S0-DHY-758

MATHEMATICAL TABLES

FROM HANDBOOK OF CHEMISTRY AND PHYSICS

NINTH EDITION

Compiled by

Charles D. Hodgman, M.S.,
Associate Professor of Physics at
Case Institute of Technology

CHEMICAL RUBBER PUBLISHING CO.
2310 Superior Ave. N.E., CLEVELAND, OHIO

PRINTED IN U. S. A.

Preface

The collection of mathematical tables and formulae, originally published in the Handbook of Chemistry and Physics was intended to provide tables of logarithms, trigonometric functions, numerical constants and mathematical formulae and equations adequate for the ordinary computations of chemistry and physics. The convenience of form and completeness of the collection led to many requests for a separate publication, which would make the tables more readily available for general computation and reference or for use by students of mathematics.

Since the first publication of the separate Mathematical Tables extensive additions and revisions have been made, the current editions presenting more than twice the material of the original volume.

Every precaution has been used to insure accuracy in the numerical values, the proofs having been read repeatedly and against several sources where possible. A large portion of the material has been computed especially for this volume. Notice of any errors which may be discovered will be sincerely appreciated.

In addition to suggestions and contributions from a large number of users of the book we wish especially to acknowledge the valuable collaboration of the following persons:

Albert A. Bennett, Brown University
W. Bruce Ross, McGill University

B. H. Brown, Dartmouth College
James W. Glover, University of Michigan
D. A. Hill, the Ohio Public Service Company
CHEMICAL RUBBER PUBLISHING COMPANY
Cleveland, Ohio.

Preface to the Ninth Edition

Several important additions have been made in recent editions of the Mathematical Tables.

A fifteen page table of natural secants and cosecants for angles in degrees and minutes has been added in response to the need developed by the increased use of computing machines.

An extensive collection of mathematical abbreviations and symbols covering about twenty-two pages has been compiled by Professor Albert A. Bennett of Brown University and has been placed at the end of the volume.

A small table for conversion of angles from arc to time has been added.

In response to several requests a collection of conversion factors and numerical constants has been assembled in a convenient location at the front of the volume.

The table of natural logarithms has been completely rearranged and is now presented in a convenient and more complete form.

There has been added to the Ninth Edition a table giving values of Sine^2, Sine × Cosine, and Cosine^2 to five significant figures. This table was computed by Professor Niel Beardsley of the University of Chicago.

A four-place table of logarithms of decimal fractions now supplements the four-place table of logarithms, and a table of powers of two has been added.

A small number of minor corrections and revisions have been made in various portions of the volume.

CHEMICAL RUBBER PUBLISHING COMPANY
Cleveland, Ohio,
September 1, 1951.

CONTENTS

CONTENTS

USE OF MATHEMATICAL TABLES

For a complete discussion of the principles and use of mathematical tables, textbooks on the subject should be consulted. The following brief statements are intended to give only sufficient information to make possible the intelligent use of the tables, omitting for the most part any attempt at treating the theory and principles.

Exponential Method of Expressing Numbers—For convenience in writing and manipulation, numbers are often expressed as factors of appropriate powers of 10. The following examples will illustrate:

2,380,000,000.	may be written	2.38×10^9
238.	may be written	2.38×10^2
.238	may be written	2.38×10^{-1}
.000000238	may be written	2.38×10^{-7}

Logarithms—The logarithm of a number is the exponent of that power to which another number, the base, must be raised to give the number first named. Any positive number greater than 1 might serve as a base. Two have been selected, yielding two systems of logarithms. One base, 2.718 . . . . usually indicated by the letter e, gives rise to a system of logarithms convenient in higher mathematics. These are called natural, Napierian, or hyperbolic logarithms. Reference will be made to their use in a subsequent paragraph.

The other base used is 10, giving logarithms particularly adapted to use in computation, called common or Briggian logarithms. Tables of logarithms given without designation are invariably of this latter type.

Since most numbers are incommensurable powers of ten, a common logarithm, in general, consists of an integer which is called the characteristic and an endless decimal, the mantissa.

It is to be observed that the common logarithms of all numbers expressed by the same figures in the same order with the decimal point in different positions have different characteristics but the same mantissa. To illustrate:—if the decimal point stand after the first figure of a number, counting from the left, the characteristic is 0; if after two figures, it is 1; if after three figures, it is 2, and so forth. If the decimal point stand before the first significant figure the characteristic is -1, usually written $\bar{1}$; if there is one zero between the decimal point and the first significant figure it is 2 and so on. For example: $\log 256 = 2.40824$, $\log 2.56 = 0.40824$, $\log 0.256 = \bar{1}.40824$, $\log 0.00256 = \bar{3}.40824$. The two latter are often written $\log 0.256 = 9.40824 - 10$, $\log 0.00256 = 7.40824 - 10$.

A method of determining characteristics of logarithms is to write the number with one figure to the left of the decimal point multiplied by the appropriate power of 10. The characteristic is then the exponent used. For example:

$$256{,}000{,}000 = 2.56 \times 10^{8} \quad \log = 8.40824$$
$$0.000000256 = 2.56 \times 10^{-7} \quad \log = \overline{7}.40824 \text{ or } 3.40824-10$$

Inasmuch as the characteristic may be determined by inspection the mantissas only are given in tables of common logarithms.

To find the logarithm of a number:

For a number of four figures, take out the tabular mantissa on a line with the first three figures of the number and under its fourth figure. The characteristic is determined as previously explained.

For a number of less than four figures, supply zeros to make a four figure number and take the value of the mantissa from the tables as before. For example: $\log 2 = \log 2.000 = 0.30103$.

For a number of more than four figures, take the tabular value of the mantissa for the first four figures; find the difference between this mantissa and the next greater tabular mantissa and multiply the difference so found by the remaining figures of the number as a decimal and add the product to the mantissa of the first four figures. For example: to find log 46.762.

$$\log 46.76 = 1.66987$$

Tabular difference between this mantissa and that for 4677 is .00010.

$$\begin{aligned} \therefore \log 46.762 &= 1.66987 + .2 \times .00010 \\ &= 1.66987 + .00002 \\ &= 1.66989 \end{aligned}$$

To find the number corresponding to a given logarithm:

If the mantissa is found exactly in the table, join the figure at the top which is directly above the given mantissa to the three figures on the line at the left and place the decimal point according to the characteristic of the logarithm. For example, $\log^{-1}$ (antilogarithm) $3.39967 = 2510$.

If the mantissa is not found exactly in the table it is necessary to interpolate. For example, $\log^{-1} 3.40028 = 2513. + {}^{9}/_{18} = 2513.5$.

The column of proportional parts at the right of each page of the table shows, under the heading of the various tabular differences, the parts of these differences which correspond to the digits from 1 to 9 in the fifth place. This makes it possible to take out a logarithm for a five figure number or to find an antilogarithm of the same number of significant figures with increased facility, usually by inspection.

The following formulae express the relations on which the use of logarithms is based:

$$\log ab = \log a + \log b$$

$$\log \frac{a}{b} = \log a - \log b$$

$$\log a^n = n \times \log a$$

$$\log \sqrt[n]{a} = \frac{\log a}{n}.$$

The following examples will serve as illustrations:

1. $52600 \times 0.00381 \times 2.74 = 549.1$

$$\begin{aligned} \log 52600 &= 4.72099 \\ \log 0.00381 &= \bar{3}.58092 \\ \log 2.74 &= 0.43775 \\ \hline \text{Sum:} &= 2.73966 \\ \text{Antilogarithm} &= 549.1 \end{aligned}$$

The sum is the logarithm of the product, the mantissa of which is 73966. On looking up this mantissa in the logarithm tables we see that it corresponds to the digits 5491. The characteristic is 2, hence there are three figures before the decimal point. The number corresponding to the logarithm, called the antilogarithm, is 549.1.

2. $0.00123 \div 52.7 = 0.00002334$

$$\begin{aligned} \log 0.00123 &= \bar{3}.08991 \\ \log 52.7 &= 1.72181 \\ \hline \text{Subtracting} &\quad \bar{5}.36810 \\ \text{Antilog} &\quad 0.00002334 \end{aligned}$$

An Alternative method:

$$\begin{aligned} \log 0.00123 &= 7.08991 - 10 \\ \log 52.7 &= 1.72181 \\ \hline &\quad 5.36810 - 10 \end{aligned}$$

The characteristic $\bar{5}$ (5. -10) shows four zeros after the decimal point before the first significant figure.

3. $\dfrac{273 \times 780}{292 \times 760} \times 15 \times 0.09 = 1.295$

$$\begin{aligned} \log 273 &= 2.43616 \\ \log 780 &= 2.89209 \\ \log 15 &= 1.17609 \\ \log 0.09 &= \bar{2}.95424 \\ \hline \log \text{sum} &= 5.45858 \end{aligned}$$

$$\begin{aligned} \log 292 &= 2.46538 \\ \log 760 &= 2.88081 \\ \hline \log \text{denominator} &= 5.34619 \end{aligned}$$

$$\begin{aligned} \log \text{numerator} &= 5.45858 \\ \log \text{denominator} &= 5.34619 \\ \hline \text{subtracting} &= 0.11239 \\ \text{antilogarithm} &= 1.295 \end{aligned}$$

As division may be accomplished by multiplying by the reciprocal of a number, the above may be considerably simplified. The logarithm of the reciprocal of a number, called the cologarithm, is readily obtained from the table by subtracting the logarithm of the number from zero. This may readily be read off from the table of mantissas. Change the sign of the characteristic algebraically adding to it -1, then mentally subtract each figure of the mantissa from 9 proceeding from left to right, the last figure being subtracted from 10. The example then is:

$$
\begin{array}{lrl}
\log & 273 & = 2.43616 \\
\log & 780 & = 2.89209 \\
\log & 15 & = \bar{1}.17609 \\
\log & 0.09 & = \bar{2}.95424 \\
\text{colog} & 292 & = \bar{3}.53462 \\
\text{colog} & 760 & = \bar{3}.11919 \\
\hline
 & & 0.11239
\end{array}
$$

4. $(0.00098)^4 = 9.224 \times 10^{-13}$

$$
\begin{array}{lrl}
\log 0.00098 & = & \bar{4}.99123 \\
 & & \underline{\qquad 4} \\
 & & 3.96492\text{(a)} \\
\bar{4} \times 4 & & \underline{\overline{16}. \qquad \text{(b)}} \\
\log (0.00098)^4 & = & \overline{13}.96492\text{(c)}
\end{array}
$$

antilog $= 9.224 \times 10^{-13}$

An alternative method:

$$
\begin{array}{rl}
\log 0.00098 = & 6.99123-10 \\
 & \underline{\qquad\qquad 4} \\
 & 27.96492-40 \\
 \text{or} & 7.96492-20 \\
 \text{or} & \overline{13}.96492
\end{array}
$$

antilog $= 9.224 \times 10^{-13}$

In the above it will be noted that the mantissa is always positive hence the multiplication of the mantissa shown at (a) while (b) shows the multiplication of the characteristic. (c) is the algebraic sum.

5. $\sqrt[5]{492} = 3.455$

$\log 492 = 2.69197$

Dividing the logarithm by 5 gives as the logarithm of the root 0.53839 the antilogarithm of which is 3.455 both characteristic and mantissa being positive. When the characteristic is negative and not evenly divisible by the root to be taken a modification of the logarithm is necessary.

6. $\sqrt[3]{0.000372} =$

$$
\begin{aligned}
\log 3.72 \times 10^{-4} &= \bar{4}.57054 && \text{(a)} \\
&= 26.57054-30 && \text{(b)}
\end{aligned}
$$

dividing (b) by 3 gives 8.85685$-$10 which may be written

$\bar{2}.85685$ and is the logarithm of the root sought, the antilogarithm of which is 0.07192.

7. $0.000372^{1.2} = 0.000076674$

$$\log 0.000372 = \bar{4}.57054$$
$$\text{or } 6.57054-10$$
$$1.2$$
$$\overline{}$$
$$7.88465-12$$

antilogarithm 0.000076674

Four-Place Logarithms—This short table on two facing pages makes possible logarithmic computation precise to four significant figures, (three without interpolation). The mantissa is given complete and the proportional parts indicated for each line.

Four-Place Antilogarithms—Some computers prefer to use separate tables for determining antilogarithms; the table being entered from the margins with the logarithm and the number being found in the body of the table. Such a table is given to accompany the four-place logarithms.

Five-Place Logarithms—For computation involving five significant figures, (four without interpolation) the five-place table will be adequate. Since the first two figures will be the same for several lines of the table they are given in the first line only. The point at which these first two figures change is indicated by an asterisk. While space does not permit the proportional parts for each line, tables will be found for each tabular difference.

The supplementary table following the five-place logarithms, giving seven-place logarithms for numbers of five significant figures from 10,000 to 12,000 will be found convenient to increase precision and avoid the inconvenience of interpolation where the differences are large.

Logarithms of the Trigonometric Functions—Logarithms of the functions are given for each minute from 0-360°.

The quantity -10 is to be appended to all logarithms of the sine and cosine, to logarithms of the tangent from 0-45° and of the cotangent from 45-90°.

With degrees indicated at either side of the top of the page use the column headings at the top. With degrees stated at the bottom of the page use the column designations at the bottom.

With degrees at the left (top or bottom) use the minute column at the left, and with degrees on the right side of the page use the minute column at the right.

To illustrate the proper employment of headings for angles in the four quadrants—

log sin 6° 24′ = 9.04715 − 10	log sin 186° 24′ = 9.04715 − 10
log sin 83° 15′ = 9.99698 − 10	log sin 263° 15′ = 9.99698 − 10
log cos 96° 41′ = 9.06589 − 10	log cos 276° 41′ = 9.06589 − 10
log cos 173° 49′ = 9.99747 − 10	log cos 353° 49′ = 9.99747 − 10

For the accurate determination of values where the tabular differences are large, the values of CS and CT are given. The following equations indicate their use.

To find the logarithm of the functions of an angle:

For angles 0–3°	For angles 87–90°
$\log \sin \theta = \log \theta'' - CS$	$\log \cos \theta = \log (90° - \theta)'' - CS$
$\log \tan \theta = \log \theta'' - CT$	$\log \cot \theta = \log (90° - \theta)'' - CT$
$\log \cot \theta = \text{colog} \tan \theta$	$\log \tan \theta = \text{colog} \cot \theta$

To find the angle:

For angles 0–3°	For angles 87–90°
$\log \theta'' = \log \sin \theta + CS$	$\log (90° - \theta)'' = \log \cos \theta + CS$
$\log \theta'' = \log \tan \theta + CT$	$\log (90° - \theta)'' = \log \cot \theta + CT$

In the above expressions, θ'' and $(90° - \theta)''$ are used to indicate the value of the angles expressed in seconds. The values in the body of the table are the cologarithms and should be used as indicated above.

The values of the logarithms S and T are also given in a separate table. For these the following relations hold:

To find the functions of an angle.

$\log \sin \theta = \log \theta'' + S$	$\log \cos \theta = \log (90° - \theta)'' + S$
$\log \tan \theta = \log \theta'' + T$	$\log \cot \theta = \log (90° - \theta)'' + T$

To find the angle.

$\log \theta'' = \log \sin \theta - S$	$\log (90° - \theta)'' = \log \cos \theta - S$
$\log \theta'' = \log \tan \theta - T$	$\log (90° - \theta)'' = \log \cot \theta - T$

Where the values of CS and CT are given, the angles expressed in seconds are given in the supplementary column at the left.

The tabular differences are given under the headings "d" and "c.d.", the latter referring to the common difference for the tangent and cotangent. Tables of proportional parts ("P.P.") facilitate interpolation. At the bottom of each column will be found special proportional parts between the tabular differences for the tangent or cotangent and those for the sine or cosine. These are useful when one function is to be obtained directly from the other without determining the angle.

For example, suppose log tan θ is given as 9.67644 and log cos θ is required. The difference between the given logarithm and that given in the table, 9.67622 (opposite 25° 23′), is 22

The tabular differences of the two logarithmic functions at this place are 32 and 6. In the proportional table for $\frac{6}{32}$, 22 corresponds to 4; this, subtracted from the tabular logarithmic cosine 9.95591, gives the required log cos θ = 9.95587.

The symbols $\bar{5}$ and $\dot{5}$ are used to indicate how the terminal 5 has been derived. For example, the logarithm 8.83075 is more fully given as 8.8307495 while the value 9.4082$\dot{5}$ is derived from 9.4082539.

Natural Trigonometric Functions—Values of the natural trigonometric functions of angles are given for each minute from 0–360°.

For degrees indicated at the top of the page use the column headings at the top. For degrees indicated at the bottom use the column indications at the bottom.

With degrees at the left of each block (top or bottom), use the minute column at the left and with degrees at the right of each block use the minute column at the right.

Natural Functions and their Logarithms are given for angles in degrees and tenths from 0 to 90 degrees.

Natural Functions and their Logarithms are given for angles in radians and hundredths, from 0 to 2 radians.

Haversines—Values of $(1 - \cos \theta)/2$ for angles between 0 and 180° are given to four significant figures. The four-place mantissas of the logarithms of the haversines are also given. The correct characteristic must be provided in each case.

The listed values of the haversines were derived from values which were computed to seven significant figures. The logarithms were independently derived from the more exact values of the haversines and are, therefore, in many cases not the exact value of the logarithm of the haversine as listed. This is notably true at the beginning of the table where the logarithm can be given with more exactness than the function.

Natural Logarithms—The natural logarithms of numbers from 0.000 to 999. are given in a group of four tables. The method of finding logarithms of numbers not included in the tables is indicated at the beginning of the third page. A convenient table of constants occurs at the top of the fourth page.

The first page gives the natural logarithms of numbers from 0.000 to 0.499. Since the characteristics change rapidly for the smaller numbers, they are indicated *above* the mantissa in the first line. In the second and following lines the characteristics are given at the left only. For example, $\log_e 0.004 = -5.52146$; $\log_e 0.014 = -4.26870$.

The succeeding pages give the natural logarithms of numbers up to 999.

Exponential Functions—Values of e^x, log e^x and e^{-x} where e is the base of the natural system of logarithms 2.71828 . . . and x has values from 0 to 10. Facilitating the solution of exponential equations, these tables also serve as a table of natural or Naperian antilogarithms. For instance if the logarithm or exponent $x = 3.26$ the corresponding number or value of e^x is 26.050. Its reciprocal e^{-x} is .038388.

Hyperbolic Functions—The table gives the values and logarithms of the hyperbolic sine x, cosine x, tangent x and cotangent x for values of x from 0 to 5.

Degrees-Radians—This table gives the value in radians to five significant figures; for each 10 minutes from 0° 0′ to 90° 0′; for each degree from 90 to 180; for each 10 degrees from 180 to 480. Values are also given for each minute from 0–60′ and for each second from 0–60″.

Tables are also provided to facilitate changing from degrees and decimal fractions to radians, from decimal fractions of a degree to minutes and seconds and the reverse operations.

Numerical Tables—The first section gives the reciprocals of numbers from 0 to 1000 and circumferences and areas of circles with diameters having these values. Reciprocals and circumferences for values not listed can be obtained by an appropriate shift of the decimal point.

The second section is devoted to squares, cubes and roots. The squares and cubes from 1 to 1000 are given exactly. The roots are given to seven significant figures. Since the square roots of $10n$ are given, values of the square roots from 1 to 10,000 may be found directly. For the square roots of numbers below and above this range, use may be made of the following relations: $\sqrt{100n} = 10\sqrt{n}$; $\sqrt{1000n} = 10\sqrt{10n}$; $\sqrt{\frac{1}{10}n} = \frac{1}{10}\sqrt{10n}$; $\sqrt{\frac{1}{100}n} = \frac{1}{10}\sqrt{n}$; $\sqrt{\frac{1}{1000}n} = \frac{1}{100}\sqrt{10n}$. For example, the square root of 0.268 may be found by using the form, $\sqrt{0.268} = \frac{1}{100}\sqrt{10 \times 268}$. The tabular value for the square root of $10n$ for 268 is 51.76872. Hence, the desired root is 0.5176872.

Values of cube roots for all numbers from 1 to 100,000 will be found directly in the table. Cube roots for numbers above or below this range will be found from the following relations: $\sqrt[3]{1000n} = 10\sqrt[3]{n}$; $\sqrt[3]{10{,}000n} = 10\sqrt[3]{10n}$; $\sqrt[3]{100{,}000n} = 10\sqrt[3]{100n}$; $\sqrt[3]{\frac{1}{10}n} = \frac{1}{10}\sqrt[3]{100n}$; $\sqrt[3]{\frac{1}{100}n} = \frac{1}{10}\sqrt[3]{10n}$; $\sqrt[3]{\frac{1}{1000}n} = \frac{1}{10}\sqrt[3]{n}$. For example, the cube root of 731,000 may be found by using the form, $\sqrt[3]{731{,}000} = 10\sqrt[3]{731}$. The tabular value of the root for 731 is 9.008223. The desired root is, therefore, 90.08223.

Powers of Numbers—This table is given to supplement the values of squares and cubes of numbers found in the preceding numerical table. The larger numbers are expressed exponentially to at least seven significant figures. The approximate value written as a whole number may be obtained by shifting the decimal point to the right by the number of places indicated in the exponent of 10 shown at the head of each group of values. For example: the approximate value of 33^8 is found in the table as 14.064086×10^{11}. Written as a whole number it is 1,406,408,600,000.

Factorials and their Logarithms—The product $n \times (n - 1) \times (n - 2) \times \cdots \times 1$ is called factorial n, expressed as $n!$ or $\underline{|n}$. For example: factorial $5 = 5 \times 4 \times 3 \times 2 \times 1 = 120$. Factorials are very often met with in series. For purposes of computation in such cases the table giving the values of the factorials and of their logarithms for numbers from 1 to 100 is provided. The values of the factorials are expressed exponentially to 5 significant figures.

A brief table of exact values and reciprocals of factorials is to be found on page 186.

Factors for Computing Probable Errors—The probable error of a series of n measures $a_1, a_2, a_3 \ldots a_n$, the mean of which is m, is given by the expression,

$$e = \frac{0.6745}{\sqrt{n-1}}\sqrt{(m-a_1)^2 + (m-a_2)^2 + \cdots (m-a_n)^2}$$

The probable error of the mean is,

$$E = \frac{0.6745}{\sqrt{n(n-1)}}\sqrt{(m-a_1)^2 + (m-a_2)^2 + \cdots (m-a_n)^2}$$

The following approximate equations are convenient forms for computation,

$$e = 0.8453\frac{\Sigma d}{\sqrt{n(n-1)}}$$

$$E = 0.8453\frac{\Sigma d}{n\sqrt{n-1}}$$

The symbol Σd represents the arithmetical sum of the deviations.

For convenience in computing the probable error the value of several of the factors involved is given for values of n from 2 to 100.

Probability of Occurrence of Deviations—The significance of deviations is indicated by this table. The probability of occurrence of deviations as great as or greater than any specific value is given for various ratios of deviation to probable error and also with respect to the standard deviation σ. The probability of occurrence is stated in per cent or chances in 100. The odds against occurrence are also stated. The probable error is $0.6745 \times (\sigma)$.

Areas, Ordinates and Derivatives of the Normal Curve of Error—If, for a large number of observations, the frequency y, of the occurrence of an error of magnitude t be plotted, a curve results whose equation may be written,

$$y = \frac{1}{\sqrt{2\pi}} e^{-t^2/2}$$

The area, ordinates and derivatives for this curve given in the table are useful in the treatment of observational data. A text on statistical methods should be consulted for a complete explanation.

Factors and Primes—The table presents the prime factors of *all* factorable numbers and the logarithms of all prime numbers from 1 to 2000.

Conversion Table

Inches		Centimeters	Centimeters		Inches
1	=	2.54001	1	=	0.39370
2	=	5.08001	2	=	0.78740
3	=	7.62002	3	=	1.1811
4	=	10.16002	4	=	1.5748
5	=	12.70003	5	=	1.9685
6	=	15.24003	6	=	2.3622
7	=	17.78004	7	=	2.7559
8	=	20.32004	8	=	3.1496
9	=	22.86005	9	=	3.5433
Feet		**Meters**	**Meters**		**Feet**
1	=	0.304801	1	=	3.28083
2	=	0.609601	2	=	6.56167
3	=	0.914402	3	=	9.84250
4	=	1.219202	4	=	13.12333
5	=	1.524003	5	=	16.40417
6	=	1.828804	6	=	19.68500
7	=	2.133604	7	=	22.96583
8	=	2.438405	8	=	26.24666
9	=	2.743205	9	=	29.52750
Yards		**Meters**	**Meters**		**Yards**
1	=	0.914402	1	=	1 093611
2	=	1.828804	2	=	2.187222
3	=	2.743205	3	=	3.280833
4	=	3.657607	4	=	4.374444
5	=	4.572009	5	=	5.468056
6	=	5.486411	6	=	6.561667
7	=	6.400813	7	=	7.655278
8	=	7.315215	8	=	8.748889
9	=	8.229616	9	=	9.842500

Conversion Tables (Continued)

Miles	Kilometers	Kilometers	Miles
1	1.60935	1	0.62137
2	3.21869	2	1.24274
3	4.82804	3	1.86411
4	6.43739	4	2.48548
5	8.04674	5	3.10685
6	9.65608	6	3.72822
7	11.26543	7	4.34959
8	12.87478	8	4.97096
9	14.48412	9	5.59233
Pounds Av.	**Kilograms**	**Kilograms**	**Pounds Av.**
1	0.45359	1	2.20462
2	0.90718	2	4.40924
3	1.36078	3	6.61387
4	1.81437	4	8.81849
5	2.26796	5	11.02311
6	2.72155	6	13.22773
7	3.17514	7	15.43236
8	3.62874	8	17.63698
9	4.08233	9	19.84160

Conversion Factors

U. S. AND METRIC UNITS

Each unit in bold face type is followed by its equivalent in other units of the same quantity.

Acre—0.0015625 square mile; 4.3560 $\times 10^4$ square feet; 0.4046873 hectare

Bushel—1.2444 cubic feet; 2150.42 cubic inches; 0.035239 cubic meter; 35.238 liters

Centimeter—0.032808 foot; 0.39370 inch.

Circular Mil.—7.854 $\times 10^{-7}$ square inch; 5.0671 $\times 10^{-6}$ square centimeter

Cubic Centimeter—0.061023 cubic inch; 0.27051 dram; 16.231 minims; 0.99997 milliliter

Cubic Foot—0.80357 bushel; 7.481 gallon; 0.02831701 cubic meter; 28.316 liters

Cubic Inch—16.387162 cubic centimeters

Cubic Meter—35.314445 cubic feet; 264.173 gallons

Foot—0.3048006 meter

Gallon—0.13368 cubic foot; 0.83268 gallons (British); 231.00 cubic inches; 0.0037854 cubic meter; 3.7853 liters

Grain—0.064798918 gram

Gram—0.00220462 pound (avoirdupois); .0352740 ounce (avoirdupois); 15.4324 grains

Hectare—2.471044 acres; 1.0764 $\times 10^5$ square feet

Inch—2.540005 centimeter

Kilogram—2.2046223 pounds (avoirdupois)

Kilometer—0.62137 mile

Liter—0.26417762 gallon; 0.035316 cubic foot; 1.056710 quarts

Meter—1.093611 yards; 3.280833 feet; 39.3700 inches

Mile—1.60935 kilometers

Ounce (fluid)—1.80469 cubic inches; 29.5737 cubic centimeters

Ounce (avoirdupois)—28.349527 grams

Ounce (apothecary or troy)—31.103481 grams

Pint (liquid)—0.473167 liter; 473.-167 cubic centimeters

Pound (avoirdupois)—0.453592 kilogram; 453.5924 grams

Pound (apothecary or troy)—0.3732418 kilogram; 373.2418 grams

Quart—1.10120 liters

Quart (liquid)—.946333 liter

Radian—57.29578 degrees

Rod—5.029210 meters

Square Centimeter—0.15500 square inches

Square Foot—0.09290341 square meter

Square Inch—645.16258 square millimeters

Square Meter—10.76387 square feet

Square Yard—0.83613 square meter

Ton (short)—907.185 kilograms

Yard—0.91440183 meter

NUMERICAL CONSTANTS

Numbers Containing π

$\pi = 3.14159\ 26536 \qquad \log_{10}\pi = 0.49714\ 98727 \quad \log_e \pi = 1.14472\ 98858$

	Number	Logarithm		Number	Logarithm
π	3.1415 927	0.4971 499	π^2	9.8696 044	0.9942 997
2π	6.2831 853	0.7981 799	$2\pi^2$	19.7392 088	1.2953 297
3π	9.4247 780	0.9742 711	$4\pi^2$	39.4784 176	1.5963 597
4π	12.5663 706	1.0992 099	$1/\pi^2$	0.1013 212	9.0057 003−10
8π	25.1327 412	1.4002 399	$1/(2\pi^2)$	0.0506 606	8.7046 703−10
$\pi/2$	1.5707 963	0.1961 199	$1/(4\pi^2)$	0.0253 303	8.4036 403−10
$\pi/3$	1.0471 976	0.0200 286	$\sqrt{\pi}$	1.7724 539	0.2485 749
$\pi/4$	0.7853 982	9.8950 899−10	$\sqrt{\pi/4}$ or	0.8862 269	9.9475 449−10
$\pi/6$	0.5235 988	9.7189 986−10	$\sqrt{\pi}/2$		
$\pi/8$	0.3926 991	9.5940 599−10	$\sqrt{\pi}/4$	0.4431 135	9.6465 149−10
$2\pi/3$	2.0943 951	0.3210 586	$\sqrt{\pi/2}$	1.2533 141	0.0980 599
$4\pi/3$	4.1887 902	0.6220 886	$\sqrt{2/\pi}$	0.7978 846	9.9019 401−10
$1/\pi$	0.3183 099	9.5028 501−10	π^3	31.0062 767	1.4914 496
$2/\pi$	0.6366 198	9.8038 801−10	$\sqrt[3]{\pi}$	1.4645 919	0.1657 166
$4/\pi$	1.2732 395	0.1049 101	$1/\sqrt[3]{\pi}$	0.6827 841	9.8342 834−10
$1/(2\pi)$	0.1591 549	9.2018 201−10	$\sqrt[3]{\pi^2}$	2.1450 294	0.3314 332
$1/(4\pi)$	0.0795 775	8.9007 901−10	$1/\sqrt{\pi}$	0.5641 896	9.7514 251−10
$1/(6\pi)$	0.0530 516	8.7246 989−10	$2/\sqrt{\pi}$ or	1.1283 792	0.0524 551
$1/(8\pi)$	0.0397 887	8.5997 601−10	$\sqrt{4/\pi}$		

Logarithmic Constants

$e = 2.71828\ 18285 \qquad M = \log_{10} e = 0.43429\ 44819$

$1/M = \log_e 10 = 2.30258\ 50930 \quad \log_{10} M = \log_{10}\log_{10} e = 9.63778\ 43113 - 10$

$1/e = 0.36787\ 94412$

$\log_e 2 = 0.69314\ 71806 \qquad \log_{10} 2 = 0.30102\ 99957$

Change of Base

$$\log_a x = \log_b x/\log_b a$$

$$\log_{10} x = \log_e x/\log_e 10 \qquad \log_e x = \log_{10} x/\log_{10} e$$

$$\log_e x = 1/M \log_{10} x = 2.30258\ 50930 \log_{10} x$$

$$\log_{10} x = M \log_e x = 0.43429\ 44819 \log_e x$$

DECIMAL EQUIVALENTS OF COMMON FRACTIONS

	1/32	2/64 =	0.03125		17/32	34/64 =	0.53125
1/16	2/32	4/64 =	.0625	9/16	18/32	36/64 =	.5625
	3/32	6/64 =	.09375		19/32	38/64 =	.59375
1/8	4/32	8/64 =	.125	5/8	20/32	40/64 =	.625
	5/32	10/64 =	.15625		21/32	42/64 =	.65625
3/16	6/32	12/64 =	.1875	11/16	22/32	44/64 =	.6875
	7/32	14/64 =	.21875		23/32	46/64 =	.71875
1/4	8/32	16/64 =	.25	3/4	24/32	48/64 =	.75
	9/32	18/64 =	.28125		25/32	50/64 =	.78125
5/16	10/32	20/64 =	.3125	13/16	26/32	52/64 =	.8125
	11/32	22/64 =	.34375		27/32	54/64 =	.84375
3/8	12/32	24/64 =	.375	7/8	28/32	56/64 =	.875
	13/32	26/64 =	.40625		29/32	58/64 =	.90625
7/16	14/32	28/64 =	.4375	15/16	30/32	60/64 =	.9375
	15/32	30/64 =	.46875		31/32	62/64 =	.96875
1/2	16/32	32/64 =	.50				

MISCELLANEOUS CONSTANTS

Mean radius of the earth, 3959 miles = 6371 kilometers.

1 degree of latitude at 40° = 69 miles.

1 nautical mile = 1′ of arc on the earth's surface at the equator.

Mean density of the earth, 5.522 grams per cm^3.

Constant of gravitation, $K = 6.670 \times 10^{-8}$ = the attraction in dynes between two gram masses one centimeter apart.

Acceleration due to gravity at sea level, lat. 45° = 980.665 cm. per sec. per sec. = 32.172 feet per sec. per sec.

Length of seconds pendulum at sea level, lat. 45° = 99.358 cm. = 39.117 in.

Density of mercury at 0°C. = 13.59509 g. per cm^3.

Density of water, maximum at 3.98° C. = 0.999973 g. per cm^3

Density of dry air at 0° C. and 760 mm. = .001293 g. per cm^3.

Velocity of sound in dry air at 0° C., 33,136 cm. per sec. = 1089 feet per sec.

Velocity of light in a vacuum = 2.99776×10^{10} cm. per sec. = 9.83514×10^8 feet per sec. = 186,272 mi./sec.

Heat equivalent of fusion of water **79.63** cal. (15° C.) per gram.

Heat equivalent of vaporization of water, 539.55 cal. (15° C.) per gram.

Coefficient of expansion of gases, .003665.

Specific heat of air, at constant pressure, 0.238.

Electrochemical equivalent of silver, 0.001118 g. per sec. per int. ampere.

Mean wave length of sodium light, .00005893 cm. or 5893. ångström units.

Absolute wave length of red cadmium line in air, 760 mm. pressure, 15° C.; 6438.4696 ångström units.

GREEK ALPHABET

Greek letter	Greek name	English equivalent	Greek letter	Greek name	English equivalent
Α α	Alpha	a	Ν ν	Nu	n
Β β	Beta	b	Ξ ξ	Xi	x
Γ γ	Gamma	g	Ο ο	Omicron	ŏ
Δ δ	Delta	d	Π π	Pi	p
Ε ε	Epsilon	ĕ	Ρ ρ	Rho	r
Ζ ζ	Zeta	z	Σ σ	Sigma	s
Η η	Eta	ē	Τ τ	Tau	t
Θ θ	Theta	th	Υ υ	Upsilon	u
Ι ι	Iota	i	Φ φ	Phi	ph
Κ κ	Kappa	k	Χ χ	Chi	ch
Λ λ	Lambda	l	Ψ ψ	Psi	ps
Μ μ	Mu	m	Ω ω	Omega	ō

N	0	1	2	3	4	5	6	7	8	9	Proportional Parts 1	2	3	4	5	6	7	8	9
10	0000	0043	0086	0128	0170	0212	0253	0294	0334	0374	*4	8	12	17	21	25	29	33	37
11	0414	0453	0492	0531	0569	0607	0645	0682	0719	0755	4	8	11	15	19	23	26	30	34
12	0792	0828	0864	0899	0934	0969	1004	1038	1072	1106	3	7	10	14	17	21	24	28	31
13	1139	1173	1206	1239	1271	1303	1335	1367	1399	1430	3	6	10	13	16	19	23	26	29
14	1461	1492	1523	1553	1584	1614	1644	1673	1703	1732	3	6	9	12	15	18	21	24	27
15	1761	1790	1818	1847	1875	1903	1931	1959	1987	2014	*3	6	8	11	14	17	20	22	25
16	2041	2068	2095	2122	2148	2175	2201	2227	2253	2279	3	5	8	11	13	16	18	21	24
17	2304	2330	2355	2380	2405	2430	2455	2480	2504	2529	2	5	7	10	12	15	17	20	22
18	2553	2577	2601	2625	2648	2672	2695	2718	2742	2765	2	5	7	9	12	14	16	19	21
19	2788	2810	2833	2856	2878	2900	2923	2945	2967	2989	2	4	7	9	11	13	16	18	20
20	3010	3032	3054	3075	3096	3118	3139	3160	3181	3201	2	4	6	8	11	13	15	17	19
21	3222	3243	3263	3284	3304	3324	3345	3365	3385	3404	2	4	6	8	10	12	14	16	18
22	3424	3444	3464	3483	3502	3522	3541	3560	3579	3598	2	4	6	8	10	12	14	15	17
23	3617	3636	3655	3674	3692	3711	3729	3747	3766	3784	2	4	6	7	9	11	13	15	17
24	3802	3820	3838	3856	3874	3892	3909	3927	3945	3962	2	4	5	7	9	11	12	14	16
25	3979	3997	4014	4031	4048	4065	4082	4099	4116	4133	2	3	5	7	9	10	12	14	15
26	4150	4166	4183	4200	4216	4232	4249	4265	4281	4298	2	3	5	7	8	10	11	13	15
27	4314	4330	4346	4362	4378	4393	4409	4425	4440	4456	2	3	5	6	8	9	11	13	14
28	4472	4487	4502	4518	4533	4548	4564	4579	4594	4609	2	3	5	6	8	9	11	12	14
29	4624	4639	4654	4669	4683	4698	4713	4728	4742	4757	1	3	4	6	7	9	10	12	13
30	4771	4786	4800	4814	4829	4843	4857	4871	4886	4900	1	3	4	6	7	9	10	11	13
31	4914	4928	4942	4955	4969	4983	4997	5011	5024	5038	1	3	4	6	7	8	10	11	12
32	5051	5065	5079	5092	5105	5119	5132	5145	5159	5172	1	3	4	5	7	8	9	11	12
33	5185	5198	5211	5224	5237	5250	5263	5276	5289	5302	1	3	4	5	6	8	9	10	12
34	5315	5328	5340	5353	5366	5378	5391	5403	5416	5428	1	3	4	5	6	8	9	10	11
35	5441	5453	5465	5478	5490	5502	5514	5527	5539	5551	1	2	4	5	6	7	9	10	11
36	5563	5575	5587	5599	5611	5623	5635	5647	5658	5670	1	2	4	5	6	7	8	10	11
37	5682	5694	5705	5717	5729	5740	5752	5763	5775	5786	1	2	3	5	6	7	8	9	10
38	5798	5809	5821	5832	5843	5855	5866	5877	5888	5899	1	2	3	5	6	7	8	9	10
39	5911	5922	5933	5944	5955	5966	5977	5988	5999	6010	1	2	3	4	5	7	8	9	10
40	6021	6031	6042	6053	6064	6075	6085	6096	6107	6117	1	2	3	4	5	6	8	9	10
41	6128	6138	6149	6160	6170	6180	6191	6201	6212	6222	1	2	3	4	5	6	7	8	9
42	6232	6243	6253	6263	6274	6284	6294	6304	6314	6325	1	2	3	4	5	6	7	8	9
43	6335	6345	6355	6365	6375	6385	6395	6405	6415	6425	1	2	3	4	5	6	7	8	9
44	6435	6444	6454	6464	6474	6484	6493	6503	6513	6522	1	2	3	4	5	6	7	8	9
45	6532	6542	6551	6561	6571	6580	6590	6599	6609	6618	1	2	3	4	5	6	7	8	9
46	6628	6637	6646	6656	6665	6675	6684	6693	6702	6712	1	2	3	4	5	6	7	7	8
47	6721	6730	6739	6749	6758	6767	6776	6785	6794	6803	1	2	3	4	5	5	6	7	8
48	6812	6821	6830	6839	6848	6857	6866	6875	6884	6893	1	2	3	4	4	5	6	7	8
49	6902	6911	6920	6928	6937	6946	6955	6964	6972	6981	1	2	3	4	4	5	6	7	8
50	6990	6998	7007	7016	7024	7033	7042	7050	7059	7067	1	2	3	3	4	5	6	7	8
51	7076	7084	7093	7101	7110	7118	7126	7135	7143	7152	1	2	3	3	4	5	6	7	8
52	7160	7168	7177	7185	7193	7202	7210	7218	7226	7235	1	2	2	3	4	5	6	7	7
53	7243	7251	7259	7267	7275	7284	7292	7300	7308	7316	1	2	2	3	4	5	6	6	7
54	7324	7332	7340	7348	7356	7364	7372	7380	7388	7396	1	2	2	3	4	5	6	6	7
N	0	1	2	3	4	5	6	7	8	9	1	2	3	4	5	6	7	8	9

* **Interpolation in this section of the table is inaccurate.**

N	0	1	2	3	4	5	6	7	8	9	Proportional Parts 1	2	3	4	5	6	7	8	9
55	7404	7412	7419	7427	7435	7443	7451	7459	7466	7474	1	2	2	3	4	5	5	6	7
56	7482	7490	7497	7505	7513	7520	7528	7536	7543	7551	1	2	2	3	4	5	5	6	7
57	7559	7566	7574	7582	7589	7597	7604	7612	7619	7627	1	2	2	3	4	5	5	6	7
58	7634	7642	7649	7657	7664	7672	7679	7686	7694	7701	1	1	2	3	4	4	5	6	7
59	7709	7716	7723	7731	7738	7745	7752	7760	7767	7774	1	1	2	3	4	4	5	6	7
60	7782	7789	7796	7803	7810	7818	7825	7832	7839	7846	1	1	2	3	4	4	5	6	6
61	7853	7860	7868	7875	7882	7889	7896	7903	7910	7917	1	1	2	3	4	4	5	6	6
62	7924	7931	7938	7945	7952	7959	7966	7973	7980	7987	1	1	2	3	3	4	5	6	6
63	7993	8000	8007	8014	8021	8028	8035	8041	8048	8055	1	1	2	3	3	4	5	5	6
64	8062	8069	8075	8082	8089	8096	8102	8109	8116	8122	1	1	2	3	3	4	5	5	6
65	8129	8136	8142	8149	8156	8162	8169	8176	8182	8189	1	1	2	3	3	4	5	5	6
66	8195	8202	8209	8215	8222	8228	8235	8241	8248	8254	1	1	2	3	3	4	5	5	6
67	8261	8267	8274	8280	8287	8293	8299	8306	8312	8319	1	1	2	3	3	4	5	5	6
68	8325	8331	8338	8344	8351	8357	8363	8370	8376	8382	1	1	2	3	3	4	4	5	6
69	8388	8395	8401	8407	8414	8420	8426	8432	8439	8445	1	1	2	2	3	4	4	5	6
70	8451	8457	8463	8470	8476	8482	8488	8494	8500	8506	1	1	2	2	3	4	4	5	6
71	8513	8519	8525	8531	8537	8543	8549	8555	8561	8567	1	1	2	2	3	4	4	5	5
72	8573	8579	8585	8591	8597	8603	8609	8615	8621	8627	1	1	2	2	3	4	4	5	5
73	8633	8639	8645	8651	8657	8663	8669	8675	8681	8686	1	1	2	2	3	4	4	5	5
74	8692	8698	8704	8710	8716	8722	8727	8733	8739	8745	1	1	2	2	3	4	4	5	5
75	8751	8756	8762	8768	8774	8779	8785	8791	8797	8802	1	1	2	2	3	3	4	5	5
76	8808	8814	8820	8825	8831	8837	8842	8848	8854	8859	1	1	2	2	3	3	4	5	5
77	8865	8871	8876	8882	8887	8893	8899	8904	8910	8915	1	1	2	2	3	3	4	4	5
78	8921	8927	8932	8938	8943	8949	8954	8960	8965	8971	1	1	2	2	3	3	4	4	5
79	8976	8982	8987	8993	8998	9004	9009	9015	9020	9025	1	1	2	2	3	3	4	4	5
80	9031	9036	9042	9047	9053	9058	9063	9069	9074	9079	1	1	2	2	3	3	4	4	5
81	9085	9090	9096	9101	9106	9112	9117	9122	9128	9133	1	1	2	2	3	3	4	4	5
82	9138	9143	9149	9154	9159	9165	9170	9175	9180	9186	1	1	2	2	3	3	4	4	5
83	9191	9196	9201	9206	9212	9217	9222	9227	9232	9238	1	1	2	2	3	3	4	4	5
84	9243	9248	9253	9258	9263	9269	9274	9279	9284	9289	1	1	2	2	3	3	4	4	5
85	9294	9299	9304	9309	9315	9320	9325	9330	9335	9340	1	1	2	2	3	3	4	4	5
86	9345	9350	9355	9360	9365	9370	9375	9380	9385	9390	1	1	2	2	3	3	4	4	5
87	9395	9400	9405	9410	9415	9420	9425	9430	9435	9440	0	1	1	2	2	3	3	4	4
88	9445	9450	9455	9460	9465	9469	9474	9479	9484	9489	0	1	1	2	2	3	3	4	4
89	9494	9499	9504	9509	9513	9518	9523	9528	9533	9538	0	1	1	2	2	3	3	4	4
90	9542	9547	9552	9557	9562	9566	9571	9576	9581	9586	0	1	1	2	2	3	3	4	4
91	9590	9595	9600	9605	9609	9614	9619	9624	9628	9633	0	1	1	2	2	3	3	4	4
92	9638	9643	9647	9652	9657	9661	9666	9671	9675	9680	0	1	1	2	2	3	3	4	4
93	9685	9689	9694	9699	9703	9708	9713	9717	9722	9727	0	1	1	2	2	3	3	4	4
94	9731	9736	9741	9745	9750	9754	9759	9763	9768	9773	0	1	1	2	2	3	3	4	4
95	9777	9782	9786	9791	9795	9800	9805	9809	9814	9818	0	1	1	2	2	3	3	4	4
96	9823	9827	9832	9836	9841	9845	9850	9854	9859	9863	0	1	1	2	2	3	3	4	4
97	9868	9872	9877	9881	9886	9890	9894	9899	9903	9908	0	1	1	2	2	3	3	4	4
98	9912	9917	9921	9926	9930	9934	9939	9943	9948	9952	0	1	1	2	2	3	3	4	4
99	9956	9961	9965	9969	9974	9978	9983	9987	9991	9996	0	1	1	2	2	3	3	3	4
N	0	1	2	3	4	5	6	7	8	9	1	2	3	4	5	6	7	8	9

N	0	1	2	3	4	5	6	7	8	9
.10	−1.000	−.9957	−.9914	−.9872	−.9830	−.9788	−.9747	−.9706	−.9666	−.9626
.11	−.9586	−.9547	−.9508	−.9469	−.9431	−.9393	−.9355	−.9318	−.9281	−.9245
.12	−.9208	−.9172	−.9136	−.9101	−.9066	−.9031	−.8996	−.8962	−.8928	−.8894
.13	−.8861	−.8827	−.8794	−.8761	−.8729	−.8697	−.8665	−.8633	−.8601	−.8570
.14	−.8539	−.8508	−.8477	−.8447	−.8416	−.8386	−.8356	−.8327	−.8297	−.8268
.15	−.8239	−.8210	−.8182	−.8153	−.8125	−.8097	−.8069	−.8041	−.8013	−.7986
.16	−.7959	−.7932	−.7905	−.7878	−.7852	−.7825	−.7799	−.7773	−.7747	−.7721
.17	−.7696	.−7670	−.7645	−.7620	−.7595	−.7570	−.7545	−.7520	−.7496	−.7471
.18	−.7447	−.7423	−.7399	−.7375	−.7352	−.7328	−.7305	−.7282	−.7258	−.7235
.19	−.7212	−.7190	−.7167	−.7144	−.7122	−.7100	−.7077	−.7055	−.7033	−.7011
.20	−.6990	−.6968	−.6946	−.6925	−.6904	−.6882	−.6861	−.6840	−.6819	−.6799
.21	−.6778	−.6757	−.6737	−.6716	−.6696	−.6676	−.6655	−.6635	−.6615	−.6596
.22	−.6576	−.6556	−.6536	−.6517	−.6498	−.6478	−.6459	−.6440	−.6421	−.6402
.23	−.6383	−.6364	−.6345	−.6326	−.6308	−.6289	−.6271	−.6253	−.6234	−.6216
.24	−.6198	−.6180	−.6162	−.6144	−.6126	−.6108	−.6091	−.6073	−.6055	−.6038
.25	−.6021	−.6003	−.5986	−.5969	−.5952	−.5935	−.5918	−.5901	−.5884	−.5867
.26	−.5850	−.5834	−.5817	−.5800	−.5784	−.5768	−.5751	−.5735	−.5719	−.5702
.27	−.5686	−.5670	−.5654	−.5638	−.5622	−.5607	−.5591	−.5575	−.5560	−.5544
.28	−.5528	−.5513	−.5498	−.5482	−.5467	−.5452	−.5436	−.5421	−.5406	−.5391
.29	−.5376	−.5361	−.5346	−.5331	−.5317	−.5302	−.5287	−.5272	−.5258	−.5243
.30	−.5229	−.5214	−.5200	−.5186	−.5171	−.5157	−.5143	−.5129	−.5114	−.5100
.31	−.5086	−.5072	−.5058	−.5045	−.5031	−.5017	−.5003	−.4989	−.4976	−.4962
.32	−.4949	−.4935	−.4921	−.4908	−.4895	−.4881	−.4868	−.4855	−.4841	−.4828
.33	−.4815	−.4802	−.4789	−.4776	−.4763	−.4750	−.4737	−.4724	−.4711	−.4698
.34	−.4685	−.4672	−.4660	−.4647	−.4634	−.4622	−.4609	−.4597	−.4584	−.4572
.35	−.4559	−.4547	−.4535	−.4522	−.4510	−.4498	−.4486	−.4473	−.4461	−.4449
.36	−.4437	−.4425	−.4413	−.4401	−.4389	−.4377	−.4365	−.4353	−.4342	−.4330
.37	−.4318	−.4306	−.4295	−.4283	−.4271	−.4260	−.4248	−.4237	−.4225	−.4214
.38	−.4202	−.4191	−.4179	−.4168	−.4157	−.4145	−.4134	−.4123	−.4112	−.4101
.39	−.4089	−.4078	−.4067	−.4056	−.4045	−.4034	−.4023	−.4012	−.4001	−.3990
.40	−.3979	−.3969	−.3958	−.3947	−.3936	−.3925	−.3915	−.3904	−.3893	−.3883
.41	−.3872	−.3862	−.3851	−.3840	−.3830	−.3820	−.3809	−.3799	−.3788	−.3778
.42	−.3768	−.3757	−.3747	−.3737	−.3726	−.3716	−.3706	−.3696	−.3686	−.3675
.43	−.3665	−.3655	−.3645	−.3635	−.3625	−.3615	−.3605	−.3595	−.3585	−.3575
.44	−.3565	−.3556	−.3546	−.3536	−.3526	−.3516	−.3507	−.3497	−.3487	−.3478
.45	−.3468	−.3458	−.3449	−.3439	−.3429	−.3420	−.3410	−.3401	−.3391	−.3382
.46	−.3372	−.3363	−.3354	−.3344	−.3335	−.3325	−.3316	−.3307	−.3298	−.3288
.47	−.3279	−.3270	−.3261	−.3251	−.3242	−.3233	−.3224	−.3215	−.3206	−.3197
.48	−.3188	−.3179	−.3170	−.3161	−.3152	−.3143	−.3134	−.3125	−.3116	−.3107
.49	−.3098	−.3089	−.3080	−.3072	−.3063	−.3054	−.3045	−.3036	−.3028	−.3019
.50	−.3010	−.3002	−.2993	−.2984	−.2976	−.2967	−.2958	−.2950	−.2941	−.2933
.51	−.2924	−.2916	−.2907	−.2899	−.2890	−.2882	−.2874	−.2865	−.2857	−.2848
.52	−.2840	−.2832	−.2823	−.2815	−.2807	−.2798	−.2790	−.2782	−.2774	−.2765
.53	−.2757	−.2749	−.2741	−.2733	−.2725	−.2716	−.2708	−.2700	−.2692	−.2684
.54	−.2676	−.2668	−.2660	−.2652	−.2644	−.2636	−.2628	−.2620	−.2612	−.2604

OF DECIMAL FRACTIONS

N	0	1	2	3	4	5	6	7	8	9
.55	−.2596	−.2588	−.2581	−.2573	−.2565	−.2557	−.2549	−.2541	−.2534	−.2526
.56	−.2518	−.2510	−.2503	−.2495	−.2487	−.2480	−.2472	−.2464	−.2457	−.2449
.57	−.2441	−.2434	−.2426	−.2418	−.2411	−.2403	−.2396	−.2388	−.2381	−.2373
.58	−.2366	−.2358	−.2351	−.2343	−.2336	−.2328	−.2321	−.2314	−.2306	−.2299
.59	−.2291	−.2284	−.2277	−.2269	−.2262	−.2255	−.2248	−.2240	−.2233	−.2226
.60	−.2218	−.2211	−.2204	−.2197	−.2190	−.2182	−.2175	−.2168	−.2161	−.2154
.61	−.2147	−.2140	−.2132	−.2125	−.2118	−.2111	−.2104	−.2097	−.2090	−.2083
.62	−.2076	−.2069	−.2062	−.2055	−.2048	−.2041	−.2034	−.2027	−.2020	−.2013
.63	−.2007	−.2000	−.1993	−.1986	−.1979	−.1972	−.1965	−.1959	−.1952	−.1945
.64	−.1938	−.1931	−.1925	−.1918	−.1911	−.1904	−.1898	−.1891	−.1884	−.1878
.65	−.1871	−.1864	−.1858	−.1851	−.1844	−.1838	−.1831	−.1824	−.1818	−.1811
.66	−.1805	−.1798	−.1791	−.1785	−.1778	−.1772	−.1765	−.1759	−.1752	−.1746
.67	−.1739	−.1733	−.1726	−.1720	−.1713	−.1707	−.1701	−.1694	−.1688	−.1681
.68	−.1675	−.1669	−.1662	−.1656	−.1649	−.1643	−.1637	−.1630	−.1624	−.1618
.69	−.1612	−.1605	−.1599	−.1593	−.1586	−.1580	−.1574	−.1568	−.1561	−.1555
.70	−.1549	−.1543	−.1537	−.1530	−.1524	−.1518	−.1512	−.1506	−.1500	−.1494
.71	−.1487	−.1481	−.1475	−.1469	−.1463	−.1457	−.1451	−.1445	−.1439	−.1433
.72	−.1427	−.1421	−.1415	−.1409	−.1403	−.1397	−.1391	−.1385	−.1379	−.1373
.73	−.1367	−.1361	−.1355	−.1349	−.1343	−.1337	−.1331	−.1325	−.1319	−.1314
.74	−.1308	−.1302	−.1296	−.1290	−.1284	−.1278	−.1273	−.1267	−.1261	−.1255
.75	−.1249	−.1244	−.1238	−.1232	−.1226	−.1221	−.1215	−.1209	−.1203	−.1198
.76	−.1192	−.1186	−.1180	−.1175	−.1169	−.1163	−.1158	−.1152	−.1146	−.1141
.77	−.1135	−.1129	−.1124	−.1118	−.1113	−.1107	−.1101	−.1096	−.1090	−.1085
.78	−.1079	−.1073	−.1068	−.1062	−.1057	−.1051	−.1046	−.1040	−.1035	−.1029
.79	−.1024	−.1018	−.1013	−.1007	−.1002	−.0996	−.0991	−.0985	−.0980	−.0975
.80	−.0969	−.0964	−.0958	−.0953	−.0947	−.0942	−.0937	−.0931	−.0926	−.0921
.81	−.0915	−.0910	−.0904	−.0899	−.0894	−.0888	−.0883	−.0878	−.0872	−.0867
.82	−.0862	−.0857	−.0851	−.0846	−.0841	−.0835	−.0830	−.0825	−.0820	−.0814
.83	−.0809	−.0804	−.0799	−.0794	−.0788	−.0783	−.0778	−.0773	−.0768	−.0762
.84	−.0757	−.0752	−.0747	−.0742	−.0737	−.0731	−.0726	−.0721	−.0716	−.0711
.85	−.0706	−.0701	−.0696	−.0691	−.0685	−.0680	−.0675	−.0670	−.0665	−.0660
.86	−.0655	−.0650	−.0645	−.0640	−.0635	−.0630	−.0625	−.0620	−.0615	−.0610
.87	−.0605	−.0600	−.0595	−.0590	−.0585	−.0580	−.0575	−.0570	−.0565	−.0560
.88	−.0555	−.0550	−.0545	−.0540	−.0535	−.0531	−.0526	−.0521	−.0516	−.0511
.89	−.0506	−.0501	−.0496	−.0491	−.0487	−.0482	−.0477	−.0472	−.0467	−.0462
.90	−.0458	−.0453	−.0448	−.0443	−.0438	−.0434	−.0429	−.0424	−.0419	−.0414
.91	−.0410	−.0405	−.0400	−.0395	−.0391	−.0386	−.0381	−.0376	−.0372	−.0367
.92	−.0362	−.0357	−.0353	−.0348	−.0343	−.0339	−.0334	−.0329	−.0325	−.0320
.93	−.0315	−.0311	−.0306	−.0301	−.0297	−.0292	−.0287	−.0283	−.0278	−.0273
.94	−.0269	−.0264	−.0259	−.0255	−.0250	−.0246	−.0241	−.0237	−.0232	−.0227
.95	−.0223	−.0218	−.0214	−.0209	−.0205	−.0200	−.0195	−.0191	−.0186	−.0182
.96	−.0177	−.0173	−.0168	−.0164	−.0159	−.0155	−.0150	−.0146	−.0141	−.0137
.97	−.0132	−.0128	−.0123	−.0119	−.0114	−.0110	−.0106	−.0101	−.0097	−.0092
.98	−.0088	−.0083	−.0079	−.0074	−.0070	−.0066	−.0061	−.0057	−.0052	−.0048
.99	−.0044	−.0039	−.0035	−.0031	−.0026	−.0022	−.0017	−.0013	−.0009	−.0004

ANTILOGARITHMS

	0	1	2	3	4	5	6	7	8	9	Proportional Parts								
											1	2	3	4	5	6	7	8	9
.00	1000	1002	1005	1007	1009	1012	1014	1016	1019	1021	0	0	1	1	1	1	2	2	2
.01	1023	1026	1028	1030	1033	1035	1038	1040	1042	1045	0	0	1	1	1	1	2	2	2
.02	1047	1050	1052	1054	1057	1059	1062	1064	1067	1069	0	0	1	1	1	1	2	2	2
.03	1072	1074	1076	1079	1081	1084	1086	1089	1091	1094	0	0	1	1	1	1	2	2	2
.04	1096	1099	1102	1104	1107	1109	1112	1114	1117	1119	0	1	1	1	1	2	2	2	2
.05	1122	1125	1127	1130	1132	1135	1138	1140	1143	1146	0	1	1	1	1	2	2	2	2
.06	1148	1151	1153	1156	1159	1161	1164	1167	1169	1172	0	1	1	1	1	2	2	2	2
.07	1175	1178	1180	1183	1186	1189	1191	1194	1197	1199	0	1	1	1	1	2	2	2	2
.08	1202	1205	1208	1211	1213	1216	1219	1222	1225	1227	0	1	1	1	1	2	2	2	3
.09	1230	1233	1236	1239	1242	1245	1247	1250	1253	1256	0	1	1	1	1	2	2	2	3
.10	1259	1262	1265	1268	1271	1274	1276	1279	1282	1285	0	1	1	1	1	2	2	2	3
.11	1288	1291	1294	1297	1300	1303	1306	1309	1312	1315	0	1	1	1	2	2	2	2	3
.12	1318	1321	1324	1327	1330	1334	1337	1340	1343	1346	0	1	1	1	2	2	2	2	3
.13	1349	1352	1355	1358	1361	1365	1368	1371	1374	1377	0	1	1	1	2	2	2	3	3
.14	1380	1384	1387	1390	1393	1396	1400	1403	1406	1409	0	1	1	1	2	2	2	3	3
.15	1413	1416	1419	1422	1426	1429	1432	1435	1439	1442	0	1	1	1	2	2	2	3	3
.16	1445	1449	1452	1455	1459	1462	1466	1469	1472	1476	0	1	1	1	2	2	2	3	3
.17	1479	1483	1486	1489	1493	1496	1500	1503	1507	1510	0	1	1	1	2	2	2	3	3
.18	1514	1517	1521	1524	1528	1531	1535	1538	1542	1545	0	1	1	1	2	2	2	3	3
.19	1549	1552	1556	1560	1563	1567	1570	1574	1578	1581	0	1	1	1	2	2	3	3	3
.20	1585	1589	1592	1596	1600	1603	1607	1611	1614	1618	0	1	1	1	2	2	3	3	3
.21	1622	1626	1629	1633	1637	1641	1644	1648	1652	1656	0	1	1	2	2	2	3	3	3
.22	1660	1663	1667	1671	1675	1679	1683	1687	1690	1694	0	1	1	2	2	2	3	3	3
.23	1698	1702	1706	1710	1714	1718	1722	1726	1730	1734	0	1	1	2	2	2	3	3	4
.24	1738	1742	1746	1750	1754	1758	1762	1766	1770	1774	0	1	1	2	2	2	3	3	4
.25	1778	1782	1786	1791	1795	1799	1803	1807	1811	1816	0	1	1	2	2	2	3	3	4
.26	1820	1824	1828	1832	1837	1841	1845	1849	1854	1858	0	1	1	2	2	3	3	3	4
.27	1862	1866	1871	1875	1879	1884	1888	1892	1897	1901	0	1	1	2	2	3	3	3	4
.28	1905	1910	1914	1919	1923	1928	1932	1936	1941	1945	0	1	1	2	2	3	3	4	4
.29	1950	1954	1959	1963	1968	1972	1977	1982	1986	1991	0	1	1	2	2	3	3	4	4
.30	1995	2000	2004	2009	2014	2018	2023	2028	2032	2037	0	1	1	2	2	3	3	4	4
.31	2042	2046	2051	2056	2061	2065	2070	2075	2080	2084	0	1	1	2	2	3	3	4	4
.32	2089	2094	2099	2104	2109	2113	2118	2123	2128	2133	0	1	1	2	2	3	3	4	4
.33	2138	2143	2148	2153	2158	2163	2168	2173	2178	2183	0	1	1	2	2	3	3	4	4
.34	2188	2193	2198	2203	2208	2213	2218	2223	2228	2234	1	1	2	2	3	3	4	4	5
.35	2239	2244	2249	2254	2259	2265	2270	2275	2280	2286	1	1	2	2	3	3	4	4	5
.36	2291	2296	2301	2307	2312	2317	2323	2328	2333	2339	1	1	2	2	3	3	4	4	5
.37	2344	2350	2355	2360	2366	2371	2377	2382	2388	2393	1	1	2	2	3	3	4	4	5
.38	2399	2404	2410	2415	2421	2427	2432	2438	2443	2449	1	1	2	2	3	3	4	4	5
.39	2455	2460	2466	2472	2477	2483	2489	2495	2500	2506	1	1	2	2	3	3	4	5	5
.40	2512	2518	2523	2529	2535	2541	2547	2553	2559	2564	1	1	2	2	3	4	4	5	5
.41	2570	2576	2582	2588	2594	2600	2606	2612	2618	2624	1	1	2	2	3	4	4	5	5
.42	2630	2636	2642	2649	2655	2661	2667	2673	2679	2685	1	1	2	2	3	4	4	5	6
.43	2692	2698	2704	2710	2716	2723	2729	2735	2742	2748	1	1	2	3	3	4	4	5	6
.44	2754	2761	2767	2773	2780	2786	2793	2799	2805	2812	1	1	2	3	3	4	4	5	6
.45	2818	2825	2831	2838	2844	2851	2858	2864	2871	2877	1	1	2	3	3	4	5	5	6
.46	2884	2891	2897	2904	2911	2917	2924	2931	2938	2944	1	1	2	3	3	4	5	5	6
.47	2951	2958	2965	2972	2979	2985	2992	2999	3006	3013	1	1	2	3	3	4	5	5	6
.48	3020	3027	3034	3041	3048	3055	3062	3069	3076	3083	1	1	2	3	4	4	5	6	6
.49	3090	3097	3105	3112	3119	3126	3133	3141	3148	3155	1	1	2	3	4	4	5	6	6
	0	1	2	3	4	5	6	7	8	9	1	2	3	4	5	6	7	8	9

ANTILOGARITHMS

	0	1	2	3	4	5	6	7	8	9	Proportional Parts								
											1	2	3	4	5	6	7	8	9
.50	3162	3170	3177	3184	3192	3199	3206	3214	3221	3228	1	1	2	3	4	4	5	6	7
.51	3236	3243	3251	3258	3266	3273	3281	3289	3296	3304	1	2	2	3	4	5	5	6	7
.52	3311	3319	3327	3334	3342	3350	3357	3365	3373	3381	1	2	2	3	4	5	5	6	7
.53	3388	3396	3404	3412	3420	3428	3436	3443	3451	3459	1	2	2	3	4	5	6	6	7
.54	3467	3475	3483	3491	3499	3508	3516	3524	3532	3540	1	2	2	3	4	5	6	6	7
.55	3548	3556	3565	3573	3581	3589	3597	3606	3614	3622	1	2	2	3	4	5	6	7	7
.56	3631	3639	3648	3656	3664	3673	3681	3690	3698	3707	1	2	3	3	4	5	6	7	8
.57	3715	3724	3733	3741	3750	3758	3767	3776	3784	3793	1	2	3	3	4	5	6	7	8
.58	3802	3811	3819	3828	3837	3846	3855	3864	3873	3882	1	2	3	4	4	5	6	7	8
.59	3890	3899	3908	3917	3926	3936	3945	3954	3963	3972	1	2	3	4	5	5	6	7	8
.60	3981	3990	3999	4009	4018	4027	4036	4046	4055	4064	1	2	3	4	5	6	6	7	8
.61	4074	4083	4093	4102	4111	4121	4130	4140	4150	4159	1	2	3	4	5	6	7	8	9
.62	4169	4178	4188	4198	4207	4217	4227	4236	4246	4256	1	2	3	4	5	6	7	8	9
.63	4266	4276	4285	4295	4305	4315	4325	4335	4345	4355	1	2	3	4	5	6	7	8	9
.64	4365	4375	4385	4395	4406	4416	4426	4436	4446	4457	1	2	3	4	5	6	7	8	9
.65	4467	4477	4487	4498	4508	4519	4529	4539	4550	4560	1	2	3	4	5	6	7	8	9
.66	4571	4581	4592	4603	4613	4624	4634	4645	4656	4667	1	2	3	4	5	6	7	9	10
.67	4677	4688	4699	4710	4721	4732	4742	4753	4764	4775	1	2	3	4	5	7	8	9	10
.68	4786	4797	4808	4819	4831	4842	4853	4864	4875	4887	1	2	3	4	6	7	8	9	10
.69	4898	4909	4920	4932	4943	4955	4966	4977	4989	5000	1	2	3	5	6	7	8	9	10
.70	5012	5023	5035	5047	5058	5070	5082	5093	5105	5117	1	2	4	5	6	7	8	9	11
.71	5129	5140	5152	5164	5176	5188	5200	5212	5224	5236	1	2	4	5	6	7	8	10	11
.72	5248	5260	5272	5284	5297	5309	5321	5333	5346	5358	1	2	4	5	6	7	9	10	11
.73	5370	5383	5395	5408	5420	5433	5445	5458	5470	5483	1	3	4	5	6	8	9	10	11
.74	5495	5508	5521	5534	5546	5559	5572	5585	5598	5610	1	3	4	5	6	8	9	10	12
.75	5623	5636	5649	5662	5675	5689	5702	5715	5728	5741	1	3	4	5	7	8	9	10	12
.76	5754	5768	5781	5794	5808	5821	5834	5848	5861	5875	1	3	4	5	7	8	9	11	12
.77	5888	5902	5916	5929	5943	5957	5970	5984	5998	6012	1	3	4	5	7	8	10	11	12
.78	6026	6039	6053	6067	6081	6095	6109	6124	6138	6152	1	3	4	6	7	8	10	11	13
.79	6166	6180	6194	6209	6223	6237	6252	6266	6281	6295	1	3	4	6	7	9	10	11	13
.80	6310	6324	6339	6353	6368	6383	6397	6412	6427	6442	1	3	4	6	7	9	10	12	13
.81	6457	6471	6486	6501	6516	6531	6546	6561	6577	6592	2	3	5	6	8	9	11	12	14
.82	6607	6622	6637	6653	6668	6683	6699	6714	6730	6745	2	3	5	6	8	9	11	12	14
.83	6761	6776	6792	6808	6823	6839	6855	6871	6887	6902	2	3	5	6	8	9	11	13	14
.84	6918	6934	6950	6966	6982	6998	7015	7031	7047	7063	2	3	5	6	8	10	11	13	15
.85	7079	7096	7112	7129	7145	7161	7178	7194	7211	7228	2	3	5	7	8	10	12	13	15
.86	7244	7261	7278	7295	7311	7328	7345	7362	7379	7396	2	3	5	7	8	10	12	13	15
.87	7413	7430	7447	7464	7482	7499	7516	7534	7551	7568	2	3	5	7	9	10	12	14	16
.88	7586	7603	7621	7638	7656	7674	7691	7709	7727	7745	2	4	5	7	9	11	12	14	16
.89	7762	7780	7798	7816	7834	7852	7870	7889	7907	7925	2	4	5	7	9	11	13	14	16
.90	7943	7962	7980	7998	8017	8035	8054	8072	8091	8110	2	4	6	7	9	11	13	15	17
.91	8128	8147	8166	8185	8204	8222	8241	8260	8279	8299	2	4	6	8	9	11	13	15	17
.92	8318	8337	8356	8375	8395	8414	8433	8453	8472	8492	2	4	6	8	10	12	14	15	17
.93	8511	8531	8551	8570	8590	8610	8630	8650	8670	8690	2	4	6	8	10	12	14	16	18
.94	8710	8730	8750	8770	8790	8810	8831	8851	8872	8892	2	4	6	8	10	12	14	16	18
.95	8913	8933	8954	8974	8995	9016	9036	9057	9078	9099	2	4	6	8	10	12	15	17	19
.96	9120	9141	9162	9183	9204	9226	9247	9268	9290	9311	2	4	6	8	11	13	15	17	19
.97	9333	9354	9376	9397	9419	9441	9462	9484	9506	9528	2	4	7	9	11	13	15	17	20
.98	9550	9572	9594	9616	9638	9661	9683	9705	9727	9750	2	4	7	9	11	13	16	18	20
.99	9772	9795	9817	9840	9863	9886	9908	9931	9954	9977	2	5	7	9	11	14	16	18	20
	0	1	2	3	4	5	6	7	8	9	1	2	3	4	5	6	7	8	9

N.		0	1	2	3	4	5	6	7	8	9	Proportional parts			
100	00	000	043	087	130	173	217	260	303	346	389		**44**	**43**	**42**
101		432	475	518	561	604	647	689	732	775	817	1	4,4	4,3	4,2
102		860	903	945	988	*030	*072	*115	*157	*199	*242	2	8,8	8,6	8,4
103	01	284	326	368	410	452	494	536	578	620	662	3	13,2	12,9	12,6
104		703	745	787	828	870	912	953	995	*036	*078	4	17,6	17,2	16,8
105	02	119	160	202	243	284	325	366	407	449	490	5	22,0	21,5	21,0
106		531	572	612	653	694	735	776	816	857	898	6	26,4	25,8	25,2
107		938	979	*019	*060	*100	*141	*181	*222	*262	*302	7	30,8	30,1	29,4
108	03	342	383	423	463	503	543	583	623	663	703	8	35,2	34,4	33,6
109		743	782	822	862	902	941	981	*021	*060	*100	9	39,6	38,7	37,8
110	04	139	179	218	258	297	336	376	415	454	493		**41**	**40**	**39**
111		532	571	610	650	689	727	766	805	844	883	1	4,1	4,0	3,9
112		922	961	999	*038	*077	*115	*154	*192	*231	*269	2	8,2	8,0	7,8
113	05	308	346	385	423	461	500	538	576	614	652	3	12,3	12,0	11,7
114		690	729	767	805	843	881	918	956	994	*032	4	16,4	16,0	15,6
115	06	070	108	145	183	221	258	296	333	371	408	5	20,5	20,0	19,5
116		446	483	521	558	595	633	670	707	744	781	6	24,6	24,0	23,4
117		819	856	893	930	967	*004	*041	*078	*115	*151	7	28,7	28,0	27,3
118	07	188	225	262	298	335	372	408	445	482	518	8	32,8	32,0	31,2
119		555	591	628	664	700	737	773	809	846	882	9	36,9	36,0	35,1
120		918	954	990	*027	*063	*099	*135	*171	*207	*243		**38**	**37**	**36**
121	08	279	314	350	386	422	458	493	529	565	600	1	3,8	3,7	3,6
122		636	672	707	743	778	814	849	884	920	955	2	7,6	7,4	7,2
123		991	*026	*061	*096	*132	*167	*202	*237	*272	*307	3	11,4	11,1	10,8
124	09	342	377	412	447	482	517	552	587	621	656	4	15,2	14,8	14,4
125		691	726	760	795	830	864	899	934	968	*003	5	19,0	18,5	18,0
126	10	037	072	106	140	175	209	243	278	312	346	6	22,8	22,2	21,6
127		380	415	449	483	517	551	585	619	653	687	7	26,6	25,9	25,2
128		721	755	789	823	857	890	924	958	992	*025	8	30,4	29,6	28,8
129	11	059	093	126	160	193	227	261	294	327	361	9	34,2	33,3	32,4
130		394	428	461	494	528	561	594	628	661	694		**35**	**34**	**33**
131		727	760	793	826	860	893	926	959	992	*024	1	3,5	3,4	3,3
132	12	057	090	123	156	189	222	254	287	320	352	2	7,0	6,8	6,6
133		385	418	450	483	516	548	581	613	646	678	3	10,5	10,2	9,9
134		710	743	775	808	840	872	905	937	969	*001	4	14,0	13,6	13,2
135	13	033	066	098	130	162	194	226	258	290	322	5	17,5	17,0	16,5
136		354	386	418	450	481	513	545	577	609	640	6	21,0	20,4	19,8
137		672	704	735	767	799	830	862	893	925	956	7	24,5	23,8	23,1
138		988	*019	*051	*082	*114	*145	*176	*208	*239	*270	8	28,0	27,2	26,4
139	14	301	333	364	395	426	457	489	520	551	582	9	31,5	30,6	29,7
140		613	644	675	706	737	768	799	829	860	891		**32**	**31**	**30**
141		922	953	983	*014	*045	*076	*106	*137	*168	*198	1	3,2	3,1	3,0
142	15	229	259	290	320	351	381	412	442	473	503	2	6,4	6,2	6,0
143		534	564	594	625	655	685	715	746	776	806	3	9,6	9,3	9,0
144		836	866	897	927	957	987	*017	*047	*077	*107	4	12,8	12,4	12,0
145	16	137	167	197	227	256	286	316	346	376	406	5	16,0	15,5	15,0
146		435	465	495	524	554	584	613	643	673	702	6	19,2	18,6	18,0
147		732	761	791	820	850	879	909	938	967	997	7	22,4	21,7	21,0
148	17	026	056	085	114	143	173	202	231	260	289	8	25,6	24,8	24,0
149		319	348	377	406	435	464	493	522	551	580	9	28,8	27,9	27,0
150		609	638	667	696	725	754	782	811	840	869				

N. 0 1 2 3 4 5 6 7 8 9 Proportional parts

N.	0	1	2	3	4	5	6	7	8	9
150	17 609	638	667	696	725	754	782	811	840	869
151	898	926	955	984	*013	*041	*070	*099	*127	*156
152	18 184	213	241	270	298	327	355	384	412	441
153	469	498	526	554	583	611	639	667	696	724
154	752	780	808	837	865	893	921	949	977	*005
155	19 033	061	089	117	145	173	201	229	257	285
156	312	340	368	396	424	451	479	507	535	562
157	590	618	645	673	700	728	756	783	811	838
158	866	893	921	948	976	*003	*030	*058	*085	*112
159	20 140	167	194	222	249	276	303	330	358	385
160	412	439	466	493	520	548	575	602	629	656
161	683	710	737	763	790	817	844	871	898	925
162	952	978	*005	*032	*059	*085	*112	*139	*165	*192
163	21 219	245	272	299	325	352	378	405	431	458
164	484	511	537	564	590	617	643	669	696	722
165	748	775	801	827	854	880	906	932	958	985
166	22 011	037	063	089	115	141	167	194	220	246
167	272	298	324	350	376	401	427	453	479	505
168	531	557	583	608	634	660	686	712	737	763
169	789	814	840	866	891	917	943	968	994	*019
170	23 045	070	096	121	147	172	198	223	249	274
171	300	325	350	376	401	426	452	477	502	528
172	553	578	603	629	654	679	704	729	754	779
173	805	830	855	880	905	930	955	980	*005	*030
174	24 055	080	105	130	155	180	204	229	254	279
175	304	329	353	378	403	428	452	477	502	527
176	551	576	601	625	650	674	699	724	748	773
177	797	822	846	871	895	920	944	969	993	*018
178	25 042	066	091	115	139	164	188	212	237	261
179	285	310	334	358	382	406	431	455	479	503
180	527	551	575	600	624	648	672	696	720	744
181	768	792	816	840	864	888	912	935	959	983
182	26 007	031	055	079	102	126	150	174	198	221
183	245	269	293	316	340	364	387	411	435	458
184	482	505	529	553	576	600	623	647	670	694
185	717	741	764	788	811	834	858	881	905	928
186	951	975	998	*021	*045	*068	*091	*114	*138	*161
187	27 184	207	231	254	277	300	323	346	370	393
188	416	439	462	485	508	531	554	577	600	623
189	646	669	692	715	738	761	784	807	830	852
190	875	898	921	944	967	989	*012	*035	*058	*081
191	28 103	126	149	171	194	217	240	262	285	307
192	330	353	375	398	421	443	466	488	511	533
193	556	578	601	623	646	668	691	713	735	758
194	780	803	825	847	870	892	914	937	959	981
195	29 003	026	048	070	092	115	137	159	181	203
196	226	248	270	292	314	336	358	380	403	425
197	447	469	491	513	535	557	579	601	623	645
198	667	688	710	732	754	776	798	820	842	863
199	885	907	929	951	973	994	*016	*038	*060	*081
200	30 103	125	146	168	190	211	233	255	276	298
N.	0	1	2	3	4	5	6	7	8	9

Proportional parts

	29	**28**	**27**	**26**	**25**	**24**	**23**	**22**	**21**
1	2,9	2,8	2,7	2,6	2,5	2,4	2,3	2,2	2,1
2	5,8	5,6	5,4	5,2	5,0	4,8	4,6	4,4	4,2
3	8,7	8,4	8,1	7,8	7,5	7,2	6,9	6,6	6,3
4	11,6	11,2	10,8	10,4	10,0	9,6	9,2	8,8	8,4
5	14,5	14,0	13,5	13,0	12,5	12,0	11,5	11,0	10,5
6	17,4	16,8	16,2	15,6	15,0	14,4	13,8	13,2	12,6
7	20,3	19,6	18,9	18,2	17,5	16,8	16,1	15,4	14,7
8	23,2	22,4	21,6	20,8	20,0	19,2	18,4	17,6	16,8
9	26,1	25,2	24,3	23,4	22,5	21,6	20,7	19,8	18,9

N.		0	1	2	3	4	5	6	7	8	9	Proportional parts		
200	30	103	125	146	168	190	211	233	255	276	298		**22**	**21**
201		320	341	363	384	406	428	449	471	492	514	1	2,2	2,1
202		535	557	578	600	621	643	664	685	707	728	2	4,4	4,2
203		750	771	792	814	835	856	878	899	920	942	3	6,6	6,3
204		963	984	*006	*027	*048	*069	*091	*112	*133	*154	4	8,8	8,4
205	31	175	197	218	239	260	281	302	323	345	366	5	11,0	10,5
206		387	408	429	450	471	492	513	534	555	576	6	13,2	12,6
207		597	618	639	660	681	702	723	744	765	785	7	15,4	14,7
208		806	827	848	869	890	911	931	952	973	994	8	17,6	16,8
209	32	015	035	056	077	098	118	139	160	181	201	9	19,8	18,9
210		222	243	263	284	305	325	346	366	387	408		**20**	
211		428	449	469	490	510	531	552	572	593	613	1	2,0	
212		634	654	675	695	715	736	756	777	797	818	2	4,0	
213		838	858	879	899	919	940	960	980	*001	*021	3	6,0	
214	33	041	062	082	102	122	143	163	183	203	224	4	8,0	
215		244	264	284	304	325	345	365	385	405	425	5	10,0	
216		445	465	486	506	526	546	566	586	606	626	6	12,0	
217		646	666	686	706	726	746	766	786	806	826	7	14,0	
218		846	866	885	905	925	945	965	985	*005	*025	8	16,0	
219	34	044	064	084	104	124	143	163	183	203	223	9	18,0	
220		242	262	282	301	321	341	361	380	400	420		**19**	
221		439	459	479	498	518	537	557	577	596	616	1	1,9	
222		635	655	674	694	713	733	753	772	792	811	2	3,8	
223		830	850	869	889	908	928	947	967	986	*005	3	5,7	
224	35	025	044	064	083	102	122	141	160	180	199	4	7,6	
225		218	238	257	276	295	315	334	353	372	392	5	9,5	
226		411	430	449	468	488	507	526	545	564	583	6	11,4	
227		603	622	641	660	679	698	717	736	755	774	7	13,3	
228		793	813	832	851	870	889	908	927	946	965	8	15,2	
229		984	*003	*021	*040	*059	*078	*097	*116	*135	*154	9	17,1	
230	36	173	192	211	229	248	267	286	305	324	342		**18**	
231		361	380	399	418	436	455	474	493	511	530	1	1,8	
232		549	568	586	605	624	642	661	680	698	717	2	3,6	
233		736	754	773	791	810	829	847	866	884	903	3	5,4	
234		922	940	959	977	996	*014	*033	*051	*070	*088	4	7,2	
235	37	107	125	144	162	181	199	218	236	254	273	5	9,0	
236		291	310	328	346	365	383	401	420	438	457	6	10,8	
237		475	493	511	530	548	566	585	603	621	639	7	12,6	
238		658	676	694	712	731	749	767	785	803	822	8	14,4	
239		840	858	876	894	912	931	949	967	985	*003	9	16,2	
240	38	021	039	057	075	093	112	130	148	166	184		**17**	
241		202	220	238	256	274	292	310	328	346	364	1	1,7	
242		382	399	417	435	453	471	489	507	525	543	2	3,4	
243		561	578	596	614	632	650	668	686	703	721	3	5,1	
244		739	757	775	792	810	828	846	863	881	899	4	6,8	
245		917	934	952	970	987	*005	*023	*041	*058	*076	5	8,5	
246	39	094	111	129	146	164	182	199	217	235	252	6	10,2	
247		270	287	305	322	340	358	375	393	410	428	7	11,9	
248		445	463	480	498	515	533	550	568	585	602	8	13,6	
249		620	637	655	672	690	707	724	742	759	777	9	15,3	
250		794	811	829	846	863	881	898	915	933	950			
N.		0	1	2	3	4	5	6	7	8	9	Proportional parts		

N.	0	1	2	3	4	5	6	7	8	9	Proportional parts	
250	39 794	811	829	846	863	881	898	915	933	950		**18**
251	967	985	*002	*019	*037	*054	*071	*088	*106	*123	1	1,8
252	40 140	157	175	192	209	226	243	261	278	295	2	3,6
253	312	329	346	364	381	398	415	432	449	466	3	5,4
254	483	500	518	535	552	569	586	603	620	637	4	7,2
255	654	671	688	705	722	739	756	773	790	807	5	9,0
256	824	841	858	875	892	909	926	943	960	976	6	10,8
257	993	*010	*027	*044	*061	*078	*095	*111	*128	*145	7	12,6
258	41 162	179	196	212	229	246	263	280	296	313	8	14,4
259	330	347	363	380	397	414	430	447	464	481	9	16,2
260	497	514	531	547	564	581	597	614	631	647		**17**
261	664	681	697	714	731	747	764	780	797	814	1	1,7
262	830	847	863	880	896	913	929	946	963	979	2	3,4
263	996	*012	*029	*045	*062	*078	*095	*111	*127	*144	3	5,1
264	42 160	177	193	210	226	243	259	275	292	308	4	6,8
265	325	341	357	374	390	406	423	439	455	472	5	8,5
266	488	504	521	537	553	570	586	602	619	635	6	10,2
267	651	667	684	700	716	732	749	765	781	797	7	11,9
268	813	830	846	862	878	894	911	927	943	959	8	13,6
269	975	991	*008	*024	*040	*056	*072	*088	*104	*120	9	15,3
270	43 136	152	169	185	201	217	233	249	265	281		**16**
271	297	313	329	345	361	377	393	409	425	441	1	1,6
272	457	473	489	505	521	537	553	569	584	600	2	3,2
273	616	632	648	664	680	696	712	727	743	759	3	4,8
274	775	791	807	823	838	854	870	886	902	917	4	6,4
275	933	949	965	981	996	*012	*028	*044	*059	*075	5	8,0
276	44 091	107	122	138	154	170	185	201	217	232	6	9,6
277	248	264	279	295	311	326	342	358	373	389	7	11,2
278	404	420	436	451	467	483	498	514	529	545	8	12,8
279	560	576	592	607	623	638	654	669	685	700	9	14,4
280	716	731	747	762	778	793	809	824	840	855		**15**
281	871	886	902	917	932	948	963	979	994	*010	1	1,5
282	45 025	040	056	071	086	102	117	133	148	163	2	3,0
283	179	194	209	225	240	255	271	286	301	317	3	4,5
284	332	347	362	378	393	408	423	439	454	469	4	6,0
285	484	500	515	530	545	561	576	591	606	621	5	7,5
286	637	652	667	682	697	712	728	743	758	773	6	9,0
287	788	803	818	834	849	864	879	894	909	924	7	10,5
288	939	954	969	984	*000	*015	*030	*045	*060	*075	8	12,0
289	46 090	105	120	135	150	165	180	195	210	225	9	13,5
290	240	255	270	285	300	315	330	345	359	374		**14**
291	389	404	419	434	449	464	479	494	509	523	1	1,4
292	538	553	568	583	598	613	627	642	657	672	2	2,8
293	687	702	716	731	746	761	776	790	805	820	3	4,2
294	835	850	864	879	894	909	923	938	953	967	4	5,6
295	982	997	*012	*026	*041	*056	*070	*085	*100	*114	5	7,0
296	47 129	144	159	173	188	202	217	232	246	261	6	8,4
297	276	290	305	319	334	349	363	378	392	407	7	9,8
298	422	436	451	465	480	494	509	524	538	553	8	11,2
299	567	582	596	611	625	640	654	669	683	698	9	12,6
300	712	727	741	756	770	784	799	813	828	842		
N.	0	1	2	3	4	5	6	7	8	9	Proportional parts	

N.	0	1	2	3	4	5	6	7	8	9
300	47 712	727	741	756	770	784	799	813	828	842
301	857	871	885	900	914	929	943	958	972	986
302	48 001	015	029	044	058	073	087	101	116	130
303	144	159	173	187	202	216	230	244	259	273
304	287	302	316	330	344	359	373	387	401	416
305	430	444	458	473	487	501	515	530	544	558
306	572	586	601	615	629	643	657	671	686	700
307	714	728	742	756	770	785	799	813	827	841
308	855	869	883	897	911	926	940	954	968	982
309	996	*010	*024	*038	*052	*066	*080	*094	*108	*122
310	49 136	150	164	178	192	206	220	234	248	262
311	276	290	304	318	332	346	360	374	388	402
312	415	429	443	457	471	485	499	513	527	541
313	554	568	582	596	610	624	638	651	665	679
314	693	707	721	734	748	762	776	790	803	817
315	831	845	859	872	886	900	914	927	941	955
316	969	982	996	*010	*024	*037	*051	*065	*079	*092
317	50 106	120	133	147	161	174	188	202	215	229
318	243	256	270	284	297	311	325	338	352	365
319	379	393	406	420	433	447	461	474	488	501
320	515	529	542	556	569	583	596	610	623	637
321	651	664	678	691	705	718	732	745	759	772
322	786	799	813	826	840	853	866	880	893	907
323	920	934	947	961	974	987	*001	*014	*028	*041
324	51 055	068	081	095	108	121	135	148	162	175
325	188	202	215	228	242	255	268	282	295	308
326	322	335	348	362	375	388	402	415	428	441
327	455	468	481	495	508	521	534	548	561	574
328	587	601	614	627	640	654	667	680	693	706
329	720	733	746	759	772	786	799	812	825	838
330	851	865	878	891	904	917	930	943	957	970
331	983	996	*009	*022	*035	*048	*061	*075	*088	*101
332	52 114	127	140	153	166	179	192	205	218	231
333	244	257	270	284	297	310	323	336	349	362
334	375	388	401	414	427	440	453	466	479	492
335	504	517	530	543	556	569	582	595	608	621
336	634	647	660	673	686	699	711	724	737	750
337	763	776	789	802	815	827	840	853	866	879
338	892	905	917	930	943	956	969	982	994	*007
339	53 020	033	046	058	071	084	097	110	122	135
340	148	161	173	186	199	212	224	237	250	263
341	275	288	301	314	326	339	352	364	377	390
342	403	415	428	441	453	466	479	491	504	517
343	529	542	555	567	580	593	605	618	631	643
344	656	668	681	694	706	719	732	744	757	769
345	782	794	807	820	832	845	857	870	882	895
346	908	920	933	945	958	970	983	995	*008	*020
347	54 033	045	058	070	083	095	108	120	133	145
348	158	170	183	195	208	220	233	245	258	270
349	283	295	307	320	332	345	357	370	382	394
350	407	419	432	444	456	469	481	494	506	518
N.	0	1	2	3	4	5	6	7	8	9

Proportional parts

	15	**14**	**13**	**12**
1	1,5	1,4	1,3	1,2
2	3,0	2,8	2,6	2,4
3	4,5	4,2	3,9	3,6
4	6,0	5,6	5,2	4,8
5	7,5	7,0	6,5	6,0
6	9,0	8,4	7,8	7,2
7	10,5	9,8	9,1	8,4
8	12,0	11,2	10,4	9,6
9	13,5	12,6	11,7	10,8

FIVE-PLACE LOGARITHMS (Continued)

N.		0	1	2	3	4	5	6	7	8	9
350	54	407	419	432	444	456	469	481	494	506	518
351		531	543	555	568	580	593	605	617	630	642
352		654	667	679	691	704	716	728	741	753	765
353		777	790	802	814	827	839	851	864	876	888
354		900	913	925	937	949	962	974	986	998	*011
355	55	023	035	047	060	072	084	096	108	121	133
356		145	157	169	182	194	206	218	230	242	255
357		267	279	291	303	315	328	340	352	364	376
358		388	400	413	425	437	449	461	473	485	497
359		509	522	534	546	558	570	582	594	606	618
360		630	642	654	666	678	691	703	715	727	739
361		751	763	775	787	799	811	823	835	847	859
362		871	883	895	907	919	931	943	955	967	979
363		991	*003	*015	*027	*038	*050	*062	*074	*086	*098
364	56	110	122	134	146	158	170	182	194	205	217
365		229	241	253	265	277	289	301	312	324	336
366		348	360	372	384	396	407	419	431	443	455
367		467	478	490	502	514	526	538	549	561	573
368		585	597	608	620	632	644	656	667	679	691
369		703	714	726	738	750	761	773	785	797	808
370		820	832	844	855	867	879	891	902	914	926
371		937	949	961	972	984	996	*008	*019	*031	*043
372	57	054	066	078	089	101	113	124	136	148	159
373		171	183	194	206	217	229	241	252	264	276
374		287	299	310	322	334	345	357	368	380	392
375		403	415	426	438	449	461	473	484	496	507
376		519	530	542	553	565	576	588	600	611	623
377		634	646	657	669	680	692	703	715	726	738
378		749	761	772	784	795	807	818	830	841	852
379		864	875	887	898	910	921	933	944	955	967
380		978	990	*001	*013	*024	*035	*047	*058	*070	*081
381	58	092	104	115	127	138	149	161	172	184	195
382		206	218	229	240	252	263	274	286	297	309
383		320	331	343	354	365	377	388	399	410	422
384		433	444	456	467	478	490	501	512	524	535
385		546	557	569	580	591	602	614	625	636	647
386		659	670	681	692	704	715	726	737	749	760
387		771	782	794	805	816	827	838	850	861	872
388		883	894	906	917	928	939	950	961	973	984
389		995	*006	*017	*028	*040	*051	*062	*073	*084	*095
390	59	106	118	129	140	151	162	173	184	195	207
391		218	229	240	251	262	273	284	295	306	318
392		329	340	351	362	373	384	395	406	417	428
393		439	450	461	472	483	494	506	517	528	539
394		550	561	572	583	594	605	616	627	638	649
395		660	671	682	693	704	715	726	737	748	759
396		770	780	791	802	813	824	835	846	857	868
397		879	890	901	912	923	934	945	956	966	977
398		988	999	*010	*021	*032	*043	*054	*065	*076	*086
399	60	097	108	119	130	141	152	163	173	184	195
400		206	217	228	239	249	260	271	282	293	304
N.		0	1	2	3	4	5	6	7	8	9

Proportional parts

	13	**12**	**11**	**10**
1	1,3	1,2	1,1	1,0
2	2,6	2,4	2,2	2,0
3	3,9	3,6	3,3	3,0
4	5,2	4,8	4,4	4,0
5	6,5	6,0	5 5	5,0
6	7,8	7,2	6,6	6,0
7	9,1	8,4	7,7	7,0
8	10,4	9,6	8,8	8,0
9	11,7	10,8	9,9	9,0

FIVE-PLACE LOGARITHMS (Continued)

N.	0	1	2	3	4	5	6	7	8	9
400	60 206	217	228	239	249	260	271	282	293	304
401	314	325	336	347	358	369	379	390	401	412
402	423	433	444	455	466	477	487	498	509	520
403	531	541	552	563	574	584	595	606	617	627
404	638	649	660	670	681	692	703	713	724	735
405	746	756	767	778	788	799	810	821	831	842
406	853	863	874	885	895	906	917	927	938	949
407	959	970	981	991	*002	*013	*023	*034	*045	*055
408	61 066	077	087	098	109	119	130	140	151	162
409	172	183	194	204	215	225	236	247	257	268
410	278	289	300	310	321	331	342	352	363	374
411	384	395	405	416	426	437	448	458	469	479
412	490	500	511	521	532	542	553	563	574	584
413	595	606	616	627	637	648	658	669	679	690
414	700	711	721	731	742	752	763	773	784	794
415	805	815	826	836	847	857	868	878	888	899
416	909	920	930	941	951	962	972	982	993	*003
417	62 014	024	034	045	055	066	076	086	097	107
418	118	128	138	149	159	170	180	190	201	211
419	221	232	242	252	263	273	284	294	304	315
420	325	335	346	356	366	377	387	397	408	418
421	428	439	449	459	469	480	490	500	511	521
422	531	542	552	562	572	583	593	603	613	624
423	634	644	655	665	675	685	696	706	716	726
424	737	747	757	767	778	788	798	808	818	829
425	839	849	859	870	880	890	900	910	921	931
426	941	951	961	972	982	992	*002	*012	*022	*033
427	63 043	053	063	073	083	094	104	114	124	134
428	144	155	165	175	185	195	205	215	225	236
429	246	256	266	276	286	296	306	317	327	337
430	347	357	367	377	387	397	407	417	428	438
431	448	458	468	478	488	498	508	518	528	538
432	548	558	568	579	589	599	609	619	629	639
433	649	659	669	679	689	699	709	719	729	739
434	749	759	769	779	789	799	809	819	829	839
435	849	859	869	879	889	899	909	919	929	939
436	949	959	969	979	988	998	*008	*018	*028	*038
437	64 048	058	068	078	088	098	108	118	128	137
438	147	157	167	177	187	197	207	217	227	237
439	246	256	266	276	286	296	306	316	326	335
440	345	355	365	375	385	395	404	414	424	434
441	444	454	464	473	483	493	503	513	523	532
442	542	552	562	572	582	591	601	611	621	631
443	640	650	660	670	680	689	699	709	719	729
444	738	748	758	768	777	787	797	807	816	826
445	836	846	856	865	875	885	895	904	914	924
446	933	943	953	963	972	982	992	*002	*011	*021
447	65 031	040	050	060	070	079	089	099	108	118
448	128	137	147	157	167	176	186	196	205	215
449	225	234	244	254	263	273	283	292	302	312
450	321	331	341	350	360	369	379	389	398	408
N.	0	1	2	3	4	5	6	7	8	9

Proportional parts

	11
1	1,1
2	2,2
3	3,3
4	4,4
5	5,5
6	6,6
7	7,7
8	8,8
9	9,9

	10
1	1,0
2	2,0
3	3,0
4	4,0
5	5,0
6	6,0
7	7,0
8	8,0
9	9,0

	9
1	0,9
2	1,8
3	2,7
4	3,6
5	4,5
6	5,4
7	6,3
8	7,2
9	8,1

FIVE-PLACE LOGARITHMS (Continued)

N.	0	1	2	3	4	5	6	7	8	9	Proportional parts
450	65 321	331	341	350	360	369	379	389	398	408	
451	418	427	437	447	456	466	475	485	495	504	
452	514	523	533	543	552	562	571	581	591	600	
453	610	619	629	639	648	658	667	677	686	696	
454	706	715	725	734	744	753	763	772	782	792	
455	801	811	820	830	839	849	858	868	877	887	
456	896	906	916	925	935	944	954	963	973	982	
457	992	*001	*011	*020	*030	*039	*049	*058	*068	*077	**10**
458	66 087	096	106	115	124	134	143	153	162	172	1 | 1,0
459	181	191	200	210	219	229	238	247	257	266	2 | 2,0
											3 | 3,0
460	276	285	295	304	314	323	332	342	351	361	4 | 4,0
461	370	380	389	398	408	417	427	436	445	455	5 | 5,0
462	464	474	483	492	502	511	521	530	539	549	6 | 6,0
463	558	567	577	586	596	605	614	624	633	642	7 | 7,0
464	652	661	671	680	689	699	708	717	727	736	8 | 8,0
465	745	755	764	773	783	792	801	811	820	829	9 | 9,0
466	839	848	857	867	876	885	894	904	913	922	
467	932	941	950	960	969	978	987	997	*006	*015	
468	67 025	034	043	052	062	071	080	089	099	108	
469	117	127	136	145	154	164	173	182	191	201	
470	210	219	228	237	247	256	265	274	284	293	
471	302	311	321	330	339	348	357	367	376	385	**9**
472	394	403	413	422	431	440	449	459	468	477	1 | 0,9
473	486	495	504	514	523	532	541	550	560	569	2 | 1,8
474	578	587	596	605	614	624	633	642	651	660	3 | 2,7
475	669	679	688	697	706	715	724	733	742	752	4 | 3,6
476	761	770	779	788	797	806	815	825	834	843	5 | 4,5
477	852	861	870	879	888	897	906	916	925	934	6 | 5,4
478	943	952	961	970	979	988	997	*006	*015	*024	7 | 6,3
479	68 034	043	052	061	070	079	088	097	106	115	8 | 7,2
											9 | 8,1
480	124	133	142	151	160	169	178	187	196	205	
481	215	224	233	242	251	260	269	278	287	296	
482	305	314	323	332	341	350	359	368	377	386	
483	395	404	413	422	431	440	449	458	467	476	
484	485	494	502	511	520	529	538	547	556	565	
485	574	583	592	601	610	619	628	637	646	655	**8**
486	664	673	681	690	699	708	717	726	735	744	1 | 0,8
487	753	762	771	780	789	797	806	815	824	833	2 | 1,6
488	842	851	860	869	878	886	895	904	913	922	3 | 2,4
489	931	940	949	958	966	975	984	993	*002	*011	4 | 3,2
											5 | 4,0
490	69 020	028	037	046	055	064	073	082	090	099	6 | 4,8
491	108	117	126	135	144	152	161	170	179	188	7 | 5,6
492	197	205	214	223	232	241	249	258	267	276	8 | 6,4
493	285	294	302	311	320	329	338	346	355	364	9 | 7,2
494	373	381	390	399	408	417	425	434	443	452	
495	461	469	478	487	496	504	513	522	531	539	
496	548	557	566	574	583	592	601	609	618	627	
497	636	644	653	662	671	679	688	697	705	714	
498	723	732	740	749	758	767	775	784	793	801	
499	810	819	827	836	845	854	862	871	880	888	
500	897	906	914	923	932	940	949	958	966	975	
N.	0	1	2	3	4	5	6	7	8	9	Proportional parts

N.		0	1	2	3	4	5	6	7	8	9
500	69	897	906	914	923	932	940	949	958	966	975
501		984	992	*001	*010	*018	*027	*036	*044	*053	*062
502	70	070	079	088	096	105	114	122	131	140	148
503		157	165	174	183	191	200	209	217	226	234
504		243	252	260	269	278	286	295	303	312	321
505		329	338	346	355	364	372	381	389	398	406
506		415	424	432	441	449	458	467	475	484	492
507		501	509	518	526	535	544	552	561	569	578
508		586	595	603	612	621	629	638	646	655	663
509		672	680	689	697	706	714	723	731	740	749
510		757	766	774	783	791	800	808	817	825	834
511		842	851	859	868	876	885	893	902	910	919
512		927	935	944	952	961	969	978	986	995	*003
513	71	012	020	029	037	046	054	063	071	079	088
514		096	105	113	122	130	139	147	155	164	172
515		181	189	198	206	214	223	231	240	248	257
516		265	273	282	290	299	307	315	324	332	341
517		349	357	366	374	383	391	399	408	416	425
518		433	441	450	458	466	475	483	492	500	508
519		517	525	533	542	550	559	567	575	584	592
520		600	609	617	625	634	642	650	659	667	675
521		684	692	700	709	717	725	734	742	750	759
522		767	775	784	792	800	809	817	825	834	842
523		850	858	867	875	883	892	900	908	917	925
524		933	941	950	958	966	975	983	991	999	*008
525	72	016	024	032	041	049	057	066	074	082	090
526		099	107	115	123	132	140	148	156	165	173
527		181	189	198	206	214	222	230	239	247	255
528		263	272	280	288	296	304	313	321	329	337
529		346	354	362	370	378	387	395	403	411	419
530		428	436	444	452	460	469	477	485	493	501
531		509	518	526	534	542	550	558	567	575	583
532		591	599	607	616	624	632	640	648	656	665
533		673	681	689	697	705	713	722	730	738	746
534		754	762	770	779	787	795	803	811	819	827
535		835	843	852	860	868	876	884	892	900	908
536		916	925	933	941	949	957	965	973	981	989
537		997	*006	*014	*022	*030	*038	*046	*054	*062	*070
538	73	078	086	094	102	111	119	127	135	143	151
539		159	167	175	183	191	199	207	215	223	231
540		239	247	255	263	272	280	288	296	304	312
541		320	328	336	344	352	360	368	376	384	392
542		400	408	416	424	432	440	448	456	464	472
543		480	488	496	504	512	520	528	536	544	552
544		560	568	576	584	592	600	608	616	624	632
545		640	648	656	664	672	679	687	695	703	711
546		719	727	735	743	751	759	767	775	783	791
547		799	807	815	823	830	838	846	854	862	870
548		878	886	894	902	910	918	926	933	941	949
549		957	965	973	981	989	997	*005	*013	*020	*028
550	74	036	044	052	060	068	076	084	092	099	107
N.		0	1	2	3	4	5	6	7	8	9

Proportional parts

	9
1	0.9
2	1.8
3	2.7
4	3.6
5	4.5
6	5.4
7	6.3
8	7.2
9	8.1

	8
1	0.8
2	1.6
3	2.4
4	3.2
5	4.0
6	4.8
7	5.6
8	6.4
9	7.2

	7
1	0.7
2	1.4
3	2.1
4	2.8
5	3.5
6	4.2
7	4.9
8	5.6
9	6.3

FIVE-PLACE LOGARITHMS (Continued)

N.	0	1	2	3	4	5	6	7	8	9	Proportional parts
550	74 036	044	052	060	068	076	084	092	099	107	
551	115	123	131	139	147	155	162	170	178	186	
552	194	202	210	218	225	233	241	249	257	265	
553	273	280	288	296	304	312	320	327	335	343	
554	351	359	367	374	382	390	398	406	414	421	
555	429	437	445	453	461	468	476	484	492	500	
556	507	515	523	531	539	547	554	562	570	578	
557	586	593	601	609	617	624	632	640	648	656	
558	663	671	679	687	695	702	710	718	726	733	
559	741	749	757	764	772	780	788	796	803	811	
560	819	827	834	842	850	858	865	873	881	889	**8**
561	896	904	912	920	927	935	943	950	958	966	1 0.8
562	974	981	989	997	*005	*012	*020	*028	*035	*043	2 1.6
563	75 051	059	066	074	082	089	097	105	113	120	3 2.4
564	128	136	143	151	159	166	174	182	189	197	4 3.2
565	205	213	220	228	236	243	251	259	266	274	5 4.0
566	282	289	297	305	312	320	328	335	343	351	6 4.8
567	358	366	374	381	389	397	404	412	420	427	7 5.6
568	435	442	450	458	465	473	481	488	496	504	8 6.4
569	511	519	526	534	542	549	557	565	572	580	9 7.2
570	587	595	603	610	618	626	633	641	648	656	
571	664	671	679	686	694	702	709	717	724	732	
572	740	747	755	762	770	778	785	793	800	808	
573	815	823	831	838	846	853	861	868	876	884	
574	891	899	906	914	921	929	937	944	952	959	
575	967	974	982	989	997	*005	*012	*020	*027	*035	
576	76 042	050	057	065	072	080	087	095	103	110	
577	118	125	133	140	148	155	163	170	178	185	
578	193	200	208	215	223	230	238	245	253	260	
579	268	275	283	290	298	305	313	320	328	335	
580	343	350	358	365	373	380	388	395	403	410	**7**
581	418	425	433	440	448	455	462	470	477	485	1 0.7
582	492	500	507	515	522	530	537	545	552	559	2 1.4
583	567	574	582	589	597	604	612	619	626	634	3 2.1
584	641	649	656	664	671	678	686	693	701	708	4 2.8
585	716	723	730	738	745	753	760	768	775	782	5 3.5
586	790	797	805	812	819	827	834	842	849	856	6 4.2
587	864	871	879	886	893	901	908	916	923	930	7 4.9
588	938	945	953	960	967	975	982	989	997	*004	8 5.6
589	77 012	019	026	034	041	048	056	063	070	078	9 6.3
590	085	093	100	107	115	122	129	137	144	151	
591	159	166	173	181	188	195	203	210	217	225	
592	232	240	247	254	262	269	276	283	291	298	
593	305	313	320	327	335	342	349	357	364	371	
594	379	386	393	401	408	415	422	430	437	444	
595	452	459	466	474	481	488	495	503	510	517	
596	525	532	539	546	554	561	568	576	583	590	
597	597	605	612	619	627	634	641	648	656	663	
598	670	677	685	692	699	706	714	721	728	735	
599	743	750	757	764	772	779	786	793	801	808	
600	815	822	830	837	844	851	859	866	873	880	
N.	0	1	2	3	4	5	6	7	8	9	Proportional parts

FIVE-PLACE LOGARITHMS (Continued)

N.	0	1	2	3	4	5	6	7	8	9	Proportional parts
600	77 815	822	830	837	844	851	859	866	873	880	
601	887	895	902	909	916	924	931	938	945	952	
602	960	967	974	981	988	996	*003	*010	*017	*025	
603	78 032	039	046	053	061	068	075	082	089	097	
604	104	111	118	125	132	140	147	154	161	168	
605	176	183	190	197	204	211	219	226	233	240	
606	247	254	262	269	276	283	290	297	305	312	
607	319	326	333	340	347	355	362	369	376	383	**8**
608	390	398	405	412	419	426	433	440	447	455	1 | 0.8
609	462	469	476	483	490	497	504	512	519	526	2 | 1.6
											3 | 2.4
610	533	540	547	554	561	569	576	583	590	597	4 | 3.2
611	004	011	010	025	000	040	047	054	001	008	5 | 4.0
612	675	682	689	696	704	711	718	725	732	739	6 | 4.8
613	746	753	760	767	774	781	789	796	803	810	7 | 5.6
614	817	824	831	838	845	852	859	866	873	880	8 | 6.4
615	888	895	902	909	916	923	930	937	944	951	9 | 7.2
616	958	965	972	979	986	993	*000	*007	*014	*021	
617	79 029	036	043	050	057	064	071	078	085	092	
618	099	106	113	120	127	134	141	148	155	162	
619	169	176	183	190	197	204	211	218	225	232	
620	239	246	253	260	267	274	281	288	295	302	**7**
621	309	316	323	330	337	344	351	358	365	372	1 | 0.7
622	379	386	393	400	407	414	421	428	435	442	2 | 1.4
623	449	456	463	470	477	484	491	498	505	511	3 | 2.1
624	518	525	532	539	546	553	560	567	574	581	4 | 2.8
625	588	595	602	609	616	623	630	637	644	650	5 | 3.5
626	657	664	671	678	685	692	699	706	713	720	6 | 4.2
627	727	734	741	748	754	761	768	775	782	789	7 | 4.9
628	796	803	810	817	824	831	837	844	851	858	8 | 5.6
629	865	872	879	886	893	900	906	913	920	927	9 | 6.3
630	934	941	948	955	962	969	975	982	989	996	
631	80 003	010	017	024	030	037	044	051	058	065	
632	072	079	085	092	099	106	113	120	127	134	
633	140	147	154	161	168	175	182	188	195	202	
634	209	216	223	229	236	243	250	257	264	271	
635	277	284	291	298	305	312	318	325	332	339	**6**
636	346	353	359	366	373	380	387	393	400	407	1 | 0.6
637	414	421	428	434	441	448	455	462	468	475	2 | 1.2
638	482	489	496	502	509	516	523	530	536	543	3 | 1.8
639	550	557	564	570	577	584	591	598	604	611	4 | 2.4
											5 | 3.0
640	618	625	632	638	645	652	659	665	672	679	6 | 3.6
641	686	693	699	706	713	720	726	733	740	747	7 | 4.2
642	754	760	767	774	781	787	794	801	808	814	8 | 4.8
643	821	828	835	841	848	855	862	868	875	882	9 | 5.4
644	889	895	902	909	916	922	929	936	943	949	
645	956	963	969	976	983	990	996	*003	*010	*017	
646	81 023	030	037	043	050	057	064	070	077	084	
647	090	097	104	111	117	124	131	137	144	151	
648	158	164	171	178	184	191	198	204	211	218	
649	224	231	238	245	251	258	265	271	278	285	
650	291	298	305	311	318	325	331	338	345	351	
N.	0	1	2	3	4	5	6	7	8	9	Proportional parts

N.	0	1	2	3	4	5	6	7	8	9	Proportional parts
650	81 291	298	305	311	318	325	331	338	345	351	
651	358	365	371	378	385	391	398	405	411	418	
652	425	431	438	445	451	458	465	471	478	485	
653	491	498	505	511	518	525	531	538	544	551	
654	558	564	571	578	584	591	598	604	611	617	
655	624	631	637	644	651	657	664	671	677	684	
656	690	697	704	710	717	723	730	737	743	750	
657	757	763	770	776	783	790	796	803	809	816	
658	823	829	836	842	849	856	862	869	875	882	
659	889	895	902	908	915	921	928	935	941	948	
660	954	961	968	974	981	987	994	*000	*007	*014	**7**
661	82 020	027	033	040	046	053	060	066	073	079	1 0,7
662	086	092	099	105	112	119	125	132	138	145	2 1,4
663	151	158	164	171	178	184	191	197	204	210	3 2,1
664	217	223	230	236	243	249	256	263	269	276	4 2,8
665	282	289	295	302	308	315	321	328	334	341	5 3,5
666	347	354	360	367	373	380	387	393	400	406	6 4,2
667	413	419	426	432	439	445	452	458	465	471	7 4,9
668	478	484	491	497	504	510	517	523	530	536	8 5,6
669	543	549	556	562	569	575	582	588	595	601	9 6,3
670	607	614	620	627	633	640	646	653	659	666	
671	672	679	685	692	698	705	711	718	724	730	
672	737	743	750	756	763	769	776	782	789	795	
673	802	808	814	821	827	834	840	847	853	860	
674	866	872	879	885	892	898	905	911	918	924	
675	930	937	943	950	956	963	969	975	982	988	
676	995	*001	*008	*014	*020	*027	*033	*040	*046	*052	
677	83 059	065	072	078	085	091	097	104	110	117	
678	123	129	136	142	149	155	161	168	174	181	
679	187	193	200	206	213	219	225	232	238	245	
680	251	257	264	270	276	283	289	296	302	308	**6**
681	315	321	327	334	340	347	353	359	366	372	1 0,6
682	378	385	391	398	404	410	417	423	429	436	2 1,2
683	442	448	455	461	467	474	480	487	493	499	3 1,8
684	506	512	518	525	531	537	544	550	556	563	4 2,4
685	569	575	582	588	594	601	607	613	620	626	5 3,0
686	632	639	645	651	658	664	670	677	683	689	6 3,6
687	696	702	708	715	721	727	734	740	746	753	7 4,2
688	759	765	771	778	784	790	797	803	809	816	8 4,8
689	822	828	835	841	847	853	860	866	872	879	9 5,4
690	885	891	897	904	910	916	923	929	935	942	
691	948	954	960	967	973	979	985	992	998	*004	
692	84 011	017	023	029	036	042	048	055	061	067	
693	073	080	086	092	098	105	111	117	123	130	
694	136	142	148	155	161	167	173	180	186	192	
695	198	205	211	217	223	230	236	242	248	255	
696	261	267	273	280	286	292	298	305	311	317	
697	323	330	336	342	348	354	361	367	373	379	
698	386	392	398	404	410	417	423	429	435	442	
699	448	454	460	466	473	479	485	491	497	504	
700	510	516	522	528	535	541	547	553	559	566	
N.	0	1	2	3	4	5	6	7	8	9	Proportional parts

N.		0	1	2	3	4	5	6	7	8	9
700	84	510	516	522	528	535	541	547	553	559	566
701		572	578	584	590	597	603	609	615	621	628
702		634	640	646	652	658	665	671	677	683	689
703		696	702	708	714	720	726	733	739	745	751
704		757	763	770	776	782	788	794	800	807	813
705		819	825	831	837	844	850	856	862	868	874
706		880	887	893	899	905	911	917	924	930	936
707		942	948	954	960	967	973	979	985	991	997
708	85	003	009	016	022	028	034	040	046	052	058
709		065	071	077	083	089	095	101	107	114	120
710		126	132	138	144	150	156	163	169	175	181
711		187	193	199	205	211	217	224	230	236	242
712		248	254	260	266	272	278	285	291	297	303
713		309	315	321	327	333	339	345	352	358	364
714		370	376	382	388	394	400	406	412	418	425
715		431	437	443	449	455	461	467	473	479	485
716		491	497	503	509	516	522	528	534	540	546
717		552	558	564	570	576	582	588	594	600	606
718		612	618	625	631	637	643	649	655	661	667
719		673	679	685	691	697	703	709	715	721	727
720		733	739	745	751	757	763	769	775	781	788
721		794	800	806	812	818	824	830	836	842	848
722		854	860	866	872	878	884	890	896	902	908
723		914	920	926	932	938	944	950	956	962	968
724		974	980	986	992	998	*004	*010	*016	*022	*028
725	86	034	040	046	052	058	064	070	076	082	088
726		094	100	106	112	118	124	130	136	141	147
727		153	159	165	171	177	183	189	195	201	207
728		213	219	225	231	237	243	249	255	261	267
729		273	279	285	291	297	303	308	314	320	326
730		332	338	344	350	356	362	368	374	380	386
731		392	398	404	410	415	421	427	433	439	445
732		451	457	463	469	475	481	487	493	499	504
733		510	516	522	528	534	540	546	552	558	564
734		570	576	581	587	593	599	605	611	617	623
735		629	635	641	646	652	658	664	670	676	682
736		688	694	700	705	711	717	723	729	735	741
737		747	753	759	764	770	776	782	788	794	800
738		806	812	817	823	829	835	841	847	853	859
739		864	870	876	882	888	894	900	906	911	917
740		923	929	935	941	947	953	958	964	970	976
741		982	988	994	999	*005	*011	*017	*023	*029	*035
742	87	040	046	052	058	064	070	075	081	087	093
743		099	105	111	116	122	128	134	140	146	151
744		157	163	169	175	181	186	192	198	204	210
745		216	221	227	233	239	245	251	256	262	268
746		274	280	286	291	297	303	309	315	320	326
747		332	338	344	349	355	361	367	373	379	384
748		390	396	402	408	413	419	425	431	437	442
749		448	454	460	466	471	477	483	489	495	500
750		506	512	518	523	529	535	541	547	552	558
N.		0	1	2	3	4	5	6	7	8	9

Proportional parts

	7
1	0,7
2	1,4
3	2·1
4	2,8
5	3,5
6	4,2
7	4,9
8	5,6
9	6,3

	6
1	0,6
2	1,2
3	1,8
4	2,4
5	3,0
6	3,6
7	4,2
8	4,8
9	5,4

	5
1	0,5
2	1,0
3	1,5
4	2,0
5	2,5
6	3,0
7	3,5
8	4,0
9	4,5

FIVE-PLACE LOGARITHMS (Continued)

N.	0	1	2	3	4	5	6	7	8	9	Proportional parts
750	87 506	512	518	523	529	535	541	547	552	558	
751	564	570	576	581	587	593	599	604	610	616	
752	622	628	633	639	645	651	656	662	668	674	
753	679	685	691	697	703	708	714	720	726	731	
754	737	743	749	754	760	766	772	777	783	789	
755	795	800	806	812	818	823	829	835	841	846	
756	852	858	864	869	875	881	887	892	898	904	
757	910	915	921	927	933	938	944	950	955	961	
758	967	973	978	984	990	996	*001	*007	*013	*018	
759	88 024	030	036	041	047	053	058	064	070	076	
760	081	087	093	098	104	110	116	121	127	133	**6**
761	138	144	150	156	161	167	173	178	184	190	1 0.6
762	195	201	207	213	218	224	230	235	241	247	2 1.2
763	252	258	264	270	275	281	287	292	298	304	3 1.8
764	309	315	321	326	332	338	343	349	355	360	4 2.4
765	366	372	377	383	389	395	400	406	412	417	5 3.0
766	423	429	434	440	446	451	457	463	468	474	6 3.6
767	480	485	491	497	502	508	513	519	525	530	7 4.2
768	536	542	547	553	559	564	570	576	581	587	8 4.8
769	593	598	604	610	615	621	627	632	638	643	9 5.4
770	649	655	660	666	672	677	683	689	694	700	
771	705	711	717	722	728	734	739	745	750	756	
772	762	767	773	779	784	790	795	801	807	812	
773	818	824	829	835	840	846	852	857	863	868	
774	874	880	885	891	897	902	908	913	919	925	
775	930	936	941	947	953	958	964	969	975	981	
776	986	992	997	*003	*009	*014	*020	*025	*031	*037	
777	89 042	048	053	059	064	070	076	081	087	092	
778	098	104	109	115	120	126	131	137	143	148	
779	154	159	165	170	176	182	187	193	198	204	
780	209	215	221	226	232	237	243	248	254	260	**5**
781	265	271	276	282	287	293	298	304	310	315	1 0.5
782	321	326	332	337	343	348	354	360	365	371	2 1.0
783	376	382	387	393	398	404	409	415	421	426	3 1.5
784	432	437	443	448	454	459	465	470	476	481	4 2.0
785	487	492	498	504	509	515	520	526	531	537	5 2.5
786	542	548	553	559	564	570	575	581	586	592	6 3.0
787	597	603	609	614	620	625	631	636	642	647	7 3.5
788	653	658	664	669	675	680	686	691	697	702	8 4.0
789	708	713	719	724	730	735	741	746	752	757	9 4.5
790	763	768	774	779	785	790	796	801	807	812	
791	818	823	829	834	840	845	851	856	862	867	
792	873	878	883	889	894	900	905	911	916	922	
793	927	933	938	944	949	955	960	966	971	977	
794	982	988	993	998	*004	*009	*015	*020	*026	*031	
795	90 037	042	048	053	059	064	069	075	080	086	
796	091	097	102	108	113	119	124	129	135	140	
797	146	151	157	162	168	173	179	184	189	195	
798	200	206	211	217	222	227	233	238	244	249	
799	255	260	266	271	276	282	287	293	298	304	
800	309	314	320	325	331	336	342	347	352	358	
N.	0	1	2	3	4	5	6	7	8	9	Proportional parts

N.	0	1	2	3	4	5	6	7	8	9	Proportional parts
800	90 309	314	320	325	331	336	342	347	352	358	
801	363	369	374	380	385	390	396	401	407	412	
802	417	423	428	434	439	445	450	455	461	466	
803	472	477	482	488	493	499	504	509	515	520	
804	526	531	536	542	547	553	558	563	569	574	
805	580	585	590	596	601	607	612	617	623	628	
806	634	639	644	650	655	660	666	671	677	682	
807	687	693	698	703	709	714	720	725	730	736	
808	741	747	752	757	763	768	773	779	784	789	
809	795	800	806	811	816	822	827	832	838	843	
810	849	854	859	865	870	875	881	886	891	897	**6**
811	902	907	913	918	924	929	934	940	945	950	1 | 0.6
812	956	961	966	972	977	982	988	993	998	*004	2 | 1.2
813	91 009	014	020	025	030	036	041	046	052	057	3 | 1.8
814	062	068	073	078	084	089	094	100	105	110	4 | 2.4
815	116	121	126	132	137	142	148	153	158	164	5 | 3.0
816	169	174	180	185	190	196	201	206	212	217	6 | 3.6
817	222	228	233	238	243	249	254	259	265	270	7 | 4.2
818	275	281	286	291	297	302	307	312	318	323	8 | 4.8
819	328	334	339	344	350	355	360	365	371	376	9 | 5.4
820	381	387	392	397	403	408	413	418	424	429	
821	434	440	445	450	455	461	466	471	477	482	
822	487	492	498	503	508	514	519	524	529	535	
823	540	545	551	556	561	566	572	577	582	587	
824	593	598	603	609	614	619	624	630	635	640	
825	645	651	656	661	666	672	677	682	687	693	
826	698	703	709	714	719	724	730	735	740	745	
827	751	756	761	766	772	777	782	787	793	798	
828	803	808	814	819	824	829	834	840	845	850	
829	855	861	866	871	876	882	887	892	897	903	
830	908	913	918	924	929	934	939	944	950	955	**5**
831	960	965	971	976	981	986	991	997	*002	*007	1 | 0.5
832	92 012	018	023	028	033	038	044	049	054	059	2 | 1.0
833	065	070	075	080	085	091	096	101	106	111	3 | 1.5
834	117	122	127	132	137	143	148	153	158	163	4 | 2.0
835	169	174	179	184	189	195	200	205	210	215	5 | 2.5
836	221	226	231	236	241	247	252	257	262	267	6 | 3.0
837	273	278	283	288	293	298	304	309	314	319	7 | 3.5
838	324	330	335	340	345	350	355	361	366	371	8 | 4.0
839	376	381	387	392	397	402	407	412	418	423	9 | 4.5
840	428	433	438	443	449	454	459	464	469	474	
841	480	485	490	495	500	505	511	516	521	526	
842	531	536	542	547	552	557	562	567	572	578	
843	583	588	593	598	603	609	614	619	624	629	
844	634	639	645	650	655	660	665	670	675	681	
845	686	691	696	701	706	711	716	722	727	732	
846	737	742	747	752	758	763	768	773	778	783	
847	788	793	799	804	809	814	819	824	829	834	
848	840	845	850	855	860	865	870	875	881	886	
849	891	896	901	906	911	916	921	927	932	937	
850	942	947	952	957	962	967	973	978	983	988	
N.	0	1	2	3	4	5	6	7	8	9	Proportional parts

FIVE-PLACE LOGARITHMS (Continued)

N.	0	1	2	3	4	5	6	7	8	9
850	92 942	947	952	957	962	967	973	978	983	988
851	993	998	*003	*008	*013	*018	*024	*029	*034	*039
852	93 044	049	054	059	064	069	075	080	085	090
853	095	100	105	110	115	120	125	131	136	141
854	146	151	156	161	166	171	176	181	186	192
855	197	202	207	212	217	222	227	232	237	242
856	247	252	258	263	268	273	278	283	288	293
857	298	303	308	313	318	323	328	334	339	344
858	349	354	359	364	369	374	379	384	389	394
859	399	404	409	414	420	425	430	435	440	445
860	450	455	460	465	470	475	480	485	490	495
861	500	505	510	515	520	526	531	536	541	546
862	551	556	561	566	571	576	581	586	591	596
863	601	606	611	616	621	626	631	636	641	646
864	651	656	661	666	671	676	682	687	692	697
865	702	707	712	717	722	727	732	737	742	747
866	752	757	762	767	772	777	782	787	792	797
867	802	807	812	817	822	827	832	837	842	847
868	852	857	862	867	872	877	882	887	892	897
869	902	907	912	917	922	927	932	937	942	947
870	952	957	962	967	972	977	982	987	992	997
871	94 002	007	012	017	022	027	032	037	042	047
872	052	057	062	067	072	077	082	086	091	096
873	101	106	111	116	121	126	131	136	141	146
874	151	156	161	166	171	176	181	186	191	196
875	201	206	211	216	221	226	231	236	240	245
876	250	255	260	265	270	275	280	285	290	295
877	300	305	310	315	320	325	330	335	340	345
878	349	354	359	364	369	374	379	384	389	394
879	399	404	409	414	419	424	429	433	438	443
880	448	453	458	463	468	473	478	483	488	493
881	498	503	507	512	517	522	527	532	537	542
882	547	552	557	562	567	571	576	581	586	591
883	596	601	606	611	616	621	626	630	635	640
884	645	650	655	660	665	670	675	680	685	689
885	694	699	704	709	714	719	724	729	734	738
886	743	748	753	758	763	768	773	778	783	787
887	792	797	802	807	812	817	822	827	832	836
888	841	846	851	856	861	866	871	876	880	885
889	890	895	900	905	910	915	919	924	929	934
890	939	944	949	954	959	963	968	973	978	983
891	988	993	998	*002	*007	*012	*017	*022	*027	*032
892	95 036	041	046	051	056	061	066	071	075	080
893	085	090	095	100	105	109	114	119	124	129
894	134	139	143	148	153	158	163	168	173	177
895	182	187	192	197	202	207	211	216	221	226
896	231	236	240	245	250	255	260	265	270	274
897	279	284	289	294	299	303	308	313	318	323
898	328	332	337	342	347	352	357	361	366	371
899	376	381	386	390	395	400	405	410	415	419
900	424	429	434	439	444	448	453	458	463	468
N.	0	1	2	3	4	5	6	7	8	9

Proportional parts

	6
1	0,6
2	1,2
3	1,8
4	2,4
5	3,0
6	3,6
7	4,2
8	4,8
9	5,4

	5
1	0,5
2	1,0
3	1,5
4	2,0
5	2,5
6	3,0
7	3,5
8	4,0
9	4,5

	4
1	0,4
2	0,8
3	1,2
4	1,6
5	2,0
6	2,4
7	2,8
8	3,2
9	3,6

Proportional parts

N.		0	1	2	3	4	5	6	7	8	9	Proportional parts	
900	95	424	429	434	439	444	448	453	458	463	468		
901		472	477	482	487	492	497	501	506	511	516		
902		521	525	530	535	540	545	550	554	559	564		
903		569	574	578	583	588	593	598	602	607	612		
904		617	622	626	631	636	641	646	650	655	660		
905		665	670	674	679	684	689	694	698	703	708		
906		713	718	722	727	732	737	742	746	751	756		
907		761	766	770	775	780	785	789	794	799	804		
908		809	813	818	823	828	832	837	842	847	852		
909		856	861	866	871	875	880	885	890	895	899		
910		904	909	914	918	923	928	933	938	942	947		**5**
911		952	957	961	966	971	976	980	985	990	995	1	0.5
912		999	*004	*009	*014	*019	*023	*028	*033	*038	*042	2	1.0
913	96	047	052	057	061	066	071	076	080	085	090	3	1.5
914		095	099	104	109	114	118	123	128	133	137	4	2.0
915		142	147	152	156	161	166	171	175	180	185	5	2.5
916		190	194	199	204	209	213	218	223	227	232	6	3.0
917		237	242	246	251	256	261	265	270	275	280	7	3.5
918		284	289	294	298	303	308	313	317	322	327	8	4.0
919		332	336	341	346	350	355	360	365	369	374	9	4.5
920		379	384	388	393	398	402	407	412	417	421		
921		426	431	435	440	445	450	454	459	464	468		
922		473	478	483	487	492	497	501	506	511	515		
923		520	525	530	534	539	544	548	553	558	562		
924		567	572	577	581	586	591	595	600	605	609		
925		614	619	624	628	633	638	642	647	652	656		
926		661	666	670	675	680	685	689	694	699	703		
927		708	713	717	722	727	731	736	741	745	750		
928		755	759	764	769	774	778	783	788	792	797		
929		802	806	811	816	820	825	830	834	839	844		
930		848	853	858	862	867	872	876	881	886	890		**4**
931		895	900	904	909	914	918	923	928	932	937	1	0.4
932		942	946	951	956	960	965	970	974	979	984	2	0.8
933		988	993	997	*002	*007	*011	*016	*021	*025	*030	3	1.2
934	97	035	039	044	049	053	058	063	067	072	077	4	1.6
935		081	086	090	095	100	104	109	114	118	123	5	2.0
936		128	132	137	142	146	151	155	160	165	169	6	2.4
937		174	179	183	188	192	197	202	206	211	216	7	2.8
938		220	225	230	234	239	243	248	253	257	262	8	3.2
939		267	271	276	280	285	290	294	299	304	308	9	3.6
940		313	317	322	327	331	336	340	345	350	354		
941		359	364	368	373	377	382	387	391	396	400		
942		405	410	414	419	424	428	433	437	442	447		
943		451	456	460	465	470	474	479	483	488	493		
944		497	502	506	511	516	520	525	529	534	539		
945		543	548	552	557	562	566	571	575	580	585		
946		589	594	598	603	607	612	617	621	626	630		
947		635	640	644	649	653	658	663	667	672	676		
948		681	685	690	695	699	704	708	713	717	722		
949		727	731	736	740	745	749	754	759	763	768		
950		772	777	782	786	791	795	800	804	809	813		
N.		0	1	2	3	4	5	6	7	8	9	Proportional parts	

FIVE-PLACE LOGARITHMS (Continued)

N.	0	1	2	3	4	5	6	7	8	9	Proportional parts
950	97 772	777	782	786	791	795	800	804	809	813	
951	818	823	827	832	836	841	845	850	855	859	
952	864	868	873	877	882	886	891	896	900	905	
953	909	914	918	923	928	932	937	941	946	950	
954	955	959	964	968	973	978	982	987	991	996	
955	98 000	005	009	014	019	023	028	032	037	041	
956	046	050	055	059	064	068	073	078	082	087	
957	091	096	100	105	109	114	118	123	127	132	
958	137	141	146	150	155	159	164	168	173	177	
959	182	186	191	195	200	204	209	214	218	223	
960	227	232	236	241	245	250	254	259	263	268	**5**
961	272	277	281	286	290	295	299	304	308	313	1 0.5
962	318	322	327	331	336	340	345	349	354	358	2 1.0
963	363	367	372	376	381	385	390	394	399	403	3 1.5
964	408	412	417	421	426	430	435	439	444	448	4 2.0
965	453	457	462	466	471	475	480	484	489	493	5 2.5
966	498	502	507	511	516	520	525	529	534	538	6 3.0
967	543	547	552	556	561	565	570	574	579	583	7 3.5
968	588	592	597	601	605	610	614	619	623	628	8 4.0
969	632	637	641	646	650	655	659	664	668	673	9 4.5
970	677	682	686	691	695	700	704	709	713	717	
971	722	726	731	735	740	744	749	753	758	762	
972	767	771	776	780	784	789	793	798	802	807	
973	811	816	820	825	829	834	838	843	847	851	
974	856	860	865	869	874	878	883	887	892	896	
975	900	905	909	914	918	923	927	932	936	941	
976	945	949	954	958	963	967	972	976	981	985	
977	989	994	998	*003	*007	*012	*016	*021	*025	*029	
978	99 034	038	043	047	052	056	061	065	069	074	
979	078	083	087	092	096	100	105	109	114	118	
980	123	127	131	136	140	145	149	154	158	162	**4**
981	167	171	176	180	185	189	193	198	202	207	1 0.4
982	211	216	220	224	229	233	238	242	247	251	2 0.8
983	255	260	264	269	273	277	282	286	291	295	3 1.2
984	300	304	308	313	317	322	326	330	335	339	4 1.6
985	344	348	352	357	361	366	370	373	379	383	5 2.0
986	388	392	396	401	405	410	414	419	423	427	6 2.4
987	432	436	441	445	449	454	458	463	467	471	7 2.8
988	476	480	484	489	493	498	502	506	511	515	8 3.2
989	520	524	528	533	537	542	546	550	555	559	9 3.6
990	564	568	572	577	581	585	590	594	599	603	
991	607	612	616	621	625	629	634	638	642	647	
992	651	656	660	664	669	673	677	682	686	691	
993	695	699	704	708	712	717	721	726	730	734	
994	739	743	747	752	756	760	765	769	774	778	
995	782	787	791	795	800	804	808	813	817	822	
996	826	830	835	839	843	848	852	856	861	865	
997	870	874	878	883	887	891	896	900	904	909	
998	913	917	922	926	930	935	939	944	948	952	
999	957	961	965	970	974	978	983	987	991	996	
1000	00 000	004	009	013	017	022	026	030	035	039	
N.	0	1	2	3	4	5	6	7	8	9	Proportional parts

LOGARITHMS (Continued)

N.	0	1	2	3	4	5	6	7	8	9	d.
1000	000 0000	0434	0869	1303	1737	2171	2605	3039	3473	3907	434
1001	4341	4775	5208	5642	6076	6510	6943	7377	7810	8244	434
1002	8677	9111	9544	9977	*0411	*0844	*1277	*1710	*2143	*2576	433
1003	001 3009	3442	3875	4308	4741	5174	5607	6039	6472	6905	433
1004	7337	7770	8202	8635	9067	9499	9932	*0364	*0796	*1228	432
1005	002 1661	2093	2525	2957	3389	3821	4253	4685	5116	5548	432
1006	5980	6411	6843	7275	7706	8138	8569	9001	9432	9863	431
1007	003 0295	0726	1157	1588	2019	2451	2882	3313	3744	4174	431
1008	4605	5036	5467	5898	6328	6759	7190	7620	8051	8481	431
1009	8912	9342	9772	*0203	*0633	*1063	*1493	*1924	*2354	*2784	430
1010	004 3214	3644	4074	4504	4933	5363	5793	6223	6652	7082	430
1011	7512	7941	8371	8800	9229	9659	*0088	*0517	*0947	*1376	429
1012	005 1805	2234	2663	3092	3521	3950	4379	4808	5237	5666	429
1013	6094	6523	6952	7380	7809	8238	8666	9094	9523	9951	429
1014	006 0380	0808	1236	1664	2092	2521	2949	3377	3805	4233	428
1015	4660	5088	5516	5944	6372	6799	7227	7655	8082	8510	428
1016	8937	9365	9792	*0219	*0647	*1074	*1501	*1928	*2355	*2782	427
1017	007 3210	3637	4064	4490	4917	5344	5771	6198	6624	7051	427
1018	7478	7904	8331	8757	9184	9610	*0037	*0463	*0889	*1316	426
1019	008 1742	2168	2594	3020	3446	3872	4298	4724	5150	5576	426
1020	6002	6427	6853	7279	7704	8130	8556	8981	9407	9832	426
1021	009 0257	0683	1108	1533	1959	2384	2809	3234	3659	4084	425
1022	4509	4934	5359	5784	6208	6633	7058	7483	7907	8332	425
1023	8756	9181	9605	*0030	*0454	*0878	*1303	*1727	*2151	*2575	424
1024	010 3000	3424	3848	4272	4696	5120	5544	5967	6391	6815	424
1025	7239	7662	8086	8510	8933	9357	9780	*0204	*0627	*1050	424
1026	011 1474	1897	2320	2743	3166	3590	4013	4436	4859	5282	423
1027	5704	6127	6550	6973	7396	7818	8241	8664	9086	9509	423
1028	9931	*0354	*0776	*1198	*1621	*2043	*2465	*2887	*3310	*3732	422
1029	012 4154	4576	4998	5420	5842	6264	6685	7107	7529	7951	422
1030	8372	8794	9215	9637	*0059	*0480	*0901	*1323	*1744	*2165	422
1031	013 2587	3008	3429	3850	4271	4692	5113	5534	5955	6376	421
1032	6797	7218	7639	8059	8480	8901	9321	9742	*0162	*0583	421
1033	014 1003	1424	1844	2264	2685	3105	3525	3945	4365	4785	420
1034	5205	5625	6045	6465	6885	7305	7725	8144	8564	8984	420
1035	9403	9823	*0243	*0662	*1082	*1501	*1920	*2340	*2759	*3178	420
1036	015 3598	4017	4436	4855	5274	5693	6112	6531	6950	7369	419
1037	7788	8206	8625	9044	9462	9881	*0300	*0718	*1137	*1555	419
1038	016 1974	2392	2810	3229	3647	4065	4483	4901	5319	5737	418
1039	6155	6573	6991	7409	7827	8245	8663	9080	9498	9916	418
1040	017 0333	0751	1168	1586	2003	2421	2838	3256	3673	4090	417
1041	4507	4924	5342	5759	6176	6593	7010	7427	7844	8260	417
1042	8677	9094	9511	9927	*0344	*0761	*1177	*1594	*2010	*2427	417
1043	018 2843	3259	3676	4092	4508	4925	5341	5757	6173	6589	416
1044	7005	7421	7837	8253	8669	9084	9500	9916	*0332	*0747	416
1045	019 1163	1578	1994	2410	2825	3240	3656	4071	4486	4902	415
1046	5317	5732	6147	6562	6977	7392	7807	8222	8637	9052	415
1047	9467	9882	*0296	*0711	*1126	*1540	*1955	*2369	*2784	*3198	415
1048	020 3613	4027	4442	4856	5270	5684	6099	6513	6927	7341	414
1049	7755	8169	8583	8997	9411	9824	*0238	*0652	*1066	*1479	414
1050	021 1893	2307	2720	3134	3547	3961	4374	4787	5201	5614	413
N.	0	1	2	3	4	5	6	7	8	9	d.

N.		0	1	2	3	4	5	6	7	8	9	d.
1050	021	1893	2307	2720	3134	3547	3961	4374	4787	5201	5614	413
1051		6027	6440	6854	7267	7680	8093	8506	8919	9332	9745	413
1052	022	0157	0570	0983	1396	1808	2221	2634	3046	3459	3871	413
1053		4284	4696	5109	5521	5933	6345	6758	7170	7582	7994	412
1054		8406	8818	9230	9642	*0054	*0466	*0878	*1289	*1701	*2113	412
1055	023	2525	2936	3348	3759	4171	4582	4994	5405	5817	6228	411
1056		6639	7050	7462	7873	8284	8695	9106	9517	9928	*0339	411
1057	024	0750	1161	1572	1982	2393	2804	3214	3625	4036	4446	411
1058		4857	5267	5678	6088	6498	6909	7319	7729	8139	8549	410
1059		8960	9370	9780	*0190	*0600	*1010	*1419	*1829	*2239	*2649	410
1060	025	3059	3468	3878	4288	4697	5107	5516	5926	6335	6744	410
1061		7154	7563	7972	8382	8791	9200	9609	*0018	*0427	*0836	409
1062	026	1245	1654	2063	2472	2881	3289	3698	4107	4515	4924	409
1063		5333	5741	6150	6558	6967	7375	7783	8192	8600	9008	408
1064		9416	9824	*0233	*0641	*1049	*1457	*1865	*2273	*2680	*3088	408
1065	027	3496	3904	4312	4719	5127	5535	5942	6350	6757	7165	408
1066		7572	7979	8387	8794	9201	9609	*0016	*0423	*0830	*1237	407
1067	028	1644	2051	2458	2865	3272	3679	4086	4492	4899	5306	407
1068		5713	6119	6526	6932	7339	7745	8152	8558	8964	9371	406
1069		9777	*0183	*0590	*0996	*1402	*1808	*2214	*2620	*3026	*3432	406
1070	029	3838	4244	4649	5055	5461	5867	6272	6678	7084	7489	406
1071		7895	8300	8706	9111	9516	9922	*0327	*0732	*1138	*1543	405
1072	030	1948	2353	2758	3163	3568	3973	4378	4783	5188	5592	405
1073		5997	6402	6807	7211	7616	8020	8425	8830	9234	9638	405
1074	031	0043	0447	0851	1256	1660	2064	2468	2872	3277	3681	404
1075		4085	4489	4893	5296	5700	6104	6508	6912	7315	7719	404
1076		8123	8526	8930	9333	9737	*0140	*0544	*0947	*1350	*1754	403
1077	032	2157	2560	2963	3367	3770	4173	4576	4979	5382	5785	403
1078		6188	6590	6993	7396	7799	8201	8604	9007	9409	9812	403
1079	033	0214	0617	1019	1422	1824	2226	2629	3031	3433	3835	402
1080		4238	4640	5042	5444	5846	6248	6650	7052	7453	7855	402
1081		8257	8659	9060	9462	9864	*0265	*0667	*1068	*1470	*1871	402
1082	034	2273	2674	3075	3477	3878	4279	4680	5081	5482	5884	401
1083		6285	6686	7087	7487	7888	8289	8690	9091	9491	9892	401
1084	035	0293	0693	1094	1495	1895	2296	2696	3096	3497	3897	400
1085		4297	4698	5098	5498	5898	6298	6698	7098	7498	7898	400
1086		8298	8698	9098	9498	9898	*0297	*0697	*1097	*1496	*1896	400
1087	036	2295	2695	3094	3494	3893	4293	4692	5091	5491	5890	399
1088		6289	6688	7087	7486	7885	8284	8683	9082	9481	9880	399
1089	037	0279	0678	1076	1475	1874	2272	2671	3070	3468	3867	399
1090		4265	4663	5062	5460	5858	6257	6655	7053	7451	7849	398
1091		8248	8646	9044	9442	9839	*0237	*0635	*1033	*1431	*1829	398
1092	038	2226	2624	3022	3419	3817	4214	4612	5009	5407	5804	398
1093		6202	6599	6996	7393	7791	8188	8585	8982	9379	9776	397
1094	039	0173	0570	0967	1364	1761	2158	2554	2951	3348	3745	397
1095		4141	4538	4934	5331	5727	6124	6520	6917	7313	7709	397
1096		8106	8502	8898	9294	9690	*0086	*0482	*0878	*1274	*1670	396
1097	040	2066	2462	2858	3254	3650	4045	4441	4837	5232	5628	396
1098		6023	6419	6814	7210	7605	8001	8396	8791	9187	9582	395
1099		9977	*0372	*0767	*1162	*1557	*1952	*2347	*2742	*3137	*3532	395
1100	041	3927	4322	4716	5111	5506	5900	6295	6690	7084	7479	395
N.		0	1	2	3	4	5	6	7	8	9	d.

LOGARITHMS—(Continued)

N	0	1	2	3	4	5	6	7	8	9	d.
1100	041 3927	4322	4716	5111	5506	5900	6295	6690	7084	7479	395
1101	7873	8268	8662	9056	9451	9845	*0239	*0633	*1028	*1422	394
1102	042 1816	2210	2604	2998	3392	3786	4180	4574	4968	5361	394
1103	5755	6149	6543	6936	7330	7723	8117	8510	8904	9297	394
1104	9691	*0084	*0477	*0871	*1264	*1657	*2050	*2444	*2837	*3230	393
1105	043 3623	4016	4409	4802	5195	5587	5980	6373	6766	7159	393
1106	7551	7944	8337	8729	9122	9514	9907	*0299	*0692	*1084	393
1107	044 1476	1869	2261	2653	3045	3437	3829	4222	4614	5006	392
1108	5398	5790	6181	6573	6965	7357	7749	8140	8532	8924	392
1109	9315	9707	*0099	*0490	*0882	*1273	*1664	*2056	*2447	*2839	392
1110	045 3230	3621	4012	4403	4795	5186	5577	5968	6359	6750	391
1111	7141	7531	7922	8313	8704	9095	9485	9876	*0267	*0657	391
1112	046 1048	1438	1829	2219	2610	3000	3391	3781	4171	4561	390
1113	4952	5342	5732	6122	6512	6902	7292	7682	8072	8462	390
1114	8852	9242	9632	*0021	*0411	*0801	*1190	*1580	*1970	*2359	390
1115	047 2749	3138	3528	3917	4306	4696	5085	5474	5864	6253	389
1116	6642	7031	7420	7809	8198	8587	8976	9365	9754	*0143	389
1117	048 0532	0921	1309	1698	2087	2475	2864	3253	3641	4030	389
1118	4418	4806	5195	5583	5972	6360	6748	7136	7525	7913	388
1119	8301	8689	9077	9465	9853	*0241	*0629	*1017	*1405	*1792	388
1120	049 2180	2568	2956	3343	3731	4119	4506	4894	5281	5669	388
1121	6056	6444	6831	7218	7606	7993	8380	8767	9154	9541	387
1122	9929	*0316	*0703	*1090	*1477	*1863	*2250	*2637	*3024	*3411	387
1123	050 3798	4184	4571	4958	5344	5731	6117	6504	6890	7277	387
1124	7663	8049	8436	8822	9208	9595	9981	*0367	*0753	*1139	386
1125	051 1525	1911	2297	2683	3069	3455	3841	4227	4612	4998	386
1126	5384	5770	6155	6541	6926	7312	7697	8083	8468	8854	386
1127	9239	9624	*0010	*0395	*0780	*1166	*1551	*1936	*2321	*2706	385
1128	052 3091	3476	3861	4246	4631	5016	5400	5785	6170	6555	385
1129	6939	7324	7709	8093	8478	8862	9247	9631	*0016	*0400	385
1130	053 0784	1169	1553	1937	2321	2706	3090	3474	3858	4242	384
1131	4626	5010	5394	5778	6162	6546	6929	7313	7697	8081	384
1132	8464	8848	9232	9615	9999	*0382	*0766	*1149	*1532	*1916	384
1133	054 2299	2682	3066	3449	3832	4215	4598	4981	5365	5748	383
1134	6131	6514	6896	7279	7662	8045	8428	8811	9193	9576	383
1135	9959	*0341	*0724	*1106	*1489	*1871	*2254	*2636	*3019	*3401	382
1136	055 3783	4166	4548	4930	5312	5694	6077	6459	6841	7223	382
1137	7605	7987	8369	8750	9132	9514	9896	*0278	*0659	*1041	382
1138	056 1423	1804	2186	2567	2949	3330	3712	4093	4475	4856	381
1139	5237	5619	6000	6381	6762	7143	7524	7905	8287	8668	381
1140	9049	9429	9810	*0191	*0572	*0953	*1334	*1714	*2095	*2476	381
1141	057 2856	3237	3618	3998	4379	4759	5140	5520	5900	6281	381
1142	6661	7041	7422	7802	8182	8562	8942	9322	9702	*0082	380
1143	058 0462	0842	1222	1602	1982	2362	2741	3121	3501	3881	380
1144	4260	4640	5019	5399	5778	6158	6537	6917	7296	7676	380
1145	8055	8434	8813	9193	9572	9951	*0330	*0709	*1088	*1467	379
1146	059 1846	2225	2604	2983	3362	3741	4119	4498	4877	5256	379
1147	5634	6013	6391	6770	7148	7527	7905	8284	8662	9041	379
1148	9419	9797	*0175	*0554	*0932	*1310	*1688	*2066	*2444	*2822	378
1149	060 3200	3578	3956	4334	4712	5090	5468	5845	6223	6601	378
1150	6978	7356	7734	8111	8489	8866	9244	9621	9999	*0376	378
N	0	1	2	3	4	5	6	7	8	9	d.

N	0	1	2	3	4	5	6	7	8	9	d.
1150	060 6978	7356	7734	8111	8489	8866	9244	9621	9999	*0376	378
1151	061 0753	1131	1508	1885	2262	2639	3017	3394	3771	4148	377
1152	4525	4902	5279	5656	6032	6409	6786	7163	7540	7916	377
1153	8293	8670	9046	9423	9799	*0176	*0552	*0929	*1305	*1682	377
1154	062 2058	2434	2811	3187	3563	3939	4316	4692	5068	5444	376
1155	5820	6196	6572	6948	7324	7699	8075	8451	8827	9203	376
1156	9578	9954	*0330	*0705	*1081	*1456	*1832	*2207	*2583	*2958	376
1157	063 3334	3709	4084	4460	4835	5210	5585	5960	6335	6711	375
1158	7086	7461	7836	8211	8585	8960	9335	9710	*0085	*0460	375
1159	064 0834	1209	1584	1958	2333	2708	3082	3457	3831	4205	375
1160	4580	4954	5329	5703	6077	6451	6826	7200	7574	7948	374
1161	8322	8696	9070	9444	9818	*0192	*0566	*0940	*1314	*1688	374
1162	065 2061	2435	2809	3182	3556	3930	4303	4677	5050	5424	374
1163	5797	6171	6544	6917	7291	7664	8037	8410	8784	9157	373
1164	9530	9903	*0276	*0649	*1022	*1395	*1768	*2141	*2514	*2886	373
1165	066 3259	3632	4005	4377	4750	5123	5495	5868	6241	6613	373
1166	6986	7358	7730	8103	8475	8847	9220	9592	9964	*0336	372
1167	067 0709	1081	1453	1825	2197	2569	2941	3313	3685	4057	372
1168	4428	4800	5172	5544	5915	6287	6659	7030	7402	7774	372
1169	8145	8517	8888	9259	9631	*0002	*0374	*0745	*1116	*1487	371
1170	068 1859	2230	2601	2972	3343	3714	4085	4456	4827	5198	371
1171	5569	5940	6311	6681	7052	7423	7794	8164	8535	8906	371
1172	9276	9647	*0017	*0388	*0758	*1129	*1499	*1869	*2240	*2610	370
1173	069 2980	3350	3721	4091	4461	4831	5201	5571	5941	6311	370
1174	6681	7051	7421	7791	8160	8530	8900	9270	9639	*0009	370
1175	070 0379	0748	1118	1487	1857	2226	2596	2965	3335	3704	369
1176	4073	4442	4812	5181	5550	5919	6288	6658	7027	7396	369
1177	7765	8134	8503	8871	9240	9609	9978	*0347	*0715	*1084	369
1178	071 1453	1822	2190	2559	2927	3296	3664	4033	4401	4770	369
1179	5138	5506	5875	6243	6611	6979	7348	7716	8084	8452	368
1180	8820	9188	9556	9924	*0292	*0660	*1028	*1396	*1763	*2131	368
1181	072 2499	2867	3234	3602	3970	4337	4705	5072	5440	5807	368
1182	6175	6542	6910	7277	7644	8011	8379	8746	9113	9480	367
1183	9847	*0215	*0582	*0949	*1316	*1683	*2050	*2416	*2783	*3150	367
1184	073 3517	3884	4251	4617	4984	5351	5717	6084	6450	6817	367
1185	7184	7550	7916	8283	8649	9016	9382	9748	*0114	*0481	366
1186	074 0847	1213	1579	1945	2311	2677	3043	3409	3775	4141	366
1187	4507	4873	5239	5605	5970	6336	6702	7068	7433	7799	366
1188	8164	8530	8895	9261	9626	9992	*0357	*0723	*1088	*1453	365
1189	075 1819	2184	2549	2914	3279	3644	4010	4375	4740	5105	365
1190	5470	5835	6199	6564	6929	7294	7659	8024	8388	8753	365
1191	9118	9482	9847	*0211	*0576	*0940	*1305	*1669	*2034	*2398	364
1192	076 2763	3127	3491	3855	4220	4584	4948	5312	5676	6040	364
1193	6404	6768	7132	7496	7860	8224	8588	8952	9316	9680	364
1194	077 0043	0407	0771	1134	1498	1862	2225	2589	2952	3316	364
1195	3679	4042	4406	4769	5133	5496	5859	6222	6585	6949	363
1196	7312	7675	8038	8401	8764	9127	9490	9853	*0216	*0579	363
1197	078 0942	1304	1667	2030	2393	2755	3118	3480	3843	4206	363
1198	4568	4931	5293	5656	6018	6380	6743	7105	7467	7830	362
1199	8192	8554	8916	9278	9640	*0003	*0365	*0727	*1089	*1451	362
1200	079 1812	2174	2536	2898	3260	3622	3983	4345	4707	5068	362
N	0	1	2	3	4	5	6	7	8	9	d.

LOGARITHMS OF THE TRIGONOMETRIC FUNCTIONS

Logarithms of the functions are given for each minute from 0-360°.

The quantity −10 is to be appended to all logarithms of the sine and cosine, to logarithms of the tangent from 0-45° and of the cotangent from 45-90°.

With degrees indicated at either side of the top of the page use the column headings at the top. With degrees stated at the bottom of the page use the column designations at the bottom.

With degrees at the left (top or bottom) use the minute column at the left, and with degrees on the right side of the page use the minute column at the right.

The method of determining the functions of small angles by the auxiliary quantities S and T is given in the section explaining the use of the mathematical tables at the front of the volume.

Min	Values of S, −10 to be appended					Values of T, −10 to be appended					Sec.
	0°	1°	2°	3°	4°	0°	1°	2°	3°	4°	
0′	4.68 557	555	549	538	522	4.68 557	562	575	597	628	0′
1	557	555	549	537	522	557	562	575	598	629	60
2	557	555	548	537	522	557	562	576	598	629	120
3	557	555	548	537	521	557	562	576	599	630	180
4	557	555	548	537	521	558	563	576	599	631	240
5	557	555	548	537	521	558	563	577	599	631	300
6	557	555	548	536	520	558	563	577	600	632	360
7	557	555	548	536	520	558	563	577	600	632	420
8	557	555	548	536	520	558	563	578	601	633	480
9	557	555	547	536	520	558	563	578	601	634	540
10	4.68 557	555	547	535	519	4.68 558	564	578	602	634	600
11	557	554	547	535	519	558	564	579	602	635	660
12	557	554	547	535	519	558	564	579	603	635	720
13	557	554	547	535	518	558	564	579	603	636	780
14	557	554	547	534	518	558	564	580	604	637	840
15	557	554	546	534	518	558	564	580	604	637	900
16	557	554	546	534	517	558	565	580	605	638	960
17	557	554	546	534	517	558	565	581	605	639	1020
18	557	554	546	534	517	558	565	581	606	639	1080
19	557	554	546	533	516	558	565	581	606	640	1140
20	4.68 557	554	546	533	516	4.68 558	565	582	607	640	1200
21	557	554	545	533	516	558	566	582	607	641	1260
22	557	553	545	533	515	558	566	582	608	642	1320
23	557	553	545	532	515	558	566	583	608	642	1380
24	557	553	545	532	515	558	566	583	609	643	1440
25	557	553	545	532	515	558	566	583	609	644	1500
26	557	553	544	532	514	558	567	584	610	644	1560
27	557	553	544	531	514	558	567	584	610	645	1620
28	557	553	544	531	514	558	567	584	611	646	1680
29	557	553	544	531	513	559	567	585	611	646	1740
30	4.68 557	553	544	531	513	4.68 559	567	585	612	647	1800
31	557	552	544	530	513	559	568	585	612	648	1860
32	557	552	543	530	512	559	568	586	613	648	1920
33	557	552	543	530	512	559	568	586	613	649	1980
34	557	552	543	529	512	559	568	587	614	650	2040
35	557	552	543	529	511	559	569	587	614	650	2100
36	557	552	543	529	511	559	569	587	615	651	2160
37	557	552	542	529	511	559	569	588	615	652	2220
38	557	552	542	528	510	559	569	588	616	652	2280
39	557	552	542	528	510	559	570	589	616	653	2340
40	4.68 557	551	542	528	510	4.68 559	570	589	617	654	2400
41	556	551	542	528	509	560	570	589	617	654	2460
42	556	551	541	527	509	560	570	590	618	655	2520
43	556	551	541	527	508	560	571	590	619	656	2580
44	556	551	541	527	508	560	571	591	619	656	2640
45	556	551	541	527	508	560	571	591	620	657	2700
46	556	551	541	526	507	560	571	591	620	658	2760
47	556	551	540	526	507	560	572	592	621	659	2820
48	556	550	540	526	507	560	572	592	621	659	2880
49	556	550	540	525	506	560	572	593	622	660	2940
50	4.68 556	550	540	525	506	4.68 561	572	593	622	661	3000
51	556	550	540	525	506	561	573	593	623	661	3060
52	556	550	539	525	505	561	573	594	624	662	3120
53	556	550	539	524	505	561	573	594	624	663	3180
54	556	550	539	524	505	561	573	595	625	664	3240
55	556	549	539	524	504	561	574	595	625	664	3300
56	556	549	539	523	504	561	574	596	626	665	3360
57	556	549	538	523	503	562	574	596	626	666	3420
58	555	549	538	523	503	562	575	596	627	667	3480
59	555	549	538	523	503	562	575	597	628	667	3540
60	4.68 555	549	538	522	502	4.68 562	575	597	628	668	3600

0° (180°) | (359°) **179°**

″	′	L. Sin.	d.	C. S.	C. T.	L. Tan.	c.d.	L. Cot.	L. Cos.	′
0	**0**	—		—	—	—		—	0.00 000	**60**
60	1	6.46 373	30103	5.31 443	5.31 443	6.46 373	30103	3.53 627	0.00 000	59
120	2	6.76 476	17609	5.31 443	5.31 443	6.76 476	17609	3.23 524	0.00 000	58
180	3	6.94 085	12494	5.31 443	5.31 443	6.94 085	12494	3.05 915	0.00 000	57
240	4	7.06 579	9691	5.31 443	5.31 442	7.06 579	9691	2.93 421	0.00 000	56
300	5	7.16 270	7918	5.31 443	5.31 442	7.16 270	7918	2.83 730	0.00 000	55
360	6	7.24 188	6694	5.31 443	5.31 442	7.24 188	6694	2.75 812	0.00 000	54
420	7	7.30 882	5800	5.31 443	5.31 442	7.30 882	5800	2.69 118	0.00 000	53
480	8	7.36 682	5115	5.31 443	5.31 442	7.36 682	5115	2.63 318	0.00 000	52
540	9	7.41 797	4576	5.31 443	5.31 442	7.41 797	4576	2.58 203	0.00 000	51
600	**10**	7.46 373	4139	5.31 443	5.31 442	7.46 373	4139	2.53 627	0.00 000	**50**
660	11	7.50 512	3779	5.31 443	5.31 442	7.50 512	3779	2.49 488	0.00 000	49
720	12	7.54 291	3476	5.31 443	5.31 442	7.54 291	3476	2.45 709	0.00 000	48
780	13	7.57 767	3218	5.31 443	5.31 442	7.57 767	3219	2.42 233	0.00 000	47
840	14	7.60 985	2997	5.31 443	5.31 442	7.60 986	2996	2.39 014	0.00 000	46
900	15	7.63 982	2802	5.31 443	5.31 442	7.63 982	2803	2.36 018	0.00 000	45
960	16	7.66 784	2633	5.31 443	5.31 442	7.66 785	2633	2.33 215	0.00 000	44
1020	17	7.69 417	2483	5.31 443	5.31 442	7.69 418	2482	2.30 582	9.99 999	43
1080	18	7.71 900	2348	5.31 443	5.31 442	7.71 900	2348	2.28 100	9.99 999	42
1140	19	7.74 248	2227	5.31 443	5.31 442	7.74 248	2228	2.25 752	9.99 999	41
1200	**20**	7.76 475	2119	5.31 443	5.31 442	7.76 476	2119	2.23 524	9.99 999	**40**
1260	21	7.78 594	2021	5.31 443	5.31 442	7.78 595	2020	2.21 405	9.99 999	39
1320	22	7.80 615	1930	5.31 443	5.31 442	7.80 615	1931	2.19 385	9.99 999	38
1380	23	7.82 545	1848	5.31 443	5.31 442	7.82 546	1848	2.17 454	9.99 999	37
1440	24	7.84 393	1773	5.31 443	5.31 442	7.84 394	1773	2.15 606	9.99 999	36
1500	25	7.86 166	1704	5.31 443	5.31 442	7.86 167	1704	2.13 833	9.99 999	35
1560	26	7.87 870	1639	5.31 443	5.31 442	7.87 871	1639	2.12 129	9.99 999	34
1620	27	7.89 509	1579	5.31 443	5.31 442	7.89 510	1579	2.10 490	9.99 999	33
1680	28	7.91 088	1524	5.31 443	5.31 442	7.91 089	1524	2.08 911	9.99 999	32
1740	29	7.92 612	1472	5.31 443	5.31 441	7.92 613	1473	2.07 387	9.99 998	31
1800	**30**	7.94 084	1424	5.31 443	5.31 441	7.94 086	1424	2.05 914	9.99 998	**30**
1860	31	7.95 508	1379	5.31 443	5.31 441	7.95 510	1379	2.04 490	9.99 998	29
1920	32	7.96 887	1336	5.31 443	5.31 441	7.96 889	1336	2.03 111	9.99 998	28
1980	33	7.98 223	1297	5.31 443	5.31 441	7.98 225	1297	2.01 775	9.99 998	27
2040	34	7.99 520	1259	5.31 443	5.31 441	7.99 522	1259	2.00 478	9.99 998	26
2100	35	8.00 779	1223	5.31 443	5.31 441	8.00 781	1223	1.99 219	9.99 998	25
2160	36	8.02 002	1190	5.31 443	5.31 441	8.02 004	1190	1.97 996	9.99 998	24
2220	37	8.03 192	1158	5.31 443	5.31 441	8.03 194	1159	1.96 806	9.99 997	23
2280	38	8.04 350	1128	5.31 443	5.31 441	8.04 353	1128	1.95 647	9.99 997	22
2340	39	8.05 478	1100	5.31 443	5.31 441	8.05 481	1100	1.94 519	9.99 997	21
2400	**40**	8.06 578	1072	5.31 443	5.31 441	8.06 581	1072	1.93 419	9.99 997	**20**
2460	41	8.07 650	1046	5.31 444	5.31 440	8.07 653	1047	1.92 347	9.99 997	19
2520	42	8.08 696	1022	5.31 444	5.31 440	8.08 700	1022	1.91 300	9.99 997	18
2580	43	8.09 718	999	5.31 444	5.31 440	8.09 722	998	1.90 278	9.99 997	17
2640	44	8.10 717	976	5.31 444	5.31 440	8.10 720	976	1.89 280	9.99 996	16
2700	45	8.11 693	954	5.31 444	5.31 440	8.11 696	955	1.88 304	9.99 996	15
2760	46	8.12 647	934	5.31 444	5.31 440	8.12 651	934	1.87 349	9.99 996	14
2820	47	8.13 581	914	5.31 444	5.31 440	8.13 585	915	1.86 415	9.99 996	13
2880	48	8.14 495	896	5.31 444	5.31 440	8.14 500	895	1.85 500	9.99 996	12
2940	49	8.15 391	877	5.31 444	5.31 440	8.15 395	878	1.84 605	9.99 996	11
3000	**50**	8.16 268	860	5.31 444	5.31 439	8.16 273	860	1.83 727	9.99 995	**10**
3060	51	8.17 128	843	5.31 444	5.31 439	8.17 133	843	1.82 867	9.99 995	9
3120	52	8.17 971	827	5.31 444	5.31 439	8.17 976	828	1.82 024	9.99 995	8
3180	53	8.18 798	812	5.31 444	5.31 439	8.18 804	812	1.81 196	9.99 995	7
3240	54	8.19 610	797	5.31 444	5.31 439	8.19 616	797	1.80 384	9.99 995	6
3300	55	8.20 407	782	5.31 444	5.31 439	8.20 413	782	1.79 587	9.99 994	5
3360	56	8.21 189	769	5.31 444	5.31 439	8.21 195	769	1.78 805	9.99 994	4
3420	57	8.21 958	755	5.31 445	5.31 439	8.21 964	756	1.78 036	9.99 994	3
3480	58	8.22 713	743	5.31 445	5.31 438	8.22 720	742	1.77 280	9.99 994	2
3540	59	8.23 456	730	5.31 445	5.31 438	8.23 462	730	1.76 538	9.99 994	1
3600	**60**	8.24 186		5.31 445	5.31 438	8.24 192		1.75 808	9.99 993	**0**
	′	L. Cos.	d.			L. Cot.	c.d.	L. Tan.	L. Sin.	′

90° (270°) | (269°) **89°**

1° (181°) (358°) **178°**

"	'	L. Sin.	d.	C. S.	C. T.	L. Tan.	c.d.	L. Cot.	L. Cos.	'
3600	**0**	8.24 186	717	5.31 445	5.31 438	8.24 192	718	1.75 808	9.99 993	**60**
3660	1	8.24 903	706	5.31 445	5.31 438	8.24 910	706	1.75 090	9.99 993	59
3720	2	8.25 609	695	5.31 445	5.31 438	8.25 616	696	1.74 384	9.99 993	58
3780	3	8.26 304	684	5.31 445	5.31 438	8.26 312	684	1.73 688	9.99 993	57
3840	4	8.26 988	673	5.31 445	5.31 437	8.26 996	673	1.73 004	9.99 992	56
3900	5	8.27 661	663	5.31 445	5.31 437	8.27 669	663	1.72 331	9.99 992	55
3960	6	8.28 324	653	5.31 445	5.31 437	8.28 332	654	1.71 668	9.99 992	54
4020	7	8.28 977	644	5.31 445	5.31 437	8.28 986	643	1.71 014	9.99 992	53
4080	8	8.29 621	634	5.31 445	5.31 437	8.29 629	634	1.70 371	9.99 992	52
4140	9	8.30 255	624	5.31 445	5.31 437	8.30 263	625	1.69 737	9.99 991	51
4200	**10**	8.30 879	616	5.31 446	5.31 437	8.30 888	617	1.69 112	9.99 991	**50**
4260	11	8.31 495	608	5.31 446	5.31 436	8.31 505	607	1.68 495	9.99 991	49
4320	12	8.32 103	599	5.31 446	5.31 436	8.32 112	599	1.67 888	9.99 990	48
4380	13	8.32 702	590	5.31 446	5.31 436	8.32 711	591	1.67 289	9.99 990	47
4440	14	8.33 292	583	5.31 446	5.31 436	8.33 302	584	1.66 698	9.99 990	46
4500	15	8.33 875	575	5.31 446	5.31 436	8.33 886	575	1.66 114	9.99 990	45
4560	16	8.34 450	568	5.31 446	5.31 435	8.34 461	568	1.65 539	9.99 989	44
4620	17	8.35 018	560	5.31 446	5.31 435	8.35 029	561	1.64 971	9.99 989	43
4680	18	8.35 578	553	5.31 446	5.31 435	8.35 590	553	1.64 410	9.99 989	42
4740	19	8.36 131	547	5.31 446	5.31 435	8.36 143	546	1.63 857	9.99 989	41
4800	**20**	8.36 678	539	5.31 446	5.31 435	8.36 689	540	1.63 311	9.99 988	**40**
4860	21	8.37 217	533	5.31 447	5.31 434	8.37 229	533	1.62 771	9.99 988	39
4920	22	8.37 750	526	5.31 447	5.31 434	8.37 762	527	1.62 238	9.99 988	38
4980	23	8.38 276	520	5.31 447	5.31 434	8.38 289	520	1.61 711	9.99 987	37
5040	24	8.38 796	514	5.31 447	5.31 434	8.38 809	514	1.61 191	9.99 987	36
5100	25	8.39 310	508	5.31 447	5.31 434	8.39 323	509	1.60 677	9.99 987	35
5160	26	8.39 818	502	5.31 447	5.31 433	8.39 832	502	1.60 168	9.99 986	34
5220	27	8.40 320	496	5.31 447	5.31 433	8.40 334	496	1.59 666	9.99 986	33
5280	28	8.40 816	491	5.31 447	5.31 433	8.40 830	491	1.59 170	9.99 986	32
5340	29	8.41 307	485	5.31 447	5.31 433	8.41 321	486	1.58 679	9.99 985	31
5400	**30**	8.41 792	480	5.31 447	5.31 433	8.41 807	480	1.58 193	9.99 985	**30**
5460	31	8.42 272	474	5.31 448	5.31 432	8.42 287	475	1.57 713	9.99 985	29
5520	32	8.42 746	470	5.31 448	5.31 432	8.42 762	470	1.57 238	9.99 984	28
5580	33	8.43 216	464	5.31 448	5.31 432	8.43 232	464	1.56 768	9.99 984	27
5640	34	8.43 680	459	5.31 448	5.31 432	8.43 696	460	1.56 304	9.99 984	26
5700	35	8.44 139	455	5.31 448	5.31 431	8.44 156	455	1.55 844	9.99 983	25
5760	36	8.44 594	450	5.31 448	5.31 431	8.44 611	450	1.55 389	9.99 983	24
5820	37	8.45 044	445	5.31 448	5.31 431	8.45 061	446	1.54 939	9.99 983	23
5880	38	8.45 489	441	5.31 448	5.31 431	8.45 507	441	1.54 493	9.99 982	22
5940	39	8.45 930	436	5.31 449	5.31 431	8.45 948	437	1.54 052	9.99 982	21
6000	**40**	8.46 366	433	5.31 449	5.31 430	8.46 385	432	1.53 615	9.99 982	**20**
6060	41	8.46 799	427	5.31 449	5.31 430	8.46 817	428	1.53 183	9.99 981	19
6120	42	8.47 226	424	5.31 449	5.31 430	8.47 245	424	1.52 755	9.99 981	18
6180	43	8.47 650	419	5.31 449	5.31 430	8.47 669	420	1.52 331	9.99 981	17
6240	44	8.48 069	416	5.31 449	5.31 429	8.48 089	416	1.51 911	9.99 980	16
6300	45	8.48 485	411	5.31 449	5.31 429	8.48 505	412	1.51 495	9.99 980	15
6360	46	8.48 896	408	5.31 449	5.31 429	8.48 917	408	1.51 083	9.99 979	14
6420	47	8.49 304	404	5.31 450	5.31 428	8.49 325	404	1.50 675	9.99 979	13
6480	48	8.49 708	400	5.31 450	5.31 428	8.49 729	401	1.50 271	9.99 979	12
6540	49	8.50 108	396	5.31 450	5.31 428	8.50 130	397	1.49 870	9.99 978	11
6600	**50**	8.50 504	393	5.31 450	5.31 428	8.50 527	393	1.49 473	9.99 978	**10**
6660	51	8.50 897	390	5.31 450	5.31 427	8.50 920	390	1.49 080	9.99 977	9
6720	52	8.51 287	386	5.31 450	5.31 427	8.51 310	386	1.48 690	9.99 977	8
6780	53	8.51 673	382	5.31 450	5.31 427	8.51 696	383	1.48 304	9.99 977	7
6840	54	8.52 055	379	5.31 450	5.31 427	8.52 079	380	1.47 921	9.99 976	6
6900	55	8.52 434	376	5.31 451	5.31 426	8.52 459	376	1.47 541	9.99 976	5
6960	56	8.52 810	373	5.31 451	5.31 426	8.52 835	373	1.47 165	9.99 975	4
7020	57	8.53 183	369	5.31 451	5.31 426	8.53 208	370	1.46 792	9.99 975	3
7080	58	8.53 552	367	5.31 451	5.31 425	8.53 578	367	1.46 422	9.99 974	2
7140	59	8.53 919	363	5.31 451	5.31 425	8.53 945	363	1.46 055	9.99 974	1
7200	**60**	8.54 282		5.31 451	5.31 425	8.54 308		1.45 692	9.99 974	**0**
	'	L. Cos.	d.			L. Cot.	c.d.	L. Tan.	L. Sin.	'

91° (271°) (268°) **88°**

2° (182°) — (357°) **177°**

″	′	L. Sin.	d.	C. S.	C. T.	L. Tan.	c.d.	L. Cot.	L. Cos.	′
7200	**0**	8.54 282	360	5.31 451	5.31 425	8.54 308	361	1.45 692	9.99 974	**60**
7260	1	8.54 642	357	5.31 451	5.31 425	8.54 669	358	1.45 331	9.99 973	59
7320	2	8.54 999	355	5.31 452	5.31 424	8.55 027	355	1.44 973	9.99 973	58
7380	3	8.55 354	351	5.31 452	5.31 424	8.55 382	352	1.44 618	9.99 972	57
7440	4	8.55 705	349	5.31 452	5.31 424	8.55 734	349	1.44 266	9.99 972	56
7500	5	8.56 054	346	5.31 452	5.31 423	8.56 083	346	1.43 917	9.99 971	55
7560	6	8.56 400	343	5.31 452	5.31 423	8.56 429	344	1.43 571	9.99 971	54
7620	7	8.56 743	341	5.31 452	5.31 423	8.56 773	341	1.43 227	9.99 970	53
7680	8	8.57 084	337	5.31 453	5.31 422	8.57 114	338	1.42 886	9.99 970	52
7740	9	8.57 421	336	5.31 453	5.31 422	8.57 452	336	1.42 548	9.99 969	51
7800	**10**	8.57 757	332	5.31 453	5.31 422	8.57 788	333	1.42 212	9.99 969	**50**
7860	11	8.58 089	330	5.31 453	5.31 421	8.58 121	330	1.41 879	9.99 968	49
7920	12	8.58 419	328	5.31 453	5.31 421	8.58 451	328	1.41 549	9.99 968	48
7980	13	8.58 747	325	5.31 453	5.31 421	8.58 779	326	1.41 221	9.99 967	47
8040	14	8.59 072	323	5.31 454	5.31 421	8.59 105	323	1.40 895	9.99 967	46
8100	15	8.59 395	320	5.31 454	5.31 420	8.59 428	321	1.40 572	9.99 967	45
8160	16	8.59 715	318	5.31 454	5.31 420	8.59 749	319	1.40 251	9.99 966	44
8220	17	8.60 033	316	5.31 454	5.31 420	8.60 068	316	1.39 932	9.99 966	43
8280	18	8.60 349	313	5.31 454	5.31 419	8.60 384	314	1.39 616	9.99 965	42
8340	19	8.60 662	311	5.31 454	5.31 419	8.60 698	311	1.39 302	9.99 964	41
8400	**20**	8.60 973	309	5.31 455	5.31 418	8.61 009	310	1.38 991	9.99 964	**40**
8460	21	8.61 282	307	5.31 455	5.31 418	8.61 319	307	1.38 681	9.99 963	39
8520	22	8.61 589	305	5.31 455	5.31 418	8.61 626	305	1.38 374	9.99 963	38
8580	23	8.61 894	302	5.31 455	5.31 417	8.61 931	303	1.38 069	9.99 962	37
8640	24	8.62 196	301	5.31 455	5.31 417	8.62 234	301	1.37 766	9.99 962	36
8700	25	8.62 497	298	5.31 455	5.31 417	8.62 535	299	1.37 465	9.99 961	35
8760	26	8.62 795	296	5.31 456	5.31 416	8.62 834	297	1.37 166	9.99 961	34
8820	27	8.63 091	294	5.31 456	5.31 416	8.63 131	295	1.36 869	9.99 960	33
8880	28	8.63 385	293	5.31 456	5.31 416	8.63 426	292	1.36 574	9.99 960	32
8940	29	8.63 678	290	5.31 456	5.31 415	8.63 718	291	1.36 282	9.99 959	31
9000	**30**	8.63 968	288	5.31 456	5.31 415	8.64 009	289	1.35 991	9.99 959	**30**
9060	31	8.64 256	287	5.31 456	5.31 415	8.64 298	287	1.35 702	9.99 958	29
9120	32	8.64 543	284	5.31 457	5.31 414	8.64 585	285	1.35 415	9.99 958	28
9180	33	8.64 827	283	5.31 457	5.31 414	8.64 870	284	1.35 130	9.99 957	27
9240	34	8.65 110	281	5.31 457	5.31 413	8.65 154	281	1.34 846	9.99 956	26
9300	35	8.65 391	279	5.31 457	5.31 413	8.65 435	280	1.34 565	9.99 956	25
9360	36	8.65 670	277	5.31 457	5.31 413	8.65 715	278	1.34 285	9.99 955	24
9420	37	8.65 947	276	5.31 458	5.31 412	8.65 993	276	1.34 007	9.99 955	23
9480	38	8.66 223	274	5.31 458	5.31 412	8.66 269	274	1.33 731	9.99 954	22
9540	39	8.66 497	272	5.31 458	5.31 412	8.66 543	273	1.33 457	9.99 954	21
9600	**40**	8.66 769	270	5.31 458	5.31 411	8.66 816	271	1.33 184	9.99 953	**20**
9660	41	8.67 039	269	5.31 458	5.31 411	8.67 087	269	1.32 913	9.99 952	19
9720	42	8.67 308	267	5.31 459	5.31 410	8.67 356	268	1.32 644	9.99 952	18
9780	43	8.67 575	266	5.31 459	5.31 410	8.67 624	266	1.32 376	9.99 951	17
9840	44	8.67 841	263	5.31 459	5.31 410	8.67 890	264	1.32 110	9.99 951	16
9900	45	8.68 104	263	5.31 459	5.31 409	8.68 154	263	1.31 846	9.99 950	15
9960	46	8.68 367	260	5.31 459	5.31 409	8.68 417	261	1.31 583	9.99 949	14
10020	47	8.68 627	259	5.31 460	5.31 408	8.68 678	260	1.31 322	9.99 949	13
10080	48	8.68 886	258	5.31 460	5.31 408	8.68 938	258	1.31 062	9.99 948	12
10140	49	8.69 144	256	5.31 460	5.31 408	8.69 196	257	1.30 804	9.99 948	11
10200	**50**	8.69 400	254	5.31 460	5.31 407	8.69 453	255	1.30 547	9.99 947	**10**
10260	51	8.69 654	253	5.31 460	5.31 407	8.69 708	254	1.30 292	9.99 946	9
10320	52	8.69 907	252	5.31 461	5.31 406	8.69 962	252	1.30 038	9.99 946	8
10380	53	8.70 159	250	5.31 461	5.31 406	8.70 214	251	1.29 786	9.99 945	7
10440	54	8.70 409	249	5.31 461	5.31 405	8.70 465	249	1.29 535	9.99 944	6
10500	55	8.70 658	247	5.31 461	5.31 405	8.70 714	248	1.29 286	9.99 944	5
10560	56	8.70 905	246	5.31 461	5.31 405	8.70 962	246	1.29 038	9.99 943	4
10620	57	8.71 151	244	5.31 462	5.31 404	8.71 208	245	1.28 792	9.99 942	3
10680	58	8.71 395	243	5.31 462	5.31 404	8.71 453	244	1.28 547	9.99 942	2
10740	59	8.71 638	242	5.31 462	5.31 403	8.71 697	243	1.28 303	9.99 941	1
10800	**60**	8.71 880		5.31 462	5.31 403	8.71 940		1.28 060	9.99 940	**0**
	′	L. Cos.	d.			L. Cot.	c.d.	L. Tan.	L. Sin.	′

92° (272°) — (267°) **87°**

LOGARITHMS OF THE FUNCTIONS (Continued)

8° (183°) (356°) **176°**

′	L. Sin.	d.	L. Tan.	c.d.	L. Cot.	L. Cos.	′
0	8.71 880	240	8.71 940	241	1.28 060	9.99 940	**60**
1	8.72 120	239	8.72 181	239	1.27 819	9.99 940	59
2	8.72 359	238	8.72 420	239	1.27 580	9.99 939	58
3	8.72 597	237	8.72 659	237	1.27 341	9.99 938	57
4	8.72 834	235	8.72 896	236	1.27 104	9.99 938	56
5	8.73 069	234	8.73 132	234	1.26 868	9.99 937	55
6	8.73 303	232	8.73 366	234	1.26 634	9.99 936	54
7	8.73 535	232	8.73 600	232	1.26 400	9.99 936	53
8	8.73 767	230	8.73 832	231	1.26 168	9.99 935	52
9	8.73 997	229	8.74 063	229	1.25 937	9.99 934	51
10	8.74 226	228	8.74 292	229	1.25 708	9.99 934	**50**
11	8.74 454	226	8.74 521	227	1.25 479	9.99 933	49
12	8.74 680	226	8.74 748	226	1.25 252	9.99 932	48
13	8.74 906	224	8.74 974	225	1.25 026	9.99 932	47
14	8.75 130	223	8.75 199	224	1.24 801	9.99 931	46
15	8.75 353	222	8.75 423	222	1.24 577	9.99 930	45
16	8.75 575	220	8.75 645	222	1.24 355	9.99 929	44
17	8.75 795	220	8.75 867	220	1.24 133	9.99 929	43
18	8.76 015	219	8.76 087	219	1.23 913	9.99 928	42
19	8.76 234	217	8.76 306	219	1.23 694	9.99 927	41
20	8.76 451	216	8.76 525	217	1.23 475	9.99 926	**40**
21	8.76 667	216	8.76 742	216	1.23 258	9.99 926	39
22	8.76 883	214	8.76 958	215	1.23 042	9.99 925	38
23	8.77 097	213	8.77 173	214	1.22 827	9.99 924	37
24	8.77 310	212	8.77 387	213	1.22 613	9.99 923	36
25	8.77 522	211	8.77 600	211	1.22 400	9.99 923	35
26	8.77 733	210	8.77 811	211	1.22 189	9.99 922	34
27	8.77 943	209	8.78 022	210	1.21 978	9.99 921	33
28	8.78 152	208	8.78 232	209	1.21 768	9.99 920	32
29	8.78 360	208	8.78 441	208	1.21 559	9.99 920	31
30	8.78 568	206	8.78 649	206	1.21 351	9.99 919	**30**
31	8.78 774	205	8.78 855	206	1.21 145	9.99 918	29
32	8.78 979	204	8.79 061	205	1.20 939	9.99 917	28
33	8.79 183	203	8.79 266	204	1.20 734	9.99 917	27
34	8.79 386	202	8.79 470	203	1.20 530	9.99 916	26
35	8.79 588	201	8.79 673	202	1.20 327	9.99 915	25
36	8.79 789	201	8.79 875	201	1.20 125	9.99 914	24
37	8.79 990	199	8.80 076	201	1.19 924	9.99 913	23
38	8.80 189	199	8.80 277	199	1.19 723	9.99 913	22
39	8.80 388	197	8.80 476	198	1.19 524	9.99 912	21
40	8.80 585	197	8.80 674	198	1.19 326	9.99 911	**20**
41	8.80 782	196	8.80 872	196	1.19 128	9.99 910	19
42	8.80 978	195	8.81 068	196	1.18 932	9.99 909	18
43	8.81 173	194	8.81 264	195	1.18 736	9.99 909	17
44	8.81 367	193	8.81 459	194	1.18 541	9.99 908	16
45	8.81 560	192	8.81 653	193	1.18 347	9.99 907	15
46	8.81 752	192	8.81 846	192	1.18 154	9.99 906	14
47	8.81 944	190	8.82 038	192	1.17 962	9.99 905	13
48	8.82 134	190	8.82 230	190	1.17 770	9.99 904	12
49	8.82 324	189	8.82 420	190	1.17 580	9.99 904	11
50	8.82 513	188	8.82 610	189	1.17 390	9.99 903	**10**
51	8.82 701	187	8.82 799	188	1.17 201	9.99 902	9
52	8.82 888	187	8.82 987	188	1.17 013	9.99 901	8
53	8.83 075	186	8.83 175	186	1.16 825	9.99 900	7
54	8.83 261	185	8.83 361	186	1.16 639	9.99 899	6
55	8.83 446	184	8.83 547	185	1.16 453	9.99 898	5
56	8.83 630	183	8.83 732	184	1.16 268	9.99 898	4
57	8.83 813	183	8.83 916	184	1.16 084	9.99 897	3
58	8.83 996	181	8.84 100	182	1.15 900	9.99 896	2
59	8.84 177	181	8.84 282	182	1.15 718	9.99 895	1
60	8.84 358		8.84 464		1.15 536	9.99 894	**0**
′	L. Cos.	d.	L. Cot.	c.d.	L. Tan.	L. Sin.	′

P. P.					
″	**241**	**239**	**237**	**235**	**234**
1	4.0	4.0	4.0	3.9	3.9
2	8.0	8.0	7.9	7.8	7.8
3	12.0	12.0	11.8	11.8	11.7
4	16.1	15.9	15.8	15.7	15.6
5	20.1	19.9	19.8	19.6	19.5
6	24.1	23.9	23.7	23.5	23.4
7	28.1	27.9	27.6	27.4	27.3
8	32.1	31.9	31.6	31.3	31.2
9	36.2	35.8	35.6	35.2	35.1
″	**232**	**229**	**227**	**225**	**223**
1	3.9	3.8	3.8	3.8	3.7
2	7.7	7.6	7.6	7.5	7.4
3	11.6	11.4	11.4	11.2	11.2
4	15.5	15.3	15.1	15.0	14.9
5	19.3	19.1	18.9	18.8	18.6
6	23.2	22.9	22.7	22.5	22.3
7	27.1	26.7	26.5	26.2	26.0
8	30.9	30.5	30.3	30.0	29.7
9	34.8	34.4	34.0	33.8	33.4
″	**222**	**220**	**217**	**215**	**213**
1	3.7	3.7	3.6	3.6	3.6
2	7.4	7.3	7.2	7.2	7.1
3	11.1	11.0	10.8	10.8	10.6
4	14.8	14.7	14.5	14.3	14.2
5	18.5	18.3	18.1	17.9	17.8
6	22.2	22.0	21.7	21.5	21.3
7	25.9	25.7	25.3	25.1	24.8
8	29.6	29.3	28.9	28.7	28.4
9	33.3	33.0	32.6	32.2	32.0
″	**211**	**208**	**206**	**203**	**201**
1	3.5	3.5	3.4	3.4	3.4
2	7.0	6.9	6.9	6.8	6.7
3	10.6	10.4	10.3	10.2	10.0
4	14.1	13.9	13.7	13.5	13.4
5	17.6	17.3	17.2	16.9	16.8
6	21.1	20.8	20.6	20.3	20.1
7	24.6	24.3	24.0	23.7	23.4
8	28.1	27.7	27.5	27.1	26.8
9	31.6	31.2	30.9	30.4	30.2
″	**199**	**197**	**195**	**193**	**192**
1	3.3	3.3	3.2	3.2	3.2
2	6.6	6.6	6.5	6.4	6.4
3	10.0	9.8	9.8	9.6	9.6
4	13.3	13.1	13.0	12.9	12.8
5	16.6	16.4	16.2	16.1	16.0
6	19.9	19.7	19.5	19.3	19.2
7	23.2	23.0	22.8	22.5	22.4
8	26.5	26.3	26.0	25.7	25.6
9	29.8	29.6	29.2	29.0	28.8
″	**189**	**187**	**185**	**183**	**181**
1	3.2	3.1	3.1	3.0	3.0
2	6.3	6.2	6.2	6.1	6.0
3	9.4	9.4	9.2	9.2	9.0
4	12.6	12.5	12.3	12.2	12.1
5	15.8	15.6	15.4	15.2	15.1
6	18.9	18.7	18.5	18.3	18.1
7	22.0	21.8	21.6	21.4	21.1
8	25.2	24.9	24.7	24.4	24.1
9	28.4	28.0	27.8	27.4	27.2
10	31.5	31.2	30.8	30.5	30.2
			P. P.		

93° (273°) (266°) **86°**

4° (184°) (355°) 175°

′	L. Sin.	d.	L. Tan.	c.d.	L. Cot.	L. Cos.	′
0	8.84 358	181	8.84 464	182	1.15 536	9.99 894	**60**
1	8.84 539	179	8.84 646	180	1.15 354	9.99 893	59
2	8.84 718	179	8.84 826	180	1.15 174	9.99 892	58
3	8.84 897	178	8.85 006	179	1.14 994	9.99 891	57
4	8.85 075̇	177	8.85 185̄	178	1.14 815̇	9.99 891	56
5	8.85 252	177	8.85 363	177	1.14 637	9.99 890	55
6	8.85 429	176	8.85 540	177	1.14 460	9.99 889	54
7	8.85 605̄	175	8.85 717	176	1.14 283	9.99 888	53
8	8.85 780	175	8.85 893	176	1.14 107	9.99 887	52
9	8.85 955̄	173	8.86 069	174	1.13 931	9.99 886	51
10	8.86 128	173	8.86 243	174	1.13 757	9.99 885̇	**50**
11	8.86 301	173	8.86 417	174	1.13 583	9.99 884	49
12	8.86 474	171	8.86 591	172	1.13 409	9.99 883	48
13	8.86 645̇	171	8.86 763	172	1.13 237	9.99 882	47
14	8.86 816	171	8.86 935̇	171	1.13 065̄	9.99 881	46
15	8.86 987	169	8.87 106	171	1.12 894	9.99 880	45
16	8.87 156	169	8.87 277	170	1.12 723	9.99 879	44
17	8.87 325̇	169	8.87 447	169	1.12 553	9.99 879	43
18	8.87 494	167	8.87 616	169	1.12 384	9.99 878	42
19	8.87 661	168	8.87 785̄	168	1.12 215̇	9.99 877	41
20	8.87 829	166	8.87 953	167	1.12 047	9.99 876	**40**
21	8.87 995̄	166	8.88 120	167	1.11 880	9.99 875̄	39
22	8.88 161	165	8.88 287	166	1.11 713	9.99 874	38
23	8.88 326	164	8.88 453	165	1.11 547	9.99 873	37
24	8.88 490	164	8.88 618	165	1.11 382	9.99 872	36
25	8.88 654	163	8.88 783	165	1.11 217	9.99 871	35
26	8.88 817	163	8.88 948	163	1.11 052	9.99 870	34
27	8.88 980	162	8.89 111	163	1.10 889	9.99 869	33
28	8.89 142	162	8.89 274	163	1.10 726	9.99 868	32
29	8.89 304	160	8.89 437	161	1.10 563	9.99 867	31
30	8.89 464	161	8.89 598	162	1.10 402	9.99 866	**30**
31	8.89 625̄	159	8.89 760	160	1.10 240	9.99 865̄	29
32	8.89 784	159	8.89 920	160	1.10 080	9.99 864	28
33	8.89 943	159	8.90 080	160	1.09 920	9.99 863	27
34	8.90 102	158	8.90 240	159	1.09 760	9.99 862	26
35	8.90 260	157	8.90 399	158	1.09 601	9.99 861	25
36	8.90 417	157	8.90 557	158	1.09 443	9.99 860	24
37	8.90 574	156	8.90 715̄	157	1.09 285̇	9.99 859	23
38	8.90 730	155	8.90 872	157	1.09 128	9.99 858	22
39	8.90 885̇	155	8.91 029	156	1.08 971	9.99 857	21
40	8.91 040	155	8.91 185̄	155	1.08 815̇	9.99 856	**20**
41	8.91 195̄	154	8.91 340	155	1.08 660	9.99 855̄	19
42	8.91 349	153	8.91 495̇	155	1.08 505̄	9.99 854	18
43	8.91 502	153	8.91 650̄	153	1.08 350̇	9.99 853	17
44	8.91 655̇	152	8.91 803	154	1.08 197	9.99 852	16
45	8.91 807	152	8.91 957	153	1.08 043	9.99 851	15
46	8.91 959	151	8.92 110	152	1.07 890	9.99 850̄	14
47	8.92 110	151	8.92 262	152	1.07 738	9.99 848	13
48	8.92 261	150	8.92 414	151	1.07 586	9.99 847	12
49	8.92 411	150	8.92 565̄	151	1.07 435̇	9.99 846	11
50	8.92 561	149	8.92 716	150	1.07 284	9.99 845̇	**10**
51	8.92 710	149	8.92 866	150	1.07 134	9.99 844	9
52	8.92 859	148	8.93 016	149	1.06 984	9.99 843	8
53	8.93 007	147	8.93 165̄	148	1.06 835̇	9.99 842	7
54	8.93 154	147	8.93 313	149	1.06 687	9.99 841	6
55	8.93 301	147	8.93 462	147	1.06 538	9.99 840	5
56	8.93 448	146	8.93 609	147	1.06 391	9.99 839	4
57	8.93 594	146	8.93 756	147	1.06 244	9.99 838	3
58	8.93 740	145	8.93 903	146	1.06 097	9.99 837	2
59	8.93 885̄	145	8.94 049	146	1.05 951	9.99 836	1
60	8.94 030		8.94 195̇		1.05 805̄	9.99 834	**0**
′	L. Cos.	d.	L. Cot.	c.d.	L. Tan.	L. Sin.	′

P. P.

″	**182**	**181**	**179**	**178**	**177**
1	3.0	3.0	3.0	3.0	3.0
2	6.1	6.0	6.0	5.9	5.9
3	9.1	9.0	9.0	8.9	8.8
4	12.1	12.1	11.9	11.9	11.8
5	15.2	15.1	14.9	14.8	14.8
6	18.2	18.1	17.9	17.8	17.7
7	21.2	21.1	20.9	20.8	20.6
8	24.3	24.1	23.9	23.7	23.6
9	27.3	27.2	26.8	26.7	26.6
″	**176**	**175**	**174**	**173**	**172**
1	2.9	2.9	2.9	2.9	2.9
2	5.9	5.8	5.8	5.8	5.7
3	8.8	8.8	8.7	8.6	8.6
4	11.7	11.7	11.6	11.5̇	11.5̄
5	14.7	14.6	14.5	14.4	14.3
6	17.6	17.5	17.4	17.3	17.2
7	20.5̇	20.4	20.3	20.2	20.1
8	23.5̄	23.3	23.2	23.1	22.9
9	26.4	26.2	26.1	26.0	25.8
″	**171**	**170**	**169**	**168**	**167**
1	2.8	2.8	2.8	2.8	2.8
2	5.7	5.7	5.6	5.6	5.6
3	8.6	8.5	8.4	8.4	8.4
4	11.4	11.3	11.3	11.2	11.1
5	14.2	14.2	14.1	14.0	13.9
6	17.1	17.0	16.9	16.8	16.7
7	20.0	19.8	19.7	19.6	19.5̄
8	22.8	22.7	22.5̇	22.4	22.3
9	25.6	25.5	25.4	25.2	25.0̇
″	**166**	**165**	**164**	**163**	**162**
1	2.8	2.8	2.7	2.7	2.7
2	5.5̇	5.5	5.5̄	5.4	5.4
3	8.3	8.2	8.2	8.2	8.1
4	11.1	11.0	10.9	10.9	10.8
5	13.8	13.8	13.7	13.6	13.5
6	16.6	16.5	16.4	16.3	16.2
7	19.4	19.2	19.1	19.0	18.9
8	22.1	22.0	21.9	21.7	21.6
9	24.9	24.8	24.6	24.4	24.3
″	**161**	**160**	**159**	**158**	**157**
1	2.7	2.7	2.6	2.6	2.6
2	5.4	5.3	5.3	5.3	5.2
3	8.0	8.0	8.0	7.9	7.8
4	10.7	10.7	10.6	10.5̇	10.5̄
5	13.4	13.3	13.2	13.2	13.1
6	16.1	16.0	15.9	15.8	15.7
7	18.8	18.7	18.6	18.4	18.3
8	21.5̄	21.3	21.2	21.1	20.9
9	24.2	24.0	23.8	23.7	23.6
″	**156**	**155**	**154**	**153**	**152**
1	2.6	2.6	2.6	2.6	2.5̇
2	5.2	5.2	5.1	5.1	5.1
3	7.8	7.8	7.7	7.6	7.6
4	10.4	10.3	10.3	10.2	10.1
5	13.0	12.9	12.8	12.8	12.7
6	15.6	15.5	15.4	15.3	15.2
7	18.2	18.1	18.0	17.8	17.7
8	20.8	20.7	20.5̇	20.4	20.3
9	23.4	23.2	23.1	23.0	22.8
10	26.0	25.8	25.7	25.5	25.3

P. P.

94° (274°) (265°) 85°

5° (185°) **(354°) 174°**

′	L. Sin.	d.	L.Tan.	c.d.	L. Cot.	L. Cos.	′	P.P.					
0	8.94 030		8.94 195		1.05 805	9.99 834	60	″	151	149	148	147	146
1	8.94 174	144	8.94 340	145	1.05 660	9.99 833	59	1	2.5	2.5	2.5	2.4	2.4
2	8.94 317	143	8.94 485	145	1.05 515	9.99 832	58	2	5.0	5.0	4.9	4.9	4.9
3	8.94 461	144	8.94 630	145	1.05 370	9.99 831	57	3	7.6	7.4	7.4	7.4	7.3
4	8.94 603	142	8.94 773	143	1.05 227	9.99 830	56	4	10.1	9.9	9.9	9.8	9.7
5	8.94 746	143	8.94 917	144	1.05 083	9.99 829	55	5	12.6	12.4	12.3	12.2	12.2
6	8.94 887	141	8.95 060	143	1.04 940	9.99 828	54	6	15.1	14.9	14.8	14.7	14.6
7	8.95 029	142	8.95 202	142	1.04 798	9.99 827	53	7	17.6	17.4	17.3	17.2	17.0
8	8.95 170	141	8.95 344	142	1.04 656	9.99 825	52	8	20.1	19.9	19.7	19.6	19.5
9	8.95 310	140	8.95 486	142	1.04 514	9.99 824	51	9	22.6	22.4	22.2	22.0	21.9
10	8.95 450	140	8.95 627	141	1.04 373	9.99 823	50	″	145	144	143	142	141
11	8.95 589	139	8.95 767	140	1.04 233	9.99 822	49	1	2.4	2.4	2.4	2.4	2.4
12	8.95 728	139	8.95 908	141	1.04 092	9.99 821	48	2	4.8	4.8	4.8	4.7	4.7
13	8.95 867	139	8.96 047	139	1.03 953	9.99 820	47	3	7.2	7.2	7.2	7.1	7.0
14	8.96 005	138	8.96 187	140	1.03 813	9.99 819	46	4	9.7	9.6	9.5	9.5	9.4
15	8.96 143	138	8.96 325	138	1.03 675	9.99 817	45	5	12.1	12.0	11.9	11.8	11.8
16	8.96 280	137	8.96 464	139	1.03 536	9.99 816	44	6	14.5	14.4	14.3	14.2	14.1
17	8.96 417	137	8.96 602	138	1.03 398	9.99 815	43	7	16.9	16.8	16.7	16.6	16.4
18	8.96 553	136	8.96 739	137	1.03 261	9.99 814	42	8	19.3	19.2	19.1	18.9	18.8
19	8.96 689	136	8.96 877	138	1.03 123	9.99 813	41	9	21.8	21.6	21.4	21.3	21.2
20	8.96 825	136	8.97 013	136	1.02 987	9.99 812	40	″	140	139	138	137	136
21	8.96 960	135	8.97 150	137	1.02 850	9.99 810	39	1	2.3	2.3	2.3	2.3	2.3
22	8.97 095	135	8.97 285	135	1.02 715	9.99 809	38	2	4.7	4.6	4.6	4.6	4.5
23	8.97 229	134	8.97 421	136	1.02 579	9.99 808	37	3	7.0	7.0	6.9	6.8	6.8
24	8.97 363	134	8.97 556	135	1.02 444	9.99 807	36	4	9.3	9.3	9.2	9.1	9.1
25	8.97 496	133	8.97 691	135	1.02 309	9.99 806	35	5	11.7	11.6	11.5	11.4	11.3
26	8.97 629	133	8.97 825	134	1.02 175	9.99 804	34	6	14.0	13.9	13.8	13.7	13.6
27	8.97 762	133	8.97 959	134	1.02 041	9.99 803	33	7	16.3	16.2	16.1	16.0	15.9
28	8.97 894	132	8.98 092	133	1.01 908	9.99 802	32	8	18.7	18.5	18.4	18.3	18.1
29	8.98 026	132	8.98 225	133	1.01 775	9.99 801	31	9	21.0	20.8	20.7	20.6	20.4
30	8.98 157	131	8.98 358	133	1.01 642	9.99 800	30	″	135	134	133	132	131
31	8.98 288	131	8.98 490	132	1.01 510	9.99 798	29	1	2.2	2.2	2.2	2.2	2.2
32	8.98 419	131	8.98 622	132	1.01 378	9.99 797	28	2	4.5	4.5	4.4	4.4	4.4
33	8.98 549	130	8.98 753	131	1.01 247	9.99 796	27	3	6.8	6.7	6.6	6.6	6.6
34	8.98 679	130	8.98 884	131	1.01 116	9.99 795	26	4	9.0	8.9	8.9	8.8	8.7
35	8.98 808	129	8.99 015	131	1.00 985	9.99 793	25	5	11.2	11.2	11.1	11.0	10.9
36	8.98 937	129	8.99 145	130	1.00 855	9.99 792	24	6	13.5	13.4	13.3	13.2	13.1
37	8.99 066	129	8.99 275	130	1.00 725	9.99 791	23	7	15.8	15.6	15.5	15.4	15.3
38	8.99 194	128	8.99 405	130	1.00 595	9.99 790	22	8	18.0	17.9	17.7	17.6	17.5
39	8.99 322	128	8.99 534	129	1.00 466	9.99 788	21	9	20.2	20.1	20.0	19.8	19.6
40	8.99 450	128	8.99 662	128	1.00 338	9.99 787	20	″	130	129	128	127	126
41	8.99 577	127	8.99 791	129	1.00 209	9.99 786	19	1	2.2	2.2	2.1	2.1	2.1
42	8.99 704	127	8.99 919	128	1.00 081	9.99 785	18	2	4.3	4.3	4.3	4.2	4.2
43	8.99 830	126	9.00 046	127	0.99 954	9.99 783	17	3	6.5	6.4	6.4	6.4	6.3
44	8.99 956	126	9.00 174	128	0.99 826	9.99 782	16	4	8.7	8.6	8.5	8.5	8.4
45	9.00 082	126	9.00 301	127	0.99 699	9.99 781	15	5	10.8	10.8	10.7	10.6	10.5
46	9.00 207	125	9.00 427	126	0.99 573	9.99 780	14	6	13.0	12.9	12.8	12.7	12.6
47	9.00 332	125	9.00 553	126	0.99 447	9.99 778	13	7	15.2	15.0	14.9	14.8	14.7
48	9.00 456	124	9.00 679	126	0.99 321	9.99 777	12	8	17.3	17.2	17.1	16.9	16.8
49	9.00 581	125	9.00 805	126	0.99 195	9.99 776	11	9	19.5	19.4	19.2	19.0	18.9
50	9.00 704	123	9.00 930	125	0.99 070	9.99 775	10	″	125	124	123	122	121
51	9.00 828	124	9.01 055	125	0.98 945	9.99 773	9	1	2.1	2.1	2.0	2.0	2.0
52	9.00 951	123	9.01 179	124	0.98 821	9.99 772	8	2	4.2	4.1	4.1	4.1	4.0
53	9.01 074	123	9.01 303	124	0.98 697	9.99 771	7	3	6.2	6.2	6.2	6.1	6.0
54	9.01 196	122	9.01 427	124	0.98 573	9.99 769	6	4	8.3	8.3	8.2	8.1	8.1
55	9.01 318	122	9.01 550	123	0.98 450	9.99 768	5	5	10.4	10.3	10.2	10.2	10.1
56	9.01 440	122	9.01 673	123	0.98 327	9.99 767	4	6	12.5	12.4	12.3	12.2	12.1
57	9.01 561	121	9.01 796	123	0.98 204	9.99 765	3	7	14.6	14.5	14.4	14.2	14.1
58	9.01 682	121	9.01 918	122	0.98 082	9.99 764	2	8	16.7	16.5	16.4	16.3	16.1
59	9.01 803	121	9.02 040	122	0.97 960	9.99 763	1	9	18.8	18.6	18.4	18.3	18.2
60	9.01 923	120	9.02 162	122	0.97 838	9.99 761	0	10	20.8	20.7	20.5	20.3	20.2
′	L. Cos.	d.	L. Cot.	c.d.	L. Tan.	L. Sin.	′	P.P.					

95° (275°) **(264°) 84°**

6° (186°) (353°) **173°**

′	L. Sin.	d.	L. Tan.	c.d.	L. Cot.	L. Cos.	′
0	9.01 923	120	9.02 162	121	0.97 838	9.99 761	**60**
1	9.02 043	120	9.02 283	121	0.97 717	9.99 760	59
2	9.02 163	120	9.02 404	121	0.97 596	9.99 759	58
3	9.02 283	119	9.02 525	120	0.97 475	9.99 757	57
4	9.02 402	118	9.02 645	121	0.97 355	9.99 756	56
5	9.02 520	119	9.02 766	119	0.97 234	9.99 755	55
6	9.02 639	118	9.02 885	120	0.97 115	9.99 753	54
7	9.02 757	117	9.03 005	119	0.96 995	9.99 752	53
8	9.02 874	118	9.03 124	118	0.96 876	9.99 751	52
9	9.02 992	117	9.03 242	119	0.96 758	9.99 749	51
10	9.03 109	117	9.03 361	118	0.96 639	9.99 748	**50**
11	9.03 226	116	9.03 479	118	0.96 521	9.99 747	49
12	9.03 342	116	9.03 597	117	0.96 403	9.99 745	48
13	9.03 458	116	9.03 714	118	0.96 286	9.99 744	47
14	9.03 574	116	9.03 832	116	0.96 168	9.99 742	46
15	9.03 690	115	9.03 948	117	0.96 052	9.99 741	45
16	9.03 805	115	9.04 065	116	0.95 935	9.99 740	44
17	9.03 920	114	9.04 181	116	0.95 819	9.99 738	43
18	9.04 034	115	9.04 297	116	0.95 703	9.99 737	42
19	9.04 149	113	9.04 413	115	0.95 587	9.99 736	41
20	9.04 262	114	9.04 528	115	0.95 472	9.99 734	**40**
21	9.04 376	114	9.04 643	115	0.95 357	9.99 733	39
22	9.04 490	113	9.04 758	115	0.95 242	9.99 731	38
23	9.04 603	112	9.04 873	114	0.95 127	9.99 730	37
24	9.04 715	113	9.04 987	114	0.95 013	9.99 728	36
25	9.04 828	112	9.05 101	113	0.94 899	9.99 727	35
26	9.04 940	112	9.05 214	114	0.94 786	9.99 726	34
27	9.05 052	112	9.05 328	113	0.94 672	9.99 724	33
28	9.05 164	111	9.05 441	112	0.94 559	9.99 723	32
29	9.05 275	111	9.05 553	113	0.94 447	9.99 721	31
30	9.05 386	111	9.05 666	112	0.94 334	9.99 720	**30**
31	9.05 497	110	9.05 778	112	0.94 222	9.99 718	29
32	9.05 607	110	9.05 890	112	0.94 110	9.99 717	28
33	9.05 717	110	9.06 002	111	0.93 998	9.99 716	27
34	9.05 827	110	9.06 113	111	0.93 887	9.99 714	26
35	9.05 937	109	9.06 224	111	0.93 776	9.99 713	25
36	9.06 046	109	9.06 335	110	0.93 665	9.99 711	24
37	9.06 155	109	9.06 445	111	0.93 555	9.99 710	23
38	9.06 264	108	9.06 556	110	0.93 444	9.99 708	22
39	9.06 372	109	9.06 666	109	0.93 334	9.99 707	21
40	9.06 481	108	9.06 775	110	0.93 225	9.99 705	**20**
41	9.06 589	107	9.06 885	109	0.93 115	9.99 704	19
42	9.06 696	108	9.06 994	109	0.93 006	9.99 702	18
43	9.06 804	107	9.07 103	108	0.92 897	9.99 701	17
44	9.06 911	107	9.07 211	109	0.92 789	9.99 699	16
45	9.07 018	106	9.07 320	108	0.92 680	9.99 698	15
46	9.07 124	107	9.07 428	108	0.92 572	9.99 696	14
47	9.07 231	106	9.07 536	107	0.92 464	9.99 695	13
48	9.07 337	105	9.07 643	108	0.92 357	9.99 693	12
49	9.07 442	106	9.07 751	107	0.92 249	9.99 692	11
50	9.07 548	105	9.07 858	106	0.92 142	9.99 690	**10**
51	9.07 653	105	9.07 964	107	0.92 036	9.99 689	9
52	9.07 758	105	9.08 071	106	0.91 929	9.99 687	8
53	9.07 863	105	9.08 177	106	0.91 823	9.99 686	7
54	9.07 968	104	9.08 283	106	0.91 717	9.99 684	6
55	9.08 072	104	9.08 389	106	0.91 611	9.99 683	5
56	9.08 176	104	9.08 495	105	0.91 505	9.99 681	4
57	9.08 280	103	9.08 600	105	0.91 400	9.99 680	3
58	9.08 383	103	9.08 705	105	0.91 295	9.99 678	2
59	9.08 486	103	9.08 810	104	0.91 190	9.99 677	1
60	9.08 589		9.08 914		0.91 086	9.99 675	**0**
′	L. Cos.	d.	L. Cot.	c.d.	L. Tan.	L. Sin.	′

P. P.				
″	**121**	**120**	**119**	**118**
1	2.0	2.0	2.0	2.0
2	4.0	4.0	4.0	3.9
3	6.0	6.0	6.0	5.9
4	8.1	8.0	7.9	7.9
5	10.1	10.0	9.9	9.8
6	12.1	12.0	11.9	11.8
7	14.1	14.0	13.9	13.8
8	16.1	16.0	15.9	15.7
9	18.2	18.0	17.8	17.7
10	20.2	20.0	19.8	19.7
20	40.3	40.0	39.7	39.3
30	60.5	60.0	59.5	59.0
40	80.7	80.0	79.3	78.7
50	100.8	100.0	99.2	98.3
″	**117**	**116**	**115**	**114**
1	2.0	1.9	1.9	1.9
2	3.9	3.9	3.8	3.8
3	5.8	5.8	5.8	5.7
4	7.8	7.7	7.7	7.6
5	9.8	9.7	9.6	9.5
6	11.7	11.6	11.5	11.4
7	13.6	13.5	13.4	13.3
8	15.6	15.5	15.3	15.2
9	17.6	17.4	17.2	17.1
10	19.5	19.3	19.2	19.0
20	39.0	38.7	38.3	38.0
30	58.5	58.0	57.5	57.0
40	78.0	77.3	76.7	76.0
50	97.5	96.7	95.8	95.0
″	**113**	**112**	**111**	**110**
1	1.9	1.9	1.8	1.8
2	3.8	3.7	3.7	3.7
3	5.6	5.6	5.6	5.5
4	7.5	7.5	7.4	7.3
5	9.4	9.3	9.2	9.2
6	11.3	11.2	11.1	11.0
7	13.2	13.1	13.0	12.8
8	15.1	14.9	14.8	14.7
9	17.0	16.8	16.6	16.5
10	18.8	18.7	18.5	18.3
20	37.7	37.3	37.0	36.7
30	56.5	56.0	55.5	55.0
40	75.3	74.7	74.0	73.3
50	94.2	93.3	92.5	91.7
″	**109**	**108**	**107**	**106**
1	1.8	1.8	1.8	1.8
2	3.6	3.6	3.6	3.5
3	5.4	5.4	5.4	5.3
4	7.3	7.2	7.1	7.1
5	9.1	9.0	8.9	8.8
6	10.9	10.8	10.7	10.6
7	12.7	12.6	12.5	12.4
8	14.5	14.4	14.3	14.1
9	16.4	16.2	16.0	15.9
10	18.2	18.0	17.8	17.7
20	36.3	36.0	35.7	35.3
30	54.5	54.0	53.5	53.0
40	72.7	72.0	71.3	70.7
50	90.8	90.0	89.2	88.3

96° (276°) (263°) **83°**

7° (187°) (352°) **172°**

′	L. Sin.	d.	L. Tan.	c.d.	L. Cot.	L. Cos.	′
0	9.08 589	103	9.08 914	105	0.91 086	9.99 675	**60**
1	9.08 692	103	9.09 019	104	0.90 981	9.99 674	59
2	9.08 795	102	9.09 123	104	0.90 877	9.99 672	58
3	9.08 897	102	9.09 227	103	0.90 773	9.99 670	57
4	9.08 999	102	9.09 330	104	0.90 670	9.99 669	56
5	9.09 101	101	9.09 434	103	0.90 566	9.99 667	55
6	9.09 202	102	9.09 537	103	0.90 463	9.99 666	54
7	9.09 304	101	9.09 640	102	0.90 360	9.99 664	53
8	9.09 405	101	9.09 742	103	0.90 258	9.99 663	52
9	9.09 506	100	9.09 845	102	0.90 155	9.99 661	51
10	9.09 606	101	9.09 947	102	0.90 053	9.99 659	**50**
11	9.09 707	100	9.10 049	101	0.89 951	9.99 658	49
12	9.09 807	100	9.10 150	102	0.89 850	9.99 656	48
13	9.09 907	99	9.10 252	101	0.89 748	9.99 655	47
14	9.10 006	100	9.10 353	101	0.89 647	9.99 653	46
15	9.10 106	99	9.10 454	101	0.89 546	9.99 651	45
16	9.10 205	99	9.10 555	101	0.89 445	9.99 650	44
17	9.10 304	98	9.10 656	100	0.89 344	9.99 648	43
18	9.10 402	99	9.10 756	100	0.89 244	9.99 647	42
19	9.10 501	98	9.10 856	100	0.89 144	9.99 645	41
20	9.10 599	98	9.10 956	100	0.89 044	9.99 643	**40**
21	9.10 697	98	9.11 056	99	0.88 944	9.99 642	39
22	9.10 795	98	9.11 155	99	0.88 845	9.99 640	38
23	9.10 893	97	9.11 254	99	0.88 746	9.99 638	37
24	9.10 990	97	9.11 353	99	0.88 647	9.99 637	36
25	9.11 087	97	9.11 452	99	0.88 548	9.99 635	35
26	9.11 184	97	9.11 551	98	0.88 449	9.99 633	34
27	9.11 281	96	9.11 649	98	0.88 351	9.99 632	33
28	9.11 377	97	9.11 747	98	0.88 253	9.99 630	32
29	9.11 474	96	9.11 845	98	0.88 155	9.99 629	31
30	9.11 570	96	9.11 943	97	0.88 057	9.99 627	**30**
31	9.11 666	95	9.12 040	98	0.87 960	9.99 625	29
32	9.11 761	96	9.12 138	97	0.87 862	9.99 624	28
33	9.11 857	95	9.12 235	97	0.87 765	9.99 622	27
34	9.11 952	95	9.12 332	96	0.87 668	9.99 620	26
35	9.12 047	95	9.12 428	97	0.87 572	9.99 618	25
36	9.12 142	94	9.12 525	96	0.87 475	9.99 617	24
37	9.12 236	95	9.12 621	96	0.87 379	9.99 615	23
38	9.12 331	94	9.12 717	96	0.87 283	9.99 613	22
39	9.12 425	94	9.12 813	96	0.87 187	9.99 612	21
40	9.12 519	93	9.12 909	95	0.87 091	9.99 610	**20**
41	9.12 612	94	9.13 004	95	0.86 996	9.99 608	19
42	9.12 706	93	9.13 099	95	0.86 901	9.99 607	18
43	9.12 799	93	9.13 194	95	0.86 806	9.99 605	17
44	9.12 892	93	9.13 289	95	0.86 711	9.99 603	16
45	9.12 985	93	9.13 384	94	0.86 616	9.99 601	15
46	9.13 078	93	9.13 478	95	0.86 522	9.99 600	14
47	9.13 171	92	9.13 573	94	0.86 427	9.99 598	13
48	9.13 263	92	9.13 667	94	0.86 333	9.99 596	12
49	9.13 355	92	9.13 761	93	0.86 239	9.99 595	11
50	9.13 447	92	9.13 854	94	0.86 146	9.99 593	**10**
51	9.13 539	91	9.13 948	93	0.86 052	9.99 591	9
52	9.13 630	92	9.14 041	93	0.85 959	9.99 589	8
53	9.13 722	91	9.14 134	93	0.85 866	9.99 588	7
54	9.13 813	91	9.14 227	93	0.85 773	9.99 586	6
55	9.13 904	90	9.14 320	92	0.85 680	9.99 584	5
56	9.13 994	91	9.14 412	92	0.85 588	9.99 582	4
57	9.14 085	90	9.14 504	93	0.85 496	9.99 581	3
58	9.14 175	91	9.14 597	91	0.85 403	9.99 579	2
59	9.14 266	90	9.14 688	92	0.85 312	9.99 577	1
60	9.14 356		9.14 780		0.85 220	9.99 575	**0**
′	L. Cos.	d.	L. Cot.	c.d.	L. Tan.	L. Sin.	′

P. P.

″	**105**	**104**	**103**	**102**
1	1.8	1.7	1.7	1.7
2	3.5	3.5	3.4	3.4
3	5.2	5.2	5.2	5.1
4	7.0	6.9	6.9	6.8
5	8.8	8.7	8.6	8.5
6	10.5	10.4	10.3	10.2
7	12.2	12.1	12.0	11.9
8	14.0	13.9	13.7	13.6
9	15.8	15.6	15.4	15.3
10	17.5	17.3	17.2	17.0
20	35.0	34.7	34.3	34.0
30	52.5	52.0	51.5	51.0
40	70.0	69.3	68.7	68.0
50	87.5	86.7	85.8	85.0
″	**101**	**100**	**99**	**98**
1	1.7	1.7	1.6	1.6
2	3.4	3.3	3.3	3.3
3	5.0	5.0	5.0	4.9
4	6.7	6.7	6.6	6.5
5	8.4	8.3	8.2	8.2
6	10.1	10.0	9.9	9.8
7	11.8	11.7	11.6	11.4
8	13.5	13.3	13.2	13.1
9	15.2	15.0	14.8	14.7
10	16.8	16.7	16.5	16.3
20	33.7	33.3	33.0	32.7
30	50.5	50.0	49.5	49.0
40	67.3	66.7	66.0	65.3
50	84.2	83.3	82.5	81.7
″	**97**	**96**	**95**	**94**
1	1.6	1.6	1.6	1.6
2	3.2	3.2	3.2	3.1
3	4.8	4.8	4.8	4.7
4	6.5	6.4	6.3	6.3
5	8.1	8.0	7.9	7.8
6	9.7	9.6	9.5	9.4
7	11.3	11.2	11.1	11.0
8	12.9	12.8	12.7	12.5
9	14.6	14.4	14.2	14.1
10	16.2	16.0	15.8	15.7
20	32.3	32.0	31.7	31.3
30	48.5	48.0	47.5	47.0
40	64.7	64.0	63.3	62.7
50	80.8	80.0	79.2	78.3
″	**93**	**92**	**91**	**90**
1	1.6	1.5	1.5	1.5
2	3.1	3.1	3.0	3.0
3	4.6	4.6	4.6	4.5
4	6.2	6.1	6.1	6.0
5	7.8	7.7	7.6	7.5
6	9.3	9.2	9.1	9.0
7	10.8	10.7	10.6	10.5
8	12.4	12.3	12.1	12.0
9	14.0	13.8	13.6	13.5
10	15.5	15.3	15.2	15.0
20	31.0	30.7	30.3	30.0
30	46.5	46.0	45.5	45.0
40	62.0	61.3	60.7	60.0
50	77.5	76.7	75.8	75.0

P. P.

97° (277°) (262°) **82°**

8° (188°) (351°) **171°**

′	L. Sin	d.	L. Tan.	c. d.	L. Cot.	L. Cos.	′
0	9.14 356	89	9.14 780	92	0.85 220	9.99 575̇	**60**
1	9.14 445̇	90	9.14 872	91	0.85 128	9.99 574	59
2	9.14 535̄	89	9.14 963	91	0.85 037	9.99 572	58
3	9.14 624	90	9.15 054	91	0.84 946	9.99 570	57
4	9.14 714	89	9.15 145̄	91	0.84 855̄	9.99 568	56
5	9.14 803	88	9.15 236	91	0.84 764	9.99 566	55
6	9.14 891	89	9.15 327	90	0.84 673	9.99 565̄	54
7	9.14 980	89	9.15 417	91	0.84 583	9.99 563	53
8	9.15 069	88	9.15 508	90	0.84 492	9.99 561	52
9	9.15 157	88	9.15 598	90	0.84 402	9.99 559	51
10	9.15 245̇	88	9.15 688	89	0.84 312	9.99 557	**50**
11	9.15 333	88	9.15 777	90	0.84 223	9.99 556	49
12	9.15 421	87	9.15 867	89	0.84 133	9.99 554	48
13	9.15 508	88	9.15 956	90	0.84 044	9.99 552	47
14	9.15 596	87	9.16 046	89	0.83 954	9.99 550̇	46
15	9.15 683	87	9.16 135̄	89	0.83 865̇	9.99 548	45
16	9.15 770	87	9.16 224	88	0.83 776	9.99 546	44
17	9.15 857	87	9.16 312	89	0.83 688	9.99 545̄	43
18	9.15 944	86	9.16 401	88	0.83 599	9.99 543	42
19	9.16 030	86	9.16 489	88	0.83 511	9.99 541	41
20	9.16 116	87	9.16 577	88	0.83 423	9.99 539	**40**
21	9.16 203	86	9.16 665̇	88	0.83 335̄	9.99 537	39
22	9.16 289	85	9.16 753	88	0.83 247	9.99 535̇	38
23	9.16 374	86	9.16 841	87	0.83 159	9.99 533	37
24	9.16 460	85	9.16 928	88	0.83 072	9.99 532	36
25	9.16 545̇	86	9.17 016	87	0.82 984	9.99 530	35
26	9.16 631	85	9.17 103	87	0.82 897	9.99 528	34
27	9.16 716	85	9.17 190	87	0.82 810	9.99 526	33
28	9.16 801	85	9.17 277	86	0.82 723	9.99 524	32
29	9.16 886	84	9.17 363	87	0.82 637	9.99 522	31
30	9.16 970	85	9.17 450	86	0.82 550̇	9.99 520	**30**
31	9.17 055̄	84	9.17 536	86	0.82 464	9.99 518	29
32	9.17 139	84	9.17 622	86	0.82 378	9.99 517	28
33	9.17 223	84	9.17 708	86	0.82 292	9.99 515̄	27
34	9.17 307	84	9.17 794	86	0.82 206	9.99 513	26
35	9.17 391	83	9.17 880	85	0.82 120	9.99 511	25
36	9.17 474	84	9.17 965̇	86	0.82 035̄	9.99 509	24
37	9.17 558	83	9.18 051	85	0.81 949	9.99 507	23
38	9.17 641	83	9.18 136	85	0.81 864	9.99 505̇	22
39	9.17 724	83	9.18 221	85	0.81 779	9.99 503	21
40	9.17 807	83	9.18 306	85	0.81 694	9.99 501	**20**
41	9.17 890	83	9.18 391	84	0.81 609	9.99 499	19
42	9.17 973	82	9.18 475̇	85	0.81 525̄	9.99 497	18
43	9.18 055̇	82	9.18 560	84	0.81 440	9.99 495̇	17
44	9.18 137	83	9.18 644	84	0.81 356	9.99 494	16
45	9.18 220	82	9.18 728	84	0.81 272	9.99 492	15
46	9.18 302	81	9.18 812	84	0.81 188	9.99 490	14
47	9.18 383	82	9.18 896	83	0.81 104	9.99 488	13
48	9.18 465̇	82	9.18 979	84	0.81 021	9.99 486	12
49	9.18 547	81	9.19 063	83	0.80 937	9.99 484	11
50	9.18 628	81	9.19 146	83	0.80 854	9.99 482	**10**
51	9.18 709	81	9.19 229	83	0.80 771	9.99 480	9
52	9.18 790	81	9.19 312	83	0.80 688	9.99 478	8
53	9.18 871	81	9.19 395̇	83	0.80 605̄	9.99 476	7
54	9.18 952	81	9.19 478	83	0.80 522	9.99 474	6
55	9.19 033	80	9.19 561	82	0.80 439	9.99 472	5
56	9.19 113	80	9.19 643	82	0.80 357	9.99 470	4
57	9.19 193	80	9.19 725̇	82	0.80 275̄	9.99 468	3
58	9.19 273	80	9.19 807	82	0.80 193	9.99 466	2
59	9.19 353	80	9.19 889	82	0.80 111	9.99 464	1
60	9.19 433		9.19 971		0.80 029	9.99 462	**0**
′	L. Cos.	d.	L. Cot.	c. d.	L. Tan.	L. Sin.	′

P. P.

″	**92**	**91**	**90**
1	1.5	1.5	1.5
2	3.1	3.0	3.0
3	4.6	4.6	4.5
4	6.1	6.1	6.0
5	7.7	7.6	7.5
6	9.2	9.1	9.0
7	10.7	10.6	10.5
8	12.3	12.1	12.0
9	13.8	13.6	13.5
10	15.3	15.2	15.0
20	30.7	30.3	30.0
30	46.0	45.5	45.0
40	61.3	60.7	60.0
50	76.7	75.8	75.0
″	**89**	**88**	**87**
1	1.5̄	1.5̄	1.4
2	3.0	2.9	2.9
3	4.4	4.4	4.4
4	5.9	5.9	5.8
5	7.4	7.3	7.2
6	8.9	8.8	8.7
7	10.4	10.3	10.2
8	11.9	11.7	11.6
9	13.4	13.2	13.0
10	14.8	14.7	14.5
20	29.7	29.3	29.0
30	44.5	44.0	43.5
40	59.3	58.7	58.0
50	74.2	73.3	72.5
″	**86**	**85**	**84**
1	1.4	1.4	1.4
2	2.9	2.8	2.8
3	4.3	4.2	4.2
4	5.7	5.7	5.6
5	7.2	7.1	7.0
6	8.6	8.5	8.4
7	10.0	9.9	9.8
8	11.5̄	11.3	11.2
9	12.9	12.8	12.6
10	14.3	14.2	14.0
20	28.7	28.3	28.0
30	43.0	42.5	42.0
40	57.3	56.7	56.0
50	71.7	70.8	70.0
″	**83**	**82**	**81**
1	1.4	1.4	1.4
2	2.8	2.7	2.7
3	4.2	4.1	4.0
4	5.5̇	5.5̄	5.4
5	6.9	6.8	6.8
6	8.3	8.2	8.1
7	9.7	9.6	9.4
8	11.1	10.9	10.8
9	12.4	12.3	12.2
10	13.8	13.7	13.5
20	27.7	27.3	27.0
30	41.5	41.0	40.5
40	55.3	54.7	54.0
50	69.2	68.3	67.5

98° (278°) (261°) **81°**

9° (189°) (350°) **170°**

′	L. Sin.	d.	L. Tan.	c.d.	L. Cot.	L. Cos.	′
0	9.19 433	80	9.19 971	82	0.80 029	9.99 462	**60**
1	9.19 513	79	9.20 053	81	0.79 947	9.99 460	59
2	9.19 592	80	9.20 134	82	0.79 866	9.99 458	58
3	9.19 672	79	9.20 216	81	0.79 784	9.99 456	57
4	9.19 751	79	9.20 297	81	0.79 703	9.99 454	56
5	9.19 830	79	9.20 378	81	0.79 622	9.99 452	55
6	9.19 909	79	9.20 459	81	0.79 541	9.99 450	54
7	9.19 988	79	9.20 540	81	0.79 460	9.99 448	53
8	9.20 067	78	9.20 621	80	0.79 379	9.99 446	52
9	9.20 145	78	9.20 701	81	0.79 299	9.99 444	51
10	9.20 223	79	9.20 782	80	0.79 218	9.99 442	**50**
11	9.20 302	78	9.20 862	80	0.79 138	9.99 440	49
12	9.20 380	78	9.20 942	80	0.79 058	9.99 438	48
13	9.20 458	77	9.21 022	80	0.78 978	9.99 436	47
14	9.20 535	78	9.21 102	80	0.78 898	9.99 434	46
15	9.20 613	78	9.21 182	79	0.78 818	9.99 432	45
16	9.20 691	77	9.21 261	80	0.78 739	9.99 429	44
17	9.20 768	77	9.21 341	79	0.78 659	9.99 427	43
18	9.20 845	77	9.21 420	79	0.78 580	9.99 425	42
19	9.20 922	77	9.21 499	79	0.78 501	9.99 423	41
20	9.20 999	77	9.21 578	79	0.78 422	9.99 421	**40**
21	9.21 076	77	9.21 657	79	0.78 343	9.99 419	39
22	9.21 153	76	9.21 736	78	0.78 264	9.99 417	38
23	9.21 229	77	9.21 814	79	0.78 186	9.99 415	37
24	9.21 306	76	9.21 893	78	0.78 107	9.99 413	36
25	9.21 382	76	9.21 971	78	0.78 029	9.99 411	35
26	9.21 458	76	9.22 049	78	0.77 951	9.99 409	34
27	9.21 534	76	9.22 127	78	0.77 873	9.99 407	33
28	9.21 610	75	9.22 205	78	0.77 795	9.99 404	32
29	9.21 685	76	9.22 283	78	0.77 717	9.99 402	31
30	9.21 761	75	9.22 361	77	0.77 639	9.99 400	**30**
31	9.21 836	76	9.22 438	78	0.77 562	9.99 398	29
32	9.21 912	75	9.22 516	77	0.77 484	9.99 396	28
33	9.21 987	75	9.22 593	77	0.77 407	9.99 394	27
34	9.22 062	75	9.22 670	77	0.77 330	9.99 392	26
35	9.22 137	74	9.22 747	77	0.77 253	9.99 390	25
36	9.22 211	75	9.22 824	77	0.77 176	9.99 388	24
37	9.22 286	75	9.22 901	76	0.77 099	9.99 385	23
38	9.22 361	74	9.22 977	77	0.77 023	9.99 383	22
39	9.22 435	74	9.23 054	76	0.76 946	9.99 381	21
40	9.22 509	74	9.23 130	76	0.76 870	9.99 379	**20**
41	9.22 583	74	9.23 206	77	0.76 794	9.99 377	19
42	9.22 657	74	9.23 283	76	0.76 717	9.99 375	18
43	9.22 731	74	9.23 359	76	0.76 641	9.99 372	17
44	9.22 805	73	9.23 435	75	0.76 565	9.99 370	16
45	9.22 878	74	9.23 510	76	0.76 490	9.99 368	15
46	9.22 952	73	9.23 586	75	0.76 414	9.99 366	14
47	9.23 025	73	9.23 661	76	0.76 339	9.99 364	13
48	9.23 098	73	9.23 737	75	0.76 263	9.99 362	12
49	9.23 171	73	9.23 812	75	0.76 188	9.99 359	11
50	9.23 244	73	9.23 887	75	0.76 113	9.99 357	**10**
51	9.23 317	73	9.23 962	75	0.76 038	9.99 355	9
52	9.23 390	72	9.24 037	75	0.75 963	9.99 353	8
53	9.23 462	73	9.24 112	74	0.75 888	9.99 351	7
54	9.23 535	72	9.24 186	75	0.75 814	9.99 348	6
55	9.23 607	72	9.24 261	74	0.75 739	9.99 346	5
56	9.23 679	73	9.24 335	75	0.75 665	9.99 344	4
57	9.23 752	71	9.24 410	74	0.75 590	9.99 342	3
58	9.23 823	72	9.24 484	74	0.75 516	9.99 340	2
59	9.23 895	72	9.24 558	74	0.75 442	9.99 337	1
60	9.23 967		9.24 632		0.75 368	9.99 335	**0**
′	L. Cos.	d.	L. Cot.	c.d.	L. Tan.	L. Sin.	′

P. P.

″	**80**	**79**	**78**	**77**
1	1.3	1.3	1.3	1.3
2	2.7	2.6	2.6	2.6
3	4.0	4.0	3.9	3.8
4	5.3	5.3	5.2	5.1
5	6.7	6.6	6.5	6.4
6	8.0	7.9	7.8	7.7
7	9.3	9.2	9.1	9.0
8	10.7	10.5	10.4	10.3
9	12.0	11.8	11.7	11.6
10	13.3	13.2	13.0	12.8
20	26.7	26.3	26.0	25.7
30	40.0	39.5	39.0	38.5
40	53.3	52.7	52.0	51.3
50	66.7	65.8	65.0	64.2

″	**76**	**75**	**74**	**73**
1	1.3	1.2	1.2	1.2
2	2.5	2.5	2.5	2.4
3	3.8	3.8	3.7	3.6
4	5.1	5.0	4.9	4.9
5	6.3	6.2	6.2	6.1
6	7.6	7.5	7.4	7.3
7	8.9	8.8	8.6	8.5
8	10.1	10.0	9.9	9.7
9	11.4	11.2	11.1	11.0
10	12.7	12.5	12.3	12.2
20	25.3	25.0	24.7	24.3
30	38.0	37.5	37.0	36.5
40	50.7	50.0	49.3	48.7
50	63.3	62.5	61.7	60.8

″	**72**	**71**	**3**	**2**
1	1.2	1.2	0.0	0.0
2	2.4	2.4	0.1	0.1
3	3.6	3.6	0.2	0.1
4	4.8	4.7	0.2	0.1
5	6.0	5.9	0.2	0.2
6	7.2	7.1	0.3	0.2
7	8.4	8.3	0.4	0.2
8	9.6	9.5	0.4	0.3
9	10.8	10.6	0.4	0.3
10	12.0	11.8	0.5	0.3
20	24.0	23.7	1.0	0.7
30	36.0	35.5	1.5	1.0
40	48.0	47.3	2.0	1.3
50	60.0	59.2	2.5	1.7

	3/79	**3/78**	**3/77**
0			
1	13.2	13.0	12.8
2	39.5	39.0	38.5
3	65.8	65.0	64.2

	3/76	**3/75**	**3/74**
0			
1	12.7	12.5	12.3
2	38.0	37.5	37.0
3	63.3	62.5	61.7

P. P.

99° (279°) (260°) **80°**

10° (190°) (349°) **169°**

′	L. Sin.	d.	L. Tan.	c.d.	L. Cot.	L. Cos.	d.	′
0	9.23 967	72	9.24 632	74	0.75 368	9.99 335	2	**60**
1	9.24 039	71	9.24 706	73	0.75 294	9.99 333	2	59
2	9.24 110	71	9.24 779	74	0.75 221	9.99 331	3	58
3	9.24 181	72	9.24 853	73	0.75 147	9.99 328	2	57
4	9.24 253	71	9.24 926	74	0.75 074	9.99 326	2	56
5	9.24 324	71	9.25 000	73	0.75 000	9.99 324	2	55
6	9.24 395	71	9.25 073	73	0.74 927	9.99 322	3	54
7	9.24 466	70	9.25 146	73	0.74 854	9.99 319	2	53
8	9.24 536	71	9.25 219	73	0.74 781	9.99 317	2	52
9	9.24 607	70	9.25 292	73	0.74 708	9.99 315	2	51
10	9.24 677	71	9.25 365	72	0.74 635	9.99 313	3	**50**
11	9.24 748	70	9.25 437	73	0.74 563	9.99 310	2	49
12	9.24 818	70	9.25 510	72	0.74 490	9.99 308	2	48
13	9.24 888	70	9.25 582	73	0.74 418	9.99 306	2	47
14	9.24 958	70	9.25 655	72	0.74 345	9.99 304	3	46
15	9.25 028	70	9.25 727	72	0.74 273	9.99 301	2	45
16	9.25 098	70	9.25 799	72	0.74 201	9.99 299	2	44
17	9.25 168	69	9.25 871	72	0.74 129	9.99 297	3	43
18	9.25 237	70	9.25 943	72	0.74 057	9.99 294	2	42
19	9.25 307	69	9.26 015	71	0.73 985	9.99 292	2	41
20	9.25 376	69	9.26 086	72	0.73 914	9.99 290	2	**40**
21	9.25 445	69	9.26 158	71	0.73 842	9.99 288	3	39
22	9.25 514	69	9.26 229	72	0.73 771	9.99 285	2	38
23	9.25 583	69	9.26 301	71	0.73 699	9.99 283	2	37
24	9.25 652	69	9.26 372	71	0.73 628	9.99 281	3	36
25	9.25 721	69	9.26 443	71	0.73 557	9.99 278	2	35
26	9.25 790	68	9.26 514	71	0.73 486	9.99 276	2	34
27	9.25 858	69	9.26 585	70	0.73 415	9.99 274	3	33
28	9.25 927	68	9.26 655	71	0.73 345	9.99 271	2	32
29	9.25 995	68	9.26 726	71	0.73 274	9.99 269	2	31
30	9.26 063	68	9.26 797	70	0.73 203	9.99 267	3	**30**
31	9.26 131	68	9.26 867	70	0.73 133	9.99 264	2	29
32	9.26 199	68	9.26 937	71	0.73 063	9.99 262	2	28
33	9.26 267	68	9.27 008	70	0.72 992	9.99 260	3	27
34	9.26 335	68	9.27 078	70	0.72 922	9.99 257	2	26
35	9.26 403	67	9.27 148	70	0.72 852	9.99 255	3	25
36	9.26 470	68	9.27 218	70	0.72 782	9.99 252	2	24
37	9.26 538	67	9.27 288	69	0.72 712	9.99 250	2	23
38	9.26 605	67	9.27 357	70	0.72 643	9.99 248	3	22
39	9.26 672	67	9.27 427	69	0.72 573	9.99 245	2	21
40	9.26 739	67	9.27 496	70	0.72 504	9.99 243	2	**20**
41	9.26 806	67	9.27 566	69	0.72 434	9.99 241	3	19
42	9.26 873	67	9.27 635	69	0.72 365	9.99 238	2	18
43	9.26 940	67	9.27 704	69	0.72 296	9.99 236	3	17
44	9.27 007	66	9.27 773	69	0.72 227	9.99 233	2	16
45	9.27 073	67	9.27 842	69	0.72 158	9.99 231	2	15
46	9.27 140	66	9.27 911	69	0.72 089	9.99 229	3	14
47	9.27 206	67	9.27 980	69	0.72 020	9.99 226	2	13
48	9.27 273	66	9.28 049	68	0.71 951	9.99 224	3	12
49	9.27 339	66	9.28 117	69	0.71 883	9.99 221	2	11
50	9.27 405	66	9.28 186	68	0.71 814	9.99 219	2	**10**
51	9.27 471	66	9.28 254	69	0.71 746	9.99 217	3	9
52	9.27 537	65	9.28 323	68	0.71 677	9.99 214	2	8
53	9.27 602	66	9.28 391	68	0.71 609	9.99 212	3	7
54	9.27 668	66	9.28 459	68	0.71 541	9.99 209	2	6
55	9.27 734	65	9.28 527	68	0.71 473	9.99 207	3	5
56	9.27 799	65	9.28 595	67	0.71 405	9.99 204	2	4
57	9.27 864	66	9.28 662	68	0.71 338	9.99 202	2	3
58	9.27 930	65	9.28 730	68	0.71 270	9.99 200	3	2
59	9.27 995	65	9.28 798	67	0.71 202	9.99 197	2	1
60	9.28 060		9.28 865		0.71 135	9.99 195		**0**
′	L. Cos.	d.	L. Cot.	c.d.	L. Tan.	L. Sin.	d.	′

P. P.

″	**74**	**73**	**72**
1	1.2	1.2	1.2
2	2.5	2.4	2.4
3	3.7	3.6	3.6
4	4.9	4.9	4.8
5	6.2	6.1	6.0
6	7.4	7.3	7.2
7	8.6	8.5	8.4
8	9.9	9.7	9.6
9	11.1	11.0	10.8
10	12.3	12.2	12.0
20	24.7	24.3	24.0
30	37.0	36.5	36.0
40	49.3	48.7	48.0
50	61.7	60.8	60.0

″	**71**	**70**	**69**
1	1.2	1.2	1.2
2	2.4	2.3	2.3
3	3.6	3.5	3.4
4	4.7	4.7	4.6
5	5.9	5.8	5.8
6	7.1	7.0	6.9
7	8.3	8.2	8.0
8	9.5	9.3	9.2
9	10.6	10.5	10.4
10	11.8	11.7	11.5
20	23.7	23.3	23.0
30	35.5	35.0	34.5
40	47.3	46.7	46.0
50	59.2	58.3	57.5

″	**68**	**67**	**66**
1	1.1	1.1	1.1
2	2.3	2.2	2.2
3	3.4	3.4	3.3
4	4.5	4.5	4.4
5	5.7	5.6	5.5
6	6.8	6.7	6.6
7	7.9	7.8	7.7
8	9.1	8.9	8.8
9	10.2	10.0	9.9
10	11.3	11.2	11.0
20	22.7	22.3	22.0
30	34.0	33.5	33.0
40	45.3	44.7	44.0
50	56.7	55.8	55.0

	3/74	**3/73**	**3/72**
0–1	12.3	12.2	12.0
1–2	37.0	36.5	36.0
2–3	61.7	60.8	60.0

	3/71	**3/70**	**3/69**	**3/68**
0–1	11.8	11.7	11.5	11.3
1–2	35.5	35.0	34.5	34.0
2–3	59.2	58.3	57.5	56.7

100° (280°) (259°) **79°**

LOGARITHMS OF THE FUNCTIONS (Continued)

11° (191°) (348°) **168°**

′	L. Sin.	d.	L. Tan.	c.d.	L. Cot.	L. Cos.	d.	′
0	9.28 060	65	9.28 865	68	0.71 135	9.99 195	3	**60**
1	9.28 125	65	9.28 933	67	0.71 067	9.99 192	2	59
2	9.28 190	64	9.29 000	67	0.71 000	9.99 190	3	58
3	9.28 254	65	9.29 067	67	0.70 933	9.99 187	2	57
4	9.28 319	65	9.29 134	67	0.70 866	9.99 185	3	56
5	9.28 384	64	9.29 201	67	0.70 799	9.99 182	2	55
6	9.28 448	64	9.29 268	67	0.70 732	9.99 180	3	54
7	9.28 512	65	9.29 335	67	0.70 665	9.99 177	2	53
8	9.28 577	64	9 29 402	66	0.70 598	9.99 175	3	52
9	9.28 641	64	9.29 468	67	0.70 532	9.99 172	2	51
10	9.28 705	64	9.29 535	66	0.70 465	9.99 170	3	**50**
11	9.28 769	64	9.29 601	67	0.70 399	9.99 167	2	49
12	9.28 833	63	9.29 668	66	0.70 332	9.99 165	3	48
13	9.28 896	64	9.29 734	66	0.70 266	9.99 162	2	47
14	9.28 960	64	9.29 800	66	0.70 200	9.99 160	3	46
15	9.29 024	63	9.29 866	66	0.70 134	9.99 157	2	45
16	9.29 087	63	9.29 932	66	0.70 068	9.99 155	3	44
17	9.29 150	64	9.29 998	66	0.70 002	9.99 152	2	43
18	9.29 214	63	9.30 064	66	0.69 936	9.99 150	3	42
19	9.29 277	63	9.30 130	65	0.69 870	9.99 147	2	41
20	9.29 340	63	9.30 195	66	0.69 805	9.99 145	3	**40**
21	9.29 403	63	9.30 261	65	0.69 739	9.99 142	2	39
22	9.29 466	63	9.30 326	65	0.69 674	9.99 140	3	38
23	9.29 529	62	9.30 391	66	0.69 609	9.99 137	2	37
24	9.29 591	63	9.30 457	65	0.69 543	9.99 135	3	36
25	9.29 654	62	9.30 522	65	0.69 478	9.99 132	2	35
26	9.29 716	63	9.30 587	65	0.69 413	9.99 130	3	34
27	9.29 779	62	9.30 652	65	0.69 348	9.99 127	3	33
28	9.29 841	62	9.30 717	65	0.69 283	9.99 124	2	32
29	9.29 903	63	9.30 782	64	0.69 218	9.99 122	3	31
30	9.29 966	62	9.30 846	65	0.69 154	9.99 119	2	**30**
31	9.30 028	62	9.30 911	64	0.69 089	9.99 117	3	29
32	9.30 090	61	9.30 975	65	0.69 025	9.99 114	2	28
33	9.30 151	62	9.31 040	64	0.68 960	9.99 112	3	27
34	9.30 213	62	9.31 104	64	0.68 896	9.99 109	3	26
35	9.30 275	61	9.31 168	65	0.68 832	9.99 106	2	25
36	9.30 336	62	9.31 233	64	0.68 767	9.99 104	3	24
37	9.30 398	61	9.31 297	64	0.68 703	9.99 101	2	23
38	9.30 459	62	9.31 361	64	0.68 639	9.99 099	3	22
39	9.30 521	61	9.31 425	64	0.68 575	9.99 096	3	21
40	9.30 582	61	9.31 489	63	0.68 511	9.99 093	2	**20**
41	9.30 643	61	9.31 552	64	0.68 448	9.99 091	3	19
42	9.30 704	61	9.31 616	63	0.68 384	9.99 088	2	18
43	9.30 765	61	9.31 679	64	0.68 321	9.99 086	3	17
44	9.30 826	61	9.31 743	63	0.68 257	9.99 083	3	16
45	9.30 887	60	9.31 806	64	0.68 194	9.99 080	2	15
46	9.30 947	61	9.31 870	63	0.68 130	9.99 078	3	14
47	9.31 008	60	9.31 933	63	0.68 067	9.99 075	3	13
48	9.31 068	61	9.31 996	63	0.68 004	9.99 072	2	12
49	9.31 129	60	9.32 059	63	0.67 941	9.99 070	3	11
50	9.31 189	61	9.32 122	63	0.67 878	9.99 067	3	**10**
51	9.31 250	60	9.32 185	63	0.67 815	9.99 064	2	9
52	9.31 310	60	9.32 248	63	0.67 752	9.99 062	3	8
53	9.31 370	60	9.32 311	62	0.67 689	9.99 059	3	7
54	9.31 430	60	9.32 373	63	0.67 627	9.99 056	2	6
55	9.31 490	59	9.32 436	62	0.67 564	9.99 054	3	5
56	9.31 549	60	9.32 498	63	0.67 502	9.99 051	3	4
57	9.31 609	60	9.32 561	62	0.67 439	9.99 048	2	3
58	9.31 669	59	9.32 623	62	0.67 377	9.99 046	3	2
59	9.31 728	60	9.32 685	62	0.67 315	9.99 043	3	1
60	9.31 788		9.32 747		0.67 253	9.99 040		**0**
′	L. Cos.	d.	L. Cot.	c.d.	L. Tan.	L. Sin.	d.	′

P. P.

″	**65**	**64**	**63**
1	1.1	1.1	1.0
2	2.2	2.1	2.1
3	3.2	3.2	3.2
4	4.3	4.3	4.2
5	5.4	5.3	5.2
6	6.5	6.4	6.3
7	7.6	7.5	7.4
8	8.7	8.5	8.4
9	9.8	9.6	9.4
10	10.8	10.7	10.5
20	21.7	21.3	21.0
30	32.5	32.0	31.5
40	43.3	42.7	42.0
50	54.2	53.3	52.5

″	**62**	**61**	**60**
1	1.0	1.0	1.0
2	2.1	2.0	2.0
3	3.1	3.0	3.0
4	4.1	4.1	4.0
5	5.2	5.1	5.0
6	6.2	6.1	6.0
7	7.2	7.1	7.0
8	8.3	8.1	8.0
9	9.3	9.2	9.0
10	10.3	10.2	10.0
20	20.7	20.3	20.0
30	31.0	30.5	30.0
40	41.3	40.7	40.0
50	51.7	50.8	50.0

″	**59**	**3**	**2**
1	1.0	0.0	0.0
2	2.0	0.1	0.1
3	3.0	0.2	0.1
4	3.9	0.2	0.1
5	4.9	0.2	0.2
6	5.9	0.3	0.2
7	6.9	0.4	0.2
8	7.9	0.4	0.3
9	8.8	0.4	0.3
10	9.8	0.5	0.3
20	19.7	1.0	0.7
30	29.5	1.5	1.0
40	39.3	2.0	1.3
50	49.2	2.5	1.7

	3/67	**3/66**	**3/65**
0	11.2	11.0	10.8
1	33.5	33.0	32.5
2	55.8	55.0	54.2
3			

	3/64	**3/63**	**3/62**
0	10.7	10.5	10.3
1	32.0	31.5	31.0
2	53.3	52.5	51.7
3			

101° (281°) (258°) **78°**

LOGARITHMS OF THE FUNCTIONS (Continued)

12° (192°) (347°) **167°**

′	L. Sin.	d.	L. Tan.	c.d.	L. Cot.	L. Cos.	d.	′
0	9.31 788		9.32 747		0.67 253	9.99 040		**60**
1	9.31 847	59	9.32 810	63	0.67 190	9.99 038	2	59
2	9.31 907	60	9.32 872	62	0.67 128	9.99 035	3	58
3	9.31 966	59	9.32 933	61	0.67 067	9.99 032	3	57
4	9.32 025	59	9.32 995	62	0.67 005	9.99 030	2	56
5	9.32 084	59	9.33 057	62	0.66 943	9.99 027	3	55
6	9.32 143	59	9.33 119	62	0.66 881	9.99 024	3	54
7	9.32 202	59	9.33 180	61	0.66 820	9.99 022	2	53
8	9.32 261	59	9.33 242	62	0.66 758	9.99 019	3	52
9	9.32 319	58	9.33 303	61	0.66 697	9.99 016	3	51
10	9.32 378	59	9.33 365	62	0.66 605	9.99 013	3	**50**
11	9.32 437	59	9.33 426	61	0.66 574	9.99 011	2	49
12	9.32 495	58	9.33 487	61	0.66 513	9.99 008	3	48
13	9.32 553	58	9.33 548	61	0.66 452	9.99 005	3	47
14	9.32 612	59	9.33 609	61	0.66 391	9.99 002	3	46
15	9.32 670	58	9.33 670	61	0.66 330	9.99 000	2	45
16	9.32 728	58	9.33 731	61	0.66 269	9.98 997	3	44
17	9.32 786	58	9.33 792	61	0.66 208	9.98 994	3	43
18	9.32 844	58	9.33 853	61	0.66 147	9.98 991	3	42
19	9.32 902	58	9.33 913	60	0.66 087	9.98 989	2	41
20	9.32 960	58	9.33 974	61	0.66 026	9.98 986	3	**40**
21	9.33 018	58	9.34 034	60	0.65 966	9.98 983	3	39
22	9.33 075	57	9.34 095	61	0.65 905	9.98 980	3	38
23	9.33 133	58	9.34 155	60	0.65 845	9.98 978	2	37
24	9.33 190	57	9.34 215	60	0.65 785	9.98 975	3	36
25	9.33 248	58	9.34 276	61	0.65 724	9.98 972	3	35
26	9.33 305	57	9.34 336	60	0.65 664	9.98 969	3	34
27	9.33 362	57	9.34 396	60	0.65 604	9.98 967	2	33
28	9.33 420	58	9.34 456	60	0.65 544	9.98 964	3	32
29	9.33 477	57	9.34 516	60	0.65 484	9.98 961	3	31
30	9.33 534	57	9.34 576	60	0.65 424	9.98 958	3	**30**
31	9.33 591	57	9.34 635	59	0.65 365	9.98 955	3	29
32	9.33 647	56	9.34 695	60	0.65 305	9.98 953	2	28
33	9.33 704	57	9.34 755	60	0.65 245	9.98 950	3	27
34	9.33 761	57	9.34 814	59	0.65 186	9.98 947	3	26
35	9.33 818	57	9.34 874	60	0.65 126	9.98 944	3	25
36	9.33 874	56	9.34 933	59	0.65 067	9.98 941	3	24
37	9.33 931	57	9.34 992	59	0.65 008	9.98 938	3	23
38	9.33 987	56	9.35 051	59	0.64 949	9.98 936	2	22
39	9.34 043	56	9.35 111	60	0.64 889	9.98 933	3	21
40	9.34 100	57	9.35 170	59	0.64 830	9.98 930	3	**20**
41	9.34 156	56	9.35 229	59	0.64 771	9.98 927	3	19
42	9.34 212	56	9.35 288	59	0.64 712	9.98 924	3	18
43	9.34 268	56	9.35 347	59	0.64 653	9.98 921	3	17
44	9.34 324	56	9.35 405	58	0.64 595	9.98 919	2	16
45	9.34 380	56	9.35 464	59	0.64 536	9.98 916	3	15
46	9.34 436	56	9.35 523	59	0.64 477	9.98 913	3	14
47	9.34 491	55	9.35 581	58	0.64 419	9.98 910	3	13
48	9.34 547	56	9.35 640	59	0.64 360	9.98 907	3	12
49	9.34 602	55	9.35 698	58	0.64 302	9.98 904	3	11
50	9.34 658	56	9.35 757	59	0.64 243	9.98 901	3	**10**
51	9.34 713	55	9.35 815	58	0.64 185	9.98 898	3	9
52	9.34 769	56	9.35 873	58	0.64 127	9.98 896	2	8
53	9.34 824	55	9.35 931	58	0.64 069	9.98 893	3	7
54	9.34 879	55	9.35 989	58	0.64 011	9.98 890	3	6
55	9.34 934	55	9.36 047	58	0.63 953	9.98 887	3	5
56	9.34 989	55	9.36 105	58	0.63 895	9.98 884	3	4
57	9.35 044	55	9.36 163	58	0.63 837	9.98 881	3	3
58	9.35 099	55	9.36 221	58	0.63 779	9.98 878	3	2
59	9.35 154	55	9.36 279	58	0.63 721	9.98 875	3	1
60	9.35 209	55	9.36 336	57	0.63 664	9.98 872	3	**0**
′	L. Cos.	d.	L. Cot.	c.d.	L. Tan.	L. Sin.	d.	′

P. P.

″	**63**	**62**	**61**
1	1.0	1.0	1.0
2	2.1	2.1	2.0
3	3.2	3.1	3.0
4	4.2	4.1	4.1
5	5.2	5.2	5.1
6	6.3	6.2	6.1
7	7.4	7.2	7.1
8	8.4	8.3	8.1
9	9.4	9.3	9.2
10	10.5	10.3	10.2
20	21.0	20.7	20.3
30	31.5	31.0	30.5
40	42.0	41.3	40.7
50	52.5	51.7	50.8
″	**60**	**59**	**58**
1	1.0	1.0	1.0
2	2.0	2.0	1.9
3	3.0	3.0	2.9
4	4.0	3.9	3.9
5	5.0	4.9	4.8
6	6.0	5.9	5.8
7	7.0	6.9	6.8
8	8.0	7.9	7.7
9	9.0	8.8	8.7
10	10.0	9.8	9.7
20	20.0	19.7	19.3
30	30.0	29.5	29.0
40	40.0	39.3	38.7
50	50.0	49.2	48.3
″	**57**	**56**	**55**
1	1.0	0.9	0.9
2	1.9	1.9	1.8
3	2.8	2.8	2.8
4	3.8	3.7	3.7
5	4.8	4.7	4.6
6	5.7	5.6	5.5
7	6.6	6.5	6.4
8	7.6	7.5	7.3
9	8.6	8.4	8.2
10	9.5	9.3	9.2
20	19.0	18.7	18.3
30	28.5	28.0	27.5
40	38.0	37.3	36.7
50	47.5	46.7	45.8

	3/**62**	**3**/**61**	**3**/**60**
0			
	10.3	10.2	10.0
1			
	31.0	30.5	30.0
2			
	51.7	50.8	50.0
3			

	3/**59**	**3**/**58**	**3**/**57**
0			
	9.8	9.7	9.5
1			
	29.5	29.0	28.5
2			
	49.2	48.3	47.5
3			

P. P.

102° (282°) (257°) **77°**

13° (193°) (346°) **166°**

′	L. Sin.	d.	L. Tan.	c.d.	L. Cot.	L. Cos.	d.	′
0	9.35 209	54	9.36 336	58	0.63 664	9.98 872	3	**60**
1	9.35 263	55	9.36 394	58	0.63 606	9.98 869	2	59
2	9.35 318	55	9.36 452	57	0.63 548	9.98 867	3	58
3	9.35 373	54	9.36 509	57	0.63 491	9.98 864	3	57
4	9.35 427	54	9.36 566	58	0.63 434	9.98 861	3	56
5	9.35 481	55	9.36 624	57	0.63 376	9.98 858	3	55
6	9.35 536	54	9.36 681	57	0.63 319	9.98 855	3	54
7	9.35 590	54	9.36 738	57	0.63 262	9.98 952	3	53
8	9.35 644	54	9.36 795	57	0.63 205	9.98 849	3	52
9	9.35 698	54	9.36 852	57	0.63 148	9.98 846	3	51
10	9.35 752	54	9.36 909	57	0.63 091	9.98 843	3	**50**
11	9.35 806	54	9.36 966	57	0.63 034	9.98 840	3	49
12	9.35 860	54	9.37 023	57	0.62 977	9.98 837	3	48
13	9.35 914	54	9.37 080	57	0.62 920	9.98 834	3	47
14	9.35 968	54	9.37 137	56	0.62 863	9.98 831	3	46
15	9.36 022	53	9.37 193	57	0.62 807	9.98 828	3	45
16	9.36 075	54	9.37 250	56	0.62 750	9.98 825	3	44
17	9.36 129	53	9.37 306	57	0.62 694	9.98 822	3	43
18	9.36 182	54	9.37 363	56	0.62 637	9.98 819	3	42
19	9.36 236	53	9.37 419	57	0.62 581	9.98 816	3	41
20	9.36 289	53	9.37 476	56	0.62 524	9.98 813	3	**40**
21	9.36 342	53	9.37 532	56	0.62 468	9.98 810	3	39
22	9.36 395	54	9.37 588	56	0.62 412	9.98 807	3	38
23	9.36 449	53	9.37 644	56	0.62 356	9.98 804	3	37
24	9.36 502	53	9.37 700	56	0.62 300	9.98 801	3	36
25	9.36 555	53	9.37 756	56	0.62 244	9.98 798	3	35
26	9.36 608	52	9.37 812	56	0.62 188	9.98 795	3	34
27	9.36 660	53	9.37 868	56	0.62 132	9.98 792	3	33
28	9.36 713	53	9.37 924	56	0.62 076	9.98 789	3	32
29	9.36 766	53	9.37 980	55	0.62 020	9.98 786	3	31
30	9.36 819	52	9.38 035	56	0.61 965	9.98 783	3	**30**
31	9.36 871	53	9.38 091	56	0.61 909	9.98 780	3	29
32	9.36 924	52	9.38 147	55	0.61 853	9.98 777	3	28
33	9.36 976	52	9.38 202	55	0.61 798	9.98 774	3	27
34	9.37 028	53	9.38 257	56	0.61 743	9.98 771	3	26
35	9.37 081	52	9.38 313	55	0.61 687	9.98 768	3	25
36	9.37 133	52	9.38 368	55	0.61 632	9.98 765	3	24
37	9.37 185	52	9.38 423	56	0.61 577	9.98 762	3	23
38	9.37 237	52	9.38 479	55	0.61 521	9.98 759	3	22
39	9.37 289	52	9.38 534	55	0.61 466	9.98 756	3	21
40	9.37 341	52	9.38 589	55	0.61 411	9.98 753	3	**20**
41	9.37 393	52	9.38 644	55	0.61 356	9.98 750	4	19
42	9.37 445	52	9.38 699	55	0.61 301	9.98 746	3	18
43	9.37 497	52	9.38 754	54	0.61 246	9.98 743	3	17
44	9.37 549	51	9.38 808	55	0.61 192	9.98 740	3	16
45	9.37 600	52	9.38 863	55	0.61 137	9.98 737	3	15
46	9.37 652	51	9.38 918	54	0.61 082	9.98 734	3	14
47	9.37 703	52	9.38 972	55	0.61 028	9.98 731	3	13
48	9.37 755	51	9.39 027	55	0.60 973	9.98 728	3	12
49	9.37 806	52	9.39 082	54	0.60 918	9.98 725	3	11
50	9.37 858	51	9.39 136	54	0.60 864	9.98 722	3	**10**
51	9.37 909	51	9.39 190	55	0.60 810	9.98 719	4	9
52	9.37 960	51	9.39 245	54	0.60 755	9.98 715	3	8
53	9.38 011	51	9.39 299	54	0.60 701	9.98 712	3	7
54	9.38 062	51	9.39 353	54	0.60 647	9.98 709	3	6
55	9.38 113	51	9.39 407	54	0.60 593	9.98 706	3	5
56	9.38 164	51	9.39 461	54	0.60 539	9.98 703	3	4
57	9.38 215	51	9.39 515	54	0.60 485	9.98 700	3	3
58	9.38 266	51	9.39 569	54	0.60 431	9.98 697	3	2
59	9.38 317	51	9.39 623	54	0.60 377	9.98 694	4	1
60	9.38 368		9.39 677		0.60 323	9.98 690		**0**
′	L. Cos.	d.	L. Cot.	c.d.	L. Tan.	L. Sin.	d.	′

103° (283°) (256°) **76°**

P. P.

″	**57**	**56**	**55**
1	1.0	0.9	0.9
2	1.9	1.9	1.8
3	2.8	2.8	2.8
4	3.8	3.7	3.7
5	4.8	4.7	4.6
6	5.7	5.6	5.5
7	6.6	6.5	6.4
8	7.6	7.5	7.3
9	8.6	8.4	8.2
10	9.5	9.3	9.2
20	19.0	18.7	18.3
30	28.5	28.0	27.5
40	38.0	37.3	36.7
50	47.5	46.7	45.8

″	**54**	**53**	**52**
1	0.9	0.9	0.9
2	1.8	1.8	1.7
3	2.7	2.6	2.6
4	3.6	3.5	3.5
5	4.5	4.4	4.3
6	5.4	5.3	5.2
7	6.3	6.2	6.1
8	7.2	7.1	6.9
9	8.1	8.0	7.8
10	9.0	8.8	8.7
20	18.0	17.7	17.3
30	27.0	26.5	26.0
40	36.0	35.3	34.7
50	45.0	44.2	43.3

″	**51**	**4**	**3**	**2**
1	0.8	0.1	0.0	0.0
2	1.7	0.1	0.1	0.1
3	2.6	0.2	0.2	0.1
4	3.4	0.3	0.2	0.1
5	4.2	0.3	0.2	0.2
6	5.1	0.4	0.3	0.2
7	6.0	0.5	0.4	0.2
8	6.8	0.5	0.4	0.3
9	7.6	0.6	0.4	0.3
10	8.5	0.7	0.5	0.3
20	17.0	1.3	1.0	0.7
30	25.5	2.0	1.5	1.0
40	34.0	2.7	2.0	1.3
50	42.5	3.3	2.5	1.7

	4/55	**4/54**	**3/58**	**3/57**
0	6.9	6.8	9.7	9.5
1	20.6	20.2	29.0	28.5
2	34.4	33.8	48.3	47.5
3	48.1	47.2	—	—
4				

	3/56	**3/55**	**3/54**
0	9.3	9.2	9.0
1	28.0	27.5	27.0
2	46.7	45.8	45.0
3			

P. P.

14° (194°) (345°) **165°**

′	L. Sin.	d.	L. Tan.	c.d.	L. Cot.	L. Cos.	d.	′
0	9.38 368	50	9.39 677	54	0.60 323	9.98 690	3	**60**
1	9.38 418	51	9.39 731	54	0.60 269	9.98 687	3	59
2	9.38 469	50	9.39 785̄	53	0.60 215̇	9.98 684	3	58
3	9.38 519	51	9.39 838	54	0.60 162	9.98 681	3	57
4	9.38 570	50	9.39 892	53	0.60 108	9.98 678	3	56
5	9.38 620	50	9.39 945̇	54	0.60 055̄	9.98 675̄	4	55
6	9.38 670	51	9.39 999	53	0.60 001	9.98 671	3	54
7	9.38 721	50	9.40 052	54	0.59 948	9.98 668	3	53
8	9.38 771	50	9.40 106	53	0.59 894	9.98 665̇	3	52
9	9.38 821	50	9.40 159	53	0.59 841	9.98 662	3	51
10	9.38 871	50	9.40 212	54	0.59 788	9.98 659	3	**50**
11	9.38 921	50	9.40 266	53	0.59 734	9.98 656	4	49
12	9.38 971	50	9.40 319	53	0.59 681	9.98 652	3	48
13	9.39 021	50	9.40 372	53	0.59 628	9.98 649	3	47
14	9.39 071	50	9.40 425̄	53	0.59 575̇	9.98 646	3	46
15	9.39 121	49	9.40 478	53	0.59 522	9.98 643	3	45
16	9.39 170	50	9.40 531	53	0.59 469	9.98 640	4	44
17	9.39 220	50	9.40 584	52	0.59 416	9.98 636	3	43
18	9.39 270	49	9.40 636	53	0.59 364	9.98 633	3	42
19	9.39 319	50	9.40 689	53	0.59 311	9.98 630	3	41
20	9.39 369	49	9.40 742	53	0.59 258	9.98 627	4	**40**
21	9.39 418	49	9.40 795̄	52	0.59 205̇	9.98 623	3	39
22	9.39 467	50	9.40 847	53	0.59 153	9.98 620	3	38
23	9.39 517	49	9.40 900	52	0.59 100	9.98 617	3	37
24	9.39 566	49	9.40 952	53	0.59 048	9.98 614	4	36
25	9.39 615̄	49	9.41 005̄	52	0.58 995̇	9.98 610	3	35
26	9.39 664	49	9.41 057	52	0.58 943	9.98 607	3	34
27	9.39 713	49	9.41 109	52	0.58 891	9.98 604	3	33
28	9.39 762	49	9.41 161	53	0.58 839	9.98 601	4	32
29	9.39 811	49	9.41 214	52	0.58 786	9.98 597	3	31
30	9.39 860	49	9.41 266	52	0.58 734	9.98 594	3	**30**
31	9.39 909	49	9.41 318	52	0.58 682	9.98 591	3	29
32	9.39 958	48	9.41 370	52	0.58 630	9.98 588	4	28
33	9.40 006	49	9.41 422	52	0.58 578	9.98 584	3	27
34	9.40 055̄	48	9.41 474	52	0.58 526	9.98 581	3	26
35	9.40 103	49	9.41 526	52	0.58 474	9.98 578	4	25
36	9.40 152	48	9.41 578	51	0.58 422	9.98 574	3	24
37	9.40 200	49	9.41 629	52	0.58 371	9.98 571	3	23
38	9.40 249	48	9.41 681	52	0.58 319	9.98 568	3	22
39	9.40 297	49	9.41 733	51	0.58 267	9.98 565̄	4	21
40	9.40 346	48	9.41 784	52	0.58 216	9.98 561	3	**20**
41	9.40 394	48	9.41 836	51	0.58 164	9.98 558	3	19
42	9.40 442	48	9.41 887	52	0.58 113	9.98 555̄	4	18
43	9.40 490	48	9.41 939	51	0.58 061	9.98 551	3	17
44	9.40 538	48	9.41 990	51	0.58 010	9.98 548	3	16
45	9.40 586	48	9.42 041	52	0.57 959	9.98 545̄	4	15
46	9.40 634	48	9.42 093	51	0.57 907	9.98 541	3	14
47	9.40 682	48	9.42 144	51	0.57 856	9.98 538	3	13
48	9.40 730	48	9.42 195̇	51	0.57 805̄	9.98 535̄	4	12
49	9.40 778	47	9.42 246	51	0.57 754	9.98 531	3	11
50	9.40 825̇	48	9.42 297	51	0.57 703	9.98 528	3	**10**
51	9.40 873	48	9.42 348	51	0.57 652	9.98 525̄	4	9
52	9.40 921	47	9.42 399	51	0.57 601	9.98 521	3	8
53	9.40 968	48	9.42 45̇0	51	0.57 55̄0	9.98 518	3	7
54	9.41 016	47	9.42 501	51	0.57 499	9.98 515̄	4	6
55	9.41 063	48	9.42 552	51	0.57 448	9.98 511	3	5
56	9.41 111	47	9.42 603	50	0.57 397	9.98 508	3	4
57	9.41 158	47	9.42 653	51	0.57 347	9.98 505̄	4	3
58	9.41 205̇	47	9.42 704	51	0.57 296	9.98 501	3	2
59	9.41 252	48	9.42 755̄	50	0.57 245̇	9.98 498	4	1
60	9.41 300		9.42 805̇		0.57 195̄	9.98 494		**0**
′	L. Cos.	d.	L. Cot.	c.d.	L. Tan.	L. Sin.	d.	′

P. P.

″	**54**	**53**	**52**
1	0.9	0.9	0.9
2	1.8	1.8	1.7
3	2.7	2.6	2.6
4	3.6	3.5̇	3.5̄
5	4.5	4.4	4.3
6	5.4	5.3	5.2
7	6.3	6.2	6.1
8	7.2	7.1	6.9
9	8.1	8.0	7.8
10	9.0	8.8	8.7
20	18.0	17.7	17.3
30	27.0	26.5	26.0
40	36.0	35.3	34.7
50	45.0	44.2	43.3

″	**51**	**50**	**49**
1	0.8	0.8	0.8
2	1.7	1.7	1.6
3	2.6	2.5	2.4
4	3.4	3.3	3.3
5	4.2	4.2	4.1
6	5.1	5.0	4.9
7	6.0	5.8	5.7̄
8	6.8	6.7	6.5̇
9	7.6	7.5	7.4
10	8.5	8.3	8.2
20	17.0	16.7	16.3
30	25.5	25.0	24.5
40	34.0	33.3	32.7
50	42.5	41.7	40.8

″	**48**	**47**	**4**	**3**
1	0.8	0.8	0.1	0.0
2	1.6	1.6	0.1	0.1
3	2.4	2.4	0.2	0.2
4	3.2	3.1	0.3	0.2
5	4.0	3.9	0.3	0.2
6	4.8	4.7	0.4	0.3
7	5.6	5.5̄	0.5̄	0.4
8	6.4	6.3	0.5̇	0.4
9	7.2	7.0	0.6	0.4
10	8.0	7.8	0.7	0.5
20	16.0	15.7	1.3	1.0
30	24.0	23.5	2.0	1.5
40	32.0	31.3	2.7	2.0
50	40.0	39.2	3.3	2.5

	4/54	**4/53**	**4/52**	**4/51**
0	6.8	6.6	6.5	6.4
1	20.2	19.9	19.5	19.1
2	33.8	33.1	32.5	31.9
3	47.2	46.4	45.5	44.6

	3/54	**3/53**	**3/52**	**3/51**
0	9.0	8.8	8.7	8.5
1	27.0	26.5	26.0	25.5
2	45.0	44.2	43.3	42.5

P. P.

104° (284°) (255°) **75°**

15° (195°) (344°) **164°**

′	L. Sin.	d.	L. Tan.	c.d.	L. Cot.	L. Cos.	d.	′
0	9.41 300		9.42 80$\dot{5}$		0.57 19$\bar{5}$	9.98 494		**60**
1	9.41 347	47	9.42 856	51	0.57 144	9.98 491	3	59
2	9.41 394	47	9.42 906	50	0.57 094	9.98 488	3	58
3	9.41 441	47	9.42 957	51	0.57 043	9.98 484	4	57
4	9.41 488	47	9.43 007	50	0.56 993	9.98 481	3	56
5	9.41 53$\bar{5}$	47	9.43 057	50	0.56 943	9.98 477	4	55
6	9.41 582	47	9.43 108	51	0.56 892	9.98 474	3	54
7	9.41 628	46	9.43 158	50	0.56 842	9.98 471	3	53
8	9.41 675	47	9.43 208	50	0.56 792	9.98 467	4	52
9	9.41 722	47	9.43 258	50	0.56 742	9.98 464	3	51
10	9.41 768	46	9.43 308	50	0.56 692	9.98 460	4	**50**
11	9.41 81$\bar{5}$	47	9.43 358	50	0.56 642	9.98 457	3	49
12	9.41 861	46	9.43 408	50	0.56 592	9.98 453	4	48
13	9.41 908	47	9.43 458	50	0.56 542	9.98 4$\dot{5}$0	3	47
14	9.41 954	46	9.43 508	50	0.56 492	9.98 447	3	46
15	9.42 001	47	9.43 558	50	0.56 442	9.98 443	4	45
16	9.42 047	46	9.43 607	49	0.56 393	9.98 440	3	44
17	9.42 093	46	9.43 657	50	0.56 343	9.98 436	4	43
18	9.42 140	47	9.43 707	50	0.56 293	9.98 433	3	42
19	9.42 186	46	9.43 756	49	0.56 244	9.98 429	4	41
20	9.42 232	46	9.43 806	50	0.56 194	9.98 426	3	**40**
21	9.42 278	46	9.43 85$\dot{5}$	49	0.56 14$\bar{5}$	9.98 422	4	39
22	9.42 324	46	9.43 90$\bar{5}$	50	0.56 09$\dot{5}$	9.98 419	3	38
23	9.42 370	46	9.43 954	49	0.56 046	9.98 41$\dot{5}$	4	37
24	9.42 416	46	9.44 004	50	0.55 996	9.98 412	3	36
25	9.42 461	45	9.44 053	49	0.55 947	9.98 409	3	35
26	9.42 507	46	9.44 102	49	0.55 898	9.98 40$\dot{5}$	4	34
27	9.42 553	46	9.44 151	49	0.55 849	9.98 402	3	33
28	9.42 599	46	9.44 201	50	0.55 799	9.98 398	4	32
29	9.42 644	45	9.44 2$\bar{5}$0	49	0.55 7$\dot{5}$0	9.98 39$\bar{5}$	3	31
30	9.42 690	46	9.44 299	49	0.55 701	9.98 391	4	**30**
31	9.42 735	45	9.44 348	49	0.55 652	9.98 388	3	29
32	9.42 781	46	9.44 397	49	0.55 603	9.98 384	4	28
33	9.42 826	45	9.44 446	49	0.55 554	9.98 381	3	27
34	9.42 872	46	9.44 49$\bar{5}$	49	0.55 50$\dot{5}$	9.98 377	4	26
35	9.42 917	45	9.44 544	49	0.55 456	9.98 373	4	25
36	9.42 962	45	9.44 592	48	0.55 408	9.98 370	3	24
37	9.43 008	46	9.44 641	49	0.55 359	9.98 366	4	23
38	9.43 053	45	9.44 690	49	0.55 310	9.98 363	3	22
39	9.43 098	45	9.44 738	48	0.55 262	9.98 359	4	21
40	9.43 143	45	9.44 787	49	0.55 213	9.98 356	3	**20**
41	9.43 188	45	9.44 836	49	0.55 164	9.98 352	4	19
42	9.43 233	45	9.44 884	48	0.55 116	9.98 349	3	18
43	9.43 278	45	9.44 933	49	0.55 067	9.98 34$\dot{5}$	4	17
44	9.43 323	45	9.44 981	48	0.55 019	9.98 342	3	16
45	9.43 367	44	9.45 029	48	0.54 971	9.98 338	4	15
46	9.43 412	45	9.45 078	49	0.54 922	9.98 334	4	14
47	9.43 457	45	9.45 126	48	0.54 874	9.98 331	3	13
48	9.43 502	45	9.45 174	48	0.54 826	9.98 327	4	12
49	9.43 546	44	9.45 222	48	0.54 778	9.98 324	3	11
50	9.43 591	45	9.45 271	49	0.54 729	9.98 320	4	**10**
51	9.43 635	44	9.45 319	48	0.54 681	9.98 317	3	9
52	9.43 680	45	9.45 367	48	0.54 633	9.98 313	4	8
53	9.43 724	44	9.45 41$\bar{5}$	48	0.54 58$\dot{5}$	9.98 309	4	7
54	9.43 769	45	9.45 463	48	0.54 537	9.98 306	3	6
55	9.43 813	44	9.45 511	48	0.54 489	9.98 302	4	5
56	9.43 857	44	9.45 559	48	0.54 441	9.98 299	3	4
57	9.43 901	44	9.45 606	47	0.54 394	9.98 29$\dot{5}$	4	3
58	9.43 946	45	9.45 654	48	0.54 346	9.98 291	4	2
59	9.43 990	44	9.45 702	48	0.54 298	9.98 288	3	1
60	9.44 034	44	9.45 7$\bar{5}$0	48	0.54 2$\dot{5}$0	9.98 284	4	**0**
′	L. Cos.	d.	L. Cot.	c.d.	L. Tan.	L. Sin.	d.	′

P. P.

″	51	50	49
1	0.8	0.8	0.8
2	1.7	1.7	1.6
3	2.6	2.5	2.4
4	3.4	3.3	3.3
5	4.2	4.2	4.1
6	5.1	5.0	4.9
7	6.0	5.8	5.7
8	6.8	6.7	6.$\dot{5}$
9	7.6	7.5	7.4
10	8.5	8.3	8.2
20	17.0	16.7	16.3
30	25.5	25.0	24.5
40	34.0	33.3	32.7
50	42.5	41.7	40.8

″	48	47	46
1	0.8	0.8	0.8
2	1.6	1.6	1.$\dot{5}$
3	2.4	2.4	2.3
4	3.2	3.1	3.1
5	4.0	3.9	3.8
6	4.8	4.7	4.6
7	5.6	5.$\bar{5}$	5.4
8	6.4	6.3	6.1
9	7.2	7.0	6.9
10	8.0	7.8	7.7
20	16.0	15.7	15.3
30	24.0	23.5	23.0
40	32.0	31.3	30.7
50	40.0	39.2	38.3

″	45	44	4	3
1	0.8	0.7	0.1	0.0
2	1.5	1.$\bar{5}$	0.1	0.1
3	2.2	2.2	0.2	0.2
4	3.0	2.9	0.3	0.2
5	3.8	3.7	0.3	0.2
6	4.5	4.4	0.4	0.3
7	5.2	5.1	0.$\bar{5}$	0.4
8	6.0	5.9	0.$\dot{5}$	0.4
9	6.8	6.6	0.6	0.4
10	7.5	7.3	0.7	0.5
20	15.0	14.7	1.3	1.0
30	22.5	22.0	2.0	1.5
40	30.0	29.3	2.7	2.0
50	37.5	36.7	3.3	2.5

	4/50	4/49	4/48	4/47
0	6.2	6.1	6.0	5.9
1	18.8	18.4	18.0	17.6
2	31.2	30.6	30.0	29.4
3	43.8	42.9	42.0	41.1
4				

	3/51	3/50	3/49	3/48
0	8.5	8.3	8.2	8.0
1	25.5	25.0	24.5	24.0
2	42.5	41.7	40.8	40.0
3				

P. P.

105° (285°) (254°) **74°**

16° (196°) (343°) **163°**

′	L. Sin.	d.	L. Tan.	c.d.	L. Cot.	L. Cos.	d.	′
0	9.44 034	44	9.45 750	47	0.54 250	9.98 284	3	60
1	9.44 078	44	9.45 797	48	0.54 203	9.98 281	4	59
2	9.44 122	44	9.45 845	47	0.54 155	9.98 277	4	58
3	9.44 166	44	9.45 892	48	0.54 108	9.98 273	3	57
4	9.44 210	43	9.45 940	47	0.54 060	9.98 270	4	56
5	9.44 253	44	9.45 987	48	0.54 013	9.98 266	4	55
6	9.44 297	44	9.46 035	47	0.53 965	9.98 262	3	54
7	9.44 341	44	9.46 082	48	0.53 918	9.98 259	4	53
8	9.44 385	43	9.46 130	47	0.53 870	9.98 255	4	52
9	9.44 428	44	9.46 177	47	0.53 823	9.98 251	3	51
10	9.44 472	44	9.46 224	47	0.53 776	9.98 248	4	50
11	9.44 516	43	9.46 271	48	0.53 729	9.98 244	4	49
12	9.44 559	43	9.46 319	47	0.53 681	9.98 240	3	48
13	9.44 602	44	9.46 366	47	0.53 634	9.98 237	4	47
14	9.44 646	43	9.46 413	47	0.53 587	9.98 233	4	46
15	9.44 689	44	9.46 460	47	0.53 540	9.98 229	3	45
16	9.44 733	43	9.46 507	47	0.53 493	9.98 226	4	44
17	9.44 776	43	9.46 554	47	0.53 446	9.98 222	4	43
18	9.44 819	43	9.46 601	47	0.53 399	9.98 218	3	42
19	9.44 862	43	9.46 648	46	0.53 352	9.98 215	4	41
20	9.44 905	43	9.46 694	47	0.53 306	9.98 211	4	40
21	9.44 948	44	9.46 741	47	0.53 259	9.98 207	3	39
22	9.44 992	43	9.46 788	47	0.53 212	9.98 204	4	38
23	9.45 035	42	9.46 835	46	0.53 165	9.98 200	4	37
24	9.45 077	43	9.46 881	47	0.53 119	9.98 196	4	36
25	9.45 120	43	9.46 928	47	0.53 072	9.98 192	3	35
26	9.45 163	43	9.46 975	46	0.53 025	9.98 189	4	34
27	9.45 206	43	9.47 021	47	0.52 979	9.98 185	4	33
28	9.45 249	43	9.47 068	46	0.52 932	9.98 181	4	32
29	9.45 292	42	9.47 114	46	0.52 886	9.98 177	3	31
30	9.45 334	43	9.47 160	47	0.52 840	9.98 174	4	30
31	9.45 377	42	9.47 207	46	0.52 793	9.98 170	4	29
32	9.45 419	43	9.47 253	46	0.52 747	9.98 166	4	28
33	9.45 462	42	9.47 299	47	0.52 701	9.98 162	3	27
34	9.45 504	43	9.47 346	46	0.52 654	9.98 159	4	26
35	9.45 547	42	9.47 392	46	0.52 608	9.98 155	4	25
36	9.45 589	43	9.47 438	46	0.52 562	9.98 151	4	24
37	9.45 632	42	9.47 484	46	0.52 516	9.98 147	3	23
38	9.45 674	42	9.47 530	46	0.52 470	9.98 144	4	22
39	9.45 716	42	9.47 576	46	0.52 424	9.98 140	4	21
40	9.45 758	43	9.47 622	46	0.52 378	9.98 136	4	20
41	9.45 801	42	9.47 668	46	0.52 332	9.98 132	3	19
42	9.45 843	42	9.47 714	46	0.52 286	9.98 129	4	18
43	9.45 885	42	9.47 760	46	0.52 240	9.98 125	4	17
44	9.45 927	42	9.47 806	46	0.52 194	9.98 121	4	16
45	9.45 969	42	9.47 852	45	0.52 148	9.98 117	4	15
46	9.46 011	42	9.47 897	46	0.52 103	9.98 113	3	14
47	9.46 053	42	9.47 943	46	0.52 057	9.98 110	4	13
48	9.46 095	41	9.47 989	46	0.52 011	9.98 106	4	12
49	9.46 136	42	9.48 035	45	0.51 965	9.98 102	4	11
50	9.46 178	42	9.48 080	46	0.51 920	9.98 098	4	10
51	9.46 220	42	9.48 126	45	0.51 874	9.98 094	4	9
52	9.46 262	41	9.48 171	46	0.51 829	9.98 090	3	8
53	9.46 303	42	9.48 217	45	0.51 783	9.98 087	4	7
54	9.46 345	41	9.48 262	45	0.51 738	9.98 083	4	6
55	9.46 386	42	9.48 307	46	0.51 693	9.98 079	4	5
56	9.46 428	41	9.48 353	45	0.51 647	9.98 075	4	4
57	9.46 469	42	9.48 398	45	0.51 602	9.98 071	4	3
58	9.46 511	41	9.48 443	46	0.51 557	9.98 067	4	2
59	9.46 552	42	9.48 489	45	0.51 511	9.98 063	3	1
60	9.46 594		9.48 534		0.51 466	9.98 060		0
′	L. Cos.	d.	L. Cot.	c.d.	L. Tan.	L. Sin.	d.	′

P.P.

″	48	47	46
1	0.8	0.8	0.8
2	1.6	1.6	1.5
3	2.4	2.4	2.3
4	3.2	3.1	3.1
5	4.0	3.9	3.8
6	4.8	4.7	4.6
7	5.6	5.5	5.4
8	6.4	6.3	6.1
9	7.2	7.0	6.9
10	8.0	7.8	7.7
20	16.0	15.7	15.3
30	24.0	23.5	23.0
40	32.0	31.3	30.7
50	40.0	39.2	38.3

″	45	44	43
1	0.8	0.7	0.7
2	1.5	1.5	1.4
3	2.2	2.2	2.2
4	3.0	2.9	2.9
5	3.8	3.7	3.6
6	4.5	4.4	4.3
7	5.2	5.1	5.0
8	6.0	5.9	5.7
9	6.8	6.6	6.4
10	7.5	7.3	7.2
20	15.0	14.7	14.3
30	22.5	22.0	21.5
40	30.0	29.3	28.7
50	37.5	36.7	35.8

″	42	41	4	3
1	0.7	0.7	0.1	0.0
2	1.4	1.4	0.1	0.1
3	2.1	2.0	0.2	0.2
4	2.8	2.7	0.3	0.2
5	3.5	3.4	0.3	0.2
6	4.2	4.1	0.4	0.3
7	4.9	4.8	0.5	0.4
8	5.6	5.5	0.5	0.4
9	6.3	6.2	0.6	0.4
10	7.0	6.8	0.7	0.5
20	14.0	13.7	1.3	1.0
30	21.0	20.5	2.0	1.5
40	28.0	27.3	2.7	2.0
50	35.0	34.2	3.3	2.5

	4/48	4/47	4/46	4/45
0	6.0	5.9	5.8	5.6
1	18.0	17.6	17.2	16.9
2	30.0	29.4	28.8	28.1
3	42.0	41.1	40.2	39.4

	3/48	3/47	3/46	3/45
0	8.0	7.8	7.7	7.5
1	24.0	23.5	23.0	22.5
2	40.0	39.2	38.3	37.5

P.P.

106° (286°) (253°) **73°**

17° (197°) (342°) **162°**

′	L. Sin.	d.	L. Tan.	c.d.	L. Cot.	L. Cos.	d.	′
0	9.46 594	41	9.48 534	45	0.51 466	9.98 060	4	**60**
1	9.46 635	41	9.48 579	45	0.51 421	9.98 056	4	59
2	9.46 676	41	9.48 624	45	0.51 376	9.98 052	4	58
3	9.46 717	41	9.48 669	45	0.51 331	9.98 048	4	57
4	9.46 758	42	9.48 714	45	0.51 286	9.98 044	4	56
5	9.46 800	41	9.48 759	45	0.51 241	9.98 040	4	55
6	9.46 841	41	9.48 804	45	0.51 196	9.98 036	4	54
7	9.46 882	41	9.48 849	45	0.51 151	9.98 032	3	53
8	9.46 923	41	9.48 894	45	0.51 106	9.98 029	4	52
9	9.46 964	41	9.48 939	45	0.51 061	9.98 025	4	51
10	9.47 005	40	9.48 984	45	0.51 016	9.98 021	4	**50**
11	9.47 045	41	9.49 029	44	0.50 971	9.98 017	4	49
12	9.47 086	41	9.49 073	45	0.50 927	9.98 013	4	48
13	9.47 127	41	9.49 118	45	0.50 882	9.98 009	4	47
14	9.47 168	41	9.49 163	44	0.50 837	9.98 005	4	46
15	9.47 209	40	9.49 207	45	0.50 793	9.98 001	4	45
16	9.47 249	41	9.49 252	44	0.50 748	9.97 997	4	44
17	9.47 290	40	9.49 296	45	0.50 704	9.97 993	4	43
18	9.47 330	41	9.49 341	44	0.50 659	9.97 989	3	42
19	9.47 371	40	9.49 385	45	0.50 615	9.97 986	4	41
20	9.47 411	41	9.49 430	44	0.50 570	9.97 982	4	**40**
21	9.47 452	40	9.49 474	45	0.50 526	9.97 978	4	39
22	9.47 492	41	9.49 519	44	0.50 481	9.97 974	4	38
23	9.47 533	40	9.49 563	44	0.50 437	9.97 970	4	37
24	9.47 573	40	9.49 607	45	0.50 393	9.97 966	4	36
25	9.47 613	41	9.49 652	44	0.50 348	9.97 962	4	35
26	9.47 654	40	9.49 696	44	0.50 304	9.97 958	4	34
27	9.47 694	40	9.49 740	44	0.50 260	9.97 954	4	33
28	9.47 734	40	9.49 784	44	0.50 216	9.97 950	4	32
29	9.47 774	40	9.49 828	44	0.50 172	9.97 946	4	31
30	9.47 814	40	9.49 872	44	0.50 128	9.97 942	4	**30**
31	9.47 854	40	9.49 916	44	0.50 084	9.97 938	4	29
32	9.47 894	40	9.49 960	44	0.50 040	9.97 934	4	28
33	9.47 934	40	9.50 004	44	0.49 996	9.97 930	4	27
34	9.47 974	40	9.50 048	44	0.49 952	9.97 926	4	26
35	9.48 014	40	9.50 092	44	0.49 908	9.97 922	4	25
36	9.48 054	40	9.50 136	44	0.49 864	9.97 918	4	24
37	9.48 094	39	9.50 180	43	0.49 820	9.97 914	4	23
38	9.48 133	40	9.50 223	44	0.49 777	9.97 910	4	22
39	9.48 173	40	9.50 267	44	0.49 733	9.97 906	4	21
40	9.48 213	39	9.50 311	44	0.49 689	9.97 902	4	**20**
41	9.48 252	40	9.50 355	43	0.49 645	9.97 898	4	19
42	9.48 292	40	9.50 398	44	0.49 602	9.97 894	4	18
43	9.48 332	39	9.50 442	43	0.49 558	9.97 890	4	17
44	9.48 371	40	9.50 485	44	0.49 515	9.97 886	4	16
45	9.48 411	39	9.50 529	43	0.49 471	9.97 882	4	15
46	9.48 450	40	9.50 572	44	0.49 428	9.97 878	4	14
47	9.48 490	39	9.50 616	43	0.49 384	9.97 874	4	13
48	9.48 529	39	9.50 659	44	0.49 341	9.97 870	4	12
49	9.48 568	39	9.50 703	43	0.49 297	9.97 866	5	11
50	9.48 607	40	9.50 746	43	0.49 254	9.97 861	4	**10**
51	9.48 647	39	9.50 789	44	0.49 211	9.97 857	4	9
52	9.48 686	39	9.50 833	43	0.49 167	9.97 853	4	8
53	9.48 725	39	9.50 876	43	0.49 124	9.97 849	4	7
54	9.48 764	39	9.50 919	43	0.49 081	9.97 845	4	6
55	9.48 803	39	9.50 962	43	0.49 038	9.97 841	4	5
56	9.48 842	39	9.51 005	43	0.48 995	9.97 837	4	4
57	9.48 881	39	9.51 048	44	0.48 952	9.97 833	4	3
58	9.48 920	39	9.51 092	43	0.48 908	9.97 829	4	2
59	9.48 959	39	9.51 135	43	0.48 865	9.97 825	4	1
60	9.48 998		9.51 178		0.48 822	9.97 821		**0**
′	L. Cos.	d.	L. Cot.	c.d.	L. Tan.	L. Sin.	d.	′

P.P.

″	**45**	**44**	**43**
1	0.8	0.7	0.7
2	1.5	1.5	1.4
3	2.2	2.2	2.2
4	3.0	2.9	2.9
5	3.8	3.7	3.6
6	4.5	4.4	4.3
7	5.2	5.1	5.0
8	6.0	5.9	5.7
9	6.8	6.6	6.4
10	7.5	7.3	7.2
20	15.0	14.7	14.3
30	22.5	22.0	21.5
40	30.0	29.3	28.7
50	37.5	36.7	35.8

″	**42**	**41**	**40**
1	0.7	0.7	0.7
2	1.4	1.4	1.3
3	2.1	2.0	2.0
4	2.8	2.7	2.7
5	3.5	3.4	3.3
6	4.2	4.1	4.0
7	4.9	4.8	4.7
8	5.6	5.5	5.3
9	6.3	6.2	6.0
10	7.0	6.8	6.7
20	14.0	13.7	13.3
30	21.0	20.5	20.0
40	28.0	27.3	26.7
50	35.0	34.2	33.3

″	**39**	**5**	**4**	**3**
1	0.6	0.1	0.1	0.0
2	1.3	0.2	0.1	0.1
3	2.0	0.2	0.2	0.2
4	2.6	0.3	0.3	0.2
5	3.2	0.4	0.3	0.2
6	3.9	0.5	0.4	0.3
7	4.6	0.6	0.5	0.4
8	5.2	0.7	0.5	0.4
9	5.8	0.8	0.6	0.4
10	6.5	0.8	0.7	0.5
20	13.0	1.7	1.3	1.0
30	19.5	2.5	2.0	1.5
40	26.0	3.3	2.7	2.0
50	32.5	4.2	3.3	2.5

	5/43	**4/45**	**4/44**
0	4.3	5.6	5.5
1	12.9	16.9	16.5
2	21.5	28.1	27.5
3	30.1	39.4	38.5
4	38.7	—	—
5			

	4/43	**3/45**	**3/44**
0	5.4	7.5	7.3
1	16.1	22.5	22.0
2	26.9	37.5	36.7
3	37.6	—	—
4			

107° (287°) (252°) **72°**

18° (198°) (341°) **161°**

′	L. Sin.	d.	L. Tan.	c.d.	L. Cot.	L. Cos.	d	′
0	9.48 998		9.51 178		0.48 822	9.97 821		**60**
1	9.49 037	39	9.51 221	43	0.48 779	9.97 817	4	59
2	9.49 076	39	9.51 264	43	0.48 736	9.97 812	5	58
3	9.49 115	39	9.51 306	42	0.48 694	9.97 808	4	57
4	9.49 153	38	9.51 349	43	0.48 651	9.97 804	4	56
5	9.49 192	39	9.51 392	43	0.48 608	9.97 800	4	55
6	9.49 231	39	9.51 435	43	0.48 565	9.97 796	4	54
7	9.49 269	38	9.51 478	43	0.48 522	9.97 792	4	53
8	9.49 308	39	9.51 520	42	0.48 480	9.97 788	4	52
9	9.49 347	39	9.51 563	43	0.48 437	9.97 784	4	51
10	9.49 385	38	9.51 606	43	0.48 394	9.97 779	5	**50**
11	9.49 424	39	9.51 648	42	0.48 352	9.97 775	4	49
12	9.49 462	38	9.51 691	43	0.48 309	9.97 771	4	48
13	9.49 500	38	9.51 734	43	0.48 266	9.97 767	4	47
14	9.49 539	39	9.51 776	42	0.48 224	9.97 763	4	46
15	9.49 577	38	9.51 819	43	0.48 181	9.97 759	4	45
16	9.49 615	38	9.51 861	42	0.48 139	9.97 754	5	44
17	9.49 654	39	9.51 903	42	0.48 097	9.97 750	4	43
18	9.49 692	38	9.51 946	43	0.48 054	9.97 746	4	42
19	9.49 730	38	9.51 988	42	0.48 012	9.97 742	4	41
20	9.49 768	38	9.52 031	43	0.47 969	9.97 738	4	**40**
21	9.49 806	38	9.52 073	42	0.47 927	9.97 734	4	39
22	9.49 844	38	9.52 115	42	0.47 885	9.97 729	5	38
23	9.49 882	38	9.52 157	42	0.47 843	9.97 725	4	37
24	9.49 920	38	9.52 200	43	0.47 800	9.97 721	4	36
25	9.49 958	38	9.52 242	42	0.47 758	9.97 717	4	35
26	9.49 996	38	9.52 284	42	0.47 716	9.97 713	4	34
27	9.50 034	38	9.52 326	42	0.47 674	9.97 708	5	33
28	9.50 072	38	9.52 368	42	0.47 632	9.97 704	4	32
29	9.50 110	38	9.52 410	42	0.47 590	9.97 700	4	31
30	9.50 148	38	9.52 452	42	0.47 548	9.97 696	4	**30**
31	9.50 185	37	9.52 494	42	0.47 506	9.97 691	5	29
32	9.50 223	38	9.52 536	42	0.47 464	9.97 687	4	28
33	9.50 261	38	9.52 578	42	0.47 422	9.97 683	4	27
34	9.50 298	37	9.52 620	42	0.47 380	9.97 679	4	26
35	9.50 336	38	9.52 661	41	0.47 339	9.97 674	5	25
36	9.50 374	38	9.52 703	42	0.47 297	9.97 670	4	24
37	9.50 411	37	9.52 745	42	0.47 255	9.97 666	4	23
38	9.50 449	38	9.52 787	42	0.47 213	9.97 662	4	22
39	9.50 486	37	9.52 829	42	0.47 171	9.97 657	5	21
40	9.50 523	37	9.52 870	41	0.47 130	9.97 653	4	**20**
41	9.50 561	38	9.52 912	42	0.47 088	9.97 649	4	19
42	9.50 598	37	9.52 953	41	0.47 047	9.97 645	4	18
43	9.50 635	37	9.52 995	42	0.47 005	9.97 640	5	17
44	9.50 673	38	9.53 037	42	0.46 963	9.97 636	4	16
45	9.50 710	37	9.53 078	41	0.46 922	9.97 632	4	15
46	9.50 747	37	9.53 120	42	0.46 880	9.97 628	4	14
47	9.50 784	37	9.53 161	41	0.46 839	9.97 623	5	13
48	9.50 821	37	9.53 202	41	0.46 798	9.97 619	4	12
49	9.50 858	37	9.53 244	42	0.46 756	9.97 615	4	11
50	9.50 896	38	9.53 285	41	0.46 715	9.97 610	5	**10**
51	9.50 933	37	9.53 327	42	0.46 673	9.97 606	4	9
52	9.50 970	37	9.53 368	41	0.46 632	9.97 602	4	8
53	9.51 007	37	9.53 409	41	0.46 591	9.97 597	5	7
54	9.51 043	36	9.53 450	41	0.46 550	9.97 593	4	6
55	9.51 080	37	9.53 492	42	0.46 508	9.97 589	4	5
56	9.51 117	37	9.53 533	41	0.46 467	9.97 584	5	4
57	9.51 154	37	9.53 574	41	0.46 426	9.97 580	4	3
58	9.51 191	37	9.53 615	41	0.46 385	9.97 576	4	2
59	9.51 227	36	9.53 656	41	0.46 344	9.97 571	5	1
60	9.51 264	37	9.53 697	41	0.46 303	9.97 567	4	**0**
′	L. Cos.	d.	L. Cot.	c.d.	L. Tan.	L. Sin.	d	′

P. P.

″	**43**	**42**	**41**
1	0.7	0.7	0.7
2	1.4	1.4	1.4
3	2.2	2.1	2.0
4	2.9	2.8	2.7
5	3.6	3.5	3.4
6	4.3	4.2	4.1
7	5.0	4.9	4.8
8	5.7	5.6	5.5
9	6.4	6.3	6.2
10	7.2	7.0	6.8
20	14.3	14.0	13.7
30	21.5	21.0	20.5
40	28.7	28.0	27.3
50	35.8	35.0	34.2

″	**39**	**38**	**37**
1	0.6	0.6	0.6
2	1.3	1.3	1.2
3	2.0	1.9	1.8
4	2.6	2.5	2.5
5	3.2	3.2	3.1
6	3.9	3.8	3.7
7	4.6	4.4	4.3
8	5.2	5.1	4.9
9	5.8	5.7	5.6
10	6.5	6.3	6.2
20	13.0	12.7	12.3
30	19.5	19.0	18.5
40	26.0	25.3	24.7
50	32.5	31.7	30.8

″	**36**	**5**	**4**
1	0.6	0.1	0.1
2	1.2	0.2	0.1
3	1.8	0.2	0.2
4	2.4	0.3	0.3
5	3.0	0.4	0.3
6	3.6	0.5	0.4
7	4.2	0.6	0.5
8	4.8	0.7	0.5
9	5.4	0.8	0.6
10	6.0	0.8	0.7
20	12.0	1.7	1.3
30	18.0	2.5	2.0
40	24.0	3.3	2.7
50	30.0	4.2	3.3

	5/43	5/42	5/41
0			
1	4.3	4.2	4.1
2	12.9	12.6	12.3
3	21.5	21.0	20.5
4	30.1	29.4	28.7
5	38.7	37.8	36.9

	4/43	4/42	4/41
0	5.4	5.2	5.1
1	16.1	15.8	15.4
2	26.9	26.2	25.6
3	37.6	36.8	35.9
4			

108° (288°) (251°) **71°**

19° (199°) (340°) **160°**

′	L. Sin.	d.	L. Tan.	c.d.	L. Cot.	L. Cos.	d.	′
0	9.51 264	37	9.53 697	41	0.46 303	9.97 567	4	60
1	9.51 301	37	9.53 738	41	0.46 262	9.97 563	5	59
2	9.51 338	36	9.53 779	41	0.46 221	9.97 558	4	58
3	9.51 374	37	9.53 820	41	0.46 180	9.97 554	4	57
4	9.51 411	36	9.53 861	41	0.46 139	9.97 550	5	56
5	9.51 447	37	9.53 902	41	0.46 098	9.97 545	4	55
6	9.51 484	36	9.53 943	41	0.46 057	9.97 541	5	54
7	9.51 520	37	9.53 984	41	0.46 016	9.97 536	4	53
8	9.51 557	36	9.54 025	40	0.45 975	9.97 532	4	52
9	9.51 593	36	9.54 065	41	0.45 935	9.97 528	5	51
10	9.51 629	37	9.54 106	41	0.45 894	9.97 523	4	50
11	9.51 666	36	9.54 147	40	0.45 853	9.97 519	4	49
12	9.51 702	36	9.54 187	41	0.45 813	9.97 515	5	48
13	9.51 738	36	9.54 228	41	0.45 772	9.97 510	4	47
14	9.51 774	37	9.54 269	40	0.45 731	9.97 506	5	46
15	9.51 811	36	9.54 309	41	0.45 691	9.97 501	4	45
16	9.51 847	36	9.54 350	40	0.45 650	9.97 497	5	44
17	9.51 883	36	9.54 390	41	0.45 610	9.97 492	4	43
18	9.51 919	36	9.54 431	40	0.45 569	9.97 488	4	42
19	9.51 955	36	9.54 471	41	0.45 529	9.97 484	5	41
20	9.51 991	36	9.54 512	40	0.45 488	9.97 479	4	40
21	9.52 027	36	9.54 552	41	0.45 448	9.97 475	5	39
22	9.52 063	36	9.54 593	40	0.45 407	9.97 470	4	38
23	9.52 099	36	9.54 633	40	0.45 367	9.97 466	5	37
24	9.52 135	36	9.54 673	41	0.45 327	9.97 461	4	36
25	9.52 171	36	9.54 714	40	0.45 286	9.97 457	4	35
26	9.52 207	35	9.54 754	40	0.45 246	9.97 453	5	34
27	9.52 242	36	9.54 794	41	0.45 206	9.97 448	4	33
28	9.52 278	36	9.54 835	40	0.45 165	9.97 444	5	32
29	9.52 314	36	9.54 875	40	0.45 125	9.97 439	4	31
30	9.52 350	35	9.54 915	40	0.45 085	9.97 435	5	30
31	9.52 385	36	9.54 955	40	0.45 045	9.97 430	4	29
32	9.52 421	35	9.54 995	40	0.45 005	9.97 426	5	28
33	9.52 456	36	9.55 035	40	0.44 965	9.97 421	4	27
34	9.52 492	35	9.55 075	40	0.44 925	9.97 417	5	26
35	9.52 527	36	9.55 115	40	0.44 885	9.97 412	4	25
36	9.52 563	35	9.55 155	40	0.44 845	9.97 408	5	24
37	9.52 598	36	9.55 195	40	0.44 805	9.97 403	4	23
38	9.52 634	35	9.55 235	40	0.44 765	9.97 399	5	22
39	9.52 669	36	9.55 275	40	0.44 725	9.97 394	4	21
40	9.52 705	35	9.55 315	40	0.44 685	9.97 390	5	20
41	9.52 740	35	9.55 355	40	0.44 645	9.97 385	4	19
42	9.52 775	36	9.55 395	39	0.44 605	9.97 381	5	18
43	9.52 811	35	9.55 434	40	0.44 566	9.97 376	4	17
44	9.52 846	35	9.55 474	40	0.44 526	9.97 372	5	16
45	9.52 881	35	9.55 514	40	0.44 486	9.97 367	4	15
46	9.52 916	35	9.55 554	39	0.44 446	9.97 363	5	14
47	9.52 951	35	9.55 593	40	0.44 407	9.97 358	5	13
48	9.52 986	35	9.55 633	40	0.44 367	9.97 353	4	12
49	9.53 021	35	9.55 673	39	0.44 327	9.97 349	5	11
50	9.53 056	36	9.55 712	40	0.44 288	9.97 344	4	10
51	9.53 092	34	9.55 752	39	0.44 248	9.97 340	5	9
52	9.53 126	35	9.55 791	40	0.44 209	9.97 335	4	8
53	9.53 161	35	9.55 831	39	0.44 169	9.97 331	5	7
54	9.53 196	35	9.55 870	40	0.44 130	9.97 326	4	6
55	9.53 231	35	9.55 910	39	0.44 090	9.97 322	5	5
56	9.53 266	35	9.55 949	40	0.44 051	9.97 317	5	4
57	9.53 301	35	9.55 989	39	0.44 011	9.97 312	4	3
58	9.53 336	34	9.56 028	39	0.43 972	9.97 308	5	2
59	9.53 370	35	9.56 067	40	0.43 933	9.97 303	4	1
60	9.53 405		9.56 107		0.43 893	9.97 299		0
′	L. Cos.	d.	L. Cot.	c.d.	L. Tan.	L. Sin.	d.	′

P. P.

″	41	40	39
1	0.7	0.7	0.6
2	1.4	1.3	1.3
3	2.0	2.0	2.0
4	2.7	2.7	2.6
5	3.4	3.3	3.2
6	4.1	4.0	3.9
7	4.8	4.7	4.6
8	5.5	5.3	5.2
9	6.2	6.0	5.8
10	6.8	6.7	6.5
20	13.7	13.3	13.0
30	20.5	20.0	19.5
40	27.3	26.7	26.0
50	34.2	33.3	32.5

″	37	36	35
1	0.6	0.6	0.6
2	1.2	1.2	1.2
3	1.8	1.8	1.8
4	2.5	2.4	2.3
5	3.1	3.0	2.9
6	3.7	3.6	3.5
7	4.3	4.2	4.1
8	4.9	4.8	4.7
9	5.6	5.4	5.2
10	6.2	6.0	5.8
20	12.3	12.0	11.7
30	18.5	18.0	17.5
40	24.7	24.0	23.3
50	30.8	30.0	29.2

″	34	5	4
1	0.6	0.1	0.1
2	1.1	0.2	0.1
3	1.7	0.2	0.2
4	2.3	0.3	0.3
5	2.8	0.4	0.3
6	3.4	0.5	0.4
7	4.0	0.6	0.5
8	4.5	0.7	0.5
9	5.1	0.8	0.6
10	5.7	0.8	0.7
20	11.3	1.7	1.3
30	17.0	2.5	2.0
40	22.7	3.3	2.7
50	28.3	4.2	3.3

	5/41	5/40	5/39
0	4.1	4.0	3.9
1	12.3	12.0	11.7
2	20.5	20.0	19.5
3	28.7	28.0	27.3
4	36.9	36.0	35.1
5			

	4/41	4/40	4/39
0	5.1	5.0	4.9
1	15.4	15.0	14.6
2	25.6	25.0	24.4
3	35.9	35.0	34.1
4			

P. P.

109° (289°) (250°) **70°**

20° (200°) **(339°) 159°**

'	L. Sin.	d.	L. Tan.	c.d.	L. Cot.	L. Cos.	d.	'
0	9.53 405	35	9.56 107	39	0.43 893	9.97 299	5	60
1	9.53 440	35	9.56 146	39	0.43 854	9.97 294	5	59
2	9.53 475	34	9.56 185	39	0.43 815	9.97 289	4	58
3	9.53 509	35	9.56 224	40	0.43 776	9.97 285	5	57
4	9.53 544	34	9.56 264	39	0.43 736	9.97 280	4	56
5	9.53 578	35	9.56 303	39	0.43 697	9.97 276	5	55
6	9.53 613	34	9.56 342	39	0.43 658	9.97 271	5	54
7	9.53 647	35	9.56 381	39	0.43 619	9.97 266	4	53
8	9.53 682	34	9.56 420	39	0.43 580	9.97 262	5	52
9	9.53 716	35	9.56 459	39	0.43 541	9.97 257	5	51
10	9.53 751	34	9.56 498	39	0.43 502	9.97 252	4	50
11	9.53 785	34	9.56 537	39	0.43 463	9.97 248	5	49
12	9.53 819	35	9.56 576	39	0.43 424	9.97 243	5	48
13	9.53 854	34	9.56 615	39	0.43 385	9.97 238	4	47
14	9.53 888	34	9.56 654	39	0.43 346	9.97 234	5	46
15	9.53 922	35	9.56 693	39	0.43 307	9.97 229	5	45
16	9.53 957	34	9.56 732	39	0.43 268	9.97 224	4	44
17	9.53 991	34	9.56 771	39	0.43 229	9.97 220	5	43
18	9.54 025	34	9.56 810	39	0.43 190	9.97 215	5	42
19	9.54 059	34	9.56 849	38	0.43 151	9.97 210	4	41
20	9.54 093	34	9.56 887	39	0.43 113	9.97 206	5	40
21	9.54 127	34	9.56 926	39	0.43 074	9.97 201	5	39
22	9.54 161	34	9.56 965	39	0.43 035	9.97 196	4	38
23	9.54 195	34	9.57 004	38	0.42 996	9.97 192	5	37
24	9.54 229	34	9.57 042	39	0.42 958	9.97 187	5	36
25	9.54 263	34	9.57 081	39	0.42 919	9.97 182	4	35
26	9.54 297	34	9.57 120	38	0.42 880	9.97 178	5	34
27	9.54 331	34	9.57 158	39	0.42 842	9.97 173	5	33
28	9.54 365	34	9.57 197	38	0.42 803	9.97 168	5	32
29	9.54 399	34	9.57 235	39	0.42 765	9.97 163	4	31
30	9.54 433	33	9.57 274	38	0.42 726	9.97 159	5	30
31	9.54 466	34	9.57 312	39	0.42 688	9.97 154	5	29
32	9.54 500	34	9.57 351	38	0.42 649	9.97 149	4	28
33	9.54 534	33	9.57 389	39	0.42 611	9.97 145	5	27
34	9.54 567	34	9.57 428	38	0.42 572	9.97 140	5	26
35	9.54 601	34	9.57 466	38	0.42 534	9.97 135	5	25
36	9.54 635	33	9.57 504	39	0.42 496	9.97 130	4	24
37	9.54 668	34	9.57 543	38	0.42 457	9.97 126	5	23
38	9.54 702	33	9.57 581	38	0.42 419	9.97 121	5	22
39	9.54 735	34	9.57 619	39	0.42 381	9.97 116	5	21
40	9.54 769	33	9.57 658	38	0.42 342	9.97 111	4	20
41	9.54 802	34	9.57 696	38	0.42 304	9.97 107	5	19
42	9.54 836	33	9.57 734	38	0.42 266	9.97 102	5	18
43	9.54 869	34	9.57 772	38	0.42 228	9.97 097	5	17
44	9.54 903	33	9.57 810	39	0.42 190	9.97 092	5	16
45	9.54 936	33	9.57 849	38	0.42 151	9.97 087	4	15
46	9.54 969	34	9.57 887	38	0.42 113	9.97 083	5	14
47	9.55 003	33	9.57 925	38	0.42 075	9.97 078	5	13
48	9.55 036	33	9.57 963	38	0.42 037	9.97 073	5	12
49	9.55 069	33	9.58 001	38	0.41 999	9.97 068	5	11
50	9.55 102	34	9.58 039	38	0.41 961	9.97 063	4	10
51	9.55 136	33	9.58 077	38	0.41 923	9.97 059	5	9
52	9.55 169	33	9.58 115	38	0.41 885	9.97 054	5	8
53	9.55 202	33	9.58 153	38	0.41 847	9.97 049	5	7
54	9.55 235	33	9.58 191	38	0.41 809	9.97 044	5	6
55	9.55 268	33	9.58 229	38	0.41 771	9.97 039	4	5
56	9.55 301	33	9.58 267	37	0.41 733	9.97 035	5	4
57	9.55 334	33	9.58 304	38	0.41 696	9.97 030	5	3
58	9.55 367	33	9.58 342	38	0.41 658	9.97 025	5	2
59	9.55 400	33	9.58 380	38	0.41 620	9.97 020	5	1
60	9.55 433		9.58 418		0.41 582	9.97 015		0
'	L. Cos.	d.	L. Cot.	c.d.	L. Tan.	L. Sin.	d.	'

P.P.

"	40	39	38
1	0.7	0.6	0.6
2	1.3	1.3	1.3
3	2.0	2.0	1.9
4	2.7	2.6	2.5
5	3.3	3.2	3.2
6	4.0	3.9	3.8
7	4.7	4.6	4.4
8	5.3	5.2	5.1
9	6.0	5.8	5.7
10	6.7	6.5	6.3
20	13.3	13.0	12.7
30	20.0	19.5	19.0
40	26.7	26.0	25.3
50	33.3	32.5	31.7

"	37	35	34
1	0.6	0.6	0.6
2	1.2	1.2	1.1
3	1.8	1.8	1.7
4	2.5	2.3	2.3
5	3.1	2.9	2.8
6	3.7	3.5	3.4
7	4.3	4.1	4.0
8	4.9	4.7	4.5
9	5.6	5.2	5.1
10	6.2	5.8	5.7
20	12.3	11.7	11.3
30	18.5	17.5	17.0
40	24.7	23.3	22.7
50	30.8	29.2	28.3

"	33	5	4
1	0.6	0.1	0.1
2	1.1	0.2	0.1
3	1.6	0.2	0.2
4	2.2	0.3	0.3
5	2.8	0.4	0.3
6	3.3	0.5	0.4
7	3.8	0.6	0.5
8	4.4	0.7	0.5
9	5.0	0.8	0.6
10	5.5	0.8	0.7
20	11.0	1.7	1.3
30	16.5	2.5	2.0
40	22.0	3.3	2.7
50	27.5	4.2	3.3

	5/40	5/39	5/38
0	4.0	3.9	3.8
1	12.0	11.7	11.4
2	20.0	19.5	19.0
3	28.0	27.3	26.6
4	36.0	35.1	34.2
5			

	5/37	4/39	4/38
0	3.7	4.9	4.8
1	11.1	14.6	14.2
2	18.5	24.4	23.8
3	25.9	34.1	33.2
4	33.3	—	—
5			

P.P.

110° (290°) **(249°) 69°**

21° (201°) (338°) **158°**

′	L. Sin.	d.	L. Tan.	c.d.	L. Cot.	L. Cos.	d.	′
0	9.55 433	33	9.58 418	37	0.41 582	9.97 015̇	5	**60**
1	9.55 466	33	9.58 455̇	38	0.41 545̄	9.97 010	5	59
2	9.55 499	33	9.58 493	38	0.41 507	9.97 005̇	4	58
3	9.55 532	32	9.58 531	38	0.41 469	9.97 001	5	57
4	9.55 564	33	9.58 569	37	0.41 431	9.96 996	5	56
5	9.55 597	33	9.58 606	38	0.41 394	9.96 991	5	55
6	9.55 630	33	9.58 644	37	0.41 356	9.96 986	5	54
7	9.55 663	32	9.58 681	38	0.41 319	9.96 981	5	53
8	9.55 695̇	33	9.58 719	38	0.41 281	9.96 976	5	52
9	9.55 728	33	9.58 757	37	0.41 243	9.96 971	5	51
10	9.55 761	32	9.58 794	38	0.41 206	9.96 966	4	**50**
11	9.55 793	33	9.58 832	37	0.41 168	9.96 962	5	49
12	9.55 826	32	9.58 869	38	0.41 131	9.96 957	5	48
13	9.55 858	33	9.58 907	37	0.41 093	9.96 952	5	47
14	9.55 891	32	9.58 944	37	0.41 056	9.96 947	5	46
15	9.55 923	33	9.58 981	38	0.41 019	9.96 942	5	45
16	9.55 956	32	9.59 019	37	0.40 981	9.96 937	5	44
17	9.55 988	33	9.59 056	38	0.40 944	9.96 932	5	43
18	9.56 021	32	9.59 094	37	0.40 906	9.96 927	5	42
19	9.56 053	32	9.59 131	37	0.40 869	9.96 922	5	41
20	9.56 085̇	33	9.59 168	37	0.40 832	9.96 917	5	**40**
21	9.56 118	32	9.59 205̇	38	0.40 795̄	9.96 912	5	39
22	9.56 150̇	32	9.59 243	37	0.40 757	9.96 907	4	38
23	9.56 182	33	9.59 280	37	0.40 720	9.96 903	5	37
24	9.56 215̄	32	9.59 317	37	0.49 683	9.96 898	5	36
25	9.56 247	32	9.59 354	37	0.40 646	9.96 893	5	35
26	9.56 279	32	9.59 391	38	0.40 609	9.96 888	5	34
27	9.56 311	32	9.59 429	37	0.40 571	9.96 883	5	33
28	9.56 343	32	9.59 466	37	0.40 534	9.96 878	5	32
29	9.56 375̇	33	9.59 503	37	0.40 497	9.96 873	5	31
30	9.56 408	32	9.59 540	37	0.40 460	9.96 868	5	**30**
31	9.56 440	32	9.59 577	37	0.40 423	9.96 863	5	29
32	9.56 472	32	9.59 614	37	0.40 386	9.96 858	5	28
33	9.56 504	32	9.59 651	37	0.40 349	9.96 853	5	27
34	9.56 536	32	9.59 688	37	0.40 312	9.96 848	5	26
35	9.56 568	31	9.59 725̄	37	0.40 275̇	9.96 843	5	25
36	9.56 599	32	9.59 762	37	0.40 238	9.96 838	5	24
37	9.56 631	32	9.59 799	36	0.40 201	9.96 833	5	23
38	9.56 663	32	9.59 835̇	37	0.40 165̄	9.96 828	5	22
39	9.56 695̇	32	9.59 872	37	0.40 128	9.96 823	5	21
40	9.56 727	32	9.59 909	37	0.40 091	9.96 818	5	**20**
41	9.56 759	31	9.59 946	37	0.40 054	9.96 813	5	19
42	9.56 790	32	9.59 983	36	0.40 017	9.96 808	5	18
43	9.56 822	32	9.60 019	37	0.39 981	9.96 803	5	17
44	9.56 854	32	9.60 056	37	0.39 944	9.96 798	5	16
45	9.56 886	31	9.60 093	37	0.39 907	9.96 793	5	15
46	9.56 917	32	9.60 130	36	0.39 870	9.96 788	5	14
47	9.56 949	31	9.60 166	37	0.39 834	9.96 783	5	13
48	9.56 980	32	9.60 203	37	0.39 797	9.96 778	6	12
49	9.57 012	32	9.60 240	36	0.39 760	9.96 772	5	11
50	9.57 044	31	9.60 276	37	0.39 724	9.96 767	5	**10**
51	9.57 075̇	32	9.60 313	36	0.39 687	9.96 762	5	9
52	9.57 107	31	9.60 349	37	0.39 651	9.96 757	5	8
53	9.57 138	31	9.60 386	36	0.39 614	9.96 752	5	7
54	9.57 169	32	9.60 422	37	0.39 578	9.96 747	5	6
55	9.57 201	31	9.60 459	36	0.39 541	9.96 742	5	5
56	9.57 232	32	9.60 495̇	37	0.39 505̄	9.96 737	5	4
57	9.57 264	31	9.60 532	36	0.39 468	9.96 732	5	3
58	9.57 295̄	31	9.60 568	37	0.39 432	9.96 727	5	2
59	9.57 326	32	9.60 605̄	36	0.39 395̇	9.96 722	5	1
60	9.57 358		9.60 641		0.39 359	9.96 717		**0**
′	L. Cos.	d.	L. Cot.	c.d.	L. Tan.	L. Sin.	d.	′

111° (291°) (248°) **68°**

P. P.

″	**38**	**37**	**36**
1	0.6	0.6	0.6
2	1.3	1.2	1.2
3	1.9	1.8	1.8
4	2.5	2.5̄	2.4
5	3.2	3.1	3.0
6	3.8	3.7	3.6
7	4.4	4.3	4.2
8	5.1	4.9	4.8
9	5.7	5.6	5.4
10	6.3	6.2	6.0
20	12.7	12.3	12.0
30	19.0	18.5	18.0
50	25.3	24.7	24.0
50	31.7	30.8	30.0

″	**33**	**32**	**31**
1	0.6	0.5̇	0.5̇
2	1.1	1.1	1.0
3	1.6	1.6	1.6
4	2.2	2.1	2.1
5	2.8	2.7	2.6
6	3.3	3.2	3.1
7	3.8	3.7	3.6
8	4.4	4.3	4.1
9	5̄.0	4.8	4.6
10	5.5	5.3	5.2
20	11.0	10.7	10.3̇
30	16.5	16.0	15.5
40	22.0	21.3	20.7
50	27.5	26.7	25.8

″	**6**	**5**	**4**
1	0.1	0.1	0.1
2	0.2	0.2	0.1
3	0.3	0.2	0.2
4	0.4	0.3	0.3
5	0.5̇	0.4	0.3
6	0.6	0.5	0.4
7	0.7	0.6	0.5̄
8	0.8	0.7	0.5̇
9	0.9	0.8	0.6
10	1.0	0.8	0.7
20	2.0	1.7	1.3
30	3.0	2.5	2.0
40	4.0	3.3	2.7
50	5.0	4.2	3.3

	6/37	**5/38**	**5/37**
0, 1, 2, 3, 4, 5, 6			
	3.1	3.8	3.7
	9.2	11.4	11.1
	15.4	19.0	18.5
	21.6	26.6	25.9
	27.8	34.2	33.3
	33.9	—	—

	5/36	**4/38**	**4/37**
0, 1, 3, 3, 4, 5			
	3.6	4.8	4.6
	10.8	14.2	13.9
	18.0	23.8	23.1
	25.2	33.2	32.4
	32.4	—	—

P. P.

LOGARITHMS OF THE FUNCTIONS (Continued)

22° (202)° (337°) **157°**

′	L. Sin.	d.	L. Tan.	c.d.	L. Cot.	L. Cos.	d.	′
0	9.57 358	31	9.60 641	36	0.39 359	9.96 717	6	**60**
1	9.57 389	31	9.60 677	37	0.39 323	9.96 711	5	59
2	9.57 420	31	9.60 714	36	0.39 286	9.96 706	5	58
3	9.57 451	31	9.60 75̄0	36	0.39 25̇0	9.96 701	5	57
4	9.57 482	32	9.60 786	37	0.39 214	9.96 696	5	56
5	9.57 514	31	9.60 823	36	0.39 177	9.96 691	5	55
6	9.57 545̄	31	9.60 859	36	0.39 141	9.97 686	5	54
7	9.57 576	31	9.60 895̇	36	0.39 105̄	9.96 681	5	53
8	9.57 607	31	9.60 931	36	0.39 069	9.96 676	6	52
9	9.57 638	31	9.60 967	37	0.39 033	9.96 670	5	51
10	9.57 669	31	9.61 004	36	0.38 996	9.96 665̇	5	**50**
11	9.57 700	31	9.61 040	36	0.38 960	9.96 660	5	49
12	9.57 731	31	9.61 076	36	0.38 924	9.96 655̇	5	48
13	9.57 762	31	9.61 112	36	0.38 888	9.96 65̄0	5	47
14	9.57 793	31	9.61 148	36	0.38 852	9.96 645̄	5	46
15	9.57 824	31	9.61 184	36	0.38 816	9.96 640	6	45
16	9.57 855̄	30	9.61 220	36	0.38 780	9.96 634	5	44
17	9.57 885̇	31	9.61 256	36	0.38 744	9.96 629	5	43
18	9.57 916	31	9.61 292	36	0.38 708	9.96 624	5	42
19	9.57 947	31	9.61 328	36	0.38 672	9.96 619	5	41
20	9.57 978	30	9.61 364	36	0.38 636	9.96 614	6	**40**
21	9.58 008	31	9.61 400	36	0.38 600	9.96 608	5	39
22	9.58 039	31	9.61 436	36	0.38 564	9.96 603	5	38
23	9.58 070	31	9.61 472	36	0.38 528	9.96 598	5	37
24	9.58 101	30	9.61 508	36	0.38 492	9.96 593	5	36
25	9.58 131	31	9.61 544	35	0.38 456	9.96 588	6	35
26	9.58 162	30	9.61 579	36	0.38 421	9.96 582	5	34
27	9.58 192	31	9.61 615̇	36	0.38 385̄	9.96 577	5	33
28	9.58 223	30	9.61 651	36	0.38 349	9.96 572	5	32
29	9.58 253	31	9.61 687	35	0.38 313	9.96 567	5	31
30	9.58 284	30	9.61 722	36	0.38 278	9.96 562	6	**30**
31	9.58 314	31	9.61 758	36	0.38 242	9.96 556	5	29
32	9.58 345̄	30	9.61 794	36	0.38 206	9.96 551	5	28
33	9.58 375̇	31	9.61 830	35	0.38 170	9.96 546	5	27
34	9.58 406	30	9.61 865̇	36	0.38 135̄	9.96 541	6	26
35	9.58 436	31	9.61 901	35	0.38 099	9.96 535̇	5	25
36	9.58 467	30	9.61 936	36	0.38 064	9.56 530	5	24
37	9.58 497	30	9.61 972	36	0.38 028	9.96 525̄	5	23
38	9.58 527	30	9.62 008	35	0.37 992	9.96 520	6	22
39	9.58 557	31	9.62 043	36	0.37 957	9.96 514	5	21
40	9.58 588	30	9.62 079	35	0.37 921	9.96 509	5	**20**
41	9.58 618	30	9.62 114	36	0.37 886	9.96 504	6	19
42	9.48 648	30	9.62 15̄0	35	0.37 85̇0	9.96 498	5	18
43	9.58 678	31	9.62 185̇	36	0.37 815̄	9.96 493	5	17
44	9.58 709	30	9.62 221	35	0.37 779	9.96 488	5	16
45	9.58 739	30	9.62 256	36	0.37 744	9.96 483	6	15
46	9.58 769	30	9.62 292	35	0.37 708	9.96 477	5	14
47	9.58 799	30	9.62 327	35	0.37 673	9.96 472	5	13
48	9.58 829	30	9.62 362	36	0.37 638	9.96 467	6	12
49	9.58 859	30	9.62 398	35	0.37 602	9.96 461	5	11
50	9.58 889	30	9.62 433	35	0.37 567	9.96 456	5	**10**
51	9.58 919	30	9.62 468	36	0.37 532	9.96 351	6	9
52	9.58 949	30	9.62 504	35	0.37 496	9.96 445̇	5	8
53	9.58 979	30	9.62 539	35	0.37 461	9.96 440	5	7
54	9.59 009	30	9.62 574	35	0.37 426	9.96 435̄	6	6
55	9.59 039	30	9.62 609	36	0.37 391	9.96 429	5	5
56	9.59 069	29	9.62 645̄	35	0.38 355̇	9.96 424	5	4
57	9.59 098	30	9.62 680	35	0.37 320	9.96 419	6	3
58	9.59 128	30	9.62 715̄	35	0.37 285̇	9.96 413	5	2
59	9.59 158	30	9.62 75̇0	35	0.37 25̄0	9.96 408	5	1
60	9.59 188		9.62 785̇		0.37 215̄	9.96 403		**0**
′	L. Cos.	d.	L. Cot.	c.d.	L. Tan.	L. Sin.	d.	′

P. P.

″	**37**	**36**	**35**
1	0.6	0.6	0.6
2	1.2	1.2	1.2
3	1.8	1.8	1.8
4	2.5̄	2.4	2.3
5	3.1	3.0	2.9
6	3.7	3.6	3.5
7	4.3	4.2	4.1
8	4.9	4.8	4.7
9	5.6	5.4	5.2
10	6.2	6.0	5.8
20	12.3	12.0	11.7
30	18.5	18.0	17.5
40	24.7	24.0	23.3
50	30.8	30.0	29.2

″	**32**	**31**	**30**
1	0.5̇	0.5̇	0.5
2	1.1	1.0	1.0
3	1.6	1.6	1.5
4	2.1	2.1	2.0
5	2.7	2.6	2.5
6	3.2	3.1	3.0
7	3.7	3.6	3.5
8	4.3	4.1	4.0
9	4.8	4.6	4.5
10	5.3	5.2	5.0
20	10.7	10.3	10.0
30	16.0	15.5	15.0
40	21.3	20.7	20.0
50	26.7	25.8	25.0

″	**29**	**6**	**5**
1	0.5̄	0.1	0.1
2	1.0	0.2	0.2
3	1.4	0.3	0.2
4	1.9	0.4	0.3
5	2.4	0.5	0.4
6	2.9	0.6	0.5
7	3.4	0.7	0.6
8	3.9	0.8	0.7
9	4.4	0.9	0.8
10	4.8	1.0	0.8
20	9.7	2.0	1.7
30	14.5	3.0	2.5
40	19.3	4.0	3.3
50	24.2	5.0	4.2

	6/36	**6/35**
0	3.0	2.9
1	9.0	8.8
2	15.0	14.6
3	21.0	20.4
4	27.0	26.2
5	33.0	32.1
6		

	5/37	**5/36**	**5/35**
0	3.7	3.6	3.5
1	11.1	10.8	10.5
2	18.5	18.0	17.5
3	25.9	25.2	24.5
4	33.3	32.4	31.5
5			

P. P.

112° (292°) (247°) **67°**

23° (203°) (336°) **156°**

′	L. Sin.	d.	L. Tan.	c.d.	L. Cot.	L. Cos.	d.	′
0	9.59 188	30	9.62 785	35	0.37 215	9.96 403	6	**60**
1	9.59 218	29	9.62 820	35	0.37 180	9.96 397	5	59
2	9.59 247	30	9.62 855	35	0.37 145	9.96 392	5	58
3	9.59 277	30	9.62 890	36	0.37 110	9.96 387	6	57
4	9.59 307	29	9.62 926	35	0.37 074	9.96 381	5	56
5	9.59 336	30	9.62 961	35	0.37 039	9.96 376	6	55
6	9.59 366	30	9.62 996	35	0.37 004	9.96 370	5	54
7	9.59 396	29	9.63 031	35	0.36 969	9.96 365	5	53
8	9.59 425	30	9.63 066	35	0.36 934	9.96 360	6	52
9	9.59 455	29	9.63 101	34	0.36 899	9.96 354	5	51
10	9.59 484	30	9.63 135	35	0.36 865	9.96 349	6	**50**
11	9.59 514	29	9.63 170	35	0.36 830	9.96 343	5	49
12	9.59 543	30	9.63 205	35	0.36 795	9.96 338	5	48
13	9.59 573	29	9.63 240	35	0.36 760	9.96 333	6	47
14	9.59 602	30	9.63 275	35	0.36 725	9.96 327	5	46
15	9.59 632	29	9.63 310	35	0.36 690	9.96 322	6	45
16	9.59 661	29	9.63 345	34	0.36 655	9.96 316	5	44
17	9.59 690	30	9.63 379	35	0.36 621	9.96 311	6	43
18	9.59 720	29	9.63 414	35	0.36 586	9.96 305	5	42
19	9.59 749	29	9.63 449	35	0.36 551	9.96 300	6	41
20	9.59 778	30	9.63 484	35	0.36 516	9.96 294	5	**40**
21	9.59 808	29	9.63 519	34	0.36 481	9.96 289	5	39
22	9.59 837	29	9.63 553	35	0.36 447	9.96 284	6	38
23	9.59 866	29	9.63 588	35	0.36 412	9.96 278	5	37
24	9.59 895	29	9.63 623	34	0.36 377	9.96 273	6	36
25	9.59 924	30	9.63 657	35	0.36 343	9.96 267	5	35
26	9.59 954	29	9.63 692	34	0.36 308	9.96 262	6	34
27	9.59 983	29	9.63 726	35	0.36 274	9.96 256	5	33
28	9.60 012	29	9.63 761	35	0.36 239	9.96 251	6	32
29	9.60 041	29	9.63 796	34	0.36 204	9.96 245	5	31
30	9.60 070	29	9.63 830	35	0.36 170	9.96 240	6	**30**
31	9.60 099	29	9.63 865	34	0.36 135	9.96 234	5	29
32	9.60 128	29	9.63 899	35	0.36 101	9.96 229	6	28
33	9.60 157	29	9.63 934	34	0.36 066	9.96 223	5	27
34	9.60 186	29	9.63 968	35	0.36 032	9.96 218	6	26
35	9.60 215	29	9.64 003	34	0.35 997	9.96 212	5	25
36	9.60 244	29	9.64 037	35	0.35 963	9.96 207	6	24
37	9.60 273	29	9.64 072	34	0.35 928	9.96 201	5	23
38	9.60 302	29	9.64 106	34	0.35 894	9.96 196	6	22
39	9.60 331	28	9.64 140	35	0.35 860	9.96 190	5	21
40	9.60 359	29	9.64 175	34	0.35 825	9.96 185	6	**20**
41	9.60 388	29	9.64 209	34	0.35 791	9.96 179	5	19
42	9.60 417	29	9.64 243	35	0.35 757	9.96 174	6	18
43	9.60 446	28	9.64 278	34	0.35 722	9.96 168	6	17
44	9.60 474	29	9.64 312	34	0.35 688	9.96 162	5	16
45	9.60 503	29	9.64 346	35	0.35 654	9.96 157	6	15
46	9.60 532	29	9.64 381	34	0.35 619	9.96 151	5	14
47	9.60 561	28	9.64 415	34	0.35 585	9.96 146	6	13
48	9.60 589	29	9.64 449	34	0.35 551	9.96 140	5	12
49	9.60 618	28	9.64 483	34	0.35 517	9.96 135	6	11
50	9.60 646	29	9.64 517	35	0.35 483	9.96 129	6	**10**
51	9.60 675	29	9.64 552	34	0.35 448	9.96 123	5	9
52	9.60 704	28	9.64 586	34	0.35 414	9.96 118	6	8
53	9.60 732	29	9.64 620	34	0.35 380	9.96 112	5	7
54	9.60 761	28	9.64 654	34	0.35 346	9.96 107	6	6
55	9.60 789	29	9.64 688	34	0.35 312	9.96 101	6	5
56	9.60 818	28	9.64 722	34	0.35 278	9.96 095	5	4
57	9.60 846	29	9.64 756	34	0.35 244	9.96 090	6	3
58	9.60 875	28	9.64 790	34	0.35 210	9.96 084	5	2
59	9.60 903	28	9.64 824	34	0.35 176	9.96 079	6	1
60	9.60 931		9.64 858		0.35 142	9.96 073		**0**
′	L. Cos.	d.	L. Cot.	c.d.	L. Tan.	L. Sin.	d.	′

P. P.

″	36	35	34
1	0.6	0.6	0.6
2	1.2	1.2	1.1
3	1.8	1.8	1.7
4	2.4	2.3	2.3
5	3.0	2.9	2.8
6	3.6	3.5	3.4
7	4.2	4.1	4.0
8	4.8	4.7	4.5
9	5.4	5.2	5.1
10	6.0	5.8	5.7
20	12.0	11.7	11.3
30	18.0	17.5	17.0
40	24.0	23.3	22.7
50	30.0	29.2	28.3

″	30	29	28
1	0.5	0.5	0.5
2	1.0	1.0	0.9
3	1.5	1.4	1.4
4	2.0	1.9	1.9
5	2.5	2.4	2.3
6	3.0	2.9	2.8
7	3.5	3.4	3.3
8	4.0	3.9	3.7
9	4.5	4.4	4.2
10	5.0	4.8	4.7
20	10.0	9.7	9.3
30	15.0	14.5	14.0
40	20.0	19.3	18.7
50	25.0	24.2	23.3

″	6	5
1	0.1	0.1
2	0.2	0.2
3	0.3	0.2
4	0.4	0.3
5	0.5	0.4
6	0.6	0.5
7	0.7	0.6
8	0.8	0.7
9	0.9	0.8
10	1.0	0.8
20	2.0	1.7
30	3.0	2.5
40	4.0	3.3
50	5.0	4.2

	6/36	6/35	6/34
0	3.0	2.9	2.8
1	9.0	8.8	8.5
2	15.0	14.6	14.2
3	21.0	20.4	19.8
4	27.0	26.2	25.5
5	33.0	32.1	31.2
6			

	5/35	5/34
0	3.5	3.4
1	10.5	10.2
2	17.5	17.0
3	24.5	23.8
4	31.5	30.6
5		

P. P.

113° (293°) (246°) **66°**

24° (204°) (335°) **155°**

′	L. Sin.	d.	L. Tan.	c.d.	L. Cot.	L. Cos.	d.	′
0	9.60 931	29	9.64 858	34	0.35 142	9.96 073	6	**60**
1	9.60 960	28	9.64 892	34	0.35 108	9.96 067	5	59
2	9.60 988	28	9.64 926	34	0.35 074	9.96 062	6	58
3	9.61 016	29	9.64 960	34	0.35 040	9.96 056	6	57
4	9.61 045̄	28	9.64 994	34	0.35 006	9.96 050̇	5	56
5	9.61 073	28	9.65 028	34	0.34 972	9.96 045̄	6	55
6	9.61 101	28	9.65 062	34	0.34 938	9.96 039	5	54
7	9.61 129	29	9.65 096	34	0.34 904	9.96 034	6	53
8	9.61 158	28	9.65 130	34	0.34 870	9.96 028	6	52
9	9.61 186	28	9.65 164	33	0.34 836	9.96 022	5	51
10	9.61 214	28	9.65 197	34	0.34 803	9.96 017	6	**50**
11	9.61 242	28	9.65 231	34	0.34 769	9.96 011̇	6	49
12	9.61 270	28	9.65 265̇	34	0.34 735̄	9.96 005̇	5	48
13	9.61 298	28	9.65 299	34	0.34 701	9.96 000	6	47
14	9.61 326	28	9.65 333	33	0.34 667	9.95 994	6	46
15	9.61 354	28	9.65 366	34	0.34 634	9.95 988	6	45
16	9.61 382	29	9.65 400	34	0.34 600	9.95 982	5	44
17	9.61 411	27	9.65 434	33	0.34 566	9.95 977	6	43
18	9.61 438	28	9.65 467	34	0.34 533	9.95 971	6	42
19	9.61 466	28	9.65 501	34	0.34 499	9.95 965̇	5	41
20	9.61 494	28	9.65 535̄	33	0.34 465̇	9.95 960	6	**40**
21	9.61 522	28	9.65 568	34	0.34 432	9.95 954	6	39
22	9.61 550̇	28	9.65 602	34	0.34 398	9.95 948	6	38
23	9.61 578	28	9.65 636	33	0.34 364	9.95 942	5	37
24	9.61 606	28	9.65 669	34	0.34 331	9.95 937	6	36
25	9.61 634	28	9.65 703	33	0.34 297	9.95 931	6	35
26	9.61 662	27	9.65 736	34	0.34 264	9.95 925̇	5	34
27	9.61 689	28	9.65 770	33	0.34 230	9.95 920	6	33
28	9.61 717	28	9.65 803	34	0.34 197	9.95 914	6	32
29	9.61 745̄	28	9.65 837	33	0.34 163	9.95 908	6	31
30	9.61 773	27	9.65 870	34	0.34 130	9.95 902	5	**30**
31	9.61 800	28	9.65 904	33	0.34 096	9.95 897	6	29
32	9.61 828	28	9.65 937	34	0.34 063	9.95 891	6	28
33	9.61 856	27	9.65 971	33	0.34 029	9.95 885̄	6	27
34	9.61 883	28	9.66 004	34	0.33 996	9.95 879	6	26
35	9.61 911	28	9.66 038	33	0.33 962	9.95 873	5	25
36	9.61 939	27	9.66 071	33	0.33 929	9.95 868	6	24
37	9.61 966	28	9.66 104	34	0.33 896	9.95 862	6	23
38	9.61 994	27	9.66 138	33	0.33 862	9.95 856	6	22
39	9.62 021	28	9.66 171	33	0.33 829	9.95 850̇	6	21
40	9.62 049	27	9.66 204	34	0.33 796	9.95 844	5	**20**
41	9.62 076	28	9.66 238	33	0.33 762	9.95 839	6	19
42	9.62 104	27	9.66 271	33	0.33 729	9.95 833	6	18
43	9.62 131	28	9.66 304	33	0.33 696	9.95 827	6	17
44	9.62 159	27	9.66 337	34	0.33 663	9.95 821	6	16
45	9.62 186	28	9.66 371	33	0.33 629	9.95 815̇	5	15
46	9.62 214	27	9.66 404	33	0.33 596	9.95 810	6	14
47	9.62 241	27	9.66 437	33	0.33 563	9.95 804	6	13
48	9.62 268	28	9.66 470	33	0.33 530	9.95 798	6	12
49	9.62 296	27	9.66 503	34	0.33 497	9.95 792	6	11
50	9.62 323	27	9.66 537	33	0.33 463	9.95 786	6	**10**
51	9.62 350̇	27	9.66 570	33	0.33 430	9.95 780	5	9
52	9.62 377	28	9.66 603	33	0.33 397	9.95 775̄	6	8
53	9.62 405̄	27	9.66 636	33	0.33 364	9.95 769	6	7
54	9.62 432	27	9.66 669	33	0.33 331	9.95 763	6	6
55	9.62 459	27	9.66 702	33	0.33 298	9.95 757	6	5
56	9.62 486	27	9.66 735̇	33	0.33 265̄	9.95 751	6	4
57	9.62 513	28	9.66 678	33	0.33 232	9.95 745̇	6	3
58	9.62 541	27	9.66 801	33	0.33 199	9.95 739	6	2
59	9.62 568	27	9.66 834	33	0.33 166	9.95 733	5	1
60	9.62 595̄		9.66 867		0.33 133	9.95 728		**0**
′	L. Cos.	d.	L. Cot.	c.d.	L. Tan.	L. Sin.	d.	′

P. P.

″	**34**	**33**
1	0.6	0.6
2	1.1	1.1
3	1.7	1.6
4	2.3	2.2
5	2.8	2.8
6	3.4	3.3
7	4.0	3.8
8	4.5̇	4.4
9	5.1	5̄.0
10	5.7	5.5
20	11.3	11.0
30	17.0	16.5
40	22.7	22.0
50	28.3	27.5

″	**29**	**28**	**27**
1	0.5̄	0.5̄	0.4
2	1.0	0.9	0.9
3	1.4	1.4	1.4
4	1.9	1.9	1.8
5	2.4	2.3	2.2
6	2.9	2.8	2.7
7	3.4	3.3	3.2
8	3.9	3.7	3.6
9	4.4	4.2	4.0
10	4.8	4.7	4.5
20	9.7	9.3	9.0
30	14.5	14.0	13.5
40	19.3	18.7	18.0
50	24.2	23.3	22.5

″	**6**	**5**
1	0.1	0.1
2	0.2	0.2
3	0.3	0.2
4	0.4	0.3
5	0.5	0.4
6	0.6	0.5
7	0.7	0.6
8	0.8	0.7
9	0.9	0.8
10	1.0	0.8
20	2.0	1.7
30	3.0	2.5
40	4.0	3.3
50	5.0	4.2

	6/34	**6/33**	**5/34**
0	2.8	2.8	3.4
1	8.5	8.2	10.2
2	14.2	13.8	17.0
3	19.8	19.2	23.8
4	25.5	24.8	30.6
5	31.2	30.2	—
6			

P. P.

114° (294°) (245°) **65°**

25° (205°) (334°) **154°**

′	L. Sin.	d.	L. Tan.	c.d.	L. Cot.	L. Cos.	d.	′
0	9.62 595	27	9.66 867	33	0.33 133	9.95 728	6	**60**
1	9.62 622	27	9.66 900	33	0.33 100	9.95 722	6	59
2	9.62 649	27	9.66 933	33	0.33 067	9.95 716	6	58
3	9.62 676	27	9.66 966	33	0.33 034	9.95 710	6	57
4	9.62 703	27	9.66 999	33	0.33 001	9.95 704	6	56
5	9.62 730	27	9.67 032	33	0.32 968	9.95 698	6	55
6	9.62 757	27	9.67 065	33	0.32 935	9.95 692	6	54
7	9.62 784	27	9.67 098	33	0.32 902	9.95 686	6	53
8	9.62 811	27	9.67 131	32	0.32 869	9.95 680	6	52
9	9.62 838	27	9.67 163	33	0.32 837	9.95 674	6	51
10	9.62 865	27	9.67 196	33	0.32 804	9.95 668	5	**50**
11	9.62 892	26	9.67 229	33	0.32 771	9.95 663	6	49
12	9.62 918	27	9.67 262	33	0.32 738	9.95 657	6	48
13	9.62 945	27	9.67 295	32	0.32 705	9.95 651	6	47
14	9.62 972	27	9.67 327	33	0.32 673	9.95 645	6	46
15	9.62 999	27	9.67 360	33	0.32 640	9.95 639	6	45
16	9.63 026	26	9.67 393	33	0.32 607	9.95 633	6	44
17	9.63 052	27	9.67 426	32	0.32 574	9.95 627	6	43
18	9.63 079	27	9.67 458	33	0.32 542	9.95 621	6	42
19	9.63 106	27	9.67 491	33	0.32 509	9.95 615	6	41
20	9.63 133	26	9.67 524	32	0.32 476	9.95 609	6	**40**
21	9.63 159	27	9.67 556	33	0.32 444	9.95 603	6	39
22	9.63 186	27	9.67 589	33	0.32 411	9.95 597	6	38
23	9.63 213	26	9.67 622	32	0.32 378	9.95 591	6	37
24	9.63 239	27	9.67 654	33	0.32 346	9.95 585	6	36
25	9.63 266	26	9.67 687	32	0.32 313	9.95 579	6	35
26	9.63 292	27	9.67 719	33	0.32 281	9.95 573	6	34
27	9.63 319	26	9.67 752	33	0.32 248	9.95 567	6	33
28	9.63 345	27	9.67 785	32	0.32 215	9.95 561	6	32
29	9.63 372	26	9.67 817	33	0.32 183	9.95 555	6	31
30	9.63 398	27	9.67 850	32	0.32 150	9.95 549	6	**30**
31	9.63 425	26	9.67 882	33	0.32 118	9.95 543	6	29
32	9.63 451	27	9.67 915	32	0.32 085	9.95 537	6	28
33	9.63 478	26	9.67 947	33	0.32 053	9.95 531	6	27
34	9.63 504	27	9.67 980	32	0.32 020	9.95 525	6	26
35	9.63 531	26	9.68 012	32	0.31 988	9.95 519	6	25
36	9.63 557	26	9.68 044	33	0.31 956	9.95 513	6	24
37	9.63 583	27	9.68 077	32	0.31 923	9.95 507	7	23
38	9.63 610	26	9.68 109	33	0.31 891	9.95 500	6	22
39	9.63 636	26	9.68 142	32	0.31 858	9.95 494	6	21
40	9.63 662	27	9.68 174	32	0.31 826	9.95 488	6	**20**
41	9.63 689	26	9.68 206	33	0.31 794	9.95 482	6	19
42	9.63 715	26	9.68 239	32	0.31 761	9.95 476	6	18
43	9.63 741	26	9.68 271	32	0.31 729	9.95 470	6	17
44	9.63 767	27	9.68 303	33	0.31 697	9.95 464	6	16
45	9.63 794	26	9.68 336	32	0.31 664	9.95 458	6	15
46	9.63 820	26	9.68 368	32	0.31 632	9.95 452	6	14
47	9.63 846	26	9.68 400	32	0.31 600	9.95 446	6	13
48	9.63 872	26	9.68 432	33	0.31 568	9.95 440	6	12
49	9.63 898	26	9.68 465	32	0.31 535	9.95 434	7	11
50	9.63 924	26	9.68 497	32	0.31 503	9.95 427	6	**10**
51	9.63 950	26	9.68 529	32	0.31 471	9.95 421	6	9
52	9.63 976	26	9.68 561	32	0.31 439	9.95 415	6	8
53	9.64 002	26	9.68 593	33	0.31 407	9.95 409	6	7
54	9.64 028	26	9.68 626	32	0.31 374	9.95 403	6	6
55	9.64 054	26	9.68 658	32	0.31 342	9.95 397	6	5
56	9.64 080	26	9.68 690	32	0.31 310	9.95 391	7	4
57	9.64 106	26	9.68 722	32	0.31 278	9.95 384	6	3
58	9.64 132	26	9.68 754	32	0.31 246	9.95 378	6	2
59	9.64 158	26	9.68 786	32	0.31 214	9.95 372	6	1
60	9.64 184		9.68 818		0.31 182	9.95 366		**0**
′	L. Cos.	d.	L. Cot.	c.d.	L. Tan.	L. Sin.	d.	′

P.P.

″	33	32
1	0.6	0.5
2	1.1	1.1
3	1.6	1.6
4	2.2	2.1
5	2.8	2.7
6	3.3	3.2
7	3.8	3.7
8	4.4	4.3
9	5.0	4.8
10	5.5	5.3
20	11.0	10.7
30	16.5	16.0
40	22.0	21.3
50	27.5	26.7

″	27	26
1	0.4	0.4
2	0.9	0.9
3	1.4	1.3
4	1.8	1.7
5	2.2	2.2
6	2.7	2.6
7	3.2	3.0
8	3.6	3.5
9	4.0	3.9
10	4.5	4.3
20	9.0	8.7
30	13.5	13.0
40	18.0	17.3
50	22.5	21.7

″	7	6	5
1	0.1	0.1	0.1
2	0.2	0.2	0.2
3	0.4	0.3	0.2
4	0.5	0.4	0.3
5	0.6	0.5	0.4
6	0.7	0.6	0.5
7	0.8	0.7	0.6
8	0.9	0.8	0.7
9	1.0	0.9	0.8
10	1.2	1.0	0.8
20	2.3	2.0	1.7
30	3.5	3.0	2.5
40	4.7	4.0	3.3
50	5.8	5.0	4.2

	7/32	6/32	5/33
0	2.3	2.7	3.3
1	6.9	8.0	9.9
2	11.4	13.3	16.5
3	16.0	18.7	23.1
4	20.6	24.0	29.7
5	25.1	29.3	—
6	29.7	—	—
7			

P.P.

115° (295°) (244°) **64°**

26° (206°) (333°) **153°**

′	L. Sin.	d.	L. Tan.	c.d.	L. Cot.	L. Cos.	d.	′
0	9.64 184	26	9.68 818	32	0.31 182	9.95 366	6	60
1	9.64 210	26	9.68 850	32	0.31 150	9.95 360	6	59
2	9.64 236	26	9.68 882	32	0.31 118	9.95 354	6	58
3	9.64 262	26	9.68 914	32	0.31 086	9.95 348	7	57
4	9.64 288	25	9.68 946	32	0.31 054	9.95 341	6	56
5	9.64 313	26	9.68 978	32	0.31 022	9.95 335	6	55
6	9.64 339	26	9.69 010	32	0.30 990	9.95 329	6	54
7	9.64 365	26	9.69 042	32	0.30 958	9.95 323	6	53
8	9.64 391	26	9.69 074	32	0.30 926	9.95 317	7	52
9	9.64 417	25	9.69 106	32	0.30 894	9.95 310	6	51
10	9.64 442	26	9.69 138	32	0.30 862	9.95 304	6	50
11	9.64 468	26	9.69 170	32	0.30 830	9.95 298	6	49
12	9.64 494	25	9.69 202	32	0.30 798	9.95 292	6	48
13	9.64 519	26	9.69 234	32	0.30 766	9.95 286	7	47
14	9.64 545	26	9.69 266	32	0.30 734	9.95 279	6	46
15	9.64 571	25	9.69 298	31	0.30 702	9.95 273	6	45
16	9.64 596	26	9.69 329	32	0.30 671	9.95 267	6	44
17	9.64 622	25	9.69 361	32	0.30 639	9.95 261	7	43
18	9.64 647	26	9.69 393	32	0.30 607	9.95 254	6	42
19	9.64 673	25	9.69 425	32	0.30 575	9.95 248	6	41
20	9.64 698	26	9.69 457	31	0.30 543	9.95 242	6	40
21	9.64 724	25	9.69 488	32	0.30 512	9.95 236	7	39
22	9.64 749	26	9.69 520	32	0.30 480	9.95 229	6	38
23	9.64 775	25	9.69 552	32	0.30 448	9.95 223	6	37
24	9.64 800	26	9.69 584	31	0.30 416	9.95 217	6	36
25	9.64 826	25	9.69 615	32	0.30 385	9.95 211	7	35
26	9.64 851	26	9.69 647	32	0.30 353	9.95 204	6	34
27	9.64 877	25	9.69 679	31	0.30 321	9.95 198	6	33
28	9.64 902	25	9.69 710	32	0.30 290	9.95 192	7	32
29	9.64 927	26	9.69 742	32	0.30 258	9.95 185	6	31
30	9.64 953	25	9.69 774	31	0.30 226	9.95 179	6	30
31	9.64 978	25	9.69 805	32	0.30 195	9.95 173	6	29
32	9.65 003	26	9.69 837	31	0.30 163	9.95 167	7	28
33	9.65 029	25	9.69 868	32	0.30 132	9.95 160	6	27
34	9.65 054	25	9.69 900	32	0.30 100	9.95 154	6	26
35	9.65 079	25	9.69 932	31	0.30 068	9.95 148	7	25
36	9.65 104	26	9.69 963	32	0.30 037	9.95 141	6	24
37	9.65 130	25	9.69 995	31	0.30 005	9.95 135	6	23
38	9.65 155	25	9.70 026	32	0.29 974	9.95 129	7	22
39	9.65 180	25	9.70 058	31	0.29 942	9.95 122	6	21
40	9.65 205	25	9.70 089	32	0.29 911	9.95 116	6	20
41	9.65 230	25	9.70 121	31	0.29 879	9.95 110	7	19
42	9.65 255	26	9.70 152	32	0.29 848	9.95 103	6	18
43	9.65 281	25	9.70 184	31	0.29 816	9.95 097	7	17
44	9.65 306	25	9.70 215	32	0.29 785	9.95 090	6	16
45	9.65 331	25	9.70 247	31	0.29 753	9.95 084	6	15
46	9.65 356	25	9.70 278	31	0.29 722	9.95 078	7	14
47	9.65 381	25	9.70 309	32	0.29 691	9.95 071	6	13
48	9.65 406	25	9.70 341	31	0.29 659	9.95 065	6	12
49	9.65 431	25	9.70 372	32	0.29 628	9.95 059	7	11
50	9.65 456	25	9.70 404	31	0.29 596	9.95 052	6	10
51	9.65 481	25	9.70 435	31	0.29 565	9.95 046	7	9
52	9.65 506	25	9.70 466	32	0.29 534	9.95 039	6	8
53	9.65 531	25	9.70 498	31	0.29 502	9.95 033	6	7
54	9.65 556	24	9.70 529	31	0.29 471	9.95 027	7	6
55	9.65 580	25	9.70 560	32	0.29 440	9.95 020	6	5
56	9.65 605	25	9.70 592	31	0.29 408	9.95 014	7	4
57	9.65 630	25	9.70 623	31	0.29 377	9.95 007	6	3
58	9.65 655	25	9.70 654	31	0.29 346	9.95 001	6	2
59	9.65 680	25	9.70 685	32	0.29 315	9.94 995	7	1
60	9.65 705		9.70 717		0.29 283	9.94 988		0
′	L. Cos.	d.	L. Cot.	c.d.	L. Tan.	L. Sin.	d.	′

P.P.

″	32	31
1	0.5	0.5
2	1.1	1.0
3	1.6	1.6
4	2.1	2.1
5	2.7	2.6
6	3.2	3.1
7	3.7	3.6
8	4.3	4.1
9	4.8	4.6
10	5.3	5.2
20	10.7	10.3
30	16.0	15.5
40	21.3	20.7
50	26.7	25.8

″	26	25	24
1	0.4	0.4	0.4
2	0.9	0.8	0.8
3	1.3	1.2	1.2
4	1.7	1.7	1.6
5	2.2	2.1	2.0
6	2.6	2.5	2.4
7	3.0	2.9	2.8
8	3.5	3.3	3.2
9	3.9	3.8	3.6
10	4.3	4.2	4.0
20	8.7	8.3	8.0
30	13.0	12.5	12.0
40	17.3	16.7	16.0
50	21.7	20.8	20.0

″	7	6
1	0.1	0.1
2	0.2	0.2
3	0.4	0.3
4	0.5	0.4
5	0.6	0.5
6	0.7	0.6
7	0.8	0.7
8	0.9	0.8
9	1.0	0.9
10	1.2	1.0
20	2.3	2.0
30	3.5	3.0
40	4.7	4.0
50	5.8	5.0

	7/32	7/31	6/32
0	2.3	2.2	2.7
1	6.9	6.6	8.0
2	11.4	11.1	13.3
3	16.0	15.5	18.7
4	20.6	19.9	24.0
5	25.1	24.4	29.3
6	29.7	28.8	—
7			

116° (296°) (243°) **63°**

27° (207°) (332°) **152°**

′	L. Sin.	d.	L. Tan.	c.d.	L. Cot.	L. Cos.	d.	′
0	9.65 705	24	9.70 717	31	0.29 283	9.94 988	6	**60**
1	9.65 729	25	9.70 748	31	0.29 252	9.94 982	7	59
2	9.65 754	25	9.70 779	31	0.29 221	9.94 975	6	58
3	9.65 779	25	9.70 810	31	0.29 190	9.94 969	7	57
4	9.65 804	24	9.70 841	32	0.29 159	9.94 962	6	56
5	9.65 828	25	9.70 873	31	0.29 127	9.94 956	7	55
6	9.65 853	25	9.70 904	31	0.29 096	9.94 949	6	54
7	9.65 878	24	9.70 935	31	0.29 065	9.94 943	7	53
8	9.65 902	25	9.70 966	31	0.29 034	9.94 936	6	52
9	9.65 927	25	9.70 997	31	0.29 003	9.94 930	7	51
10	9.65 952	24	9.71 028	31	0.28 972	9.94 923	6	**50**
11	9.65 976	25	9.71 059	31	0.28 941	9.94 917	6	49
12	9.66 001	24	9.71 090	31	0.28 910	9.94 911	7	48
13	9.66 025	25	9.71 121	32	0.28 879	9.94 904	6	47
14	9.66 050	25	9.71 153	31	0.28 847	9.94 898	7	46
15	9.66 075	24	9.71 184	31	0.28 816	9.94 891	6	45
16	9.66 099	25	9.71 215	31	0.28 785	9.94 885	7	44
17	9.66 124	24	9.71 246	31	0.28 754	9.94 878	7	43
18	9.66 148	25	9.71 277	31	0.28 723	9.94 871	6	42
19	9.66 173	24	9.71 308	31	0.28 692	9.94 865	7	41
20	9.66 197	24	9.71 339	31	0.28 661	9.94 858	6	**40**
21	9.66 221	25	9.71 370	31	0.28 630	9.94 852	7	39
22	9.66 246	24	9.71 401	30	0.28 599	9.94 845	6	38
23	9.66 270	25	9.71 431	31	0.28 569	9.94 839	7	37
24	9.66 295	24	9.71 462	31	0.28 538	9.94 832	6	36
25	9.66 319	24	9.71 493	31	0.28 507	9.94 826	7	35
26	9.66 343	25	9.71 524	31	0.28 476	9.94 819	6	34
27	9.66 368	24	9.71 555	31	0.28 445	9.94 813	7	33
28	9.66 392	24	9.71 586	31	0.28 414	9.94 806	7	32
29	9.66 416	25	9.71 617	31	0.28 383	9.94 799	6	31
30	9.66 441	24	9.71 648	31	0.28 352	9.94 793	7	**30**
31	9.66 465	24	9.71 679	30	0.28 321	9.94 786	6	29
32	9.66 489	24	9.71 709	31	0.28 291	9.94 780	7	28
33	9.66 513	24	9.71 740	31	0.28 260	9.94 773	6	27
34	9.66 537	25	9.71 771	31	0.28 229	9.94 767	7	26
35	9.66 562	24	9.71 802	31	0.28 198	9.94 760	7	25
36	9.66 586	24	9.71 833	30	0.28 167	9.94 753	6	24
37	9.66 610	24	9.71 863	31	0.28 137	9.94 747	7	23
38	9.66 634	24	9.71 894	31	0.28 106	9.94 740	6	22
39	9.66 658	24	9.71 925	30	0.28 075	9.94 734	7	21
40	9.66 682	24	9.71 955	31	0.28 045	9.94 727	7	**20**
41	9.66 706	25	9.71 986	31	0.28 014	9.94 720	6	19
42	9.66 731	24	9.72 017	31	0.27 983	9.94 714	7	18
43	9.66 755	24	9.72 048	30	0.27 952	9.94 707	7	17
44	9.66 779	24	9.72 078	31	0.27 922	9.94 700	6	16
45	9.66 803	24	9.72 109	31	0.27 891	9.94 694	7	15
46	9.66 827	24	9.72 140	30	0.27 860	9.94 687	7	14
47	9.66 851	24	9.72 170	31	0.27 830	9.94 680	6	13
48	9.66 875	24	9.72 201	30	0.27 799	9.94 674	7	12
49	9.66 899	23	9.72 231	31	0.27 769	9.94 667	7	11
50	9.66 922	24	9.72 262	31	0.27 738	9.94 660	6	**10**
51	9.66 946	24	9.72 293	30	0.27 707	9.94 654	7	9
52	9.66 970	24	9.72 323	31	0.27 677	9.94 647	7	8
53	9.66 994	24	9.72 354	30	0.27 646	9.94 640	6	7
54	9.67 018	24	9.72 384	31	0.27 616	9.94 634	7	6
55	9.67 042	24	9.72 415	30	0.27 585	9.94 627	7	5
56	9.67 066	24	9.72 445	31	0.27 555	9.94 620	6	4
57	9.67 090	23	9.72 476	30	0.27 524	9.94 614	7	3
58	9.67 113	24	9.72 506	31	0.27 494	9.94 607	7	2
59	9.67 137	24	9.72 537	30	0.27 463	9.94 600	7	1
60	9.67 161		9.72 567		0.27 433	9.94 593		**0**
′	L. Cos.	d.	L. Cot.	c.d.	L. Tan.	L. Sin.	d.	′

P. P.

″	32	31	30
1	0.5	0.5	0.5
2	1.1	1.0	1.0
3	1.6	1.6	1.5
4	2.1	2.1	2.0
5	2.7	2.6	2.5
6	3.2	3.1	3.0
7	3.7	3.6	3.5
8	4.3	4.1	4.0
9	4.8	4.6	4.5
10	5.3	5.2	5.0
20	10.7	10.3	10.0
30	16.0	15.5	15.0
40	21.3	20.7	20.0
50	26.7	25.8	25.0

″	25	24	23
1	0.4	0.4	0.4
2	0.8	0.8	0.8
3	1.2	1.2	1.2
4	1.7	1.6	1.5
5	2.1	2.0	1.9
6	2.5	2.4	2.3
7	2.9	2.8	2.7
8	3.3	3.2	3.1
9	3.8	3.6	3.4
10	4.2	4.0	3.8
20	8.3	8.0	7.7
30	12.5	12.0	11.5
40	16.7	16.0	15.3
50	20.8	20.0	19.2

″	7	6
1	0.1	0.1
2	0.2	0.2
3	0.4	0.3
4	0.5	0.4
5	0.6	0.5
6	0.7	0.6
7	0.8	0.7
8	0.9	0.8
9	1.0	0.9
10	1.2	1.0
20	2.3	2.0
30	3.5	3.0
40	4.7	4.0
50	5.8	5.0

	7/30	6/31	6/30
0	2.1	2.6	2.5
1	6.4	7.8	7.5
2	10.7	12.9	12.5
3	15.0	18.1	17.5
4	19.3	23.2	22.5
5	23.6	28.4	27.5
6	27.9	—	—
7			

P. P.

117° (297°) (242°) **62°**

28° (208°) (331°) **151°**

′	L. Sin.	d.	L. Tan.	c.d.	L. Cot.	L. Cos.	d.	′
0	9.67 161	24	9.72 567	31	0.27 433	9.94 593	6	60
1	9.67 185	23	9.72 598	30	0.27 402	9.94 587	7	59
2	9.67 208	24	9.72 628	31	0.27 372	9.94 580	7	58
3	9.67 232	24	9.72 659	30	0.27 341	9.94 573	6	57
4	9.67 256	24	9.72 689	31	0.27 311	9.94 567	7	56
5	9.67 280	23	9.72 720	30	0.27 280	9.94 560	7	55
6	9.67 303	24	9.72 750	30	0.27 250	9.94 553	7	54
7	9.67 327	23	9.72 780	31	0.27 220	9.94 546	6	53
8	9.67 350	24	9.72 811	30	0.27 189	9.94 540	7	52
9	9.67 374	24	9.72 841	31	0.27 159	9.94 533	7	51
10	9.67 398	23	9.72 872	30	0.27 128	9.94 526	7	50
11	9.67 421	24	9.72 902	30	0.27 098	9.94 519	6	49
12	9.67 445	23	9.72 932	31	0.27 068	9.94 513	7	48
13	9.67 468	24	9.72 963	30	0.27 037	9.94 506	7	47
14	9.67 492	23	9.72 993	30	0.27 007	9.94 499	7	46
15	9.67 515	24	9.73 023	31	0.26 977	9.94 492	7	45
16	9.67 539	23	9.73 054	30	0.26 946	9.94 485	6	44
17	9.67 562	24	9.73 084	30	0.26 916	9.94 479	7	43
18	9.67 586	23	9.73 114	30	0.26 886	9.94 472	7	42
19	9.67 609	24	9.73 144	31	0.26 856	9.94 465	7	41
20	9.67 633	23	9.73 175	30	0.26 825	9.94 458	7	40
21	9.67 656	24	9.73 205	30	0.26 795	9.94 451	6	39
22	9.67 680	23	9.73 235	30	0.26 765	9.94 445	7	38
23	9.67 703	23	9.73 265	30	0.26 735	9.94 438	7	37
24	9.67 726	24	9.73 295	31	0.26 705	9.94 431	7	36
25	9.67 750	23	9.73 326	30	0.26 674	9.94 424	7	35
26	9.67 773	23	9.73 356	30	0.26 644	9.94 417	7	34
27	9.67 796	24	9.73 386	30	0.26 614	9.94 410	6	33
28	9.67 820	23	9.73 416	30	0.26 584	9.94 404	7	32
29	9.67 843	23	9.73 446	30	0.26 554	9.94 397	7	31
30	9.67 866	24	9.73 476	31	0.26 524	9.94 390	7	30
31	9.67 890	23	9.73 507	30	0.26 493	9.94 383	7	29
32	9.67 913	23	9.73 537	30	0.26 463	9.94 376	7	28
33	9.67 936	23	9.73 567	30	0.26 433	9.94 369	7	27
34	9.67 959	23	9.73 597	30	0.26 403	9.94 362	7	26
35	9.67 982	24	9.73 627	30	0.26 373	9.94 355	6	25
36	9.68 006	23	9.73 657	30	0.26 343	9.94 349	7	24
37	9.68 029	23	9.73 687	30	0.26 313	9.94 342	7	23
38	9.68 052	23	9.73 717	30	0.26 283	9.94 335	7	22
39	9.68 075	23	9.73 747	30	0.26 253	9.94 328	7	21
40	9.68 098	23	9.73 777	30	0.26 223	9.94 321	7	20
41	9.68 121	23	9.73 807	30	0.26 193	9.94 314	7	19
42	9.68 144	23	9.73 837	30	0.26 163	9.94 307	7	18
43	9.68 167	23	9.73 867	30	0.26 133	9.94 300	7	17
44	9.68 190	23	9.73 897	30	0.26 103	9.94 293	7	16
45	9.68 213	24	9.73 927	30	0.26 073	9.94 286	7	15
46	9.68 237	23	9.73 957	30	0.26 043	9.94 279	6	14
47	9.68 260	23	9.73 987	30	0.26 013	9.94 273	7	13
48	9.68 283	22	9.74 017	30	0.25 983	9.94 266	7	12
49	9.68 305	23	9.74 047	30	0.25 953	9.94 259	7	11
50	9.68 328	23	9.74 077	30	0.25 923	9.94 252	7	10
51	9.68 351	23	9.74 107	30	0.25 893	9.94 245	7	9
52	9.68 374	23	9.74 137	29	0.25 863	9.94 238	7	8
53	9.68 397	23	9.74 136	30	0.25 834	9.94 231	7	7
54	9.68 420	23	9.74 196	30	0.25 804	9.94 224	7	6
55	9.68 443	23	9.74 226	30	0.25 774	9.94 217	7	5
56	9.68 466	23	9.74 256	30	0.25 744	9.94 210	7	4
57	9.68 489	23	9.74 286	30	0.25 714	9.94 203	7	3
58	9.68 512	22	9.74 316	29	0.25 684	9.94 196	7	2
59	9.68 534	23	9.74 345	30	0.25 655	9.94 189	7	1
60	9.68 557		9.74 375		0.25 625	9.94 182		0
′	L. Cos.	d.	L. Cot.	c.d.	L. Tan.	L. Sin.	d	′

P. P.

″	31	30	29
1	0.5	0.5	0.5
2	1.0	1.0	1.0
3	1.6	1.5	1.4
4	2.1	2.0	1.9
5	2.6	2.5	2.4
6	3.1	3.0	2.9
7	3.6	3.5	3.4
8	4.1	4.0	3.9
9	4.6	4.5	4.4
10	5.2	5.0	4.8
20	10.3	10.0	9.7
30	15.5	15.0	14.5
40	20.7	20.0	19.3
50	25.8	25.0	24.2

″	24	23	22
1	0.4	0.4	0.4
2	0.8	0.8	0.7
3	1.2	1.2	1.1
4	1.6	1.5	1.5
5	2.0	1.9	1.8
6	2.4	2.3	2.2
7	2.8	2.7	2.6
8	3.2	3.1	2.9
9	3.6	3.4	3.3
10	4.0	3.8	3.7
20	8.0	7.7	7.3
30	12.0	11.5	11.0
40	16.0	15.3	14.7
50	20.0	19.2	18.3

″	7	6
1	0.1	0.1
2	0.2	0.2
3	0.4	0.3
4	0.5	0.4
5	0.6	0.5
6	0.7	0.6
7	0.8	0.7
8	0.9	0.8
9	1.0	0.9
10	1.2	1.0
20	2.3	2.0
30	3.5	3.0
40	4.7	4.0
50	5.8	5.0

	7/31	6/31	6/30
0	2.2	2.6	2.5
1	6.6	7.8	7.5
2	11.1	12.9	12.5
3	15.5	18.1	17.5
4	19.9	23.2	22.5
5	24.4	28.4	27.5
6	28.8	—	—
7			

P. P.

118° (298°) (241°) **61°**

29° (209°) (330°) **150°**

′	L. Sin.	d.	L. Tan.	c.d.	L. Cot.	L. Cos.	d.	′
0	9.68 557	23	9.74 375	30	0.25 625	9.94 182	7	60
1	9.68 580	23	9.74 405	30	0.25 595	9.94 175	7	59
2	9.68 603	22	9.74 435	30	0.25 565	9.94 168	7	58
3	9.68 625	23	9.74 465	29	0.25 535	9.94 161	7	57
4	9.68 648	23	9.74 494	30	0.25 506	9.94 154	7	56
5	9.68 671	23	9.74 524	30	0.25 476	9.94 147	7	55
6	9.68 694	22	9.74 554	29	0.25 446	9.94 140	7	54
7	9.68 716	23	9.74 583	30	0.25 417	9.94 133	7	53
8	9.68 739	23	9.74 613	30	0.25 387	9.94 126	7	52
9	9.68 762	22	9.74 643	30	0.25 357	9.94 119	7	51
10	9.68 784	23	9.74 673	29	0.25 327	9.94 112	7	50
11	9.68 807	22	9.74 702	30	0.25 298	9.94 105	7	49
12	9.68 829	23	9.74 732	30	0.25 268	9.94 098	8	48
13	9.68 852	23	9.74 762	29	0.25 238	9.94 090	7	47
14	9.68 875	22	9.74 791	30	0.25 209	9.94 083	7	46
15	9.68 897	23	9.74 821	30	0.25 179	9.94 076	7	45
16	9.68 920	22	9.74 851	29	0.25 149	9.94 069	7	44
17	9.68 942	23	9.74 880	30	0.25 120	9.94 062	7	43
18	9.68 965	22	9.74 910	29	0.25 090	9.94 055	7	42
19	9.68 987	23	9.74 939	30	0.25 061	9.94 048	7	41
20	9.69 010	22	9.74 969	29	0.25 031	9.94 041	7	40
21	9.69 032	23	9.74 998	30	0.25 002	9.94 034	7	39
22	9.69 055	22	9.75 028	30	0.24 972	9.94 027	7	38
23	9.69 077	23	9.75 058	29	0.24 942	9.94 020	8	37
24	9.69 100	22	9.75 087	30	0.24 913	9.94 012	7	36
25	9.69 122	22	9.75 117	29	0.24 883	9.94 005	7	35
26	9.69 144	23	9.75 146	30	0.24 854	9.93 998	7	34
27	9.69 167	22	9.75 176	29	0.24 824	9.93 991	7	33
28	9.69 189	23	9.75 205	30	0.24 795	9.93 984	7	32
29	9.69 212	22	9.75 235	29	0.24 765	9.93 977	7	31
30	9.69 234	22	9.75 264	30	0.24 736	9.93 970	7	30
31	9.69 256	23	9.75 294	29	0.24 706	9.93 963	8	29
32	9.69 279	22	9.75 323	30	0.24 677	9.93 955	7	28
33	9.69 301	22	9.75 353	29	0.24 647	9.93 948	7	27
34	9.69 323	22	9.75 382	29	0.24 618	9.93 941	7	26
35	9.69 345	23	9.75 411	30	0.24 589	9.93 934	7	25
36	9.69 368	22	9.75 441	29	0.24 559	9.93 927	7	24
37	9.69 390	22	9.75 470	30	0.24 530	9.93 920	8	23
38	9.69 412	22	9.75 500	29	0.24 500	9.93 912	7	22
39	9.69 434	22	9.75 529	29	0.24 471	9.93 905	7	21
40	9.69 456	23	9.75 558	30	0.24 442	9.93 898	7	20
41	9.69 479	22	9.75 588	29	0.24 412	9.93 891	7	19
42	9.69 501	22	9.75 617	30	0.24 383	9.93 884	8	18
43	9.69 523	22	9.75 647	29	0.24 353	9.93 876	7	17
44	9.69 545	22	9.75 676	29	0.24 324	9.93 869	7	16
45	9.69 567	22	9.75 705	30	0.24 295	9.93 862	7	15
46	9.69 589	22	9.75 735	29	0.24 265	9.93 855	8	14
47	9.69 611	22	9.75 764	29	0.24 236	9.93 847	7	13
48	9.69 633	22	9.75 793	29	0.24 207	9.93 840	7	12
49	9.69 655	22	9.75 822	30	0.24 178	9.93 833	7	11
50	9.69 677	22	9.75 852	29	0.24 148	9.93 826	7	10
51	9.69 699	22	9.75 881	29	0.24 119	9.93 819	8	9
52	9.69 721	22	9.75 910	29	0.24 090	9.93 811	7	8
53	9.69 743	22	9.75 939	30	0.24 061	9.93 804	7	7
54	9.69 765	22	9.75 969	29	0.24 031	9.93 797	8	6
55	9.69 787	22	9.75 998	29	0.24 002	9.93 789	7	5
56	9.69 809	22	9.76 027	29	0.23 973	9.93 782	7	4
57	9.69 831	22	9.76 056	30	0.23 944	9.93 775	7	3
58	9.69 853	22	9.76 086	29	0.23 914	9.93 768	8	2
59	9.69 875	22	9.76 115	29	0.23 885	9.93 760	7	1
60	9.69 897		9.76 144		0.23 856	9.93 753		0
′	L. Cos.	d.	L. Cot.	c.d.	L. Tan.	L. Sin.	d.	′

P. P.

″	30	29	23
1	0.5	0.5	0.4
2	1.0	1.0	0.8
3	1.5	1.4	1.2
4	2.0	1.9	1.5
5	2.5	2.4	1.9
6	3.0	2.9	2.3
7	3.5	3.4	2.7
8	4.0	3.9	3.1
9	4.5	4.4	3.4
10	5.0	4.8	3.8
20	10.0	9.7	7.7
30	15.0	14.5	11.5
40	20.0	19.3	15.3
50	25.0	24.2	19.2

″	22	8	7
1	0.4	0.1	0.1
2	0.7	0.3	0.2
3	1.1	0.4	0.4
4	1.5	0.5	0.5
5	1.8	0.7	0.6
6	2.2	0.8	0.7
7	2.6	0.9	0.8
8	2.9	1.1	0.9
9	3.3	1.2	1.0
10	3.7	1.3	1.2
20	7.3	2.7	2.3
30	11.0	4.0	3.5
40	14.7	5.3	4.7
50	18.3	6.7	5.8

	8/30	8/29
0	1.9	1.8
1	5.6	5.4
2	9.4	9.1
3	13.1	12.7
4	16.9	16.3
5	20.6	19.9
6	24.4	23.6
7	28.1	27.2
8		

	7/30	7/29
0	2.1	2.1
1	6.4	6.2
2	10.7	10.4
3	15.0	14.5
4	19.3	18.6
5	23.6	22.8
6	27.9	26.9
7		

P. P.

119° (299°) (240°) **60°**

30° (210°) (329°) **149°**

′	L. Sin.	d.	L. Tan.	c.d.	L. Cot.	L. Cos.	d.	′
0	9.69 897	22	9.76 144	29	0.23 856	9.93 753	7	**60**
1	9.69 919	22	9.76 173	29	0.23 827	9.93 746	8	59
2	9.69 941	22	9.76 202	29	0.23 798	9.93 738	7	58
3	9.69 963	21	9.76 231	30	0.23 769	9.93 731	7	57
4	9.69 984	22	9.76 261	29	0.23 739	9.93 724	7	56
5	9.70 006	22	9.76 290	29	0.23 710	9.93 717	8	55
6	9.70 028	22	9.76 319	29	0.23 681	9.93 709	7	54
7	9.70 050	22	9.76 348	29	0.23 652	9.93 702	7	53
8	9.70 072	21	9.76 377	29	0.23 623	9.93 695	8	52
9	9.70 093	22	9.76 406	29	0.23 594	9.93 687	7	51
10	9.70 115	22	9.76 435	29	0.23 565	9.93 680	7	**50**
11	9.70 137	22	9.76 464	29	0.23 536	9.93 673	8	49
12	9.70 159	21	9.76 493	29	0.23 507	9.93 665	7	48
13	9.70 180	22	9.76 522	29	0.23 478	9.93 658	8	47
14	9.70 202	22	9.76 551	29	0.23 449	9.93 650	7	46
15	9.70 224	21	9.76 580	29	0.23 420	9.93 643	7	45
16	9.70 245	22	9.76 609	30	0.23 391	9.93 636	8	44
17	9.70 267	21	9.76 639	29	0.23 361	9.93 628	7	43
18	9.70 288	22	9.76 668	29	0.23 332	9.93 621	7	42
19	9.70 310	22	9.76 697	28	0.23 303	9.93 614	8	41
20	9.70 332	21	9.76 725	29	0.23 275	9.93 606	7	**40**
21	9.70 353	22	9.76 754	29	0.23 246	9.93 599	8	39
22	9.70 375	21	9.76 783	29	0.23 217	9.93 591	7	38
23	9.70 396	22	9.76 812	29	0.23 188	9.93 584	7	37
24	9.70 418	21	9.76 841	29	0.23 159	9.93 577	8	36
25	9.70 439	22	9.76 870	29	0.23 130	9.93 569	7	35
26	9.70 461	21	9.76 899	29	0.23 101	9.93 562	8	34
27	9.70 482	22	9.76 928	29	0.23 072	9.93 554	7	33
28	9.70 504	21	9.76 957	29	0.23 043	9.93 547	8	32
29	9.70 525	22	9.76 986	29	0.23 014	9.93 539	7	31
30	9.70 547	21	9.77 015	29	0.22 985	9.93 532	7	**30**
31	9.70 568	22	9.77 044	29	0.22 956	9.93 525	8	29
32	9.70 590	21	9.77 073	28	0.22 927	9.93 517	7	28
33	9.70 611	22	9.77 101	29	0.22 899	9.93 510	8	27
34	9.70 633	21	9.77 130	29	0.22 870	9.93 502	7	26
35	9.70 654	21	9.77 159	29	0.22 841	9.93 495	8	25
36	9.70 675	22	9.77 188	29	0.22 812	9.93 487	7	24
37	9.70 697	21	9.77 217	29	0.22 783	9.93 480	8	23
38	9.70 718	21	9.77 246	28	0.22 754	9.93 472	7	22
39	9.70 739	22	9.77 274	29	0.22 726	9.93 465	8	21
40	9.70 761	21	9.77 303	29	0.22 697	9.93 457	7	**20**
41	9.70 782	21	9.77 332	29	0.22 668	9.93 450	8	19
42	9.70 803	21	9.77 361	29	0.22 639	9.93 442	7	18
43	9.70 824	22	9.77 390	28	0.22 610	9.93 435	8	17
44	9.70 846	21	9.77 418	29	0.22 582	9.93 427	7	16
45	9.70 867	21	9.77 447	29	0.22 553	9.93 420	8	15
46	9.70 888	21	9.77 476	29	0.22 524	9.93 412	7	14
47	9.70 909	22	9.77 505	28	0.22 495	9.93 405	8	13
48	9.70 931	21	9.77 533	29	0.22 467	9.93 397	7	12
49	9.70 952	21	9.77 562	29	0.22 438	9.93 390	8	11
50	9.70 973	21	9.77 591	28	0.22 409	9.93 382	7	**10**
51	9.70 994	21	9.77 619	29	0.22 381	9.93 375	8	9
52	9.71 015	21	9.77 648	29	0.22 352	9.93 367	7	8
53	9.71 036	22	9.77 677	29	0.22 323	9.93 360	8	7
54	9.71 058	21	9.77 706	28	0.22 294	9.93 352	8	6
55	9.71 079	21	9.77 734	29	0.22 266	9.93 344	7	5
56	9.71 100	21	9.77 763	28	0.22 237	9.93 337	8	4
57	9.71 121	21	9.77 791	29	0.22 209	9.93 329	7	3
58	9.71 142	21	9.77 820	29	0.22 180	9.93 322	8	2
59	9.71 163	21	9.77 849	28	0.22 151	9.93 314	7	1
60	9.71 184		9.77 877		0.22 123	9.93 307		**0**
′	L. Cos.	d.	L. Cot.	c.d.	L. Tan.	L. Sin.	d.	′

P.P.

″	**30**	**29**	**28**
1	0.5	0.5	0.5
2	1.0	1.0	0.9
3	1.5	1.4	1.4
4	2.0	1.9	1.9
5	2.5	2.4	2.3
6	3.0	2.9	2.8
7	3.5	3.4	3.3
8	4.0	3.9	3.7
9	4.5	4.4	4.2
10	5.0	4.8	4.7
20	10.0	9.7	9.3
30	15.0	14.5	14.0
40	20.0	19.3	18.7
50	25.0	24.2	23.3

″	**22**	**21**
1	0.4	0.4
2	0.7	0.7
3	1.1	1.0
4	1.5	1.4
5	1.8	1.8
6	2.2	2.1
7	2.6	2.4
8	2.9	2.8
9	3.3	3.2
10	3.7	3.5
20	7.3	7.0
30	11.0	10.5
40	14.7	14.0
50	18.3	17.5

″	**8**	**7**
1	0.1	0.1
2	0.3	0.2
3	0.4	0.4
4	0.5	0.5
5	0.7	0.6
6	0.8	0.7
7	0.9	0.8
8	1.1	0.9
9	1.2	1.0
10	1.3	1.2
20	2.7	2.3
30	4.0	3.5
40	5.3	4.7
50	6.7	5.8

	7/30	**7/29**	**7/28**
0	2.1	2.1	2.0
1	6.4	6.2	6.0
2	10.7	10.4	10.0
3	15.0	14.5	14.0
4	19.3	18.6	18.0
5	23.6	22.8	22.0
6	27.9	26.9	26.0
7			

P.P.

120° (300°) (239°) **59°**

31° (211°) (328°) **148°**

′	L. Sin.	d.	L. Tan.	c.d.	L. Cot.	L. Cos.	d.	′
0	9.71 184	21	9.77 877	29	0.22 123	9.93 307	8	60
1	9.71 205	21	9.77 906	29	0.22 094	9.93 299	8	59
2	9.71 226	21	9.77 935	28	0.22 065	9.93 291	7	58
3	9.71 247	21	9.77 963	29	0.22 037	9.93 284	8	57
4	9.71 268	21	9.77 992	28	0.22 008	9.93 276	7	56
5	9.71 289	21	9.78 020	29	0.21 980	9.93 269	8	55
6	9.71 310	21	9.78 049	28	0.21 951	9.93 261	8	54
7	9.71 331	21	9.78 077	29	0.21 923	9.93 253	7	53
8	9.71 352	21	9.78 106	29	0.21 894	9.93 246	8	52
9	9.71 373	20	9.78 135	28	0.21 865	9.93 238	8	51
10	9.71 393	21	9.78 163	29	0.21 837	9.93 230	7	50
11	9.71 414	21	9.78 192	28	0.21 808	9.93 223	8	49
12	9.71 435	21	9.78 220	29	0.21 780	9.93 215	8	48
13	9.71 456	21	9.78 249	28	0.21 751	9.93 207	7	47
14	9.71 477	21	9.78 277	29	0.21 723	9.93 200	8	46
15	9.71 498	21	9.78 306	28	0.21 694	9.93 192	8	45
16	9.71 519	20	9.78 334	29	0.21 666	9.93 184	7	44
17	9.71 539	21	9.78 363	28	0.21 637	9.93 177	8	43
18	9.71 560	21	9.78 391	28	0.21 609	9.93 169	8	42
19	9.71 581	21	9.78 419	29	0.21 581	9.93 161	7	41
20	9.71 602	20	9.78 448	28	0.21 552	9.93 154	8	40
21	9.71 622	21	9.78 476	29	0.21 524	9.93 146	8	39
22	9.71 643	21	9.78 505	28	0.21 495	9.93 138	7	38
23	9.71 664	21	9.78 533	29	0.21 467	9.93 131	8	37
24	9.71 685	20	9.78 562	28	0.21 438	9.93 123	8	36
25	9.71 705	21	9.78 590	28	0.21 410	9.93 115	7	35
26	9.71 726	21	9.78 618	29	0.21 382	9.93 108	8	34
27	9.71 747	20	9.78 647	28	0.21 353	9.93 100	8	33
28	9.71 767	21	9.78 675	29	0.21 325	9.93 092	8	32
29	9.71 788	21	9.78 704	28	0.21 296	9.93 084	7	31
30	9.71 809	20	9.78 732	28	0.21 268	9.93 077	8	30
31	9.71 829	21	9.78 760	29	0.21 240	9.93 069	8	29
32	9.71 850	20	9.78 789	28	0.21 211	9.93 061	8	28
33	9.71 870	21	9.78 817	28	0.21 183	9.93 053	7	27
34	9.71 891	20	9.78 845	29	0.21 155	9.93 046	8	26
35	9.71 911	21	9.78 874	28	0.21 126	9.93 038	8	25
36	9.71 932	20	9.78 902	28	0.21 098	9.93 030	8	24
37	9.71 952	21	9.78 930	29	0.21 070	9.93 022	8	23
38	9.71 973	21	9.78 959	28	0.21 041	9.93 014	7	22
39	9.71 994	20	9.78 987	28	0.21 013	9.93 007	8	21
40	9.72 014	20	9.79 015	28	0.20 985	9.92 999	8	20
41	9.72 034	21	9.79 043	29	0.20 957	9.92 991	8	19
42	9.72 055	20	9.79 072	28	0.20 928	9.92 983	7	18
43	9.72 075	21	9.79 100	28	0.20 900	9.92 976	8	17
44	9.72 096	20	9.79 128	28	0.20 872	9.92 968	8	16
45	9.72 116	21	9.79 156	29	0.20 844	9.92 960	8	15
46	9.72 137	20	9.79 185	28	0.20 815	9.92 952	8	14
47	9.72 157	20	9.79 213	28	0.20 787	9.92 944	8	13
48	9.72 177	21	9.79 241	28	0.20 759	9.92 936	7	12
49	9.72 198	20	9.79 269	28	0.20 731	9.92 929	8	11
50	9.72 218	20	9.79 297	29	0.20 703	9.92 921	8	10
51	9.72 238	21	9.79 326	28	0.20 674	9.92 913	8	9
52	9.72 259	20	9.79 354	28	0.20 646	9.92 905	8	8
53	9.72 279	20	9.79 382	28	0.20 618	9.92 897	8	7
54	9.72 299	21	9.79 410	28	0.20 590	9.92 889	8	6
55	9.72 320	20	9.79 438	28	0.20 562	9.92 881	7	5
56	9.72 340	20	9.79 466	29	0.20 534	9.92 874	8	4
57	9.72 360	21	9.79 495	28	0.20 505	9.92 866	8	3
58	9.72 381	20	9.79 523	28	0.20 477	9.92 858	8	2
59	9.72 401	20	9.79 551	28	0.20 449	9.92 850	8	1
60	9.72 421		9.79 579		0.20 421	9.92 842		0
′	L. Cos.	d.	L. Cot.	c.d.	L. Tan.	L. Sin.	d.	′

P.P.

″	29	28
1	0.5	0.5
2	1.0	0.9
3	1.4	1.4
4	1.9	1.9
5	2.4	2.3
6	2.9	2.8
7	3.4	3.3
8	3.9	3.7
9	4.4	4.2
10	4.8	4.7
20	9.7	9.3
30	14.5	14.0
40	19.3	18.7
50	24.2	23.3

″	21	20
1	0.4	0.3
2	0.7	0.7
3	1.0	1.0
4	1.4	1.3
5	1.8	1.7
6	2.1	2.0
7	2.4	2.3
8	2.8	2.7
9	3.2	3.0
10	3.5	3.3
20	7.0	6.7
30	10.5	10.0
40	14.0	13.3
50	17.5	16.7

″	8	7
1	0.1	0.1
2	0.3	0.2
3	0.4	0.4
4	0.5	0.5
5	0.7	0.6
6	0.8	0.7
7	0.9	0.8
8	1.1	0.9
9	1.2	1.0
10	1.3	1.2
20	2.7	2.3
30	4.0	3.5
40	5.3	4.7
50	6.7	5.8

	8/30	8/29	8/28
0			
1	1.9	1.8	1.8
2	5.6	5.4	5.2
3	9.4	9.1	8.8
4	13.1	12.7	12.2
5	16.9	16.3	15.8
6	20.6	19.9	19.2
7	24.4	23.6	22.8
8	28.1	27.2	26.2

P.P.

121° (301°) (238°) **58°**

LOGARITHMS OF THE FUNCTIONS (Continued)

32° (212°) (327°) **147°**

′	L. Sin.	d.	L. Tan.	c.d.	L. Cot.	L. Cos.	d.	′
0	9.72 421	20	9.79 579	28	0.20 421	9.92 842	8	**60**
1	9.72 441	20	9.79 607	28	0.20 393	9.92 834	8	59
2	9.72 461	21	9.79 635̇	28	0.20 365̄	9.92 826	8	58
3	9.72 482	20	9.79 663	28	0.20 337	9.92 818	8	57
4	9.72 502	20	9.79 691	28	0.20 309	9.92 810	7	56
5	9.72 522	20	9.79 719	28	0.20 281	9.92 803	8	55
6	9.72 542	20	9.79 747	29	0.20 253	9.92 795̄	8	54
7	9.72 562	20	9.79 776	28	0.20 224	9.92 787	8	53
8	9.72 582	20	9.79 804	28	0.20 196	9.92 779	8	52
9	9.72 602	20	9.79 832	28	0.20 168	9.92 771	8	51
10	9.72 622	21	9.79 860	28	0.20 140	9.92 763	8	**50**
11	9.72 643	20	9.79 888	28	0.20 112	9.92 755̄	8	49
12	9.72 663	20	9.79 916	28	0.20 084	9.92 747	8	48
13	9.72 683	20	9.79 944	28	0.20 056	9.92 739	8	47
14	9.72 703	20	9.79 972	28	0.20 028	9.92 731	8	46
15	9.72 723	20	9.80 000	28	0.20 000	9.92 723	8	45
16	9.72 743	20	9.80 028	28	0.19 972	9.92 715̇	8	44
17	9.72 763	20	9.80 056	28	0.19 944	9.92 707	8	43
18	9.72 783	20	9.80 084	28	0.19 916	9.92 699	8	42
19	9.72 803	20	9.80 112	28	0.19 888	9.92 691	8	41
20	9.72 823	20	9.80 140	28	0.19 860	9.92 683	8	**40**
21	9.72 843	20	9.80 168	27	0.19 832	9.92 675̇	8	39
22	9.72 863	20	9.80 195̇	28	0.19 805̄	9.92 667	8	38
23	9.72 883	19	9.80 223	28	0.19 777	9.92 659	8	37
24	9.72 902	20	9.80 251	28	0.19 749	9.92 651	8	36
25	9.72 922	20	9.80 279	28	0.19 721	9.92 643	8	35
26	9.72 942	20	9.80 307	28	0.19 693	9.92 635̇	8	34
27	9.72 962	20	9.80 335̇	28	0.19 665̄	9.92 627	8	33
28	9.72 982	20	9.80 363	28	0.19 637	9.92 619	8	32
29	9.73 002	20	9.80 391	28	0.19 609	9.92 611	8	31
30	9.73 022	19	9.80 419	28	0.19 581	9.92 603	8	**30**
31	9.73 041	20	9.80 447	27	0.19 553	9.92 595	8	29
32	9.73 061	20	9.80 474	28	0.19 526	9.92 587	8	28
33	9.73 081	20	9.80 502	28	0.19 498	9.92 579	8	27
34	9.73 101	20	9.80 530	28	0.19 470	9.92 571	8	26
35	9.73 121	19	9.80 558	28	0.19 442	9.92 563	8	25
36	9.73 140	20	9.80 586	28	0.19 414	9.92 555̄	9	24
37	9.73 160	20	9.80 614	28	0.19 386	9.92 546	8	23
38	9.73 180	20	9.80 642	27	0.19 358	9.92 538	8	22
39	9.73 200	19	9.80 669	28	0.19 331	9.92 530	8	21
40	9.73 219	20	9.80 697	28	0.19 303	9.92 522	8	**20**
41	9.73 239	20	9.80 725̄	28	0.19 275̇	9.92 514	8	19
42	9.73 259	19	9.80 753	28	0.19 247	9.92 506	8	18
43	9.73 278	20	9.80 781	27	0.19 219	9.92 498	8	17
44	9.73 298	20	9.80 808	28	0.19 192	9.92 490	8	16
45	9.73 318	19	9.80 836	28	0.19 164	9.92 482	9	15
46	9.73 337	20	9.80 864	28	0.19 136	9.92 473	8	14
47	9.73 357	20	9.80 892	27	0.19 108	9.92 465̇	8	13
48	9.73 377	19	9.80 919	28	0.19 081	9.92 457	8	12
49	9.73 396	20	9.80 947	28	0.19 053	9.92 449	8	11
50	9.73 416	19	9.80 975̄	28	0.19 025̇	9.92 441	8	**10**
51	9.73 435	20	9.81 003	27	0.18 997	9.92 433	8	9
52	9.73 455̄	19	9.81 030	28	0.18 970	9.92 425̄	9	8
53	9.73 474	20	9.81 058	28	0.18 942	9.92 416	8	7
54	9.73 494	19	9.81 086	27	0.18 914	9.92 408	8	6
55	9.73 513	20	9.81 113	28	0.18 887	9.92 400	8	5
56	9.73 533	19	9.81 141	28	0.18 859	9.92 392	8	4
57	9.73 552	20	9.81 169	27	0.18 831	9.92 384	8	3
58	9.73 572	19	9.81 196	28	0.18 804	9.92 376	9	2
59	9.73 591	20	9.81 224	28	0.18 776	9.92 367	8	1
60	9.73 611		9.81 252		0.18 748	9.92 359		**0**
′	L. Cos.	d.	L. Cot.	c.d.	L. Tan.	L. Sin.	d.	′

P. P.

″	29	28	27
1	0.5̄	0.5̄	0.4
2	1.0	0.9	0.9
3	1.4	1.4	1.4
4	1.9	1.9	1.8
5	2.4	2.3	2.2
6	2.9	2.8	2.7
7	3.4	3.3	3.2
8	3.9	3.7	3.6
9	4.4	4.2	4.0
10	4.8	4.7	4.5
20	9.7	9.3	9.0
30	14.5	14.0	13.5
40	19.3	18.7	18.0
50	24.2	23.3	22.5
″	**21**	**20**	**19**
1	0.4	0.3	0.3
2	0.7	0.7	0.6
3	1.0	1.0	1.0
4	1.4	1.3	1.3
5	1.8	1.7	1.6
6	2.1	2.0	1.9
7	2.4	2.3	2.2
8	2.8	2.7	2.5̇
9	3.2	3.0	2.8
10	3.5	3.3	3.2
20	7.0	6.7	6.3
30	10.5	10.0	9.5
40	14.0	13.3	12.7
50	17.5	16.7	15.8
″	**9**	**8**	**7**
1	0.2	0.1	0.1
2	0.3	0.3	0.2
3	0.4	0.4	0.4
4	0.6	0.5̇	0.5̄
5	0.8	0.7	0.6
6	0.9	0.8	0.7
7	1.0	0.9	0.8
8	1.2	1.1	0.9
9	1.4	1.2	1.0
10	1.5	1.3	1.2
20	3.0	2.7	2.3
30	4.5	4.0	3.5
40	6.0	5.3	4.7
50	7.5	6.7	5.8

	8/29	8/28	7/28
0	1.8	1.8	2.0
1	5.4	5.2	6.0
2	9.1	8.8	10.0
3	12.7	12.2	14.0
4	16.3	15.8	18.0
5	19.9	19.2	22.0
6	23.6	22.8	26.0
7	27.2	26.2	—
8			

P. P.

122° (302°) (237°) **57°**

LOGARITHMS OF THE FUNCTIONS (Continued)

33° (213°) (326°) **146°**

′	L. Sin.	d.	L. Tan.	c.d.	L. Cot.	L. Cos.	d.	′
0	9.73 611	19	9.81 252	27	0.18 748	9.92 359	8	**60**
1	9.73 630	20	9.81 279	28	0.18 721	9.92 351	8	59
2	9.73 650	19	9.81 307	28	0.18 693	9.92 343	8	58
3	9.73 669	20	9.81 335̄	27	0.18 665̇	9.92 335̄	9	57
4	9.73 689	19	9.81 362	28	0.18 638	9.92 326	8	56
5	9.73 708	19	9.81 390	28	0.18 610	9.92 318	8	55
6	9.73 727	20	9.81 418	27	0.18 582	9.92 310	8	54
7	9.73 747	19	9.81 445̇	28	0.18 555̄	9.92 302	9	53
8	9.73 766	19	9.81 473	27	0.18 527	9.92 293	8	52
9	9.73 785̇	20	9.81 500	28	0.18 500	9.92 285̇	8	51
10	9.73 805̄	19	9.81 528	28	0.18 472	9.92 277	8	**50**
11	9.73 824	19	9.81 556	27	0.18 444	9.92 269	9	49
12	9.73 843	20	9.81 583	28	0.18 417	9.92 260	8	48
13	9.73 863	19	9.81 611	27	0.18 389	9.92 252	8	47
14	9.73 882	19	9.81 638	28	0.18 362	9.92 244	9	46
15	9.73 901	20	9.81 666	27	0.18 334	9.92 235̇	8	45
16	9.73 921	19	9.81 693	28	0.18 307	9.92 227	8	44
17	9.73 940	19	9.81 721	27	0.18 279	9.92 219	8	43
18	9.73 959	19	9.81 748	28	0.18 252	9.92 211	9	42
19	9.73 978	19	9.81 776	27	0.18 224	9.92 202	8	41
20	9.73 997	20	9.81 803	28	0.18 197	9.92 194	8	**40**
21	9.74 017	19	9.81 831	27	0.18 169	9.92 186	9	39
22	9.74 036	19	9.81 858	28	0.18 142	9.92 177	8	38
23	9.74 055̇	19	9.81 886	27	0.18 114	9.92 169	8	37
24	9.74 074	19	9.81 913	28	0.18 087	9.92 161	9	36
25	9.74 093	20	9.81 941	27	0.18 059	9.92 152	8	35
26	9.74 113	19	9.81 968	28	0.18 032	9.92 144	8	34
27	9.74 132	19	9.81 996	27	0.18 004	9.92 136	9	33
28	9.74 151	19	9.82 023	28	0.17 977	9.92 127	8	32
29	9.74 170	19	9.82 051	27	0.17 949	9.92 119	8	31
30	9.74 189	19	9.82 078	28	0.17 922	9.92 111	9	**30**
31	9.74 208	19	9.82 106	27	0.17 894	9.92 102	8	29
32	9.74 227	19	9.82 133	28	0.17 867	9.92 094	8	28
33	9.74 246	19	9.82 161	27	0.17 839	9.92 086	9	27
34	9.74 265̇	19	9.82 188	27	0.17 812	9.92 077	8	26
35	9.74 284	19	9.82 215̇	28	0.17 785̄	9.92 069	9	25
36	9.74 303	19	9.82 243	27	0.17 757	9.92 060	8	24
37	9.74 322	19	9.82 270	28	0.17 730	9.92 052	8	23
38	9.74 341	19	9.82 298	27	0.17 702	9.92 044	9	22
39	9.74 360	19	9.82 325̇	27	0.17 675̄	9.92 035̇	8	21
40	9.74 379	19	9.82 352	28	0.17 648	9.92 027	9	**20**
41	9.74 398	19	9.82 380	27	0.17 620	9.92 018	8	19
42	9.74 417	19	9.82 407	28	0.17 593	9.92 010	8	18
43	9.74 436	19	9.82 435̄	27	0.17 565̇	9.92 002	9	17
44	9.74 455̄	19	9.82 462	27	0.17 538	9.91 993	8	16
45	9.74 474	19	9.82 489	28	0.17 511	9.91 985̄	9	15
46	9.74 493	19	9.82 517	27	0.17 483	9.91 976	8	14
47	9.74 512	19	9.82 544	27	0.17 456	9.91 968	9	13
48	9.74 531	18	9.82 571	28	0.17 429	9.91 959	8	12
49	9.74 549	19	9.82 599	27	0.17 401	9.91 951	9	11
50	9.74 568	19	9.82 626	27	0.17 374	9.91 942	8	**10**
51	9.74 587	19	9.82 653	28	0.17 347	9.91 934	9	9
52	9.74 606	19	9.82 681	27	0.17 319	9.91 925̇	8	8
53	9.74 625̄	19	9.82 708	27	0.17 292	9.91 917	9	7
54	9.74 644	18	9.82 735̇	27	0.17 265̄	9.91 908	8	6
55	9.74 662	19	9.82 762	28	0.17 238	9.91 900	9	5
56	9.74 681	19	9.82 790	27	0.17 210	9.91 891	8	4
57	9.74 700	19	9.82 817	27	0.17 183	9.91 883	9	3
58	9.74 719	18	9.82 844	27	0.17 156	9.91 874	8	2
59	9.74 737	19	9.82 871	28	0.17 129	9.91 866	9	1
60	9.74 756		9.82 899		0.17 101	9.91 857		**0**
′	L. Cos.	d.	L. Cot.	c.d.	L. Tan	L. Sin.	d.	′

P. P.

″	**28**	**27**
1	0.5̄	0.4
2	0.9	0.9
3	1.4	1.4
4	1.9	1.8
5	2.3	2.2
6	2.8	2.7
7	3.3	3.2
8	3.7	3.6
9	4.2	4.0
10	4.7	4.5
20	9.3	9.0
30	14.0	13.5
40	18.7	18.0
50	23.3	22.5

″	**20**	**19**	**18**
1	0.3	0.3	0.3
2	0.7	0.6	0.6
3	1.0	1.0	0.9
4	1.3	1.3	1.2
5	1.7	1.6	1.5
6	2.0	1.9	1.8
7	2.3	2.2	2.1
8	2.7	2.5̇	2.4
9	3.0	2.8	2.7
10	3.3	3.2	3.0
20	6.7	6.3	6.0
30	10.0	9.5	9.0
40	13.3	12.7	12.0
50	16.7	15.8	15.0

″	**9**	**8**
1	0.2	0.1
2	0.3	0.3
3	0.4	0.4
4	0.6	0.5̇
5	0.8	0.7
6	0.9	0.8
7	1.0	0.9
8	1.2	1.1
9	1.4	1.2
10	1.5	1.3
20	3.0	2.7
30	4.5	4.0
40	6.0	5.3
50	7.5	6.7

	9/28	**9/27**	**8/27**
0	1.6	1.5	1.7
1	4.7	4.5	5.1
2	7.8	7.5	8.4
3	10.9	10.5	11.8
4	14.0	13.5	15.2
5	17.1	16.5	18.6
6	20.2	19.5	21.9
7	23.3	22.5	25.3
8	26.4	25.5	—
9			

P. P.

123° (303°) (236°) **56°**

LOGARITHMS OF THE FUNCTIONS (Continued)

34° (214°) (325°) **145°**

′	L. Sin.	d.	L. Tan.	c.d.	L. Cot.	L. Cos.	d.	′
0	9.74 756	19	9.82 899	27	0.17 101	9.91 857	8	**60**
1	9.74 775	19	9.82 926	27	0.17 074	9.91 849	9	59
2	9.74 794	18	9.82 953	27	0.17 047	9.91 840	8	58
3	9.74 812	19	9.82 980	28	0.17 020	9.91 832	9	57
4	9.74 831	19	9.83 008	27	0.16 992	9.91 823	8	56
5	9.74 850	18	9.83 035	27	0.16 965	9.91 815	9	55
6	9.74 868	19	9.83 062	27	0.16 938	9.91 806	8	54
7	9.74 887	19	9.83 089	28	0.16 911	9.91 798	9	53
8	9.74 906	18	9.83 117	27	0.16 883	9.91 789	8	52
9	9.74 924	19	9.83 144	27	0.16 856	9.91 781	9	51
10	9.74 943	18	9.83 171	27	0.16 829	9.91 772	9	**50**
11	9.74 961	19	9.83 198	27	0.16 802	9.91 763	8	49
12	9.74 980	19	9.83 225	27	0.16 775	9.91 755	9	48
13	9.74 999	18	9.83 252	28	0.16 748	9.91 746	8	47
14	9.75 017	19	9.83 280	27	0.16 720	9.91 738	9	46
15	9.75 036	18	9.83 307	27	0.16 693	9.91 729	9	45
16	9.75 054	19	9.83 334	27	0.16 666	9.91 720	8	44
17	9.75 073	18	9.83 361	27	0.16 639	9.91 712	9	43
18	9.75 091	19	9.83 388	27	0.16 612	9.91 703	8	42
19	9.75 110	18	9.83 415	27	0.16 585	9.91 695	9	41
20	9.75 128	19	9.83 442	28	0.16 558	9.91 686	9	**40**
21	9.75 147	18	9.83 470	27	0.16 530	9.91 677	8	39
22	9.75 165	19	9.83 497	27	0.16 503	9.91 669	9	38
23	9.75 184	18	9.83 524	27	0.16 476	9.91 660	9	37
24	9.75 202	19	9.83 551	27	0.16 449	9.91 651	8	36
25	9.75 221	18	9.83 578	27	0.16 422	9.91 643	9	35
26	9.75 239	19	9.83 605	27	0.16 395	9.91 634	9	34
27	9.75 258	18	9.83 632	27	0.16 368	9.91 625	8	33
28	9.75 276	18	9.83 659	27	0.16 341	9.91 617	9	32
29	9.75 294	19	9.83 686	27	0.16 314	9.91 608	9	31
30	9.75 313	18	9.83 713	27	0.16 287	9.91 599	8	**30**
31	9.75 331	19	9.83 740	28	0.16 260	9.91 591	9	29
32	9.75 350	18	9.83 768	27	0.16 232	9.91 582	9	28
33	9.75 368	18	9.83 795	27	0.16 205	9.91 573	8	27
34	9.75 386	19	9.83 822	27	0.16 178	9.91 565	9	26
35	9.75 405	18	9.83 849	27	0.16 151	9.91 556	9	25
36	9.75 423	18	9.83 876	27	0.16 124	9.91 547	9	24
37	9.75 441	18	9.83 903	27	0.16 097	9.91 538	8	23
38	9.75 459	19	9.83 930	27	0.16 070	9.91 530	9	22
39	9.75 478	18	9.83 957	27	0.16 043	9.91 521	9	21
40	9.75 496	18	9.83 984	27	0.16 016	9.91 512	8	**20**
41	9.75 514	19	9.84 011	27	0.15 989	9.91 504	9	19
42	9.75 533	18	9.84 038	27	0.15 962	9.91 495	9	18
43	9.75 551	18	9.84 065	27	0.15 935	9.91 486	9	17
44	9.75 569	18	9.84 092	27	0.15 908	9.91 477	8	16
45	9.75 587	18	9.84 119	27	0.15 881	9.91 469	9	15
46	9.75 605	19	9.84 146	27	0.15 854	9.91 460	9	14
47	9.75 624	18	9.84 173	27	0.15 827	9.91 451	9	13
48	9.75 642	18	9.84 200	27	0.15 800	9.91 442	9	12
49	9.75 660	18	9.84 227	27	0.15 773	9.91 433	8	11
50	9.75 678	18	9.84 254	26	0.15 746	9.91 425	9	**10**
51	9.75 696	18	9.84 280	27	0.15 720	9.91 416	9	9
52	9.75 714	19	9.84 307	27	0.15 693	9.91 407	9	8
53	9.75 733	18	9.84 334	27	0.15 666	9.91 398	9	7
54	9.75 751	18	9.84 361	27	0.15 639	9.91 389	8	6
55	9.75 769	18	9.84 388	27	0.15 612	9.91 381	9	5
56	9.75 787	18	9.84 415	27	0.15 585	9.91 372	9	4
57	9.75 805	18	9.84 442	27	0.15 558	9.91 363	9	3
58	9.75 823	18	9.84 469	27	0.15 531	9.91 354	9	2
59	9.75 841	18	9.84 496	27	0.15 504	9.91 345	9	1
60	9.75 859		9.84 523		0.15 477	9.91 336		**0**
′	L. Cos.	d.	L. Cot.	c.d.	L. Tan.	L. Sin.	d.	′

P.P.

″	28	27	26
1	0.5	0.4	0.4
2	0.9	0.9	0.9
3	1.4	1.4	1.3
4	1.9	1.8	1.7
5	2.3	2.2	2.2
6	2.8	2.7	2.6
7	3.3	3.2	3.0
8	3.7	3.6	3.5
9	4.2	4.0	3.9
10	4.7	4.5	4.3
20	9.3	9.0	8.7
30	14.0	13.5	13.0
40	18.7	18.0	17.3
50	23.3	22.5	21.7

″	19	18
1	0.3	0.3
2	0.6	0.6
3	1.0	0.9
4	1.3	1.2
5	1.6	1.5
6	1.9	1.8
7	2.2	2.1
8	2.5	2.4
9	2.8	2.7
10	3.2	3.0
20	6.3	6.0
30	9.5	9.0
40	12.7	12.0
50	15.8	15.0

″	9	8
1	0.2	0.1
2	0.3	0.3
3	0.4	0.4
4	0.6	0.5
5	0.8	0.7
6	0.9	0.8
7	1.0	0.9
8	1.2	1.1
9	1.4	1.2
10	1.5	1.3
20	3.0	2.7
30	4.5	4.0
40	6.0	5.3
50	7.5	6.7

	9/28	8/28	8/27
0	1.6	1.8	1.7
1	4.7	5.2	5.1
2	7.8	8.8	8.4
3	10.9	12.2	11.8
4	14.0	15.8	15.2
5	17.1	19.2	18.6
6	20.2	22.8	21.9
7	23.3	26.2	25.3
8	26.4	—	—
9			

P.P.

124° (304°) (235°) **55°**

35° (215°) (324°) **144°**

′	L. Sin.	d.	L. Tan.	c.d.	L. Cot.	L. Cos.	d.	′
0	9.75 859	18	9.84 523	27	0.15 477	9.91 336	8	**60**
1	9.75 877	18	9.84 550	26	0.15 450	9.91 328	9	59
2	9.75 895	18	9.84 576	27	0.15 424	9.91 319	9	58
3	9.75 913	18	9.84 603	27	0.15 397	9.91 310	9	57
4	9.75 931	18	9.84 630	27	0.15 370	9.91 301	9	56
5	9.75 949	18	9.84 657	27	0.15 343	9.91 292	9	55
6	9.75 967	18	9.84 684	27	0.15 316	9.91 283	9	54
7	9.75 985	18	9.84 711	27	0.15 289	9.91 274	8	53
8	9.76 003	18	9.84 738	26	0.15 262	9.91 266	9	52
9	9.76 021	18	9.84 764	27	0.15 236	9.91 257	9	51
10	9.76 039	18	9.84 791	27	0.15 209	9.91 248	9	**50**
11	9.76 057	18	9.84 818	27	0.15 182	9.91 239	9	49
12	9.76 075	18	9.84 845	27	0.15 155	9.91 230	9	48
13	9.76 093	18	9.84 872	27	0.15 128	9.91 221	9	47
14	9.76 111	18	9.84 899	26	0.15 101	9.91 212	9	46
15	9.76 129	17	9.84 925	27	0.15 075	9.91 203	9	45
16	9.76 146	18	9.84 952	27	0.15 048	9.91 194	9	44
17	9.76 164	18	9.84 979	27	0.15 021	9.91 185	9	43
18	9.76 182	18	9.85 006	27	0.14 994	9.91 176	9	42
19	9.76 200	18	9.85 033	26	0.14 967	9.91 167	9	41
20	9.76 218	18	9.85 059	27	0.14 941	9.91 158	9	**40**
21	9.76 236	17	9.85 086	27	0.14 914	9.91 149	8	39
22	9.76 253	18	9.85 113	27	0.14 887	9.91 141	9	38
23	9.76 271	18	9.85 140	26	0.14 860	9.91 132	9	37
24	9.76 289	18	9.85 166	27	0.14 834	9.91 123	9	36
25	9.76 307	17	9.85 193	27	0.14 807	9.91 114	9	35
26	9.76 324	18	9.85 220	27	0.14 780	9.91 105	9	34
27	9.76 342	18	9.85 247	26	0.14 753	9.91 096	9	33
28	9.76 360	18	9.85 273	27	0.14 727	9.91 087	9	32
29	9.76 378	17	9.85 300	27	0.14 700	9.91 078	9	31
30	9.76 395	18	9.85 327	27	0.14 673	9.91 069	9	**30**
31	9.76 413	18	9.85 354	26	0.14 646	9.91 060	9	29
32	9.76 431	17	9.85 380	27	0.14 620	9.91 051	9	28
33	9.76 448	18	9.85 407	27	0.14 593	9.91 042	9	27
34	9.76 466	18	9.85 434	26	0.14 566	9.91 033	10	26
35	9.76 484	17	9.85 460	27	0.14 540	9.91 023	9	25
36	9.76 501	18	9.85 487	27	0.14 513	9.91 014	9	24
37	9.76 519	18	9.85 514	26	0.14 486	9.91 005	9	23
38	9.76 537	17	9.85 540	27	0.14 460	9.90 996	9	22
39	9.76 554	18	9.85 567	27	0.14 433	9.90 987	9	21
40	9.76 572	18	9.85 594	26	0.14 406	9.90 978	9	**20**
41	9.76 590	17	9.85 620	27	0.14 380	9.90 969	9	19
42	9.76 607	18	9.85 647	27	0.14 353	9.90 960	9	18
43	9.76 625	17	9.85 674	26	0.14 326	9.90 951	9	17
44	9.76 642	18	9.85 700	27	0.14 300	9.90 942	9	16
45	9.76 660	17	9.85 727	27	0.14 273	9.90 933	9	15
46	9.76 677	18	9.85 754	26	0.14 246	9.90 924	9	14
47	9.76 695	17	9.85 780	27	0.14 220	9.90 915	9	13
48	9.76 712	18	9.85 807	27	0.14 193	9.90 906	10	12
49	9.76 730	17	9.85 834	26	0.14 166	9.90 896	9	11
50	9.76 747	18	9.85 860	27	0.14 140	9.90 887	9	**10**
51	9.76 765	17	9.85 887	26	0.14 113	9.90 878	9	9
52	9.76 782	18	9.85 913	27	0.14 087	9.90 869	9	8
53	9.76 800	17	9.85 940	27	0.14 060	9.90 860	9	7
54	9.76 817	18	9.85 967	26	0.14 033	9.90 851	9	6
55	9.76 835	17	9.85 993	27	0.14 007	9.90 842	10	5
56	9.76 852	18	9.86 020	26	0.13 980	9.90 832	9	4
57	9.76 870	17	9.86 046	27	0.13 954	9.90 823	9	3
58	9.76 887	17	9.86 073	27	0.13 927	9.90 814	9	2
59	9.76 904	18	9.86 100	26	0.13 900	9.90 805	9	1
60	9.76 922		9.86 126		0.13 874	9.90 796		**0**
′	L. Cos.	d.	L. Cot.	c.d.	L. Tan.	L. Sin.	d.	′

P.P.

″	27	26	18
1	0.4	0.4	0.3
2	0.9	0.9	0.6
3	1.4	1.3	0.9
4	1.8	1.7	1.2
5	2.2	2.2	1.5
6	2.7	2.6	1.8
7	3.2	3.0	2.1
8	3.6	3.5	2.4
9	4.0	3.9	2.7
10	4.5	4.3	3.0
20	9.0	8.7	6.0
30	13.5	13.0	9.0
40	18.0	17.3	12.0
50	22.5	21.7	15.0

″	17	10	9	8
1	0.3	0.2	0.2	0.1
2	0.6	0.3	0.3	0.3
3	0.8	0.5	0.4	0.4
4	1.1	0.7	0.6	0.5
5	1.4	0.8	0.8	0.7
6	1.7	1.0	0.9	0.8
7	2.0	1.2	1.0	0.9
8	2.3	1.3	1.2	1.1
9	2.6	1.5	1.4	1.2
10	2.8	1.7	1.5	1.3
20	5.7	3.3	3.0	2.7
30	8.5	5.0	4.5	4.0
40	11.3	6.7	6.0	5.3
50	14.2	8.3	7.5	6.7

	10/27	10/26
0	1.4	1.3
1	4.1	3.9
2	6.8	6.5
3	9.4	9.1
4	12.2	11.7
5	14.8	14.3
6	17.6	16.9
7	20.2	19.5
8	22.9	22.1
9	25.6	24.7
10		

	9/27	9/26
0	1.5	1.4
1	4.5	4.3
2	7.5	7.2
3	10.5	10.1
4	13.5	13.0
5	16.5	15.9
6	19.5	18.8
7	22.5	21.7
8	25.5	24.6
9		

125° (305°) (234°) **54°**

36° (216°) (323°) **143°**

′	L. Sin.	d.	L. Tan.	c.d.	L. Cot.	L. Cos.	d.	′
0	9.76 922	17	9.86 126	27	0.13 874	9.90 796	9	**60**
1	9.76 939	18	9.86 153	26	0.13 847	9.90 787	10	59
2	9.76 957	17	9.86 179	27	0.13 821	9.90 777	9	58
3	9.76 974	17	9.86 206	26	0.13 794	9.90 768	9	57
4	9.76 991	18	9.86 232	27	0.13 768	9.90 759	9	56
5	9.77 009	17	9.86 259	26	0.13 741	9.90 750	9	55
6	9.77 026	17	9.86 285	27	0.13 715	9.90 741	10	54
7	9.77 043	18	9.86 312	26	0.13 688	9.90 731	9	53
8	9.77 061	17	9.86 338	27	0.13 662	9.90 722	9	52
9	9.77 078	17	9.86 365	27	0.13 635	9.90 713	9	51
10	9.77 095	17	9.86 392	26	0.13 608	9.90 704	10	**50**
11	9.77 112	18	9.86 418	27	0.13 582	9.90 694	9	49
12	9.77 130	17	9.86 445	26	0.13 555	9.90 685	9	48
13	9.77 147	17	9.86 471	27	0.13 529	9.90 676	9	47
14	9.77 164	17	9.86 498	26	0.13 502	9.90 667	10	46
15	9.77 181	18	9.86 524	27	0.13 476	9.90 657	9	45
16	9.77 199	17	9.86 551	26	0.13 449	9.90 648	9	44
17	9.77 216	17	9.86 577	26	0.13 423	9.90 639	9	43
18	9.77 233	17	9.86 603	27	0.13 397	9.90 630	10	42
19	9.77 250	18	9.86 630	26	0.13 370	9.90 620	9	41
20	9.77 268	17	9.86 656	27	0.13 344	9.90 611	9	**40**
21	9.77 285	17	9.86 683	26	0.13 317	9.90 602	10	39
22	9.77 302	17	9.86 709	27	0.13 291	9.90 592	9	38
23	9.77 319	17	9.86 736	26	0.13 264	9.90 583	9	37
24	9.77 336	17	9.86 762	27	0.13 238	9.90 574	9	36
25	9.77 353	17	9.86 789	26	0.13 211	9.90 565	10	35
26	9.77 370	17	9.86 815	27	0.13 185	9.90 555	9	34
27	9.77 387	18	9.86 842	26	0.13 158	9.90 546	9	33
28	9.77 405	17	9.86 868	26	0.13 132	9.90 537	10	32
29	9.77 422	17	9.86 894	27	0.13 106	9.90 527	9	31
30	9.77 439	17	9.86 921	26	0.13 079	9.90 518	9	**30**
31	9.77 456	17	9.86 947	27	0.13 053	9.90 509	10	29
32	9.77 473	17	9.86 974	26	0.13 026	9.90 499	9	28
33	9.77 490	17	9.87 000	27	0.13 000	9.90 490	10	27
34	9.77 507	17	9.87 027	26	0.12 973	9.90 480	9	26
35	9.77 524	17	9.87 053	26	0.12 947	9 90 471	9	25
36	9.77 541	17	9.87 079	27	0.12 921	9.90 462	10	24
37	9.77 558	17	9.87 106	26	0.12 894	9.90 452	9	23
38	9.77 575	17	9.87 132	26	0.12 868	9.90 443	9	22
39	9.77 592	17	9.87 158	27	0.12 842	9.90 434	10	21
40	9.77 609	17	9.87 185	26	0.12 815	9.90 424	9	**20**
41	9.77 626	17	9.87 211	27	0.12 789	9.90 415	10	19
42	9.77 643	17	9.87 238	26	0.12 762	9.90 405	9	18
43	9.77 660	17	9.87 264	26	0.12 736	9.90 396	10	17
44	9.77 677	17	9.87 290	27	0.12 710	9.90 386	9	16
45	9.77 694	17	9.87 317	26	0.12 683	9.90 377	9	15
46	9.77 711	17	9.87 343	26	0.12 657	9.90 368	10	14
47	9.77 728	16	9.87 369	27	0.12 631	9.90 358	9	13
48	9.77 744	17	9.87 396	26	0.12 604	9.90 349	10	12
49	9.77 761	17	9.87 422	26	0.12 578	9.90 339	9	11
50	9.77 778	17	9.87 448	27	0.12 552	9.90 330	10	**10**
51	9.77 795	17	9.87 475	26	0.12 525	9.90 320	9	9
52	9.77 812	17	9.87 501	26	0.12 499	9.90 311	10	8
53	9.77 829	17	9.87 527	27	0.12 473	9.90 301	9	7
54	9.77 846	16	9.87 554	26	0.12 446	9.90 292	10	6
55	9.77 862	17	9.87 580	26	0.12 420	9.90 282	9	5
56	9.77 879	17	9.87 606	27	0.12 394	9.90 273	10	4
57	9.77 896	17	9.87 633	26	0.12 367	9.90 263	9	3
58	9.77 913	17	9.87 659	26	0.12 341	9.90 254	10	2
59	9.77 930	16	9.87 685	26	0.12 315	9.90 244	9	1
60	9.77 946		9.87 711		0.12 289	9.90 235		**0**
′	L. Cos.	d.	L. Cot.	c.d.	L. Tan.	L. Sin.	d.	′

126° (306°) (233°) **53°**

P. P.

″	27	26
1	0.4	0.4
2	0.9	0.9
3	1.4	1.3
4	1.8	1.7
5	2.2	2.2
6	2.7	2.6
7	3.2	3.0
8	3.6	3.5
9	4.0	3.9
10	4.5	4.3
20	9.0	8.7
30	13.5	13.0
40	18.0	17.3
50	22.5	21.7

″	18	17	16
1	0.3	0.3	0.3
2	0.6	0.6	0.5
3	0.9	0.8	0.8
4	1.2	1.1	1.1
5	1.5	1.4	1.3
6	1.8	1.7	1.6
7	2.1	2.0	1.9
8	2.4	2.3	2.1
9	2.7	2.6	2.4
10	3.0	2.8	2.7
20	6.0	5.7	5.3
30	9.0	8.5	8.0
40	12.0	11.3	10.7
50	15.0	14.2	13.3

″	10	9
1	0.2	0.2
2	0.3	0.3
3	0.5	0.4
4	0.7	0.6
5	0.8	0.8
6	1.0	0.9
7	1.2	1.0
8	1.3	1.2
9	1.5	1.4
10	1.7	1.5
20	3.3	3.0
30	5.0	4.5
40	6.7	6.0
50	8.3	7.5

	9/27	9/26
0	1.5	1.4
1	4.5	4.3
2	7.5	7.2
3	10.5	10.1
4	13.5	13.0
5	16.5	15.9
6	19.5	18.8
7	22.5	21.7
8	25.5	24.6
9		

P. P.

37° (217°) (322°) **142°**

′	L. Sin.	d.	L. Tan.	c.d.	L. Cot.	L. Cos.	d.	′
0	9.77 946	17	9.87 711	27	0.12 289	9.90 235	10	**60**
1	9.77 963	17	9.87 738	26	0.12 262	9.90 225	9	59
2	9.77 980	17	9.87 764	26	0.12 236	9.90 216	10	58
3	9.77 997	16	9.87 790	27	0.12 210	9.90 206	9	57
4	9.78 013	17	9.87 817	26	0.12 183	9.90 197	10	56
5	9.78 030	17	9.87 843	26	0.12 157	9.90 187	9	55
6	9.78 047	16	9.87 869	26	0.12 131	9.90 178	10	54
7	9.78 063	17	9.87 895	27	0.12 105	9.90 168	9	53
8	9.78 080	17	9.87 922	26	0.12 078	9.90 159	10	52
9	9.78 097	16	9.87 948	26	0.12 052	9.90 149	10	51
10	9.78 113	17	9.87 974	26	0.12 026	9.90 139	9	**50**
11	9.78 130	17	9.88 000	27	0.12 000	9.90 130	10	49
12	9.78 147	16	9.88 027	26	0.11 973	9.90 120	9	48
13	9.78 163	17	9.88 053	26	0.11 947	9.90 111	10	47
14	9.78 180	17	9.88 079	26	0.11 921	9.90 101	10	46
15	9.78 197	16	9.88 105	26	0.11 895	9.90 091	9	45
16	9.78 213	17	9.88 131	27	0.11 869	9.90 082	10	44
17	9.78 230	16	9.88 158	26	0.11 842	9.90 072	9	43
18	9.78 246	17	9.88 184	26	0.11 816	9.90 063	10	42
19	9.78 263	17	9.88 210	26	0.11 790	9.90 053	10	41
20	9.78 280	16	9.88 236	26	0.11 764	9.90 043	9	**40**
21	9.78 296	17	9.88 262	27	0.11 738	9.90 034	10	39
22	9.78 313	16	9.88 289	26	0.11 711	9.90 024	10	38
23	9.78 329	17	9.88 315	26	0.11 685	9.90 014	9	37
24	9.78 346	16	9.88 341	26	0.11 659	9.90 005	10	36
25	9.78 362	17	9.88 367	26	0.11 633	9.89 995	10	35
26	9.78 379	16	9.88 393	27	0.11 607	9.89 985	9	34
27	9.78 395	17	9.88 420	26	0.11 580	9.89 976	10	33
28	9.78 412	16	9.88 446	26	0.11 554	9.89 966	10	32
29	9.78 428	17	9.88 472	26	0.11 528	9.89 956	9	31
30	9.78 445	16	9.88 498	26	0.11 502	9.89 947	10	**30**
31	9.78 461	17	9.88 524	26	0.11 476	9.89 937	10	29
32	9.78 478	16	9.88 550	27	0.11 450	9.89 927	9	28
33	9.78 494	16	9.88 577	26	0.11 423	9.89 918	10	27
34	9.78 510	17	9.88 603	26	0.11 397	9.89 908	10	26
35	9.78 527	16	9.88 629	26	0.11 371	9.89 898	10	25
36	9.78 543	17	9.88 655	26	0.11 345	9.89 888	9	24
37	9.78 560	16	9.88 681	26	0.11 319	9.89 879	10	23
38	9.78 576	16	9.88 707	26	0.11 293	9.89 869	10	22
39	9.78 592	17	9.88 733	26	0.11 267	9.89 859	10	21
40	9.78 609	16	9.88 759	27	0.11 241	9.89 849	9	**20**
41	9.78 625	17	9.88 786	26	0.11 214	9.89 840	10	19
42	9.78 642	16	9.88 812	26	0.11 188	9.89 830	10	18
43	9.78 658	16	9.88 838	26	0.11 162	9.89 820	10	17
44	9.78 674	17	9.88 864	26	0.11 136	9.89 810	9	16
45	9.78 691	16	9.88 890	26	0.11 110	9.89 801	10	15
46	9.78 707	16	9.88 916	26	0.11 084	9.89 791	10	14
47	9.78 723	16	9.88 942	26	0.11 058	9.89 781	10	13
48	9.78 739	17	9.88 968	26	0.11 032	9.89 771	10	12
49	9.78 756	16	9.88 994	26	0.11 006	9.89 761	9	11
50	9.78 772	16	9.89 020	26	0.10 980	9.89 752	10	**10**
51	9.78 788	17	9.89 046	27	0.10 954	9.89 742	10	9
52	9.78 805	16	9.89 073	26	0.10 927	9.89 732	10	8
53	9.78 821	16	9.89 099	26	0.10 901	9.89 722	10	7
54	9.78 837	16	9.89 125	26	0.10 875	9.89 712	10	6
55	9.78 853	16	9.89 151	26	0.10 849	9.89 702	9	5
56	9.78 869	17	9.89 177	26	0.10 823	9.89 693	10	4
57	9.78 886	16	9.89 203	26	0.10 797	9.89 683	10	3
58	9.78 902	16	9.89 229	26	0.10 771	9.89 673	10	2
59	9.78 918	16	9.89 255	26	0.10 745	9.89 663	10	1
60	9.78 934		9.89 281		0.10 719	9.89 653		**0**
′	L. Cos.	d.	L. Cot.	c.d.	L. Tan.	L. Sin.	d.	′

P. P.

″	**27**	**26**
1	0.4	0.4
2	0.9	0.9
3	1.4	1.3
4	1.8	1.7
5	2.2	2.2
6	2.7	2.6
7	3.2	3.0
8	3.6	3.5
9	4.0	3.9
10	4.5	4.3
20	9.0	8.7
30	13.5	13.0
40	18.0	17.3
50	22.5	21.7

″	**17**	**16**
1	0.3	0.3
2	0.6	0.5
3	0.8	0.8
4	1.1	1.1
5	1.4	1.3
6	1.7	1.6
7	2.0	1.9
8	2.3	2.1
9	2.6	2.4
10	2.8	2.7
20	5.7	5.3
30	8.5	8.0
40	11.3	10.7
50	14.2	13.3

″	**10**	**9**
1	0.2	0.2
2	0.3	0.3
3	0.5	0.4
4	0.7	0.6
5	0.8	0.8
6	1.0	0.9
7	1.2	1.0
8	1.3	1.2
9	1.5	1.4
10	1.7	1.5
20	3.3	3.0
30	5.0	4.5
40	6.7	6.0
50	8.3	7.5

	10/27	**10/26**
0	1.4	1.3
1	4.1	3.9
2	6.8	6.5
3	9.4	9.1
4	12.2	11.7
5	14.8	14.3
6	17.6	16.9
7	20.2	19.5
8	22.9	22.1
9	25.6	24.7
10		

P. P.

127° (307°) (232°) **52°**

′	L. Sin.	d.	L. Tan.	c.d.	L. Cot.	L. Cos.	d.	′
0	9.78 934	16	9.89 281	26	0.10 719	9.89 653	10	60
1	9.78 950	17	9.89 307	26	0.10 693	9.89 643	10	59
2	9.78 967	16	9.89 333	26	0.10 667	9.89 633	9	58
3	9.78 983	16	9.89 359	26	0.10 641	9.89 624	10	57
4	9.78 999	16	9.89 385	26	0.10 615	9.89 614	10	56
5	9.79 015	16	9.89 411	26	0.10 589	9.89 604	10	55
6	9.79 031	16	9.89 437	26	0.10 563	9.89 594	10	54
7	9.79 047	16	9.89 463	26	0.10 537	9.89 584	10	53
8	9.79 063	16	9.89 489	26	0.10 511	9.89 574	10	52
9	9.79 079	16	9.89 515	26	0.10 485	9.89 564	10	51
10	9.79 095	16	9.89 541	26	0.10 459	9.89 554	10	50
11	9.79 111	17	9.89 567	26	0.10 433	9.89 544	10	49
12	9.79 128	16	9.89 593	26	0.10 407	9.89 534	10	48
13	9.79 144	16	9.89 619	26	0.10 381	9.89 524	10	47
14	9.79 160	16	9.89 645	26	0.10 355	9.89 514	10	46
15	9.79 176	16	9.89 671	26	0.10 329	9.89 504	9	45
16	9.79 192	16	9.89 697	26	0.10 303	9.89 495	10	44
17	9.79 208	16	9.89 723	26	0.10 277	9.89 485	10	43
18	9.79 224	16	9.89 749	26	0.10 251	9.89 475	10	42
19	9.79 240	16	9.89 775	26	0.10 225	9.89 465	10	41
20	9.79 256	16	9.89 801	26	0.10 199	9.89 455	10	40
21	9.79 272	16	9.89 827	26	0.10 173	9.89 445	10	39
22	9.79 288	16	9.89 853	26	0.10 147	9.89 435	10	38
23	9.79 304	15	9.89 879	26	0.10 121	9.89 425	10	37
24	9.79 319	16	9.89 905	26	0.10 095	9.89 415	10	36
25	9.79 335	16	9.89 931	26	0.10 069	9.89 405	10	35
26	9.79 351	16	9.89 957	26	0.10 043	9.89 395	10	34
27	9.79 367	16	9.89 983	26	0.10 017	9.89 385	10	33
28	9.79 383	16	9.90 009	26	0.09 991	9.89 375	11	32
29	9.79 399	16	9.90 035	26	0.09 965	9.89 364	10	31
30	9.79 415	16	9.90 061	25	0.09 939	9.89 354	10	30
31	9.79 431	16	9.90 086	26	0.09 914	9.89 344	10	29
32	9.79 447	16	9.90 112	26	0.09 888	9.89 334	10	28
33	9.79 463	15	9.90 138	26	0.09 862	9.89 324	10	27
34	9.79 478	16	9.90 164	26	0.09 836	9.89 314	10	26
35	9.79 494	16	9.90 190	26	0.09 810	9.89 304	10	25
36	9.79 510	16	9.90 216	26	0.09 784	9.89 294	10	24
37	9.79 526	16	9.90 242	26	0.09 758	9.89 284	10	23
38	9.79 542	16	9.90 268	26	0.09 732	9.89 274	10	22
39	9.79 558	15	9.90 294	26	0.09 706	9.89 264	10	21
40	9.79 573	16	9.90 320	26	0.09 680	9.89 254	10	20
41	9.79 589	16	9.90 346	25	0.09 654	9.89 244	11	19
42	9.79 605	16	9.90 371	26	0.09 629	9.89 233	10	18
43	9.79 621	15	9.90 397	26	0.09 603	9.89 223	10	17
44	9.79 636	16	9.90 423	26	0.09 577	9.89 213	10	16
45	9.79 652	16	9.90 449	26	0.09 551	9.89 203	10	15
46	9.79 668	16	9.90 475	26	0.09 525	9.89 193	10	14
47	9.79 684	15	9.90 501	26	0.09 499	9.89 183	10	13
48	9.79 699	16	9.90 527	26	0.09 473	9.89 173	11	12
49	9.79 715	16	9.90 553	25	0.09 447	9.89 162	10	11
50	9.79 731	15	9.90 578	26	0.09 422	9.89 152	10	10
51	9.79 746	16	9.90 604	26	0.09 396	9.89 142	10	9
52	9.79 762	16	9.90 630	26	0.09 370	9.89 132	10	8
53	9.79 778	15	9.90 656	26	0.09 344	9.89 122	10	7
54	9.79 793	16	9.90 682	26	0.09 318	9.89 112	11	6
55	9.79 809	16	9.90 708	26	0.09 292	9.89 101	10	5
56	9.79 825	15	9.90 734	25	0.09 266	9.89 091	10	4
57	9.79 840	16	9.90 759	26	0.09 241	9.89 081	10	3
58	9.79 856	16	9.90 785	26	0.09 215	9.89 071	11	2
59	9.79 872	15	9.90 811	26	0.09 189	9.89 060	10	1
60	9.79 887		9.90 837		0.09 163	9.89 050		0
′	L. Cos.	d.	L. Cot.	c.d.	L. Tan.	L. Sin.	d.	′

P. P.

″	26	25
1	0.4	0.4
2	0.9	0.8
3	1.3	1.2
4	1.7	1.7
5	2.2	2.1
6	2.6	2.5
7	3.0	2.9
8	3.5	3.3
9	3.9	3.8
10	4.3	4.2
20	8.7	8.3
30	13.0	12.5
40	17.3	16.7
50	21.7	20.8

″	17	16	15
1	0.3	0.3	0.2
2	0.6	0.5	0.5
3	0.8	0.8	0.8
4	1.1	1.1	1.0
5	1.4	1.3	1.2
6	1.7	1.6	1.5
7	2.0	1.9	1.8
8	2.3	2.1	2.0
9	2.6	2.4	2.2
10	2.8	2.7	2.5
20	5.7	5.3	5.0
30	8.5	8.0	7.5
40	11.3	10.7	10.0
50	14.2	13.3	12.5

″	11	10	9
1	0.2	0.2	0.2
2	0.4	0.3	0.3
3	0.6	0.5	0.4
4	0.7	0.7	0.6
5	0.9	0.8	0.8
6	1.1	1.0	0.9
7	1.3	1.2	1.0
8	1.5	1.3	1.2
9	1.6	1.5	1.4
10	1.8	1.7	1.5
20	3.7	3.3	3.0
30	5.5	5.0	4.5
40	7.3	6.7	6.0
50	9.2	8.3	7.5

	10/26	10/25	9/26
0			
1	1.3	1.2	1.4
2	3.9	3.8	4.3
3	6.5	6.2	7.2
4	9.1	8.8	10.1
5	11.7	11.2	13.0
6	14.3	13.8	15.9
7	16.9	16.2	18.8
8	19.5	18.8	21.7
9	22.1	21.2	24.6
10	24.7	23.8	—

P. P.

39° (219°) (320°) **140°**

′	L. Sin.	d.	L. Tan.	c.d.	L. Cot.	L. Cos.	d.	′
0	9.79 887	16	9.90 837	26	0.09 163	9.89 050	10	**60**
1	9.79 903	15	9.90 863	26	0.09 137	9.89 040	10	59
2	9.79 918	16	9.90 889	25	0.09 111	9.89 030	10	58
3	9.79 934	16	9.90 914	26	0.09 086	9.89 020	11	57
4	9.79 950	15	9.90 940	26	0.09 060	9.89 009	10	56
5	9.79 965	16	9.90 966	26	0.09 034	9.88 999	10	55
6	9.79 981	15	9.90 992	26	0.09 008	9.88 989	11	54
7	9.79 996	16	9.91 018	25	0.08 982	9.88 978	10	53
8	9.80 012	15	9.91 043	26	0.08 957	9.88 968	10	52
9	9.80 027	16	9.91 069	26	0.08 931	9.88 958	10	51
10	9.80 043	15	9.91 095	26	0.08 905	9.88 948	11	**50**
11	9.80 058	16	9.91 121	26	0.08 879	9.88 937	10	49
12	9.80 074	15	9.91 147	25	0.08 853	9.88 927	10	48
13	9.80 089	16	9.91 172	26	0.08 828	9.88 917	11	47
14	9.80 105	15	9.91 198	26	0.08 802	9.88 906	10	46
15	9.80 120	16	9.91 224	26	0.08 776	9.88 896	10	45
16	9.80 136	15	9.91 250	26	0.08 750	9.88 886	11	44
17	9.80 151	15	9.91 276	25	0.08 724	9.88 875	10	43
18	9.80 166	16	9.91 301	26	0.08 699	9.88 865	10	42
19	9.80 182	15	9.91 327	26	0.08 673	9.88 855	11	41
20	9.80 197	16	9.91 353	26	0.08 647	9.88 844	10	**40**
21	9.80 213	15	9.91 379	25	0.08 621	9.88 834	10	39
22	9.80 228	16	9.91 404	26	0.08 596	9.88 824	11	38
23	9.80 244	15	9.91 430	26	0.08 570	9.88 813	10	37
24	9.80 259	15	9.91 456	26	0.08 544	9.88 803	10	36
25	9.80 274	16	9.91 482	25	0.08 518	9.88 793	11	35
26	9.80 290	15	9.91 507	26	0.08 493	9.88 782	10	34
27	9.80 305	15	9.91 533	26	0.08 467	9.88 772	11	33
28	9.80 320	16	9.91 559	26	0.08 441	9.88 761	10	32
29	9.80 336	15	9.91 585	25	0.08 415	9.88 751	10	31
30	9.80 351	15	9.91 610	26	0.08 390	9.88 741	11	**30**
31	9.80 366	16	9.91 636	26	0.08 364	9.88 730	10	29
32	9.80 382	15	9.91 662	26	0.08 338	9.88 720	11	28
33	9.80 397	15	9.91 688	25	0.08 312	9.88 709	10	27
34	9.80 412	16	9.91 713	26	0.08 287	9.88 699	11	26
35	9.80 428	15	9.91 739	26	0.08 261	9.88 688	10	25
36	9.80 443	15	9.91 765	26	0.08 235	9.88 678	10	24
37	9.80 458	15	9.91 791	25	0.08 209	9.88 668	11	23
38	9.80 473	16	9.91 816	26	0.08 184	9.88 657	10	22
39	9.80 489	15	9.91 842	26	0.08 158	9.88 647	11	21
40	9.80 504	15	9.91 868	25	0.08 132	9.88 636	10	**20**
41	9.80 519	15	9.91 893	26	0.08 107	9.88 626	11	19
42	9.80 534	16	9.91 919	26	0.08 081	9.88 615	10	18
43	9.80 550	15	9.91 945	26	0.08 055	9.88 605	11	17
44	9.80 565	15	9.91 971	25	0.08 029	9.88 594	10	16
45	9.80 580	15	9.91 996	26	0.08 004	9.88 584	11	15
46	9.80 595	15	9.92 022	26	0.07 978	9.88 573	10	14
47	9.80 610	15	9.92 048	25	0.07 952	9.88 563	11	13
48	9.80 625	16	9.92 073	26	0.07 927	9.88 552	10	12
49	9.80 641	15	9.92 099	26	0.07 901	9.88 542	11	11
50	9.80 656	15	9.92 125	25	0.07 875	9.88 531	10	**10**
51	9.80 671	15	9.92 150	26	0.07 850	9.88 521	11	9
52	9.80 686	15	9.92 176	26	0.07 824	9.88 510	11	8
53	9.80 701	15	9.92 202	25	0.07 798	9.88 499	10	7
54	9.80 716	15	9.92 227	26	0.07 773	9.88 489	11	6
55	9.80 731	15	9.92 253	26	0.07 747	9.88 478	10	5
56	9.80 746	16	9.92 279	25	0.07 721	9.88 468	11	4
57	9.80 762	15	9.92 304	26	0.07 696	9.88 457	10	3
58	9.80 777	15	9.92 330	26	0.07 670	9.88 447	11	2
59	9.80 792	15	9.92 356	25	0.07 644	9.88 436	11	1
60	9.80 807		9.92 381		0.07 619	9.88 425		**0**
′	L. Cos.	d.	L. Cot.	c.d.	L. Tan.	L. Sin.	d.	′

P. P.

″	**26**	**25**
1	0.4	0.4
2	0.9	0.8
3	1.3	1.2
4	1.7	1.7
5	2.2	2.1
6	2.6	2.5
7	3.0	2.9
8	3.5	3.3
9	3.9	3.8
10	4.3	4.2
20	8.7	8.3
30	13.0	12.5
40	17.3	16.7
50	21.7	20.8

″	**16**	**15**
1	0.3	0.2
2	0.5	0.5
3	0.8	0.8
4	1.1	1.0
5	1.3	1.2
6	1.6	1.5
7	1.9	1.8
8	2.1	2.0
9	2.4	2.2
10	2.7	2.5
20	5.3	5.0
30	8.0	7.5
40	10.7	10.0
50	13.3	12.5

″	**11**	**10**
1	0.2	0.2
2	0.4	0.3
3	0.6	0.5
4	0.7	0.7
5	0.9	0.8
6	1.1	1.0
7	1.3	1.2
8	1.5	1.3
9	1.6	1.5
10	1.8	1.7
20	3.7	3.3
30	5.5	5.0
40	7.3	6.7
50	9.2	8.3

	11/26	**11/25**
0	1.2	1.1
1	3.5	3.4
2	5.9	5.7
3	8.3	7.9
4	10.6	10.2
5	13.0	12.5
6	15.4	14.8
7	17.7	17.1
8	20.1	19.3
9	22.5	21.6
10	24.8	23.9
11		

P. P.

129° (309°) (230°) **50°**

40° (220°) (319°) **139°**

′	L. Sin.	d.	L. Tan.	c.d.	L. Cot.	L. Cos.	d.	′
0	9.80 807	15	9.92 381	26	0.07 619	9.88 425	10	**60**
1	9.80 822	15	9.92 407	26	0.07 593	9.88 415	11	59
2	9.80 837	15	9.92 433	25	0.07 567	9.88 404	10	58
3	9.80 852	15	9.92 458	26	0.07 542	9.88 394	11	57
4	9.80 867	15	9.92 484	26	0.07 516	9.88 383	11	56
5	9.80 882	15	9.92 510	25	0.07 490	9.88 372	10	55
6	9.80 897	15	9.92 535	26	0.07 465	9.88 362	11	54
7	9.80 912	15	9.92 561	26	0.07 439	9.88 351	11	53
8	9.80 927	15	9.92 587	25	0.07 413	9.88 340	10	52
9	9.80 942	15	9.92 612	26	0.07 388	9.88 330	11	51
10	9.80 957	15	9.92 638	25	0.07 362	9.88 319	11	**50**
11	9.80 972	15	9.92 663	26	0.07 337	9.88 308	10	49
12	9.80 987	15	9.92 689	26	0.07 311	9.88 298	11	48
13	9.81 002	15	9.92 715	25	0.07 285	9.88 287	11	47
14	9.81 017	15	9.92 740	26	0.07 260	9.88 276	10	46
15	9.81 032	15	9.92 766	26	0.07 234	9.88 266	11	45
16	9.81 047	14	9.92 792	25	0.07 208	9.88 255	11	44
17	9.81 061	15	9.92 817	26	0.07 183	9.88 244	10	43
18	9.81 076	15	9.92 843	25	0.07 157	9.88 234	11	42
19	9.81 091	15	9.92 868	26	0.07 132	9.88 223	11	41
20	9.81 106	15	9.92 894	26	0.07 106	9.88 212	11	**40**
21	9.81 121	15	9.92 920	25	0.07 080	9.88 201	10	39
22	9.81 136	15	9.92 945	26	0.07 055	9.88 191	11	38
23	9.81 151	15	9.92 971	25	0.07 029	9.88 180	11	37
24	9.81 166	14	9.92 996	26	0.07 004	9.88 169	11	36
25	9.81 180	15	9.93 022	26	0.06 978	9.88 158	10	35
26	9.81 195	15	9.93 048	25	0.06 952	9.88 148	11	34
27	9.81 210	15	9.93 073	26	0.06 927	9.88 137	11	33
28	9.81 225	15	9.93 099	25	0.06 901	9.88 126	11	32
29	9.81 240	14	9.93 124	26	0.06 876	9.88 115	10	31
30	9.81 254	15	9.93 150	25	0.06 850	9.88 105	11	**30**
31	9.81 269	15	9.93 175	26	0.06 825	9.88 094	11	29
32	9.81 284	15	9.93 201	26	0.06 799	9.88 083	11	28
33	9.81 299	15	9.93 227	25	0.06 773	9.88 072	11	27
34	9.81 314	14	9.93 252	26	0.06 748	9.88 061	10	26
35	9.81 328	15	9.93 278	25	0.06 722	9.88 051	11	25
36	9.81 343	15	9.93 303	26	0.06 697	9.88 040	11	24
37	9.81 358	14	9.93 329	25	0.06 671	9.88 029	11	23
38	9.81 372	15	9.93 354	26	0.06 646	9.88 018	11	22
39	9.81 387	15	9.93 380	26	0.06 620	9.88 007	11	21
40	9.81 402	15	9.93 406	25	0.06 594	9.87 996	11	**20**
41	9.81 417	14	9.93 431	26	0.06 569	9.87 985	10	19
42	9.81 431	15	9.93 457	25	0.06 543	9.87 975	11	18
43	9.81 446	15	9.93 482	26	0.06 518	9.87 964	11	17
44	9.81 461	14	9.93 508	25	0.06 492	9.87 953	11	16
45	9.81 475	15	9.93 533	26	0.06 467	9.87 942	11	15
46	9.81 490	15	9.93 559	25	0.06 441	9.87 931	11	14
47	9.81 505	14	9.93 584	26	0.06 416	9.87 920	11	13
48	9.81 519	15	9.93 610	26	0.06 390	9.87 909	11	12
49	9.81 534	15	9.93 636	25	0.06 364	9.87 898	11	11
50	9.81 549	14	9.93 661	26	0.06 339	9.87 887	10	**10**
51	9.81 563	15	9.93 687	25	0.06 313	9.87 877	11	9
52	9.81 578	14	9.93 712	26	0.06 288	9.87 866	11	8
53	9.81 592	15	9.93 738	25	0.06 262	9.87 855	11	7
54	9.81 607	15	9.93 763	26	0.06 237	9.87 844	11	6
55	9.81 622	14	9.93 789	25	0.06 211	9.87 833	11	5
56	9.81 636	15	9.93 814	26	0.06 186	9.87 822	11	4
57	9.81 651	14	9.93 840	25	0.06 160	9.87 811	11	3
58	9.81 665	15	9.93 865	26	0.06 135	9.87 800	11	2
59	9.81 680	14	9.93 891	25	0.06 109	9.87 789	11	1
60	9.81 694		9.93 916		0.06 084	9.87 778		**0**
′	L. Cos.	d.	L. Cot.	c.d.	L. Tan.	L. Sin.	d.	′

130° (310°) (229°) **49°**

P. P.

″	**26**	**25**
1	0.4	0.4
2	0.9	0.8
3	1.3	1.2
4	1.7	1.7
5	2.2	2.1
6	2.6	2.5
7	3.0	2.9
8	3.5	3.3
9	3.9	3.8
10	4.3	4.2
20	8.7	8.3
30	13.0	12.5
40	17.3	16.7
50	21.7	20.8

″	**15**	**14**
1	0.2	0.2
2	0.5	0.5
3	0.8	0.7
4	1.0	0.9
5	1.2	1.2
6	1.5	1.4
7	1.8	1.6
8	2.0	1.9
9	2.2	2.1
10	2.5	2.3
20	5.0	4.7
30	7.5	7.0
40	10.0	9.3
50	12.5	11.7

″	**11**	**10**
1	0.2	0.2
2	0.4	0.3
3	0.6	0.5
4	0.7	0.7
5	0.9	0.8
6	1.1	1.0
7	1.3	1.2
8	1.5	1.3
9	1.6	1.5
10	1.8	1.7
20	3.7	3.3
30	5.5	5.0
40	7.3	6.7
50	9.2	8.3

	11/26	**10/26**	**10/25**
0			
1	1.2	1.3	1.2
2	3.5	3.9	3.8
3	5.9	6.5	6.2
4	8.3	9.1	8.8
5	10.6	11.7	11.2
6	13.0	14.3	13.8
7	15.4	16.9	16.2
8	17.7	19.5	18.8
9	20.1	22.1	21.2
10	22.5	24.7	23.8
11	24.8	—	—

P. P.

41° (221°) (318°) **138°**

′	L. Sin.	d.	L. Tan.	c.d.	L. Cot.	L. Cos.	d.	′
0	9.81 694	15	9.93 916	26	0.06 084	9.87 778	11	**60**
1	9.81 709	14	9.93 942	25	0.06 058	9.87 767	11	59
2	9.81 723	15	9.93 967	26	0.06 033	9.87 756	11	58
3	9.81 738	14	9.93 993	25	0.06 007	9.87 745̇	11	57
4	9.81 752	15	9.94 018	26	0.05 982	9.87 734	11	56
5	9.81 767	14	9.94 044	25	0.05 956	9.87 723	11	55
6	9.81 781	15	9.94 069	26	0.05 931	9.87 712	11	54
7	9.81 796	14	9.94 095̄	25	0.05 905̇	9.87 701	11	53
8	9.81 810	15	9.94 120	26	0.05 880	9.87 690	11	52
9	9.81 825̄	14	9.94 146	25	0.05 854	9.87 679	11	51
10	9.81 839	15	9.94 171	26	0.05 829	9.87 668	11	**50**
11	9.81 854	14	9.94 197	25	0.05 803	9.87 657	11	49
12	9.81 868	14	9.94 222	26	0.05 778	9.87 646	11	48
13	9.81 882	15	9.94 248	25	0.05 752	9.87 635̄	11	47
14	9.81 897	14	9.94 273	26	0.05 727	9.87 624	11	46
15	9.81 911	15	9.94 299	25	0.05 701	9.87 613	12	45
16	9.81 926	14	9.94 324	26	0.05 676	9.87 601	11	44
17	9.81 940	15	9.94 350̄	25	0.05 650̇	9.87 590	11	43
18	9.81 955̄	14	9.94 375̇	26	0.05 625̄	9.87 579	11	42
19	9.81 969	14	9.94 401	25	0.05 599	9.87 568	11	41
20	9.81 983	15	9.94 426	26	0.05 574	9.87 557	11	**40**
21	9.81 998	14	9.94 452	25	0.05 548	9.87 546	11	39
22	9.82 012	14	9.94 477	26	0.05 523	9.87 535̄	11	38
23	9.82 026	15	9.94 503	25	0.05 497	9.87 524	11	37
24	9.82 041	14	9.94 528	26	0.05 472	9.87 513	12	36
25	9.82 055̄	14	9.94 554	25	0.05 446	9.87 501	11	35
26	9.82 069	15	9.94 579	25	0.05 421	9.87 490	11	34
27	9.82 084	14	9.94 604	26	0.05 396	9.87 479	11	33
28	9.82 098	14	9.94 630	25	0.05 370	9.87 468	11	32
29	9.82 112	14	9.94 655̇	26	0.05 345̄	9.87 457	11	31
30	9.82 126	15	9.94 681	25	0.05 319	9.87 446	12	**30**
31	9.82 141	14	9.94 706	26	0.05 294	9.87 434	11	29
32	9.82 155̄	14	9.94 732	25	0.05 268	9.87 423	11	28
33	9.82 169	15	9.94 757	26	0.05 243	9.87 412	11	27
34	9.82 184	14	9.94 783	25	0.05 217	9.87 401	11	26
35	9.82 198	14	9.94 808	26	0.05 192	9.87 390	12	25
36	9.82 212	14	9.94 834	25	0.05 166	9.87 378	11	24
37	9.82 226	14	9.94 859	25	0.05 141	9.87 367	11	23
38	9.82 240	15	9.94 884	26	0.05 116	9.87 356	11	22
39	9.82 255̄	14	9.94 910	25	0.05 090	9.87 345̄	11	21
40	9.82 269	14	9.94 935̇	26	0.05 065̄	9.87 334	12	**20**
41	9.82 283	14	9.94 961	25	0.05 039	9.87 322	11	19
42	9.82 297	14	9.94 986	26	0.05 014	9.87 311	11	18
43	9.82 311	15	9.95 012	25	0.04 988	9.87 300	12	17
44	9.82 326	14	9.95 037	25	0.04 963	9.87 288	11	16
45	9.82 340	14	9.95 062	26	0.04 938	9.87 277	11	15
46	9.82 354	14	9.95 088	25	0.04 912	9.87 266	11	14
47	9.82 368	14	9.95 113	26	0.04 887	9.87 255̄	12	13
48	9.82 382	14	9.95 139	25	0.04 861	9.87 243	11	12
49	9.82 396	14	9.95 164	26	0.04 836	9.87 232	11	11
50	9.82 410	14	9.95 190	25	0.04 810	9.87 221	12	**10**
51	9.82 424	15	9.95 215̇	25	0.04 785̄	9.87 209	11	9
52	9.82 439	14	9.95 240	26	0.04 760	9.87 198	11	8
53	9.82 453	14	9.95 266	25	0.04 734	9.87 187	12	7
54	9.82 467	14	9.95 291	26	0.04 709	9.87 175̇	11	6
55	9.82 481	14	9.95 317	25	0.04 683	9.87 164	11	5
56	9.82 495̄	14	9.95 342	26	0.04 658	9.87 153	12	4
57	9.82 509	14	9.95 368	25	0.04 632	9.87 141	11	3
58	9.82 523	14	9.95 393	25	0.04 607	9.87 130	11	2
59	9.82 537	14	9.95 418	26	0.04 582	9.87 119	12	1
60	9.82 551		9.95 444		0.04 556	9.87 107		**0**
′	L. Cos.	d.	L. Cot.	c.d.	L. Tan.	L. Sin.	d.	′

P. P.

″	**26**	**25**
1	0.4	0.4
2	0.9	0.8
3	1.3	1.2
4	1.7	1.7
5	2.2	2.1
6	2.6	2.5
7	3.0	2.9
8	3.5̄	3.3
9	3.9	3.8
10	4.3	4.2
20	8.7	8.3
30	13.0	12.5
40	17.3	16.7
50	21.7	20.8

″	**15**	**14**
1	0.2	0.2
2	0.5	0.5̄
3	0.8	0.7
4	1.0	0.9
5	1.2	1.2
6	1.5	1.4
7	1.8	1.6
8	2.0	1.9
9	2.2	2.1
10	2.5	2.3
20	5.0	4.7
30	7.5	7.0
40	10.0	9.3
50	12.5	11.7

″	**12**	**11**
1	0.2	0.2
2	0.4	0.4
3	0.6	0.6
4	0.8	0.7
5	1.0	0.9
6	1.2	1.1
7	1.4	1.3
8	1.6	1.5̄
9	1.8	1.6
10	2.0	1.8
20	4.0	3.7
30	6.0	5.5
40	8.0	7.3
50	10.0	9.2

	12/26	**12/25**	**11/25**
0			
1	1.1	1.1	1.1
2	3.2	3.1	3.4
3	5.4	5.2	5.7
4	7.6	7.3	7.9
5	9.8	9.4	10.2
6	11.9	11.5̄	12.5
7	14.1	13.5̇	14.8
8	16.2	15.6	17.1
9	18.4	17.7	19.3
10	20.6	19.8	21.6
11	22.8	21.9	23.9
12	24.9	23.9	—

P. P.

131° (311°) (228°) **48°**

42° (222°) (317°) **137°**

′	L. Sin.	d.	L. Tan.	c.d.	L. Cot.	L. Cos.	d.	′
0	9.82 551	14	9.95 444	25	0.04 556	9.87 107	11	**60**
1	9.82 565	14	9.95 469	26	0.04 531	9.87 096	11	59
2	9.82 579	14	9.95 495	25	0.04 505	9.87 085	12	58
3	9.82 593	14	9.95 520	25	0.04 480	9.87 073	11	57
4	9.82 607	14	9.95 545	26	0.04 455	9.87 062	12	56
5	9.82 621	14	9.95 571	25	0.04 429	9.87 050	11	55
6	9.82 635	14	9.95 596	26	0.04 404	9.87 039	11	54
7	9.82 649	14	9.95 622	25	0.04 378	9.87 028	12	53
8	9.82 663	14	9.95 647	25	0.04 353	9.87 016	11	52
9	9.82 677	14	9.95 672	26	0.04 328	9.87 005	12	51
10	9.82 691	14	9.95 698	25	0.04 302	9.86 993	11	**50**
11	9.82 705	14	9.95 723	25	0.04 277	9.86 982	12	49
12	9.82 719	14	9.95 748	26	0.04 252	9.86 970	11	48
13	9.82 733	14	9.95 774	25	0.04 226	9.86 959	12	47
14	9.82 747	14	9.95 799	26	0.04 201	9.86 947	11	46
15	9.82 761	14	9.95 825	25	0.04 175	9.86 936	12	45
16	9.82 775	13	9.95 850	25	0.04 150	9.86 924	11	44
17	9.82 788	14	9.95 875	26	0.04 125	9.86 913	11	43
18	9.82 802	14	9.95 901	25	0.04 099	9.86 902	12	42
19	9.82 816	14	9.95 926	26	0.04 074	9.86 890	11	41
20	9.82 830	14	9.95 952	25	0.04 048	9.86 879	12	**40**
21	9.82 844	14	9.95 977	25	0.04 023	9.86 867	12	39
22	9.82 858	14	9.96 002	26	0.03 998	9.86 855	11	38
23	9.82 872	13	9.96 028	25	0.03 972	9.86 844	12	37
24	9.82 885	14	9.96 053	25	0.03 947	9.86 832	11	36
25	9.82 899	14	9.96 078	26	0.03 922	9.86 821	12	35
26	9.82 913	14	9.96 104	25	0.03 896	9.86 809	11	34
27	9.82 927	14	9.96 129	26	0.03 871	9.86 798	12	33
28	9.82 941	14	9.96 155	25	0.03 845	9.86 786	11	32
29	9.82 955	13	9.96 180	25	0.03 820	9.86 775	12	31
30	9.82 968	14	9.96 205	26	0.03 795	9.86 763	11	**30**
31	9.82 982	14	9.96 231	25	0.03 769	9.86 752	12	29
32	9.82 996	14	9.96 256	25	0.03 744	9.86 740	12	28
33	9.83 010	13	9.96 281	26	0.03 719	9.86 728	11	27
34	9.83 023	14	9.96 307	25	0.03 693	9.86 717	12	26
35	9.83 037	14	9.96 332	25	0.03 668	9.86 705	11	25
36	9.83 051	14	9.96 357	26	0.03 643	9.86 694	12	24
37	9.83 065	13	9.96 383	25	0.03 617	9.86 682	12	23
38	9.83 078	14	9.96 408	25	0.03 592	9.86 670	11	22
39	9.83 092	14	9.96 433	26	0.03 567	9.86 659	12	21
40	9.83 106	14	9.96 459	25	0.03 541	9.86 647	12	**20**
41	9.83 120	13	9.96 484	26	0.03 516	9.86 635	11	19
42	9.83 133	14	9.96 510	25	0.03 490	9.86 624	12	18
43	9.83 147	14	9.96 535	25	0.03 465	9.86 612	12	17
44	9.83 161	13	9.96 560	26	0.03 440	9.86 600	11	16
45	9.83 174	14	9.96 586	25	0.03 414	9.86 589	12	15
46	9.83 188	14	9.96 611	25	0.03 389	9.86 577	12	14
47	9.83 202	13	9.96 636	26	0.03 364	9.86 565	11	13
48	9.83 215	14	9.96 662	25	0.03 338	9.86 554	12	12
49	9.83 229	13	9.96 687	25	0.03 313	9.86 542	12	11
50	9.83 242	14	9.96 712	26	0.03 288	9.86 530	12	**10**
51	9.83 256	14	9.96 738	25	0.03 262	9.86 518	11	9
52	9.83 270	13	9.96 763	25	0.03 237	9.86 507	12	8
53	9.83 283	14	9.96 788	26	0.03 212	9.86 495	12	7
54	9.83 297	13	9.96 814	25	0.03 186	9.86 483	11	6
55	9.83 310	14	9.96 839	25	0.03 161	9.86 472	12	5
56	9.83 324	14	9.96 864	26	0.03 136	9.86 460	12	4
57	9.83 338	13	9.96 890	25	0.03 110	9.86 448	12	3
58	9.83 351	14	9.96 915	25	0.03 085	9.86 436	11	2
59	9.83 365	13	9.96 940	26	0.03 060	9.86 425	12	1
60	9.83 378		9.96 966		0.03 034	9.86 413		**0**
′	L. Cos.	d.	L. Cot.	c.d.	L. Tan.	L. Sin.	d.	′

P. P.

″	**26**	**25**
1	0.4	0.4
2	0.9	0.8
3	1.3	1.2
4	1.7	1.7
5	2.2	2.1
6	2.6	2.5
7	3.0	2.9
8	3.5	3.3
9	3.9	3.8
10	4.3	4.2
20	8.7	8.3
30	13.0	12.5
40	17.3	16.7
50	21.7	20.8

″	**14**	**13**
1	0.2	0.2
2	0.5	0.4
3	0.7	0.6
4	0.9	0.9
5	1.2	1.1
6	1.4	1.3
7	1.6	1.5
8	1.9	1.7
9	2.1	2.0
10	2.3	2.2
20	4.7	4.3
30	7.0	6.5
40	9.3	8.7
50	11.7	10.8

″	**12**	**11**
1	0.2	0.2
2	0.4	0.4
3	0.6	0.6
4	0.8	0.7
5	1.0	0.9
6	1.2	1.1
7	1.4	1.3
8	1.6	1.5
9	1.8	1.6
10	2.0	1.8
20	4.0	3.7
30	6.0	5.5
40	8.0	7.3
50	10.0	9.2

	12/26	**11/26**	**11/25**
0			
1	1.1	1.2	1.1
2	3.2	3.5	3.4
3	5.4	5.9	5.7
4	7.6	8.3	7.9
5	9.8	10.6	10.2
6	11.9	13.0	12.5
7	14.1	15.4	14.8
8	16.2	17.7	17.1
9	18.4	20.1	19.3
10	20.6	22.5	21.6
11	22.8	24.8	23.9
12	24.9	—	—

P. P.

132° (312°) (227°) **47°**

43° (223°) (316°) **136°**

′	L. Sin.	d.	L. Tan.	c.d.	L. Cot.	L. Cos.	d.	′
0	9.83 378	14	9.96 966	25	0.03 034	9.86 413	12	60
1	9.83 392	13	9.96 991	25	0.03 009	9.86 401	12	59
2	9.83 405	14	9.97 016	26	0.02 984	9.86 389	12	58
3	9.83 419	13	9.97 042	25	0.02 958	9.86 377	11	57
4	9.83 432	14	9.97 067	25	0.02 933	9.86 366	12	56
5	9.83 446	13	9.97 092	26	0.02 908	9.86 354	12	55
6	9.83 459	14	9.97 118	25	0.02 882	9.86 342	12	54
7	9.83 473	13	9.97 143	25	0.02 857	9.86 330	12	53
8	9.83 486	14	9.97 168	25	0.02 832	9.86 318	12	52
9	9.83 500	13	9.97 193	26	0.02 807	9.86 306	11	51
10	9.83 513	14	9.97 219	25	0.02 781	9.86 295	12	50
11	9.83 527	13	9.97 244	25	0.02 756	9.86 283	12	49
12	9.83 540	14	9.97 269	26	0.02 731	9.86 271	12	48
13	9.83 554	13	9.97 295	25	0.02 705	9.86 259	12	47
14	9.83 567	14	9.97 320	25	0.02 680	9.86 247	12	46
15	9.83 581	13	9.97 345	26	0.02 655	9.86 235	12	45
16	9.83 594	14	9.97 371	25	0.02 629	9.86 223	12	44
17	9.83 608	13	9.97 396	25	0.02 604	9.86 211	11	43
18	9.83 621	13	9.97 421	26	0.02 579	9.86 200	12	42
19	9.83 634	14	9.97 447	25	0.02 553	9.86 188	12	41
20	9.83 648	13	9.97 472	25	0.02 528	9.86 176	12	40
21	9.83 661	13	9.97 497	26	0.02 503	9.86 164	12	39
22	9.83 674	14	9.97 523	25	0.02 477	9.86 152	12	38
23	9.83 688	13	9.97 548	25	0.02 452	9.86 140	12	37
24	9.83 701	14	9.97 573	25	0.02 427	9.86 128	12	36
25	9.83 715	13	9.97 598	26	0.02 402	9.86 116	12	35
26	9.83 728	13	9.97 624	25	0.02 376	9.86 104	12	34
27	9.83 741	14	9.97 649	25	0.02 351	9.86 092	12	33
28	9.83 755	13	9.97 674	26	0.02 326	9.86 080	12	32
29	9.83 768	13	9.97 700	25	0.02 300	9.86 068	12	31
30	9.83 781	14	9.97 725	25	0.02 275	9.86 056	12	30
31	9.83 795	13	9.97 750	26	0.02 250	9.86 044	12	29
32	9.83 808	13	9.97 776	25	0.02 224	9.86 032	12	28
33	9.83 821	13	9.97 801	25	0.02 199	9.86 020	12	27
34	9.83 834	14	9.97 826	25	0.02 174	9.86 008	12	26
35	9.83 848	13	9.97 851	26	0.02 149	9.85 996	12	25
36	9.83 861	13	9.97 877	25	0.02 123	9.85 984	12	24
37	9.83 874	13	9.97 902	25	0.02 098	9.85 972	12	23
38	9.83 887	14	9.97 927	26	0.02 073	9.85 960	12	22
39	9.83 901	13	9.97 953	25	0.02 047	9.85 948	12	21
40	9.83 914	13	9.97 978	25	0.02 022	9.85 936	12	20
41	9.83 927	13	9.98 003	26	0.01 997	9.85 924	12	19
42	9.83 940	14	9.98 029	25	0.01 971	9.85 912	12	18
43	9.83 954	13	9.98 054	25	0.01 946	9.85 900	12	17
44	9.83 967	13	9.98 079	25	0.01 921	9.85 888	12	16
45	9.83 980	13	9.98 104	26	0.01 896	9.85 876	12	15
46	9.83 993	13	9.98 130	25	0.01 870	9.85 864	13	14
47	9.84 006	14	9.98 155	25	0.01 845	9.85 851	12	13
48	9.84 020	13	9.98 180	26	0.01 820	9.85 839	12	12
49	9.84 033	13	9.98 206	25	0.01 794	9.85 827	12	11
50	9.84 046	13	9.98 231	25	0.01 769	9.85 815	12	10
51	9.84 059	13	9.98 256	25	0.01 744	9.85 803	12	9
52	9.84 072	13	9.98 281	26	0.01 719	9.85 791	12	8
53	9.84 085	13	9.98 307	25	0.01 693	9.85 779	13	7
54	9.84 098	14	9.98 332	25	0.01 668	9.85 766	12	6
55	9.84 112	13	9.98 357	26	0.01 643	9.85 754	12	5
56	9.84 125	13	9.98 383	25	0.01 617	9.85 742	12	4
57	9.84 138	13	9.98 408	25	0.01 592	9.85 730	12	3
58	9.84 151	13	9.98 433	25	0.01 567	9.85 718	12	2
59	9.84 164	13	9.98 458	26	0.01 542	9.85 706	13	1
60	9.84 177		9.98 484		0.01 516	9.85 693		0
′	L. Cos.	d.	L. Cot.	c.d.	L. Tan.	L. Sin.	d.	′

P. P.

″	26	25
1	0.4	0.4
2	0.9	0.8
3	1.3	1.2
4	1.7	1.7
5	2.2	2.1
6	2.6	2.5
7	3.0	2.9
8	3.5	3.3
9	3.9	3.8
10	4.3	4.2
20	8.7	8.3
30	13.0	12.5
40	17.3	16.7
50	21.7	20.8

″	14	13
1	0.2	0.2
2	0.5	0.4
3	0.7	0.6
4	0.9	0.9
5	1.2	1.1
6	1.4	1.3
7	1.6	1.5
8	1.9	1.7
9	2.1	2.0
10	2.3	2.2
20	4.7	4.3
30	7.0	6.5
40	9.3	8.7
50	11.7	10.8

″	12	11
1	0.2	0.2
2	0.4	0.4
3	0.6	0.6
4	0.8	0.7
5	1.0	0.9
6	1.2	1.1
7	1.4	1.3
8	1.6	1.5
9	1.8	1.6
10	2.0	1.8
20	4.0	3.7
30	6.0	5.5
40	8.0	7.3
50	10.0	9.2

		13/26	13/25	12/25
0	1	1.0	0.9	1.1
1	2	3.0	2.9	3.1
2	3	5.0	4.8	5.2
3	4	7.0	6.7	7.3
4	5	9.0	8.7	9.4
5	6	11.0	10.6	11.5
6	7	13.0	12.5	13.5
7	8	15.0	14.4	15.6
8	9	17.0	16.3	17.7
9	10	19.0	18.3	19.8
10	11	21.0	20.2	21.9
11	12	23.0	22.1	23.9
12	13	25.0	24.1	—

P. P.

133° (313°) (226°) **46°**

44° (224°) (315°) **135°**

′	L. Sin.	d.	L. Tan.	c.d.	L. Cot.	L. Cos.	d.	′
0	9.84 177	13	9.98 484	25	0.01 516	9.85 693	12	**60**
1	9.84 190	13	9.98 509	25	0.01 491	9.85 681	12	59
2	9.84 203	13	9.98 534	26	0.01 466	9.85 669	12	58
3	9.84 216	13	9.98 560	25	0.01 440	9.85 657	12	57
4	9.84 229	13	9.98 58̄5	25	0.01 41̇5	9.85 64̄5	13	56
5	9.84 242	13	9.98 610	25	0.01 390	9.85 632	12	55
6	9.84 25̇5	14	9.98 63̇5	26	0.01 36̄5	9.85 620	12	54
7	9.84 269	13	9.98 661	25	0.01 339	9.85 608	12	53
8	9.84 282	13	9.98 686	25	0.01 314	9.85 596	13	52
9	9.84 29̄5	13	9.98 711	26	0.01 289	9.85 583	12	51
10	9.84 308	13	9.98 737	25	0.01 263	9.85 571	12	**50**
11	9.84 321	13	9.98 762	25	0.01 238	9.85 559	12	49
12	9.84 334	13	9.98 787	25	0.01 213	9.85 547	13	48
13	9.84 347	13	9.98 812	26	0.01 188	9.85 534	12	47
14	9.84 360	13	9.98 838	25	0.01 162	9.85 522	12	46
15	9.84 373	12	9.98 863	25	0.01 137	9.85 510	13	45
16	9.84 38̇5	13	9.98 888	25	0.01 112	9.85 497	12	44
17	9.84 398	13	9.98 913	26	0.01 087	9.85 48̄5	12	43
18	9.84 411	13	9.98 939	25	0.01 061	9.85 473	13	42
19	9.84 424	13	9.98 964	25	0.01 036	9.85 460	12	41
20	9.84 437	13	9.98 989	26	0.01 011	9.85 448	12	**40**
21	9.84 450	13	9.99 01̄5	25	0.00 98̇5	9.85 436	13	39
22	9.84 463	13	9.99 040	25	0.00 960	9.85 423	12	38
23	9.84 476	13	9.99 06̇5	25	0.00 93̄5	9.85 411	12	37
24	9.84 489	13	9.99 090	26	0.00 910	9.85 399	13	36
25	9.84 502	13	9.99 116	25	0.00 884	9.85 386	12	35
26	9.84 51̄5	13	9.99 141	25	0.00 859	9.85 374	13	34
27	9.84 528	12	9.99 166	25	0.00 834	9.85 361	12	33
28	9.84 540	13	9.99 191	26	0.00 809	9.85 349	12	32
29	9.84 553	13	9.99 217	25	0.00 783	9.85 337	13	31
30	9.84 566	13	9.99 242	25	0.00 758	9.85 324	12	**30**
31	9.84 579	13	9.99 267	26	0.00 733	9.85 312	13	29
32	9.84 592	13	9.99 293	25	0.00 707	9.85 299	12	28
33	9.84 60̄5	13	9.99 318	25	0.00 682	9.85 287	13	27
34	9.84 618	12	9.99 343	25	0.00 657	9.85 274	12	26
35	9.84 630	13	9.99 368	26	0.00 632	9.85 262	12	25
36	9.84 643	13	9.99 394	25	0.00 606	9.85 250	13	24
37	9.84 656	13	9.99 419	25	0.00 581	9.85 237	12	23
38	9.84 669	13	9.99 444	25	0.00 556	9.85 22̄5	13	22
39	9.84 682	12	9.99 469	26	0.00 531	9.85 212	12	21
40	9.84 694	13	9.99 49̄5	25	0.00 50̇5	9.85 200	13	**20**
41	9.84 707	13	9.99 520	25	0.00 480	9.85 187	12	19
42	9.84 720	13	9.99 54̇5	25	0.00 45̄5	9.85 17̄5	13	18
43	9.84 733	12	9.99 570	26	0.00 430	9.85 162	12	17
44	9.84 74̇5	13	9.99 596	25	0.00 404	9.85 150	13	16
45	9.84 758	13	9.99 621	25	0.00 379	9.85 137	12	15
46	9.84 771	13	9.99 646	26	0.00 354	9.85 12̄5	13	14
47	9.84 784	12	9.99 672	25	0.00 328	9.85 112	12	13
48	9.84 796	13	9.99 697	25	0.00 303	9.85 100	13	12
49	9.84 809	13	9.99 722	25	0.00 278	9.85 087	13	11
50	9.84 822	13	9.99 747	26	0.00 253	9.85 074	12	**10**
51	9.84 83̄5	12	9.99 773	25	0.00 227	9.85 062	13	9
52	9.84 847	13	9.99 798	25	0.00 202	9.85 049	12	8
53	9.84 860	13	9.99 823	25	0.00 177	9.85 037	13	7
54	9.84 873	12	9.99 848	26	0.00 152	9.85 024	12	6
55	9.84 88̇5	13	9.99 874	25	0.00 126	9.85 012	13	5
56	9.84 898	13	9.99 899	25	0.00 101	9.84 999	13	4
57	9.84 911	12	9.99 924	25	0.00 076	9.84 986	12	3
58	9.84 923	13	9.99 949	26	0.00 051	9.84 974	13	2
59	9.84 936	13	9.99 97̄5	25	0.00 02̇5	9.84 961	12	1
60	9.84 949		0.00 000		0.00 000	9.84 949		**0**
′	L. Cos.	d.	L. Cot.	c.d.	L. Tan.	L. Sin.	d.	′

134° (314°) (225°) **45°**

P. P.

″	26	25
1	0.4	0.4
2	0.9	0.8
3	1.3	1.2
4	1.7	1.7
5	2.2	2.1
6	2.6	2.5
7	3.0	2.9
8	3.̄5	3.3
9	3.9	3.8
10	4.3	4.2
20	8.7	8.3
30	13.0	12.5
40	17.3	16.7
50	21.7	20.8

″	14	13	12
1	0.2	0.2	0.2
2	0.̄5	0.4	0.4
3	0.7	0.6	0.6
4	0.9	0.9	0.8
5	1.2	1.1	1.0
6	1.4	1.3	1.2
7	1.6	1.̇5	1.4
8	1.9	1.7	1.6
9	2.1	2.0	1.8
10	2.3	2.2	2.0
20	4.7	4.3	4.0
30	7.0	6.5	6.0
40	9.3	8.7	8.0
50	11.7	10.8	10.0

	13/26	13/25
0		
1	1.0	0.9
2	3.0	2.9
3	5 0	4.8
4	7.0	6.7
5	9.0	8.7
6	11.0	10.6
7	13.0	12.5
8	15.0	14.4
9	17.0	16.3
10	19.0	18.3
11	21.0	20.2
12	23.0	22.1
13	25.0	24.1

	12/26	12/25
0		
1	1.1	1.1
2	3.2	3.1
3	5.4	5.2
4	7.6	7.3
5	9.8	9.4
6	11.9	11.̄5
7	14.1	13.̇5
8	16.2	15.6
9	18.4	17.7
10	20.6	19.8
11	22.8	21.9
12	24.9	23.9

P. P.

NATURAL TRIGONOMETRIC FUNCTIONS

Values of the trigonometric functions of angles for each minute from 0–360°.

For degrees indicated at the top of the page use the column headings at the top. For degrees indicated at the bottom use the column indications at the bottom.

With degrees at the left of each block (top or bottom), use the minute column at the left and with degrees at the right of each block use the minute column at the right.

0° (180°) (359°) **179°**

′	Sin	Tan	Cot	Cos	′
0	.00000	.00000	——	1.0000	**60**
1	.00029	.00029	3437.7	1.0000	59
2	.00058	.00058	1718.9	1.0000	58
3	.00087	.00087	1145.9	1.0000	57
4	.00116	.00116	859.44	1.0000	56
5	.00145	.00145	687.55	1.0000	**55**
6	.00175	.00175	572.96	1.0000	54
7	.00204	.00204	491.11	1.0000	53
8	.00233	.00233	429.72	1.0000	52
9	.00262	.00262	381.97	1.0000	51
10	.00291	.00291	343.77	1.0000	**50**
11	.00320	.00320	312.52	.99999	49
12	.00349	.00349	286.48	.99999	48
13	.00378	.00378	264.44	.99999	47
14	.00407	.00407	245.55	.99999	46
15	.00436	.00436	229.18	.99999	**45**
16	.00465	.00465	214.86	.99999	44
17	.00495	.00495	202.22	.99999	43
18	.00524	.00524	190.98	.99999	42
19	.00553	.00553	180.93	.99998	41
20	.00582	.00582	171.89	.99998	**40**
21	.00611	.00611	163.70	.99998	39
22	.00640	.00640	156.26	.99998	38
23	.00669	.00669	149.47	.99998	37
24	.00698	.00698	143.24	.99998	36
25	.00727	.00727	137.51	.99997	**35**
26	.00756	.00756	132.22	.99997	34
27	.00785	.00785	127.32	.99997	33
28	.00814	.00815	122.77	.99997	32
29	.00844	.00844	118.54	.99996	31
30	.00873	.00873	114.59	.99996	**30**
31	.00902	.00902	110.89	.99996	29
32	.00931	.00931	107.43	.99996	28
33	.00960	.00960	104.17	.99995	27
34	.00989	.00989	101.11	.99995	26
35	.01018	.01018	98.218	.99995	**25**
36	.01047	.01047	95.489	.99995	24
37	.01076	.01076	92.908	.99994	23
38	.01105	.01105	90.463	.99994	22
39	.01134	.01135	88.144	.99994	21
40	.01164	.01164	85.940	.99993	**20**
41	.01193	.01193	83.844	.99993	19
42	.01222	.01222	81.847	.99993	18
43	.01251	.01251	79.943	.99992	17
44	.01280	.01280	78.126	.99992	16
45	.01309	.01309	76.390	.99991	**15**
46	.01338	.01338	74.729	.99991	14
47	.01367	.01367	73.139	.99991	13
48	.01396	.01396	71.615	.99990	12
49	.01425	.01425	70.153	.99990	11
50	.01454	.01455	68.750	.99989	**10**
51	.01483	.01484	67.402	.99989	9
52	.01513	.01513	66.105	.99989	8
53	.01542	.01542	64.858	.99988	7
54	.01571	.01571	63.657	.99988	6
55	.01600	.01600	62.499	.99987	**5**
56	.01629	.01629	61.383	.99987	4
57	.01658	.01658	60.306	.99986	3
58	.01687	.01687	59.266	.99986	2
59	.01716	.01716	58.261	.99985	1
60	.01745	.01746	57.290	.99985	**0**
′	Cos	Cot	Tan	Sin	′

90° (270°) (269°) **89°**

1° (181°) (358°) **178°**

′	Sin	Tan	Cot	Cos	′
0	.01745	.01746	57.290	.99985	**60**
1	.01774	.01775	56.351	.99984	59
2	.01803	.01804	55.442	.99984	58
3	.01832	.01833	54.561	.99983	57
4	.01862	.01862	53.709	.99983	56
5	.01891	.01891	52.882	.99982	**55**
6	.01920	.01920	52.081	.99982	54
7	.01949	.01949	51.303	.99981	53
8	.01978	.01978	50.549	.99980	52
9	.02007	.02007	49.816	.99980	51
10	.02036	.02036	49.104	.99979	**50**
11	.02065	.02066	48.312	.99979	49
12	.02094	.02095	47.740	.99978	48
13	.02123	.02124	47.085	.99977	47
14	.02152	.02153	46.449	.99977	46
15	.02181	.02182	45.829	.99976	**45**
16	.02211	.02211	45.226	.99976	44
17	.02240	.02240	44.639	.99975	43
18	.02269	.02269	44.066	.99974	42
19	.02298	.02298	43.508	.99974	41
20	.02327	.02328	42.964	.99973	**40**
21	.02356	.02357	42.433	.99972	39
22	.02385	.02386	41.916	.99972	38
23	.02414	.02415	41.411	.99971	37
24	.02443	.02444	40.917	.99970	36
25	.02472	.02473	40.436	.99969	**35**
26	.02501	.02502	39.965	.99969	34
27	.02530	.02531	39.506	.99968	33
28	.02560	.02560	39.057	.99967	32
29	.02589	.02589	38.618	.99966	31
30	.02618	.02619	38.188	.99966	**30**
31	.02647	.02648	37.769	.99965	29
32	.02676	.02677	37.358	.99964	28
33	.02705	.02706	36.956	.99963	27
34	.02734	.02735	36.563	.99963	26
35	.02763	.02764	36.178	.99962	**25**
36	.02792	.02793	35.801	.99961	24
37	.02821	.02822	35.431	.99960	23
38	.02850	.02851	35.070	.99959	22
39	.02879	.02881	34.715	.99959	21
40	.02908	.02910	34.368	.99958	**20**
41	.02938	.02939	34.027	.99957	19
42	.02967	.02968	33.694	.99956	18
43	.02996	.02997	33.366	.99955	17
44	.03025	.03026	33.045	.99954	16
45	.03054	.03055	32.730	.99953	**15**
46	.03083	.03084	32.421	.99952	14
47	.03112	.03114	32.118	.99952	13
48	.03141	.03143	31.821	.99951	12
49	.03170	.03172	31.528	.99950	11
50	.03199	.03201	31.242	.99949	**10**
51	.03228	.03230	30.960	.99948	9
52	.03257	.03259	30.683	.99947	8
53	.03286	.03288	30.412	.99946	7
54	.03316	.03317	30.145	.99945	6
55	.03345	.03346	29.882	.99944	**5**
56	.03374	.03376	29.624	.99943	4
57	.03403	.03405	29.371	.99942	3
58	.03432	.03434	29.122	.99941	2
59	.03461	.03463	28.877	.99940	1
60	.03490	.03492	28.636	.99939	**0**
′	Cos	Cot	Tan	Sin	′

91° (271°) (268°) **88°**

NATURAL FUNCTIONS (Continued)

2° (182°) (357°) **177°**

′	Sin	Tan	Cot	Cos	′
0	.03490	.03492	28.636	.99939	**60**
1	.03519	.03521	28.399	.99938	59
2	.03548	.03550	28.166	.99937	58
3	.03577	.03579	27.937	.99936	57
4	.03606	.03609	27.712	.99935	56
5	.03635	.03638	27.490	.99934	**55**
6	.03664	.03667	27.271	.99933	54
7	.03693	.03696	27.057	.99932	53
8	.03723	.03725	26.845	.99931	52
9	.03752	.03754	26.637	.99930	51
10	.03781	.03783	26.432	.99929	**50**
11	.03810	.03812	26.230	.99927	49
12	.03839	.03842	26.031	.99926	48
13	.03868	.03871	25.835	.99925	47
14	.03897	.03900	25.642	.99924	46
15	.03926	.03929	25.452	.99923	**45**
16	.03955	.03958	25.264	.99922	44
17	.03984	.03987	25.080	.99921	43
18	.04013	.04016	24.898	.99919	42
19	.04042	.04046	24.719	.99918	41
20	.04071	.04075	24.542	.99917	**40**
21	.04100	.04104	24.368	.99916	39
22	.04129	.04133	24.196	.99915	38
23	.04159	.04162	24.026	.99913	37
24	.04188	.04191	23.859	.99912	36
25	.04217	.04220	23.695	.99911	**35**
26	.04246	.04250	23.532	.99910	34
27	.04275	.04279	23.372	.99909	33
28	.04304	.04308	23.214	.99907	32
29	.04333	.04337	23.058	.99906	31
30	.04362	.04366	22.904	.99905	**30**
31	.04391	.04395	22.752	.99904	29
32	.04420	.04424	22.602	.99902	28
33	.04449	.04454	22.454	.99901	27
34	.04478	.04483	22.308	.99900	26
35	.04507	.04512	22.164	.99898	**25**
36	.04536	.04541	22.022	.99897	24
37	.04565	.04570	21.881	.99896	23
38	.04594	.04599	21.743	.99894	22
39	.04623	.04628	21.606	.99893	21
40	.04653	.04658	21.470	.99892	**20**
41	.04682	.04687	21.337	.99890	19
42	.04711	.04716	21.205	.99889	18
43	.04740	.04745	21.075	.99888	17
44	.04769	.04774	20.946	.99886	16
45	.04798	.04803	20.819	.99885	**15**
46	.04827	.04833	20.693	.99883	14
47	.04856	.04862	20.569	.99882	13
48	.04885	.04891	20.446	.99881	12
49	.04914	.04920	20.325	.99879	11
50	.04943	.04949	20.206	.99876	**10**
51	.04972	.04978	20.087	.99876	9
52	.05001	.05007	19.970	.99875	8
53	.05030	.05037	19.885	.99873	7
54	.05059	.05066	19.740	.99872	6
55	.05088	.05095	19.627	.99870	**5**
56	.05117	.05124	19.516	.99869	4
57	.05146	.05153	19.405	.99867	3
58	.05175	.05182	19.296	.99866	2
59	.05205	.05212	19.188	.99864	1
60	.05234	.05241	19.081	.99863	**0**
′	Cos	Cot	Tan	Sin	′

92° (272°) (267°) **87°**

3° (183°) (356°) **176°**

′	Sin	Tan	Cot	Cos	′
0	.05234	.05241	19.081	.99863	**60**
1	.05263	.05270	18.976	.99861	59
2	.05292	.05299	18.871	.99860	58
3	.05321	.05328	18.768	.99858	57
4	.05350	.05357	18.666	.99857	56
5	.05379	.05387	18.564	.99855	**55**
6	.05408	.05416	18.464	.99854	54
7	.05437	.05445	18.366	.99852	53
8	.05466	.05474	18.268	.99851	52
9	.05495	.05503	18.171	.99849	51
10	.05524	.05533	18.075	.99847	**50**
11	.05553	.05562	17.980	.99846	49
12	.05582	.05591	17.886	.99844	48
13	.05611	.05620	17.793	.99842	47
14	.05640	.05649	17.702	.99841	46
15	.05669	.05678	17.611	.99839	**45**
16	.05698	.05708	17.521	.99838	44
17	.05727	.05737	17.431	.99836	43
18	.05756	.05766	17.343	.99834	42
19	.05785	.05795	17.256	.99833	41
20	.05814	.05824	17.169	.99831	**40**
21	.05844	.05854	17.084	.99829	39
22	.05873	.05883	16.999	.99827	38
23	.05902	.05912	16.915	.99826	37
24	.05931	.05941	16.832	.99824	36
25	.05960	.05970	16.750	.99822	**35**
26	.05989	.05999	16.668	.99821	34
27	.06018	.06029	16.587	.99819	33
28	.06047	.06058	16.507	.99817	32
29	.06076	.06087	16.428	.99815	31
30	.06105	.06116	16.350	.99813	**30**
31	.06134	.06145	16.272	.99812	29
32	.06163	.06175	16.195	.99810	28
33	.06192	.06204	16.119	.99808	27
34	.06221	.06233	16.043	.99806	26
35	.06250	.06262	15.969	.99804	**25**
36	.06279	.06291	15.895	.99803	24
37	.06308	.06321	15.821	.99801	23
38	.06337	.06350	15.748	.99799	22
39	.06366	.06379	15.676	.99797	21
40	.06395	.06408	15.605	.99795	**20**
41	.06424	.06438	15.534	.99793	19
42	.06453	.06467	15.464	.99792	18
43	.06482	.06496	15.394	.99790	17
44	.06511	.06525	15.325	.99788	16
45	.06540	.06554	15.257	.99786	**15**
56	.06569	.06584	15.189	.99784	14
47	.06598	.06613	15.122	.99782	13
48	.06627	.06642	15.056	.99780	12
49	.06656	.06671	14.990	.99778	11
50	.06685	.06700	14.924	.99776	**10**
51	.06714	.06730	14.860	.99774	9
52	.06743	.06759	14.795	.99772	8
53	.06773	.06788	14.732	.99770	7
54	.06802	.06817	14.669	.99768	6
55	.06831	.06847	14.606	.99766	**5**
56	.06860	.06876	14.544	.99764	4
57	.06889	.06905	14.482	.99762	3
58	.06918	.06934	14.421	.99760	2
59	.06947	.06963	14.361	.99758	1
60	.06976	.06993	14.301	.99756	**0**
′	Cos	Cot	Tan	Sin	′

93° (273°) (266°) **86°**

NATURAL FUNCTIONS (Continued)

4° (184°) (355°) **175°**

′	Sin	Tan	Cot	Cos	′
0	.06976	.06993	14.301	.99756	**60**
1	.07005	.07022	14.241	.99754	59
2	.07034	.07051	14.182	.99752	58
3	.07063	.07080	14.124	.99750	57
4	.07092	.07110	14.065	.99748	56
5	.07121	.07139	14.008	.99746	**55**
6	.07150	.07168	13.951	.99744	54
7	.07179	.07197	13.894	.99742	53
8	.07208	.07227	13.838	.99740	52
9	.07237	.07256	13.782	.99738	51
10	.07266	.07285	13.727	.99736	**50**
11	.07295	.07314	13.672	.99734	49
12	.07324	.07344	13.617	.99731	48
13	.07353	.07373	13.563	.99729	47
14	.07382	.07402	13.510	.99727	46
15	.07411	.07431	13.457	.99725	**45**
16	.07440	.07461	13.404	.99723	44
17	.07469	.07490	13.352	.99721	43
18	.07498	.07519	13.300	.99719	42
19	.07527	.07548	13.248	.99716	41
20	.07556	.07578	13.197	.99714	**40**
21	.07585	.07607	13.146	.99712	39
22	.07614	.07636	13.096	.99710	38
23	.07643	.07665	13.046	.99708	37
24	.07672	.07695	12.996	.99705	36
25	.07701	.07724	12.947	.99703	**35**
26	.07730	.07753	12.898	.99701	34
27	.07759	.07782	12.850	.99699	33
28	.07788	.07812	12.801	.99696	32
29	.07817	.07841	12.754	.99694	31
30	.07846	.07870	12.706	.99692	**30**
31	.07875	.07899	12.659	.99689	29
32	.07904	.07929	12.612	.99687	28
33	.07933	.07958	12.566	.99685	27
34	.07962	.07987	12.520	.99683	26
35	.07991	.08017	12.474	.99680	**25**
36	.08020	.08046	12.429	.99678	24
37	.08049	.08075	12.384	.99676	23
38	.08078	.08104	12.339	.99673	22
39	.08107	.08134	12.295	.99671	21
40	.08136	.08163	12.251	.99668	**20**
41	.08165	.08192	12.207	.99666	19
42	.08194	.08221	12.163	.99664	18
43	.08223	.08251	12.120	.99661	17
44	.08252	.08280	12.077	.99659	16
45	.08281	.08309	12.035	.99657	**15**
46	.08310	.08339	11.992	.99654	14
47	.08339	.08368	11.950	.99652	13
48	.08368	.08397	11.909	.99649	12
49	.08397	.08427	11.867	.99647	11
50	.08426	.08456	11.826	.99644	**10**
51	.08455	.08485	11.785	.99642	9
52	.08484	.08514	11.745	.99639	8
53	.08513	.08544	11.705	.99637	7
54	.08542	.08573	11.664	.99635	6
55	.08571	.08602	11.625	.99632	**5**
56	.08600	.08632	11.585	.99630	4
57	.08629	.08661	11.546	.99627	3
58	.08658	.08690	11.507	.99625	2
59	.08687	.08720	11.468	.99622	1
60	.08716	.08749	11.430	.99619	**0**
′	Cos	Cot	Tan	Sin	′

94° (274°) (265°) **85°**

5° (185°) (354°) **174°**

′	Sin	Tan	Cot	Cos	′
0	.08716	.08749	11.430	.99619	**60**
1	.08745	.08778	11.392	.99617	59
2	.08774	.08807	11.354	.99614	58
3	.08803	.08837	11.316	.99612	57
4	.08831	.08866	11.279	.99609	56
5	.08860	.08895	11.242	.99607	**55**
6	.08889	.08925	11.205	.99604	54
7	.08918	.08954	11.168	.99602	53
8	.08947	.08983	11.132	.99599	52
9	.08976	.09013	11.095	.99596	51
10	.09005	.09042	11.059	.99594	**50**
11	.09034	.09071	11.024	.99591	49
12	.09063	.09101	10.988	.99588	48
13	.09092	.09130	10.953	.99586	47
14	.09121	.09159	10.918	.99583	46
15	.09150	.09189	10.883	.99580	**45**
16	.09179	.09218	10.848	.99578	44
17	.09208	.09247	10.814	.99575	43
18	.09237	.09277	10.780	.99572	42
19	.09266	.09306	10.746	.99570	41
20	.09295	.09335	10.712	.99567	**40**
21	.09324	.09365	10.678	.99564	39
22	.09353	.09394	10.645	.99562	38
23	.09382	.09423	10.612	.99559	37
24	.09411	.09453	10.579	.99556	36
25	.09440	.09482	10.546	.99553	**35**
26	.09469	.09511	10.514	.99551	34
27	.09498	.09541	10.481	.99548	33
28	.09527	.09570	10.449	.99545	32
29	.09556	.09600	10.417	.99542	31
30	.09585	.09629	10.385	.99540	**30**
31	.09614	.09658	10.354	.99537	29
32	.09642	.09688	10.322	.99534	28
33	.09671	.09717	10.291	.99531	27
34	.09700	.09746	10.260	.99528	26
35	.09729	.09776	10.229	.99526	**25**
36	.09758	.09805	10.199	.99523	24
37	.09787	.09834	10.168	.99520	23
38	.09816	.09864	10.138	.99517	22
39	.09845	.09893	10.108	.99514	21
40	.09874	.09923	10.078	.99511	**20**
41	.09903	.09952	10.048	.99508	19
42	.09932	.09981	10.019	.99506	18
43	.09961	.10011	9.9893	.99503	17
44	.09990	.10040	9.9601	.99500	16
45	.10019	.10069	9.9310	.99497	**15**
46	.10048	.10099	9.9021	.99494	14
47	.10077	.10128	9.8734	.99491	13
48	.10106	.10158	9.8448	.99488	12
49	.10135	.10187	9.8164	.99485	11
50	.10164	.10216	9.7882	.99482	**10**
51	.10192	.10246	9.7601	.99479	9
52	.10221	.10275	9.7322	.99476	8
53	.10250	.10305	9.7044	.99473	7
54	.10279	.10334	9.6768	.99470	6
55	.10308	.10363	9.6943	.99467	**5**
56	.10337	.10393	9.6220	.99464	4
57	.10366	.10422	9.5949	.99461	3
58	.10395	.10452	9.5679	.99458	2
59	.10424	.10481	9.5411	.99455	1
60	.10453	.10510	9.5144	.99452	**0**
′	Cos	Cot	Tan	Sin	′

95° (275°) (264°) **84°**

NATURAL FUNCTIONS (Continued)

6° (186°) (353°) **173°**

′	Sin	Tan	Cot	Cos	′
0	.10453	.10510	9.5144	.99452	**60**
1	.10482	.10540	9.4878	.99449	59
2	.10511	.10569	9.4614	.99446	58
3	.10540	.10599	9.4352	.99443	57
4	.10569	.10628	9.4090	.99440	56
5	.10597	.10657	9.3831	.99437	**55**
6	.10626	.10687	9.3572	.99434	54
7	.10655	.10716	9.3315	.99431	53
8	.10684	.10746	9.3060	.99428	52
9	.10713	.10775	9.2806	.99424	51
10	.10742	.10805	9.2553	.99421	**50**
11	.10771	.10834	9.2302	.99418	49
12	.10800	.10863	9.2052	.99415	48
13	.10829	.10893	9.1803	.99412	47
14	.10858	.10922	9.1555	.99409	56
15	.10887	.10952	9.1309	.99406	**45**
16	.10916	.10981	9.1065	.99402	44
17	.10945	.11011	9.0821	.99399	43
18	.10973	.11040	9.0579	.99396	42
19	.11002	.11070	9.0338	.99393	41
20	.11031	.11099	9.0098	.99390	**40**
21	.11060	.11128	8.9860	.99386	39
22	.11089	.11158	8.9623	.99383	38
23	.11118	.11187	8.9387	.99380	37
24	.11147	.11217	8.9152	.99377	36
25	.11176	.11246	8.8919	.99374	**35**
26	.11205	.11276	8.8686	.99370	34
27	.11234	.11305	8.8455	.99367	33
28	.11263	.11335	8.8225	.99364	32
29	.11291	.11364	8.7996	.99360	31
30	.11320	.11394	8.7769	.99357	**30**
31	.11349	.11423	8.7542	.99354	29
32	.11378	.11452	8.7317	.99351	28
33	.11407	.11482	8.7093	.99347	27
34	.11436	.11511	8.6870	.99344	26
35	.11465	.11541	8.6648	.99341	**25**
36	.11494	.11570	8.6427	.99337	24
37	.11523	.11600	8.6208	.99334	23
38	.11552	.11629	8.5989	.99331	22
39	.11580	.11659	8.5772	.99327	21
40	.11609	.11688	8.5555	.99324	**20**
41	.11638	.11718	8.5340	.99320	19
42	.11667	.11747	8.5126	.99317	18
43	.11696	.11777	8.4913	.99314	17
44	.11725	.11806	8.4701	.99310	16
45	.11754	.11836	8.4490	.99307	**15**
46	.11783	.11865	8.4280	.99303	14
47	.11812	.11895	8.4071	.99300	13
48	.11840	.11924	8.3863	.99297	12
49	.11869	.11954	8.3656	.99293	11
50	.11898	.11983	8.3450	.99290	**10**
51	.11927	.12013	8.3245	.99286	9
52	.11956	.12042	8.3041	.99283	8
53	.11985	.12072	8.2838	.99279	7
54	.12014	.12101	8.2636	.99276	6
55	.12043	.12131	8.2434	.99272	**5**
56	.12071	.12160	8.2234	.99269	4
57	.12100	.12190	8.2035	.99265	3
58	.12129	.12219	8.1837	.99262	2
59	.12158	.12249	8.1640	.99258	1
60	.12187	.12278	8.1443	.99255	**0**
′	Cos	Cot	Tan	Sin	′

96° (276°) (263°) **83°**

7° (187°) (352°) **172°**

′	Sin	Tan	Cot	Cos	′
0	.12187	.12278	8.1443	.99255	**60**
1	.12216	.12308	8.1248	.99251	59
2	.12245	.12338	8.1054	.99248	58
3	.12274	.12367	8.0860	.99244	57
4	.12302	.12397	8.0667	.99240	56
5	.12331	.12426	8.0476	.99237	**55**
6	.12360	.12456	8.0285	.99233	54
7	.12389	.12485	8.0095	.99230	53
8	.12418	.12515	7.9906	.99226	52
9	.12447	.12544	7.9718	.99222	51
10	.12476	.12574	7.9530	.99219	**50**
11	.12504	.12603	7.9344	.99215	49
12	.12533	.12633	7.9158	.99211	48
13	.12562	.12662	7.8973	.99208	47
14	.12591	.12692	7.8789	.99204	46
15	.12620	.12722	7.8606	.99200	**45**
16	.12649	.12751	7.8424	.99197	44
17	.12678	.12781	7.8243	.99193	43
18	.12706	.12810	7.8062	.99189	42
19	.12735	.12840	7.7882	.99186	41
20	.12764	.12869	7.7704	.99182	**40**
21	.12793	.12899	7.7525	.99178	39
22	.12822	.12929	7.7348	.99175	38
23	.12851	.12958	7.7171	.99171	37
24	.12880	.12988	7.6996	.99167	36
25	.12908	.13017	7.6821	.99163	**35**
26	.12937	.13047	7.6647	.99160	34
27	.12966	.13076	7.6473	.99156	33
28	.12995	.13106	7.6301	.99152	32
29	.13024	.13136	7.6129	.99148	31
30	.13053	.13165	7.5958	.99144	**30**
31	.13081	.13195	7.5787	.99141	29
32	.13110	.13224	7.5618	.99137	28
33	.13139	.13254	7.5449	.99133	27
34	.13168	.13284	7.5281	.99129	26
35	.13197	.13313	7.5113	.99125	**25**
36	.13226	.13343	7.4947	.99122	24
37	.13254	.13372	7.4781	.99118	23
38	.13283	.13402	7.4615	.99114	22
39	.13312	.13432	7.4451	.99110	21
40	.13341	.13461	7.4287	.99106	**20**
41	.13370	.13491	7.4124	.99102	19
42	.13399	.13521	7.3962	.99098	18
43	.13427	.13550	7.3800	.99094	17
44	.13456	.13580	7.3639	.99091	16
45	.13485	.13609	7.3479	.99087	**15**
46	.13514	.13639	7.3319	.99083	14
47	.13543	.13669	7.3160	.99079	13
48	.13572	.13698	7.3002	.99075	12
49	.13600	.13728	7.2844	.99071	11
50	.13629	.13758	7.2687	.99067	**10**
51	.13658	.13787	7.2531	.99063	9
52	.13687	.13817	7.2375	.99059	8
53	.13716	.13846	7.2220	.99055	7
54	.13744	.13876	7.2066	.99051	6
55	.13773	.13906	7.1912	.99047	**5**
56	.13802	.13935	7.1759	.99043	4
57	.13831	.13965	7.1607	.99039	3
58	.13860	.13995	7.1455	.99035	2
59	.13889	.14024	7.1304	.99031	1
60	.13917	.14054	7.1154	.99027	**0**
′	Cos	Cot	Tan	Sin	′

97° (277°) (262°) **82°**

NATURAL FUNCTIONS (Continued)

8° (188°) (351°) **171°**

′	Sin	Tan	Cot	Cos	′
0	.13917	.14054	7.1154	.99027	**60**
1	.13946	.14084	7.1004	.99023	59
2	.13975	.14113	7.0855	.99019	58
3	.14004	.14143	7.0706	.99015	57
4	.14033	.14173	7.0558	.99011	56
5	.14061	.14202	7.0410	.99006	**55**
6	.14090	.14232	7.0264	.99002	54
7	.14119	.14262	7.0117	.98998	53
8	.14148	.14291	6.9972	.98994	52
9	.14177	.14321	6.9827	.98900	51
10	.14205	.14351	6.9682	.98986	**50**
11	.14234	.14381	6.9538	.98982	49
12	.14263	.14410	6.9395	.98978	48
13	.14292	.14440	6.9252	.98973	47
14	.14320	.14470	6.9110	.98969	46
15	.14349	.14499	6.8969	.98965	**45**
16	.14378	.14529	6.8828	.98961	44
17	.14407	.14559	6.8687	.98957	43
18	.14436	.14588	6.8548	.98953	42
19	.14464	.14618	6.8408	.98948	41
20	.14493	.14648	6.8269	.98944	**40**
21	.14522	.14678	6.8131	.98940	39
22	.14551	.14707	6.7994	.98936	38
23	.14580	.14737	6.7856	.98931	37
24	.14608	.14767	6.7720	.98927	36
25	.14637	.14796	6.7584	.98923	**35**
26	.14666	.14826	6.7448	.98919	34
27	.14695	.14856	6.7313	.98914	33
28	.14723	.14886	6.7179	.98910	32
29	.14752	.14915	6.7045	.98906	31
30	.14781	.14945	6.6912	.98902	**30**
31	.14810	.14975	6.6779	.98897	29
32	.14838	.15005	6.6646	.98893	28
33	.14867	.15034	6.6514	.98889	27
34	.14896	.15064	6.6383	.98884	26
35	.14925	.15094	6.6252	.98880	**25**
36	.14954	.15124	6.6122	.98876	24
37	.14982	.15153	6.5992	.98871	23
38	.15011	.15183	6.5863	.98867	22
39	.15040	.15213	6.5734	.98863	21
40	.15069	.15243	6.5606	.98858	**20**
41	.15097	.15272	6.5478	.98854	19
42	.15126	.15302	6.5350	.98849	18
43	.15155	.15332	6.5223	.98845	17
44	.15184	.15362	6.5097	.98841	16
45	.15212	.15391	6.4971	.98836	**15**
46	.15241	.15421	6.4846	.98832	14
47	.15270	.15451	6.4721	.98827	13
48	.15299	.15481	6.4596	.98823	12
49	.15327	.15511	6.4472	.98818	11
50	.15356	.15540	6.4348	.98814	**10**
51	.15385	.15570	6.4225	.98809	9
52	.15414	.15600	6.4103	.98805	8
53	.15442	.15630	6.3980	.98800	7
54	.15471	.15660	6.3859	.98796	6
55	.15500	.15689	6.3737	.98791	**5**
56	.15529	.15719	6.3617	.98787	4
57	.15557	.15749	6.3496	.98782	3
58	.15586	.15779	6.3376	.98778	2
59	.15615	.15809	6.3257	.98773	1
60	.15643	.15838	6.3138	.98769	**0**
′	Cos	Cot	Tan	Sin	′

98° (278°) (261°) **81°**

9° (189°) (350°) **170°**

′	Sin	Tan	Cot	Cos	′
0	.15643	.15838	6.3138	.98769	**60**
1	.15672	.15868	6.3019	.98764	59
2	.15701	.15898	6.2901	.98760	58
3	.15730	.15928	6.2783	.98755	57
4	.15758	.15958	6.2666	.98751	56
5	.15787	.15988	6.2549	.98746	**55**
6	.15816	.16017	6.2432	.98741	54
7	.15845	.16047	6.2316	.98737	53
8	.15873	.16077	6.2200	.98732	52
9	.15902	.16107	6.2085	.98728	51
10	.15931	.16137	6.1970	.98723	**50**
11	.15959	.16167	6.1856	.98718	49
12	.15988	.16196	6.1742	.98714	48
13	.16017	.16226	6.1628	.98709	47
14	.16046	.16256	6.1515	.98704	46
15	.16074	.16286	6.1402	.98700	**45**
16	.16103	.16316	6.1290	.98695	44
17	.16132	.16346	6.1178	.98690	43
18	.16160	.16376	6.1066	.98686	42
19	.16189	.16405	6.0955	.98681	41
20	.16218	.16435	6.0844	.98676	**40**
21	.16246	.16465	6.0734	.98671	39
22	.16275	.16495	6.0624	.98667	38
23	.16304	.16525	6.0514	.98662	37
24	.16333	.16555	6.0405	.98657	36
25	.16361	.16585	6.0296	.98652	**35**
26	.16390	.16615	6.0188	.98648	34
27	.16419	.16645	6.0080	.98643	33
28	.16447	.16674	5.9972	.98638	32
29	.16476	.16704	5.9865	.98633	31
30	.16505	.16734	5.9758	.98629	**30**
31	.16533	.16764	5.9651	.98624	29
32	.16562	.16794	5.9545	.98619	28
33	.16591	.16824	5.9439	.98614	27
34	.16620	.16854	5.9333	.98609	26
35	.16648	.16884	5.9228	.98604	**25**
36	.16677	.16914	5.9124	.98600	24
37	.16706	.16944	5.9019	.98595	23
38	.16734	.16974	5.8915	.98590	22
39	.16763	.17004	5.8811	.98585	21
40	.16792	.17033	5.8708	.98580	**20**
41	.16820	.17063	5.8605	.98575	19
42	.16849	.17093	5.8502	.98570	18
43	.16878	.17123	5.8400	.98565	17
44	.16906	.17153	5.8298	.98561	16
45	.16935	.17183	5.8197	.98556	**15**
46	.16964	.17213	5.8095	.98551	14
47	.16992	.17243	5.7994	.98546	13
48	.17021	.17273	5.7894	.98541	12
49	.17050	.17303	5.7794	.98536	11
50	.17078	.17333	5.7694	.98531	**10**
51	.17107	.17363	5.7594	.98526	9
52	.17136	.17393	5.7495	.98521	8
53	.17164	.17423	5.7396	.98516	7
54	.17193	.17453	5.7297	.98511	6
55	.17222	.17483	5.7199	.98506	**5**
56	.17250	.17513	5.7101	.98501	4
57	.17279	.17543	5.7004	.98496	3
58	.17308	.17573	5.6906	.98491	2
59	.17336	.17603	5.6809	.98486	1
60	.17365	.17633	5.6713	.98481	**0**
′	Cos	Cot	Tan	Sin	′

99° (279°) (260°) **80°**

10° (190°) (349°) **169°**

′	Sin	Tan	Cot	Cos	′
0	.17365	.17633	5.6713	.98481	**60**
1	.17393	.17663	5.6617	.98476	59
2	.17422	.17693	5.6521	.98471	58
3	.17451	.17723	5.6425	.98466	57
4	.17479	.17753	5.6329	.98461	56
5	.17508	.17783	5.6234	.98455	**55**
6	.17537	.17813	5.6140	.98450	54
7	.17565	.17843	5.6045	.98445	53
8	.17594	.17873	5.5951	.98440	52
9	.17623	.17903	5.5857	.98435	51
10	.17651	.17933	5.5764	.98430	**50**
11	.17680	.17963	5.5671	.98425	49
12	.17708	.17993	5.5578	.98420	48
13	.17737	.18023	5.5485	.98414	47
14	.17766	.18053	5.5393	.98409	46
15	.17794	.18083	5.5301	.98404	**45**
16	.17823	.18113	5.5209	.98399	44
17	.17852	.18143	5.5118	.98394	43
18	.17880	.18173	5.5026	.98389	42
19	.17909	.18203	5.4936	.98383	41
20	.17937	.18233	5.4845	.98378	**40**
21	.17966	.18263	5.4755	.98373	39
22	.17995	.18293	5.4665	.98368	38
23	.18023	.18323	5.4575	.98362	37
24	.18052	.18353	5.4486	.98357	36
25	.18081	.18384	5.4397	.98352	**35**
26	.18109	.18414	5.4308	.98347	34
27	.18138	.18444	5.4219	.98341	33
28	.18166	.18474	5.4131	.98336	32
29	.18195	.18504	5.4043	.98331	31
30	.18224	.18534	5.3955	.98325	**30**
31	.18252	.18564	5.3868	.98320	29
32	.18281	.18594	5.3781	.98315	28
33	.18309	.18624	5.3694	.98310	27
34	.18338	.18654	5.3607	.98304	26
35	.18367	.18684	5.3521	.98299	**25**
36	.18395	.18714	5.3435	.98294	24
37	.18424	.18745	5.3349	.98288	23
38	.18452	.18775	5.3263	.98283	22
39	.18481	.18805	5.3178	.98277	21
40	.18509	.18835	5.3093	.98272	**20**
41	.18538	.18865	5.3008	.98267	19
42	.18567	.18895	5.2924	.98261	18
43	.18595	.18925	5.2839	.98256	17
44	.18624	.18955	5.2755	.98250	16
45	.18652	.18986	5.2672	.98245	**15**
46	.18681	.19016	5.2588	.98240	14
47	.18710	.19046	5.2505	.98234	13
48	.18738	.19076	5.2422	.98229	12
49	.18767	.19106	5.2339	.98223	11
50	.18795	.19136	5.2257	.98218	**10**
51	.18824	.19166	5.2174	.98212	9
52	.18852	.19197	5.2092	.98207	8
53	.18881	.19227	5.2011	.98201	7
54	.18910	.19257	5.1929	.98196	6
55	.18938	.19287	5.1848	.98190	**5**
56	.18967	.19317	5.1767	.98185	4
57	.18995	.19347	5.1686	.98179	3
58	.19024	.19378	5.1606	.98174	2
59	.19052	.19408	5.1526	.98168	1
60	.19081	.19438	5.1446	.98163	**0**
′	Cos	Cot	Tan	Sin	′

100° (280°) (259°) **79°**

11° (191°) (348°) **168°**

′	Sin	Tan	Cot	Cos	′
0	.19081	.19438	5.1446	.98163	**60**
1	.19109	.19468	5.1366	.98157	59
2	.19138	.19498	5.1286	.98152	58
3	.19167	.19529	5.1207	.98146	57
4	.19195	.19559	5.1128	.98140	56
5	.19224	.19589	5.1049	.98135	**55**
6	.19252	.19619	5.0970	.98129	54
7	.19281	.19649	5.0892	.98124	53
8	.19309	.19680	5.0814	.98118	52
9	.19338	.19710	5.0736	.98112	51
10	.19366	.19740	5.0658	.98107	**50**
11	.19395	.19770	5.0581	.98101	49
12	.19423	.19801	5.0504	.98096	48
13	.19452	.19831	5.0427	.98090	47
14	.19481	.19861	5.0350	.98084	46
15	.19509	.19891	5.0273	.98079	**45**
16	.19538	.19921	5.0197	.98073	44
17	.19566	.19952	5.0121	.98067	43
18	.19595	.19982	5.0045	.98061	42
19	.19623	.20012	4.9969	.98056	41
20	.19652	.20042	4.9894	.98050	**40**
21	.19680	.20073	4.9819	.98044	39
22	.19709	.20103	4.9744	.98039	38
23	.19737	.20133	4.9669	.98033	37
24	.19766	.20164	4.9594	.98027	36
25	.19794	.20194	4.9520	.98021	**35**
26	.19823	.20224	4.9446	.98016	34
27	.19851	.20254	4.9372	.98010	33
28	.19880	.20285	4.9298	.98004	32
29	.19908	.20315	4.9225	.97998	31
30	.19937	.20345	4.9152	.97992	**30**
31	.19965	.20376	4.9078	.97987	29
32	.19994	.20406	4.9006	.97981	28
33	.20022	.20436	4.8933	.97975	27
34	.20051	.20466	4.8860	.97969	26
35	.20079	.20497	4.8788	.97963	**25**
36	.20108	.20527	4.8716	.97958	24
37	.20136	.20557	4.8644	.97952	23
38	.20165	.20588	4.8573	.97946	22
39	.20193	.20618	4.8501	.97940	21
40	.20222	.20648	4.8430	.97934	**20**
41	.20250	.20679	4.8359	.97938	19
42	.20279	.20709	4.8288	.97922	18
43	.20307	.20739	4.8218	.97916	17
44	.20336	.20770	4.8147	.97910	16
45	.20364	.20800	4.8077	.97905	**15**
46	.20393	.20830	4.8007	.97899	14
47	.20421	.20861	4.7937	.97893	13
48	.20450	.20891	4.7867	.97887	12
49	.20478	.20921	4.7798	.97881	11
50	.20507	.20952	4.7729	.97875	**10**
51	.20535	.20982	4.7659	.97869	9
52	.20563	.21013	4.7591	.97863	8
53	.20592	.21043	4.7522	.97857	7
54	.20620	.21073	4.7453	.97851	6
55	.20649	.21104	4.7385	.97845	**5**
56	.20677	.21134	4.7317	.97839	4
57	.20706	.21164	4.7249	.97833	3
58	.20734	.21195	4.7181	.97827	2
59	.20763	.21225	4.7114	.97821	1
60	.20791	.21256	4.7046	.97815	**0**
′	Cos	Cot	Tan	Sin	′

101° (281°) (258°) **78°**

12° (192°) (347°) **167°**

′	Sin	Tan	Cot	Cos	′
0	.20791	.21256	4.7046	.97815	**60**
1	.20820	.21286	4.6979	.97809	59
2	.20848	.21316	4.6912	.97803	58
3	.20877	.21347	4.6845	.97797	57
4	.20905	.21377	4.6779	.97791	56
5	.20933	.21408	4.6712	.97784	**55**
6	.20962	.21438	4.6646	.97778	54
7	.20990	.21469	4.6580	.97772	53
8	.21019	.21499	4.6514	.97766	52
9	.21047	.21529	4.6448	.97760	51
10	.21076	.21560	4.6382	.97754	**50**
11	.21104	.21590	4.6317	.97748	49
12	.21132	.21621	4.6252	.97742	48
13	.21161	.21651	4.6187	.97735	47
14	.21189	.21682	4.6122	.97729	46
15	.21218	.21712	4.6057	.97723	**45**
16	.21246	.21743	4.5993	.97717	44
17	.21275	.21773	4.5928	.97711	43
18	.21303	.21804	4.5864	.97705	42
19	.21331	.21834	4.5800	.97698	41
20	.21360	.21864	4.5736	.97692	**40**
21	.21388	.21895	4.5673	.97686	39
22	.21417	.21925	4.5609	.97680	38
23	.21445	.21956	4.5546	.97673	37
24	.21474	.21986	4.5483	.97667	36
25	.21502	.22017	4.5420	.97661	**35**
26	.21530	.22047	4.5357	.97655	34
27	.21559	.22078	4.5294	.97648	33
28	.21587	.22108	4.5232	.97642	32
29	.21616	.22139	4.5169	.97636	31
30	.21644	.22169	4.5107	.97630	**30**
31	.21672	.22200	4.5045	.97623	29
32	.21701	.22231	4.4983	.97617	28
33	.21729	.22261	4.4922	.97611	27
34	.21758	.22292	4.4860	.97604	26
35	.21786	.22322	4.4799	.97598	**25**
36	.21814	.22353	4.4737	.97592	24
37	.21843	.22383	4.4676	.97585	23
38	.21871	.22414	4.4615	.97579	22
39	.21899	.22444	4.4555	.97573	21
40	.21928	.22475	4.4494	.97566	**20**
41	.21956	.22505	4.4434	.97560	19
42	.21985	.22536	4.4373	.97553	18
43	.22013	.22567	4.4313	.97547	17
44	.22041	.22597	4.4253	.97541	16
45	.22070	.22628	4.4194	.97534	**15**
46	.22098	.22658	4.4134	.97528	14
47	.22126	.22689	4.4075	.97521	13
48	.22155	.22719	4.4015	.97515	12
49	.22183	.22750	4.3956	.97508	11
50	.22212	.22781	4.3897	.97502	**10**
51	.22240	.22811	4.3838	.97496	9
52	.22268	.22842	4.3779	.97489	8
53	.22297	.22872	4.3721	.97483	7
54	.22325	.22903	4.3662	.97476	6
55	.22353	.22934	4.3604	.97470	**5**
56	.22382	.22964	4.3546	.97463	4
57	.22410	.22995	4.3488	.97457	3
58	.22438	.23026	4.3430	.97450	2
59	.22467	.23056	4.3372	.97444	1
60	.22495	.23087	4.3315	.97437	**0**
′	Cos	Cot	Tan	Sin	′

102° (282°) (257°) **77°**

13° (193°) (346°) **166°**

′	Sin	Tan	Cot	Cos	′
0	.22495	.23087	4.3315	.97437	**60**
1	.22523	.23117	4.3257	.97430	59
2	.22552	.23148	4.3200	.97424	58
3	.22580	.23179	4.3143	.97417	57
4	.22608	.23209	4.3086	.97411	56
5	.22637	.23240	4.3029	.97404	**55**
6	.22665	.23271	4.2972	.97398	54
7	.22693	.23301	4.2916	.97391	53
8	.22722	.23332	4.2859	.97384	52
9	.22750	.23363	4.2803	.97378	51
10	.22778	.23393	4.2747	.97371	**50**
11	.22807	.23424	4.2691	.97365	49
12	.22835	.23455	4.2635	.97358	48
13	.22863	.23485	4.2580	.97351	47
14	.22892	.23516	4.2524	.97345	46
15	.22920	.23547	4.2468	.97338	**45**
16	.22948	.23578	4.2413	.97331	44
17	.22977	.23608	4.2358	.97325	43
18	.23005	.23639	4.2303	.97318	42
19	.23033	.23670	4.2248	.97311	41
20	.23062	.23700	4.2193	.97304	**40**
21	.23090	.23731	4.2139	.97298	39
22	.23118	.23762	4.2084	.97291	38
23	.23146	.23793	4.2030	.97284	37
24	.23175	.23823	4.1976	.97278	36
25	.23203	.23854	4.1922	.97271	**35**
26	.23231	.23885	4.1868	.97264	34
27	.23260	.23916	4.1814	.97257	33
28	.23288	.23946	4.1760	.97251	32
29	.23316	.23977	4.1706	.97244	31
30	.23345	.24008	4.1653	.97237	**30**
31	.23373	.24039	4.1600	.97230	29
32	.23401	.24069	4.1547	.97223	28
33	.23429	.24100	4.1493	.97217	27
34	.23458	.24131	4.1441	.97210	26
35	.23486	.24162	4.1388	.97203	**25**
36	.23514	.24193	4.1335	.97196	24
37	.23542	.24223	4.1282	.97189	23
38	.23571	.24254	4.1230	.97182	22
39	.23599	.24285	4.1178	.97176	21
40	.23627	.24316	4.1126	.97169	**20**
41	.23656	.24347	4.1074	.97162	19
42	.23684	.24377	4.1022	.97155	18
43	.23712	.24408	4.0970	.97148	17
44	.23740	.24439	4.0918	.97141	16
45	.23769	.24470	4.0867	.97134	**15**
46	.23797	.24501	4.0815	.97127	14
47	.23825	.24532	4.0764	.97120	13
48	.23853	.24562	4.0713	.97113	12
49	.23882	.24593	4.0662	.97106	11
50	.23910	.24624	4.0611	.97100	**10**
51	.23938	.24655	4.0560	.97093	9
52	.23966	.24686	4.0509	.97086	8
53	.23995	.24717	4.0459	.97079	7
54	.24023	.24747	4.0408	.97072	6
55	.24051	.24778	4.0358	.97065	**5**
56	.24079	.24809	4.0308	.97058	4
57	.24108	.24840	4.0257	.97051	3
58	.24136	.24871	4.0207	.97044	2
59	.24164	.24902	4.0158	.97037	1
60	.24192	.24933	4.0108	.97030	**0**
′	Cos	Cot	Tan	Sin	′

103° (283°) (256°) **76°**

14° (194°) (345°) **165°**

′	Sin	Tan	Cot	Cos	′
0	.24192	.24933	4.0108	.97030	**60**
1	.24220	.24964	4.0058	.97023	59
2	.24249	.24995	4.0009	.97015	58
3	.24277	.25026	3.9959	.97008	57
4	.24305	.25056	3.9910	.97001	56
5	.24333	.25087	3.9861	.96994	**55**
6	.24362	.25118	3.9812	.96987	54
7	.24390	.25149	3.9763	.96980	53
8	.24418	.25180	3.9714	.96973	52
9	.24446	.25211	3.9665	.96966	51
10	.24474	.25242	3.9617	.96959	**50**
11	.24503	.25273	3.9568	.96952	49
12	.24531	.25304	3.9520	.96945	48
13	.24559	.25335	3.9471	.96937	47
14	.24587	.25366	3.9423	.96930	46
15	.24615	.25397	3.9375	.96923	**45**
16	.24644	.25428	3.9327	.96916	44
17	.24672	.25459	3.9279	.96909	43
18	.24700	.25490	3.9232	.96902	42
19	.24728	.25521	3.9184	.96894	41
20	.24756	.25552	3.9136	.96887	**40**
21	.24784	.25583	3.9089	.96880	39
22	.24813	.25614	3.9042	.96873	38
23	.24841	.25645	3.8995	.96866	37
24	.24869	.25676	3.8947	.96858	36
25	.24897	.25707	3.8900	.96851	**35**
26	.24925	.25738	3.8854	.96844	34
27	.24954	.25769	3.8807	.96837	33
28	.24982	.25800	3.8760	.96829	32
29	.25010	.25831	3.8714	.96822	31
30	.25038	.25862	3.8667	.96815	**30**
31	.25066	.25893	3.8621	.96807	29
32	.25094	.25924	3.8575	.96800	28
33	.25122	.25955	3.8528	.96793	27
34	.25151	.25986	3.8482	.96786	26
35	.25179	.26017	3.8436	.96778	**25**
36	.25207	.26048	3.8391	.96771	24
37	.25235	.26079	3.8345	.96764	23
38	.25263	.26110	3.8299	.96756	22
39	.25291	.26141	3.8254	.96749	21
40	.25320	.26172	3.8208	.96742	**20**
41	.25348	.26203	3.8163	.96734	19
42	.25376	.26235	3.8118	.96727	18
43	.25404	.26266	3.8073	.96719	17
44	.25432	.26297	3.8028	.96712	16
45	.25460	.26328	3.7983	.96705	**15**
46	.25488	.26359	3.7938	.96697	14
47	.25516	.26390	3.7893	.96690	13
48	.25545	.26421	3.7848	.96682	12
49	.25573	.26452	3.7804	.96675	11
50	.25601	.26483	3.7760	.96667	**10**
51	.25629	.26515	3.7715	.96660	9
52	.25657	.26546	3.7671	.96653	8
53	.25685	.26577	3.7627	.96645	7
54	.25713	.26608	3.7583	.96638	6
55	.25741	.26639	3.7539	.96630	**5**
56	.25769	.26670	3.7495	.96623	4
57	.25798	.26701	3.7451	.96615	3
58	.25826	.26733	3.7408	.96608	2
59	.25854	.26764	3.7364	.96600	1
60	.25882	.26795	3.7321	.96593	**0**
′	Cos	Cot	Tan	Sin	′

104° (284°) (255°) **75°**

15° (195°) (344°) **164°**

′	Sin	Tan	Cot	Cos	′
0	.25882	.26795	3.7321	.96593	**60**
1	.25910	.26826	3.7277	.96585	59
2	.25938	.26857	3.7234	.96578	58
3	.25966	.26888	3.7191	.96570	57
4	.25994	.26920	3.7148	.96562	56
5	.26022	.26951	3.7105	.96555	**55**
6	.26050	.26982	3.7062	.96547	54
7	.26079	.27013	3.7019	.96540	53
8	.26107	.27044	3.6976	.96532	52
9	.26135	.27076	3.6933	.96524	51
10	.26163	.27107	3.6891	.96517	**50**
11	.26191	.27138	3.6848	.96509	49
12	.26219	.27169	3.6806	.96502	48
13	.26247	.27201	3.6764	.96494	47
14	.26275	.27232	3.6722	.96486	46
15	.26303	.27263	3.6680	.96479	**45**
16	.26331	.27294	3.6638	.96471	44
17	.26359	.27326	3.6596	.96463	43
18	.26387	.27357	3.6554	.96456	42
19	.26415	.27388	3.6512	.96448	41
20	.26443	.27419	3.6470	.96440	**40**
21	.26471	.27451	3.6429	.96433	39
22	.26500	.27482	3.6387	.96425	38
23	.26528	.27513	3.6346	.96417	37
24	.26556	.27545	3.6305	.96410	36
25	.26584	.27576	3.6264	.96402	**35**
26	.26612	.27607	3.6222	.96394	34
27	.26640	.27638	3.6181	.96386	33
28	.26668	.27670	3.6140	.96379	32
29	.26696	.27701	6.6100	.96371	31
30	.26724	.27732	3.6059	.96363	**30**
31	.26572	.27764	3.6018	.96355	29
32	.26780	.27795	3.5978	.96347	28
33	.26808	.27826	3.5937	.96340	27
34	.26836	.27858	3.5897	.96332	26
35	.26864	.27889	3.5856	.96324	**25**
36	.26892	.27921	3.5816	.96316	24
37	.26920	.27952	3.5776	.96308	23
38	.26948	.27983	3.5736	.96301	22
39	.26976	.28015	3.5696	.96293	21
40	.27004	.28046	3.5656	.96285	**20**
41	.27032	.28077	3.5616	.96277	19
42	.27060	.28109	3.5576	.96269	18
43	.27088	.28140	3.5536	.96261	17
44	.27116	.28172	3.5497	.96253	16
45	.27144	.28203	3.5457	.96246	**15**
46	.27172	.28234	3.5418	.96238	14
47	.27200	.28266	3.5379	.96230	13
48	.27228	.28297	3.5339	.96222	12
49	.27256	.28329	3.5300	.96214	11
50	.27284	.28360	3.5261	.96206	**10**
51	.27312	.28391	3.5222	.96198	9
52	.27340	.28423	3.5183	.96190	8
53	.27368	.28454	3.5144	.96182	7
54	.27396	.28486	3.5105	.96174	6
55	.27424	.28517	3.5067	.96166	**5**
56	.27452	.28549	3.5028	.96158	4
57	.27480	.28580	3.4989	.96150	3
58	.27508	.28612	3.4951	.96142	2
59	.27536	.28643	3.4912	.96134	1
60	.27564	.28675	3.4874	.96126	**0**
′	Cos	Cot	Tan	Sin	′

105° (285°) (254°) **74°**

NATURAL FUNCTIONS (Continued)

16° (196°) (343°) **163°**

′	Sin	Tan	Cot	Cos	′
0	.27564	.28675	3.4874	.96126	**60**
1	.27592	.28706	3.4836	.96118	59
2	.27620	.28738	3.4798	.96110	58
3	.27648	.28769	3.4760	.96102	57
4	.27676	.28801	3.4722	.96094	56
5	.27704	.28832	3.4684	.96086	**55**
6	.27731	.28864	3.4646	.96078	54
7	.27759	.28895	3.4608	.96070	53
8	.27787	.28927	3.4570	.96062	52
9	.27815	.28958	3.4533	.96054	51
10	.27843	.28990	3.4495	.96046	**50**
11	.27871	.29021	3.4458	.96037	49
12	.27899	.29053	3.4420	.96029	48
13	.27927	.29084	3.4383	.96021	47
14	.27955	.29116	3.4346	.96013	46
15	.27983	.29147	3.4308	.96005	**45**
16	.28011	.29179	3.4271	.95997	44
17	.28039	.29210	3.4234	.95989	43
18	.28067	.29242	3.4197	.95981	42
19	.28095	.29274	3.4160	.95972	41
20	.28123	.29305	3.4124	.95964	**40**
21	.28150	.29337	3.4087	.95956	39
22	.28178	.29368	3.4050	.95948	38
23	.28206	.29400	3.4014	.95940	37
24	.28234	.29432	3.3977	.95931	36
25	.28262	.29463	3.3941	.95923	**35**
26	.28290	.29495	3.3904	.95915	34
27	.28318	.29526	3.3868	.95907	33
28	.28346	.29558	3.3832	.95898	32
29	.28374	.29590	3.3796	.95890	31
30	.28402	.29621	3.3759	.95882	**30**
31	.28429	.29653	3.3723	.95874	29
32	.28457	.29685	3.3687	.95865	28
33	.28485	.29716	3.3652	.95857	27
34	.28513	.29748	3.3616	.95849	26
35	.28541	.29780	3.3580	.95841	**25**
36	.28569	.29811	3.3544	.95832	24
37	.28597	.29843	3.3509	.95824	23
38	.28625	.29875	3.3473	.95816	22
39	.28652	.29906	3.3438	.95807	21
40	.28680	.29938	3.3402	.95799	**20**
41	.28708	.29970	3.3367	.95791	19
42	.28736	.30001	3.3332	.95782	18
43	.28764	.30033	3.3297	.95774	17
44	.28792	.30065	3.3261	.95766	16
45	.28820	.30097	3.3226	.95757	**15**
46	.28847	.30128	3.3191	.95749	14
47	.28875	.30160	3.3156	.95740	13
48	.28903	.30192	3.3122	.95732	12
49	.28931	.30224	3.3087	.95724	11
50	.28959	.30255	3.3052	.95715	**10**
51	.28987	.30287	3.3017	.95707	9
52	.29015	.30319	3.2983	.95698	8
53	.29042	.30351	3.2948	.95690	7
54	.29070	.30382	3.2914	.95681	6
55	.29098	.30414	3.2879	.95673	**5**
56	.29126	.30446	3.2845	.95664	4
57	.29154	.30478	3.2811	.95656	3
58	.29182	.30509	3.2777	.95647	2
59	.29209	.30541	3.2743	.95639	1
60	.29237	.30573	3.2709	.95630	**0**
′	Cos	Cot	Tan	Sin	′

106° (286°) (253°) **73°**

17° (197°) (342°) **162°**

′	Sin	Tan	Cot	Cos	′
0	.29237	.30573	3.2709	.95630	**60**
1	.29265	.30605	3.2675	.95622	59
2	.29293	.30637	3.2641	.95613	58
3	.29321	.30669	3.2607	.95605	57
4	.29348	.30700	3.2573	.95596	56
5	.29376	.30732	3.2539	.95588	**55**
6	.29404	.30764	3.2506	.95579	54
7	.29432	.30796	3.2472	.95571	53
8	.29460	.30828	3.2438	.95562	52
9	.29487	.30860	3.2405	.95554	51
10	.29515	.30891	3.2371	.95545	**50**
11	.29543	.30923	3.2338	.95536	49
12	.29571	.30955	3.2305	.95528	48
13	.29599	.30987	3.2272	.95519	47
14	.29626	.31019	3.2238	.95511	46
15	.29654	.31051	3.2205	.95502	**45**
16	.29682	.31083	3.2172	.95493	44
17	.29710	.31115	3.2139	.95485	43
18	.29737	.31147	3.2106	.95476	42
19	.29765	.41178	3.2073	.95467	41
20	.29793	.31210	3.2041	.95459	**40**
21	.29821	.31242	3.2008	.95450	39
22	.29849	.31274	3.1975	.95441	38
23	.29876	.31306	3.1943	.95433	37
24	.29904	.31338	3.1910	.95424	36
25	.29932	.31370	3.1878	.95415	**35**
26	.29960	.31402	3.1845	.95407	34
27	.29987	.31434	3.1813	.95398	33
28	.30015	.31466	3.1780	.95389	32
29	.30043	.31498	3.1748	.95380	31
30	.30071	.31530	3.1716	.95372	**30**
31	.30098	.31562	3.1684	.95363	29
32	.30126	.31594	3.1652	.95354	28
33	.30154	.31626	3.1620	.95345	27
34	.30182	.31658	3.1588	.95337	26
35	.30209	.31690	3.1556	.95328	**25**
36	.30237	.31722	3.1524	.95319	24
37	.30265	.31754	3.1492	.95310	23
38	.30292	.31786	3.1460	.95301	22
39	.30320	.31818	3.1429	.95293	21
40	.30348	.31850	3.1397	.95284	**20**
41	.30376	.31882	3.1366	.95275	19
42	.30403	.31914	3.1334	.95266	18
43	.30431	.31946	3.1303	.95257	17
44	.30459	.31978	3.1271	.95248	16
45	.30486	.32010	3.1240	.95240	**15**
46	.30514	.32042	3.1209	.95231	14
47	.30542	.32074	3.1178	.95222	13
48	.30570	.32106	3.1146	.95213	12
49	.30597	.32139	3.1115	.95204	11
50	.30625	.32171	3.1084	.95195	**10**
51	.30653	.32203	3.1053	.95186	9
52	.30680	.32235	3.1022	.95177	8
53	.30708	.32267	3.0991	.95168	7
54	.30736	.32299	3.0961	.95159	6
55	.30763	.32331	3.0930	.95150	**5**
56	.30791	.32363	3.0899	.95142	4
57	.30819	.32396	3.0868	.95133	3
58	.30846	.32428	3.0838	.95124	2
59	.30874	.32460	3.0807	.95115	1
60	.30902	.32492	3.0777	.95106	**0**
′	Cos	Cot	Tan	Sin	′

107° (287°) (252°) **72°**

NATURAL FUNCTIONS (Continued)

18° (198°) (341°) **161°**

′	Sin	Tan	Cot	Cos	′
0	.30902	.32492	3.0777	.95106	**60**
1	.30929	.32524	3.0746	.95097	59
2	.30957	.32556	3.0716	.95088	58
3	.30985	.32588	3.0686	.95079	57
4	.31012	.32621	3.0655	.95070	56
5	.31040	.32653	3.0625	.95061	**55**
6	.31068	.32685	3.0595	.95052	54
7	.31095	.32717	3.0565	.95043	53
8	.31123	.32749	3.0535	.95033	52
9	.31151	.32782	3.0505	.95024	51
10	.31178	.32814	3.0475	.95015	**50**
11	.31206	.32846	3.0445	.95006	49
12	.31233	.32878	3.0415	.94997	48
13	.31261	.32911	3.0385	.94988	47
14	.31289	.32943	3.0356	.94979	46
15	.31316	.32975	3.0326	.94970	**45**
16	.31344	.33007	3.0296	.94961	44
17	.31372	.33040	3.0267	.94952	43
18	.31399	.33072	3.0237	.94943	42
19	.31427	.33104	3.0208	.94933	41
20	.31454	.33136	3.0178	.94924	**40**
21	.31482	.33169	3.0149	.94915	39
22	.31510	.33201	3.0120	.94906	38
23	.31537	.33233	3.0090	.94897	37
24	.31565	.33266	3.0061	.94888	36
25	.31593	.33298	3.0032	.94878	**35**
26	.31620	.33330	3.0003	.94869	34
27	.31648	.33363	2.9974	.94860	33
28	.31675	.33395	2.9945	.94851	32
29	.31703	.33427	2.9916	.94842	31
30	.31730	.33460	2.9887	.94832	**30**
31	.31758	.33492	2.9858	.94823	29
32	.31786	.33524	2.9829	.94814	28
33	.31813	.33557	2.9800	.94805	27
34	.31841	.33589	2.9772	.94795	26
35	.31868	.33621	2.9743	.94786	**25**
36	.31896	.33654	2.9714	.94777	24
37	.31923	.33686	2.9686	.94768	23
38	.31951	.33718	2.9657	.94758	22
39	.31979	.33751	2.9629	.94749	21
40	.32006	.33783	2.9600	.94740	**20**
41	.32034	.33816	2.9572	.94730	19
42	.32061	.33848	2.9544	.94721	18
43	.32089	.33881	2.9515	.94712	17
44	.32116	.33913	2.9487	.94702	16
45	.32144	.33945	2.9459	.94693	**15**
46	.32171	.33978	2.9431	.94684	14
47	.32199	.34010	2.9403	.94674	13
48	.32227	.34043	2.9375	.94665	12
49	.32254	.34075	2.9347	.94656	11
50	.32282	.34108	2.9319	.94646	**10**
51	.32309	.34140	2.9291	.94637	9
52	.32337	.34173	2.9263	.94627	8
53	.32364	.34205	2.9235	.94618	7
54	.32392	.34238	2.9208	.94609	6
55	.32419	.34270	2.9180	.94599	**5**
56	.32447	.34303	2.9152	.94590	4
57	.32474	.34335	2.9125	.94580	3
58	.32502	.34368	2.9097	.94571	2
59	.32529	.34400	2.9070	.94561	1
60	.32557	.34433	2.9042	.94552	**0**
′	Cos	Cot	Tan	Sin	′

108° (288°) (251°) **71°**

19° (199°) (340°) **160°**

′	Sin	Tan	Cot	Cos	′
0	.32557	.34433	2.9042	.94552	**60**
1	.32584	.34465	2.9015	.94542	59
2	.32612	.34498	2.8987	.94533	58
3	.32639	.34530	2.8960	.94523	57
4	.32667	.34563	2.8933	.94514	56
5	.32694	.34596	2.8905	.94504	**55**
6	.32722	.34628	2.8878	.94495	54
7	.32749	.34661	2.8851	.94485	53
8	.32777	.34693	2.8824	.94476	52
9	.32804	.34726	2.8797	.94466	51
10	.32832	.34758	2.8770	.94457	**50**
11	.32859	.34791	2.8743	.94447	49
12	.32887	.34824	2.8716	.94438	48
13	.32914	.34856	2.8689	.94428	47
14	.32942	.34889	2.8662	.94418	46
15	.32969	.34922	2.8636	.94409	**45**
16	.32997	.34954	2.8609	.94399	44
17	.33024	.34987	2.8582	.94390	43
18	.33051	.35020	2.8556	.94380	42
19	.33079	.35052	2.8529	.94370	41
20	.33106	.35085	2.8502	.94361	**40**
21	.33134	.35118	2.8476	.94351	39
22	.33161	.35150	2.8449	.94342	38
23	.33189	.35183	2.8423	.94332	37
24	.33216	.35216	2.8397	.94322	36
25	.33244	.35248	2.8370	.94313	**35**
26	.33271	.35281	2.8344	.94303	24
27	.33298	.35314	2.8318	.94293	33
28	.33326	.35346	2.8291	.94284	32
29	.33353	.35379	2.8265	.94274	31
30	.33381	.35412	2.8239	.94264	**30**
31	.33408	.35445	2.8213	.94254	29
32	.33436	.35477	2.8187	.94245	28
33	.33463	.35510	2.8161	.94235	27
34	.33490	.35543	2.8135	.94225	26
35	.33518	.35576	2.8109	.94215	**25**
36	.33545	.35608	2.8083	.94206	24
37	.33573	.35641	2.8057	.94196	23
38	.33600	.35674	2.8032	.94186	22
39	.33627	.35707	2.8006	.94176	21
40	.33655	.35740	2.7980	.94167	**20**
41	.33682	.35772	2.7955	.94157	19
42	.33710	.35805	2.7929	.94147	18
43	.33737	.35838	2.7903	.94137	17
44	.33764	.35871	2.7878	.94127	16
45	.33792	.35904	2.7852	.94118	**15**
46	.33819	.35937	2.7827	.94108	14
47	.33846	.35969	2.7801	.94098	13
48	.33874	.36002	2.7776	.94088	12
49	.33901	.36035	2.7751	.94078	11
50	.33929	.36068	2.7725	.94068	**10**
51	.33956	.36101	2.7700	.94058	9
52	.33983	.36134	2.7675	.94049	8
53	.34011	.36167	2.7650	.94039	7
54	.34038	.36199	2.7625	.94029	6
55	.34065	.36232	2.7600	.94019	**5**
56	.34093	.36265	2.7575	.94009	4
57	.34120	.36298	2.7550	.93999	3
58	.34147	.36331	2.7525	.93989	2
59	.34175	.36364	2.7500	.93979	1
60	.34202	.36397	2.7475	.93969	**0**
′	Cos	Cot	Tan	Sin	′

109° (289°) (250°) **70°**

NATURAL FUNCTIONS (Continued)

20° (200°) (339°) **159°**

′	Sin	Tan	Cot	Cos	′
0	.34202	.36397	2.7475	.93969	**60**
1	.34229	.36430	2.7450	.93959	59
2	.34257	.36463	2.7425	.93949	58
3	.34284	.36496	2.7400	.93939	57
4	.34311	.36529	2.7376	.93929	56
5	.34339	.36562	2.7351	.93919	**55**
6	.34366	.36595	2.7326	.93909	54
7	.34393	.36628	2.7302	.93899	53
8	.34421	.36661	2.7277	.93889	52
9	.34448	.36694	2.7253	.93879	51
10	.34475	.36727	2.7228	.93869	**50**
11	.34503	.36760	2.7204	.93859	49
12	.34530	.36793	2.7179	.93849	48
13	.34557	.36826	2.7155	.93839	47
14	.34584	.36859	2.7130	.93829	46
15	.34612	.36892	2.7106	.93819	**45**
16	.34639	.36925	2.7082	.93809	44
17	.34666	.36958	2.7058	.93799	43
18	.34694	.36991	2.7034	.93789	42
19	.34721	.37024	2.7009	.93779	41
20	.34748	.37057	2.6985	.93769	**40**
21	.34775	.37090	2.6961	.93759	39
22	.34803	.37123	2.6937	.93748	38
23	.34830	.37157	2.6913	.93738	37
24	.34857	.37190	2.6889	.93728	36
25	.34884	.37223	2.6865	.93718	**35**
26	.34912	.37256	2.6841	.93708	34
27	.34939	.37289	2.6818	.93698	33
28	.34966	.37322	2.6794	.93688	32
29	.34993	.37355	2.6770	.93677	31
30	.35021	.37388	2.6746	.93667	**30**
31	.35048	.37422	2.6723	.93657	29
32	.35075	.37455	2.6699	.93647	28
33	.35102	.37488	2.6675	.93637	27
34	.35130	.37521	2.6652	.93626	26
35	.35157	.37554	2.6628	.93616	**25**
36	.35184	.37588	2.6605	.93606	24
37	.35211	.37621	2.6581	.93596	23
38	.35239	.37654	2.6558	.93585	22
39	.35266	.37687	2.6534	.93575	21
40	.35293	.37720	2.6511	.93565	**20**
41	.35320	.37754	2.6488	.93555	19
42	.35347	.37787	2.6464	.93544	18
43	.35375	.37820	2.6441	.93534	17
44	.35402	.37853	2.6418	.93524	16
45	.35429	.37887	2.6395	.93514	**15**
46	.35456	.37920	2.6371	.93503	14
47	.35484	.37953	2.6348	.93493	13
48	.35511	.37986	2.6325	.93483	12
49	.35538	.38020	2.6302	.93472	11
50	.35565	.38053	2.6279	.93462	**10**
51	.35592	.38086	2.6256	.93452	9
52	.35619	.38120	2.6233	.93441	8
53	.35647	.38153	2.6210	.93431	7
54	.35674	.38186	2.6187	.93420	6
55	.35701	.38220	2.6165	.93410	**5**
56	.35728	.38253	2.6142	.93400	4
57	.35755	.38286	2.6119	.93389	3
58	.35782	.38320	2.6096	.93379	2
59	.35810	.38353	2.6074	.93368	1
60	.35837	.38386	2.6051	.93358	**0**
′	Cos	Cot	Tan	Sin	′

110° (290°) (249°) **69°**

21° (201°) (338°) **158°**

′	Sin	Tan	Cot	Cos	′
0	.35837	.38386	2.6051	.93358	**60**
1	.35864	.38420	2.6028	.93348	59
2	.35891	.38453	2.6006	.93337	58
3	.35918	.38487	2.5983	.93327	57
4	.35945	.38520	2.5961	.93316	56
5	.35973	.38553	2.5938	.93306	**55**
6	.36000	.38587	2.5916	.93295	54
7	.36027	.38620	2.5893	.93285	53
8	.36054	.38654	2.5871	.93274	52
9	.36081	.38687	2.5848	.93264	51
10	.36108	.38721	2.5826	.93253	**50**
11	.36135	.38754	2.5804	.93243	49
12	.36162	.38787	2.5782	.93232	48
13	.36190	.38821	2.5759	.93222	47
14	.36217	.38854	2.5737	.93211	46
15	.36244	.38888	2.5715	.93201	**45**
16	.36271	.38921	2.5693	.93190	44
17	.36298	.38955	2.5671	.93180	43
18	.36325	.38988	2.5649	.93169	42
19	.36352	.39022	2.5627	.93159	41
20	.36379	.39055	2.5605	.93148	**40**
21	.36406	.39089	2.5583	.93137	39
22	.36434	.39122	2.5561	.93127	38
23	.36461	.39156	2.5539	.93116	37
24	.36488	.39190	2.5517	.93106	36
25	.36515	.39223	2.5495	.93095	**35**
26	.36542	.39257	2.5473	.93084	34
27	.36569	.39290	2.5452	.93074	33
28	.36596	.39324	2.5430	.93063	32
29	.36623	.39357	2.5408	.93052	31
30	.36650	.39391	2.5386	.93042	**30**
31	.36677	.39425	2.5365	.93031	29
32	.36704	.39458	2.5343	.93020	28
33	.36731	.39492	2.5322	.93010	27
34	.36758	.39526	2.5300	.92999	26
35	.36785	.39559	2.5279	.92988	**25**
36	.36812	.39593	2.5257	.92978	24
37	.36839	.39626	2.5236	.93967	23
38	.36867	.39660	2.5214	.92956	22
39	.36894	.39694	2.5193	.92945	21
40	.36921	.39727	2.5172	.92935	**20**
41	.36948	.39761	2.5150	.92924	19
42	.36975	.39795	2.5129	.92913	18
43	.37002	.39829	2.5108	.92902	17
44	.37029	.39862	2.5086	.92892	16
45	.37056	.39896	2.5065	.92881	**15**
46	.37083	.39930	2.5044	.92870	14
47	.37110	.39963	2.5023	.92859	13
48	.37137	.39997	2.5002	.92849	12
49	.37164	.40031	2.4981	.92838	11
50	.37191	.40065	2.4960	.92827	**10**
51	.37218	.40098	2.4939	.92816	9
52	.37245	.40132	2.4918	.92805	8
53	.37272	.40166	2.4897	.92794	7
54	.37299	.40200	2.4876	.92784	6
55	.37326	.40234	2.4855	.92773	**5**
56	.37353	.40267	2.4834	.92762	4
57	.37380	.40301	2.4813	.92751	3
58	.37407	.40335	2.4792	.92740	2
59	.37434	.40369	2.4772	.92729	1
60	.37461	.40403	2.4751	.92718	**0**
′	Cos	Cot	Tan	Sin	′

111° (291°) (248°) **68°**

NATURAL FUNCTIONS (Continued)

22° (202°) (337°) **157°**

′	Sin	Tan	Cot	Cos	′
0	.37461	.40403	2.4751	.92718	**60**
1	.37488	.40436	2.4730	.92707	59
2	.37515	.40470	2.4709	.92697	58
3	.37542	.40504	2.4689	.92686	57
4	.37569	.40538	2.4668	.92675	56
5	.37595	.40572	2.4648	.92664	**55**
6	.37622	.40606	2.4627	.92653	54
7	.37649	.40640	2.4606	.92642	53
8	.37676	.40674	2.4586	.92631	52
9	.37703	.40707	2.4566	.92620	51
10	.37730	.40741	2.4545	.92609	**50**
11	.37757	.40775	2.4525	.92598	49
12	.37784	.40809	2.4504	.92587	48
13	.37811	.40843	2.4484	.92576	47
14	.37838	.40877	2.4464	.92565	46
15	.37865	.40911	2.4443	.92554	**45**
16	.37892	.40945	2.4423	.92543	44
17	.37919	.40979	2.4403	.92532	43
18	.37946	.41013	2.4383	.92521	42
19	.37973	.41047	2.4362	.92510	41
20	.37999	.41081	2.4342	.92499	**40**
21	.38026	.41115	2.4322	.92488	39
22	.38053	.41149	2.4302	.92477	38
23	.38080	.41183	2.4282	.92466	37
24	.38107	.41217	2.4262	.92455	36
25	.38134	.41251	2.4242	.92444	**35**
26	.38161	.41285	2.4222	.92432	34
27	.38188	.41319	2.4202	.92421	33
28	.38215	.41353	2.4182	.92410	32
29	.38241	.41387	2.4162	.92399	31
30	.38268	.41421	2.4142	.92388	**30**
31	.38295	.41455	2.4122	.92377	29
32	.38322	.41490	2.4102	.92366	28
33	.38349	.41524	2.4083	.92355	27
34	.38376	.41558	2.4063	.92343	26
35	.38403	.41592	2.4043	.92332	**25**
36	.38430	.41626	2.4023	.92321	24
37	.38456	.41660	2.4004	.92310	23
38	.38483	.41694	2.3984	.92299	22
39	.38510	.41728	2.3964	.92287	21
40	.38537	.41763	2.3945	.92276	**20**
41	.38564	.41797	2.3925	.92265	19
42	.38591	.41831	2.3906	.92254	18
43	.38617	.41865	2.3886	.92243	17
44	.38644	.41899	2.3867	.92231	16
45	.38671	.41933	2.3847	.92220	**15**
46	.38698	.41968	2.3828	.92209	14
47	.38725	.42002	2.3808	.92198	13
48	.38752	.42036	2.3789	.92186	12
49	.38778	.42070	2.3770	.92175	11
50	.38805	.42105	2.3750	.92164	**10**
51	.38832	.42139	2.3731	.92152	9
52	.38859	.42173	2.3712	.92141	8
53	.38886	.42207	2.3693	.92130	7
54	.38912	.42242	2.3673	.92119	6
55	.38939	.42276	2.3654	.92107	**5**
56	.38966	.42310	2.3635	.92096	4
57	.38993	.42345	2.3616	.92085	3
58	.39020	.42379	2.3597	.92073	2
59	.39046	.42413	2.3578	.92062	1
60	.39073	.42447	2.3559	.92050	**0**
′	Cos	Cot	Tan	Sin	′

112° (292°) (247°) **67°**

23° (203°) (336°) **156°**

′	Sin	Tan	Cot	Cos	′
0	.39073	.42447	2.3559	.92050	**60**
1	.39100	.42482	2.3539	.92039	59
2	.39127	.42516	2.3520	.92028	58
3	.39153	.42551	2.3501	.92016	57
4	.39180	.42585	2.3483	.92005	56
5	.39207	.42619	2.3464	.91994	**55**
6	.39234	.42654	2.3445	.91982	54
7	.39260	.42688	2.3426	.91971	53
8	.39287	.42722	2.3407	.91959	52
9	.39314	.42757	2.3388	.91948	51
10	.39341	.42791	2.3369	.91936	**50**
11	.39367	.42826	2.3351	.91925	49
12	.39394	.42860	2.3332	.91914	48
13	.39421	.42894	2.3313	.91902	47
14	.39448	.42929	2.3294	.91891	46
15	.39474	.42963	2.3276	.91879	**45**
16	.39501	.42998	2.3257	.91868	44
17	.39528	.43032	2.3238	.91856	43
18	.39555	.43067	2.3220	.91845	42
19	.39581	.43101	2.3201	.91833	41
20	.39608	.43136	2.3183	.91822	**40**
21	.39635	.43170	2.3164	.91810	39
22	.39661	.43205	2.3146	.91799	38
23	.39688	.43239	2.3127	.91878	37
24	.39715	.43274	2.3109	.91775	36
25	.39741	.43308	2.3090	.91764	**35**
26	.39768	.43343	2.3072	.91752	34
27	.39795	.43378	2.3053	.91741	33
28	.39822	.43412	2.3035	.91729	32
29	.39848	.43447	2.3017	.91718	31
30	.39875	.43481	2.2998	.91706	**30**
31	.39902	.43516	2.2980	.91694	29
32	.39928	.43550	2.2962	.91683	28
33	.39955	.43585	2.2944	.91671	27
34	.39982	.43620	2.2925	.91660	26
35	.40008	.43654	2.2907	.91648	**25**
36	.40035	.43689	2.2889	.91636	24
37	.40062	.43724	2.2871	.91625	23
38	.40088	.43758	2.2853	.91613	22
39	.40115	.43793	2.2835	.91601	21
40	.40141	.43828	2.2817	.91590	**20**
41	.40168	.43862	2.2799	.91578	19
42	.40195	.43897	2.2781	.91566	18
43	.40221	.43932	2.2763	.91555	17
44	.40248	.43966	2.2745	.91543	16
45	.40275	.44001	2.2727	.91531	**15**
46	.40301	.44036	2.2709	.91519	14
47	.40328	.44071	2.2691	.91508	13
48	.40355	.44105	2.2673	.91496	12
49	.40381	.44140	2.2655	.91484	11
50	.40408	.44175	2.2637	.91472	**10**
51	.40434	.44210	2.2620	.91461	9
52	.40461	.44244	2.2602	.91449	8
53	.40488	.44279	2.2584	.91437	7
54	.40514	.44314	2.2566	.91425	6
55	.40541	.44349	2.2549	.91414	**5**
56	.40567	.44384	2.2531	.91402	4
57	.40594	.44418	2.2513	.91390	3
58	.40621	.44453	2.2496	.91378	2
59	.40647	.44488	2.2478	.91366	1
60	.40674	.44523	2.2460	.91355	**0**
′	Cos	Cot	Tan	Sin	′

113° (293°) (246°) **66°**

24° (204°) (335°) **155°**

′	Sin	Tan	Cot	Cos	′
0	.40674	.44523	2.2460	.91355	**60**
1	.40700	.44558	2.2443	.91343	59
2	.40727	.44593	2.2425	.91331	58
3	.40753	.44627	2.2408	.91319	57
4	.40780	.44662	2.2390	.91307	56
5	.40806	.44697	2.2373	.91295	**55**
6	.40833	.44732	2.2355	.91283	54
7	.40860	.44767	2.2338	.91272	53
8	.40886	.44802	2.2320	.91260	52
9	.40913	.44837	2.2303	.91248	51
10	.40939	.44872	2.2286	.91236	**50**
11	.40966	.44907	2.2268	.91224	49
12	.40992	.44942	2.2251	.91212	48
13	.41019	.44977	2.2234	.91200	47
14	.41045	.45012	2.2216	.91188	46
15	.41072	.45047	2.2199	.91176	**45**
16	.41098	.45082	2.2182	.91164	44
17	.41125	.45117	2.2165	.91152	43
18	.41151	.45152	2.2148	.91140	42
19	.41178	.45187	2.2130	.91128	41
20	.41204	.45222	2.2113	.91116	**40**
21	.41231	.45257	2.2096	.91104	39
22	.41257	.45292	2.2079	.91092	38
23	.41284	.45327	2.2062	.91080	37
24	.41310	.45362	2.2045	.91068	36
25	.41337	.45397	2.2028	.91056	**35**
26	.41363	.45432	2.2011	.91044	34
27	.41390	.45467	2.1994	.91032	33
28	.41416	.45502	2.1977	.91020	32
29	.41443	.45538	2.1960	.91008	31
30	.41469	.45573	2.1943	.90996	**30**
31	.41496	.45608	2.1926	.90984	29
32	.41522	.45643	2.1909	.90972	28
33	.41549	.45678	2.1892	.90960	27
34	.41575	.45713	2.1876	.90948	26
35	.41602	.45748	2.1859	.90936	**25**
36	.41628	.45784	2.1842	.90924	24
37	.41655	.45819	2.1825	.90911	23
38	.41681	.45854	2.1808	.90899	22
39	.41707	.45889	2.1792	.90887	21
40	.41734	.45924	2.1775	.90875	**20**
41	.41760	.45960	2.1758	.90863	19
42	.41787	.45995	2.1742	.90851	18
43	.41813	.46030	2.1725	.90839	17
44	.41840	.46065	2.1708	.90826	16
45	.41866	.46101	2.1692	.90814	**15**
46	.41892	.46136	2.1675	.90802	14
47	.41919	.46171	2.1659	.90790	13
48	.41945	.46206	2.1642	.90778	12
49	.41972	.46242	2.1625	.90766	11
50	.41998	.46277	2.1609	.90753	**10**
51	.42024	.46312	2.1592	.90741	9
52	.42051	.46348	2.1576	.90729	8
53	.42077	.46383	2.1560	.90717	7
54	.42104	.46418	2.1543	.90704	6
55	.42130	.46454	2.1527	.90692	**5**
56	.42156	.46489	2.1510	.90680	4
57	.42183	.46525	2.1494	.90668	3
58	.42209	.46560	2.1478	.90655	2
59	.42235	.46595	2.1461	.90643	1
60	.42262	.46631	2.1445	.90631	**0**
′	Cos	Cot	Tan	Sin	′

114° (294°) (245°) **65°**

25° (205°) (334°) **154°**

′	Sin	Tan	Cot	Cos	′
0	.42262	.46631	2.1445	.90631	**60**
1	.42288	.46666	2.1429	.90618	59
2	.42315	.46702	2.1413	.90606	58
3	.42341	.46737	2.1396	.90594	57
4	.42367	.46772	2.1380	.90582	56
5	.42394	.46808	2.1364	.90569	**55**
6	.42420	.46843	2.1348	.90557	54
7	.42446	.46879	2.1332	.90545	53
8	.42473	.46914	2.1315	.90532	52
9	.42499	.46950	2.1299	.90520	51
10	.42525	.46985	2.1283	.90507	**50**
11	.42552	.47021	2.1267	.90495	49
12	.42578	.47056	2.1251	.90483	48
13	.42604	.47092	2.1235	.90470	47
14	.42631	.47128	2.1219	.90458	46
15	.42657	.47163	2.1203	.90446	**45**
16	.42683	.47199	2.1187	.90433	44
17	.42709	.47234	2.1171	.90421	43
18	.42736	.47270	2.1155	.90408	42
19	.42762	.47305	2.1139	.90396	41
20	.42788	.47341	2.1123	.90383	**40**
21	.42815	.47377	2.1107	.90371	39
22	.42841	.47412	2.1092	.90358	38
23	.42867	.47448	2.1076	.90346	37
24	.42894	.47483	2.1060	.90334	36
25	.42920	.47519	2.1044	.90321	**35**
26	.42946	.47555	2.1028	.90309	34
27	.42972	.47590	2.1013	.90296	33
28	.42999	.47626	2.0997	.90284	32
29	.43025	.47662	2.0981	.90271	31
30	.43051	.47698	2.0965	.90259	**30**
31	.43077	.47733	2.0950	.90246	29
32	.43104	.47769	2.0934	.90233	28
33	.43130	.47805	2.0918	.90221	27
34	.43156	.46840	2.0903	.90208	26
35	.43182	.47876	2.0887	.90196	**25**
36	.43209	.47912	2.0872	.90183	24
37	.43235	.47948	2.0856	.90171	23
38	.43261	.47984	2.0840	.90158	22
39	.43287	.48019	2.0825	.90146	21
40	.43313	.48055	2.0809	.90133	**20**
41	.43340	.48091	2.0794	.90120	19
42	.43366	.48127	2.0778	.90108	18
43	.43392	.48163	2.0763	.90095	17
44	.43418	.48198	2.0748	.90082	16
45	.43445	.48234	2.0732	.90070	**15**
46	.43471	.48270	2.0717	.90057	14
47	.43497	.48306	2.0701	.90045	13
48	.43523	.48342	2.0686	.90032	12
49	.43549	.48378	2.0671	.90019	11
50	.43575	.48414	2.0655	.90007	**10**
51	.43602	.48450	2.0640	.89994	9
52	.43628	.48486	2.0625	.89981	8
53	.43654	.48521	2.0609	.89968	7
54	.43680	.48557	2.0594	.89956	6
55	.43706	.48593	2.0579	.89943	**5**
56	.43733	.48629	2.0564	.89930	4
57	.43759	.48665	2.0549	.89918	3
58	.43785	.48701	2.0533	.89905	2
59	.43811	.48737	2.0518	.89892	1
60	.43837	.48773	2.0503	.89879	**0**
′	Cos	Cot	Tan	Sin	′

115° (295°) (244°) **64°**

NATURAL FUNCTIONS (Continued)

26° (206°) (333°) **153°**

′	Sin	Tan	Cot	Cos	′
0	.43837	.48773	2.0503	.89879	**60**
1	.43863	.48809	2.0488	.89867	59
2	.43889	.48845	2.0473	.89854	58
3	.43916	.48881	2.0458	.89841	57
4	.43942	.48917	2.0443	.89828	56
5	.43968	.48953	2.0428	.89816	**55**
6	.43994	.48989	2.0413	.89803	54
7	.44020	.49026	2.0398	.89790	53
8	.44046	.49062	2.0383	.89777	52
9	.44072	.49098	2.0368	.89764	51
10	.44098	.49134	2.0353	.89752	**50**
11	.44124	.49170	2.0338	.89739	49
12	.44151	.49206	2.0323	.89726	48
13	.44177	.49242	2.0308	.89713	47
14	.44203	.49278	2.0293	.89700	46
15	.44229	.49315	2.0278	.89687	**45**
16	.44255	.49351	2.0263	.89674	44
17	.44281	.49387	2.0248	.89662	43
18	.44307	.49423	2.0233	.89649	42
19	.44333	.49459	2.0219	.89636	41
20	.44359	.49495	2.0204	.89623	**40**
21	.44385	.49532	2.0189	.89610	39
22	.44411	.49568	2.0174	.89597	38
23	.44437	.49604	2.0160	.89584	37
24	.44464	.49640	2.0145	.89571	36
25	.44490	.49677	2.0130	.89558	**35**
26	.44516	.49713	2.0115	.89545	34
27	.44542	.49749	2.0101	.89532	33
28	.44568	.49786	2.0086	.89519	32
29	.44594	.49822	2.0072	.89506	31
30	.44620	.49858	2.0057	.89493	**30**
31	.44646	.49894	2.0042	.89480	29
32	.44672	.49931	2.0028	.89467	28
33	.44698	.49967	2.0013	.89454	27
34	.44724	.50004	1.9999	.89441	26
35	.44750	.50040	1.9984	.89428	**25**
36	.44776	.50076	1.9970	.89415	24
37	.44802	.50113	1.9955	.89402	23
38	.44828	.50149	1.9941	.89389	22
39	.44854	.50185	1.9926	.89376	21
40	.44880	.50222	1.9912	.89363	**20**
41	.44906	.50258	1.9897	.89350	19
42	.44932	.50295	1.9883	.89337	18
43	.44958	.50331	1.9868	.89324	17
44	.44984	.50368	1.9854	.89311	16
45	.45010	.50404	1.9840	.89298	**15**
46	.45036	.50441	1.9825	.89285	14
47	.45062	.50477	1.9811	.89272	13
48	.45088	.50514	1.9797	.89259	12
49	.45114	.50550	1.9782	.89245	11
50	.45140	.50587	1.9768	.89232	**10**
51	.45166	.50623	1.9754	.89219	9
52	.45192	.50660	1.9740	.89206	8
53	.45218	.50696	1.9725	.89193	7
54	.45243	.50733	1.9711	.89180	6
55	.45269	.50769	1.9697	.89167	**5**
56	.45295	.50806	1.9683	.89153	4
57	.45321	.50843	1.9669	.89140	3
58	.45347	.50879	1.9654	.89127	2
59	.45373	.50916	1.9640	.89114	1
60	.45399	.50953	1.9626	.89101	**0**
′	Cos	Cot	Tan	Sin	′

116° (296°) (243°) **63°**

27° (207°) (332°) **152°**

′	Sin	Tan	Cot	Cos	′
0	.45399	.50953	1.9626	.89101	**60**
1	.45425	.50989	1.9612	.89087	59
2	.45451	.51026	1.9598	.89074	58
3	.45477	.51063	1.9584	.89061	57
4	.45503	.51099	1.9570	.89048	56
5	.45529	.51136	1.9556	.89035	**55**
6	.45554	.51173	1.9542	.89021	54
7	.45580	.51209	1.9528	.89008	53
8	.45606	.51246	1.9514	.88995	52
9	.45632	.51283	1.9500	.88981	51
10	.45658	.51319	1.9486	.88968	**50**
11	.45684	.51356	1.9472	.88955	49
12	.45710	.51393	1.9458	.88942	48
13	.45736	.51430	1.9444	.88928	47
14	.45762	.51467	1.9430	.88915	46
15	.45787	.51503	1.9416	.88902	**45**
16	.45813	.51540	1.9402	.88888	44
17	.45839	.51577	1.9388	.88875	43
18	.45865	.51614	1.9375	.88862	42
19	.45891	.51651	1.9361	.88848	41
20	.45917	.51688	1.9347	.88835	**40**
21	.45942	.51724	1.9333	.88822	39
22	.45968	.51761	1.9319	.88808	38
23	.45994	.51798	1.9306	.88795	37
24	.46020	.51835	1.9292	.88782	36
25	.46046	.51872	1.9278	.88768	**35**
26	.46072	.51909	1.9265	.88755	34
27	.46097	.51946	1.9251	.88741	33
28	.46123	.51983	1.9237	.88728	32
29	.46149	.52020	1.9223	.88715	31
30	.46175	.52057	1.9210	.88701	**30**
31	.46201	.52094	1.9196	.88688	29
32	.46226	.52131	1.9183	.88674	28
33	.46252	.52168	1.9169	.88661	27
34	.46278	.52205	1.9155	.88647	26
35	.46304	.52242	1.9142	.88634	**25**
36	.46330	.52279	1.9128	.88620	24
37	.46355	.52316	1.9115	.88607	23
38	.46381	.52353	1.9101	.88953	22
39	.46407	.52390	1.9088	.88580	21
40	.46433	.52427	1.9074	.88566	**20**
41	.46458	.52464	1.9061	.88553	19
42	.46484	.52501	1.9047	.88539	18
43	.46510	.52538	1.9034	.88526	17
44	.46536	.52575	1.9020	.88512	16
45	.46561	.52613	1.9007	.88499	**15**
46	.46587	.52650	1.8993	.88485	14
47	.46613	.52687	1.8980	.88472	13
48	.46639	.52724	1.8967	.88458	12
49	.46664	.52761	1.8953	.88445	11
50	.46690	.52798	1.8940	.88431	**10**
51	.46716	.52836	1.8927	.88417	9
52	.46742	.52873	1.8913	.88404	8
53	.46767	.52910	1.8900	.88390	7
54	.46793	.52947	1.8887	.88377	6
55	.46819	.52985	1.8873	.88363	**5**
56	.46844	.53022	1.8860	.88349	4
57	.46870	.53059	1.8847	.88336	3
58	.46896	.53096	1.8834	.88322	2
59	.46921	.53134	1.8820	.88308	1
60	.46947	.53171	1.8807	.88295	**0**
′	Cos	Cot	Tan	Sin	′

117° (297°) (242°) **62°**

NATURAL FUNCTIONS (Continued)

28° (208°) — (331°) **151°**

′	Sin	Tan	Cot	Cos	′
0	.46947	.53171	1.8807	.88295	**60**
1	.46973	.53208	1.8794	.88281	59
2	.46999	.53246	1.8781	.88267	58
3	.47024	.53283	1.8768	.88254	57
4	.47050	.53320	1.8755	.88240	56
5	.47076	.53358	1.8741	.88226	**55**
6	.47101	.53395	1.8728	.88213	54
7	.47127	.53432	1.8715	.88199	53
8	.47153	.53470	1.8702	.88185	52
9	.47178	.53507	1.8689	.88172	51
10	.47204	.53545	1.8676	.88158	**50**
11	.47229	.53582	1.8663	.88144	49
12	.47255	.53620	1.8650	.88130	48
13	.47281	.53657	1.8637	.88117	47
14	.47306	.53694	1.8624	.88103	46
15	.47332	.53732	1.8611	.88089	**45**
16	.47358	.53769	1.8598	.88075	44
17	.47383	.53807	1.8585	.88062	43
18	.47409	.53844	1.8572	.88048	42
19	.47434	.53882	1.8559	.88034	41
20	.47460	.53920	1.8546	.88020	**40**
21	.47486	.53957	1.8533	.88006	39
22	.47511	.53995	1.8520	.87993	38
23	.47537	.54032	1.8507	.87979	37
24	.47562	.54070	1.8495	.87965	36
25	.47588	.54107	1.8482	.87951	**35**
26	.47614	.54145	1.8469	.87937	34
27	.47639	.54183	1.8456	.87923	33
28	.47665	.54220	1.8443	.87909	32
29	.47690	.54258	1.8430	.87896	31
30	.47716	.54296	1.8418	.87882	**30**
31	.47741	.54333	1.8405	.87868	29
32	.47767	.54371	1.8392	.87854	28
33	.47793	.54409	1.8379	.87840	27
34	.47818	.54446	1.8367	.87826	26
35	.47844	.54484	1.8354	.87812	**25**
36	.47869	.54522	1.8341	.87798	24
37	.47895	.54560	1.8329	.87784	23
38	.47920	.54597	1.8316	.87770	22
39	.47946	.54635	1.8303	.87756	21
40	.47971	.54673	1.8291	.87743	**20**
41	.47997	.54711	1.8278	.87729	19
42	.48022	.54748	1.8265	.87715	18
43	.48048	.54786	1.8253	.87701	17
44	.48073	.54824	1.8240	.87687	16
45	.48099	.54862	1.8228	.87673	**15**
46	.48124	.54900	1.8215	.87659	14
47	.48150	.54938	1.8202	.87645	13
48	.48175	.54975	1.8190	.87631	12
49	.48201	.55013	1.8177	.87617	11
50	.48226	.55051	1.8165	.87603	**10**
51	.48252	.55089	1.8152	.87589	9
52	.48277	.55127	1.8140	.87575	8
53	.48303	.55165	1.8127	.87561	7
54	.48328	.55203	1.8115	.87546	6
55	.48354	.55241	1.8103	.87532	**5**
56	.48379	.55279	1.8090	.87518	4
57	.48405	.55317	1.8078	.87504	3
58	.48430	.55355	1.8065	.87490	2
59	.48456	.55393	1.8053	.87476	1
60	.48481	.55431	1.8040	.87462	**0**
′	Cos	Cot	Tan	Sin	′

118° (298°) — (241°) **61°**

29° (209°) — (330°) **150°**

′	Sin	Tan	Cot	Cos	′
0	.48481	.55431	1.8040	.87462	**60**
1	.48506	.55469	1.8028	.87448	59
2	.48532	.55507	1.8016	.87434	58
3	.48557	.55545	1.8003	.87420	57
4	.48583	.55583	1.7991	.87406	56
5	.48608	.55621	1.7979	.87391	**55**
6	.48634	.55659	1.7966	.87377	54
7	.48659	.55697	1.7954	.87363	53
8	.48684	.55736	1.7942	.87349	52
9	.48710	.55774	1.7930	.87335	51
10	.48735	.55812	1.7917	.87321	**50**
11	.48761	.55850	1.7905	.87306	49
12	.48786	.55888	1.7893	.87292	48
13	.48811	.55926	1.7881	.87278	47
14	.48837	.55964	1.7868	.87264	46
15	.48862	.56003	1.7856	.87250	**45**
16	.48888	.56041	1.7844	.87235	44
17	.48913	.56079	1.7832	.87221	43
18	.48938	.56117	1.7820	.87207	42
19	.48964	.56156	1.7808	.87193	41
20	.48989	.56194	1.7796	.87178	**40**
21	.49014	.56232	1.7783	.87164	39
22	.49040	.56270	1.7771	.87150	38
23	.49065	.56309	1.7759	.87136	37
24	.49090	.56347	1.7747	.87121	36
25	.49116	.56385	1.7735	.87107	**35**
26	.49141	.56424	1.7723	.87093	34
27	.49166	.56462	1.7711	.87079	33
28	.49192	.56501	1.7699	.87064	32
29	.49217	.56539	1.7687	.87050	31
30	.49242	.56577	1.7675	.87036	**30**
31	.49268	.56616	1.7663	.87021	29
32	.49293	.56654	1.7651	.87007	28
33	.49318	.56693	1.7639	.86993	27
34	.49344	.56731	1.7627	.86978	26
35	.49369	.56769	1.7615	.86964	**25**
36	.49394	.56808	1.7603	.86949	24
37	.49419	.56846	1.7591	.86935	23
38	.49445	.56885	1.7579	.86921	22
39	.49470	.56923	1.7567	.86906	21
40	.49495	.56962	1.7556	.86892	**20**
41	.49521	.57000	1.7544	.86878	19
42	.49546	.57039	1.7532	.86863	18
43	.49571	.57078	1.7520	.86849	17
44	.49596	.57116	1.7508	.86834	16
45	.49622	.57155	1.7496	.86820	**15**
46	.49647	.57193	1.7485	.86805	14
47	.49672	.57232	1.7473	.86791	13
48	.49697	.57271	1.7461	.86777	12
49	.49723	.57309	1.7449	.86762	11
50	.49748	.57348	1.7437	.86748	**10**
51	.49773	.57386	1.7426	.86733	9
52	.49798	.57425	1.7414	.86719	8
53	.49824	.57464	1.7402	.86704	7
54	.49849	.57503	1.7391	.86690	6
55	.49874	.57541	1.7379	.86675	**5**
56	.49899	.57580	1.7367	.86661	4
57	.49924	.57619	1.7355	.86646	3
58	.49950	.57657	1.7344	.86632	2
59	.49975	.57696	1.7332	.86617	1
60	.50000	.57735	1.7321	.86603	**0**
′	Cos	Cot	Tan	Sin	′

119° (299°) — (240°) **60°**

30° (210°) (329°) **149°**

′	Sin	Tan	Cot	Cos	′
0	.50000	.57735	1.7321	.86603	**60**
1	.50025	.57774	1.7309	.86588	59
2	.50050	.57813	1.7297	.86573	58
3	.50076	.57851	1.7286	.86559	57
4	.50101	.57890	1.7274	.86544	56
5	.50126	.57929	1.7262	.86530	**55**
6	.50151	.57968	1.7251	.86515	54
7	.50176	.58007	1.7239	.86501	53
8	.50201	.58046	1.7228	.86486	52
9	.50227	.58085	1.7216	.86471	51
10	.50252	.58124	1.7205	.86457	**50**
11	.50277	.58162	1.7193	.86442	49
12	.50302	.58201	1.7182	.86427	48
13	.50327	.58240	1.7170	.86413	47
14	.50352	.58279	1.7159	.86398	46
15	.50377	.58318	1.7147	.86384	**45**
16	.50403	.58357	1.7136	.86369	44
17	.50428	.58396	1.7124	.86354	43
18	.50453	.58435	1.7113	.86340	42
19	.50478	.58474	1.7102	.86325	41
20	.50503	.58513	1.7090	.86310	**40**
21	.50528	.58552	1.7079	.86295	39
22	.50553	.58591	1.7067	.86281	38
23	.50578	.58631	1.7056	.86266	37
24	.50603	.58670	1.7045	.86251	36
25	.50628	.58709	1.7033	.86237	**35**
26	.50654	.58748	1.7022	.86222	34
27	.50679	.58787	1.7011	.86207	33
28	.50704	.58826	1.6999	.86192	32
29	.50729	.58865	1.6988	.86178	31
30	.50754	.58905	1.6977	.86163	**30**
31	.50779	.58944	1.6965	.86148	29
32	.50804	.58983	1.6954	.86133	28
33	.50829	.59022	1.6943	.86119	27
34	.50854	.59061	1.6932	.86104	26
35	.50879	.59101	1.6920	.86089	**25**
36	.50904	.59140	1.6909	.86074	24
37	.50929	.59179	1.6898	.86059	23
38	.50954	.59218	1.6887	.86045	22
39	.50979	.59258	1.6875	.86030	21
40	.51004	.59297	1.6864	.86015	**20**
41	.51029	.59336	1.6853	.86000	19
42	.51054	.59376	1.6842	.85985	18
43	.51079	.59415	1.6831	.85970	17
44	.51104	.59454	1.6820	.85956	16
45	.51129	.59494	1.6808	.85941	**15**
46	.51154	.59533	1.6797	.85926	14
47	.51179	.59573	1.6786	.85911	13
48	.51204	.59612	1.6775	.85896	12
49	.51229	.59651	1.6764	.85881	11
50	.51254	.59691	1.6753	.85866	**10**
51	.51279	.59730	1.6742	.85851	9
52	.51304	.59770	1.6731	.85836	8
53	.51329	.59809	1.6720	.85821	7
54	.51354	.59849	1.6709	.85806	6
55	.51379	.59888	1.6698	.85792	**5**
56	.51404	.59928	1.6687	.85777	4
57	.51429	.59967	1.6676	.85762	3
58	.51454	.60007	1.6665	.85747	2
59	.51479	.60046	1.6654	.85732	1
60	.51504	.60086	1.6643	.85717	**0**
′	Cos	Cot	Tan	Sin	′

120° (300°) (239°) **59°**

31° (211°) (328°) **148°**

′	Sin	Tan	Cot	Cos	′
0	.51504	.60086	1.6643	.85717	**60**
1	.51529	.60126	1.6632	.85702	59
2	.51554	.60165	1.6621	.85687	58
3	.51579	.60205	1.6610	.85672	57
4	.51604	.60245	1.6599	.85657	56
5	.51628	.60284	1.6588	.85642	**55**
6	.51653	.60324	1.6577	.85627	54
7	.51678	.60364	1.6566	.85612	53
8	.51703	.60403	1.6555	.85597	52
9	.51728	.60443	1.6545	.85582	51
10	.51753	.60483	1.6534	.85567	**50**
11	.51778	.60522	1.6523	.85551	49
12	.51803	.60562	1.6512	.85536	48
13	.51828	.60602	1.6501	.85521	47
14	.51852	.60642	1.6490	.85506	46
15	.51877	.60681	1.6479	.85491	**45**
16	.51902	.60721	1.6469	.85476	44
17	.51927	.60761	1.6458	.85461	43
18	.51952	.60801	1.6447	.85446	42
19	.51977	.60841	1.6436	.85431	41
20	.52002	.60881	1.6426	.85416	**40**
21	.52026	.60921	1.6415	.85401	39
22	.52051	.60960	1.6404	.85385	38
23	.52076	.61000	1.6393	.85370	37
24	.52101	.61040	1.6383	.85355	36
25	.52126	.61080	1.6372	.85340	**35**
26	.52151	.61120	1.6361	.85325	34
27	.52175	.61160	1.6351	.85310	33
28	.52200	.61200	1.6340	.85294	32
29	.52225	.61240	1.6329	.85279	31
30	.52250	.61280	1.6319	.85264	**30**
31	.52275	.61320	1.6308	.85249	29
32	.52299	.61360	1.6297	.85234	28
33	.52324	.61400	1.6287	.85218	27
34	.52349	.61440	1.6276	.85203	26
35	.52374	.61480	1.6265	.85188	**25**
36	.52399	.61520	1.6255	.85173	24
37	.52423	.61561	1.6244	.85157	23
38	.52448	.61601	1.6234	.85142	22
39	.52473	.61641	1.6223	.85127	21
40	.52498	.61681	1.6212	.85112	**20**
41	.52522	.61721	1.6202	.85096	19
42	.52547	.61761	1.6191	.85081	18
43	.52572	.61801	1.6181	.85066	17
44	.52597	.61842	1.6170	.85051	16
45	.52621	.61882	1.6160	.85035	**15**
46	.52646	.61922	1.6149	.85020	14
47	.52671	.61962	1.6139	.85005	13
48	.52696	.62003	1.6128	.84989	12
49	.52720	.62043	1.6118	.84974	11
50	.52745	.62083	1.6107	.84959	**10**
51	.52770	.62124	1.6097	.84943	9
52	.52794	.62164	1.6087	.84928	8
53	.52819	.62204	1.6076	.84913	7
54	.52844	.62245	1.6066	.84897	6
55	.52869	.62285	1.6055	.84882	**5**
56	.52893	.62325	1.6045	.84866	4
57	.52918	.62366	1.6034	.84851	3
58	.52943	.62406	1.6024	.84836	2
59	.52967	.62446	1.6014	.84820	1
60	.52992	.62487	1.6003	.84805	**0**
′	Cos	Cot	Tan	Sin	′

121° (301°) (238°) **58°**

NATURAL FUNCTIONS (Continued)

32° (212°) (327°) **147°**

′	Sin	Tan	Cot	Cos	′
0	.52992	.62487	1.6003	.84805	**60**
1	.53017	.62527	1.5993	.84789	59
2	.53041	.62568	1.5983	.84774	58
3	.53066	.62608	1.5972	.84759	57
4	.53091	.62649	1.5962	.84743	56
5	.53115	.62689	1.5952	.84728	**55**
6	.53140	.62730	1.5941	.84712	54
7	.53164	.62770	1.5931	.84697	53
8	.53189	.62811	1.5921	.84681	52
9	.53214	.62852	1.5911	.84666	51
10	.53238	.62892	1.5900	.84650	**50**
11	.53263	.62933	1.5890	.84635	49
12	.53288	.62973	1.5880	.84619	48
13	.53312	.63014	1.5869	.84604	47
14	.53337	.63055	1.5859	.84588	46
15	.53361	.63095	1.5849	.84573	**45**
16	.53386	.63136	1.5839	.84557	44
17	.53411	.63177	1.5829	.84542	43
18	.53435	.63217	1.5818	.84526	42
19	.53460	.63258	1.5808	.84511	41
20	.53484	.63299	1.5798	.84495	**40**
21	.53509	.63340	1.5788	.84480	39
22	.53534	.63380	1.5778	.84464	38
23	.53558	.63421	1.5768	.84448	37
24	.53583	.63462	1.5757	.84433	36
25	.53607	.63503	1.5747	.84417	**35**
26	.53632	.63544	1.5737	.84402	34
27	.53656	.63584	1.5727	.84386	33
28	.53681	.63625	1.5717	.84370	32
29	.53705	.63666	1.5707	.84355	31
30	.53730	.63707	1.5697	.84339	**30**
31	.53754	.63748	1.5687	.84324	29
32	.53779	.63789	1.5677	.84308	28
33	.53804	.63830	1.5667	.84292	27
34	.53828	.63871	1.5657	.84277	26
35	.53853	.63912	1.5647	.84261	**25**
36	.53877	.63953	1.5637	.84245	24
37	.53902	.63994	1.5627	.84230	23
38	.53926	.64035	1.5617	.84214	22
39	.53951	.64076	1.5607	.84198	21
40	.53975	.64117	1.5597	.84182	**20**
41	.54000	.64158	1.5587	.84167	19
42	.54024	.64199	1.5577	.84151	18
43	.54049	.64240	1.5567	.84135	17
44	.54073	.64281	1.5557	.84120	16
45	.54097	.64322	1.5547	.84104	**15**
46	.54122	.64363	1.5537	.84088	14
47	.54146	.64404	1.5527	.84072	13
48	.54171	.64446	1.5517	.84057	12
49	.54195	.64487	1.5507	.84041	11
50	.54220	.64528	1.5497	.84025	**10**
51	.54244	.64569	1.5487	.84009	9
52	.54269	.64610	1.5477	.83994	8
53	.54293	.64652	1.5468	.83978	7
54	.54317	.64693	1.5458	.83962	6
55	.54342	.64734	1.5448	.83946	**5**
56	.54366	.64775	1.5438	.83930	4
57	.54391	.64817	1.5428	.83915	3
58	.54415	.64858	1.5418	.83899	2
59	.54440	.64899	1.5408	.83883	1
60	.54464	.64941	1.5399	.83867	**0**
′	Cos	Cot	Tan	Sin	′

122° (302°) (237°) **57°**

33° (213°) (326°) **146°**

′	Sin	Tan	Cot	Cos	′
0	.54464	.64941	1.5399	.83867	**60**
1	.54488	.64982	1.5389	.83851	59
2	.54513	.65024	1.5379	.83835	58
3	.54537	.65065	1.5369	.83819	57
4	.54561	.65106	1.5359	.83804	56
5	.54586	.65148	1.5350	.83788	**55**
6	.54610	.65189	1.5340	.83772	54
7	.54635	.65231	1.5330	.83756	53
8	.54659	.65272	1.5320	.83740	52
9	.54683	.65314	1.5311	.83724	51
10	.54708	.65355	1.5301	.83708	**50**
11	.54732	.65397	1.5291	.83692	49
12	.54756	.65438	1.5282	.83676	48
13	.54781	.65480	1.5272	.83660	47
14	.54805	.65521	1.5262	.83645	46
15	.54829	.65563	1.5253	.83629	**45**
16	.54854	.65604	1.5243	.83613	44
17	.54878	.65646	1.5233	.83597	43
18	.54902	.65688	1.5224	.83581	42
19	.54927	.65729	1.5214	.83565	41
20	.54951	.65771	1.5204	.83549	**40**
21	.54975	.65813	1.5195	.83533	39
22	.54999	.65854	1.5185	.83517	38
23	.55024	.65896	1.5175	.83501	37
24	.55048	.65938	1.5166	.83485	36
25	.55072	.65980	1.5156	.83469	**35**
26	.55097	.66021	1.5147	.83453	34
27	.55121	.66063	1.5137	.83437	33
28	.55145	.66105	1.5127	.83421	32
29	.55169	.66147	1.5118	.83405	31
30	.55194	.66189	1.5108	.83389	**30**
31	.55218	.66230	1.5099	.83373	29
32	.55242	.66272	1.5089	.83356	28
33	.55266	.66314	1.5080	.83340	27
34	.55291	.66356	1.5070	.83324	26
35	.55315	.66398	1.5061	.83308	**25**
36	.55339	.66440	1.5051	.83292	24
37	.55363	.66482	1.5042	.83276	23
38	.55388	.66254	1.5032	.83260	22
39	.55412	.66566	1.5023	.83244	21
40	.55436	.66608	1.5013	.83228	**20**
41	.55460	.66650	1.5004	.83212	19
42	.55484	.66692	1.4994	.83195	18
43	.55509	.66734	1.4985	.83179	17
44	.55533	.66776	1.4975	.83163	16
45	.55557	.66818	1.4966	.83147	**15**
46	.55581	.66860	1.4957	.83131	14
47	.55605	.66902	1.4947	.83115	13
48	.55630	.66944	1.4938	.83098	12
49	.55654	.66986	1.4928	.83082	11
50	.55678	.67028	1.4919	.83066	**10**
51	.55702	.67071	1.4910	.83050	9
52	.55726	.67113	1.4900	.83034	8
53	.55750	.67155	1.4891	.83017	7
54	.55775	.67197	1.4882	.83001	6
55	.55799	.67239	1.4872	.82985	**5**
56	.55823	.67282	1.4863	.82969	4
57	.55847	.67324	1.4854	.82953	3
58	.55871	.67366	1.4844	.82936	2
59	.55895	.67409	1.4835	.82920	1
60	.55919	.67451	1.4826	.82904	**0**
′	Cos	Cot	Tan	Sin	′

123° (303°) (236°) **56°**

NATURAL FUNCTIONS (Continued)

34° (214°) (325°) **145°**

′	Sin	Tan	Cot	Cos	′
0	.55919	.67451	1.4826	.82904	**60**
1	.55943	.67493	1.4816	.82887	59
2	.55968	.67536	1.4807	.82871	58
3	.55992	.67578	1.4798	.82855	57
4	.56016	.67620	1.4788	.82839	56
5	.56040	.67663	1.4779	.82822	**55**
6	.56064	.67705	1.4770	.82806	54
7	.56088	.67748	1.4761	.82790	53
8	.56112	.67790	1.4751	.82773	52
9	.56136	.67832	1 4742	.82757	51
10	.56160	.67875	1.4733	.82741	**50**
11	.56184	.67917	1.4724	.82724	49
12	.56208	.67960	1.4715	.82708	48
13	.56232	.68002	1.4705	.82692	47
14	.56256	.68045	1.4696	.82675	46
15	.56280	.68088	1.4687	.82659	**45**
16	.56305	.68130	1.4678	.82643	44
17	.56329	.68173	1.4669	.82626	43
18	.56353	.68215	1.4659	.82610	42
19	.56377	.68258	1.4650	.82593	41
20	.56401	.68301	1.4641	.82577	**40**
21	.56425	.68343	1.4632	.82561	39
22	.56449	.68386	1.4623	.82544	38
23	.56473	.68429	1.4614	.82528	37
24	.56497	.68471	1.4605	.82511	36
25	.56521	.68514	1.4596	.82495	**35**
26	.56545	.68557	1.4586	.82478	34
27	.56569	.68600	1.4577	.82462	33
28	.56593	.68642	1.4568	.82446	32
29	.56617	.68685	1.4559	.82429	31
30	.56641	.68728	1.4550	.82413	**30**
31	.56665	.68771	1.4541	.82396	29
32	.56689	.68814	1.4532	.82380	28
33	.56713	.68857	1.4523	.82363	27
34	.56736	.68900	1.4514	.82347	26
35	.56760	.68942	1.4505	.82330	**25**
36	.56784	.68985	1.4496	.82314	24
37	.56808	.69028	1.4487	.82297	23
38	.56832	.69071	1.4478	.82281	22
39	.56856	.69114	1.4469	.82264	21
40	.56880	.69157	1.4460	.82248	**20**
41	.56904	.69200	1.4451	.82231	19
42	.56928	.69243	1.4442	.82214	18
43	.56952	.69286	1.4433	.82198	17
44	.56976	.69329	1.4424	.82181	16
45	.57000	.69372	1.4415	.82165	**15**
46	.57024	.69416	1.4406	.82148	14
47	.57047	.69459	1.4397	.82132	13
48	.57071	.69502	1.4388	.82115	12
49	.57095	.69545	1.4379	.82098	11
50	.57119	.69588	1.4370	.82082	**10**
51	.57143	.69631	1.4361	.82065	9
52	.57167	.69675	1.4352	.82048	8
53	.57191	.69718	1.4344	.82032	7
54	.57215	.69761	1.4335	.82015	6
55	.57238	.69804	1.4326	.81999	**5**
56	.57262	.69847	1.4317	.81982	4
57	.57286	.69891	1.4308	.81965	3
58	.57310	.69934	1.4299	.81949	2
59	.57334	.69977	1.4290	.81932	1
60	.57358	.70021	1.4281	.81915	**0**
′	Cos	Cot	Tan	Sin	′

124° (304°) (235°) **55°**

35° (215°) (324°) **144°**

′	Sin	Tan	Cot	Cos	′
0	.57358	.70021	1.4281	.81915	**60**
1	.57381	.70064	1.4273	.81899	59
2	.57405	.70107	1.4264	.81882	58
3	.57429	.70151	1.4255	.81865	57
4	.57453	.70194	1.4246	.81848	56
5	.57477	.70238	1.4237	.81832	**55**
6	.57501	.70281	1.4229	.81815	54
7	.57524	.70325	1.4220	.81798	53
8	.57548	.70368	1.4211	.81782	52
9	.57572	.70412	1.4202	.81765	51
10	.57596	.70455	1.4193	.81748	**50**
11	.57619	.70499	1.4185	.81731	49
12	.57643	.70542	1.4176	.81714	48
13	.57667	.70586	1.4167	.81698	47
14	.57691	.70629	1.4158	.81681	46
15	.57715	.70673	1.4150	.81664	**45**
16	.57738	.70717	1.4141	.81647	44
17	.57762	.70760	1.4132	.81631	43
18	.57786	.70804	1.4124	.81614	42
19	.57810	.70848	1.4115	.81597	41
20	.57833	.70891	1.4106	.81580	**40**
21	.57857	.70935	1.4097	.81563	39
22	.57881	.70979	1.4089	.81546	38
23	.57904	.71023	1.4080	.81530	37
24	.57928	.71066	1.4071	.81513	36
25	.57952	.71110	1.4063	.81496	**35**
26	.57976	.71154	1.4054	.81479	34
27	.57999	.71198	1.4045	.81462	33
28	.58023	.71242	1.4037	.81445	32
29	.58047	.71285	1.4028	.81428	31
30	.58070	.71329	1.4019	.81412	**30**
31	.58094	.71373	1.4011	.81395	29
32	.58118	.71417	1.4002	.81378	28
33	.58141	.71461	1.3994	.81361	27
34	.58165	.71505	1.3985	.81344	26
35	.58189	.71549	1.3976	.81327	**25**
36	.58212	.71593	1.3968	.81310	24
37	.58236	.71637	1.3959	.81293	23
38	.58260	.71681	1.3951	.81276	22
39	.58283	.71725	1.3942	.81259	21
40	.58307	.71769	1.3934	.81242	**20**
41	.58330	.71813	1.3925	.81225	19
42	.58354	.71857	1.3916	.81208	18
43	.58378	.71901	1.3908	.81191	17
44	.58401	.71946	1.3899	.81174	16
45	.58425	.71990	1.3891	.81157	**15**
46	.58449	.72034	1.3882	.81140	14
47	.58472	.72078	1.3874	.81123	13
48	.58496	.72122	1.3865	.81106	12
49	.58519	.72167	1.3857	.81089	11
50	.58543	.72211	1.3848	.81072	**10**
51	.58567	.72255	1.3840	.81055	9
52	.58590	.72299	1.3831	.81038	8
53	.58614	.72344	1.3823	.81021	7
54	.58637	.72388	1.3814	.81004	6
55	.58661	.72432	1.3806	.80987	**5**
56	.58684	.72477	1.3798	.80970	4
57	.58708	.72521	1.3789	.80953	3
58	.58731	.72565	1.3781	.80936	2
59	.58755	.72610	1.3772	.80919	1
60	.58779	.72654	1.3764	.80902	**0**
′	Cos	Cot	Tan	Sin	′

125° (305°) (234°) **54°**

NATURAL FUNCTIONS (Continued)

36° (216°) (323°) **143°**

′	Sin	Tan	Cot	Cos	′
0	.58779	.72654	1.3764	.80902	**60**
1	.58802	.72699	1.3755	.80885	59
2	.58826	.72743	1.3747	.80867	58
3	.58849	.72788	1.3739	.80850	57
4	.58873	.72832	1.3730	.80833	56
5	.58896	.72877	1.3722	.80816	**55**
6	.58920	.72921	1.3713	.80799	54
7	.58943	.72966	1.3705	.80782	53
8	.58967	.73010	1.3697	.80765	52
9	.58990	.73055	1.3688	.80748	51
10	.59014	.73100	1.3680	.80730	**50**
11	.59037	.73144	1.3672	.80713	49
12	.59061	.73189	1.3663	.80696	48
13	.59084	.73234	1.3655	.80679	47
14	.59108	.73278	1.3647	.80662	46
15	.59131	.73323	1.3638	.80644	**45**
16	.59154	.73368	1.3630	.80627	44
17	.59178	.73413	1.3622	.80610	43
18	.59201	.73457	1.3613	.80593	42
19	.59225	.73502	1.3605	.80576	41
20	.59248	.73547	1.3597	.80558	**40**
21	.59272	.73592	1.3588	.80541	39
22	.59295	.73637	1.3580	.80524	38
23	.59318	.73681	1.3572	.80507	37
24	.59342	.73726	1.3564	.80489	36
25	.59365	.73771	1.3555	.80472	**35**
26	.59389	.73816	1.3547	.80455	34
27	.59412	.73861	1.3539	.80438	33
28	.59436	.73906	1.3531	.80420	32
29	.59459	.73951	1.3522	.80403	31
30	.59482	.73996	1.3514	.80386	**30**
31	.59506	.74041	1.3506	.80368	29
32	.59529	.74086	1.3498	.80351	28
33	.59552	.74131	1.3490	.80334	27
34	.59576	.74176	1.3481	.80316	26
35	.59599	.74221	1.3473	.80299	**25**
36	.59622	.74267	1.3465	.80282	24
37	.59646	.74312	1.3457	.80264	23
38	.59669	.74357	1.3449	.80247	22
39	.59693	.74402	1.3440	.80230	21
40	.59716	.74447	1.3432	.80212	**20**
41	.59739	.74492	1.3424	.80195	19
42	.59763	.74538	1.3416	.80178	18
43	.59786	.74583	1.3408	.80160	17
44	.59809	.74628	1.3400	.80143	16
45	.59832	.74674	1.3392	.80125	**15**
46	.59856	.74719	1.3384	.80108	14
47	.59879	.74764	1.3375	.80091	13
48	.59902	.74810	1.3367	.80073	12
49	.59926	.74855	1.3359	.80056	11
50	.59949	.74900	1.3351	.80038	**10**
51	.59972	.74946	1.3343	.80021	9
52	.59995	.74991	1.3335	.80003	8
53	.60019	.75037	1.3327	.79986	7
54	.60042	.75082	1.3319	.79968	6
55	.60065	.75128	1.3311	.79951	**5**
56	.60089	.75173	1.3303	.79934	4
57	.60112	.75219	1.3295	.79916	3
58	.60135	.75264	1.3287	.79899	2
59	.60158	.75310	1.3278	.79881	1
60	.60182	.75355	1.3270	.79864	**0**
′	Cos	Cot	Tan	Sin	′

126° (306°) (233°) **53°**

37° (217°) (322°) **142°**

′	Sin	Tan	Cot	Cos	′
0	.60182	.75355	1.3270	.79864	**60**
1	.60205	.75401	1.3262	.79846	59
2	.60228	.75447	1.3254	.79829	58
3	.60251	.75492	1.3246	.79811	57
4	.60274	.75538	1.3238	.79793	56
5	.60298	.75584	1.3230	.79776	**55**
6	.60321	.75629	1.3222	.79758	54
7	.60344	.75675	1.3214	.79741	53
8	.60367	.75721	1.3206	.79723	52
9	.60390	.75767	1.3198	.79706	51
10	.60414	.75812	1.3190	.79688	**50**
11	.60437	.75858	1.3182	.79671	49
12	.60460	.75904	1.3175	.79653	48
13	.60483	.75950	1.3167	.79635	47
14	.60506	.75996	1.3159	.79618	46
15	.60529	.76042	1.3151	.79600	**45**
16	.60553	.76088	1.3143	.79583	44
17	.60576	.76134	1.3135	.79565	43
18	.60599	.76180	1.3127	.79547	42
19	.60622	.76226	1.3119	.79530	41
20	.60645	.76272	1.3111	.79512	**40**
21	.60668	.76318	1.3103	.79494	39
22	.60691	.76364	1.3095	.79477	38
23	.60714	.76410	1.3087	.79459	37
24	.60738	.76456	1.3079	.79441	36
25	.60761	.76502	1.3072	.79424	**35**
26	.60784	.76548	1.3064	.79406	34
27	.60807	.76594	1.3056	.79388	33
28	.60830	.76640	1.3048	.79371	32
29	.60853	.76686	1.3040	.79353	31
30	.60876	.76733	1.3032	.79335	**30**
31	.60899	.76779	1.3024	.79318	29
32	.60922	.76825	1.3017	.79300	28
33	.60945	.76871	1.3009	.79282	27
34	.60968	.76918	1.3001	.79264	26
35	.60991	.76964	1.2993	.79247	**25**
36	.61015	.77010	1.2985	.79229	24
37	.61038	.77057	1.2977	.79211	23
38	.61061	.77103	1.2970	.79193	22
39	.61084	.77149	1.2962	.79176	21
40	.61107	.77196	1.2954	.79158	**20**
41	.61130	.77242	1.2946	.79140	19
42	.61153	.77289	1.2938	.79122	18
43	.61176	.77335	1.2931	.79105	17
44	.61199	.77382	1.2923	.79087	16
45	.61222	.77428	1.2915	.79069	**15**
46	.61245	.77475	1.2907	.79051	14
47	.61268	.77521	1.2900	.79033	13
48	.61291	.77568	1.2892	.79016	12
49	.61314	.77615	1.2884	.78998	11
50	.61337	.77661	1.2876	.78980	**10**
51	.61360	.77708	1.2869	.78962	9
52	.61383	.77754	1.2861	.78944	8
53	.61406	.77801	1.2853	.78926	7
54	.61429	.77848	1.2846	.78908	6
55	.61451	.77895	1.2838	.78891	**5**
56	.61474	.77941	1.2830	.78873	4
57	.61497	.77988	1.2822	.78855	3
58	.61520	.78035	1.2815	.78837	2
59	.61543	.78082	1.2807	.78819	1
60	.61566	.78129	1.2799	.78801	**0**
′	Cos	Cot	Tan	Sin	′

127° (307°) (232°) **52°**

NATURAL FUNCTIONS (Continued)

38° (218°) (321°) **141°**

′	Sin	Tan	Cot	Cos	′
0	.61566	.78129	1.2799	.78801	**60**
1	.61589	.78175	1.2792	.78783	59
2	.61612	.78222	1.2784	.78765	58
3	.61635	.78269	1.2776	.78747	57
4	.61658	.78316	1.2769	.78729	56
5	.61681	.78363	1.2761	.78711	**55**
6	.61704	.78410	1.2753	.78694	54
7	.61726	.78457	1.2746	.78676	53
8	.61749	.78504	1.2738	.78658	52
9	.61772	.78551	1.2731	.78640	51
10	.61795	.78598	1.2723	.78622	**50**
11	.61818	.78645	1.2715	.78604	49
12	.61841	.78692	1.2708	.78586	48
13	.61864	.78739	1.2700	.78568	47
14	.61887	.78786	1.2693	.78550	46
15	.61909	.78834	1.2685	.78532	**45**
16	.61932	.78881	1.2677	.78514	44
17	.61955	.78928	1.2670	.78496	43
18	.61978	.78975	1.2662	.78478	42
19	.62001	.79022	1.2655	.78460	41
20	.62024	.79070	1.2647	.78442	**40**
21	.62046	.79117	1.2640	.78424	39
22	.62069	.79164	1.2632	.78405	38
23	.62092	.79212	1.2624	.78387	37
24	.62115	.79259	1.2617	.78369	36
25	.62138	.79306	1.2609	.78351	**35**
26	.62160	.79354	1.2602	.78333	34
27	.62183	.79401	1.2594	.78315	33
28	.62206	.79449	1.2587	.78297	32
29	.62229	.79496	1.2579	.78279	31
30	.62251	.79544	1.2572	.78261	**30**
31	.62274	.79591	1.2564	.78243	29
32	.62297	.79639	1.2557	.78225	28
33	.62320	.79686	1.2549	.78206	27
34	.62342	.79734	1.2542	.78188	26
35	.62365	.79781	1.2534	.78170	**25**
36	.62388	.79829	1.2527	.78152	24
37	.62411	.79877	1.2519	.78134	23
38	.62433	.79924	1.2512	.78116	22
39	.62456	.79972	1.2504	.78098	21
40	.62479	.80020	1.2497	.78079	**20**
41	.62502	.80067	1.2489	.78061	19
42	.62524	.80115	1.2482	.78043	18
43	.62547	.80163	1.2475	.78025	17
44	.62570	.80211	1.2467	.78007	16
45	.62592	.80258	1.2460	.77988	**15**
46	.62615	.80306	1.2452	.77970	14
47	.62638	.80354	1.2445	.77952	13
48	.62660	.80402	1.2437	.77934	12
49	.62683	.80450	1.2430	.77916	11
50	.62706	.80498	1.2423	.77897	**10**
51	.62728	.80546	1.2415	.77879	9
52	.62751	.80594	1.2408	.77861	8
53	.62774	.80642	1.2401	.77843	7
54	.62796	.80690	1.2393	.77824	6
55	.62819	.80738	1.2386	.77806	**5**
56	.62842	.80786	1.2378	.77788	4
57	.62864	.80834	1.2371	.77769	3
58	.62887	.80882	1.2364	.77751	2
59	.62909	.80930	1.2356	.77733	1
60	.62932	.80978	1.2349	.77715	**0**
′	Cos	Cot	Tan	Sin	′

128° (308°) (231°) **51°**

39° (219°) (320°) **140°**

′	Sin	Tan	Cot	Cos	′
0	.62932	.80978	1.2349	.77715	**60**
1	.62955	.81027	1.2342	.77696	59
2	.62977	.81075	1.2334	.77678	58
3	.63000	.81123	1.2327	.77660	57
4	.63022	.81171	1.2320	.77641	56
5	.63045	.81220	1.2312	.77623	**55**
6	.63068	.81268	1.2305	.77605	54
7	.63090	.81316	1.2298	.77586	53
8	.63113	.81364	1.2290	.77568	52
9	.63135	.81413	1.2283	.77550	51
10	.63158	.81461	1.2276	.77531	**50**
11	.63180	.81510	1.2268	.77513	49
12	.63203	.81558	1.2261	.77494	48
13	.63225	.81606	1.2254	.77476	47
14	.63248	.81655	1.2247	.77458	46
15	.63271	.81703	1.2239	.77439	**45**
16	.63293	.81752	1.2232	.77421	44
17	.63316	.81800	1.2225	.77402	43
18	.63338	.81849	1.2218	.77384	42
19	.63361	.81898	1.2210	.77366	41
20	.63383	.81946	1.2203	.77347	**40**
21	.63406	.81995	1.2196	.77329	39
22	.63428	.82044	1.2189	.77310	38
23	.63451	.82092	1.2181	.77292	37
24	.63473	.82141	1.2174	.77273	36
25	.63496	.82190	1.2167	.77255	**35**
26	.63518	.82238	1.2160	.77236	34
27	.63540	.82287	1.2153	.77218	33
28	.63563	.82336	1.2145	.77199	32
29	.63585	.82385	1.2138	.77181	31
30	.63608	.82434	1.2131	.77162	**30**
31	.63630	.82483	1.2124	.77144	29
32	.63653	.82531	1.2117	.77125	28
33	.63675	.82580	1.2109	.77107	27
34	.63698	.82629	1.2102	.77088	26
35	.63720	.82678	1.2095	.77070	**25**
36	.63742	.82727	1.2088	.77051	24
37	.63765	.82776	1.2081	.77033	23
38	.63787	.82825	1.2074	.77014	22
39	.63810	.82874	1.2066	.76996	21
40	.63832	.82923	1.2059	.76977	**20**
41	.63854	.82972	1.2052	.76959	19
42	.63877	.83022	1.2045	.76940	18
43	.63899	.83071	1.2038	.76921	17
44	.63922	.83120	1.2031	.76903	16
45	.63944	.83169	1.2024	.76884	**15**
46	.63966	.83218	1.2017	.76866	14
47	.63989	.83268	1.2009	.76847	13
48	.64011	.83317	1.2002	.76828	12
49	.64033	.83366	1.1995	.76810	11
50	.64056	.83415	1.1988	.76791	**10**
51	.64078	.83465	1.1981	.76772	9
52	.64100	.83514	1.1974	.76754	8
53	.64123	.83564	1.1967	.76735	7
54	.64145	.83613	1.1960	.76717	6
55	.64167	.83662	1.1953	.76698	**5**
56	.64190	.83712	1.1946	.76679	4
57	.64212	.83761	1.1939	.76661	3
58	.64234	.83811	1.1932	.76642	2
59	.64256	.83860	1.1925	.76623	1
60	.64279	.83910	1.1918	.76604	**0**
′	Cos	Cot	Tan	Sin	′

129° (309°) (230°) **50°**

40° (220°) (319°) **139°**

′	Sin	Tan	Cot	Cos	′
0	.64279	.83910	1.1918	.76604	**60**
1	.64301	.83960	1.1910	.76586	59
2	.64323	.84009	1.1903	.76567	58
3	.64346	.84059	1.1896	.76548	57
4	.64368	.84108	1.1889	.76530	56
5	.64390	.84158	1.1882	.76511	**55**
6	.64412	.84208	1.1875	.76492	54
7	.64435	.84258	1.1868	.76473	53
8	.64457	.84307	1.1861	.76455	52
9	.64479	.84357	1.1854	.76436	51
10	.64501	.84407	1.1847	.76417	**50**
11	.64524	.84457	1.1840	.76398	49
12	.64546	.84507	1.1833	.76380	48
13	.64568	.84556	1.1826	.76361	47
14	.64590	.84606	1.1819	.76342	46
15	.64612	.84656	1.1812	.76323	**45**
16	.64635	.84706	1.1806	.76304	44
17	.64657	.84756	1.1799	.76286	43
18	.64679	.84806	1.1792	.76267	42
19	.64701	.84856	1.1785	.76248	41
20	.64723	.84906	1.1778	.76229	**40**
21	.64746	.84956	1.1771	.76210	39
22	.64768	.85006	1.1764	.76192	38
23	.64790	.85057	1.1757	.76173	37
24	.64812	.85107	1.1750	.76154	36
25	.64834	.85157	1.1743	.76135	**35**
26	.64856	.85207	1.1736	.76116	34
27	.64878	.85257	1.1729	.76097	33
28	.64901	.85308	1.1722	.76078	32
29	.64923	.85358	1.1715	.76059	31
30	.64945	.85408	1.1708	.76041	**30**
31	.64967	.85458	1.1702	.76022	29
32	.64989	.85509	1.1695	.76003	28
33	.65011	.85559	1.1688	.75984	27
34	.65033	.85609	1.1681	.75965	26
35	.65055	.85660	1.1674	.75946	**25**
36	.65077	.85710	1.1667	.75927	24
37	.65100	.85761	1.1660	.75908	23
38	.65122	.85811	1.1653	.75889	22
39	.65144	.85862	1.1647	.75870	21
40	.65166	.85912	1.1640	.75851	**20**
41	.65188	.85963	1.1633	.75832	19
42	.65210	.86014	1.1626	.75813	18
43	.65232	.86064	1.1619	.75794	17
44	.65254	.86115	1.1612	.75775	16
45	.65276	.86166	1.1606	.75756	**15**
46	.65298	.86216	1.1599	.75738	14
47	.65320	.86267	1.1592	.75719	13
48	.65342	.86318	1.1585	.75700	12
49	.65364	.86368	1.1578	.75680	11
50	.65386	.86419	1.1571	.75661	**10**
51	.65408	.86470	1.1565	.75642	9
52	.65430	.86521	1.1558	.75623	8
53	.65452	.86572	1.1551	.75604	7
54	.65474	.86623	1.1544	.75585	6
55	.65496	.86674	1.1538	.75566	**5**
56	.65518	.86725	1.1531	.75547	4
57	.65540	.86776	1.1524	.75528	3
58	.65562	.86827	1.1517	.75509	2
59	.65584	.86878	1.1510	.75490	1
60	.65606	.86929	1.1504	.75471	**0**
′	Cos	Cot	Tan	Sin	′

130° (310°) (229°) **49°**

41° (221°) (318°) **138°**

′	Sin	Tan	Cot	Cos	′
0	.65606	.86929	1.1504	.75471	**60**
1	.65628	.86980	1.1497	.75452	59
2	.65650	.87031	1.1490	.75433	58
3	.65672	.87082	1.1483	.75414	57
4	.65694	.87133	1.1477	.75395	56
5	.65716	.87184	1.1470	.75375	**55**
6	.65738	.87236	1.1463	.75356	54
7	.65759	.87287	1.1456	.75337	53
8	.65781	.87338	1.1450	.75318	52
9	.65803	.87389	1.1443	.75299	51
10	.65825	.87441	1.1436	.75280	**50**
11	.65847	.87492	1.1430	.75261	49
12	.65869	.87543	1.1423	.75241	48
13	.65891	.87595	1.1416	.75222	47
14	.65913	.87646	1.1410	.75203	46
15	.65935	.87698	1.1403	.75184	**45**
16	.65956	.87749	1.1396	.75165	44
17	.65978	.87801	1.1389	.75146	43
18	.66000	.87852	1.1383	.75126	42
19	.66022	.87904	1.1376	.75107	41
20	.66044	.87955	1.1369	.75088	**40**
21	.66066	.88007	1.1363	.75069	39
22	.66088	.88059	1.1356	.75050	38
23	.66109	.88110	1.1349	.75030	37
24	.66131	.88162	1.1343	.75011	36
25	.66153	.88214	1.1336	.74992	**35**
26	.66175	.88265	1.1329	.74973	34
27	.66197	.88317	1.1323	.74953	33
28	.66218	.88369	1.1316	.74934	32
29	.66240	.88421	1.1310	.74915	31
30	.66262	.88473	1.1303	.74896	**30**
31	.66284	.88524	1.1296	.74876	29
32	.66306	.88576	1.1290	.74857	28
33	.66327	.88628	1.1283	.74838	27
34	.66349	.88680	1.1276	.74818	26
35	.66371	.88732	1.1270	.74799	**25**
36	.66393	.88748	1.1263	.74780	24
37	.66414	.88836	1.1257	.74760	23
38	.66436	.88888	1.1250	.74741	22
39	.66458	.88940	1.1243	.74722	21
40	.66480	.88992	1.1237	.74703	**20**
41	.66501	.89045	1.1230	.74683	19
42	.66523	.89097	1.1224	.74664	18
43	.66545	.89149	1.1217	.74644	17
44	.66566	.89201	1.1211	.74625	16
45	.66588	.89253	1.1204	.74606	**15**
46	.66610	.89306	1.1197	.74586	14
47	.66632	.89358	1.1191	.74567	13
48	.66653	.89410	1.1184	.74548	12
49	.66675	.89463	1.1178	.74528	11
50	.66697	.89515	1.1171	.74509	**10**
51	.66718	.89567	1.1165	.74489	9
52	.66740	.89620	1.1158	.74470	8
53	.66762	.89672	1 1152	.74451	7
54	.66783	.89725	1.1145	.74431	6
55	.66805	.89777	1.1139	.74412	**5**
56	.66827	.89830	1.1132	.74392	4
57	.66848	.89883	1.1126	.74373	3
58	.66870	.89935	1.1119	.74353	2
59	.66891	.89988	1.1113	.74334	1
60	.66913	.90040	1.1106	.74314	**0**
′	Cos	Cot	Tan	Sin	′

131° (311°) (228°) **48°**

NATURAL FUNCTIONS (Continued)

42° (222°) (317°) **137°**

′	Sin	Tan	Cot	Cos	′
0	.66913	.90040	1.1106	.74314	**60**
1	.66935	.90093	1.1100	.74295	59
2	.66956	.90146	1.1093	.74276	58
3	.66978	.90199	1.1087	.74256	57
4	.66999	.90251	1.1080	.74237	56
5	.67021	.90304	1.1074	.74217	**55**
6	.67043	.90357	1.1067	.74198	54
7	.67064	.90410	1.1061	.74178	53
8	.67086	.90463	1.1054	.74159	52
9	.67107	.90516	1.1048	.74139	51
10	.67129	.90569	1.1041	.74120	**50**
11	.67151	.90621	1.1035	.74100	49
12	.67172	.90674	1.1028	.74080	48
13	.67194	.90727	1.1022	.74061	47
14	.67215	.90781	1.1016	.74041	46
15	.67237	.90834	1.1009	.74022	**45**
16	.67258	.90887	1.1003	.74002	44
17	.67280	.90940	1.0996	.73983	43
18	.67301	.90993	1.0990	.73963	42
19	.67323	.91046	1.0983	.73944	41
20	.67344	.91099	1.0977	.73924	**40**
21	.67366	.91153	1.0971	.73904	39
22	.67387	.91206	1.0964	.73885	38
23	.67409	.91259	1.0958	.73865	37
24	.67430	.91313	1.0951	.73846	36
25	.67452	.91366	1.0945	.73826	**35**
26	.67473	.91419	1.0939	.73806	34
27	.67495	.91473	1.0932	.73787	33
28	.67516	.91526	1.0926	.73767	32
29	.67538	.91580	1.0919	.73747	31
30	.67559	.91633	1.0913	.73728	**30**
31	.67580	.91687	1.0907	.73708	29
32	.67602	.91740	1.0900	.73688	28
33	.67623	.91794	1.0894	.73669	27
34	.67645	.91847	1.0888	.73649	26
35	.67666	.91901	1.0881	.73629	**25**
36	.67688	.91955	1.0875	.73610	24
37	.67709	.92008	1.0869	.73590	23
38	.67730	.92062	1.0862	.73570	22
39	.67752	.92116	1.0856	.73551	21
40	.67773	.92170	1.0850	.73531	**20**
41	.67795	.92224	1.0843	.73511	19
42	.67816	.92277	1.0837	.73491	18
43	.67837	.92331	1.0831	.73472	17
44	.67859	.92385	1.0824	.73452	16
45	.67880	.92439	1.0818	.73432	**15**
46	.67901	.92493	1.0812	.73413	14
47	.67923	.92547	1.0805	.73393	13
48	.67944	.92601	1.0799	.73373	12
49	.67965	.92655	1.0793	.73353	11
50	.67987	.92709	1.0786	.73333	**10**
51	.68008	.92763	1.0780	.73314	9
52	.68029	.92817	1.0774	.73294	8
53	.68051	.92872	1.0768	.73274	7
54	.68072	.92926	1.0761	.73254	6
55	.68093	.92980	1.0755	.73234	**5**
56	.68115	.93034	1.0749	.73215	4
57	.68136	.93088	1.0742	.73195	3
58	.68157	.93143	1.0736	.73175	2
59	.68179	.93197	1.0730	.73155	1
60	.68200	.93252	1.0724	.73135	**0**
′	Cos	Cot	Tan	Sin	′

132° (312°) (227°) **47°**

43° (223°) (316°) **136°**

′	Sin	Tan	Cot	Cos	′
0	.68200	.93252	1.0724	.73135	**60**
1	.68221	.93306	1.0717	.73116	59
2	.68242	.93360	1.0711	.73096	58
3	.68264	.93415	1.0705	.73076	57
4	.68285	.93469	1.0699	.73056	56
5	.68306	.93524	1.0692	.73036	**55**
6	.68327	.93578	1.0686	.73016	54
7	.68349	.93633	1.0680	.72996	53
8	.68370	.93688	1.0674	.72976	52
9	.68391	.93742	1.0668	.72957	51
10	.68412	.93796	1.0661	.72937	**50**
11	.68434	.93852	1.0655	.72917	49
12	.68455	.93906	1.0649	.72897	48
13	.68476	.93961	1.0643	.72877	47
14	.68497	.94016	1.0637	.72857	46
15	.68518	.94071	1.0630	.72837	**45**
16	.68539	.94125	1.0624	.72817	44
17	.68561	.94180	1.0618	.72797	43
18	.68582	.94235	1.0612	.72777	42
19	.68603	.94290	1.0606	.72757	41
20	.68624	.94345	1.0599	.72737	**40**
21	.68645	.94400	1.0593	.72717	39
22	.68666	.94455	1.0587	.72697	38
23	.68688	.94510	1.0581	.72677	37
24	.68709	.94565	1.0575	.72657	36
25	.68730	.94620	1.0569	.72637	**35**
26	.68751	.94676	1.0562	.72617	34
27	.68772	.94731	1.0556	.72597	33
28	.68793	.94786	1.0550	.72577	32
29	.68814	.94841	1.0544	.72557	31
30	.68835	.94896	1.0538	.72537	**30**
31	.68857	.94952	1.0532	.72517	29
32	.68878	.95007	1.0526	.72497	28
33	.68899	.95062	1.0519	.72477	27
34	.68920	.95118	1.0513	.72457	26
35	.68941	.95173	1.0507	.72437	**25**
36	.68962	.95229	1.0501	.72417	24
37	.68983	.95284	1.0495	.72397	23
38	.69004	.95340	1.0489	.72377	22
39	.69025	.95395	1.0483	.72357	21
40	.69046	.95451	1.0477	.72337	**20**
41	.69067	.95506	1.0470	.72317	19
42	.69088	.95562	1.0464	.72297	18
43	.69109	.95618	1.0458	.72277	17
44	.69130	.95673	1.0452	.72257	16
45	.69151	.95729	1.0446	.72236	**15**
46	.69172	.95785	1.0440	.72216	14
47	.69193	.95841	1.0434	.72196	13
48	.69214	.95897	1.0428	.72176	12
49	.69235	.95952	1.0422	.72156	11
50	.69256	.96008	1.0416	.72136	**10**
51	.69277	.96064	1.0410	.72116	9
52	.69298	.96120	1.0404	.72095	8
53	.69319	.96176	1.0398	.72075	7
54	.69340	.96232	1.0392	.72055	6
55	.69361	.96288	1.0385	.72035	**5**
56	.69382	.96344	1.0379	.72015	4
57	.69403	.96400	1.0373	.71995	3
58	.69424	.96457	1.0367	.71974	2
59	.69445	.96513	1.0361	.71954	1
60	.69466	.96569	1.0355	.71934	**0**
′	Cos	Cot	Tan	Sin	′

133° (313°) (226°) **46°**

NATURAL FUNCTIONS (Continued)

44° (224°) (315°) **135°**

′	Sin	Tan	Cot	Cos	′
0	.69466	.96569	1.0355	.71934	**60**
1	.69487	.96625	1.0349	.71914	59
2	.69508	.96681	1.0343	.71894	58
3	.69529	.96738	1.0337	.71873	57
4	.69549	.96794	1.0331	.71853	56
5	.69570	.96850	1.0325	.71833	**55**
6	.69591	.96907	1.0319	.71813	54
7	.69612	.96963	1.0313	.71792	53
8	.69633	.97020	1.0307	.71772	52
9	.69654	.97076	1.0301	.71752	51
10	.69675	.97133	1.0295	.71732	**50**
11	.69696	.97189	1.0289	.71711	49
12	.69717	.97246	1.0283	.71691	48
13	.69737	.97302	1.0277	.71671	47
14	.69758	.97359	1.0271	.71650	46
15	.69779	.97416	1.0265	.71630	**45**
16	.69800	.97472	1.0259	.71610	44
17	.69821	.97529	1.0253	.71590	43
18	.69842	.97586	1.0247	.71569	42
19	.69862	.97643	1.0241	.71549	41
20	.69883	.97700	1.0235	.71529	**40**
21	.69904	.97756	1.0230	.71508	39
22	.69925	.97813	1.0224	.71488	38
23	.69946	.97870	1.0218	.71468	37
24	.69966	.97927	1.0212	.71447	36
25	.69987	.97984	1.0206	.71427	**35**
26	.70008	.98041	1.0200	.71407	34
27	.70029	.98098	1.0194	.71386	33
28	.70049	.98155	1.0188	.71366	32
29	.70070	.98213	1.0182	.71345	31
30	.70091	.98270	1.0176	.71325	**30**
31	.70112	.98327	1.0170	.71305	29
32	.70132	.98384	1.0164	.71284	28
33	.70153	.98441	1.0158	.71264	27
34	.70174	.98499	1.0152	.71243	26
35	.70195	.98556	1.0147	.71223	**25**
36	.70215	.98613	1.0141	.71203	24
37	.70236	.98671	1.0135	.71182	23
38	.70257	.98728	1.0129	.71162	22
39	.70277	.98786	1.0123	.71141	21
40	.70298	.98843	1.0117	.71121	**20**
41	.70319	.98901	1.0111	.71100	19
42	.70339	.98958	1.0105	.71080	18
43	.70360	.99016	1.0099	.71059	17
44	.70381	.99073	1.0094	.71039	16
45	.70401	.99131	1.0088	.71019	**15**
46	.70422	.99189	1.0082	.70998	14
47	.70443	.99247	1.0076	.70978	13
48	.70463	.99304	1.0070	.70957	12
49	.70484	.99362	1.0064	.70937	11
50	.70505	.99420	1.0058	.70916	**10**
51	.70525	.99478	1.0052	.70896	9
52	.70546	.99536	1.0047	.70875	8
53	.70567	.99594	1.0041	.70855	7
54	.70587	.99652	1.0035	.70834	6
55	.70608	.99710	1.0029	.70813	**5**
56	.70628	.99768	1.0023	.70793	4
57	.70649	.99826	1.0017	.70772	3
58	.70670	.99884	1.0012	.70752	2
59	.70690	.99942	1.0006	.70731	1
60	.70711	1.0000	1.0000	.70711	**0**
′	Cos	Cot	Tan	Sin	′

134° (314°) (225°) **45°**

NATURAL FUNCTIONS—SECANTS AND COSECANTS

0° (180°) (359°) **179°**

′	Sec	Csc	′
0	1.0000		**60**
1	1.0000	3437.7	59
2	1.0000	1718.9	58
3	1.0000	1145.9	57
4	1.0000	859.44	56
5	1.0000	687.55	**55**
6	1.0000	572.96	54
7	1.0000	491.11	53
8	1.0000	429.72	52
9	1.0000	381.97	51
10	1.0000	343.78	**50**
11	1.0000	312.52	49
12	1.0000	286.48	48
13	1.0000	264.44	47
14	1.0000	245.55	46
15	1.0000	229.18	**45**
16	1.0000	214.86	44
17	1.0000	202.22	43
18	1.0000	190.99	42
19	1.0000	180.93	41
20	1.0000	171.89	**40**
21	1.0000	163.70	39
22	1.0000	156.26	38
23	1.0000	149.47	37
24	1.0000	143.24	36
25	1.0000	137.51	**35**
26	1.0000	132.22	34
27	1.0000	127.33	33
28	1.0000	122.78	32
29	1.0000	118.54	31
30	1.0000	114.59	**30**
31	1.0000	110.90	29
32	1.0000	107.43	28
33	1.0000	104.18	27
34	1.0000	101.11	26
35	1.0001	98.223	**25**
36	1.0001	95.495	24
37	1.0001	92.914	23
38	1.0001	90.469	22
39	1.0001	88.149	21
40	1.0001	85.946	**20**
41	1.0001	83.849	19
42	1.0001	81.853	18
43	1.0001	79.950	17
44	1.0001	78.133	16
45	1.0001	76.397	**15**
46	1.0001	74.736	14
47	1.0001	73.146	13
48	1.0001	71.622	12
49	1.0001	70.160	11
50	1.0001	68.757	**10**
51	1.0001	67.409	9
52	1.0001	66.113	8
53	1.0001	64.866	7
54	1.0001	63.665	6
55	1.0001	62.507	**5**
56	1.0001	61.391	4
57	1.0001	60.314	3
58	1.0001	59.274	2
59	1.0001	58.270	1
60	1.0002	57.299	**0**
′	Csc	Sec	′

90° (270°) (269°) **89°**

1° (181°) (358°) **178°**

′	Sec	Csc	′
0	1.0002	57.299	**60**
1	1.0002	56.359	59
2	1.0002	55.451	58
3	1.0002	54.570	57
4	1.0002	53.718	56
5	1.0002	52.892	**55**
6	1.0002	52.090	54
7	1.0002	51.313	53
8	1.0002	50.558	52
9	1.0002	49.826	51
10	1.0002	49.114	**50**
11	1.0002	48.422	49
12	1.0002	47.750	48
13	1.0002	47.096	47
14	1.0002	46.460	46
15	1.0002	45.840	**45**
16	1.0002	45.237	44
17	1.0003	44.650	43
18	1.0003	44.077	42
19	1.0003	43.520	41
20	1.0003	42.976	**40**
21	1.0003	42.445	39
22	1.0003	41.928	38
23	1.0003	41.423	37
24	1.0003	40.930	36
25	1.0003	40.448	**35**
26	1.0003	39.978	34
27	1.0003	39.519	33
28	1.0003	39.070	32
29	1.0003	38.631	31
30	1.0003	38.202	**30**
31	1.0004	37.782	29
32	1.0004	37.371	28
33	1.0004	36.970	27
34	1.0004	36.576	26
35	1.0004	36.191	**25**
36	1.0004	35.815	24
37	1.0004	35.445	23
38	1.0004	35.084	22
39	1.0004	34.730	21
40	1.0004	34.382	**20**
41	1.0004	34.042	19
42	1.0004	33.708	18
43	1.0004	33.381	17
44	1.0005	33.060	16
45	1.0005	32.746	**15**
46	1.0005	32.437	14
47	1.0005	32.134	13
48	1.0005	31.836	12
49	1.0005	31.544	11
50	1.0005	31.258	**10**
51	1.0005	30.976	9
52	1.0005	30.700	8
53	1.0005	30.428	7
54	1.0006	30.161	6
55	1.0006	29.899	**5**
56	1.0006	29.641	4
57	1.0006	29.388	3
58	1.0006	29.139	2
59	1.0006	28.894	1
60	1.0006	28 654	**0**
′	Csc	Sec	′

91° (271°) (268°) **88°**

2° (182°) (357°) **177°**

′	Sec	Csc	′
0	1.0006	28.654	**60**
1	1.0006	28.417	59
2	1.0006	28.184	58
3	1.0006	27.955	57
4	1.0007	27.730	56
5	1.0007	27.508	**55**
6	1.0007	27.290	54
7	1.0007	27.075	53
8	1.0007	26.864	52
9	1.0007	26.655	51
10	1.0007	26.451	**50**
11	1.0007	26.249	49
12	1.0007	26.050	48
13	1.0007	25.854	47
14	1.0008	25.661	46
15	1.0008	25.471	**45**
16	1.0008	25.284	44
17	1.0008	25.100	43
18	1.0008	24.918	42
19	1.0008	24.739	41
20	1.0008	24.562	**40**
21	1.0008	24.388	39
22	1.0009	24.216	38
23	1.0009	24.047	37
24	1.0009	23.880	36
25	1.0009	23.716	**35**
26	1.0009	23.553	34
27	1.0009	23.393	33
28	1.0009	23.235	32
29	1.0009	23.079	31
30	1.0010	22.926	**30**
31	1.0010	22.774	29
32	1.0010	22.624	28
33	1.0010	22.476	27
34	1.0010	22.330	26
35	1.0010	22.187	**25**
36	1.0010	22.044	24
37	1.0010	21.904	23
38	1.0011	21.766	22
39	1.0011	21.629	21
40	1.0011	21.494	**20**
41	1.0011	21.360	19
42	1.0011	21.229	18
43	1.0011	21.098	17
44	1.0011	20.970	16
45	1.0012	20.843	**15**
46	1.0012	20.717	14
47	1.0012	20.593	13
48	1.0012	20.471	12
49	1.0012	20.350	11
50	1.0012	20.230	**10**
51	1.0012	20.112	9
52	1.0013	19.995	8
53	1.0013	19.880	7
54	1.0013	19.766	6
55	1.0013	19.653	**5**
56	1.0013	19.541	4
57	1.0013	19.431	3
58	1.0013	19.322	2
59	1.0014	19.214	1
60	1.0014	19.107	**0**
′	Csc	Sec	′

92° (272°) (267°) **87°**

3° (183°) (356°) **176°**

′	Sec	Csc	′
0	1.0014	19.107	**60**
1	1.0014	19.002	59
2	1.0014	18.898	58
3	1.0014	18.794	57
4	1.0014	18.692	56
5	1.0014	18.591	**55**
6	1.0015	18.492	54
7	1.0015	18.393	53
8	1.0015	18.295	52
9	1.0015	18.198	51
10	1.0015	18.103	**50**
11	1.0015	18.008	49
12	1.0016	17.914	48
13	1.0016	17.822	47
14	1.0016	17.730	46
15	1.0016	17.639	**45**
16	1.0016	17.549	44
17	1.0016	17.460	43
18	1.0017	17.372	42
19	1.0017	17.285	41
20	1.0017	17.198	**40**
21	1.0017	17.113	39
22	1.0017	17.028	38
23	1.0017	16.945	37
24	1.0018	16.862	36
25	1.0018	16.779	**35**
26	1.0018	16.698	34
27	1.0018	16.618	33
28	1.0018	16.538	32
29	1.0019	16.459	31
30	1.0019	16.380	**30**
31	1.0019	16.303	29
32	1.0019	16.226	28
33	1.0019	16.150	27
34	1.0019	16.075	26
35	1.0020	16.000	**25**
36	1.0020	15.926	24
37	1.0020	15.853	23
38	1.0020	15.780	22
39	1.0020	15.708	21
40	1.0021	15.637	**20**
41	1.0021	15.566	19
42	1.0021	15.496	18
43	1.0021	15.427	17
44	1.0021	15.358	16
45	1.0021	15.290	**15**
46	1.0022	15.222	14
47	1.0022	15.155	13
48	1.0022	15.089	12
49	1.0022	15.023	11
50	1.0022	14.958	**10**
51	1.0023	14.893	9
52	1.0023	14.829	8
53	1.0023	14.766	7
54	1.0023	14.703	6
55	1.0023	14.640	**5**
56	1.0024	14.578	4
57	1.0024	14.517	3
58	1.0024	14.456	2
59	1.0024	14.395	1
60	1.0024	14.336	**0**
′	Csc	Sec	′

93° (273°) (266°) **86°**

4° (184°) (355°) **175°**

′	Sec	Csc	′
0	1.0024	14.336	**60**
1	1.0025	14.276	59
2	1.0025	14.217	58
3	1.0025	14.159	57
4	1.0025	14.101	56
5	1.0025	14.044	**55**
6	1.0026	13.987	54
7	1.0026	13.930	53
8	1.0026	13.874	52
9	1.0026	13.818	51
10	1.0027	13.763	**50**
11	1.0027	13.708	49
12	1.0027	13.654	48
13	1.0027	13.600	47
14	1.0027	13.547	46
15	1.0028	13.494	**45**
16	1.0028	13.441	44
17	1.0028	13.389	43
18	1.0028	13.337	42
19	1.0028	13.286	41
20	1.0029	13.235	**40**
21	1.0029	13.184	39
22	1.0029	13.134	38
23	1.0029	13.084	37
24	1.0030	13.035	36
25	1.0030	12.985	**35**
26	1.0030	12.937	34
27	1.0030	12.888	33
28	1.0030	12.840	32
29	1.0031	12.793	31
30	1.0031	12.745	**30**
31	1.0031	12.699	29
32	1.0031	12.652	28
33	1.0032	12.606	27
34	1.0032	12.560	26
35	1.0032	12.514	**25**
36	1.0032	12.469	24
37	1.0033	12.424	23
38	1.0033	12.379	22
39	1.0033	12.335	21
40	1.0033	12.291	**20**
41	1.0034	12.248	19
42	1.0034	12.204	18
43	1.0034	12.161	17
44	1.0034	12.119	16
45	1.0034	12.076	**15**
46	1.0035	12.034	14
47	1.0035	11.992	13
48	1.0035	11.951	12
49	1.0035	11.909	11
50	1.0036	11.868	**10**
51	1.0036	11.828	9
52	1.0036	11.787	8
53	1.0036	11.747	7
54	1.0037	11.707	6
55	1.0037	11.668	**5**
56	1.0037	11.628	4
57	1.0037	11.589	3
58	1.0038	11.551	2
59	1.0038	11.512	1
60	1.0038	11.474	**0**
′	Csc	Sec	′

94° (274°) (265°) **85°**

5° (185°) (354°) **174°**

′	Sec	Csc	′
0	1.0038	11.474	**60**
1	1.0038	11.436	59
2	1.0039	11.398	58
3	1.0039	11.360	57
4	1.0039	11.323	56
5	1.0039	11.286	**55**
6	1.0040	11.249	54
7	1.0040	11.213	53
8	1.0040	11.176	52
9	1.0041	11.140	51
10	1.0041	11.105	**50**
11	1.0041	11.069	49
12	1.0041	11.034	48
13	1.0042	10.998	47
14	1.0042	10.963	46
15	1.0042	10.929	**45**
16	1.0042	10.894	44
17	1.0043	10.860	43
18	1.0043	10.826	42
19	1.0043	10.792	41
20	1.0043	10.758	**40**
21	1.0044	10.725	39
22	1.0044	10.692	38
23	1.0044	10.659	37
24	1.0045	10.626	36
25	1.0045	10.593	**35**
26	1.0045	10.561	34
27	1.0045	10.529	33
28	1.0046	10.497	32
29	1.0046	10.465	31
30	1.0046	10.433	**30**
31	1.0047	10.402	29
32	1.0047	10.371	28
33	1.0047	10.340	27
34	1.0047	10.309	26
35	1.0048	10.278	**25**
36	1.0048	10.248	24
37	1.0048	10.217	23
38	1.0049	10.187	22
39	1.0049	10.157	21
40	1.0049	10.128	**20**
41	1.0049	10.098	19
42	1.0050	10.068	18
43	1.0050	10.039	17
44	1.0050	10.010	16
45	1.0051	9.9812	**15**
46	1.0051	9.9525	14
47	1.0051	9.9239	13
48	1.0051	9.8955	12
49	1.0052	9.8672	11
50	1.0052	9.8391	**10**
51	1.0052	9.8112	9
52	1.0053	9.7834	8
53	1.0053	9.7558	7
54	1.0053	9.7283	6
55	1.0054	9.7010	**5**
56	1.0054	9.6739	4
57	1.0054	9.6469	3
58	1.0054	9.6200	2
59	1.0055	9.5933	1
60	1.0055	9.5668	**0**
′	Csc	Sec	′

95° (275°) (264°) **84°**

6° (186°) (353°) **173°**

′	Sec	Csc	′
0	1.0055	9.5668	**60**
1	1.0055	9.5404	59
2	1.0056	9.5141	58
3	1.0056	9.4880	57
4	1.0056	9.4620	56
5	1.0057	9.4362	**55**
6	1.0057	9.4105	54
7	1.0057	9.3850	53
8	1.0058	9.3596	52
9	1.0058	9.3343	51
10	1.0058	9.3092	**50**
11	1.0059	9.2842	49
12	1.0059	9.2593	48
13	1.0059	9.2346	47
14	1.0059	9.2100	46
15	1.0060	9.1855	**45**
16	1.0060	9.1612	44
17	1.0060	9.1370	43
18	1.0061	9.1129	42
19	1.0061	9.0890	41
20	1.0061	9.0652	**40**
21	1.0062	9.0415	39
22	1.0062	9.0179	38
23	1.0062	8.9944	37
24	1.0063	8.9711	36
25	1.0063	8.9479	**35**
26	1.0063	8.9248	34
27	1.0064	8.9019	33
28	1.0064	8.8790	32
29	1.0064	8.8563	31
30	1.0065	8.8337	**30**
31	1.0065	8.8112	29
32	1.0065	8.7888	28
33	1.0066	8.7665	27
34	1.0066	8.7444	26
35	1.0066	8.7223	**25**
36	1.0067	8.7004	24
37	1.0067	8.6786	23
38	1.0067	8.6569	22
39	1.0068	8.6353	21
40	1.0068	8.6138	**20**
41	1.0068	8.5924	19
42	1.0069	8.5711	18
43	1.0069	8.5500	17
44	1.0069	8.5289	16
45	1.0070	8.5079	**15**
46	1.0070	8.4871	14
47	1.0070	8.4663	13
48	1.0071	8.4457	12
49	1.0071	8.4251	11
50	1.0072	8.4047	**10**
51	1.0072	8.3843	9
52	1.0072	8.3641	8
53	1.0073	8.3439	7
54	1.0073	8.3238	6
55	1.0073	8.3039	**5**
56	1.0074	8.2840	4
57	1.0074	8.2642	3
58	1.0074	8.2446	2
59	1.0075	8.2250	1
60	1.0075	8.2055	**0**
′	Csc	Sec	′

96° (276°) (263°) **83°**

7° (187°) (352°) **172°**

′	Sec	Csc	′
0	1.0075	8.2055	**60**
1	1.0075	8.1861	59
2	1.0076	8.1668	58
3	1.0076	8.1476	57
4	1.0077	8.1285	56
5	1.0077	8.1095	**55**
6	1.0077	8.0905	54
7	1.0078	8.0717	53
8	1.0078	8.0529	52
9	1.0078	8.0342	51
10	1.0079	8.0156	**50**
11	1.0079	7.9971	49
12	1.0079	7.9787	48
13	1.0080	7.9604	47
14	1.0080	7.9422	46
15	1.0081	7.9240	**45**
16	1.0081	7.9059	44
17	1.0081	7.8879	43
18	1.0082	7.8700	42
19	1.0082	7.8522	41
20	1.0082	7.8344	**40**
21	1.0083	7.8168	39
22	1.0083	7.7992	38
23	1.0084	7.7817	37
24	1.0084	7.7642	36
25	1.0084	7.7469	**35**
26	1.0085	7.7296	34
27	1.0085	7.7124	33
28	1.0086	7.6953	32
29	1.0086	7.6783	31
30	1.0086	7.6613	**30**
31	1.0087	7.6444	29
32	1.0087	7.6276	28
33	1.0087	7.6109	27
34	1.0088	7.5942	26
35	1.0088	7.5776	**25**
36	1.0089	7.5611	24
37	1.0089	7.5446	23
38	1.0089	7.5282	22
39	1.0090	7.5119	21
40	1.0090	7.4957	**20**
41	1.0091	7.4795	19
42	1.0091	7.4635	18
43	1.0091	7.4474	17
44	1.0092	7.4315	16
45	1.0092	7.4156	**15**
46	1.0093	7.3998	14
47	1.0093	7.3840	13
48	1.0093	7.3684	12
49	1.0094	7.3527	11
50	1.0094	7.3372	**10**
51	1.0095	7.3217	9
52	1.0095	7.3063	8
53	1.0095	7.2909	7
54	1.0096	7.2757	6
55	1.0096	7.2604	**5**
56	1.0097	7.2453	4
57	1.0097	7.2302	3
58	1.0097	7.2152	2
59	1.0098	7.2002	1
60	1.0098	7.1853	**0**
′	Csc	Sec	′

97° (277°) (262°) **82°**

8° (188°) (351°) **171°**

′	Sec	Csc	′
0	1.0098	7.1853	**60**
1	1.0099	7.1705	59
2	1.0099	7.1557	58
3	1.0100	7.1410	57
4	1.0100	7.1263	56
5	1.0100	7.1117	**55**
6	1.0101	7.0972	54
7	1.0101	7.0827	53
8	1.0102	7.0683	52
9	1.0102	7.0539	51
10	1.0102	7.0396	**50**
11	1.0103	7.0254	49
12	1.0103	7.0112	48
13	1.0104	6.9971	47
14	1.0104	6.9830	46
15	1.0105	6.9690	**45**
16	1.0105	6.9550	44
17	1.0105	6.9411	43
18	1.0106	6.9273	42
19	1.0106	6.9135	41
20	1.0107	6.8998	**40**
21	1.0107	6.8861	39
22	1.0108	6.8725	38
23	1.0108	6.8589	37
24	1.0108	6.8454	36
25	1.0109	6.8320	**35**
26	1.0109	6.8186	34
27	1.0110	6.8052	33
28	1.0110	6.7919	32
29	1.0111	6.7787	31
30	1.0111	6.7655	**30**
31	1.0112	6.7523	29
32	1.0112	6.7392	28
33	1.0112	6.7262	27
34	1.0113	6.7132	26
35	1.0113	6.7003	**25**
36	1.0114	6.6874	24
37	1.0114	6.6745	23
38	1.0115	6.6618	22
39	1.0115	6.6490	21
40	1.0116	6.6363	**20**
41	1.0116	6.6237	19
42	1.0116	6.6111	18
43	1.0117	6.5986	17
44	1.0117	6.5861	16
45	1.0118	6.5736	**15**
46	1.0118	6.5612	14
47	1.0119	6.5489	13
48	1.0119	6.5366	12
49	1.0120	6.5243	11
50	1.0120	6.5121	**10**
51	1.0120	6.4999	9
52	1.0121	6.4878	8
53	1.0121	6.4757	7
54	1.0122	6.4637	6
55	1.0122	6.4517	**5**
56	1.0123	6.4398	4
57	1.0123	6.4279	3
58	1.0124	6.4160	2
59	1.0124	6.4042	1
60	1.0125	6.3925	**0**
′	Csc	Sec	′

98° (278°) (261°) **81°**

9° (189°) (350°) **170°**

′	Sec	Csc	′
0	1.0125	6.3925	**60**
1	1.0125	6.3807	59
2	1.0126	6.3691	58
3	1.0126	6.3574	57
4	1.0127	6.3458	56
5	1.0127	6.3343	**55**
6	1.0127	6.3228	54
7	1.0128	6.3113	53
8	1.0128	6.2999	52
9	1.0129	6.2885	51
10	1.0129	6.2772	**50**
11	1.0130	6.2659	49
12	1.0130	6.2546	48
13	1.0131	6.2434	47
14	1.0131	6.2323	46
15	1.0132	6.2211	**45**
16	1.0132	6.2100	44
17	1.0133	6.1990	43
18	1.0133	6.1880	42
19	1.0134	6.1770	41
20	1.0134	6.1661	**40**
21	1.0135	6.1552	39
22	1.0135	6.1443	38
23	1.0136	6.1335	37
24	1.0136	6.1227	36
25	1.0137	6.1120	**35**
26	1.0137	6.1013	34
27	1.0138	6.0906	33
28	1.0138	6.0800	32
29	1.0139	6.0694	31
30	1.0139	6.0589	**30**
31	1.0140	6.0483	29
32	1.0140	6.0379	28
33	1.0141	6.0274	27
34	1.0141	6.0170	26
35	1.0142	6.0067	**25**
36	1.0142	5.9963	24
37	1.0143	5.9860	23
38	1.0143	5.9758	22
39	1.0144	5.9656	21
40	1.0144	5.9554	**20**
41	1.0145	5.9452	19
42	1.0145	5.9351	18
43	1.0146	5.9250	17
44	1.0146	5.9150	16
45	1.0147	5.9049	**15**
46	1.0147	5.8950	14
47	1.0148	5.8850	13
48	1.0148	5.8751	12
49	1.0149	5.8652	11
50	1.0149	5.8554	**10**
51	1.0150	5.8456	9
52	1.0150	5.8358	8
53	1.0151	5.8261	7
54	1.0151	5.8164	6
55	1.0152	5.8067	**5**
56	1.0152	5.7970	4
57	1.0153	5.7874	3
58	1.0153	5.7778	2
59	1.0154	5.7683	1
60	1.0154	5.7588	**0**
′	Csc	Sec	′

99° (279°) (260°) **80°**

10° (190°) (349°) **169°**

′	Sec	Csc	′
0	1.0154	5.7588	**60**
1	1.0155	5.7493	59
2	1.0155	5.7398	58
3	1.0156	5.7304	57
4	1.0156	5.7210	56
5	1.0157	5.7117	**55**
6	1.0157	5.7023	54
7	1.0158	5.6930	53
8	1.0158	5.6838	52
9	1.0159	5.6745	51
10	1.0160	5.6653	**50**
11	1.0160	5.6562	49
12	1.0161	5.6470	48
13	1.0161	5.6379	47
14	1.0162	5.6288	46
15	1.0162	5.6198	**45**
16	1.0163	5.6107	44
17	1.0163	5.6017	43
18	1.0164	5.5928	42
19	1.0164	5.5838	41
20	1.0165	5.5749	**40**
21	1.0165	5.5660	39
22	1.0166	5.5572	38
23	1.0166	5.5484	37
24	1.0167	5.5396	36
25	1.0168	5.5308	**35**
26	1.0168	5.5221	34
27	1.0169	5.5134	33
28	1.0169	5.5047	32
29	1.0170	5.4960	31
30	1.0170	5.4874	**30**
31	1.0171	5.4788	29
32	1.0171	5.4702	28
33	1.0172	5.4617	27
34	1.0173	5.4532	26
35	1.0173	5.4447	**25**
36	1.0174	5.4362	24
37	1.0174	5.4278	23
38	1.0175	5.4194	22
39	1.0175	5.4110	21
40	1.0176	5.4026	**20**
41	1.0176	5.3943	19
42	1.0177	5.3860	18
43	1.0178	5.3777	17
44	1.0178	5.3695	16
45	1.0179	5.3612	**15**
46	1.0179	5.3530	14
47	1.0180	5.3449	13
48	1.0180	5.3367	12
49	1.0181	5.3286	11
50	1.0181	5.3205	**10**
51	1.0182	5.3124	9
52	1.0183	5.3044	8
53	1.0183	5.2963	7
54	1.0184	5.2883	6
55	1.0184	5.2804	**5**
56	1.0185	5.2724	4
57	1.0185	5.2645	3
58	1.0186	5.2566	2
59	1.0187	5.2487	1
60	1.0187	5.2408	**0**
′	Csc	Sec	′

100° (280°) (259°) **79°**

11° (191°) (348°) **168°**

′	Sec	Csc	′
0	1.0187	5.2408	**60**
1	1.0188	5.2330	59
2	1.0188	5.2252	58
3	1.0189	5.2174	57
4	1.0189	5.2097	56
5	1.0190	5.2019	**55**
6	1.0191	5.1942	54
7	1.0191	5.1865	53
8	1.0192	5.1789	52
9	1.0192	5.1712	51
10	1.0193	5.1636	**50**
11	1.0194	5.1560	49
12	1.0194	5.1484	48
13	1.0195	5.1409	47
14	1.0195	5.1333	46
15	1.0196	5.1258	**45**
16	1.0197	5.1183	44
17	1.0197	5.1109	43
18	1.0198	5.1034	42
19	1.0198	5.0960	41
20	1.0199	5.0886	**40**
21	1.0199	5.0813	39
22	1.0200	5.0739	38
23	1.0201	5.0666	37
24	1.0201	5.0593	36
25	1.0202	5.0520	**35**
26	1.0202	5.0447	34
27	1.0203	5.0375	33
28	1.0204	5.0302	32
29	1.0204	5.0230	31
30	1.0205	5.0159	**30**
31	1.0205	5.0087	29
32	1.0206	5.0016	28
33	1.0207	4.9944	27
34	1.0207	4.9873	26
35	1.0208	4.9803	**25**
36	1.0209	4.9732	24
37	1.0209	4.9662	23
38	1.0210	4.9591	22
39	1.0210	4.9521	21
40	1.0211	4.9452	**20**
41	1.0212	4.9382	19
42	1.0212	4.9313	18
43	1.0213	4.9244	17
44	1.0213	4.9175	16
45	1.0214	4.9106	**15**
46	1.0215	4.9037	14
47	1.0215	4.8969	13
48	1.0216	4.8901	12
49	1.0217	4.8833	11
50	1.0217	4.8765	**10**
51	1.0218	4.8697	9
52	1.0218	4.8630	8
53	1.0219	4.8563	7
54	1.0220	4.8496	6
55	1.0220	4.8429	**5**
56	1.0221	4.8362	4
57	1.0222	4.8296	3
58	1.0222	4.8229	2
59	1.0223	4.8163	1
60	1.0223	4.8097	**0**
′	Csc	Sec	′

101° (281°) (258°) **78°**

12° (192°) (347°) **167°**

′	Sec	Csc	′
0	1.0223	4.8097	**60**
1	1.0224	4.8032	59
2	1.0225	4.7966	58
3	1.0225	4.7901	57
4	1.0226	4.7836	56
5	1.0227	4.7771	**55**
6	1.0227	4.7706	54
7	1.0228	4.7641	53
8	1.0228	4.7577	52
9	1.0229	4.7512	51
10	1.0230	4.7448	**50**
11	1.0230	4.7384	49
12	1.0231	4.7321	48
13	1.0232	4.7257	47
14	1.0232	4.7194	46
15	1.0233	4.7130	**45**
16	1.0234	4.7067	44
17	1.0234	4.7004	43
18	1.0235	4.6942	42
19	1.0236	4.6879	41
20	1.0236	4.6817	**40**
21	1.0237	4.6755	39
22	1.0238	4.6693	38
23	1.0238	4.6631	37
24	1.0239	4.6569	36
25	1.0240	4.6507	**35**
26	1.0240	4.6446	34
27	1.0241	4.6385	33
28	1.0241	4.6324	32
29	1.0242	4.6263	31
30	1.0243	4.6202	**30**
31	1.0243	4.6142	29
32	1.0244	4.6081	28
33	1.0245	4.6021	27
34	1.0245	4.5961	26
35	1.0246	4.5901	**25**
36	1.0247	4.5841	24
37	1.0247	4.5782	23
38	1.0248	4.5722	22
39	1.0249	4.5663	21
40	1.0249	4.5604	**20**
41	1.0250	4.5545	19
42	1.0251	4.5486	18
43	1.0251	4.5428	17
44	1.0252	4.5369	16
45	1.0253	4.5311	**15**
46	1.0253	4.5253	14
47	1.0254	4.5195	13
48	1.0255	4.5137	12
49	1.0256	4.5079	11
50	1.0256	4.5022	**10**
51	1.0257	4.4964	9
52	1.0258	4.4907	8
53	1.0258	4.4850	7
54	1.0259	4.4793	6
55	1.0260	4.4736	**5**
56	1.0260	4.4679	4
57	1.0261	4.4623	3
58	1.0262	4.4566	2
59	1.0262	4.4510	1
60	1.0263	4.4454	**0**
′	Csc	Sec	′

102° (282°) (257°) **77°**

13° (193°) (346°) **166°**

′	Sec	Csc	′
0	1.0263	4.4454	**60**
1	1.0264	4.4398	59
2	1.0264	4.4342	58
3	1.0265	4.4287	57
4	1.0266	4.4231	56
5	1.0266	4.4176	**55**
6	1.0267	4.4121	54
7	1.0268	4.4066	53
8	1.0269	4.4011	52
9	1.0269	4.3956	51
10	1.0270	4.3901	**50**
11	1.0271	4.3847	49
12	1.0271	4.3792	48
13	1.0272	4.3738	47
14	1.0273	4.3684	46
15	1.0273	4.3630	**45**
16	1.0274	4.3576	44
17	1.0275	4.3522	43
18	1.0276	4.3469	42
19	1.0276	4.3415	41
20	1.0277	4.3362	**40**
21	1.0278	4.3309	39
22	1.0278	4.3256	38
23	1.0279	4.3203	37
24	1.0280	4.3150	36
25	1.0281	4.3098	**35**
26	1.0281	4.3045	34
27	1.0282	4.2993	33
28	1.0283	4.2941	32
29	1.0283	4.2889	31
30	1.0284	4.2837	**30**
31	1.0285	4.2785	29
32	1.0286	4.2733	28
33	1.0286	4.2681	27
34	1.0287	4.2630	26
35	1.0288	4.2579	**25**
36	1.0288	4.2527	24
37	1.0289	4.2476	23
38	1.0290	4.2425	22
39	1.0291	4.2375	21
40	1.0291	4.2324	**20**
41	1.0292	4.2273	19
42	1.0293	4.2223	18
43	1.0294	4.2173	17
44	1.0294	4.2122	16
45	1.0295	4.2072	**15**
46	1.0296	4.2022	14
47	1.0297	4.1973	13
48	1.0297	4.1923	12
49	1.0298	4.1873	11
50	1.0299	4.1824	**10**
51	1.0299	4.1774	9
52	1.0300	4.1725	8
53	1.0301	4.1676	7
54	1.0302	4.1627	6
55	1.0302	4.1578	**5**
56	1.0303	4.1529	4
57	1.0304	4.1481	3
58	1.0305	4.1432	2
59	1.0305	4.1384	1
60	1.0306	4.1336	**0**
′	Csc	Sec	′

103° (283°) (256°) **76°**

14° (194°) (345°) **165°**

′	Sec	Csc	′
0	1.0306	4.1336	**60**
1	1.0307	4.1287	59
2	1.0308	4.1239	58
3	1.0308	4.1191	57
4	1.0309	4.1144	56
5	1.0310	4.1096	**55**
6	1.0311	4.1048	54
7	1.0311	4.1001	53
8	1.0312	4.0954	52
9	1.0313	4.0906	51
10	1.0314	4.0859	**50**
11	1.0314	4.0812	49
12	1.0315	4.0765	48
13	1.0316	4.0718	47
14	1.0317	4.0672	46
15	1.0317	4.0625	**45**
16	1.0318	4.0579	44
17	1.0319	4.0532	43
18	1.0320	4.0486	42
19	1.0321	4.0440	41
20	1.0321	4.0394	**40**
21	1.0322	4.0348	39
22	1.0323	4.0302	38
23	1.0324	4.0256	37
24	1.0324	4.0211	36
25	1.0325	4.0165	**35**
26	1.0326	4.0120	34
27	1.0327	4.0075	33
28	1.0327	4.0029	32
29	1.0328	3.9984	31
30	1.0329	3.9939	**30**
31	1.0330	3.9894	29
32	1.0331	3.9850	28
33	1.0331	3.9805	27
34	1.0332	3.9760	26
35	1.0333	3.9716	**25**
36	1.0334	3.9672	24
37	1.0334	3.9627	23
38	1.0335	3.9583	22
39	1.0336	3.9539	21
40	1.0337	3.9495	**20**
41	1.0338	3.9451	19
42	1.0338	3.9408	18
43	1.0339	3.9364	17
44	1.0340	3.9320	16
45	1.0341	3.9277	**15**
46	1.0342	3.9234	14
47	1.0342	3.9190	13
48	1.0343	3.9147	12
49	1.0344	3.9104	11
50	1.0345	3.9061	**10**
51	1.0346	3.9018	9
52	1.0346	3.8976	8
53	1.0347	3.8933	7
54	1.0348	3.8890	6
55	1.0349	3.8848	**5**
56	1.0350	3.8806	4
57	1.0350	3.8763	3
58	1.0351	3.8721	2
59	1.0352	3.8679	1
60	1.0353	3.8637	**0**
′	Csc	Sec	′

104° (284°) (255°) **75°**

15° (195°) (344°) **164°**

′	Sec	Csc	′
0	1.0353	3.8637	**60**
1	1.0354	3.8595	59
2	1.0354	3.8553	58
3	1.0355	3.8512	57
4	1.0356	3.8470	56
5	1.0357	3.8428	**55**
6	1.0358	3.8387	54
7	1.0358	3.8346	53
8	1.0359	3.8304	52
9	1.0360	3.8263	51
10	1.0361	3.8222	**50**
11	1.0362	3.8181	49
12	1.0363	3.8140	48
13	1.0363	3.8100	47
14	1.0364	3.8059	46
15	1.0365	3.8018	**45**
16	1.0366	3.7978	44
17	1.0367	3.7937	43
18	1.0367	3.7897	42
19	1.0368	3.7857	41
20	1.0369	3.7817	**40**
21	1.0370	3.7777	39
22	1.0371	3.7737	38
23	1.0372	3.7697	37
24	1.0372	3.7657	36
25	1.0373	3.7617	**35**
26	1.0374	3.7577	34
27	1.0375	3.7538	33
28	1.0376	3.7498	32
29	1.0377	3.7459	31
30	1.0377	3.7420	**30**
31	1.0378	3.7381	29
32	1.0379	3.7341	28
33	1.0380	3.7302	27
34	1.0381	3.7263	26
35	1.0382	3.7225	**25**
36	1.0382	3.7186	24
37	1.0383	3.7147	23
38	1.0384	3.7108	22
39	1.0385	3.7070	21
40	1.0386	3.7032	**20**
41	1.0387	3.6993	19
42	1.0388	3.6955	18
43	1.0388	3.6917	17
44	1.0389	3.6879	16
45	1.0390	3.6840	**15**
46	1.0391	3.6803	14
47	1.0392	3.6765	13
48	1.0393	3.6727	12
49	1.0394	3.6689	11
50	1.0394	3.6652	**10**
51	1.0395	3.6614	9
52	1.0396	3.6576	8
53	1.0397	3.6539	7
54	1.0398	3.6502	6
55	1.0399	3.6465	**5**
56	1.0400	3.6427	4
57	1.0400	3.6390	3
58	1.0401	3.6353	2
59	1.0402	3.6316	1
60	1.0403	3.6280	**0**
′	Csc	Sec	′

105° (285°) (254°) **74°**

16° (196°) (343°) **163°**

′	Sec	Csc	′
0	1.0403	3.6280	**60**
1	1.0404	3.6243	59
2	1.0405	3.6206	58
3	1.0406	3.6169	57
4	1.0406	3.6133	56
5	1.0407	3.6097	**55**
6	1.0408	3.6060	54
7	1.0409	3.6024	53
8	1.0410	3.5988	52
9	1.0411	3.5951	51
10	1.0412	3.5915	**50**
11	1.0413	3.5879	49
12	1.0413	3.5843	48
13	1.0414	3.5808	47
14	1.0415	3.5772	46
15	1.0416	3.5736	**45**
16	1.0417	3.5700	44
17	1.0418	3.5665	43
18	1.0419	3.5629	42
19	1.0420	3.5594	41
20	1.0421	3.5559	**40**
21	1.0421	3.5523	39
22	1.0422	3.5488	38
23	1.0423	3.5453	37
24	1.0424	3.5418	36
25	1.0425	3.5383	**35**
26	1.0426	3.5348	34
27	1.0427	3.5313	33
28	1.0428	3.5279	32
29	1.0429	3.5244	31
30	1.0429	3.5209	**30**
31	1.0430	3.5175	29
32	1.0431	3.5140	28
33	1.0432	3.5106	27
34	1.0433	3.5072	26
35	1.0434	3.5037	**25**
36	1.0435	3.5003	24
37	1.0436	3.4969	23
38	1.0437	3.4935	22
39	1.0438	3.4901	21
40	1.0439	3.4867	**20**
41	1.0439	3.4833	19
42	1.0440	3.4799	18
43	1.0441	3.4766	17
44	1.0442	3.4732	16
45	1.0443	3.4699	**15**
46	1.0444	3.4665	14
47	1.0445	3.4632	13
48	1.0446	3.4598	12
49	1.0447	3.4565	11
50	1.0448	3.4532	**10**
51	1.0449	3.4499	9
52	1.0450	3.4465	8
53	1.0450	3.4432	7
54	1.0451	3.4399	6
55	1.0452	3.4367	**5**
56	1.0453	3.4334	4
57	1.0454	3.4301	3
58	1.0455	3.4268	2
59	1.0456	3.4236	1
60	1.0457	3.4203	**0**
′	Csc	Sec	′

106° (286°) (253°) **73°**

17° (197°) (342°) **162°**

′	Sec	Csc	′
0	1.0457	3.4203	**60**
1	1.0458	3.4171	59
2	1.0459	3.4138	58
3	1.0460	3.4106	57
4	1.0461	3.4073	56
5	1.0462	3.4041	**55**
6	1.0463	3.4009	54
7	1.0463	3.3977	53
8	1.0464	3.3945	52
9	1.0465	3.3913	51
10	1.0466	3.3881	**50**
11	1.0467	3.3849	49
12	1.0468	3.3817	48
13	1.0469	3.3785	47
14	1.0470	3.3754	46
15	1.0471	3.3722	**45**
16	1.0472	3.3691	44
17	1.0473	3.3659	43
18	1.0474	3.3628	42
19	1.0475	3.3596	41
20	1.0476	3.3565	**40**
21	1.0477	3.3534	39
22	1.0478	3.3502	38
23	1.0479	3.3471	37
24	1.0480	3.3440	36
25	1.0480	3.3409	**35**
26	1.0481	3.3378	34
27	1.0482	3.3347	33
28	1.0483	3.3317	32
29	1.0484	3.3286	31
30	1.0485	3.3255	**30**
31	1.0486	3.3224	29
32	1.0487	3.3194	28
33	1.0488	3.3163	27
34	1.0489	3.3133	26
35	1.0490	3.3102	**25**
36	1.0491	3.3072	24
37	1.0492	3.3042	23
38	1.0493	3.3012	22
39	1.0494	3.2981	21
40	1.0495	3.2951	**20**
41	1.0496	3.2921	19
42	1.0497	3.2891	18
43	1.0498	3.2861	17
44	1.0499	3.2831	16
45	1.0500	3.2801	**15**
46	1.0501	3.2772	14
47	1.0502	3.2742	13
48	1.0503	3.2712	12
49	1.0504	3.2683	11
50	1.0505	3.2653	**10**
51	1.0506	3.2624	9
52	1.0507	3.2594	8
53	1.0508	3.2565	7
54	1.0509	3.2535	6
55	1.0510	3.2506	**5**
56	1.0511	3.2477	4
57	1.0512	3.2448	3
58	1.0513	3.2419	2
59	1.0514	3.2390	1
60	1.0515	3.2361	**0**
′	Csc	Sec	′

107° (287°) (252°) **72°**

18° (198°)		(341°) 161°	
′	Sec	Csc	′
0	1.0515	3.2361	**60**
1	1.0516	3.2332	59
2	1.0517	3.2303	58
3	1.0518	3.2274	57
4	1.0519	3.2245	56
5	1.0520	3.2217	**55**
6	1.0521	3.2188	54
7	1.0522	3.2159	53
8	1.0523	3.2131	52
9	1.0524	3.2102	51
10	1.0525	3.2074	**50**
11	1.0526	3.2045	49
12	1.0527	3.2017	48
13	1.0528	3.1989	47
14	1.0529	3.1960	46
15	1.0530	3.1932	**45**
16	1.0531	3.1904	44
17	1.0532	3.1876	43
18	1.0533	3.1848	42
19	1.0534	3.1820	41
20	1.0535	3.1792	**40**
21	1.0536	3.1764	39
22	1.0537	3.1736	38
23	1.0538	3.1708	37
24	1.0539	3.1681	36
25	1.0540	3.1653	**35**
26	1.0541	3.1625	34
27	1.0542	3.1598	33
28	1.0543	3.1570	32
29	1.0544	3.1543	31
30	1.0545	3.1515	**30**
31	1.0546	3.1488	29
32	1.0547	3.1461	28
33	1.0548	3.1433	27
34	1.0549	3.1406	26
35	1.0550	3.1379	**25**
36	1.0551	3.1352	24
37	1.0552	3.1325	23
38	1.0553	3.1298	22
39	1.0554	3.1271	21
40	1.0555	3.1244	**20**
41	1.0556	3.1217	19
42	1.0557	3.1190	18
43	1.0558	3.1163	17
44	1.0559	3.1137	16
45	1.0560	3.1110	**15**
46	1.0561	3.1083	14
47	1.0563	3.1057	13
48	1.0564	3.1030	12
49	1.0565	3.1004	11
50	1.0566	3.0977	**10**
51	1.0567	3.0951	9
52	1.0568	3.0925	8
53	1.0569	3.0898	7
54	1.0570	3.0872	6
55	1.0571	3.0846	**5**
56	1.0572	3.0820	4
57	1.0573	3.0794	3
58	1.0574	3.0768	2
59	1.0575	3.0742	1
60	1.0576	3.0716	**0**
′	Csc	Sec	′
108° (288°)		(251°) 71°	

19° (199°)		(340°) 160°	
′	Sec	Csc	′
0	1.0576	3.0716	**60**
1	1.0577	3.0690	59
2	1.0578	3.0664	58
3	1.0579	3.0638	57
4	1.0580	3.0612	56
5	1.0582	3.0586	**55**
6	1.0583	3.0561	54
7	1.0584	3.0535	53
8	1.0585	3.0509	52
9	1.0586	3.0484	51
10	1.0587	3.0458	**50**
11	1.0588	3.0433	49
12	1.0589	3.0407	48
13	1.0590	3.0382	47
14	1.0591	3.0357	46
15	1.0592	3.0331	**45**
16	1.0593	3.0306	44
17	1.0594	3.0281	43
18	1.0595	3.0256	42
19	1.0597	3.0231	41
20	1.0598	3.0206	**40**
21	1.0599	3.0181	39
22	1.0600	3.0156	38
23	1.0601	3.0131	37
24	1.0602	3.0106	36
25	1.0603	3.0081	**35**
26	1.0604	3.0056	34
27	1.0605	3.0031	33
28	1.0606	3.0007	32
29	1.0607	2.9982	31
30	1.0608	2.9957	**30**
31	1.0610	2.9933	29
32	1.0611	2.9908	28
33	1.0612	2.9884	27
34	1.0613	2.9859	26
35	1.0614	2.9835	**25**
36	1.0615	2.9811	24
37	1.0616	2.9786	23
38	1.0617	2.9762	22
39	1.0618	2.9738	21
40	1.0619	2.9713	**20**
41	1.0621	2.9689	19
42	1.0622	2.9665	18
43	1.0623	2.9641	17
44	1.0624	2.9617	16
45	1.0625	2.9593	**15**
46	1.0626	2.9569	14
47	1.0627	2.9545	13
48	1.0628	2.9521	12
49	1.0629	2.9498	11
50	1.0631	2.9474	**10**
51	1.0632	2.9450	9
52	1.0633	2.9426	8
53	1.0634	2.9403	7
54	1.0635	2.9379	6
55	1.0636	2.9355	**5**
56	1.0637	2.9332	4
57	1.0638	2.9308	3
58	1.0640	2.9285	2
59	1.0641	2.9261	1
60	1.0642	2.9238	**0**
′	Csc	Sec	′
109° (289°)		(250°) 70°	

20° (200°)		(339°) 159°	
′	Sec	Csc	′
0	1.0642	2.9238	**60**
1	1.0643	2.9215	59
2	1.0644	2.9191	58
3	1.0645	2.9168	57
4	1.0646	2.9145	56
5	1.0647	2.9122	**55**
6	1.0649	2.9099	54
7	1.0650	2.9075	53
8	1.0651	2.9052	52
9	1.0652	2.9029	51
10	1.0653	2.9006	**50**
11	1.0654	2.8983	49
12	1.0655	2.8960	48
13	1.0657	2.8938	47
14	1.0658	2.8915	46
15	1.0659	2.8892	**45**
16	1.0660	2.8869	44
17	1.0661	2.8846	43
18	1.0662	2.8824	42
19	1.0663	2.8801	41
20	1.0665	2.8779	**40**
21	1.0666	2.8756	39
22	1.0667	2.8733	38
23	1.0668	2.8711	37
24	1.0669	2.8688	36
25	1.0670	2.8666	**35**
26	1.0671	2.8644	34
27	1.0673	2.8621	33
28	1.0674	2.8599	32
29	1.0675	2.8577	31
30	1.0676	2.8555	**30**
31	1.0677	2.8532	29
32	1.0678	2.8510	28
33	1.0680	2.8488	27
34	1.0681	2.8466	26
35	1.0682	2.8444	**25**
36	1.0683	2.8422	24
37	1.0684	2.8400	23
38	1.0685	2.8378	22
39	1.0687	2.8356	21
40	1.0688	2.8334	**20**
41	1.0689	2.8312	19
42	1.0690	2.8291	18
43	1.0691	2.8269	17
44	1.0692	2.8247	16
45	1.0694	2.8225	**15**
46	1.0695	2.8204	14
47	1.0696	2.8182	13
48	1.0697	2.8161	12
49	1.0698	2.8139	11
50	1.0700	2.8117	**10**
51	1.0701	2.8096	9
52	1.0702	2.8075	8
53	1.0703	2.8053	7
54	1.0704	2.8032	6
55	1.0705	2.8010	**5**
56	1.0707	2.7989	4
57	1.0708	2.7968	3
58	1.0709	2.7947	2
59	1.0710	2.7925	1
60	1.0711	2.7904	**0**
′	Csc	Sec	′
110° (290°)		(249°) 69°	

21° (201°) (338°) **158°**

′	Sec	Csc	′
0	1.0711	2.7904	**60**
1	1.0713	2.7883	59
2	1.0714	2.7862	58
3	1.0715	2.7841	57
4	1.0716	2.7820	56
5	1.0717	2.7799	**55**
6	1.0719	2.7778	54
7	1.0720	2.7757	53
8	1.0721	2.7736	52
9	1.0722	2.7715	51
10	1.0723	2.7695	**50**
11	1.0725	2.7674	49
12	1.0726	2.7653	48
13	1.0727	2.7632	47
14	1.0728	2.7612	46
15	1.0730	2.7591	**45**
16	1.0731	2.7570	44
17	1.0732	2.7550	43
18	1.0733	2.7529	42
19	1.0734	2.7509	41
20	1.0736	2.7488	**40**
21	1.0737	2.7468	39
22	1.0738	2.7447	38
23	1.0739	2.7427	37
24	1.0740	2.7407	36
25	1.0742	2.7386	**35**
26	1.0743	2.7366	34
27	1.0744	2.7346	33
28	1.0745	2.7325	32
29	1.0747	2.7305	31
30	1.0748	2.7285	**30**
31	1.0749	2.7265	29
32	1.0750	2.7245	28
33	1.0752	2.7225	27
34	1.0753	2.7205	26
35	1.0754	2.7185	**25**
36	1.0755	2.7165	24
37	1.0757	2.7145	23
38	1.0758	2.7125	22
39	1.0759	2.7105	21
40	1.0760	2.7085	**20**
41	1.0761	2.7065	19
42	1.0763	2.7046	18
43	1.0764	2.7026	17
44	1.0765	2.7006	16
45	1.0766	2.6986	**15**
46	1.0768	2.6967	14
47	1.0769	2.6947	13
48	1.0770	2.6927	12
49	1.0771	2.6908	11
50	1.0773	2.6888	**10**
51	1.0774	2.6869	9
52	1.0775	2.6849	8
53	1.0777	2.6830	7
54	1.0778	2.6811	6
55	1.0779	2.6791	**5**
56	1.0780	2.6772	4
57	1.0782	2.6752	3
58	1.0783	2.6733	2
59	1.0784	2.6714	1
60	1.0785	2.6695	**0**
′	Csc	Sec	′

111° (291°) (248°) **68°**

22° (202°) (337°) **157°**

′	Sec	Csc	′
0	1.0785	2.6695	**60**
1	1.0787	2.6675	59
2	1.0788	2.6656	58
3	1.0789	2.6637	57
4	1.0790	2.6618	56
5	1.0792	2.6599	**55**
6	1.0793	2.6580	54
7	1.0794	2.6561	53
8	1.0796	2.6542	52
9	1.0797	2.6523	51
10	1.0798	2.6504	**50**
11	1.0799	2.6485	49
12	1.0801	2.6466	48
13	1.0802	2.6447	47
14	1.0803	2.6429	46
15	1.0804	2.6410	**45**
16	1.0806	2.6391	44
17	1.0807	2.6372	43
18	1.0808	2.6354	42
19	1.0810	2.6335	41
20	1.0811	2.6316	**40**
21	1.0812	2.6298	39
22	1.0814	2.6279	38
23	1.0815	2.6260	37
24	1.0816	2.6242	36
25	1.0817	2.6223	**35**
26	1.0819	2.6205	34
27	1.0820	2.6186	33
28	1.0821	2.6168	32
29	1.0823	2.6150	31
30	1.0824	2.6131	**30**
31	1.0825	2.6113	29
32	1.0827	2.6095	28
33	1.0828	2.6076	27
34	1.0829	2.6058	26
35	1.0830	2.6040	**25**
36	1.0832	2.6022	24
37	1.0833	2.6003	23
38	1.0834	2.5985	22
39	1.0836	2.5967	21
40	1.0837	2.5949	**20**
41	1.0838	2.5931	19
42	1.0840	2.5913	18
43	1.0841	2.5895	17
44	1.0842	2.5877	16
45	1.0844	2.5859	**15**
46	1.0845	2.5841	14
47	1.0846	2.5823	13
48	1.0848	2.5805	12
49	1.0849	2.5788	11
50	1.0850	2.5770	**10**
51	1.0852	2.5752	9
52	1.0853	2.5734	8
53	1.0854	2.5716	7
54	1.0856	2.5699	6
55	1.0857	2.5681	**5**
56	1.0858	2.5663	4
57	1.0860	2.5646	3
58	1.0861	2.5628	2
59	1.0862	2.5611	1
60	1.0864	2.5593	**0**
′	Csc	Sec	′

112° (292°) (247°) **67°**

23° (203°) (336°) **156°**

′	Sec	Csc	′
0	1.0864	2.5593	**60**
1	1.0865	2.5576	59
2	1.0866	2.5558	58
3	1.0868	2.5541	57
4	1.0869	2.5523	56
5	1.0870	2.5506	**55**
6	1.0872	2.5488	54
7	1.0873	2.5471	53
8	1.0874	2.5454	52
9	1.0876	2.5436	51
10	1.0877	2.5419	**50**
11	1.0878	2.5402	49
12	1.0880	2.5384	48
13	1.0881	2.5367	47
14	1.0883	2.5350	46
15	1.0884	2.5333	**45**
16	1.0885	2.5316	44
17	1.0887	2.5299	43
18	1.0888	2.5282	42
19	1.0889	2.5264	41
20	1.0891	2.5247	**40**
21	1.0892	2.5230	39
22	1.0893	2.5213	38
23	1.0895	2.5196	37
24	1.0896	2.5180	36
25	1.0898	2.5163	**35**
26	1.0899	2.5146	34
27	1.0900	2.5129	33
28	1.0902	2.5112	32
29	1.0903	2.5095	31
30	1.0904	2.5078	**30**
31	1.0906	2.5062	29
32	1.0907	2.5045	28
33	1.0909	2.5028	27
34	1.0910	2.5012	26
35	1.0911	2.4995	**25**
36	1.0913	2.4978	24
37	1.0914	2.4962	23
38	1.0915	2.4945	22
39	1.0917	2.4928	21
40	1.0918	2.4912	**20**
41	1.0920	2.4895	19
42	1.0921	2.4879	18
43	1.0922	2.4862	17
44	1.0924	2.4846	16
45	1.0925	2.4830	**15**
46	1.0927	2.4813	14
47	1.0928	2.4797	13
48	1.0929	2.4780	12
49	1.0931	2.4764	11
50	1.0932	2.4748	**10**
51	1.0934	2.4731	9
52	1.0935	2.4715	8
53	1.0936	2.4699	7
54	1.0938	2.4683	6
55	1.0939	2.4667	**5**
56	1.0941	2.4650	4
57	1.0942	2.4634	3
58	1.0944	2.4618	2
59	1.0945	2.4602	1
60	1.0946	2.4586	**0**
′	Csc	Sec	′

113° (293°) (246°) **66°**

NATURAL FUNCTIONS—SECANTS AND COSECANTS (Continued)

24° (204°) (335°) **155°**

′	Sec	Csc	′
0	1.0946	2.4586	**60**
1	1.0948	2.4570	59
2	1.0949	2.4554	58
3	1.0951	2.4538	57
4	1.0952	2.4522	56
5	1.0953	2.4506	**55**
6	1.0955	2.4490	54
7	1.0956	2.4474	53
8	1.0958	2.4458	52
9	1.0959	2.4442	51
10	1.0961	2.4426	**50**
11	1.0962	2.4411	49
12	1.0963	2.4395	48
13	1.0965	2.4379	47
14	1.0966	2.4363	46
15	1.0968	2.4348	**45**
16	1.0969	2.4332	44
17	1.0971	2.4316	43
18	1.0972	2.4300	42
19	1.0974	2.4285	41
20	1.0975	2.4269	**40**
21	1.0976	2.4254	39
22	1.0978	2.4238	38
23	1.0979	2.4222	37
24	1.0981	2.4207	36
25	1.0982	2.4191	**35**
26	1.0984	2.4176	34
27	1.0985	2.4160	33
28	1.0987	2.4145	32
29	1.0988	2.4130	31
30	1.0989	2.4114	**30**
31	1.0991	2.4099	29
32	1.0992	2.4083	28
33	1.0994	2.4068	27
34	1.0995	2.4053	26
35	1.0997	2.4038	**25**
36	1.0998	2.4022	24
37	1.1000	2.4007	23
38	1.1001	2.3992	22
39	1.1003	2.3977	21
40	1.1004	2.3961	**20**
41	1.1006	2.3946	19
42	1.1007	2.3931	18
43	1.1009	2.3916	17
44	1.1010	2.3901	16
45	1.1011	2.3886	**15**
46	1.1013	2.3871	14
47	1.1014	2.3856	13
48	1.1016	2.3841	12
49	1.1017	2.3826	11
50	1.1019	2.3811	**10**
51	1.1020	2.3796	9
52	1.1022	2.3781	8
53	1.1023	2.3766	7
54	1.1025	2.3751	6
55	1.1026	2.3736	**5**
56	1.1028	2.3721	4
57	1.1029	2.3706	3
58	1.1031	2.3692	2
59	1.1032	2.3677	1
60	1.1034	2.3662	**0**
′	Csc	Sec	′

114° (294°) (245°) **65°**

25° (205°) (334°) **154°**

′	Sec	Csc	′
0	1.1034	2.3662	**60**
1	1.1035	2.3647	59
2	1.1037	2.3633	58
3	1.1038	2.3618	57
4	1.1040	2.3603	56
5	1.1041	2.3588	**55**
6	1.1043	2.3574	54
7	1.1044	2.3559	53
8	1.1046	2.3545	52
9	1.1047	2.3530	51
10	1.1049	2.3515	**50**
11	1.1050	2.3501	49
12	1.1052	2.3486	48
13	1.1053	2.3472	47
14	1.1055	2.3457	46
15	1.1056	2.3443	**45**
16	1.1058	2.3428	44
17	1.1059	2.3414	43
18	1.1061	2.3400	42
19	1.1062	2.3385	41
20	1.1064	2.3371	**40**
21	1.1066	2.3356	39
22	1.1067	2.3342	38
23	1.1069	2.3328	37
24	1.1070	2.3314	36
25	1.1072	2.3299	**35**
26	1.1073	2.3285	34
27	1.1075	2.3271	33
28	1.1076	2.3257	32
29	1.1078	2.3242	31
30	1.1079	2.3228	**30**
31	1.1081	2.3214	29
32	1.1082	2.3200	28
33	1.1084	2.3186	27
34	1.1085	2.3172	26
35	1.1087	2.3158	**25**
36	1.1089	2.3144	24
37	1.1090	2.3130	23
38	1.1092	2.3115	22
39	1.1093	2.3101	21
40	1.1095	2.3088	**20**
41	1.1096	2.3074	19
42	1.1098	2.3060	18
43	1.1099	2.3046	17
44	1.1101	2.3032	16
45	1.1102	2.3018	**15**
46	1.1104	2.3004	14
47	1.1106	2.2990	13
48	1.1107	2.2976	12
49	1.1109	2.2962	11
50	1.1110	2.2949	**10**
51	1.1112	2.2935	9
52	1.1113	2.2921	8
53	1.1115	2.2907	7
54	1.1117	2.2894	6
55	1.1118	2.2880	**5**
56	1.1120	2.2866	4
57	1.1121	2.2853	3
58	1.1123	2.2839	2
59	1.1124	2.2825	1
60	1.1126	2.2812	**0**
′	Csc	Sec	′

115° (295°) (244°) **64°**

26° (206°) (333°) **153°**

′	Sec	Csc	′
0	1.1126	2.2812	**60**
1	1.1128	2.2798	59
2	1.1129	2.2785	58
3	1.1131	2.2771	57
4	1.1132	2.2757	56
5	1.1134	2.2744	**55**
6	1.1136	2.2730	54
7	1.1137	2.2717	53
8	1.1139	2.2703	52
9	1.1140	2.2690	51
10	1.1142	2.2677	**50**
11	1.1143	2.2663	49
12	1.1145	2.2650	48
13	1.1147	2.2636	47
14	1.1148	2.2623	46
15	1.1150	2.2610	**45**
16	1.1151	2.2596	44
17	1.1153	2.2583	43
18	1.1155	2.2570	42
19	1.1156	2.2556	41
20	1.1158	2.2543	**40**
21	1.1159	2.2530	39
22	1.1161	2.2517	38
23	1.1163	2.2504	37
24	1.1164	2.2490	36
25	1.1166	2.2477	**35**
26	1.1168	2.2464	34
27	1.1169	2.2451	33
28	1.1171	2.2438	32
29	1.1172	2.2425	31
30	1.1174	2.2412	**30**
31	1.1176	2.2399	29
32	1.1177	2.2385	28
33	1.1179	2.2372	27
34	1.1180	2.2359	26
35	1.1182	2.2346	**25**
36	1.1184	2.2333	24
37	1.1185	2.2320	23
38	1.1187	2.2308	22
39	1.1189	2.2295	21
40	1.1190	2.2282	**20**
41	1.1192	2.2269	19
42	1.1194	2.2256	18
43	1.1195	2.2243	17
44	1.1197	2.2230	16
45	1.1198	2.2217	**15**
46	1.1200	2.2205	14
47	1.1202	2.2192	13
48	1.1203	2.2179	12
49	1.1205	2.2166	11
50	1.1207	2.2153	**10**
51	1.1208	2.2141	9
52	1.1210	2.2128	8
53	1.1212	2.2115	7
54	1.1213	2.2103	6
55	1.1215	2.2090	**5**
56	1.1217	2.2077	4
57	1.1218	2.2065	3
58	1.1220	2.2052	2
59	1.1222	2.2039	1
60	1.1223	2.2027	**0**
′	Csc	Sec	′

116° (296°) (243°) **63°**

27° (207°) (332°) **152°**

′	Sec	Csc	′
0	1.1223	2.2027	**60**
1	1.1225	2.2014	59
2	1.1227	2.2002	58
3	1.1228	2.1989	57
4	1.1230	2.1977	56
5	1.1232	2.1964	**55**
6	1.1233	2.1952	54
7	1.1235	2.1939	53
8	1.1237	2.1927	52
9	1.1238	2.1914	51
10	1.1240	2.1902	**50**
11	1.1242	2.1890	49
12	1.1243	2.1877	48
13	1.1245	2.1865	47
14	1.1247	2.1852	46
15	1.1248	2.1840	**45**
16	1.1250	2.1828	44
17	1.1252	2.1815	43
18	1.1253	2.1803	42
19	1.1255	2.1791	41
20	1.1257	2.1779	**40**
21	1.1259	2.1766	39
22	1.1260	2.1754	38
23	1.1262	2.1742	37
24	1.1264	2.1730	36
25	1.1265	2.1718	**35**
26	1.1267	2.1705	34
27	1.1269	2.1693	33
28	1.1270	2.1681	32
29	1.1272	2.1669	31
30	1.1274	2.1657	**30**
31	1.1276	2.1645	29
32	1.1277	2.1633	28
33	1.1279	2.1621	27
34	1.1281	2.1609	26
35	1.1282	2.1596	**25**
36	1.1284	2.1584	24
37	1.1286	2.1572	23
38	1.1288	2.1560	22
39	1.1289	2.1549	21
40	1.1291	2.1537	**20**
41	1.1293	2.1525	19
42	1.1294	2.1513	18
43	1.1296	2.1501	17
44	1.1298	2.1489	16
45	1.1300	2.1477	**15**
46	1.1301	2.1465	14
47	1.1303	2.1453	13
48	1.1305	2.1441	12
49	1.1307	2.1430	11
50	1.1308	2.1418	**10**
51	1.1310	2.1406	9
52	1.1312	2.1394	8
53	1.1313	2.1382	7
54	1.1315	2.1371	6
55	1.1317	2.1359	**5**
56	1.1319	2.1347	4
57	1.1320	2.1336	3
58	1.1322	2.1324	2
59	1.1324	2.1312	1
60	1.1326	2.1301	**0**
′	Csc	Sec	′

117° (297°) (242°) **62°**

28° (208°) (331°) **151°**

′	Sec	Csc	′
0	1.1326	2.1301	**60**
1	1.1327	2.1289	59
2	1.1329	2.1277	58
3	1.1331	2.1266	57
4	1.1333	2.1254	56
5	1.1334	2.1242	**55**
6	1.1336	2.1231	54
7	1.1338	2.1219	53
8	1.1340	2.1208	52
9	1.1342	2.1196	51
10	1.1343	2.1185	**50**
11	1.1345	2.1173	49
12	1.1347	2.1162	48
13	1.1349	2.1150	47
14	1.1350	2.1139	46
15	1.1352	2.1127	**45**
16	1.1354	2.1116	44
17	1.1356	2.1105	43
18	1.1357	2.1093	42
19	1.1359	2.1082	41
20	1.1361	2.1070	**40**
21	1.1363	2.1059	39
22	1.1365	2.1048	38
23	1.1366	2.1036	37
24	1.1368	2.1025	36
25	1.1370	2.1014	**35**
26	1.1372	2.1002	34
27	1.1374	2.0991	33
28	1.1375	2.0980	32
29	1.1377	2.0969	31
30	1.1379	2.0957	**30**
31	1.1381	2.0946	29
32	1.1383	2.0935	28
33	1.1384	2.0924	27
34	1.1386	2.0913	26
35	1.1388	2.0901	**25**
36	1.1390	2.0890	24
37	1.1392	2.0879	23
38	1.1393	2.0868	22
39	1.1395	2.0857	21
40	1.1397	2.0846	**20**
41	1.1399	2.0835	19
42	1.1401	2.0824	18
43	1.1402	2.0813	17
44	1.1404	2.0802	16
45	1.1406	2.0791	**15**
46	1.1408	2.0779	14
47	1.1410	2.0768	13
48	1.1412	2.0757	12
49	1.1413	2.0747	11
50	1.1415	2.0736	**10**
51	1.1417	2.0725	9
52	1.1419	2.0714	8
53	1.1421	2.0703	7
54	1.1423	2.0692	6
55	1.1424	2.0681	**5**
56	1.1426	2.0670	4
57	1.1428	2.0659	3
58	1.1430	2.0648	2
59	1.1432	2.0637	1
60	1.1434	2.0627	**0**
′	Csc	Sec	′

118° (298°) (241°) **61°**

29° (209°) (330°) **150°**

′	Sec	Csc	′
0	1.1434	2.0627	**60**
1	1.1435	2.0616	59
2	1.1437	2.0605	58
3	1.1439	2.0594	57
4	1.1441	2.0583	56
5	1.1443	2.0573	**55**
6	1.1445	2.0562	54
7	1.1446	2.0551	53
8	1.1448	2.0540	52
9	1.1450	2.0530	51
10	1.1452	2.0519	**50**
11	1.1454	2.0508	49
12	1.1456	2.0498	48
13	1.1458	2.0487	47
14	1.1460	2.0476	46
15	1.1461	2.0466	**45**
16	1.1463	2.0455	44
17	1.1465	2.0445	43
18	1.1467	2.0434	42
19	1.1469	2.0423	41
20	1.1471	2.0413	**40**
21	1.1473	2.0402	39
22	1.1474	2.0392	38
23	1.1476	2.0381	37
24	1.1478	2.0371	36
25	1.1480	2.0360	**35**
26	1.1482	2.0350	34
27	1.1484	2.0339	33
28	1.1486	2.0329	32
29	1.1488	2.0318	31
30	1.1490	2.0308	**30**
31	1.1491	2.0297	29
32	1.1493	2.0287	28
33	1.1495	2.0276	27
34	1.1497	2.0266	26
35	1.1499	2.0256	**25**
36	1.1501	2.0245	24
37	1.1503	2.0235	23
38	1.1505	2.0225	22
39	1.1507	2.0214	21
40	1.1509	2.0204	**20**
41	1.1510	2.0194	19
42	1.1512	2.0183	18
43	1.1514	2.0173	17
44	1.1516	2.0163	16
45	1.1518	2.0152	**15**
46	1.1520	2.0142	14
47	1.1522	2.0132	13
48	1.1524	2.0122	12
49	1.1526	2.0112	11
50	1.1528	2.0101	**10**
51	1.1530	2.0091	9
52	1.1532	2.0081	8
53	1.1533	2.0071	7
54	1.1535	2.0061	6
55	1.1537	2.0051	**5**
56	1.1539	2.0040	4
57	1.1541	2.0030	3
58	1.1543	2.0020	2
59	1.1545	2.0010	1
60	1.1547	2.0000	**0**
′	Csc	Sec	′

119° (299°) (240°) **60°**

30° (210°) (329°) **149°**

′	Sec	Csc	′
0	1.1547	2.0000	**60**
1	1.1549	1.9990	59
2	1.1551	1.9980	58
3	1.1553	1.9970	57
4	1.1555	1.9960	56
5	1.1557	1.9950	**55**
6	1.1559	1.9940	54
7	1.1561	1.9930	53
8	1.1563	1.9920	52
9	1.1565	1.9910	51
10	1.1566	1.9900	**50**
11	1.1568	1.9890	49
12	1.1570	1.9880	48
13	1.1572	1.9870	47
14	1.1574	1.9860	46
15	1.1576	1.9850	**45**
16	1.1578	1.9840	44
17	1.1580	1.9830	43
18	1.1582	1.9821	42
19	1.1584	1.9811	41
20	1.1586	1.9801	**40**
21	1.1588	1.9791	39
22	1.1590	1.9781	38
23	1.1592	1.9771	37
24	1.1594	1.9762	36
25	1.1596	1.9752	**35**
26	1.1598	1.9742	34
27	1.1600	1.9732	33
28	1.1602	1.9722	32
29	1.1604	1.9713	31
30	1.1606	1.9703	**30**
31	1.1608	1.9693	29
32	1.1610	1.9684	28
33	1.1612	1.9674	27
34	1.1614	1.9664	26
35	1.1616	1.9654	**25**
36	1.1618	1.9645	24
37	1.1620	1.9635	23
38	1.1622	1.9625	22
39	1.1624	1.9616	21
40	1.1626	1.9606	**20**
41	1.1628	1.9597	19
42	1.1630	1.9587	18
43	1.1632	1.9577	17
44	1.1634	1.9568	16
45	1.1636	1.9558	**15**
46	1.1638	1.9549	14
47	1.1640	1.9539	13
48	1.1642	1.9530	12
49	1.1644	1.9520	11
50	1.1646	1.9511	**10**
51	1.1648	1.9501	9
52	1.1650	1.9492	8
53	1.1652	1.9482	7
54	1.1654	1.9473	6
55	1.1656	1.9463	**5**
56	1.1658	1.9454	4
57	1.1660	1.9444	3
58	1.1662	1.9435	2
59	1.1664	1.9425	1
60	1.1666	1.9416	**0**
′	Csc	Sec	′

120° (300°) (239°) **59°**

31° (211°) (328°) **148°**

′	Sec	Csc	′
0	1.1666	1.9416	**60**
1	1.1668	1.9407	59
2	1.1670	1.9397	58
3	1.1672	1.9388	57
4	1.1675	1.9379	56
5	1.1677	1.9369	**55**
6	1.1679	1.9360	54
7	1.1681	1.9351	53
8	1.1683	1.9341	52
9	1.1685	1.9332	51
10	1.1687	1.9323	**50**
11	1.1689	1.9313	49
12	1.1691	1.9304	48
13	1.1693	1.9295	47
14	1.1695	1.9285	46
15	1.1697	1.9276	**45**
16	1.1699	1.9267	44
17	1.1701	1.9258	43
18	1.1703	1.9249	42
19	1.1705	1.9239	41
20	1.1707	1.9230	**40**
21	1.1710	1.9221	39
22	1.1712	1.9212	38
23	1.1714	1.9203	37
24	1.1716	1.9194	36
25	1.1718	1.9184	**35**
26	1.1720	1.9175	34
27	1.1722	1.9166	33
28	1.1724	1.9157	32
29	1.1726	1.9148	31
30	1.1728	1.9139	**30**
31	1.1730	1.9130	29
32	1.1732	1.9121	28
33	1.1735	1.9112	27
34	1.1737	1.9103	26
35	1.1739	1.9094	**25**
36	1.1741	1.9084	24
37	1.1743	1.9075	23
38	1.1745	1.9066	22
39	1.1747	1.9057	21
40	1.1749	1.9048	**20**
41	1.1751	1.9039	19
42	1.1753	1.9031	18
43	1.1756	1.9022	17
44	1.1758	1.9013	16
45	1.1760	1.9004	**15**
46	1.1762	1.8995	14
47	1.1764	1.8986	13
48	1.1766	1.8977	12
49	1.1768	1.8968	11
50	1.1770	1.8959	**10**
51	1.1773	1.8950	9
52	1.1775	1.8941	8
53	1.1777	1.8933	7
54	1.1779	1.8924	6
55	1.1781	1.8915	**5**
56	1.1783	1.8906	4
57	1.1785	1.8897	3
58	1.1788	1.8888	2
59	1.1790	1.8880	1
60	1.1792	1.8871	**0**
′	Csc	Sec	′

121° (301°) (238°) **58°**

32° (212°) (327°) **147°**

′	Sec	Csc	′
0	1.1792	1.8871	**60**
1	1.1794	1.8862	59
2	1.1796	1.8853	58
3	1.1798	1.8844	57
4	1.1800	1.8836	56
5	1.1803	1.8827	**55**
6	1.1805	1.8818	54
7	1.1807	1.8810	53
8	1.1809	1.8801	52
9	1.1811	1.8792	51
10	1.1813	1.8783	**50**
11	1.1815	1.8775	49
12	1.1818	1.8766	48
13	1.1820	1.8757	47
14	1.1822	1.8749	46
15	1.1824	1.8740	**45**
16	1.1826	1.8731	44
17	1.1828	1.8723	43
18	1.1831	1.8714	42
19	1.1833	1.8706	41
20	1.1835	1.8697	**40**
21	1.1837	1.8688	39
22	1.1839	1.8680	38
23	1.1842	1.8671	37
24	1.1844	1.8663	36
25	1.1846	1.8654	**35**
26	1.1848	1.8646	34
27	1.1850	1.8637	33
28	1.1852	1.8629	32
29	1.1855	1.8620	31
30	1.1857	1.8612	**30**
31	1.1859	1.8603	29
32	1.1861	1.8595	28
33	1.1863	1.8586	27
34	1.1866	1.8578	26
35	1.1868	1.8569	**25**
36	1.1870	1.8561	24
37	1.1872	1.8552	23
38	1.1875	1.8544	22
39	1.1877	1.8535	21
40	1.1879	1.8527	**20**
41	1.1881	1.8519	19
42	1.1883	1.8510	18
43	1.1886	1.8502	17
44	1.1888	1.8494	16
45	1.1890	1.8485	**15**
46	1.1892	1.8477	14
47	1.1895	1.8468	13
48	1.1897	1.8460	12
49	1.1899	1.8452	11
50	1.1901	1.8443	**10**
51	1.1903	1.8435	9
52	1.1906	1.8427	8
53	1.1908	1.8419	7
54	1.1910	1.8410	6
55	1.1912	1.8402	**5**
56	1.1915	1.8394	4
57	1.1917	1.8385	3
58	1.1919	1.8377	2
59	1.1921	1.8369	1
60	1.1924	1.8361	**0**
′	Csc	Sec	′

122° (302°) (237°) **57°**

33° (213°) (326°) **146°**

′	Sec	Csc	′
0	1.1924	1.8361	**60**
1	1.1926	1.8353	59
2	1.1928	1.8344	58
3	1.1930	1.8336	57
4	1.1933	1.8328	56
5	1.1935	1.8320	**55**
6	1.1937	1.8312	54
7	1.1939	1.8303	53
8	1.1942	1.8295	52
9	1.1944	1.8287	51
10	1.1946	1.8279	**50**
11	1.1949	1.8271	49
12	1.1951	1.8263	48
13	1.1953	1.8255	47
14	1.1955	1.8247	46
15	1.1958	1.8238	**45**
16	1.1960	1.8230	44
17	1.1962	1.8222	43
18	1.1964	1.8214	42
19	1.1967	1.8206	41
20	1.1969	1.8198	**40**
21	1.1971	1.8190	39
22	1.1974	1.8182	38
23	1.1976	1.8174	37
24	1.1978	1.8166	36
25	1.1981	1.8158	**35**
26	1.1983	1.8150	34
27	1.1985	1.8142	33
28	1.1987	1.8134	32
29	1.1990	1.8126	31
30	1.1992	1.8118	**30**
31	1.1994	1.8110	29
32	1.1997	1.8102	28
33	1.1999	1.8094	27
34	1.2001	1.8086	26
35	1.2004	1.8078	**25**
36	1.2006	1.8070	24
37	1.2008	1.8062	23
38	1.2011	1.8055	22
39	1.2013	1.8047	21
40	1.2015	1.8039	**20**
41	1.2018	1.8031	19
42	1.2020	1.8023	18
43	1.2022	1.8015	17
44	1.2025	1.8007	16
45	1.2027	1.8000	**15**
46	1.2029	1.7992	14
47	1.2032	1.7984	13
48	1.2034	1.7976	12
49	1.2036	1.7968	11
50	1.2039	1.7960	**10**
51	1.2041	1.7953	9
52	1.2043	1.7945	8
53	1.2046	1.7937	7
54	1.2048	1.7929	6
55	1.2050	1.7922	**5**
56	1.2053	1.7914	4
57	1.2055	1.7906	3
58	1.2057	1.7898	2
59	1.2060	1.7891	1
60	1.2062	1.7883	**0**
′	Csc	Sec	′

123° (303°) (236°) **56°**

34° (214°) (325°) **145°**

′	Sec	Csc	′
0	1.2062	1.7883	**60**
1	1.2065	1.7875	59
2	1.2067	1.7868	58
3	1.2069	1.7860	57
4	1.2072	1.7852	56
5	1.2074	1.7844	**55**
6	1.2076	1.7837	54
7	1.2079	1.7829	53
8	1.2081	1.7821	52
9	1.2084	1.7814	51
10	1.2086	1.7806	**50**
11	1.2088	1.7799	49
12	1.2091	1.7791	48
13	1.2093	1.7783	47
14	1.2096	1.7776	46
15	1.2098	1.7768	**45**
16	1.2100	1.7761	44
17	1.2103	1.7753	43
18	1.2105	1.7745	42
19	1.2108	1.7738	41
20	1.2110	1.7730	**40**
21	1.2112	1.7723	39
22	1.2115	1.7715	38
23	1.2117	1.7708	37
24	1.2120	1.7700	36
25	1.2122	1.7693	**35**
26	1.2124	1.7685	34
27	1.2127	1.7678	33
28	1.2129	1.7670	32
29	1.2132	1.7663	31
30	1.2134	1.7655	**30**
31	1.2136	1.7648	29
32	1.2139	1.7640	28
33	1.2141	1.7633	27
34	1.2144	1.7625	26
35	1.2146	1.7618	**25**
36	1.2149	1.7610	24
37	1.2151	1.7603	23
38	1.2154	1.7596	22
39	1.2156	1.7588	21
40	1.2158	1.7581	**20**
41	1.2161	1.7573	19
42	1.2163	1.7566	18
43	1.2166	1.7559	17
44	1.2168	1.7551	16
45	1.2171	1.7544	**15**
46	1.2173	1.7537	14
47	1.2176	1.7529	13
48	1.2178	1.7522	12
49	1.2181	1.7515	11
50	1.2183	1.7507	**10**
51	1.2185	1.7500	9
52	1.2188	1.7493	8
53	1.2190	1.7485	7
54	1.2193	1.7478	6
55	1.2195	1.7471	**5**
56	1.2198	1.7463	4
57	1.2200	1.7456	3
58	1.2203	1.7449	2
59	1.2205	1.7442	1
60	1.2208	1.7434	**0**
′	Csc	Sec	′

124° (304°) (235°) **55°**

35° (215°) (324°) **144°**

′	Sec	Csc	′
0	1.2208	1.7434	**60**
1	1.2210	1.7427	59
2	1.2213	1.7420	58
3	1.2215	1.7413	57
4	1.2218	1.7406	56
5	1.2220	1.7398	**55**
6	1.2223	1.7391	54
7	1.2225	1.7384	53
8	1.2228	1.7377	52
9	1.2230	1.7370	51
10	1.2233	1.7362	**50**
11	1.2235	1.7355	49
12	1.2238	1.7348	48
13	1.2240	1.7341	47
14	1.2243	1.7334	46
15	1.2245	1.7327	**45**
16	1.2248	1.7320	44
17	1.2250	1.7312	43
18	1.2253	1.7305	42
19	1.2255	1.7298	41
20	1.2258	1.7291	**40**
21	1.2260	1.7284	39
22	1.2263	1.7277	38
23	1.2265	1.7270	37
24	1.2268	1.7263	36
25	1.2271	1.7256	**35**
26	1.2273	1.7249	34
27	1.2276	1.7242	33
28	1.2278	1.7235	32
29	1.2281	1.7228	31
30	1.2283	1.7221	**30**
31	1.2286	1.7213	29
32	1.2288	1.7206	28
33	1.2291	1.7199	27
34	1.2293	1.7192	26
35	1.2296	1.7185	**25**
36	1.2299	1.7179	24
37	1.2301	1.7172	23
38	1.2304	1.7165	22
39	1.2306	1.7158	21
40	1.2309	1.7151	**20**
41	1.2311	1.7144	19
42	1.2314	1.7137	18
43	1.2317	1.7130	17
44	1.2319	1.7123	16
45	1.2322	1.7116	**15**
46	1.2324	1.7109	14
47	1.2327	1.7102	13
48	1.2329	1.7095	12
49	1.2332	1.7088	11
50	1.2335	1.7081	**10**
51	1.2337	1.7075	9
52	1.2340	1.7068	8
53	1.2342	1.7061	7
54	1.2345	1.7054	6
55	1.2348	1.7047	**5**
56	1.2350	1.7040	4
57	1.2353	1.7033	3
58	1.2355	1.7027	2
59	1.2358	1.7020	1
60	1.2361	1.7013	**0**
′	Csc	Sec	′

125° (305°) (234°) **54°**

36° (216°)		(323°) **143°**	
′	Sec	Csc	′
0	1.2361	1.7013	**60**
1	1.2363	1.7006	59
2	1.2366	1.6999	58
3	1.2369	1.6993	57
4	1.2371	1.6986	56
5	1.2374	1.6979	**55**
6	1.2376	1.6972	54
7	1.2379	1.6966	53
8	1.2382	1.6959	52
9	1.2384	1.6952	51
10	1.2387	1.6945	**50**
11	1.2390	1.6939	49
12	1.2392	1.6932	48
13	1.2395	1.6925	47
14	1.2397	1.6918	46
15	1.2400	1.6912	**45**
16	1.2403	1.6905	44
17	1.2405	1.6898	43
18	1.2408	1.6892	42
19	1.2411	1.6885	41
20	1.2413	1.6878	**40**
21	1.2416	1.6871	39
22	1.2419	1.6865	38
23	1.2421	1.6858	37
24	1.2424	1.6852	36
25	1.2427	1.6845	**35**
26	1.2429	1.6838	34
27	1.2432	1.6832	33
28	1.2435	1.6825	32
29	1.2437	1.6818	31
30	1.2440	1.6812	**30**
31	1.2443	1.6805	29
32	1.2445	1.6799	28
33	1.2448	1.6792	27
34	1.2451	1.6785	26
35	1.2453	1.6779	**25**
36	1.2456	1.6772	24
37	1.2459	1.6766	23
38	1.2462	1.6759	22
39	1.2464	1.6753	21
40	1.2467	1.6746	**20**
41	1.2470	1.6739	19
42	1.2472	1.6733	18
43	1.2475	1.6726	17
44	1.2478	1.6720	16
45	1.2480	1.6713	**15**
46	1.2483	1.6707	14
47	1.2486	1.6700	13
48	1.2489	1.6694	12
49	1.2491	1.6687	11
50	1.2494	1.6681	**10**
51	1.2497	1.6674	9
52	1.2499	1.6668	8
53	1.2502	1.6661	7
54	1.2505	1.6655	6
55	1.2508	1.6649	**5**
56	1.2510	1.6642	4
57	1.2513	1.6636	3
58	1.2516	1.6629	2
59	1.2519	1.6623	1
60	1.2521	1.6616	**0**
′	Csc	Sec	′
126° (306°)		(233°) **53°**	

37° (217°)		(322°) **142°**	
′	Sec	Csc	′
0	1.2521	1.6616	**60**
1	1.2524	1.6610	59
2	1.2527	1.6604	58
3	1.2530	1.6597	57
4	1.2532	1.6591	56
5	1.2535	1.6584	**55**
6	1.2538	1.6578	54
7	1.2541	1.6572	53
8	1.2543	1.6565	52
9	1.2546	1.6559	51
10	1.2549	1.6553	**50**
11	1.2552	1.6546	49
12	1.2554	1.6540	48
13	1.2557	1.6534	47
14	1.2560	1.6527	46
15	1.2563	1.6521	**45**
16	1.2566	1.6515	44
17	1.2568	1.6508	43
18	1.2571	1.6502	42
19	1.2574	1.6496	41
20	1.2577	1.6489	**40**
21	1.2579	1.6483	39
22	1.2582	1.6477	38
23	1.2585	1.6471	37
24	1.2588	1.6464	36
25	1.2591	1.6458	**35**
26	1.2593	1.6452	34
27	1.2596	1.6446	33
28	1.2599	1.6439	32
29	1.2602	1.6433	31
30	1.2605	1.6427	**30**
31	1.2608	1.6421	29
32	1.2610	1.6414	28
33	1.2613	1.6408	27
34	1.2616	1.6402	26
35	1.2619	1.6396	**25**
36	1.2622	1.6390	24
37	1.2624	1.6383	23
38	1.2627	1.6377	22
39	1.2630	1.6371	21
40	1.2633	1.6365	**20**
41	1.2636	1.6359	19
42	1.2639	1.6353	18
43	1.2641	1.6346	17
44	1.2644	1.6340	16
45	1.2647	1.6334	**15**
46	1.2650	1.6328	14
47	1.2653	1.6322	13
48	1.2656	1.6316	12
49	1.2659	1.6310	11
50	1.2661	1.6303	**10**
51	1.2664	1.6297	9
52	1.2667	1.6291	8
53	1.2670	1.6285	7
54	1.2673	1.6279	6
55	1.2676	1.6273	**5**
56	1.2679	1.6267	4
57	1.2682	1.6261	3
58	1.2684	1.6255	2
59	1.2687	1.6249	1
60	1.2690	1.6243	**0**
′	Csc	Sec	′
127° (307°)		(232°) **52°**	

38° (218°)		(321°) **141°**	
′	Sec	Csc	′
0	1.2690	1.6243	**60**
1	1.2693	1.6237	59
2	1.2696	1.6231	58
3	1.2699	1.6225	57
4	1.2702	1.6219	56
5	1.2705	1.6213	**55**
6	1.2708	1.6207	54
7	1.2710	1.6201	53
8	1.2713	1.6195	52
9	1.2716	1.6189	51
10	1.2719	1.6183	**50**
11	1.2722	1.6177	49
12	1.2725	1.6171	48
13	1.2728	1.6165	47
14	1.2731	1.6159	46
15	1.2734	1.6153	**45**
16	1.2737	1.6147	44
17	1.2740	1.6141	43
18	1.2742	1.6135	42
19	1.2745	1.6129	41
20	1.2748	1.6123	**40**
21	1.2751	1.6117	39
22	1.2754	1.6111	38
23	1.2757	1.6105	37
24	1.2760	1.6099	36
25	1.2763	1.6093	**35**
26	1.2766	1.6087	34
27	1.2769	1.6082	33
28	1.2772	1.6076	32
29	1.2775	1.6070	31
30	1.2778	1.6064	**30**
31	1.2781	1.6058	29
32	1.2784	1.6052	28
33	1.2787	1.6046	27
34	1.2790	1.6040	26
35	1.2793	1.6035	**25**
36	1.2796	1.6029	24
37	1.2799	1.6023	23
38	1.2802	1.6017	22
39	1.2804	1.6011	21
40	1.2807	1.6005	**20**
41	1.2810	1.6000	19
42	1.2813	1.5994	18
43	1.2816	1.5988	17
44	1.2819	1.5982	16
45	1.2822	1.5976	**15**
46	1.2825	1.5971	14
47	1.2828	1.5965	13
48	1.2831	1.5959	12
49	1.2834	1.5953	11
50	1.2837	1.5948	**10**
51	1.2840	1.5942	9
52	1.2843	1.5936	8
53	1.2846	1.5930	7
54	1.2849	1.5925	6
55	1.2852	1.5919	**5**
56	1.2855	1.5913	4
57	1.2859	1.5907	3
58	1.2862	1.5902	2
59	1.2865	1.5896	1
60	1.2868	1.5890	**0**
′	Csc	Sec	′
128° (308°)		(231°) **51°**	

39° (219°) (320°) **140°**

′	Sec	Csc	′
0	1.2868	1.5890	**60**
1	1.2871	1.5884	59
2	1.2874	1.5879	58
3	1.2877	1.5873	57
4	1.2880	1.5867	56
5	1.2883	1.5862	**55**
6	1.2886	1.5856	54
7	1.2889	1.5850	53
8	1.2892	1.5845	52
9	1.2895	1.5839	51
10	1.2898	1.5833	**50**
11	1.2901	1.5828	49
12	1.2904	1.5822	48
13	1.2907	1.5816	47
14	1.2910	1.5811	46
15	1.2913	1.5805	**45**
16	1.2916	1.5800	44
17	1.2919	1.5794	43
18	1.2923	1.5788	42
19	1.2926	1.5783	41
20	1.2929	1.5777	**40**
21	1.2932	1.5771	39
22	1.2935	1.5766	38
23	1.2938	1.5760	37
24	1.2941	1.5755	36
25	1.2944	1.5749	**35**
26	1.2947	1.5744	34
27	1.2950	1.5738	33
28	1.2953	1.5732	32
29	1.2957	1.5727	31
30	1.2960	1.5721	**30**
31	1.2963	1.5716	29
32	1.2966	1.5710	28
33	1.2969	1.5705	27
34	1.2972	1.5699	26
35	1.2975	1.5694	**25**
36	1.2978	1.5688	24
37	1.2981	1.5683	23
38	1.2985	1.5677	22
39	1.2988	1.5672	21
40	1.2991	1.5666	**20**
41	1.2994	1.5661	19
42	1.2997	1.5655	18
43	1.3000	1.5650	17
44	1.3003	1.5644	16
45	1.3007	1.5639	**15**
46	1.3010	1.5633	14
47	1.3013	1.5628	13
48	1.3016	1.5622	12
49	1.3019	1.5617	11
50	1.3022	1.5611	**10**
51	1.3026	1.5606	9
52	1.3029	1.5601	8
53	1.3032	1.5595	7
54	1.3035	1.5590	6
55	1.3038	1.5584	**5**
56	1.3041	1.5579	4
57	1.3045	1.5573	3
58	1.3048	1.5568	2
59	1.3051	1.5563	1
60	1.3054	1.5557	**0**
′	Csc	Sec	′

129° (309°) (230°) **50°**

40° (220°) (319°) **139°**

′	Sec	Csc	′
0	1.3054	1.5557	**60**
1	1.3057	1.5552	59
2	1.3060	1.5546	58
3	1.3064	1.5541	57
4	1.3067	1.5536	56
5	1.3070	1.5530	**55**
6	1.3073	1.5525	54
7	1.3076	1.5520	53
8	1.3080	1.5514	52
9	1.3083	1.5509	51
10	1.3086	1.5504	**50**
11	1.3089	1.5498	49
12	1.3093	1.5493	48
13	1.3096	1.5488	47
14	1.3099	1.5482	46
15	1.3102	1.5477	**45**
16	1.3105	1.5472	44
17	1.3109	1.5466	43
18	1.3112	1.5461	42
19	1.3115	1.5456	41
20	1.3118	1.5450	**40**
21	1.3122	1.5445	39
22	1.3125	1.5440	38
23	1.3128	1.5435	37
24	1.3131	1.5429	36
25	1.3135	1.5424	**35**
26	1.3138	1.5419	34
27	1.3141	1.5413	33
28	1.3144	1.5408	32
29	1.3148	1.5403	31
30	1.3151	1.5398	**30**
31	1.3154	1.5392	29
32	1.3157	1.5387	28
33	1.3161	1.5382	27
34	1.3164	1.5377	26
35	1.3167	1.5372	**25**
36	1.3171	1.5366	24
37	1.3174	1.5361	23
38	1.3177	1.5356	22
39	1.3180	1.5351	21
40	1.3184	1.5345	**20**
41	1.3187	1.5340	19
42	1.3190	1.5335	18
43	1.3194	1.5330	17
44	1.3197	1.5325	16
45	1.3200	1.5320	**15**
46	1.3203	1.5314	14
47	1.3207	1.5309	13
48	1.3210	1.5304	12
49	1.3213	1.5299	11
50	1.3217	1.5294	**10**
51	1.3220	1.5289	9
52	1.3223	1.5283	8
53	1.3227	1.5278	7
54	1.3230	1.5273	6
55	1.3233	1.5268	**5**
56	1.3237	1.5263	4
57	1.3240	1.5258	3
58	1.3243	1.5253	2
59	1.3247	1.5248	1
60	1.3250	1.5243	**0**
′	Csc	Sec	′

130° (310°) (229°) **49°**

41° (221°) (318°) **138°**

′	Sec	Csc	′
0	1.3250	1.5243	**60**
1	1.3253	1.5237	59
2	1.3257	1.5232	58
3	1.3260	1.5227	57
4	1.3264	1.5222	56
5	1.3267	1.5217	**55**
6	1.3270	1.5212	54
7	1.3274	1.5207	53
8	1.3277	1.5202	52
9	1.3280	1.5197	51
10	1.3284	1.5192	**50**
11	1.3287	1.5187	49
12	1.3291	1.5182	48
13	1.3294	1.5177	47
14	1.3297	1.5172	46
15	1.3301	1.5167	**45**
16	1.3304	1.5162	44
17	1.3307	1.5156	43
18	1.3311	1.5151	42
19	1.3314	1.5146	41
20	1.3318	1.5141	**40**
21	1.3321	1.5136	39
22	1.3325	1.5131	38
23	1.3328	1.5126	37
24	1.3331	1.5121	36
25	1.3335	1.5116	**35**
26	1.3338	1.5111	34
27	1.3342	1.5107	33
28	1.3345	1.5102	32
29	1.3348	1.5097	31
30	1.3352	1.5092	**30**
31	1.3355	1.5087	29
32	1.3359	1.5082	28
33	1.3362	1.5077	27
34	1.3366	1.5072	26
35	1.3369	1.5067	**25**
36	1.3373	1.5062	24
37	1.3376	1.5057	23
38	1.3380	1.5052	22
39	1.3383	1.5047	21
40	1.3386	1.5042	**20**
41	1.3390	1.5037	19
42	1.3393	1.5032	18
43	1.3397	1.5027	17
44	1.3400	1.5023	16
45	1.3404	1.5018	**15**
46	1.3407	1.5013	14
47	1.3411	1.5008	13
48	1.3414	1.5003	12
49	1.3418	1.4998	11
50	1.3421	1.4993	**10**
51	1.3425	1.4988	9
52	1.3428	1.4984	8
53	1.3432	1.4979	7
54	1.3435	1.4974	6
55	1.3439	1.4969	**5**
56	1.3442	1.4964	4
57	1.3446	1.4959	3
58	1.3449	1.4954	2
59	1.3453	1.4950	1
60	1.3456	1.4945	**0**
′	Csc	Sec	′

131° (311°) (228°) **48°**

42° (222°) (317°) **137°**

′	Sec	Csc	′
0	1.3456	1.4945	**60**
1	1.3460	1.4940	59
2	1.3463	1.4935	58
3	1.3467	1.4930	57
4	1.3470	1.4925	56
5	1.3474	1.4921	**55**
6	1.3478	1.4916	54
7	1.3481	1.4911	53
8	1.3485	1.4906	52
9	1.3488	1.4901	51
10	1.3492	1.4897	**50**
11	1.3495	1.4892	49
12	1.3499	1.4887	48
13	1.3502	1.4882	47
14	1.3506	1.4878	46
15	1.3510	1.4873	**45**
16	1.3513	1.4868	44
17	1.3517	1.4863	43
18	1.3520	1.4859	42
19	1.3524	1.4854	41
20	1.3527	1.4849	**40**
21	1.3531	1.4844	39
22	1.3535	1.4840	38
23	1.3538	1.4835	37
24	1.3542	1.4830	36
25	1.3545	1.4825	**35**
26	1.3549	1.4821	34
27	1.3553	1.4816	33
28	1.3556	1.4811	32
29	1.3560	1.4807	31
30	1.3563	1.4802	**30**
31	1.3567	1.4797	29
32	1.3571	1.4792	28
33	1.3574	1.4788	27
34	1.3578	1.4783	26
35	1.3582	1.4778	**25**
36	1.3585	1.4774	24
37	1.3589	1.4769	23
38	1.3592	1.4764	22
39	1.3596	1.4760	21
40	1.3600	1.4755	**20**
41	1.3603	1.4750	19
42	1.3607	1.4746	18
43	1.3611	1.4741	17
44	1.3614	1.4737	16
45	1.3618	1.4732	**15**
46	1.3622	1.4727	14
47	1.3625	1.4723	13
48	1.3629	1.4718	12
49	1.3633	1.4713	11
50	1.3636	1.4709	**10**
51	1.3640	1.4704	9
52	1.3644	1.4700	8
53	1.3647	1.4695	7
54	1.3651	1.4690	6
55	1.3655	1.4686	**5**
56	1.3658	1.4681	4
57	1.3662	1.4677	3
58	1.3666	1.4672	2
59	1.3670	1.4667	1
60	1.3673	1.4663	**0**
′	Csc	Sec	′

132° (312°) (227°) **47°**

43° (223°) (316°) **136°**

′	Sec	Csc	′
0	1.3673	1.4663	**60**
1	1.3677	1.4658	59
2	1.3681	1.4654	58
3	1.3684	1.4649	57
4	1.3688	1.4645	56
5	1.3692	1.4640	**55**
6	1.3696	1.4635	54
7	1.3699	1.4631	53
8	1.3703	1.4626	52
9	1.3707	1.4622	51
10	1.3711	1.4617	**50**
11	1.3714	1.4613	49
12	1.3718	1.4608	48
13	1.3722	1.4604	47
14	1.3726	1.4599	46
15	1.3729	1.4595	**45**
16	1.3733	1.4590	44
17	1.3737	1.4586	43
18	1.3741	1.4581	42
19	1.3744	1.4577	41
20	1.3748	1.4572	**40**
21	1.3752	1.4568	39
22	1.3756	1.4563	38
23	1.3759	1.4559	37
24	1.3763	1.4554	36
25	1.3767	1.4550	**35**
26	1.3771	1.4545	34
27	1.3775	1.4541	33
28	1.3778	1.4536	32
29	1.3782	1.4532	31
30	1.3786	1.4527	**30**
31	1.3790	1.4523	29
32	1.3794	1.4518	28
33	1.3797	1.4514	27
34	1.3801	1.4510	26
35	1.3805	1.4505	**25**
36	1.3809	1.4501	24
37	1.3813	1.4496	23
38	1.3817	1.4492	22
39	1.3820	1.4487	21
40	1.3824	1.4483	**20**
41	1.3828	1.4479	19
42	1.3832	1.4474	18
43	1.3836	1.4470	17
44	1.3840	1.4465	16
45	1.3843	1.4461	**15**
46	1.3847	1.4457	14
47	1.3851	1.4452	13
48	1.3855	1.4448	12
49	1.3859	1.4443	11
50	1.3863	1.4439	**10**
51	1.3867	1.4435	9
52	1.3871	1.4430	8
53	1.3874	1.4426	7
54	1.3878	1.4422	6
55	1.3882	1.4417	**5**
56	1.3886	1.4413	4
57	1.3890	1.4409	3
58	1.3894	1.4404	2
59	1.3898	1.4400	1
60	1.3902	1.4396	**0**
′	Csc	Sec	

133° (313°) (226°) **46°**

44° (224°) (315°) **135°**

′	Sec	Csc	′
0	1.3902	1.4396	**60**
1	1.3906	1.4391	59
2	1.3909	1.4387	58
3	1.3913	1.4383	57
4	1.3917	1.4378	56
5	1.3921	1.4374	**55**
6	1.3925	1.4370	54
7	1.3929	1.4365	53
8	1.3933	1.4361	52
9	1.3937	1.4357	51
10	1.3941	1.4352	**50**
11	1.3945	1.4348	49
12	1.3949	1.4344	48
13	1.3953	1.4340	47
14	1.3957	1.4335	46
15	1.3961	1.4331	**45**
16	1.3965	1.4327	44
17	1.3969	1.4322	43
18	1.3972	1.4318	42
19	1.3976	1.4314	41
20	1.3980	1.4310	**40**
21	1.3984	1.4305	39
22	1.3988	1.4301	38
23	1.3992	1.4297	37
24	1.3996	1.4293	36
25	1.4000	1.4288	**35**
26	1.4004	1.4284	34
27	1.4008	1.4280	33
28	1.4012	1.4276	32
29	1.4016	1.4271	31
30	1.4020	1.4267	**30**
31	1.4024	1.4263	29
32	1.4028	1.4259	28
33	1.4032	1.4255	27
34	1.4036	1.4250	26
35	1.4040	1.4246	**25**
36	1.4044	1.4242	24
37	1.4048	1.4238	23
38	1.4052	1.4234	22
39	1.4057	1.4229	21
40	1.4061	1.4225	**20**
41	1.4065	1.4221	19
42	1.4069	1.4217	18
43	1.4073	1.4213	17
44	1.4077	1.4208	16
45	1.4081	1.4204	**15**
46	1.4085	1.4200	14
47	1.4089	1.4196	13
48	1.4093	1.4192	12
49	1.4097	1.4188	11
50	1.4101	1.4183	**10**
51	1.4105	1.4179	9
52	1.4109	1.4175	8
53	1.4113	1.4171	7
54	1.4118	1.4167	6
55	1.4122	1.4163	**5**
56	1.4126	1.4159	4
57	1.4130	1.4154	3
58	1.4134	1.4150	2
59	1.4138	1.4146	1
60	1.4142	1.4142	**0**
	Csc	Sec	′

134° (314°) (225°) **45°**

NATURAL TRIGONOMETRIC FUNCTIONS FOR ANGLES IN DEGREES AND DECIMALS

Deg.	Sin	Tan	Cot	Cos	Deg.
0.0	.00000	.00000	∞	1.0000	**90.0**
.1	.00175	.00175	573.0	1.0000	89.9
.2	.00349	.00349	286.5	1.0000	.8
.3	.00524	.00524	191.0	1.0000	.7
.4	.00698	.00698	143.24	1.0000	.6
.5	.00873	.00873	114.59	1.0000	.5
.6	.01047	.01047	95.49	0.9999	.4
.7	.01222	.01222	81.85	.9999	.3
.8	.01396	.01396	71.62	.9999	.2
.9	.01571	.01571	63.66	.9999	89.1
1.0	.01745	.01746	57.29	0.9998	**89.0**
.1	.01920	.01920	52.08	.9998	88.9
.2	.02094	.02095	47.74	.9998	.8
.3	.02269	.02269	44.07	.9997	.7
.4	.02443	.02444	40.92	.9997	.6
.5	.02618	.02619	38.19	.9997	.5
.6	.02792	.02793	35.80	.9996	.4
.7	.02967	.02968	33.69	.9996	.3
.8	.03141	.03143	31.82	.9995	.2
.9	.03316	.03317	30.14	.9995	88.1
2.0	.03490	.03492	28.64	0.9994	**88.0**
.1	.03664	.03667	27.27	.9993	87.9
.2	.03839	.03842	26.03	.9993	.8
.3	.04013	.04016	24.90	.9992	.7
.4	.04188	.04191	23.86	.9991	.6
.5	.04362	.04366	22.90	.9990	.5
.6	.04536	.04541	22.02	.9990	.4
.7	.04711	.04716	21.20	.9989	.3
.8	.04885	.04891	20.45	.9988	.2
.9	.05059	.05066	19.74	.9987	87.1
3.0	.05234	.05241	19.081	0.9986	**87.0**
.1	.05408	.05416	18.464	.9985	86.9
.2	.05582	.05591	17.886	.9984	.8
.3	.05756	.05766	17.343	.9983	.7
.4	.05931	.05941	16.832	.9982	.6
.5	.06105	.06116	16.350	.9981	.5
.6	.06279	.06291	15.895	.9980	.4
.7	.06453	.06467	15.464	.9979	.3
.8	.06627	.06642	15.056	.9978	.2
.9	.06802	.06817	14.669	.9977	86.1
4.0	.06976	.06993	14.301	0.9976	**86.0**
.1	.07150	.07168	13.951	.9974	85.9
.2	.07324	.07344	13.617	.9973	.8
.3	.07498	.07519	13.300	.9972	.7
.4	.07672	.07695	12.996	.9971	.6
.5	.07846	.07870	12.706	.9969	.5
.6	.08020	.08046	12.429	.9968	.4
.7	.08194	.08221	12.163	.9966	.3
.8	.08368	.08397	11.909	.9965	.2
.9	.08542	.08573	11.664	.9963	85.1
5.0	.08716	.08749	11.430	0.9962	**85.0**
.1	.08889	.08925	11.205	.9960	84.9
.2	.09063	.09101	10.988	.9959	.8
.3	.09237	.09277	10.780	.9957	.7
.4	.09411	.09453	10.579	.9956	.6
.5	.09585	.09629	10.385	.9954	.5
.6	.09758	.09805	10.199	.9952	.4
.7	.09932	.09981	10.019	.9951	.3
.8	.10106	.10158	9.845	.9949	.2
.9	.10279	.10334	9.677	.9947	84.1
6.0	.10453	.10510	9.514	0.9945	**84.0**
Deg.	Cos	Cot	Tan	Sin	Deg.

Deg.	Sin	Tan	Cot	Cos	Deg.
6.0	.10453	.10510	9.514	0.9945	**84.0**
.1	.10626	.10687	9.357	.9943	83.9
.2	.1080	.10863	9.205	.9942	.8
.3	.10973	.11040	9.058	.9940	.7
.4	.11147	.11217	8.915	.9938	.6
.5	.11320	.11394	8.777	.9936	.5
.6	.11494	.11570	8.643	.9934	.4
.7	.11667	.11747	8.513	.9932	.3
.8	.11840	.11924	8.386	.9930	.2
.9	.12014	.12101	8.264	.9928	83.1
7.0	.12187	.12278	8.144	0.9925	**83.0**
.1	.12360	.12456	8.028	.9923	82.9
.2	.12533	.12633	7.916	.9921	.8
.3	.12706	.12810	7.806	.9919	.7
.4	.12880	.12988	7.700	.9917	.6
.5	.13053	.13165	7.596	.9914	.5
.6	.13226	.13343	7.495	.9912	.4
.7	.13399	.13521	7.396	.9910	.3
.8	.13572	.13698	7.300	.9907	.2
.9	.13744	.13876	7.207	.9905	82.1
8.0	.13917	.14054	7.115	0.9903	**82.0**
.1	.14090	.14232	7.026	.9900	81.9
.2	.14263	.14410	6.940	.9898	.8
.3	.14436	.14588	6.855	.9895	.7
.4	.14608	.14767	6.772	.9893	.6
.5	.14781	.14945	6.691	.9890	.5
.6	.14954	.15124	6.612	.9888	.4
.7	.15126	.15302	6.535	.9885	.3
.8	.15299	.15481	6.460	.9882	.2
.9	.15471	.15660	6.386	.9880	81.1
9.0	.15643	.15838	6.314	0.9877	**81.0**
.1	.15816	.16017	6.243	.9874	80.9
.2	.15988	.16196	6.174	.9871	.8
.3	.16160	.16376	6.107	.9869	.7
.4	.16333	.16555	6.041	.9866	.6
.5	.16505	.16734	5.976	.9863	.5
.6	.16677	.16914	5.912	.9860	.4
.7	.16849	.17093	5.850	.9857	.3
.8	.17021	.17273	5.789	.9854	.2
.9	.17193	.17453	5.730	.9851	80.1
10.0	.1736	.1763	5.671	0.9848	**80.0**
.1	.1754	.1781	5.614	.9845	79.9
.2	.1771	.1799	5.558	.9842	.8
.3	.1788	.1817	5.503	.9839	.7
.4	.1805	.1835	5.449	.9836	.6
.5	.1822	.1853	5.396	.9833	.5
.6	.1840	.1871	5.343	.9829	.4
.7	.1857	.1890	5.292	.9826	.3
.8	.1874	.1908	5.242	.9823	.2
.9	.1891	.1926	5.193	.9820	79.1
11.0	.1908	.1944	5.145	0.9816	**79.0**
.1	.1925	.1962	5.097	.9813	78.9
.2	.1942	.1980	5.050	.9810	.8
.3	.1959	.1998	5.005	.9806	.7
.4	.1977	.2016	4.959	.9803	.6
.5	.1994	.2035	4.915	.9799	.5
.6	.2011	.2053	4.872	.9796	.4
.7	.2028	.2071	4.829	.9792	.3
.8	.2045	.2089	4.787	.9789	.2
.9	.2062	.2107	4.745	.9785	78.1
12.0	.2079	.2126	4.705	0.9781	**78.0**
Deg.	Cos	Cot	Tan	Sin	Deg.

NATURAL FUNCTIONS FOR DEGREES AND DECIMALS (Continued)

Deg.	Sin	Tan	Cot	Cos	Deg.
12.0	0.2079	0.2126	4.705	0.9781	**78.0**
.1	.2096	.2144	4.665	.9778	77.9
.2	.2113	.2162	4.625	.9774	.8
.3	.2130	.2180	4.586	.9770	.7
.4	.2147	.2199	4.548	.9767	.6
.5	.2164	.2217	4.511	.9763	.5
.6	.2181	.2235	4.474	.9759	.4
.7	.2198	.2254	4.437	.9755	.3
.8	.2215	.2272	4.402	.9751	.2
.9	.2233	.2290	4.366	.9748	77.1
13.0	0.2250	0.2309	4.331	0.9744	**77.0**
.1	.2267	.2327	4.297	.9740	76.9
.2	.2284	.2345	4.264	.9736	.8
.3	.2300	.2364	4.230	.9732	.7
.4	.2317	.2382	4.198	.9728	.6
.5	.2334	.2401	4.165	.9724	.5
.6	.2351	.2419	4.134	.9720	.4
.7	.2368	.2438	4.102	.9715	.3
.8	.2385	.2456	4.071	.9711	.2
.9	.2402	.2475	4.041	.9707	76.1
14.0	0.2419	0.2493	4.011	0.9703	**76.0**
.1	.2436	.2512	3.981	.9699	75.9
.2	.2453	.2530	3.952	.9694	.8
.3	.2470	.2549	3.923	.9690	.7
.4	.2487	.2568	3.895	.9686	.6
.5	.2504	.2586	3.867	.9681	.5
.6	.2521	.2605	3.839	.9677	.4
.7	.2538	.2623	3.812	.9673	.3
.8	.2554	.2642	3.785	.9668	.2
.9	.2571	.2661	3.758	.9664	75.1
15.0	0.2588	0.2679	3.732	0.9659	**75.0**
.1	.2605	.2698	3.706	.9655	74.9
.2	.2622	.2717	3.681	.9650	.8
.3	.2639	.2736	3.655	.9646	.7
.4	.2656	.2754	3.630	.9641	.6
.5	.2672	.2773	3.606	.9636	.5
.6	.2689	.2792	3.582	.9632	.4
.7	.2706	.2811	3.558	.9627	.3
.8	.2723	.2830	3.534	.9622	.2
.9	.2740	.2849	3.511	.9617	74.1
16.0	0.2756	0.2867	3.487	0.9613	**74.0**
.1	.2773	.2886	3.465	.9608	73.9
.2	.2790	.2905	3.442	.9603	.8
.3	.2807	.2924	3.420	.9598	.7
.4	.2823	.2943	3.398	.9593	.6
.5	.2840	.2962	3.376	9588	.5
.6	.2857	.2981	3.354	.9583	.4
.7	.2874	.3000	3.333	.9578	.3
.8	.2890	.3019	3.312	.9573	.2
.9	.2907	.3038	3.291	.9568	73.1
17.0	0.2924	0.3057	3.271	0.9563	**73.0**
.1	.2940	.3076	3.251	.9558	72.9
.2	.2957	.3096	3.230	.9553	.8
.3	.2974	.3115	3.211	.9548	.7
.4	.2990	.3134	3.191	.9542	.6
.5	.3007	.3153	3.172	.9537	.5
.6	.3024	.3172	3.152	.9532	.4
.7	.3040	.3191	3.133	.9527	.3
.8	.3057	.3211	3.115	.9521	.2
.9	.3074	.3230	3.096	.9516	72.1
18.0	0.3090	0.3249	3.078	0.9511	**72.0**
Deg.	Cos	Cot	Tan	Sin	Deg.

Deg.	Sin	Tan	Cot	Cos	Deg.
18.0	0.3090	0.3249	3.078	0.9511	**72.0**
.1	.3107	.3269	3.060	.9505	71.9
.2	.3123	.3288	3.042	.9500	.8
.3	.3140	.3307	3.024	.9494	.7
.4	.3156	.3327	3.006	.9489	.6
.5	.3173	.3346	2.989	.9483	.5
.6	.3190	.3365	2.971	.9478	.4
.7	.3206	.3385	2.954	.9472	.3
.8	.3223	.3404	2.937	.9466	.2
.9	.3239	.3424	2.921	.9461	71.1
19.0	0.3256	0.3443	2.904	0.9455	**71.0**
.1	.3272	.3463	2.888	.9449	70.9
.2	.3289	.3482	2.872	.9444	.8
.3	.3305	.3502	2.856	.9438	.7
.4	.3322	.3522	2.840	.9432	.6
.5	.3338	.3541	2.824	.9426	.5
.6	.3355	.3561	2.808	.9421	.4
.7	.3371	.3581	2.793	.9415	.3
.8	.3387	.3600	2.778	.9409	.2
.9	.3404	.3620	2.762	.9403	70.1
20.0	0.3420	0.3640	2.747	0.9397	**70.0**
.1	.3437	.3659	2.733	.9391	69.9
.2	.3453	.3679	2.718	.9385	.8
.3	.3469	.3699	2.703	.9379	.7
.4	.3486	.3719	2.689	.9373	.6
.5	.3502	.3739	2.675	.9367	.5
.6	.3518	.3759	2.660	.9361	.4
.7	.3535	.3779	2.646	.9354	.3
.8	.3551	.3799	2.633	.9348	.2
.9	.3567	.3819	2.619	.9342	69.1
21.0	0.3584	0.3839	2.605	0.9336	**69.0**
.1	.3600	.3859	2.592	.9330	68.9
.2	.3616	.3879	2.578	.9323	.8
.3	.3633	.3899	2.565	.9317	.7
.4	.3649	.3919	2.552	.9311	.6
.5	.3665	.3939	2.539	.9304	.5
.6	.3681	.3959	2.526	.9298	.4
.7	.3697	.3979	2.513	.9291	.3
.8	.3714	.4000	2.500	.9285	.2
.9	.3730	.4020	2.488	.9278	68.1
22.0	0.3746	0.4040	2.475	0.9272	**68.0**
.1	.3762	.4061	2.463	.9265	67.9
.2	.3778	.4081	2.450	.9259	.8
.3	.3795	.4101	2.438	.9252	.7
.4	.3811	.4122	2.426	.9245	.6
.5	.3827	.4142	2.414	.9239	.5
.6	.3843	.4163	2.402	.9232	.4
.7	.3859	.4183	2.391	.9225	.3
.8	.3875	.4204	2.379	.9219	.2
.9	.3891	.4224	2.367	.9212	67.1
23.0	0.3907	0.4245	2.356	0.9205	**67.0**
.1	.3923	.4265	2.344	.9198	66.9
.2	.3939	.4286	2.333	.9191	.8
.3	.3955	.4307	2.322	.9184	.7
.4	.3971	.4327	2.311	.9178	.6
.5	.3987	.4348	2.300	.9171	.5
.6	.4003	.4369	2.289	.9164	.4
.7	.4019	.4390	2.278	.9157	.3
.8	.4035	.4411	2.267	.9150	.2
.9	.4051	.4431	2.257	.9143	66.1
24.0	0.4067	0.4452	2.246	0.9135	**66.0**
Deg.	Cos	Cot	Tan	Sin	Deg.

NATURAL FUNCTIONS FOR DEGREES AND DECIMALS (Continued)

Deg.	Sin	Tan	Cot	Cos	Deg.
24.0	0.4067	0.4452	2.246	0.9135	**66.0**
.1	.4083	.4473	2.236	.9128	65.9
.2	.4099	.4494	2.225	.9121	.8
.3	.4115	.4515	2.215	.9114	.7
.4	.4131	.4536	2.204	.9107	.6
.5	.4147	.4557	2.194	.9100	.5
.6	.4163	.4578	2.184	.9092	.4
.7	.4179	.4599	2.174	.9085	.3
.8	.4195	.4621	2.164	.9078	.2
.9	.4210	.4642	2.154	.9070	65.1
25.0	0.4226	0.4663	2.145	0.9063	**65.0**
.1	.4242	.4684	2.135	.9056	64.9
.2	.4258	.4706	2.125	.9048	.8
.3	.4274	.4727	2.116	.9041	.7
.4	.4289	.4748	2.106	.9033	.6
.5	.4305	.4770	2.097	.9026	.5
.6	.4321	.4791	2.087	.9018	.4
.7	.4337	.4813	2.078	.9011	.3
.8	.4352	.4834	2.069	.9003	.2
.9	.4368	.4856	2.059	.8996	64.1
26.0	0.4384	0.4877	2.050	0.8988	**64.0**
.1	.4399	.4899	2.041	.8980	63.9
.2	.4415	.4921	2.032	.8973	.8
.3	.4431	.4942	2.023	.8965	.7
.4	.4446	.4964	2.014	.8957	.6
.5	.4462	.4986	2.006	.8949	.5
.6	.4478	.5008	1.997	.8942	.4
.7	.4493	.5029	1.988	.8934	.3
.8	.4509	.5051	1.980	.8926	.2
.9	.4524	.5073	1.971	.8918	63.1
27.0	0.4540	0.5095	1.963	0.8910	**63.0**
.1	.4555	.5117	1.954	.8902	62.9
.2	.4571	.5139	1.946	.8894	.8
.3	.4586	.5161	1.937	.8886	.7
.4	.4602	.5184	1.929	.8878	.6
.5	.4617	.5206	1.921	.8870	.5
.6	.4633	.5228	1.913	.8862	.4
.7	.4648	.5250	1.905	.8854	.3
.8	.4664	.5272	1.897	.8846	.2
.9	.4679	.5295	1.889	.8838	62.1
28.0	0.4695	0.5317	1.881	0.8829	**62.0**
.1	.4710	.5340	1.873	.8821	61.9
.2	.4726	.5362	1.865	.8813	.8
.3	.4741	.5384	1.857	.8805	.7
.4	.4756	.5407	1.849	.8796	.6
.5	.4772	.5430	1.842	.8788	.5
.6	.4787	.5452	1.834	.8780	.4
.7	.4802	.5475	1.827	.8771	.3
.8	.4818	.5498	1.819	.8763	.2
.9	.4833	.5520	1.811	.8755	61.1
29.0	0.4848	0.5543	1.804	0.8746	**61.0**
.1	.4863	.5566	1.797	.8738	60.9
.2	.4879	.5589	1.789	.8729	.8
.3	.4894	.5612	1.782	.8721	.7
.4	.4909	.5635	1.775	.8712	.6
.5	.4924	.5658	1.767	.8704	.5
.6	.4939	.5681	1.760	.8695	.4
.7	.4955	.5704	1.753	.8686	.3
.8	.4970	.5727	1.746	.8678	.2
.9	.4985	.5750	1.739	.8669	60.1
30.0	0.5000	0.5774	1.732	0.8660	**60.0**
Deg.	Cos	Cot	Tan	Sin	Deg.

Deg.	Sin	Tan	Cot	Cos	Deg.
30.0	0.5000	0.5774	1.7321	0.8660	**60.0**
.1	.5015	.5797	1.7251	.8652	59.9
.2	.5030	.5820	1.7182	.8643	.8
.3	.5045	.5844	1.7113	.8634	.7
.4	.5060	.5867	1.7045	.8625	.6
.5	.5075	.5890	1.6977	.8616	.5
.6	.5090	.5914	1.6909	.8607	.4
.7	.5105	.5938	1.6842	.8599	.3
.8	.5120	.5961	1.6775	.8590	.2
.9	.5135	.5985	1.6709	.8581	59.1
31.0	0.5150	0.6009	1.6643	0.8572	**59.0**
.1	.5165	.6032	1.6577	.8563	58.9
.2	.5180	.6056	1.6512	.8554	.8
.3	.5195	.6080	1.6447	.8545	.7
.4	.5210	.6104	1.6383	.8536	.6
.5	.5225	.6128	1.6319	.8526	.5
.6	.5240	.6152	1.6255	.8517	.4
.7	.5255	.6176	1.6191	.8508	.3
.8	.5270	.6200	1.6128	.8499	.2
.9	.5284	.6224	1.6066	.8490	58.1
32.0	0.5299	0.6249	1.6003	0.8480	**58.0**
.1	.5314	.6273	1.5941	.8471	57.9
.2	.5329	.6297	1.5880	.8462	.8
.3	.5344	.6322	1.5818	.8453	.7
.4	.5358	.6346	1.5757	.8443	.6
.5	.5373	.6371	1.5697	.8434	.5
.6	.5388	.6395	1.5637	.8425	.4
.7	.5402	.6420	1.5577	.8415	.3
.8	.5417	.6445	1.5517	.8406	.2
.9	.5432	.6469	1.5458	.8396	57.1
33.0	0.5446	0.6494	1.5399	0.8387	**57.0**
.1	.5461	.6519	1.5340	.8377	56.9
.2	.5476	.6544	1.5282	.8368	.8
.3	.5490	.6569	1.5224	.8358	.7
.4	.5505	.6594	1.5166	.8348	.6
.5	.5519	.6619	1.5108	.8339	.5
.6	.5534	.6644	1.5051	.8329	.4
.7	.5548	.6669	1.4994	.8320	.3
.8	.5563	.6694	1.4938	.8310	.2
.9	.5577	.6720	1.4882	.8300	56.1
34.0	0.5592	0.6745	1.4826	0.8290	**56.0**
.1	.5606	.6771	1.4770	.8281	55.9
.2	.5621	.6796	1.4715	.8271	.8
.3	.5635	.6822	1.4659	.8261	.7
.4	.5650	.6847	1.4605	.8251	.6
.5	.5664	.6873	1.4550	.8241	.5
.6	.5678	.6899	1.4496	.8231	.4
.7	.5693	.6924	1.4442	.8221	.3
.8	.5707	.6950	1.4388	.8211	.2
.9	.5721	.6976	1.4335	.8202	55.1
35.0	0.5736	0.7002	1.4281	0.8192	**55.0**
.1	.5750	.7028	1.4229	.8181	54.9
.2	.5764	.7054	1.4176	.8171	.8
.3	.5779	.7080	1.4124	.8161	.7
.4	.5793	.7107	1.4071	.8151	.6
.5	.5807	.7133	1.4019	.8141	.5
.6	.5821	.7159	1.3968	.8131	.4
.7	.5835	.7186	1.3916	.8121	.3
.8	.5850	.7212	1.3865	.8111	.2
.9	.5864	.7239	1.3814	.8100	54.1
36.0	0.5878	0.7265	1.3764	0.8090	**54.0**
Deg.	Cos	Cot	Tan	Sin	Deg.

NATURAL FUNCTIONS FOR DEGREES AND DECIMALS (Continued)

Deg.	Sin	Tan	Cot	Cos	Deg.
36.0	0.5878	0.7265	1.3764	0.8090	**54.0**
.1	.5892	.7292	1.3713	.8080	53.9
.2	.5906	.7319	1.3663	.8070	.8
.3	.5920	.7346	1.3613	.8059	.7
.4	.5934	.7373	1.3564	.8049	.6
.5	.5948	.7400	1.3514	.8039	.5
.6	.5962	.7427	1.3465	.8028	.4
.7	.5976	.7454	1.3416	.8018	.3
.8	.5990	.7481	1.3367	.8007	.2
.9	.6004	.7508	1.3319	.7997	53.1
37.0	0.6018	0.7536	1.3270	0.7986	**53.0**
.1	.6032	.7563	1.3222	.7976	52.9
.2	.6046	.7590	1.3175	.7965	.8
.3	.6060	.7618	1.3127	.7955	.7
.4	.6074	.7646	1.3079	.7944	.6
.5	.6088	.7673	1.3032	.7934	.5
.6	.6101	.7701	1.2985	.7923	.4
.7	.6115	.7729	1.2938	.7912	.3
.8	.6129	.7757	1.2892	.7902	.2
.9	.6143	.7785	1.2846	.7891	52.1
38.0	0.6157	0.7813	1.2799	0.7880	**52.0**
.1	.6170	.7841	1.2753	.7869	51.9
.2	.6184	.7869	1.2708	.7859	.8
.3	.6198	.7898	1.2662	.7848	.7
.4	.6211	.7926	1.2617	.7837	.6
.5	.6225	.7954	1.2572	.7826	.5
.6	.6239	.7983	1.2527	.7815	.4
.7	.6252	.8012	1.2482	.7804	.3
.8	.6266	.8040	1.2437	.7793	.2
.9	.6280	.8069	1.2393	.7782	51.1
39.0	0.6293	0.8098	1.2349	0.7771	**51.0**
.1	.6307	.8127	1.2305	.7760	50.9
.2	.6320	.8156	1.2261	.7749	.8
.3	.6334	.8185	1.2218	.7738	.7
.4	.6347	.8214	1.2174	.7727	.6
.5	.6361	.8243	1.2131	.7716	.5
.6	.6374	.8273	1.2088	.7705	.4
.7	.6388	.8302	1.2045	.7694	.3
.8	.6401	.8332	1.2002	.7683	.2
.9	.6414	.8361	1.1960	.7672	50.1
40.0	0.6428	0.8391	1.1918	0.7660	**50.0**
.1	.6441	.8421	1.1875	.7649	49.9
.2	.6455	.8451	1.1833	.7638	.8
.3	.6468	.8481	1.1792	.7627	.7
.4	.6481	.8511	1.1750	.7615	.6
40.5	0.6494	0.8541	1.1708	0.7604	**49.5**
Deg.	Cos	Cot	Tan	Sin	Deg.

Deg.	Sin	Tan	Cot	Cos	Deg.
40.5	0.6494	0.8541	1.1708	0.7604	**49.5**
.6	.6508	.8571	1 1667	.7593	.4
.7	.6521	.8601	1.1626	.7581	.3
.8	.6534	.8632	1.1585	.7570	.2
.9	.6547	.8662	1.1544	.7559	49.1
41.0	0.6561	0.8693	1.1504	0.7547	**49.0**
.1	.6574	.8724	1.1463	.7536	48.9
.2	.6587	.8754	1.1423	.7524	.8
.3	.6600	.8785	1.1383	.7513	.7
.4	.6613	.8816	1.1343	.7501	.6
.5	.6626	.8847	1.1303	.7490	.5
.6	.6639	.8878	1.1263	.7478	.4
.7	.6652	.8910	1.1224	.7466	.3
.8	.6665	.8941	1.1184	.7455	.2
.9	.6678	.8972	1.1145	.7443	48.1
42.0	0.6691	0.9004	1 1106	0.7431	**48.0**
.1	.6704	.9036	1.1067	.7420	47 9
.2	.6717	.9067	1.1028	.7408	8
.3	.6730	.9099	1.0990	.7396	.7
.4	.6743	.9131	1.0951	.7385	.6
.5	.6756	.9163	1.0913	.7373	.5
.6	.6769	.9195	1.0875	.7361	.4
.7	.6782	.9228	1.0837	.7349	.3
.8	.6794	.9260	1.0799	.7337	.2
.9	.6807	.9293	1.0761	.7325	47.1
43.0	0.6820	0.9325	1.0724	0.7314	**47.0**
.1	.6833	.9358	1 0686	.7302	46.9
.2	.6845	.9391	1.0649	.7290	.8
.3	.6858	.9424	1.0612	.7278	.7
.4	.6871	.9457	1.0575	.7266	.6
.5	.6884	.9490	1.0538	.7254	.5
.6	.6896	.9523	1.0501	.7242	.4
.7	.6909	.9556	1.0464	.7230	.3
.8	.6921	.9590	1.0428	.7218	.2
.9	.6934	.9623	1.0392	.7206	46.1
44.0	0.6947	0.9657	1.0355	0.7193	**46.0**
.1	.6959	.9691	1.0319	.7181	45.9
.2	.6972	.9725	1.0283	.7169	.8
.3	.6984	.9759	1.0247	.7157	.7
.4	.6997	.9793	1.0212	.7145	.6
.5	.7009	.9827	1.0176	.7133	.5
.6	.7022	.9861	1.0141	.7120	.4
.7	.7034	.9896	1.0105	.7108	.3
.8	.7046	.9930	1.0070	.7096	.2
.9	.7059	.9965	1.0035	.7083	45.1
45.0	0.7071	1.0000	1.0000	0.7071	**45.0**
Deg.	Cos	Cot	Tan	Sin	Deg.

LOGARITHMS OF TRIGONOMETRIC FUNCTIONS FOR ANGLES IN DEGREES AND DECIMALS

Deg.	L. Sin	L. Tan	L. Cot	L. Cos	Deg.
0.0	— ∞	— ∞	∞	0.0000	**90.0**
.1	7.2419	7.2419	2.7581	0.0000	89.9
.2	7.5429	7.5429	2.4571	0 0000	.8
.3	7.7190	7.7190	2.2810	0.0000	.7
.4	7.8439	7.8439	2.1561	0.0000	.6
.5	7.9408	7.9409	2 0591	0.0000	.5
.6	8.0200	8.0200	1.9800	0.0000	.4
.7	8.0870	8.0870	1.9130	0.0000	.3
.8	8.1450	8 1450	1.8550	0.0000	.2
.9	8.1961	8.1962	1.8038	9.9999	89.1
1.0	8.2419	8.2419	1.7581	9.9999	**89.0**
.1	8.2832	8.2833	1.7167	9.9999	88.9
.2	8.3210	8.3211	1.6789	9.9999	.8
.3	8.3558	8.3559	1.6441	9.9999	.7
.4	8.3880	8.3881	1.6119	9.9999	.6
.5	8.4179	8.4181	1.5819	9.9999	.5
.6	8.4459	8.4461	1.5539	9.9998	.4
.7	8.4723	8.4725	1.5275	9.9998	.3
.8	8.4971	8.4973	1.5027	9.9998	.2
.9	8.5206	8.5208	1.4792	9.9998	88.1
2.0	8.5428	8.5431	1.4569	9.9997	**88.0**
1	8.5640	8.5643	1.4357	9.9997	87.9
.2	8.5842	8.5845	1.4155	9.9997	.8
.3	8.6035	8.6038	1.3962	9.9996	.7
4	8.6220	8.6223	1.3777	9.9996	.6
.5	8.6397	8.6401	1.3599	9.9996	.5
.6	8.6567	8 6571	1.3429	9.9996	.4
.7	8.6731	8.6736	1.3264	9.9995	.3
.8	8 6889	8.6894	1.3106	9.9995	.2
9	8.7041	8.7046	1.2954	9.9994	87.1
3.0	8.7188	8.7194	1.2806	9.9994	**87.0**
.1	8.7330	8.7337	1.2663	9.9994	86.9
2	8.7468	8.7475	1.2525	9.9993	.8
.3	8.7602	8.7609	1.2391	9.9993	.7
.4	8.7731	8.7739	1.2261	9.9992	.6
.5	8.7857	8.7865	1.2135	9.9992	.5
.6	8.7979	8 7988	1.2012	9.9991	.4
.7	8.8098	8.8107	1.1893	9.9991	.3
.8	8.8213	8.8223	1.1777	9.9990	.2
.9	8.8326	8.8336	1.1664	9.9990	86.1
4.0	8 8436	8.8446	1.1554	9.9989	**86.0**
.1	8.8543	8.8554	1.1446	9.9989	85.9
.2	8.8647	8.8659	1.1341	9.9988	.8
.3	8.8749	8.8762	1.1238	9.9988	.7
.4	8.8849	8.8862	1.1138	9.9987	.6
.5	8.8946	8.8960	1.1040	9.9987	.5
.6	8.9042	8.9056	1.0944	9.9986	.4
.7	8.9135	8.9150	1.0850	9.9985	.3
.8	8 9226	8.9241	1.0759	9.9985	.2
.9	8 9315	8.9331	1.0669	9.9984	85.1
5.0	8 9403	8.9420	1.0580	9.9983	**85.0**
.1	8.9489	8.9506	1.0494	9.9983	84.9
.2	8.9573	8.9591	1.0409	9.9982	.8
.3	8.9655	8.9674	1.0326	9.9981	.7
.4	8.9736	8.9756	1.0244	9.9981	.6
.5	8.9816	8.9836	1.0164	9.9980	.5
6	8.9894	8.9915	1.0085	9.9979	.4
.7	8.9970	8.9992	1.0008	9.9978	.3
.8	9.0046	9.0068	0.9932	9.9978	.2
.9	9.0120	9.0143	0.9857	9.9977	84.1
6.0	9.0192	9.0216	0.9784	9.9976	**84.0**
Deg.	L. Cos	L. Cot	L. Tan	L. Sin	Deg.

Deg.	L. Sin	L. Tan	L. Cot	L. Cos	Deg.
6.0	9.0192	9.0216	0 9784	9.9976	**84.0**
.1	9 0264	9.0289	0 9711	9.9975	83.9
.2	9.0334	9.0360	0 9640	9.9975	.8
.3	9.0403	9.0430	0 9570	9.9974	.7
.4	9.0472	9.0499	0.9501	9.9973	.6
.5	9.0539	9.0567	0.9433	9.9972	.5
.6	9.0605	9.0633	0.9367	9.9971	.4
.7	9.0670	9.0699	0.9301	9.9970	.3
.8	9.0734	9.0764	0.9236	9.9969	.2
.9	9.0797	9.0828	0.9172	9.9968	83.1
7.0	9.0859	9.0891	0.9109	9.9968	**83.0**
.1	9.0920	9.0954	0.9046	9.9967	82.9
.2	9.0981	9.1015	0.8985	9.9966	.8
.3	9 1040	9.1076	0.8924	9.9965	.7
.4	9.1099	9.1135	0.8865	9.9964	.6
.5	9.1157	9.1194	0.8806	9.9963	.5
.6	9.1214	9.1252	0.8748	9.9962	.4
.7	9.1271	9.1310	0.8690	9.9961	.3
.8	9.1326	9.1367	0.8633	9.9960	.2
.9	9.1381	9.1423	0.8577	9.9959	82.1
8.0	9.1436	9.1478	0.8522	9.9958	**82.0**
.1	9.1489	9.1533	0.8467	9.9956	81.9
.2	9.1542	9.1587	0.8413	9.9955	.8
.3	9.1594	9.1640	0.8360	9.9954	.7
.4	9.1646	9.1693	0.8307	9.9953	.6
.5	9.1697	9.1745	0.8255	9.9952	.5
.6	9.1747	9.1797	0.8203	9.9951	.4
.7	9.1797	9.1848	0.8152	9.9950	.3
.8	9.1847	9.1898	0.8102	9.9949	.2
.9	9.1895	9.1948	0.8052	9.9947	81.1
9.0	9.1943	9.1997	0.8003	9.9946	**81.0**
.1	9.1991	9.2046	0.7954	9.9945	80.9
.2	9.2038	9.2094	0.7906	9.9944	.8
.3	9.2085	9.2142	0.7858	9.9943	.7
.4	9.2131	9.2189	0.7811	9.9941	.6
.5	9.2176	9.2236	0.7764	9.9940	.5
.6	9.2221	9.2282	0.7718	9.9939	.4
.7	9.2266	9.2328	0.7672	9.9937	.3
.8	9.2310	9.2374	0.7626	9.9936	.2
.9	9.2353	9.2419	0.7581	9.9935	80.1
10.0	9.2397	9.2463	0.7537	9.9934	**80.0**
.1	9.2439	9.2507	0.7493	9.9932	79.9
.2	9.2482	9.2551	0.7449	9.9931	.8
.3	9.2524	9.2594	0.7406	9.9929	.7
.4	9.2565	9.2637	0.7363	9.9928	.6
.5	9.2606	9.2680	0.7320	9.9927	.5
.6	9.2647	9.2722	0.7278	9.9925	.4
.7	9.2687	9.2764	0.7236	9.9924	.3
.8	9.2727	9.2805	0.7195	9.9922	.2
.9	9.2767	9.2846	0.7154	9.9921	79.1
11.0	9.2806	9.2887	0.7113	9.9919	**79.0**
.1	9.2845	9.2927	0.7073	9.9918	78.9
.2	9.2883	9.2967	0.7033	9.9916	.8
.3	9.2921	9.3006	0.6994	9.9915	.7
.4	9.2959	9.3046	0.6954	9.9913	.6
.5	9.2997	9.3085	0.6915	9.9912	.5
.6	9.3034	9.3123	0.6877	9.9910	.4
.7	9.3070	9.3162	0.6838	9.9909	.3
.8	9.3107	9.3200	0.6800	9.9907	.2
.9	9.3143	9.3237	0.6763	9.9906	78.1
12.0	9.3179	9.3275	0.6725	9.9904	**78.0**
Deg.	L. Cos	L. Cot	L. Tan	L. Sin	Deg.

LOGARITHMS OF FUNCTIONS FOR DEGREES AND DECIMALS (Continued)

Deg	L. Sin	L. Tan	L. Cot	L. Cos	Deg
12.0	9.3179	9.3275	0.6725	9.9904	**78.0**
.1	9.3214	9.3312	0.6688	9.9902	77.9
.2	9.3250	9.3349	0.6651	9.9901	.8
.3	9.3284	9.3385	0.6615	9.9899	.7
.4	9.3319	9.3422	0.6578	9.9897	.6
.5	9.3353	9.3458	0.6542	9.9896	.5
.6	9.3387	9.3493	0.6507	9.9894	.4
.7	9.3421	9.3529	0.6471	9.9892	.3
.8	9.3455	9.3564	0.6436	9.9891	.2
.9	9.3488	9.3599	0.6401	9.9889	77.1
13.0	9.3521	9.3634	0.6366	9.9887	**77.0**
.1	9.3554	9.3668	0.6332	9.9885	76.9
.2	9.3586	9.3702	0.6298	9.9884	.8
.3	9.3618	9.3736	0.6264	9.9882	.7
.4	9.3650	9.3770	0.6230	9.9880	.6
.5	9.3682	9.3804	0.6196	9.9878	.5
.6	9.3713	9.3837	0.6163	9.9876	.4
.7	9.3745	9.3870	0.6130	9.9875	.3
.8	9.3775	9.3903	0.6097	9.9873	.2
.9	9.3806	9.3935	0.6065	9.9871	76.1
14.0	9.3837	9.3968	0.6032	9.9869	**76.0**
.1	9.3867	9.4000	0.6000	9.9867	75.9
.2	9.3897	9.4032	0.5968	9.9865	.8
.3	9.3927	9.4064	0.5936	9.9863	.7
.4	9.3957	9.4095	0.5905	9.9861	.6
.5	9.3986	9.4127	0.5873	9.9859	.5
.6	9.4015	9.4158	0.5842	9.9857	.4
.7	9.4044	9.4189	0.5811	9.9855	.3
.8	9.4073	9.4220	0.5780	9.9853	.2
.9	9.4102	9.4250	0.5750	9.9851	75.1
15.0	9.4130	9.4281	0.5719	9.9849	**75.0**
.1	9.4158	9.4311	0.5689	9.9847	74.9
.2	9.4186	9.4341	0.5659	9.9845	.8
.3	9.4214	9.4371	0.5629	9.9843	.7
.4	9.4242	9.4400	0.5600	9.9841	.6
.5	9.4269	9.4430	0.5570	9.9839	.5
.6	9.4296	9.4459	0.5541	9.9837	.4
.7	9.4323	9.4488	0.5512	9.9835	.3
.8	9.4350	9.4517	0.5483	9.9833	.2
.9	9.4377	9.4546	0.5454	9.9831	74.1
16.0	9.4403	9.4575	0.5425	9.9828	**74.0**
.1	9.4430	9.4603	0.5397	9.9826	73.9
.2	9.4456	9.4632	0.5368	9.9824	.8
.3	9.4482	9.4660	0.5340	9.9822	.7
.4	9.4508	9.4688	0.5312	9.9820	.6
.5	9.4533	9.4716	0.5284	9.9817	.5
.6	9.4559	9.4744	0.5256	9.9815	.4
.7	9.4584	9.4771	0.5229	9.9813	.3
.8	9.4609	9.4799	0.5201	9.9811	.2
.9	9.4634	9.4826	0.5174	9.9808	73.1
17.0	9.4659	9.4853	0.5147	9.9806	**73.0**
.1	9.4684	9.4880	0.5120	9.9804	72.9
.2	9.4709	9.4907	0.5093	9.9801	.8
.3	9.4733	9.4934	0.5066	9.9799	.7
.4	9.4757	9.4961	0.5039	9.9797	.6
.5	9.4781	9.4987	0.5013	9.9794	.5
.6	9.4805	9.5014	0.4986	9.9792	.4
.7	9.4829	9.5040	0.4960	9.9789	.3
.8	9.4853	9.5066	0.4934	9.9787	.2
.9	9.4876	9.5092	0.4908	9.9785	72.1
18.0	9.4900	9.5118	0.4882	9.9782	**72.0**
Deg.	L. Cos	L. Cot	L. Tan	L. Sin	Deg.

Deg.	L. Sin	L. Tan	L. Cot	L. Cos	Deg
18.0	9.4900	9.5118	0.4882	9.9782	**72.0**
.1	9.4923	9.5143	0.4857	9.9780	71.9
.2	9.4946	9.5169	0.4831	9.9777	.8
.3	9.4969	9.5195	0.4805	9.9775	.7
.4	9.4992	9.5220	0.4780	9.9772	.6
.5	9.5015	9.5245	0.4755	9.9770	.5
.6	9.5037	9.5270	0.4730	9.9767	.4
.7	9.5060	9.5295	0.4705	9.9764	.3
.8	9.5082	9.5320	0.4680	9.9762	.2
.9	9.5104	9.5345	0.4655	9.9759	71.1
19.0	9.5126	9.5370	0.4630	9.9757	**71.0**
.1	9.5148	9.5394	0.4606	9.9754	70.9
.2	9.5170	9.5419	0.4581	9.9751	.8
.3	9.5192	9.5443	0.4557	9.9749	.7
.4	9.5213	9.5467	0.4533	9.9746	.6
.5	9.5235	9.5491	0.4509	9.9743	.5
.6	9.5256	9.5516	0.4484	9.9741	.4
.7	9.5278	9.5539	0.4461	9.9738	.3
.8	9.5299	9.5563	0.4437	9.9735	.2
.9	9.5320	9.5587	0.4413	9.9733	70.1
20.0	9.5341	9.5611	0.4389	9.9730	**70.0**
.1	9.5361	9.5634	0.4366	9.9727	69.9
.2	9.5382	9.5658	0.4342	9.9724	.8
.3	9.5402	9.5681	0.4319	9.9722	.7
.4	9.5423	9.5704	0.4296	9.9719	.6
.5	9.5443	9.5727	0.4273	9.9716	.5
.6	9.5463	9.5750	0.4250	9.9713	.4
.7	9.5484	9.5773	0.4227	9.9710	.3
.8	9.5504	9.5796	0.4204	9.9707	.2
.9	9.5523	9.5819	0.4181	9.9704	69.1
21.0	9.5543	9.5842	0.4158	9.9702	**69.0**
.1	9.5563	9.5864	0.4136	9.9699	68.9
.2	9.5583	9.5887	0.4113	9.9696	.8
.3	9.5602	9.5909	0.4091	9.9693	.7
.4	9.5621	9.5932	0.4068	9.9690	.6
.5	9.5641	9.5954	0.4046	9.9687	.5
.6	9.5660	9.5976	0.4024	9.9684	.4
.7	9.5679	9.5998	0.4002	9.9681	.3
.8	9.5698	9.6020	0.3980	9.9678	.2
.9	9.5717	9.6042	0.3958	9.9675	68.1
22.0	9.5736	9.6064	0.3936	9.9672	**68.0**
.1	9.5754	9.6086	0.3914	9.9669	67.9
.2	9.5773	9.6108	0.3892	9.9666	.8
.3	9.5792	9.6129	0.3871	9.9662	.7
.4	9.5810	9.6151	0.3849	9.9659	.6
.5	9.5828	9.6172	0.3828	9.9656	.5
.6	9.5847	9.6194	0.3806	9.9653	.4
.7	9.5865	9.6215	0.3785	9.9650	.3
.8	9.5883	9.6236	0.3764	9.9647	.2
.9	9.5901	9.6257	0.3743	9.9643	67.1
23.0	9.5919	9.6279	0.3721	9.9640	**67.0**
.1	9.5937	9.6300	0.3700	9.9637	66.9
.2	9.5954	9.6321	0.3679	9.9634	.8
.3	9.5972	9.6341	0.3659	9.9631	.7
.4	9.5990	9.6362	0.3638	9.9627	.6
.5	9.6007	9.6383	0.3617	9.9624	.5
.6	9.6024	9.6404	0.3596	9.9621	.4
.7	9.6042	9.6424	0.3576	9.9617	.3
.8	9.6059	9.6445	0.3555	9.9614	.2
.9	9.6076	9.6465	0.3535	9.9611	66.1
24.0	9.6093	9.6486	0.3514	9.9607	**66.0**
Deg.	L. Cos	L. Cot	L. Tan	L. Sin	Deg.

LOGARITHMS OF FUNCTIONS FOR DEGREES AND DECIMALS (Continued)

Deg.	L. Sin	L. Tan	L. Cot	L. Cos	Deg.
24.0	9.6093	9.6486	0.3514	9.9607	**66.0**
.1	9 6110	9.6506	0.3494	9.9604	65.9
.2	9.6127	9.6527	0.3473	9.9601	.8
.3	9.6144	9.6547	0.3453	9.9597	.7
.4	9.6161	9.6567	0.3433	9.9594	.6
.5	9.6177	9.6587	0.3413	9 9590	.5
.6	9 6194	9.6607	0.3393	9.9587	.4
.7	9 6210	9.6627	0.3373	9.9583	.3
.8	9.6227	9.6647	0.3353	9.9580	.2
.9	9.6243	9.6667	0.3333	9.9576	65.1
25.0	9.6259	9.6687	0.3313	9.9573	**65.0**
.1	9.6276	9.6706	0.3294	9.9560	64.9
.2	9.6292	9.6726	0 3274	9.9566	.8
.3	9.6308	9.6746	0.3254	9.9562	.7
.4	9.6324	9.6765	0.3235	9.9558	.6
.5	9.6340	9.6785	0 3215	9.9555	.5
.6	9.6356	9.6804	0.3196	9.9551	.4
.7	9.6371	9.6824	0.3176	9.9548	.3
.8	9.6387	9.6843	0.3157	9.9544	.2
.9	9 6403	9.6863	0.3137	9.9540	64.1
26.0	9.6418	9.6882	0.3118	9.9537	**64.0**
.1	9.6434	9.6901	0.3099	9.9533	63.9
.2	9.6449	9.6920	0.3080	9.9529	.8
.3	9.6465	9.6939	0.3061	9 9525	.7
.4	9.6480	9.6958	0.3042	9.9522	.6
.5	9.6495	9.6977	0.3023	9.9518	.5
.6	9.6510	9.6996	0 3004	9.9514	.4
.7	9.6526	9.7015	0.2985	9.9510	.3
.8	9.6541	9.7034	0.2966	9.9506	.2
.9	9.6556	9.7053	0.2947	9.9503	63.1
27.0	9.6570	9.7072	0.2928	9.9499	**63.0**
.1	9.6585	9.7090	0.2910	9.9495	62.9
.2	9.6600	9.7109	0.2891	9.9491	.8
.3	9.6615	9.7128	0.2872	9.9487	.7
.4	9.6629	9.7146	0.2854	9.9483	.6
.5	9.6644	9.7165	0.2835	9.9479	.5
.6	9.6659	9.7183	0.2817	9.9475	.4
.7	9.6673	9.7202	0.2798	9.9471	.3
.8	9.6687	9.7220	0.2780	9.9467	.2
.9	9.6702	9.7238	0.2762	9.9463	62.1
28.0	9.6716	9.7257	0.2743	0.9459	**62.0**
.1	9.6730	9.7275	0.2725	9.9455	61.9
.2	9.6744	9.7293	0.2707	9.9451	.8
.3	9.6759	9.7311	0.2689	9.9447	.7
.4	9.6773	9.7330	0.2670	9.9443	.6
.5	9.6787	9.7348	0.2652	9.9439	.5
.6	9.6801	9.7366	0.2634	9.9435	.4
.7	9.6814	9.7384	0.2616	9.9431	.3
.8	9.6828	9.7402	0.2598	9.9427	.2
.9	9.6842	9.7420	0.2580	9.9422	61.1
29.0	9.6856	9.7438	0.2562	9.9418	**61.0**
.1	9.6869	9.7455	0.2545	9.9414	60.9
.2	9.6883	9.7473	0.2527	9.9410	.8
.3	9.6896	9.7491	0.2509	9.9406	.7
.4	9.6910	9.7509	0.2491	9.9401	.6
.5	9.6923	9.7526	0.2474	9.9397	.5
.6	9.6937	9.7544	0.2456	9.9393	.4
.7	9.6950	9.7562	0.2438	9.9388	.3
.8	9.6963	9.7579	0.2421	9.9384	.2
.9	9.6977	9.7597	0.2403	9.9380	60.1
30.0	9.6990	9 7614	0.2386	9.9375	**60.0**
Deg.	L. Cos	L. Cot	L. Tan	L. Sin	Deg.

Deg.	L. Sin	L. Tan	L. Cot	L. Cos	Deg.
30.0	9.6990	9.7614	0.2386	9.9375	**60.0**
.1	9.7003	9.7632	0.2368	9.9371	59.9
.2	9.7016	9.7649	0.2351	9.9367	.8
3	9.7029	9.7667	0.2333	9 9362	.7
.4	9.7042	9.7684	0.2316	9 9358	.6
.5	9.7055	9.7701	0.2299	9.9353	.5
.6	9.7068	9.7719	0.2281	9.9349	.4
.7	9.7080	9.7736	0.2264	9.9344	.3
.8	9.7093	9.7753	0.2247	9.9340	.2
.9	9.7106	9.7771	0.2229	9.9335	59.1
31.0	9.7118	9.7788	0.2212	9.9331	**59.0**
.1	9.7131	9.7805	0.2195	9.9326	58.9
.2	9.7144	9.7822	0.2178	9.9322	.8
.3	9.7156	9.7839	0.2161	9.9317	.7
.4	9.7168	9.7856	0.2144	9.9312	.6
.5	9.7181	9.7873	0.2127	9.9308	.5
.6	9.7193	9.7890	0.2110	9.9303	.4
.7	9.7205	9.7907	0.2093	9.9298	.3
.8	9.7218	9.7924	0.2076	9.9294	.2
.9	9.7230	9.7941	0 2059	9.9289	58.1
32.0	9.7242	9.7958	0.2042	9.9284	**58.0**
.1	9.7254	9.7975	0.2025	9.9279	57.9
.2	9.7266	9.7992	0.2008	9.9275	.8
.3	9.7278	9.8008	0.1992	9.9270	.7
.4	9.7290	9.8025	0.1975	9.9265	.6
.5	9 7302	9.8042	0.1958	9.9260	.5
.6	9.7314	9.8059	0.1941	9.9255	.4
.7	9.7326	9.8075	0.1925	9.9251	.3
.8	9.7338	9.8092	0.1908	9.9246	.2
.9	9.7349	9.8109	0.1891	9.9241	57.1
33.0	9.7361	9.8125	0.1875	9.9236	**57.0**
.1	9.7373	9.8142	0.1858	9.9231	56.9
.2	9.7384	9.8158	0.1842	9.9226	.8
.3	9.7396	9.8175	0.1825	9.9221	.7
.4	9.7407	9.8191	0.1809	9.9216	.6
.5	9.7419	9.8208	0.1792	9.9211	.5
.6	9.7430	9.8224	0.1776	9.9206	.4
.7	9.7442	9.8241	0.1759	9.9201	.3
.8	9.7453	9.8257	0.1743	9.9196	.2
.9	9.7464	9.8274	0.1726	9.9191	56.1
34.0	9.7476	9.8290	0.1710	9.9186	**56.0**
.1	9.7487	9.8306	0.1694	9.9181	55.9
.2	9.7498	9.8323	0.1677	9.9175	.8
.3	9.7509	9.8339	0.1661	9.9170	.7
.4	9.7520	9.8355	0.1645	9 9165	6
.5	9.7531	9.8371	0.1629	9.9160	.5
.6	9.7542	9.8388	0.1612	9.9155	.4
.7	9.7553	9.8404	0.1596	9.9149	.3
.8	9.7564	9.8420	0.1580	9.9144	.2
.9	9.7575	9.8436	0.1564	9.9139	55.1
35.0	9.7586	9.8452	0.1548	9.9134	**55.0**
.1	9.7597	9.8468	0.1532	9.9128	54.9
.2	9.7607	9.8484	0.1516	9.9123	.8
.3	9 7618	9.8501	0.1499	9.9118	.7
.4	9.7629	9.8517	0.1483	9 9112	.6
.5	9.7640	9.8533	0.1467	9.9107	.5
.6	9.7650	9.8549	0.1451	9.9101	.4
.7	9.7661	9.8565	0.1435	9.9096	.3
.8	9.7671	9 8581	0.1419	9.9091	.2
.9	9.7682	9.8597	0 1403	9.9085	54.1
36.0	9.7692	9.8613	0 1387	9 9080	**54.0**
Deg.	L. Cos	L Cot	L. Tan	L. Sin	Deg.

LOGARITHMS OF FUNCTIONS FOR DEGREES AND DECIMALS (Continued)

Deg.	L. Sin	L. Tan	L. Cot	L. Cos	Deg.
36.0	9.7692	9.8613	0.1387	9.9080	**54.0**
.1	9.7703	9.8629	0.1371	9.9074	53.9
.2	9.7713	9.8644	0.1356	9.9069	.8
.3	9.7723	9.8660	0.1340	9.9063	.7
.4	9.7734	9.8676	0.1324	9.9057	.6
.5	9.7744	9.8692	0.1308	9.9052	.5
.6	9.7754	9.8708	0.1292	9.9046	.4
.7	9.7764	9.8724	0.1276	9.9041	.3
.8	9.7774	9.8740	0.1260	9.9035	.2
.9	9.7785	9.8755	0.1245	9.9029	53.1
37.0	9.7795	9.8771	0.1229	9.9023	**53.0**
.1	9.7805	9.8787	0.1213	9.9018	52.9
.2	9.7815	9.8803	0.1197	9.9012	.8
.3	9.7825	9.8818	0.1182	9.9006	.7
.4	9.7835	9.8834	0.1166	9.9000	.6
.5	9.7844	9.8850	0.1150	9.8995	5
.6	9.7854	9 8865	0.1135	9.8989	.4
.7	9.7864	9 8881	0.1119	9.8983	.3
.8	9.7874	9.8897	0.1103	9.8977	.2
.9	9.7884	9.8912	0.1088	9.8971	52.1
38.0	9.7893	9.8928	0.1072	9.8965	**52.0**
1	9.7903	9.8944	0.1056	9.8959	51.9
.2	9.7913	9.8959	0.1041	9.8953	.8
.3	9.7922	9.8975	0.1025	9.8947	.7
.4	9.7932	9.8990	0.1010	9.8941	.6
.5	9.7941	9.9006	0.0994	9.8935	.5
.6	9.7951	9.9022	0.0978	9 8929	.4
.7	9.7960	9.9037	0.0963	9.8923	.3
.8	9.7970	9.9053	0 0947	9.8917	.2
.9	9.7979	9.9068	0.0932	9.8911	51.1
39.0	9.7989	9.9084	0.0916	9.8905	**51.0**
.1	9.7998	9.9099	0.0901	9.8899	50.9
.2	9.8007	9.9115	0.0885	9.8893	.8
.3	9.8017	9.9130	0.0870	9.8887	.7
.4	9.8026	9 9146	0.0854	9.8880	.6
.5	9.8035	9.9161	0.0839	9.8874	.5
.6	9.8044	9.9176	0.0824	9.8868	.4
.7	9.8053	9.9192	0.0808	9.8862	.3
.8	9.8063	9.9207	0.0793	9.8855	.2
.9	9.8072	9.9223	0.0777	9.8849	50.1
40.0	9.8081	9.9238	0.0762	9.8843	**50.0**
.1	9.8090	9.9254	0.0746	9.8836	49.9
.2	9.8099	9.9269	0.0731	9.8830	.8
.3	9.8101	9.9284	0.0716	9.8823	.7
.4	9.8117	9.9300	0.0700	9.8817	.6
.5	9.8125	9.9315	0.0685	9.8810	.5
.6	9.8134	9.9330	0.0670	9.8804	.4
.7	9.8143	9.9346	0.0654	9.8797	.3
8	9.8152	9.9361	0.0639	9.8791	2
.9	9.8161	9.9376	0.0624	9.8784	49.1
41.0	9.8169	9.9392	0.0608	9.8778	**49.0**
Deg.	L. Cos	L. Cot	L. Tan	L. Sin	Deg.

Deg.	L. Sin	L. Tan	L. Cot	L. Cos	Deg.
41.0	9.8169	9.9392	0.0608	9.8778	**49.0**
.1	9.8178	9.9407	0.0593	9.8771	48.9
.2	9.8187	9.9422	0.0578	9.8765	.8
.3	9.8195	9.9438	0.0562	9.8758	.7
.4	9.8204	9.9453	0.0547	9.8751	.6
.5	9.8213	9.9468	0.0532	9.8745	.5
.6	9.8221	9.9483	0.0517	9.8738	.4
.7	9.8230	9.9499	0.0501	9.8731	.3
.8	9.8238	9.9514	0.0486	9.8724	.2
.9	9.8247	9.9529	0.0471	9.8718	48.1
42.0	9.8255	9.9544	0.0456	9.8711	**48.0**
.1	9.8264	9.9560	0.0440	9.8704	47.9
.2	9.8272	9.9575	0.0425	9.8697	.8
.3	9.8280	9.9590	0.0410	9.8690	.7
.4	9.8289	9.9605	0.0395	9.8683	.6
.5	9.8297	9.9621	0.0379	9.8676	.5
.6	9.8305	9.9636	0.0364	9.8669	.4
.7	9.8313	9.9651	0.0349	9.8662	.3
.8	9.8322	9.9666	0.0334	9.8655	.2
9	9.8330	9.9681	0.0319	9.8648	47.1
43.0	9.8338	9.9697	0.0303	9.8641	**47.0**
.1	9.8346	9.9712	0.0288	9.8634	46.9
2	9.8354	9.9727	0.0273	9.8627	.8
.3	9.8362	9.9742	0.0258	9.8620	.7
.4	9.8370	9.9757	0.0243	9.8613	.6
.5	9.8378	9.9772	0.0228	9.8606	.5
.6	9.8386	9.9788	0.0212	9.8598	.4
.7	9.8394	9.9803	0.0197	9.8591	.3
.8	9.8402	9.9818	0.0182	9.8584	.2
.9	9.8410	9.9833	0.0167	9.8577	46.1
44.0	9.8418	9.9848	0.0152	9.8569	**46.0**
.1	9.8426	9.9864	0.0136	9.8562	45.9
.2	9.8433	9.9879	0.0121	9.8555	.8
.3	9.8441	9.9894	0.0106	9.8547	.7
.4	9.8449	9.9909	0.0091	9.8540	.6
.5	9.8457	9.9924	0.0076	9.8532	.5
.6	9.8464	9.9939	0.0061	9.8525	.4
.7	9.8472	9.9955	0.0045	9.8517	.3
.8	9.8480	9.9970	0.0030	9.8510	.2
.9	9.8487	9.9985	0.0015	9.8502	45.1
45.0	9.8495	0.0000	0.0000	9.8495	**45.0**
Deg.	L. Cos	L. Cot	L. Tan	L. Sin	Deg.

NATURAL FUNCTIONS FOR ANGLES IN RADIANS

Rad.	Sin	Tan	Cot	Cos	Rad.	Sin	Tan	Cot	Cos
.00	.00000	.00000	∞	1.0000	**.50**	.47943	.54630	1.8305	.87758
.01	.01000	.01000	99.997	.99995	.51	.48818	.55936	1.7878	.87274
.02	.02000	.02000	49.993	.99980	.52	.49688	.57256	1.7465	.86782
.03	.03000	.03001	33.323	.99955	.53	.50553	.58592	1.7067	.86281
.04	.03999	.04002	24.987	.99920	.54	.51414	.59943	1.6683	.85771
.05	.04998	.05004	19.983	.99875	.55	.52269	.61311	1.6310	.85252
.06	.05996	.06007	16.647	.99820	.56	.53119	.62695	1.5950	.84726
.07	.06994	.07011	14.262	.99755	.57	.53963	.64097	1.5601	.84190
.08	.07991	.08017	12.473	.99680	.58	.54802	.65517	1.5263	.83646
.09	.08988	.09024	11.081	.99595	.59	.55636	.66956	1.4935	.83094
.10	.09983	.10033	9.9666	.99500	**.60**	.56464	.68414	1.4617	.82534
.11	.10978	.11045	9.0542	.99396	.61	.57287	.69892	1.4308	.81965
.12	.11971	.12058	8.2933	.99281	.62	.58104	.71391	1.4007	.81388
.13	.12963	.13074	7.6489	.99156	.63	.58914	.72911	1.3715	.80803
.14	.13954	.14092	7.0961	.99022	.64	.59720	.74454	1.3431	.80210
.15	.14944	.15114	6.6166	.98877	.65	.60519	.76020	1.3154	.79608
.16	.15932	.16138	6.1966	.98723	.66	.61312	.77610	1.2885	.78999
.17	.16918	.17166	5.8256	.98558	.67	.62099	.79225	1.2622	.78382
.18	.17903	.18197	5.4954	.98384	.68	.62879	.80866	1.2366	.77757
.19	.18886	.19232	5.1997	.98200	.69	.63654	.82534	1.2116	.77125
.20	.19867	.20271	4.9332	.98007	**.70**	.64422	.84229	1.1872	.76484
.21	.20846	.21314	4.6917	.97803	.71	.65183	.85953	1.1634	.75836
.22	.21823	.22362	4.4719	.97590	.72	.65938	.87707	1.1402	.75181
.23	.22798	.23414	4.2709	.97367	.73	.66687	.89492	1.1174	.74517
.24	.23770	.24472	4.0864	.97134	.74	.67429	.91309	1.0952	.73847
.25	.24740	.25534	3.9163	.96891	.75	.68164	.93160	1.0734	.73169
.26	.25708	.26602	3.7591	.96639	.76	.68892	.95045	1.0521	.72484
.27	.26673	.27676	3.6133	.96377	.77	.69614	.96967	1.0313	.71791
.28	.27636	.28755	3.4776	.96106	.78	.70328	.98926	1.0109	.71091
.29	.28595	.29841	3.3511	.95824	.79	.71035	1.0092	.99084	.70385
.30	.29552	.30934	3.2327	.95534	**.80**	.71736	1.0296	.97121	.69671
.31	.30506	.32033	3.1218	.95233	.81	.72429	1.0505	.95197	.68950
.32	.31457	.33139	3.0176	.94924	.82	.73115	1.0717	.93309	.68222
.33	.32404	.34252	2.9195	.94604	.83	.73793	1.0934	.91455	.67488
.34	.33349	.35374	2.8270	.94275	.84	.74464	1.1156	.89635	.66746
.35	.34290	.36503	2.7395	.93937	.85	.75128	1.1383	.87848	.65998
.36	.35227	.37640	2.6567	.93590	.86	.75784	1.1616	.86091	.65244
.37	.36162	.38786	2.5782	.93233	.87	.76433	1.1853	.84365	.64483
.38	.37092	.39941	2.5037	.92866	.88	.77074	1.2097	.82668	.63715
.39	.38019	.41105	2.4328	.92491	.89	.77707	1.2346	.80998	.62941
.40	.38942	.42279	2.3652	.92106	**.90**	.78333	1.2602	.79355	.62161
.41	.39861	.43463	2.3008	.91712	.91	.78950	1.2864	.77738	.61375
.42	.40776	.44657	2.2393	.91309	.92	.79560	1.3133	.76146	.60582
.43	.41687	.45862	2.1804	.90897	.93	.80162	1.3409	.74578	.59783
.44	.42594	.47078	2.1241	.90475	.94	.80756	1.3692	.73034	.58979
.45	.43497	.48306	2.0702	.90045	.95	.81342	1.3984	.71511	.58168
.46	.44395	.49545	2.0184	.89605	.96	.81919	1.4284	.70010	.57352
.47	.45289	.50797	1.9686	.89157	.97	.82489	1.4592	.68531	.56530
.48	.46178	.52061	1.9208	.88699	.98	.83050	1.4910	.67071	.55702
.49	.47063	.53339	1.8748	.88233	.99	.83603	1.5237	.65631	.54869
.50	.47943	.54630	1.8305	.87758	**1.00**	.84147	1.5574	.64209	.54030
Rad.	Sin	Tan	Cot	Cos	Rad.	Sin	Tan	Cot	Cos

FUNCTIONS FOR ANGLES IN RADIANS (Continued)

Rad.	Sin	Tan	Cot	Cos
1.00	.84147	1.5574	.64209	.54030
1.01	.84683	1.5922	.62806	.53186
1.02	.85211	1.6281	.61420	.52337
1.03	.85730	1.6652	.60051	.51482
1.04	.86240	1.7036	.58699	.50622
1.05	.86742	1.7433	.57362	.49757
1.06	.87236	1.7844	.56040	.48887
1.07	.87720	1.8270	.54734	.48012
1.08	.88196	1.8712	.53441	.47133
1.09	.88663	1.9171	.52162	.46249
1.10	.89121	1.9648	.50897	.45360
1.11	.89570	2.0143	.49644	.44466
1.12	.90010	2.0660	.48404	.43568
1.13	.90441	2.1198	.47175	.42666
1.14	.90863	2.1759	.45959	.41759
1.15	.91276	2.2345	.44753	.40849
1.16	.91680	2.2958	.43558	.39934
1.17	.92075	2.3600	.42373	.39015
1.18	.92461	2.4273	.41199	.38092
1.19	.92837	2.4979	.40034	.37166
1.20	.93204	2.5722	.38878	.36236
1.21	.93562	2.6503	.37731	.35302
1.22	.93910	2.7328	.36593	.34365
1.23	.94249	2.8198	.35463	.33424
1.24	.94578	2.9119	.34341	.32480
1.25	.94898	3.0096	.33227	.31532
1.26	.95209	3.1133	.32121	.30582
1.27	.95510	3.2236	.31021	.29628
1.28	.95802	3.3413	.29928	.28672
1.29	.96084	3.4672	.28842	.27712
1.30	.96356	3.6021	.27762	.26750
1.31	.96618	3.7471	.26687	.25785
1.32	.96872	3.9033	.25619	.24818
1.33	.97115	4.0723	.24556	.23848
1.34	.97348	4.2556	.23498	.22875
1.35	.97572	4.4552	.22446	.21901
1.36	.97786	4.6734	.21398	.20924
1.37	.97991	4.9131	.20354	.19945
1.38	.98185	5.1774	.19315	.18964
1.39	.98370	5.4707	.18279	.17981
1.40	.98545	5.7979	.17248	.16997
1.41	.98710	6.1654	.16220	.16010
1.42	.98865	6.5811	.15195	.15023
1.43	.99010	7.0555	.14173	.14033
1.44	.99146	7.6018	.13155	.13042
1.45	.99271	8.2381	.12139	.12050
1.46	.99387	8.9886	.11125	.11057
1.47	.99492	9.8874	.10114	.10063
1.48	.99588	10.983	.09105	.09067
1.49	.99674	12.350	.08097	.08071
1.50	.99749	14.101	.07091	.07074
Rad.	**Sin**	**Tan**	**Cot**	**Cos**

Rad.	Sin	Tan	Cot	Cos
1.50	.99749	14.101	.07091	.07074
1.51	.99815	16.428	.06087	.06076
1.52	.99871	19.670	.05084	.05077
1.53	99917	24.498	.04082	.04079
1.54	.99953	32.461	.03081	.03079
1.55	.99978	48.078	.02080	.02079
1.56	.99994	92.621	.01080	.01080
1.57	1.0000	1255.8	.00080	.00080
1.58	.99996	−108.65	−.00920	−.00920
1.59	.99982	−52.067	−.01921	−.01920
1.60	.99957	−34.233	−.02921	−.02920
1.61	.99923	−25.495	−.03922	−.03919
1.62	.99879	−20.307	−.04924	−.04918
1.63	.99825	−16.871	−.05927	−.05917
1.64	.99761	−14.427	−.06931	−.06915
1.65	.99687	−12.599	−.07937	−.07912
1.66	.99602	−11.181	−.08944	−.08909
1.67	.99508	−10.047	−.09953	−.09904
1.68	.99404	−9.1208	−.10964	−.10899
1.69	.99290	−8.3492	−.11977	−.11892
1.70	.99166	−7.6966	−.12993	−.12884
1.71	.99033	−7.1373	−.14011	−.13875
1.72	.98889	−6.6524	−.15032	−.14865
1.73	.98735	−6.2281	−.16056	−.15853
1.74	.98572	−5.8535	−.17084	−.16840
1.75	.98399	−5.5204	−.18115	−.17825
1.76	.98215	−5.2221	−.19149	−.18808
1.77	.98022	−4.9534	−.20188	−.19789
1.78	.97820	−4.7101	−.21231	−.20768
1.79	.97607	−4.4887	−.22278	−.21745
1.80	.97385	−4.2863	−.23330	−.22720
1.81	.97153	−4.1005	−.24387	−.23693
1.82	.96911	−3.9294	−.25449	−.24663
1.83	.96659	−3.7712	−.26517	−.25631
1.84	.96398	−3.6245	−.27590	−.26596
1.85	.96128	−3.4881	−.28669	−.27559
1.86	.95847	−3.3608	−.29755	−.28519
1.87	.95557	−3.2419	−.30846	−.29476
1.88	.95258	−3.1304	−.31945	−.30430
1.89	.94949	−3.0257	−.33051	−.31381
1.90	.94630	−2.9271	−.34164	−.32329
1.91	.94302	−2.8341	−.35284	−.33274
1.92	.93965	−2.7463	−.36413	−.34215
1.93	.93618	−2.6632	−.37549	−.35153
1.94	.93262	−2.5843	−.38695	−.36087
1.95	.92896	−2.5095	−.39849	−.37018
1.96	.92521	−2.4383	−.41012	−.37945
1.97	.92137	−2.3705	−.42185	−.38868
1.98	.91744	−2.3058	−.43368	−.39788
1.99	.91341	−2.2441	−.44562	−.40703
2.00	.90930	−2.1850	−.45766	−.41615
Rad.	Sin	Tan	Cot	Cos

LOGARITHMS OF THE FUNCTIONS FOR ANGLES IN RADIANS

Rad.	L. Sin	L. Tan	L. Cot	L. Cos
.00	− ∞	− ∞	∞	0.00000
.01	7.99999	8.00001	1.99999	9.99998
.02	8.30100	8.30109	1.69891	9.99991
.03	8.47706	8.47725	1.52275	9.99980
.04	8.60194	8.60229	1.39771	9.99965
.05	8 69879	8.69933	1.30067	9.99946
.06	8.77789	8.77867	1.22133	9.99922
.07	8.84474	8.84581	1.15419	9.99894
.08	8.90263	8.90402	1.09598	9.99861
.09	8.95366	8.95542	1.04458	9.99824
.10	8.99928	9.00145	0.99855	9.99782
.11	9.04052	9.04315	0.95685	9.99737
.12	9.07814	9.08127	0.91873	9.99687
.13	9.11272	9.11640	0.88360	9.99632
.14	9.14471	9.14898	0.85102	9.99573
.15	9.17446	9.17937	0.82063	9.99510
.16	9.20227	9.20785	0.79215	9.99442
.17	9.22836	9.23466	0.76534	9.99369
.18	9.25292	9.26000	0.74000	9.99293
.19	9.27614	9.28402	0.71598	9.99211
.20	9.29813	9.30688	0.69312	9.99126
.21	9.31902	9.32867	0.67133	9.99035
.22	9.33891	9.34951	0.65049	9.98940
.23	9.35789	9.36948	0.63052	9.98841
.24	9.37603	9.38866	0.61134	9.98737
.25	9.39341	9.40712	0.59288	9.98628
.26	9.41007	9.42492	0.57508	9.98515
.27	9.42607	9.44210	0.55790	9.98397
.28	9.44147	9.45872	0.54128	9.98275
.29	9.45629	9.47482	0.52518	9.98148
.30	9.47059	9.49043	0.50957	9.98016
.31	9.48438	9.50559	0.49441	9.97879
.32	9.49771	9.52034	0.47966	9.97737
.33	9.51060	9.53469	0.46531	9.97591
.34	9.52308	9.54868	0.45132	9.97440
.35	9 53516	9.56233	0.43767	9.97284
.36	9.54688	9.57565	0.42435	9.97123
.37	9.55825	9.58868	0.41132	9.96957
.38	9.56928	9.60142	0.39858	9.96786
.39	9.58000	9.61390	0.38610	9.96610
.40	9.59042	9.62613	0.37387	9.96429
.41	9.60055	9.63812	0.36188	9.96243
.42	9.61041	9.64989	0.35011	9.96051
.43	9.62000	9.66145	0.33855	9.95855
.44	9.62935	9.67282	0.32718	9.95653
.45	9.63845	9.68400	0.31600	9.95446
.46	9.64733	9.69500	0 30500	9.95233
.47	9.65599	9.70583	0.29417	9.95015
.48	9.66443	9.71651	0.28349	9.94792
.49	9.67268	9.72704	0.27296	9.94563
.50	9.68072	9.73743	0.26257	9.94329
Rad	L. Sin	L. Tan	L. Cot	L. Cos

Rad.	L. Sin	L. Tan	L. Cot	L. Cos
.50	9.68072	9.73743	0.26257	9.94329
.51	9.68858	9.74769	0.25231	9.94089
.52	9.69625	9.75782	0.24218	9.93843
.53	9.70375	9.76784	0.23216	9.93591
.54	9.71108	9.77774	0.22226	9.93334
.55	9.71824	9.78754	0.21246	9.93071
.56	9.72525	9.79723	0.20277	9.92801
.57	9.73210	9.80684	0.19316	9.92526
.58	9.73880	9.81635	0.18365	9.92245
.59	9.74536	9.82579	0.17421	9.91957
.60	9.75177	9.83514	0.16486	9.91663
.61	9.75805	9.84443	0.15557	9.91363
.62	9.76420	9.85364	0.14636	9.91056
.63	9.77022	9.86280	0.13720	9.90743
.64	9.77612	9.87189	0.12811	9 90423
.65	9.78189	9.88093	0.11907	9.90096
.66	9.78754	9.88992	0.11008	9.89762
.67	9.79308	9.89886	0.10114	9.89422
.68	9.79851	9.90777	0.09223	9.89074
.69	9.80382	9.91663	0.08337	9.88719
70	9.80903	9.92546	0.07454	9.88357
.71	9.81414	9.93426	0.06574	9.87988
.72	9.81914	9.94303	0.05697	9.87611
.73	9.82404	9.95178	0.04822	9.87226
.74	9.82885	9.96051	0.03949	9.86833
.75	9.83355	9 96923	0.03077	9.86433
.76	9.83817	9.97793	0.02207	9.86024
.77	9.84269	9.98662	0.01338	9.85607
.78	9.84713	9.99531	0.00469	9.85182
.79	9.85147	0.00400	9.99600	9.84748
.80	9.85573	0.01268	9.98732	9.84305
.81	9.85991	0.02138	9.97862	9.83853
.82	9.86400	0.03008	9.96992	9.83393
.83	9.86802	0.03879	9.96121	9.82922
.84	9.87195	0.04752	9.95248	9.82443
.85	9.87580	0.05627	9.94373	9.81953
.86	9.87958	0.06504	9.93496	9.81454
.87	9.88328	0.07384	9.92616	9.80944
.88	9.88691	0.08266	9.91734	9.80424
.89	9.89046	0.09153	9.90847	9.79894
.90	9.89394	0.10043	9.89957	9.79352
.91	9.89735	0.10937	9.89063	9.78799
.92	9.90070	0.11835	9.88165	9.78234
.93	9.90397	0.12739	9.87261	9.77658
.94	9.90717	0.13648	9.86352	9.77070
95	9.91031	0.14563	9.85437	9.76469
.96	9.91339	0.15484	9.84516	9.75855
.97	9.91639	0.16412	9.83588	9.75228
.98	9.91934	0.17347	9.82653	9.74587
.99	9.92222	0.18289	9.81711	9.73933
1.00	9.92504	0.19240	9.80760	9.73264
Rad.	L. Sin	L. Tan	L. Cot	L. Cos

LOGARITHMS OF FUNCTIONS FOR ANGLES IN RADIANS (Continued)

Rad.	L. Sin	L. Tan	L. Cot	L. Cos
1.00	9.92504	0.19240	9.80760	9.73264
1.01	9.92780	0.20200	9.79800	9.72580
1.02	9.93049	0.21169	9.78831	9.71881
1.03	9.93313	0.22148	9.77852	9.71165
1.04	9.93571	0.23137	9.76863	9.70434
1.05	9.93823	0.24138	9.75862	9.69686
1.06	9.94069	0.25150	9.74850	9.68920
1.07	9.94310	0.26175	9.73825	9.68135
1.08	9.94545	0.27212	9.72788	9.67332
1.09	9.94774	0.28264	9.71736	9.66510
1.10	9.94998	0.29331	9.70669	9.65667
1.11	9.95216	0.30413	9.69587	9.64803
1.12	9.95429	0.31512	9.68488	9.63917
1.13	9.95637	0.32628	9.67372	9 63008
1.14	9.95839	0.33763	9.66237	9.62075
1.15	9.96036	0 34918	9.65082	9.61118
1.16	9 96228	0.36093	9.63907	9.60134
1.17	9.96414	0.37291	9.62709	9 59123
1.18	9.96596	0.38512	9.61488	9.58084
1.19	9.96772	0.39757	9.60243	9.57015
1.20	9.96943	0.41030	9.58970	9.55914
1.21	9.97110	0.42330	9.57670	9.54780
1.22	9.97271	0.43660	9.56340	9.53611
1.23	9.97428	0.45022	9.54978	9.52406
1.24	9.97579	0.46418	9.53582	9.51161
1.25	9 97726	0.47850	9.52150	9 49875
1.26	9.97868	0.49322	9.50678	9.48546
1.27	9.98005	0.50835	9.49165	9.47170
1.28	9.98137	0.52392	9.47608	9.45745
1.29	9.98265	0.53998	9.46002	9.44267
1.30	9.98388	0.55656	9.44344	9.42732
1.31	9.98506	0.57369	9.42631	9.41137
1.32	9.98620	0.59144	9.40856	9.39476
1.33	9.98729	0.60984	9.39016	9.37744
1.34	9.98833	0.62896	9.37104	9.35937
1.35	9.98933	0.64887	9.35113	9.34046
1.36	9.99028	0.66964	9.33036	9.32064
1.37	9.99119	0.69135	9.30865	9.29983
1.38	9.99205	0.71411	9.28589	9.27793
1.39	9.99286	0.73804	9.26196	9.25482
1.40	9.99363	0.76327	9.23673	9.23036
1.41	9.99436	0.78996	9.21004	9.20440
1.42	9.99504	0.81830	9.18170	9.17674
1.43	9.99568	0.84853	9.15147	9.14716
1.44	9.99627	0.88092	9.11908	9.11536
1.45	9.99682	0.91583	9.08417	9.08100
1.46	9.99733	0.95369	9.04631	9.04364
1.47	9.99779	0.99508	9.00492	9.00271
1.48	9.99821	1.04074	8.95926	8.95747
1.49	9.99858	1.09166	8.90834	8.90692
1.50	9.99891	1.14926	8.85074	8.84965
Rad.	L. Sin	L. Tan	L. Cot	L. Cos

Rad	L. Sin	L. Tan	L. Cot	L. Cos
1.50	9.99891	1.14926	8.85074	8 84965
1.51	9.99920	1.21559	8.78441	8.78361
1.52	9.99944	1.29379	8.70621	8.70565
1.53	9.99964	1.38914	8.61086	8.61050
1.54	9.99979	1.51136	8.48864	8 48843
1.55	9.99991	1.68195	8.31805	8.31796
1.56	9.99997	1.96671	8.03329	8.03327
1.57	0.00000	3.09891	6.90109	6.90109
1.58	9.99998	2.03603*	7.96397*	7 96396*
1.59	9.99992	1.71656	8.28344	8.28336
1.60	9.99981	1.53444	8.46556	8.46538
1.61	9.99967	1.40645	8.59355	8.59323
1.62	9.99947	1.30765	8.69235	8.69182
1.63	9.99924	1.22714	8.77286	8.77209
1.64	9.99896	1.15918	8.84082	8.83978
1.65	9.99864	1.10035	8.89965	8.89829
1.66	9.99827	1.04847	8.95154	8.94981
1.67	9.99786	1.00204	8.99796	8.99582
1.68	9.99741	0.96003	9.03997	9.03737
1.69	9.99691	0.92165	9.07835	9.07526
1.70	9.99636	0 88630	9.11370	9.11007
1.71	9.99578	0.85353	9.14647	9.14225
1.72	9.99515	0.82298	9.17702	9.17217
1.73	9.99447	0.79436	9.20564	9.20012
1.74	9.99375	0.76742	9.23258	9.22634
1.75	9.99299	0.74197	9.25803	9.25102
1.76	9.99218	0.71784	9.28216	9.27434
1.77	9.99133	0.69490	9.30510	9.29642
1.78	9.99043	0.67303	9.32697	9.31740
1.79	9.98948	0.65212	9.34788	9.33736
1.80	9.98849	0.63208	9.36792	9.35641
1.81	9.98745	0.61284	9.38716	9.37462
1.82	9.98637	0.59432	9.40568	9.39205
1.83	9.98524	0.57648	9.42352	9.40877
1.84	9.98407	0.55925	9.44075	9.42482
1.85	9.98285	0.54258	9.45742	9.44026
1.86	9.98158	0.52645	9.47355	9.45513
1.87	9.98026	0.51080	9.48920	9.46947
1.88	9.97890	0.49560	9.50440	9.48330
1.89	9.97749	0.48082	9.51918	9.49667
1.90	9.97603	0.46644	9.53356	9.50959
1.91	9.97452	0.45242	9.54758	9.52210
1.92	9.97296	0.43875	9.56125	9.53422
1.93	9.97136	0.42540	9.57460	9.54597
1.94	9.96970	0.41235	9.58765	9.55735
1.95	9.96800	0.39958	9.60042	9.56841
1.96	9.96624	0.38708	9.61292	9.57916
1.97	9.96443	0.37484	9.62516	9.58960
1.98	9.96258	0.36283	9.63717	9.59975
1.99	9.96067	0.35104	9.64896	9.60963
2.00	9.95871	0.33946	9.66054	9.61925
Rad.	L. Sin	L. Tan	L. Cot	L. Cos

* Values of the cosine, tangent and cotangent for angles in the table, 1.58 radians and above, are negative.

HAVERSINES

The following table gives the values of the haversines and their logarithms for angles from 0 to 180° at 10 minute intervals. Characteristics of the logarithms are omitted.

°	0′ Value	0′ Log	10′ Value	10′ Log	20′ Value	20′ Log	30′ Value	30′ Log	40′ Value	40′ Log	50′ Value	50′ Log
0	.0000	—	.0000	$\bar{6}$.3254	.0000	$\bar{6}$.9275	.0000	$\bar{5}$.2796	.0000	$\bar{5}$.5295	.0001	$\bar{5}$.7233
1	.0001	$\bar{5}$.8817	.0001	.0156	.0001	.1316	.0002	.2339	.0002	.3254	.0003	.4081
2	.0003	.4837	.0004	.5532	.0004	.6176	.0005	.6775	.0005	.7336	.0006	.7862
3	.0007	.8358	.0008	.8828	.0008	.9273	.0009	.9697	.0010	.0101	.0011	.0487
4	.0012	.0856	.0013	.1211	.0014	.1551	.0015	.1879	.0017	.2195	.0018	.2499
5	.0019	.2794	.0020	.3078	.0022	.3354	.0023	.3621	.0024	.3880	.0026	.4132
6	.0027	.4376	.0029	.4614	.0031	.4845	.0032	.5071	.0034	.5290	.0036	.5504
7	.0037	.5714	.0039	.5918	.0041	.6117	.0043	.6312	.0045	.6503	.0047	.6689
8	.0049	.6872	.0051	.7051	.0053	.7226	.0055	.7397	.0057	.7566	.0059	.7731
9	.0062	.7893	.0064	.8052	.0066	.8208	.0069	.8361	.0071	.8512	.0073	.8660
10	.0076	.8806	.0079	.8949	.0081	.9090	.0084	.9229	.0086	.9365	.0089	.9499
11	.0092	.9631	.0095	.9762	.0097	.9890	.0100	.0016	.0103	.0141	.0106	.0264
12	.0109	.0385	.0112	.0504	.0115	.0622	.0119	.0738	.0122	.0852	.0125	.0966
13	.0128	.1077	.0131	.1187	.0135	.1296	.0138	.1404	.0142	.1510	.0145	.1614
14	.0149	.1718	.0152	.1820	.0156	.1921	.0159	.2021	.0163	.2120	.0167	.2217
15	.0170	.2314	.0174	.2409	.0178	.2504	.0182	.2597	.0186	.2689	.0190	.2781
16	.0194	.2871	.0198	.2961	.0202	.3049	.0206	.3137	.0210	.3223	.0214	.3309
17	.0218	.3394	.0223	.3478	.0227	.3561	.0231	.3644	.0236	.3726	.0240	.3807
18	.0245	.3887	.0249	.3966	.0254	.4045	.0258	.4123	.0263	.4200	.0268	.4276
19	.0272	.4352	.0277	.4427	.0282	.4502	.0287	.4576	.0292	.4649	.0297	.4721
20	.0302	.4793	.0307	.4865	.0312	.4935	.0317	.5006	.0322	.5075	.0327	.5144
21	.0332	.5213	.0337	.5281	.0343	.5348	.0348	.5415	.0353	.5481	.0359	.5547
22	.0364	.5612	.0370	.5677	.0375	.5741	.0381	.5805	.0386	.5868	.0392	.5931
23	.0397	.5993	.0403	.6055	.0409	.6116	.0415	.6177	.0421	.6238	.0426	.6298
24	.0432	.6358	.0438	.6417	.0444	.6476	.0450	.6534	.0456	.6592	.0462	.6650
25	.0468	.6707	.0475	.6764	.0481	.6820	.0487	.6876	.0493	.6932	.0500	.6987
26	.0506	.7042	.0512	.7096	.0519	.7150	.0525	.7204	.0532	.7258	.0538	.7311
27	.0545	.7364	.0552	.7416	.0558	.7468	.0565	.7520	.0572	.7572	.0578	.7623
28	.0585	.7674	.0592	.7724	.0599	.7774	.0606	.7824	.0613	.7874	.0620	.7923
29	.0627	.7972	.0634	.8021	.0641	.8069	.0648	.8117	.0655	.8165	.0663	.8213
30	.0670	.8260	.0677	.8307	.0684	.8354	.0692	.8400	.0699	.8446	.0707	.8492
31	.0714	.8538	.0722	.8583	.0729	.8629	.0737	.8673	.0744	.8718	.0752	.8763
32	.0760	.8807	.0767	.8851	.0775	.8894	.0783	.8938	.0791	.8981	.0799	.9024
33	.0807	.9067	.0815	.9109	.0823	.9152	.0831	.9194	.0839	.9236	.0847	.9277
34	.0855	.9319	.0863	.9360	.0871	.9401	.0879	.9442	.0888	.9482	.0896	.9523
35	.0904	.9563	.0913	.9603	.0921	.9643	.0929	.9682	.0938	.9721	.0946	.9761
36	.0955	.9800	.0963	.9838	.0972	.9877	.0981	.9915	.0989	.9954	.0998	.9992
37	.1007	.0030	.1016	.0067	.1024	.0105	.1033	.0142	.1042	.0179	.1051	.0216
38	.1060	.0253	.1069	.0289	.1078	.0326	.1087	.0362	.1096	.0398	.1105	.0434
39	.1114	.0470	.1123	.0505	.1133	.0541	.1142	.0576	.1151	.0611	.1160	.0646
40	.1170	.0681	.1179	.0716	.1189	.0750	.1198	.0784	.1207	.0819	.1217	.0853
41	.1226	.0887	.1236	.0920	.1246	.0954	.1255	.0987	.1265	.1020	.1275	.1054
42	.1284	.1087	.1294	.1119	.1304	.1152	.1314	.1185	.1323	.1217	.1333	.1249
43	.1343	.1282	.1353	.1314	.1363	.1345	.1373	.1377	.1383	.1409	.1393	.1440
44	.1403	.1472	.1413	.1503	.1424	.1534	.1434	.1565	.1444	.1596	.1454	.1626
45	.1464	.1657	.1475	.1687	.1485	.1718	.1495	.1748	.1506	.1778	.1516	.1808
46	.1527	.1838	.1537	.1867	.1548	.1897	.1558	.1926	.1569	.1956	.1579	.1985
47	.1590	.2014	.1601	.2043	.1611	.2072	.1622	.2101	.1633	.2129	.1644	.2158
48	.1654	.2186	.1665	.2215	.1676	.2243	.1687	.2271	.1698	.2299	.1709	.2327
49	.1720	.2355	.1731	.2382	.1742	.2410	.1753	.2437	.1764	.2465	.1775	.2492
50	.1786	.2519	.1797	.2546	.1808	.2573	.1820	.2600	.1831	.2627	.1842	.2653
51	.1853	.2680	.1865	.2706	.1876	.2732	.1887	.2759	.1899	.2785	.1910	.2811
52	.1922	.2837	.1933	.2863	.1945	.2888	.1956	.2914	.1968	.2940	.1979	.2965
53	.1991	.2991	.2003	.3016	.2014	.3041	.2026	.3066	.2038	.3091	.2049	.3116
54	2061	.3141	.2073	.3166	.2085	.3190	.2096	.3215	.2108	.3239	.2120	.3264
55	.2132	.3288	.2144	.3312	.2156	.3336	.2168	.3361	.2180	.3384	.2192	.3408
56	.2204	.3432	.2216	.3456	.2228	.3480	.2240	.3503	.2252	.3527	.2265	.3550
57	.2277	.3573	.2289	.3596	.2301	.3620	.2314	.3643	.2326	.3666	.2338	.3689
58	.2350	.3711	.2363	.3734	.2375	.3757	.2388	.3779	.2400	.3802	.2412	.3824
59	.2425	.3847	.2437	.3869	.2450	.3891	.2462	.3913	.2475	.3935	.2487	.3957

HAVERSINES (Continued)

Characteristics of the logarithms are omitted.

°	0′ Value	0′ Log	10′ Value	10′ Log	20′ Value	20′ Log	30′ Value	30′ Log	40′ Value	40′ Log	50′ Value	50′ Log
60	.2500	.3979	.2513	.4001	.2525	.4023	.2538	.4045	.2551	.4066	.2563	.4088
61	.2576	.4109	.2589	.4131	.2601	.4152	.2614	.4173	.2627	.4195	.2640	.4216
62	.2653	.4237	.2665	.4258	.2678	.4279	.2691	.4300	.2704	.4320	.2717	.4341
63	.2730	.4362	.2743	.4382	.2756	.4403	.2769	.4423	.2782	.4444	.2795	.4464
64	.2808	.4484	.2821	.4504	.2834	.4524	.2847	.4545	.2861	.4565	.2874	.4584
65	.2887	.4604	.2900	.4624	.2913	.4644	.2927	.4664	.2940	.4683	.2953	.4703
66	.2966	.4722	.2980	.4742	.2993	.4761	.3006	.4780	.3020	.4799	.3033	.4819
67	.3046	.4838	.3060	.4857	.3073	.4876	.3087	.4895	.3100	.4914	.3113	.4932
68	.3127	.4951	.3140	.4970	.3154	.4989	.3167	.5007	.3181	.5026	.3195	.5044
69	.3208	.5063	.3222	.5081	.3235	.5099	.3249	.5117	.3263	.5136	.3276	.5154
70	.3290	.5172	.3304	.5190	.3317	.5208	.3331	.5226	.3345	.5244	.3358	.5261
71	.3372	.5279	.3386	.5297	.3400	.5314	.3413	.5332	.3427	.5349	.3441	.5367
72	.3455	.5384	.3469	.5402	.3483	.5419	.3496	.5436	.3510	.5454	.3524	.5471
73	.3538	.5488	.3552	.5505	.3566	.5522	.3580	.5539	.3594	.5556	.3608	.5572
74	.3622	.5589	.3636	.5606	.3650	.5623	.3664	.5639	.3678	.5656	.3692	.5672
75	.3706	.5689	.3720	.5705	.3734	.5722	.3748	.5738	.3762	.5754	.3776	.5771
76	.3790	.5787	.3805	.5803	.3819	.5819	.3833	.5835	.3847	.5851	.3861	.5867
77	.3875	.5883	.3889	.5899	.3904	.5915	.3918	.5930	.3932	.5946	.3946	.5962
78	.3960	.5977	.3975	.5993	.3989	.6009	.4008	.6024	.4017	.6039	.4032	.6055
79	.4046	.6070	.4060	.6086	.4075	.6101	.4089	.6116	.4103	.6131	.4117	.6146
80	.4132	.6161	.4146	.6176	.4160	.6191	.4175	.6206	.4189	.6221	.4203	.6236
81	.4218	.6251	.4232	.6266	.4247	.6280	.4261	.6295	.4275	.6310	.4290	.6324
82	.4304	.6339	.4319	.6353	.4333	.6368	.4347	.6382	.4362	.6397	.4376	.6411
83	.4391	.6425	.4405	.6440	.4420	.6454	.4434	.6468	.4448	.6482	.4463	.6496
84	.4477	.6510	.4492	.6524	.4506	.6538	.4521	.6552	.4535	.6566	.4550	.6580
85	.4564	.6594	.4579	.6607	.4593	.6621	.4608	.6635	.4622	.6648	.4637	.6662
86	.4651	.6676	.4666	.6689	.4680	.6703	.4695	.6716	.4709	.6730	.4724	.6743
87	.4738	.6756	.4753	.6770	.4767	.6783	.4782	.6796	.4796	.6809	.4811	.6822
88	.4826	.6835	.4840	.6848	.4855	.6862	.4869	.6875	.4884	.6887	.4898	.6900
89	.4913	.6913	.4927	.6926	.4942	.6939	.4956	.6952	.4971	.6964	.4985	.6977
90	.5000	.6990	.5015	.7002	.5029	.7015	.5044	.7027	.5058	.7040	.5073	.7052
91	.5087	.7065	.5102	.7077	.5116	.7090	.5131	.7102	.5145	.7114	.5160	.7126
92	.5174	.7139	.5189	.7151	.5204	.7163	.5218	.7175	.5233	.7187	.5247	.7199
93	.5262	.7211	.5276	.7223	.5291	.7235	.5305	.7247	.5320	.7259	.5334	.7271
94	.5349	.7283	.5363	.7294	.5378	.7306	.5392	.7318	.5407	.7329	.5421	.7341
95	.5436	.7353	.5450	.7364	.5465	.7376	.5479	.7387	.5494	.7399	.5508	.7410
96	.5523	.7421	.5537	.7433	.5552	.7444	.5566	.7455	.5580	.7467	.5595	.7478
97	.5609	.7489	.5624	.7500	.5638	.7511	.5653	.7523	.5667	.7534	.5681	.7545
98	.5696	.7556	.5710	.7567	.5725	.7577	.5739	.7588	.5753	.7599	.5768	.7610
99	.5782	.7621	.5797	.7632	.5811	.7642	.5825	.7653	.5840	.7664	.5854	.7674
100	.5868	.7685	.5883	.7696	.5897	.7706	.5911	.7717	.5925	.7727	.5940	.7738
101	.5954	.7748	.5968	.7759	.5983	.7769	.5997	.7779	.6011	.7790	.6025	.7800
102	.6040	.7810	.6054	.7820	.6068	.7830	.6082	.7841	.6096	.7851	.6111	.7861
103	.6125	.7871	.6139	.7881	.6153	.7891	.6167	.7901	.6181	.7911	.6195	.7921
104	.6210	.7931	.6224	.7940	.6238	.7950	.6252	.7960	.6266	.7970	.6280	.7980
105	.6294	.7989	.6308	.7999	.6322	.8009	.6336	.8018	.6350	.8028	.6364	.8037
106	.6378	.8047	.6392	.8056	.6406	.8066	.6420	.8075	.6434	.8085	.6448	.8094
107	.6462	.8104	.6476	.8113	.6490	.8122	.6504	.8131	.6517	.8141	.6531	.8150
108	.6545	.8159	.6559	.8168	.6573	.8177	.6587	.8187	.6600	.8196	.6614	.8205
109	.6628	.8214	.6642	.8223	.6655	.8232	.6669	.8241	.6683	.8250	.6696	.8258
110	.6710	.8267	.6724	.8276	.6737	.8285	.6751	.8294	.6765	.8302	.6778	.8311
111	.6792	.8320	.6805	.8329	.6819	.8337	.6833	.8346	.6846	.8354	.6860	.8363
112	.6873	.8371	.6887	.8380	.6900	.8388	.6913	.8397	.6927	.8405	.6940	.8414
113	.6954	.8422	.6967	.8430	.6980	.8439	.6994	.8447	.7007	.8455	.7020	.8464
114	.7034	.8472	.7047	.8480	.7060	.8488	.7073	.8496	.7087	.8504	.7100	.8513
115	.7113	.8521	.7126	.8529	.7139	.8537	.7153	.8545	.7166	.8553	.7179	.8561
116	.7192	.8568	.7205	.8576	.7218	.8584	.7231	.8592	.7244	.8600	.7257	8608
117	.7270	.8615	.7283	.8623	.7296	.8631	.7309	.8638	.7322	.8646	.7335	.8654
118	.7347	.8661	.7360	.8669	.7373	.8676	.7386	.8684	.7399	.8691	.7411	.8699
119	.7424	.8706	.7437	.8714	.7449	.8721	.7462	.8729	.7475	.8736	.7487	.8743

HAVERSINES (Continued)

Characteristics of the logarithms are omitted.

°	0′ Value	0′ Log	10′ Value	10′ Log	20′ Value	20′ Log	30′ Value	30′ Log	40′ Value	40′ Log	50′ Value	50′ Log
120	.7500	.8751	.7513	.8758	.7525	.8765	.7538	.8772	.7550	.8780	.7563	.8787
121	.7575	.8794	.7588	.8801	.7600	.8808	.7612	.8815	.7625	.8822	.7637	.8829
122	.7650	.8836	.7662	.8843	.7674	.8850	.7686	.8857	.7699	.8864	.7711	.8871
123	.7723	.8878	.7735	.8885	.7748	.8892	.7760	.8898	.7772	.8905	.7784	.8912
124	.7796	.8919	.7808	.8925	.7820	.8932	.7832	.8939	.7844	.8945	.7856	.8952
125	.7868	.8959	.7880	.8965	.7892	.8972	.7904	.8978	.7915	.8985	.7927	.8991
126	.7939	.8998	.7951	.9004	.7962	.9010	.7974	.9017	.7986	.9023	.7997	.9030
127	.8009	.9036	.8021	.9042	.8032	.9048	.8044	.9055	.8055	.9061	.8067	.9067
128	.8078	.9073	.8090	.9079	.8101	.9085	.8113	.9092	.8124	.9098	.8135	.9104
129	.8147	.9110	.8158	.9116	.8169	.9122	.8180	.9128	.8192	.9134	.8203	.9140
130	.8214	.9146	.8225	.9151	.8236	.9157	.8247	.9163	.8258	.9169	.8269	.9175
131	.8280	.9180	.8291	.9186	.8302	.9192	.8313	.9198	.8324	.9203	.8335	.9209
132	.8346	.9215	.8356	.9220	.8367	.9226	.8378	.9231	.8389	.9237	.8399	.9242
133	.8410	.9248	.8421	.9253	.8431	.9259	.8442	.9264	.8452	.9270	.8463	.9275
134	.8473	.9281	.8484	.9286	.8494	.9291	.8505	.9297	.8515	.9302	.8525	.9307
135	.8536	.9312	.8546	.9318	.8556	.9323	.8566	.9328	.8576	.9333	.8587	.9338
136	.8597	.9343	.8607	.9348	.8617	.9353	.8627	.9359	.8637	.9364	.8647	.9369
137	.8657	.9374	.8667	.9379	.8677	.9383	.8686	.9388	.8696	.9393	.8706	.9398
138	.8716	.9403	.8725	.9408	.8735	.9413	.8745	.9417	.8754	.9422	.8764	.9427
139	.8774	.9432	.8783	.9436	.8793	.9441	.8802	.9446	.8811	.9450	.8821	.9455
140	.8830	.9460	.8840	.9464	.8849	.9469	.8858	.9473	.8867	.9478	.8877	.9482
141	.8886	.9487	.8895	.9491	.8904	.9496	.8913	.9500	.8922	.9505	.8931	.9509
142	.8940	.9513	.8949	.9518	.8958	.9522	.8967	.9526	.8976	.9531	.8984	.9535
143	.8993	.9539	.9002	.9543	.9011	.9548	.9019	.9552	.9028	.9556	.9037	.9560
144	.9045	.9564	.9054	.9568	.9062	.9572	.9071	.9576	.9079	.9580	.9087	.9584
145	.9096	.9588	.9104	.9592	.9112	.9596	.9121	.9600	.9129	.9604	.9137	.9608
146	.9145	.9612	.9153	.9616	.9161	.9620	.9169	.9623	.9177	.9627	.9185	.9631
147	.9193	.9635	.9201	.9638	.9209	.9642	.9217	.9646	.9225	.9650	.9233	.9653
148	.9240	.9657	.9248	.9660	.9256	.9664	.9263	.9668	.9271	.9671	.9278	.9675
149	.9286	.9678	.9293	.9682	.9301	.9685	.9308	.9689	.9316	.9692	.9323	.9695
150	.9330	.9699	.9337	.9702	.9345	.9706	.9352	.9709	.9359	.9712	.9366	.9716
151	.9373	.9719	.9380	.9722	.9387	.9725	.9394	.9729	.9401	.9732	.9408	.9735
152	.9415	.9738	.9422	.9741	.9428	.9744	.9435	.9747	.9442	.9751	.9448	.9754
153	.9455	.9757	.9462	.9760	.9468	.9763	.9475	.9766	.9481	.9769	.9488	.9772
154	.9494	.9774	.9500	.9777	.9507	.9780	.9513	.9783	.9519	.9786	.9525	.9789
155	.9532	.9792	.9538	.9794	.9544	.9797	.9550	.9800	.9556	.9803	.9562	.9805
156	.9568	.9808	.9574	.9811	.9579	.9813	.9585	.9816	.9591	.9819	.9597	.9821
157	.9603	.9824	.9608	.9826	.9614	.9829	.9619	.9831	.9625	.9834	.9630	.9836
158	.9636	.9839	.9641	.9841	.9647	.9844	.9652	.9846	.9657	.9849	.9663	.9851
159	.9668	.9853	.9673	.9856	.9678	.9858	.9683	.9860	.9688	.9863	.9693	.9865
160	.9698	.9867	.9703	.9869	.9708	.9871	.9713	.9874	.9718	.9876	.9723	.9878
161	.9728	.9880	.9732	.9882	.9737	.9884	.9742	.9886	.9746	.9888	.9751	.9890
162	.9755	.9892	.9760	.9894	.9764	.9896	.9769	.9898	.9773	.9900	.9777	.9902
163	.9782	.9904	.9786	.9906	.9790	.9908	.9794	.9910	.9798	.9911	.9802	.9913
164	.9806	.9915	.9810	.9917	.9814	.9919	.9818	.9920	.9822	.9922	.9826	.9924
165	.9830	.9925	.9833	.9927	.9837	.9929	.9841	.9930	.9844	.9932	.9848	.9933
166	.9851	.9935	.9855	.9937	.9858	.9938	.9862	.9940	.9865	.9941	.9869	.9943
167	.9872	.9944	.9875	.9945	.9878	.9947	.9881	.9948	.9885	.9950	.9888	.9951
168	.9891	.9952	.9894	.9954	.9897	.9955	.9900	.9956	.9903	.9957	.9905	.9959
169	.9908	.9960	.9911	.9961	.9914	.9962	.9916	.9963	.9919	.9965	.9921	.9966
170	.9924	.9967	.9927	.9968	.9929	.9969	.9931	.9970	.9934	.9971	.9936	.9972
171	.9938	.9973	.9941	.9974	.9943	.9975	.9945	.9976	.9947	.9977	.9949	.9978
172	.9951	.9979	.9953	.9980	.9955	.9981	.9957	.9981	.9959	.9982	.9961	.9983
173	.9963	.9984	.9964	.9985	.9966	.9985	.9968	.9986	.9969	.9987	.9971	.9987
174	.9973	.9988	.9974	.9989	.9976	.9989	.9977	.9990	.9978	.9991	.9980	.9991
175	.9981	.9992	.9982	.9992	.9983	.9993	.9985	.9993	.9986	.9994	.9987	.9994
176	.9988	.9995	.9989	.9995	.9990	.9996	.9991	.9996	.9992	.9996	.9992	.9997
177	.9993	.9997	.9994	.9997	.9995	.9998	.9995	.9998	.9996	.9998	.9996	.9998
178	.9997	.9999	.9997	.9999	.9998	.9999	.9998	.9999	.9999	.9999	.9999	.9999
179	.9999	.9999	.9999	.9999	1.0000	.0000	1.0000	.0000	1.0000	.0000	1.0000	.0000
180	1.0000	.0000										

SQUARE OF THE SINE AND COSINE AND THEIR PRODUCT

Compiled by Niel F. Beardsley

0° (180°) — (359°) **179°**

′	Sin^2	Sin · Cos	Cos^2	′
0	.00000	.00000	1.00000	**60**
1	.00000	.00029	1.00000	59
2	.00000	.00058	1.00000	58
3	.00000	.00087	1.00000	57
4	.00000	.00116	1.00000	56
5	.00000	.00145	1.00000	**55**
6	.00000	.00175	1.00000	54
7	.00000	.00204	1.00000	53
8	.00001	.00233	.99999	52
9	.00001	.00262	.99999	51
10	.00001	.00291	.99999	**50**
11	.00001	.00320	.99999	49
12	.00001	.00349	.99999	48
13	.00001	.00378	.99999	47
14	.00002	.00407	.99998	46
15	.00002	.00436	.99998	**45**
16	.00002	.00465	.99998	44
17	.00002	.00495	.99998	43
18	.00003	.00524	.99997	42
19	.00003	.00553	.99997	41
20	.00003	.00582	.99997	**40**
21	.00004	.00611	.99996	39
22	.00004	.00640	.99996	38
23	.00004	.00669	.99996	37
24	.00005	.00698	.99995	36
25	.00005	.00727	.99995	**35**
26	.00006	.00756	.99994	34
27	.00006	.00785	.99994	33
28	.00007	.00814	.99993	32
29	.00007	.00844	.99993	31
30	.00008	.00873	.99992	**30**
31	.00008	.00902	.99992	29
32	.00009	.00931	.99991	28
33	.00009	.00960	.99991	27
34	.00010	.00989	.99990	26
35	.00010	.01018	.99990	**25**
36	.00011	.01047	.99989	24
37	.00012	.01076	.99988	23
38	.00012	.01105	.99988	22
39	.00013	.01134	.99987	21
40	.00014	.01163	.99986	**20**
41	.00014	.01193	.99986	19
42	.00015	.01222	.99985	18
43	.00016	.01251	.99984	17
44	.00016	.01280	.99984	16
45	.00017	.01309	.99983	**15**
46	.00018	.01338	.99982	14
47	.00019	.01367	.99981	13
48	.00019	.01396	.99981	12
49	.00020	.01425	.99980	11
50	.00021	.01454	.99979	**10**
51	.00022	.01483	.99978	9
52	.00023	.01512	.99977	8
53	.00024	.01541	.99976	7
54	.00025	.01571	.99975	6
55	.00026	.01600	.99974	**5**
56	.00027	.01629	.99973	4
57	.00027	.01658	.99973	3
58	.00028	.01687	.99972	2
59	.00029	.01716	.99971	1
60	.00030	.01745	.99970	**0**
′	Cos^2	Sin · Cos	Sin^2	′

90° (270°) — (269°) **89°**

1° (181°) — (358°) **178°**

′	Sin^2	Sin · Cos	Cos^2	′
0	.00030	.01745	.99970	**60**
1	.00031	.01774	.99969	59
2	.00033	.01803	.99967	58
3	.00034	.01832	.99966	57
4	.00035	.01861	.99965	56
5	.00036	.01890	.99964	**55**
6	.00037	.01919	.99963	54
7	.00038	.01948	.99962	53
8	.00039	.01978	.99961	52
9	.00040	.02007	.99960	51
10	.00041	.02036	.99959	**50**
11	.00043	.02065	.99957	49
12	.00044	.02094	.99956	48
13	.00045	.02123	.99955	47
14	.00046	.02152	.99954	46
15	.00048	.02181	.99952	**45**
16	.00049	.02210	.99951	44
17	.00050	.02239	.99950	43
18	.00051	.02268	.99949	42
19	.00053	.02297	.99947	41
20	.00054	.02326	.99946	**40**
21	.00056	.02355	.99944	39
22	.00057	.02384	.99943	38
23	.00058	.02413	.99942	37
24	.00060	.02442	.99940	36
25	.00061	.02472	.99939	**35**
26	.00063	.02501	.99937	34
27	.00064	.02530	.99936	33
28	.00066	.02559	.99934	32
29	.00067	.02588	.99933	31
30	.00069	.02617	.99931	**30**
31	.00070	.02646	.99930	29
32	.00072	.02675	.99928	28
33	.00073	.02704	.99927	27
34	.00075	.02733	.99925	26
35	.00076	.02762	.99924	**25**
36	.00078	.02791	.99922	24
37	.00080	.02820	.99920	23
38	.00081	.02849	.99919	22
39	.00083	.02878	.99917	21
40	.00085	.02907	.99915	**20**
41	.00086	.02936	.99914	19
42	.00088	.02965	.99912	18
43	.00090	.02994	.99910	17
44	.00091	.03023	.99909	16
45	.00093	.03052	.99907	**15**
46	.00095	.03081	.99905	14
47	.00097	.03110	.99903	13
48	.00099	.03140	.99901	12
49	.00100	.03169	.99900	11
50	.00102	.03198	.99898	**10**
51	.00104	.03227	.99896	9
52	.00106	.03256	.99894	8
53	.00108	.03285	.99892	7
54	.00110	.03314	.99890	6
55	.00112	.03343	.99888	**5**
56	.00114	.03372	.99886	4
57	.00116	.03401	.99884	3
58	.00118	.03430	.99882	2
59	.00120	.03459	.99880	1
60	.00122	.03488	.99878	**0**
′	Cos^2	Sin · Cos	Sin^2	′

91° (271°) — (268°) **88°**

Sin² x Cos² x Sin x Cos x

2° (182°) (357°) **177°**

′	Sin²	Sin · Cos	Cos²	′
0	.00122	.03488	.99878	**60**
1	.00124	.03517	.99876	59
2	.00126	.03546	.99874	58
3	.00128	.03575	.99872	57
4	.00130	.03604	.99870	56
5	.00132	.03633	.99868	**55**
6	.00134	.03662	.99866	54
7	.00136	.03691	.99864	53
8	.00139	.03720	.99861	52
9	.00141	.03749	.99859	51
10	.00143	.03778	.99857	**50**
11	.00145	.03807	.99855	49
12	.00147	.03836	.99853	48
13	.00150	.03865	.99850	47
14	.00152	.03894	.99848	46
15	.00154	.03923	.99846	**45**
16	.00156	.03952	.99844	44
17	.00159	.03981	.99841	43
18	.00161	.04010	.99839	42
19	.00163	.04039	.99837	41
20	.00166	.04068	.99834	**40**
21	.00168	.04097	.99832	39
22	.00171	.04126	.99829	38
23	.00173	.04155	.99827	37
24	.00175	.04184	.99825	36
25	.00178	.04213	.99822	**35**
26	.00180	.04242	.99820	34
27	.00183	.04271	.99817	33
28	.00185	.04300	.99815	32
29	.00188	.04329	.99812	31
30	.00190	.04358	.99810	**30**
31	.00193	.04387	.99807	29
32	.00195	.04416	.99805	28
33	.00198	.04445	.99802	27
34	.00201	.04474	.99799	26
35	.00203	.04503	.99797	**25**
36	.00206	.04532	.99794	24
37	.00208	.04561	.99792	23
38	.00211	.04590	.99789	22
39	.00214	.04619	.99786	21
40	.00216	.04647	.99784	**20**
41	.00219	.04676	.99781	19
42	.00222	.04705	.99778	18
43	.00225	.04734	.99775	17
44	.00227	.04763	.99773	16
45	.00230	.04792	.99770	**15**
46	.00233	.04821	.99767	14
47	.00236	.04850	.99764	13
48	.00239	.04879	.99761	12
49	.00241	.04908	.99759	11
50	.00244	.04937	.99756	**10**
51	.00247	.04966	.99753	9
52	.00250	.04995	.99750	8
53	.00253	.05024	.99747	7
54	.00256	.05053	.99744	6
55	.00259	.05082	.99741	**5**
56	.00262	.05111	.99738	4
57	.00265	.05140	.99735	3
58	.00268	.05169	.99732	2
59	.00271	.05197	.99729	1
60	.00274	.05226	.99726	**0**
′	Cos²	Sin · Cos	Sin²	′

92° (272°) (267°) **87°**

3° (183°) (356°) **176°**

′	Sin²	Sin · Cos	Cos²	′
0	.00274	.05226	.99726	**60**
1	.00277	.05255	.99723	59
2	.00280	.05284	.99720	58
3	.00283	.05313	.99717	57
4	.00286	.05342	.99714	56
5	.00289	.05371	.99711	**55**
6	.00292	.05400	.99708	54
7	.00296	.05429	.99704	53
8	.00299	.05458	.99701	52
9	.00302	.05487	.99698	51
10	.00305	.05516	.99695	**50**
11	.00308	.05545	.99692	49
12	.00312	.05573	.99688	48
13	.00315	.05602	.99685	47
14	.00318	.05631	.99682	46
15	.00321	.05660	.99679	**45**
16	.00325	.05689	.99675	44
17	.00328	.05718	.99672	43
18	.00331	.05747	.99669	42
19	.00335	.05776	.99665	41
20	.00338	.05805	.99662	**40**
21	.00341	.05834	.99659	39
22	.00345	.05862	.99655	38
23	.00348	.05891	.99652	37
24	.00352	.05920	.99648	36
25	.00355	.05949	.99645	**35**
26	.00359	.05978	.99641	34
27	.00362	.06007	.99638	33
28	.00366	.06036	.99634	32
29	.00369	.06065	.99631	31
30	.00373	.06093	.99627	**30**
31	.00376	.06122	.99624	29
32	.00380	.06151	.99620	28
33	.00383	.06180	.99617	27
34	.00387	.06209	.99613	26
35	.00391	.06238	.99609	**25**
36	.00394	.06267	.99606	24
37	.00398	.06296	.99602	23
38	.00402	.06324	.99598	22
39	.00405	.06353	.99595	21
40	.00409	.06382	.99591	**20**
41	.00413	.06411	.99587	19
42	.00416	.06440	.99584	18
43	.00420	.06469	.99580	17
44	.00424	.06497	.99576	16
45	.00428	.06526	.99572	**15**
46	.00432	.06555	.99568	14
47	.00435	.06584	.99565	13
48	.00439	.06613	.99561	12
49	.00443	.06642	.99557	11
50	.00447	.06670	.99553	**10**
51	.00451	.06699	.99549	9
52	.00455	.06728	.99545	8
53	.00459	.06757	.99541	7
54	.00463	.06786	.99537	6
55	.00467	.06815	.99533	**5**
56	.00471	.06843	.99529	4
57	.00475	.06872	.99525	3
58	.00479	.06901	.99521	2
59	.00483	.06930	.99517	1
60	.00487	.06959	.99513	**0**
′	Cos²	Sin · Cos	Sin²	′

93° (273°) (266°) **86°**

$\text{Sin}^2 x$ $\text{Cos}^2 x$ Sin x Cos x

4° (184°) (355°) **175°**

′	Sin²	Sin · Cos	Cos²	′
0	.00487	.06959	.99513	**60**
1	.00491	.06987	.99509	59
2	.00495	.07016	.99505	58
3	.00499	.07045	.99501	57
4	.00503	.07074	.99497	56
5	.00507	.07103	.99493	**55**
6	.00511	.07131	.99489	54
7	.00515	.07160	.99485	53
8	.00520	.07189	.99480	52
9	.00524	.07218	.99476	51
10	.00528	.07247	.99472	**50**
11	.00532	.07275	.99468	49
12	.00536	.07304	.99464	48
13	.00541	.07333	.99459	47
14	.00545	.07362	.99455	46
15	.00549	.07390	.99451	**45**
16	.00554	.07419	.99446	44
17	.00558	.07448	.99442	43
18	.00562	.07477	.99438	42
19	.00567	.07506	.99433	41
20	.00571	.07534	.99429	**40**
21	.00575	.07563	.99425	39
22	.00580	.07592	.99420	38
23	.00584	.07621	.99416	37
24	.00589	.07649	.99411	36
25	.00593	.07678	.99407	**35**
26	.00598	.07707	.99402	34
27	.00602	.07736	.99398	33
28	.00607	.07764	.99393	32
29	.00611	.07793	.99389	31
30	.00616	.07822	.99384	**30**
31	.00620	.07850	.99380	29
32	.00625	.07879	.99375	28
33	.00629	.07908	.99371	27
34	.00634	.07937	99366	26
35	.00639	.07965	.99361	**25**
36	.00643	.07994	.99357	24
37	.00648	.08023	.99352	23
38	.00653	.08051	.99347	22
39	.00657	.08080	.99343	21
40	.00662	.08109	.99338	**20**
41	.00667	.08138	.99333	19
42	.00671	.08166	.99329	18
43	.00676	.08195	.99324	17
44	.00681	.08224	.99319	16
45	.00686	.08252	.99314	**15**
46	.00691	.08281	.99309	14
47	.00695	.08310	.99305	13
48	.00700	.08338	.99300	12
49	.00705	.08367	.99295	11
50	.00710	.08396	.99290	**10**
51	.00715	.08424	.99285	9
52	.00720	.08453	.99280	8
53	.00725	.08482	.99275	7
54	.00730	.08510	.99270	6
55	.00735	.08539	.99265	**5**
56	.00740	.08568	.99260	4
57	.00745	.08596	.99255	3
58	.00750	.08625	.99250	2
59	.00755	.08654	.99245	1
60	.00760	.08682	.99240	**0**
′	Cos²	Sin · Cos	Sin²	′

94° (274°) (265°) **85°**

5° (185°) (354°) **(174°)**

′	Sin²	Sin · Cos	Cos²	′
0	.00760	.08682	.99240	**60**
1	.00765	.08711	.99235	59
2	.00770	.08740	.99230	58
3	.00775	.08768	.99225	57
4	.00780	.08797	.99220	56
5	.00785	.08826	.99215	**55**
6	.00790	.08854	.99210	54
7	.00795	.08883	.99205	53
8	.00801	.08911	.99199	52
9	.00806	.08940	.99194	51
10	.00811	.08969	.99189	**50**
11	.00816	.08997	.99184	49
12	.00821	.09026	.99179	48
13	.00827	.09055	.99173	47
14	.00832	.09083	.99168	46
15	.00837	.09112	.99163	**45**
16	.00843	.09140	.99157	44
17	.00848	.09169	.99152	43
18	.00853	.09198	.99147	42
19	.00859	.09226	.99141	41
20	.00864	.09255	.99136	**40**
21	.00869	.09283	.99131	39
22	.00875	.09312	.99125	38
23	.00880	.09340	.99120	37
24	.00886	.09369	.99114	36
25	.00891	.09398	.99109	**35**
26	.00897	.09426	.99103	34
27	.00902	.09455	.99098	33
28	.00908	.09483	.99092	32
29	.00913	.09512	.99087	31
30	.00919	.09540	.99081	**30**
31	.00924	.09569	.99076	29
32	.00930	.09598	.99070	28
33	.00935	.09626	.99065	27
34	.00941	.09655	.99059	26
35	.00947	.09683	.99053	**25**
36	.00952	.09712	.99048	24
37	.00958	.09740	.99042	23
38	.00964	.09769	.99036	22
39	.00969	.09797	.99031	21
40	.00975	.09826	.99025	**20**
41	.00981	.09854	.99019	19
42	.00986	.09883	.99014	18
43	.00992	.09911	.99008	17
44	.00998	.09940	.99002	16
45	.01004	.09968	.98996	**15**
46	.01010	.09997	.98990	14
47	.01015	.10025	.98985	13
48	.01021	.10054	.98979	12
49	.01027	.10082	.98973	11
50	.01033	.10111	.98967	**10**
51	.01039	.10139	.98961	9
52	.01045	.10168	.98955	8
53	.01051	.10196	.98949	7
54	.01057	.10225	.98943	6
55	.01063	.10253	.98937	**5**
56	.01069	.10282	.98931	4
57	.01075	.10310	.98925	3
58	.01081	.10339	.98919	2
59	.01087	.10367	.98913	1
60	.01093	.10396	.98907	**0**
′	Cos²	Sin · Cos	Sin²	′

95° (275°) (264°) **84°**

$Sin^2 x$ $Cos^2 x$ Sin x Cos x

6° (186°) (353°) **173°**

′	Sin²	Sin · Cos	Cos²	′
0	.01093	.10396	.98907	**60**
1	.01099	.10424	.98901	59
2	.01105	.10452	.98895	58
3	.01111	.10481	.98889	57
4	.01117	.10509	.98883	56
5	.01123	.10538	.98877	**55**
6	.01129	.10566	.98871	54
7	.01135	.10595	.98865	53
8	.01142	.10623	.98858	52
9	.01148	.10652	.98852	51
10	.01154	.10680	.98846	**50**
11	.01160	.10708	.98840	49
12	.01166	.10737	.98834	48
13	.01173	.10765	.98827	47
14	.01179	.10794	.98821	46
15	.01185	.10822	.98815	**45**
16	.01192	.10850	.98808	44
17	.01198	.10879	.98802	43
18	.01204	.10907	.98796	42
19	.01211	.10936	.98789	41
20	.01217	.10964	.98783	**40**
21	.01223	.10992	.98777	39
22	.01230	.11021	.98770	38
23	.01236	.11049	.98764	37
24	.01243	.11077	.98757	36
25	.01249	.11106	.98751	**35**
26	.01255	.11134	.98745	34
27	.01262	.11163	.98738	33
28	.01268	.11191	.98732	32
29	.01275	.11219	.98725	31
30	.01281	.11248	.98719	**30**
31	.01288	.11276	.98712	29
32	.01295	.11304	.98705	28
33	.01301	.11333	.98699	27
34	.01308	.11361	.98692	26
35	.01314	.11389	.98686	**25**
36	.01321	.11418	.98679	24
37	.01328	.11446	.98672	23
38	.01334	.11474	.98666	22
39	.01341	.11502	.98659	21
40	.01348	.11531	.98652	**20**
41	.01354	.11559	.98646	19
42	.01361	.11587	.98639	18
43	.01368	.11616	.98632	17
44	.01375	.11644	.98625	16
45	.01382	.11672	.98618	**15**
46	.01388	.11701	.98612	14
47	.01395	.11729	.98605	13
48	.01402	.11757	.98598	12
49	.01409	.11785	.98591	11
50	.01416	.11814	.98584	**10**
51	.01423	.11842	.98577	9
52	.01429	.11870	.98571	8
53	.01436	.11898	.98564	7
54	.01443	.11927	.98557	6
55	.01450	.11955	.98550	**5**
56	.01457	.11983	.98543	4
57	.01464	.12011	.98536	3
58	.01471	.12040	.98529	2
59	.01478	.12068	.98522	1
60	.01485	.12096	.98515	**0**
′	Cos²	Sin · Cos	Sin²	′

96° (276°) (263°) **83°**

7° (187°) (352°) **172°**

′	Sin²	Sin · Cos	Cos²	′
0	.01485	.12096	.98515	**60**
1	.01492	.12124	.98508	59
2	.01499	.12153	.98501	58
3	.01506	.12181	.98494	57
4	.01513	.12209	.98487	56
5	.01521	.12237	.98479	**55**
6	.01528	.12265	.98472	54
7	.01535	.12294	.98465	53
8	.01542	.12322	.98458	52
9	.01549	.12350	.98451	51
10	.01556	.12378	.98444	**50**
11	.01564	.12406	.98436	49
12	.01571	.12434	.98429	48
13	.01578	.12463	.98422	47
14	.01585	.12491	.98415	46
15	.01593	.12519	.98407	**45**
16	.01600	.12547	.98400	44
17	.01607	.12575	.98393	43
18	.01615	.12603	.98385	42
19	.01622	.12632	.98378	41
20	.01629	.12660	.98371	**40**
21	.01637	.12688	.98363	39
22	.01644	.12716	.98356	38
23	.01651	.12744	.98349	37
24	.01659	.12772	.98341	36
25	.01666	.12800	.98334	**35**
26	.01674	.12829	.98326	34
27	.01681	.12857	.98319	33
28	.01689	.12885	.98311	32
29	.01696	.12913	.98304	31
30	.01704	.12941	.98296	**30**
31	.01711	.12969	.98289	29
32	.01719	.12997	.98281	28
33	.01726	.13025	.98274	27
34	.01734	.13053	.98266	26
35	.01742	.13081	.98258	**25**
36	.01749	.13109	.98251	24
37	.01757	.13138	.98243	23
38	.01764	.13166	.98236	22
39	.01772	.13194	.98228	21
40	.01780	.13222	.98220	**20**
41	.01788	.13250	.98212	19
42	.01795	.13278	.98205	18
43	.01803	.13306	.98197	17
44	.01811	.13334	.98189	16
45	.01818	.13362	.98182	**15**
46	.01826	.13390	.98174	14
47	.01834	.13418	.98166	13
48	.01842	.13446	.98158	12
49	.01850	.13474	.98150	11
50	.01858	.13502	.98142	**10**
51	.01865	.13530	.98135	9
52	.01873	.13558	.98127	8
53	.01881	.13586	.98119	7
54	.01889	.13614	.98111	6
55	.01897	.13642	.98103	**5**
56	.01905	.13670	.98095	4
57	.01913	.13698	.98087	3
58	.01921	.13726	.98079	2
59	.01929	.13754	.98071	1
60	.01937	.13782	.98063	**0**
′	Cos²	Sin · Cos	Sin²	′

97° (277°) (262°) **82°**

8° (188°) (351°) **171°**

′	Sin²	Sin · Cos	Cos²	′
0	.01937	.13782	.98063	**60**
1	.01945	.13810	.98055	59
2	.01953	.13838	.98047	58
3	.01961	.13866	.98039	57
4	.01969	.13894	.98031	56
5	.01977	.13922	.98023	**55**
6	.01985	.13950	.98015	54
7	.01993	.13977	.98007	53
8	.02002	.14005	.97998	52
9	.02010	.14033	.97990	51
10	.02018	.14061	.97982	**50**
11	.02026	.14089	.97974	49
12	.02034	.14117	.97966	48
13	.02043	.14145	.97957	47
14	.02051	.14173	.97949	46
15	.02059	.14201	.97941	**45**
16	.02067	.14229	.97933	44
17	.02076	.14257	.97924	43
18	.02084	.14284	.97916	42
19	.02092	.14312	.97908	41
20	.02101	.14340	.97899	**40**
21	.02109	.14368	.97891	39
22	.02117	.14396	.97883	38
23	.02126	.14424	.97874	37
24	.02134	.14452	.97866	36
25	.02142	.14479	.97858	**35**
26	.02151	.14507	.97849	34
27	.02159	.14535	.97841	33
28	.02168	.14563	.97832	32
29	.02176	.14591	.97824	31
30	.02185	.14619	.97815	**30**
31	.02193	.14646	.97807	29
32	.02202	.14674	.97798	28
33	.02210	.14702	.97790	27
34	.02219	.14730	.97781	26
35	.02227	.14758	.97773	**25**
36	.02236	.14785	.97764	24
37	.02245	.14813	.97755	23
38	.02253	.14841	.97747	22
39	.02262	.14869	.97738	21
40	.02271	.14897	.97729	**20**
41	.02279	.14924	.97721	19
42	.02288	.14952	.97712	18
43	.02297	.14980	.97703	17
44	.02305	.15008	.97695	16
45	.02314	.15035	.97686	**15**
46	.02323	.15063	.97677	14
47	.02332	.15091	.97668	13
48	.02340	.15118	.97660	12
49	.02349	.15146	.97651	11
50	.02358	.15174	.97642	**10**
51	.02367	.15202	.97633	9
52	.02376	.15229	.97624	8
53	.02385	.15257	.97615	7
54	.02394	.15285	.97606	6
55	.02402	.15312	.97598	**5**
56	.02411	.15340	.97589	4
57	.02420	.15368	.97580	3
58	.02429	.15396	.97571	2
59	.02438	.15423	.97562	1
60	.02447	.15451	.97553	**0**
′	Cos²	Sin · Cos	Sin²	′

98° (278°) (261°) **81°**

9° (189°) (350°) **170°**

′	Sin²	Sin · Cos	Cos²	′
0	.02447	.15451	.97553	**60**
1	.02456	.15479	.97544	59
2	.02465	.15506	.97535	58
3	.02474	.15534	.97526	57
4	.02483	.15561	.97517	56
5	.02492	.15589	.97508	**55**
6	.02501	.15617	.97499	54
7	.02510	.15644	.97490	53
8	.02520	.15672	.97480	52
9	.02529	.15700	.97471	51
10	.02538	.15727	.97462	**50**
11	.02547	.15755	.97453	49
12	.02556	.15782	.97444	48
13	.02565	.15810	.97435	47
14	.02575	.15838	.97425	46
15	.02584	.15865	.97416	**45**
16	.02593	.15893	.97407	44
17	.02602	.15920	.97398	43
18	.02612	.15948	.97388	42
19	.02621	.15976	.97379	41
20	.02630	.16003	.97370	**40**
21	.02639	.16031	.97361	39
22	.02649	.16058	.97351	38
23	.02658	.16086	.97342	37
24	.02668	.16113	.97332	36
25	.02677	.16141	.97323	**35**
26	.02686	.16168	.97314	34
27	.02696	.16196	.97304	33
28	.02705	.16223	.97295	32
29	.02715	.16251	.97285	31
30	.02724	.16278	.97276	**30**
31	.02734	.16306	.97266	29
32	.02743	.16333	.97257	28
33	.02753	.16361	.97247	27
34	.02762	.16388	.97238	26
35	.02772	.16416	.97228	**25**
36	.02781	.16443	.97219	24
37	.02791	.16471	.97209	23
38	.02800	.16498	.97200	22
39	.02810	.16526	.97190	21
40	.02820	.16553	.97180	**20**
41	.02829	.16581	.97171	19
42	.02839	.16608	.97161	18
43	.02849	.16635	.97151	17
44	.02858	.16663	.97142	16
45	.02868	.16690	.97132	**15**
46	.02878	.16718	.97122	14
47	.02887	.16745	.97113	13
48	.02897	.16773	.97103	12
49	.02907	.16800	.97093	11
50	.02917	.16827	.97083	**10**
51	.02926	.16855	.97074	9
52	.02936	.16882	.97064	8
53	.02946	.16910	.97054	7
54	.02956	.16937	.97044	6
55	.02966	.16964	.97034	**5**
56	.02976	.16992	.97024	4
57	.02986	.17019	.97014	3
58	.02996	.17046	.97004	2
59	.03005	.17074	.96995	1
60	.03015	.17101	.96985	**0**
′	Cos²	Sin · Cos	Sin²	′

99° (279°) (260°) **80°**

$Sin^2 x$ $Cos^2 x$ Sin x Cos x

10° (190°) (349°) **169°**

′	Sin²	Sin · Cos	Cos²	′
0	.03015	.17101	.96985	**60**
1	.03025	.17128	.96975	59
2	.03035	.17156	.96965	58
3	.03045	.17183	.96955	57
4	.03055	.17210	.96945	56
5	.03065	.17238	.96935	**55**
6	.03075	.17265	.96925	54
7	.03085	.17292	.96915	53
8	.03095	.17319	.96905	52
9	.03106	.17347	.96894	51
10	.03116	.17374	.96884	**50**
11	.03126	.17401	.96874	49
12	.03136	.17429	.96864	48
13	.03146	.17456	.96854	47
14	.03156	.17483	.96844	46
15	.03166	.17510	.96834	**45**
16	.03177	.17538	.96823	44
17	.03187	.17565	.96813	43
18	.03197	.17592	.96803	42
19	.03207	.17619	.96793	41
20	.03218	.17647	.96782	**40**
21	.03228	.17674	.96772	39
22	.03238	.17701	.96762	38
23	.03248	.17728	.96752	37
24	.03259	.17755	.96741	36
25	.03269	.17783	.96731	**35**
26	.03279	.17810	.96721	34
27	.03290	.17837	.96710	33
28	.03300	.17864	.96700	32
29	.03311	.17891	.96689	31
30	.03321	.17918	.96679	**30**
31	.03331	.17946	.96669	29
32	.03342	.17973	.96658	28
33	.03352	.18000	.96648	27
34	.03363	.18027	.96637	26
35	.03373	.18054	.96627	**25**
36	.03384	.18081	.96616	24
37	.03394	.18108	.96606	23
38	.03405	.18135	.96595	22
39	.03415	.18163	.96585	21
40	.03426	.18190	.96574	**20**
41	.03437	.18217	.96563	19
42	.03447	.18244	.96553	18
43	.03458	.18271	.96542	17
44	.03468	.18298	.96532	16
45	.03479	.18325	.96521	**15**
46	.03490	.18352	.96510	14
47	.03500	.18379	.96500	13
48	.03511	.18406	.96489	12
49	.03522	.18433	.96478	11
50	.03533	.18460	.96467	**10**
51	.03543	.18487	.96457	9
52	.03554	.18514	.96446	8
53	.03565	.18541	.96435	7
54	.03576	.18568	.96424	6
55	.03587	.18595	.96413	**5**
56	.03597	.18622	.96403	4
57	.03608	.18649	.96392	3
58	.03619	.18676	.96381	2
59	.03630	.18703	.96370	1
60	.03641	.18730	.96359	**0**
′	Cos²	Sin · Cos	Sin²	′

100° (280°) (259°) **79°**

11° (191°) (348°) **168°**

′	Sin²	Sin · Cos	Cos²	′
0	.03641	.18730	.96359	**60**
1	.03652	.18757	.96348	59
2	.03663	.18784	.96337	58
3	.03674	.18811	.96326	57
4	.03685	.18838	.96315	56
5	.03695	.18865	.96305	**55**
6	.03706	.18892	.96294	54
7	.03717	.18919	.96283	53
8	.03728	.18946	.96272	52
9	.03740	.18973	.96260	51
10	.03751	.19000	.96249	**50**
11	.03762	.19027	.96238	49
12	.03773	.19054	.96227	48
13	.03784	.19080	.96216	47
14	.03795	.19107	.96205	46
15	.03806	.19134	.96194	**45**
16	.03817	.19161	.96183	44
17	.03828	.19188	.96172	43
18	.03839	.19215	.96161	42
19	.03851	.19242	.96149	41
20	.03862	.19268	.96138	**40**
21	.03873	.19295	.96127	39
22	.03884	.19322	.96116	38
23	.03896	.19349	.96104	37
24	.03907	.19376	.96093	36
25	.03918	.19403	.96082	**35**
26	.03929	.19429	.96071	34
27	.03941	.19456	.96059	33
28	.03952	.19483	.96048	32
29	.03963	.19510	.96037	31
30	.03975	.19537	.96025	**30**
31	.03986	.19563	.96014	29
32	.03998	.19590	.96002	28
33	.04009	.19617	.95991	27
34	.04020	.19644	.95980	26
35	.04032	.19670	.95968	**25**
36	.04043	.19697	.95957	24
37	.04055	.19724	.95945	23
38	.04066	.19751	.95934	22
39	.04078	.19777	.95922	21
40	.04089	.19804	.95911	**20**
41	.04101	.19831	.95899	19
42	.04112	.19857	.95888	18
43	.04124	.19884	.95876	17
44	.04135	.19911	.95865	16
45	.04147	.19937	.95853	**15**
46	.04159	.19964	.95841	14
47	.04170	.19991	.95830	13
48	.04182	.20017	.95818	12
49	.04194	.20044	.95806	11
50	.04205	.20071	.95795	**10**
51	.04217	.20097	.95783	9
52	.04229	.20124	.95771	8
53	.04240	.20151	.95760	7
54	.04252	.20177	.95748	6
55	.04264	.20204	.95736	**5**
56	.04276	.20230	.95724	4
57	.04287	.20257	.95713	3
58	.04299	.20284	.95701	2
59	.04311	.20310	.95689	1
60	.04323	.20337	.95677	**0**
′	Cos²	Sin · Cos	Sin²	′

101° (281°) (258°) **78°**

12° (192°) (347°) **167°**

′	Sin²	Sin · Cos	Cos²	′
0	.04323	.20337	.95677	**60**
1	.04335	.20363	.95665	59
2	.04346	.20390	.95654	58
3	.04358	.20417	.95642	57
4	.04370	.20443	.95630	56
5	.04382	.20470	.95618	**55**
6	.04394	.20496	.95606	54
7	.04406	.20523	.95594	53
8	.04418	.20549	.95582	52
9	.04430	.20576	.95570	51
10	.04442	.20602	.95558	**50**
11	.04454	.20629	.95546	49
12	.04466	.20655	.95534	48
13	.04478	.20682	.95522	47
14	.04490	.20708	.95510	46
15	.04502	.20735	.95498	**45**
16	.04514	.20761	.95486	44
17	.04526	.20788	.95474	43
18	.04538	.20814	.95462	42
19	.04550	.20840	.95450	41
20	.04562	.20867	.95438	**40**
21	.04575	.20893	.95425	39
22	.04587	.20920	.95413	38
23	.04599	.20946	.95401	37
24	.04611	.20973	.95389	36
25	.04623	.20999	.95377	**35**
26	.04636	.21025	.95364	34
27	.04648	.21052	.95352	33
28	.04660	.21078	.95340	32
29	.04672	.21105	.95328	31
30	.04685	.21131	.95315	**30**
31	.04697	.21157	.95303	29
32	.04709	.21184	.95291	28
33	.04722	.21210	.95278	27
34	.04734	.21236	.95266	26
35	.04746	.21263	.95254	**25**
36	.04759	.21289	.95241	24
37	.04771	.21315	.95229	23
38	.04783	.21342	.95217	22
39	.04796	.21368	.95204	21
40	.04808	.21394	.95192	**20**
41	.04821	.21420	.95179	19
42	.04833	.21447	.95167	18
43	.04846	.21473	.95154	17
44	.04858	.21499	.95142	16
45	.04871	.21526	.95129	**15**
46	.04883	.21552	.95117	14
47	.04896	.21578	.95104	13
48	.04908	.21604	.95092	12
49	.04921	.21631	.95079	11
50	.04934	.21657	.95066	**10**
51	.04946	.21683	.95054	9
52	.04959	.21709	.95041	8
53	.04971	.21735	.95029	7
54	.04984	.21762	.95016	6
55	.04997	.21788	.95003	**5**
56	.05009	.21814	.94991	4
57	.05022	.21840	.94978	3
58	.05035	.21866	.94965	2
59	.05048	.21892	.94952	1
60	.05060	.21919	.94940	**0**
′	Cos²	Sin · Cos	Sin²	′

102° (282°) (257°) **77°**

13° (193°) (346°) **166°**

′	Sin²	Sin · Cos	Cos²	′
0	.05060	.21919	.94940	**60**
1	.05073	.21945	.94927	59
2	.05086	.21971	.94914	58
3	.05099	.21997	.94901	57
4	.05111	.22023	.94889	56
5	.05124	.22049	.94876	**55**
6	.05137	.22075	.94863	54
7	.05150	.22101	.94850	53
8	.05163	.22127	.94837	52
9	.05176	.22154	.94824	51
10	.05189	.22180	.94811	**50**
11	.05201	.22206	.94799	49
12	.05214	.22232	.94786	48
13	.05227	.22258	.94773	47
14	.05240	.22284	.94760	46
15	.05253	.22310	.94747	**45**
16	.05266	.22336	.94734	44
17	.05279	.22362	.94721	43
18	.05292	.22388	.94708	42
19	.05305	.22414	.94695	41
20	.05318	.22440	.94682	**40**
21	.05331	.22466	.94669	39
22	.05345	.22492	.94655	38
23	.05358	.22518	.94642	37
24	.05371	.22544	.94629	36
25	.05384	.22570	.94616	**35**
26	.05397	.22596	.94603	34
27	.05410	.22622	.94590	33
28	.05423	.22648	.94577	32
29	.05436	.22674	.94564	31
30	.05450	.22700	.94550	**30**
31	.05463	.22725	.94537	29
32	.05476	.22751	.94524	28
33	.05489	.22777	.94511	27
34	.05503	.22803	.94497	26
35	.05516	.22829	.94484	**25**
36	.05529	.22855	.94471	24
37	.05542	.22881	.94458	23
38	.05556	.22907	.94444	22
39	.05569	.22932	.94431	21
40	.05582	.22958	.94418	**20**
41	.05596	.22984	.94404	19
42	.05609	.23010	.94391	18
43	.05623	.23036	.94377	17
44	.05636	.23062	.94364	16
45	.05649	.23087	.94351	**15**
46	.05663	.23113	.94337	14
47	.05676	.23139	.94324	13
48	.05690	.23165	.94310	12
49	.05703	.23191	.94297	11
50	.05717	.23216	.94283	**10**
51	.05730	.23242	.94270	9
52	.05744	.23268	.94256	8
53	.05757	.23294	.94243	7
54	.05771	.23319	.94229	6
55	.05785	.23345	.94215	**5**
56	.05798	.23371	.94202	4
57	.05812	.23396	.94188	3
58	.05825	.23422	.94175	2
59	.05839	.23448	.94161	1
60	.05853	.23474	.94147	**0**
′	Cos²	Sin · Cos	Sin²	′

103° (283°) (256°) **76°**

$\sin^2 x$ $\cos^2 x$ $\sin x \cos x$

14° (194°) — (345°) **165°**

′	Sin²	Sin · Cos	Cos²	′
0	.05853	.23474	.94147	**60**
1	.05866	.23499	.94134	59
2	.05880	.23525	.94120	58
3	.05894	.23551	.94106	57
4	.05907	.23576	.94093	56
5	.05921	.23602	.94079	**55**
6	.05935	.23628	.94065	54
7	.05949	.23653	.94051	53
8	.05962	.23679	.94038	52
9	.05976	.23704	.94024	51
10	.05990	.23730	.94010	**50**
11	.06004	.23756	.93996	49
12	.06018	.23781	.93982	48
13	.06031	.23807	.93969	47
14	.06045	.23832	.93955	46
15	.06059	.23858	.93941	**45**
16	.06073	.23883	.93927	44
17	.06087	.23909	.93913	43
18	.06101	.23935	.93899	42
19	.06115	.23960	.93885	41
20	.06129	.23986	.93871	**40**
21	.06143	.24011	.93857	39
22	.06157	.24037	.93843	38
23	.06171	.24062	.93829	37
24	.06185	.24088	.93815	36
25	.06199	.24113	.93801	**35**
26	.06213	.24139	.93787	34
27	.06227	.24164	.93773	33
28	.06241	.24190	.93759	32
29	.06255	.24215	.93745	31
30	.06269	.24240	.93731	**30**
31	.06283	.24266	.93717	29
32	.06297	.24291	.93703	28
33	.06311	.24317	.93689	27
34	.06326	.24342	.93674	26
35	.06340	.24368	.93660	**25**
36	.06354	.24393	.93646	24
37	.06368	.24418	.93632	23
38	.06382	.24444	.93618	22
39	.06397	.24469	.93603	21
40	.06411	.24494	.93589	**20**
41	.06425	.24520	.93575	19
42	.06439	.24545	.93561	18
43	.06454	.24571	.93546	17
44	.06468	.24596	.93532	16
45	.06482	.24621	.93518	**15**
46	.06497	.24646	.93503	14
47	.06511	.24672	.93489	13
48	.06525	.24697	.93475	12
49	.06540	.24722	.93460	11
50	.06554	.24748	.93446	**10**
51	.06568	.24773	.93432	9
52	.06583	.24798	.93417	8
53	.06597	.24823	.93403	7
54	.06612	.24849	.93388	6
55	.06626	.24874	.93374	**5**
56	.06641	.24899	.93359	4
57	.06655	.24924	.93345	3
58	.06670	.24950	.93330	2
59	.06684	.24975	.93316	1
60	.06699	.25000	.93301	**0**
′	Cos²	Sin · Cos	Sin²	′

104° (284°) — (255°) **75°**

15° (195°) — (344°) **164°**

′	Sin²	Sin · Cos	Cos²	′
0	.06699	.25000	.93301	**60**
1	.06713	.25025	.93287	59
2	.06728	.25050	.93272	58
3	.06742	.25076	.93258	57
4	.06757	.25101	.93243	56
5	.06772	.25126	.93228	**55**
6	.06786	.25151	.93214	54
7	.06801	.25176	.93199	53
8	.06816	.25201	.93184	52
9	.06830	.25226	.93170	51
10	.06845	.25251	.93155	**50**
11	.06860	.25277	.93140	49
12	.06874	.25302	.93126	48
13	.06889	.25327	.93111	47
14	.06904	.25352	.93096	46
15	.06919	.25377	.93081	**45**
16	.06933	.25402	.93067	44
17	.06948	.25427	.93052	43
18	.06963	.25452	.93037	42
19	.06978	.25477	.93022	41
20	.06993	.25502	.93007	**40**
21	.07007	.25527	.92993	39
22	.07022	.25552	.92978	38
23	.07037	.25577	.92963	37
24	.07052	.25602	.92948	36
25	.07067	.25627	.92933	**35**
26	.07082	.25652	.92918	34
27	.07097	.25677	.92903	33
28	.07112	.25702	.92888	32
29	.07127	.25727	.92873	31
30	.07142	.25752	.92858	**30**
31	.07157	.25777	.92843	29
32	.07172	.25802	.92828	28
33	.07187	.25827	.92813	27
34	.07202	.25852	.92798	26
35	.07217	.25876	.92783	**25**
36	.07232	.25901	.92768	24
37	.07247	.25926	.92753	23
38	.07262	.25951	.92738	22
39	.07277	.25976	.92723	21
40	.07292	.26001	.92708	**20**
41	.07307	.26026	.92693	19
42	.07322	.26050	.92678	18
43	.07338	.26075	.92662	17
44	.07353	.26100	.92647	16
45	.07368	.26125	.92632	**15**
46	.07383	.26150	.92617	14
47	.07398	.26175	.92602	13
48	.07414	.26199	.92586	12
49	.07429	.26224	.92571	11
50	.07444	.26249	.92556	**10**
51	.07459	.26274	.92541	9
52	.07475	.26298	.92525	8
53	.07490	.26323	.92510	7
54	.07505	.26348	.92495	6
55	.07521	.26373	.92479	**5**
56	.07536	.26397	.92464	4
57	.07551	.26422	.92449	3
58	.07567	.26447	.92433	2
59	.07582	.26471	.92418	1
60	.07598	.26496	.92402	**0**
′	Cos²	Sin · Cos	Sin²	′

105° (285°) — (254°) **74°**

Sin² x Cos² x Sin x Cos x

16° (196°) (343°) **163°**

′	Sin²	Sin · Cos	Cos²	′
0	.07598	.26494	.92402	**60**
1	.07613	.26521	.92387	59
2	.07628	.26545	.92372	58
3	.07644	.26570	.92356	57
4	.07659	.26595	.92341	56
5	.07675	.26619	.92325	**55**
6	.07690	.26644	.92310	54
7	.07706	.26668	.92294	53
8	.07721	.26693	.92279	52
9	.07737	.26718	.92263	51
10	.07752	.26742	.92248	**50**
11	.07768	.26767	.92232	49
12	.07784	.26791	.92216	48
13	.07799	.26816	.92201	47
14	.07815	.26840	.92185	46
15	.07830	.26865	.92170	**45**
16	.07846	.26890	.92154	44
17	.07862	.26914	.92138	43
18	.07877	.26939	.92123	42
19	.07893	.26963	.92107	41
20	.07909	.26988	.92091	**40**
21	.07924	.27012	.92076	39
22	.07940	.27036	.92060	38
23	.07956	.27061	.92044	37
24	.07972	.27085	.92028	36
25	.07987	.27110	.92013	**35**
26	.08003	.27134	.91997	34
27	.08019	.27159	.91981	33
28	.08035	.27183	.91965	32
29	.08051	.27208	.91949	31
30	.08066	.27232	.91934	**30**
31	.08082	.27256	.91918	29
32	.08098	.27281	.91902	28
33	.08114	.27305	.91886	27
34	.08130	.27329	.91870	26
35	.08146	.27354	.91854	**25**
36	.08162	.27378	.91838	24
37	.08178	.27402	.91822	23
38	.08194	.27427	.91806	22
39	.08210	.27451	.91790	21
40	.08226	.27475	.91774	**20**
41	.08242	.27500	.91758	19
42	.08258	.27524	.91742	18
43	.08274	.27548	.91726	17
44	.08290	.27573	.91710	16
45	.08306	.27597	.91694	**15**
46	.08322	.27621	.91678	14
47	.08338	.27645	.91662	13
48	.08354	.27670	.91646	12
49	.08370	.27694	.91630	11
50	.08386	.27718	.91614	**10**
51	.08402	.27742	.91598	9
52	.08418	.27766	.91582	8
53	.08435	.27791	.91565	7
54	.08451	.27815	.91549	6
55	.08467	.27839	.91533	**5**
56	.08483	.27863	.91517	4
57	.08499	.27887	.91501	3
58	.08516	.27911	.91484	2
59	.08532	.27936	.91468	1
60	.08548	.27960	.91452	**0**
′	Cos²	Sin · Cos	Sin²	′

106° (286°) (253°) **73°**

17° (197°) (342°) **162°**

′	Sin²	Sin · Cos	Cos²	′
0	.08548	.27960	.91452	**60**
1	.08564	.27984	.91436	59
2	.08581	.28008	.91419	58
3	.08597	.28032	.91403	57
4	.08613	.28056	.91387	56
5	.08630	.28080	.91370	**55**
6	.08646	.28104	.91354	54
7	.08662	.28128	.91338	53
8	.08679	.28152	.91321	52
9	.08695	.28176	.91305	51
10	.08711	.28200	.91289	**50**
11	.08728	.28224	.91272	49
12	.08744	.28248	.91256	48
13	.08761	.28272	.91239	47
14	.08777	.28296	.91223	46
15	.08794	.28320	.91206	**45**
16	.08810	.28344	.91190	44
17	.08827	.28368	.91173	43
18	.08843	.28392	.91157	42
19	.08860	.28416	.91140	41
20	.08876	.28440	.91124	**40**
21	.08893	.28464	.91107	39
22	.08909	.28488	.91091	38
23	.08926	.28512	.91074	37
24	.08943	.28536	.91057	36
25	.08959	.28560	.91041	**35**
26	.08976	.28583	.91024	34
27	.08992	.28607	.91008	33
28	.09009	.28631	.90991	32
29	.09026	.28655	.90974	31
30	.09042	.28679	.90958	**30**
31	.09059	.28703	.90941	29
32	.09076	.28726	.90924	28
33	.09093	.28750	.90907	27
34	.09109	.28774	.90891	26
35	.09126	.28798	.90874	**25**
36	.09143	.28822	.90857	24
37	.09160	.28845	.90840	23
38	.09176	.28869	.90824	22
39	.09193	.28893	.90807	21
40	.09210	.28917	.90790	**20**
41	.09227	.28940	.90773	19
42	.09244	.28964	.90756	18
43	.09260	.28988	.90740	17
44	.09277	.29011	.90723	16
45	.09294	.29035	.90706	**15**
46	.09311	.29059	.90689	14
47	.09328	.29082	.90672	13
48	.09345	.29106	.90655	12
49	.09362	.29130	.90638	11
50	.09379	.29153	.90621	**10**
51	.09396	.29177	.90604	9
52	.09413	.29201	.90587	8
53	.09430	.29224	.90570	7
54	.09447	.29248	.90553	6
55	.09464	.29271	.90536	**5**
56	.09481	.29295	.90519	4
57	.09498	.29319	.90502	3
58	.09515	.29342	.90485	2
59	.09532	.29366	.90468	1
60	.09549	.29389	.90451	**0**
′	Cos²	Sin · Cos	Sin²	′

107° (287°) (252°) **72°**

18° (198°) (341°) **161°**

′	Sin²	Sin · Cos	Cos²	′
0	.09549	.29389	.90451	**60**
1	.09566	.29413	.90434	59
2	.09583	.29436	.90417	58
3	.09601	.29460	.90399	57
4	.09618	.29483	.90382	56
5	.09635	.29507	.90365	**55**
6	.09652	.29530	.90348	54
7	.09669	.29554	.90331	53
8	.09686	.29577	.90314	52
9	.09704	.29601	.90296	51
10	.09721	.29624	.90279	**50**
11	.09738	.29648	.90262	49
12	.09755	.29671	.90245	48
13	.09773	.29694	.90227	47
14	.09790	.29718	.90210	46
15	.09807	.29741	.90193	**45**
16	.09824	.29765	.90176	44
17	.09842	.29788	.90158	43
18	.09859	.29811	.90141	42
19	.09876	.29835	.90124	41
20	.09894	.29858	.90106	**40**
21	.09911	.29881	.90089	39
22	.09929	.29905	.90071	38
23	.09946	.29928	.90054	37
24	.09963	.29951	.90037	36
25	.09981	.29974	.90019	**35**
26	.09998	.29998	.90002	34
27	.10016	.30021	.89984	33
28	.10033	.30044	.89967	32
29	.10051	.30068	.89949	31
30	.10068	.30091	.89932	**30**
31	.10086	.30114	.89914	29
32	.10103	.30137	.89897	28
33	.10121	.30160	.89879	27
34	.10138	.30184	.89862	26
35	.10156	.30207	.89844	**25**
36	.10174	.30230	.89826	24
37	.10191	.30253	.89809	23
38	.10209	.30276	.89791	22
39	.10226	.30299	.89774	21
40	.10244	.30323	.89756	**20**
41	.10262	.30346	.89738	19
42	.10279	.30369	.89721	18
43	.10297	.30392	.89703	17
44	.10315	.30415	.89685	16
45	.10332	.30438	.89668	**15**
46	.10350	.30461	.89650	14
47	.10368	.30484	.89632	13
48	.10386	.30507	.89614	12
49	.10403	.30530	.89597	11
50	.10421	.30553	.89579	**10**
51	.10439	.30576	.89561	9
52	.10457	.30599	.89543	8
53	.10474	.30622	.89526	7
54	.10492	.30645	.89508	6
55	.10510	.30668	.89490	**5**
56	.10528	.30691	.89472	4
57	.10546	.30714	.89454	3
58	.10564	.30737	.89436	2
59	.10582	.30760	.89418	1
60	.10599	.30783	.89401	**0**
′	Cos²	Sin · Cos	Sin²	′

108° (288°) (251°) **71°**

19° (199°) (340°) **160°**

′	Sin²	Sin · Cos	Cos²	′
0	.10599	.30783	.89401	**60**
1	.10617	.30806	.89383	59
2	.10635	.30829	.89365	58
3	.10653	.30852	.89347	57
4	.10671	.30875	.89329	56
5	.10689	.30898	.89311	**55**
6	.10707	.30920	.89293	54
7	.10725	.30943	.89275	53
8	.10743	.30966	.89257	52
9	.10761	.30989	.89239	51
10	.10779	.31012	.89221	**50**
11	.10797	.31035	.89203	49
12	.10815	.31057	.89185	48
13	.10833	.31080	.89167	47
14	.10851	.31103	.89149	46
15	.10870	.31126	.89130	**45**
16	.10888	.31148	.89112	44
17	.10906	.31171	.89094	43
18	.10924	.31194	.89076	42
19	.10942	.31217	.89058	41
20	.10960	.31239	.89040	**40**
21	.10978	.31262	.89022	39
22	.10997	.31285	.89003	38
23	.11015	.31308	.88985	37
24	.11033	.31330	.88967	36
25	.11051	.31353	.88949	**35**
26	.11070	.31376	.88930	34
27	.11088	.31398	.88912	33
28	.11106	.31421	.88894	32
29	.11124	.31443	.88876	31
30	.11143	.31466	.88857	**30**
31	.11161	.31489	.88839	29
32	.11179	.31511	.88821	28
33	.11198	.31534	.88802	27
34	.11216	.31556	.88784	26
35	.11234	.31579	.88766	**25**
36	.11253	.31601	.88747	24
37	.11271	.31624	.88729	23
38	.11290	.31647	.88710	22
39	.11308	.31669	.88692	21
40	.11326	.31692	.88674	**20**
41	.11345	.31714	.88655	19
42	.11363	.31737	.88637	18
43	.11382	.31759	.88618	17
44	.11400	.31781	.88600	16
45	.11419	.31804	.88581	**15**
46	.11437	.31826	.88563	14
47	.11456	.31849	.88544	13
48	.11474	.31871	.88526	12
49	.11493	.31894	.88507	11
50	.11511	.31916	.88489	**10**
51	.11530	.31938	.88470	9
52	.11549	.31961	.88451	8
53	.11567	.31983	.88433	7
54	.11586	.32005	.88414	6
55	.11604	.32028	.88396	**5**
56	.11623	.32050	.88377	4
57	.11642	.32072	.88358	3
58	.11660	.32095	.88340	2
59	.11679	.32117	.88321	1
60	.11698	.32139	.88302	**0**
′	Cos²	Sin · Cos	Sin²	′

109° (289°) (250°) **70°**

Sin^2 x Cos^2 x Sin x Cos x

20° (200°) (339°) **159°**

′	Sin^2	Sin · Cos	Cos^2	′
0	.11698	.32139	.88302	**60**
1	.11716	.32162	.88284	59
2	.11735	.32184	.88265	58
3	.11754	.32206	.88246	57
4	.11773	.32228	.88227	56
5	.11791	.32251	.88209	**55**
6	.11810	.32273	.88190	54
7	.11829	.32295	.88171	53
8	.11848	.32317	.88152	52
9	.11867	.32339	.88133	51
10	.11885	.32362	.88115	**50**
11	.11904	.32384	.88096	49
12	.11923	.32406	.88077	48
13	.11942	.32428	.88058	47
14	.11961	.32450	.88039	46
15	.11980	.32472	.88020	**45**
16	.11999	.32495	.88001	44
17	.12018	.32517	.87982	43
18	.12036	.32539	.87964	42
19	.12055	.32561	.87945	41
20	.12074	.32583	.87926	**40**
21	.12093	.32605	.87907	39
22	.12112	.32627	.87888	38
23	.12131	.32649	.87869	37
24	.12150	.32671	.87850	36
25	.12169	.32693	.87831	**35**
26	.12188	.32715	.87812	34
27	.12207	.32737	.87793	33
28	.12226	.32759	.87774	32
29	.12245	.32781	.87755	31
30	.12265	.32803	.87735	**30**
31	.12284	.32825	.87716	29
32	.12303	.32847	.87697	28
33	.12322	.32869	.87678	27
34	.12341	.32891	.87659	26
35	.12360	.32913	.87640	**25**
36	.12379	.32934	.87621	24
37	.12398	.32956	.87602	23
38	.12418	.32978	.87582	22
39	.12437	.33000	.87563	21
40	.12456	.33022	.87544	**20**
41	.12475	.33044	.87525	19
42	.12494	.33066	.87506	18
43	.12514	.33087	.87486	17
44	.12533	.33109	.87467	16
45	.12552	.33131	.87448	**15**
46	.12571	.33153	.87429	14
47	.12591	.33175	.87409	13
48	.12610	.33196	.87390	12
49	.12629	.33218	.87371	11
50	.12649	.33240	.87351	**10**
51	.12668	.33262	.87332	9
52	.12687	.33283	.87313	8
53	.12707	.33305	.87293	7
54	.12726	.33327	.87274	6
55	.12746	.33348	.87254	**5**
56	.12765	.33370	.87235	4
57	.12784	.33392	.87216	3
58	.12804	.33413	.87196	2
59	.12823	.33435	.87177	1
60	.12843	.33457	.87157	**0**
′	Cos^2	Sin · Cos	Sin^2	′

110° (290°) (249°) **69°**

21° (201°) (338°) **158°**

′	Sin^2	Sin · Cos	Cos^2	′
0	.12843	.33457	.87157	**60**
1	.12862	.33478	.87138	59
2	.12882	.33500	.87118	58
3	.12901	.33521	.87099	57
4	.12921	.33543	.87079	56
5	.12940	.33564	.87060	**55**
6	.12960	.33586	.87040	54
7	.12979	.33608	.87021	53
8	.12999	.33629	.87001	52
9	.13018	.33651	.86982	51
10	.13038	.33672	.86962	**50**
11	.13058	.33694	.86942	49
12	.13077	.33715	.86923	48
13	.13097	.33737	.86903	47
14	.13116	.33758	.86884	46
15	.13136	.33780	.86864	**45**
16	.13156	.33801	.86844	44
17	.13175	.33822	.86825	43
18	.13195	.33844	.86805	42
19	.13215	.33865	.86785	41
20	.13235	.33887	.86765	**40**
21	.13254	.33908	.86746	39
22	.13274	.33929	.86726	38
23	.13294	.33951	.86706	37
24	.13314	.33972	.86686	36
25	.13333	.33993	.86667	**35**
26	.13353	.34015	.86647	34
27	.13373	.34036	.86627	33
28	.13393	.34057	.86607	32
29	.13412	.34079	.86588	31
30	.13432	.34100	.86568	**30**
31	.13452	.34121	.86548	29
32	.13472	.34142	.86528	28
33	.13492	.34164	.86508	27
34	.13512	.34185	.86488	26
35	.13532	.34206	.86468	**25**
36	.13552	.34227	.86448	24
37	.13571	.34249	.86429	23
38	.13591	.34270	.86409	22
39	.13611	.34291	.86389	21
40	.13631	.34312	.86369	**20**
41	.13651	.34333	.86349	19
42	.13671	.34354	.86329	18
43	.13691	.34376	.86309	17
44	.13711	.34397	.86289	16
45	.13731	.34418	.86269	**15**
46	.13751	.34439	.86249	14
47	.13771	.34460	.86229	13
48	.13791	.34481	.86209	12
49	.13811	.34502	.86189	11
50	.13832	.34523	.86168	**10**
51	.13852	.34544	.86148	9
52	.13872	.34565	.86128	8
53	.13892	.34586	.86108	7
54	.13912	.34607	.86088	6
55	.13932	.34628	.86068	**5**
56	.13952	.34649	.86048	4
57	.13972	.34670	.86028	3
58	.13993	.34691	.86007	2
59	.14013	.34712	.85987	1
60	.14033	.34733	.85967	**0**
′	Cos^2	Sin · Cos	Sin^2	′

111° (291°) (248°) **68°**

Sin² x Cos² x Sin x Cos x

22° (202°) (337°) **157°**

′	Sin²	Sin · Cos	Cos²	′
0	.14033	.34733	.85967	**60**
1	.14053	.34754	.85947	59
2	.14073	.34775	.85927	58
3	.14094	.34796	.85906	57
4	.14114	.34817	.85886	56
5	.14134	.34837	.85866	**55**
6	.14154	.34858	.85846	54
7	.14175	.34879	.85825	53
8	.14195	.34900	.85805	52
9	.14215	.34921	.85785	51
10	.14236	.34942	.85764	**50**
11	.14256	.34962	.85744	49
12	.14276	.34983	.85724	48
13	.14297	.35004	.85703	47
14	.14317	.35025	.85683	46
15	.14337	.35045	.85663	**45**
16	.14358	.35066	.85642	44
17	.14378	.35087	.85622	43
18	.14399	.35108	.85601	42
19	.14419	.35128	.85581	41
20	.14440	.35149	.85560	**40**
21	.14460	.35170	.85540	39
22	.14480	.35190	.85520	38
23	.14501	.35211	.85499	37
24	.14521	.35232	.85479	36
25	.14542	.35252	.85458	**35**
26	.14562	.35273	.85438	34
27	.14583	.35294	.85417	33
28	.14604	.35314	.85396	32
29	.14624	.35335	.85376	31
30	.14645	.35355	.85355	**30**
31	.14665	.35376	.85335	29
32	.14686	.35396	.85314	28
33	.14706	.35417	.85294	27
34	.14727	.35438	.85273	26
35	.14748	.35458	.85252	**25**
36	.14768	.35479	.85232	24
37	.14789	.35499	.85211	23
38	.14810	.35520	.85190	22
39	.14830	.35540	.85170	21
40	.14851	.35560	.85149	**20**
41	.14872	.35581	.85128	19
42	.14892	.35601	.85108	18
43	.14913	.35622	.85087	17
44	.14934	.35642	.85066	16
45	.14955	.35663	.85045	**15**
46	.14975	.35683	.85025	14
47	.14996	.35703	.85004	13
48	.15017	.35724	.84983	12
49	.15038	.35744	.84962	11
50	.15058	.35764	.84942	**10**
51	.15079	.35785	.84921	9
52	.15100	.35805	.84900	8
53	.15121	.35825	.84879	7
54	.15142	.35846	.84858	6
55	.15163	.35866	.84837	**5**
56	.15183	.35886	.84817	4
57	.15204	.35906	.84796	3
58	.15225	.35927	.84775	2
59	.15246	.35947	.84754	1
60	.15267	.35967	.84733	**0**
′	Cos²	Sin · Cos	Sin²	′

112° (292°) (247°) **67°**

23° (203°) (336°) **156°**

′	Sin²	Sin · Cos	Cos²	′
0	.15267	.35967	.84733	**60**
1	.15288	.35987	.84712	59
2	.15309	.36007	.84691	58
3	.15330	.36028	.84670	57
4	.15351	.36048	.84649	56
5	.15372	.36068	.84628	**55**
6	.15393	.36088	.84607	54
7	.15414	.36108	.84586	53
8	.15435	.36128	.84565	52
9	.15456	.36148	.84544	51
10	.15477	.36168	.84523	**50**
11	.15498	.36189	.84502	49
12	.15519	.36209	.84481	48
13	.15540	.36229	.84460	47
14	.15561	.36249	.84439	46
15	.15582	.36269	.84418	**45**
16	.15603	.36289	.84397	44
17	.15624	.36309	.84376	43
18	.15646	.36329	.84354	42
19	.15667	.36349	.84333	41
20	.15688	.36369	.84312	**40**
21	.15709	.36389	.84291	39
22	.15730	.36409	.84270	38
23	.15751	.36429	.84249	37
24	.15773	.36448	.84227	36
25	.15794	.36468	.84206	**35**
26	.15815	.36488	.84185	34
27	.15836	.36508	.84164	33
28	.15858	.36528	.84142	32
29	.15879	.36548	.84121	31
30	.15900	.36568	.84100	**30**
31	.15921	.36588	.84079	29
32	.15943	.36607	.84057	28
33	.15964	.36627	.84036	27
34	.15985	.36647	.84015	26
35	.16007	.36667	.83993	**25**
36	.16028	.36686	.83972	24
37	.16049	.36706	.83951	23
38	.16071	.36726	.83929	22
39	.16092	.36746	.83908	21
40	.16113	.36765	.83887	**20**
41	.16135	.36785	.83865	19
42	.16156	.36805	.83844	18
43	.16178	.36825	.83822	17
44	.16199	.36844	.83801	16
45	.16220	.36864	.83780	**15**
46	.16242	.36884	.83758	14
47	.16263	.36903	.83737	13
48	.16285	.36923	.83715	12
49	.16306	.36942	.83694	11
50	.16328	.36962	.83672	**10**
51	.16349	.36982	.83651	9
52	.16371	.37001	.83629	8
53	.16392	.37021	.83608	7
54	.16414	.37040	.83586	6
55	.16436	.37060	.83564	**5**
56	.16457	.37079	.83543	4
57	.16479	.37099	.83521	3
58	.16500	.37118	.83500	2
59	.16522	.37138	.83478	1
60	.16543	.37157	.83457	**0**
′	Cos²	Sin · Cos	Sin²	′

113° (293°) (246°) **66°**

$\sin^2 x$ $\cos^2 x$ $\sin x \cos x$

24° (204°) — (335°) **155°**

′	Sin²	Sin · Cos	Cos²	′
0	.16543	.37157	.83457	**60**
1	.16565	.37177	.83435	59
2	.16587	.37196	.83413	58
3	.16608	.37216	.83392	57
4	.16630	.37235	.83370	56
5	.16652	.37254	.83348	**55**
6	.16673	.37274	.83327	54
7	.16695	.37293	.83305	53
8	.16717	.37313	.83283	52
9	.16738	.37332	.83262	51
10	.16760	.37351	.83240	**50**
11	.16782	.37371	.83218	49
12	.16804	.37390	.83196	48
13	.16825	.37409	.83175	47
14	.16847	.37429	.83153	46
15	.16869	.37448	.83131	**45**
16	.16891	.37467	.83109	44
17	.16913	.37486	.83087	43
18	.16934	.37506	.83066	42
19	.16956	.37525	.83044	41
20	.16978	.37544	.83022	**40**
21	.17000	.37563	.83000	39
22	.17022	.37582	.82978	38
23	.17044	.37602	.82956	37
24	.17066	.37621	.82934	36
25	.17087	.37640	.82913	**35**
26	.17109	.37659	.82891	34
27	.17131	.37678	.82869	33
28	.17153	.37697	.82847	32
29	.17175	.37716	.82825	31
30	.17197	.37735	.82803	**30**
31	.17219	.37755	.82781	29
32	.17241	.37774	.82759	28
33	.17263	.37793	.82737	27
34	.17285	.37812	.82715	26
35	.17307	.37831	.82693	**25**
36	.17329	.37850	.82671	24
37	.17351	.37869	.82649	23
38	.17373	.37888	.82627	22
39	.17395	.37907	.82605	21
40	.17417	.37926	.82583	**20**
41	.17439	.37945	.82561	19
42	.17461	.37964	.82539	18
43	.17483	.37982	.82517	17
44	.17505	.38001	.82495	16
45	.17528	.38020	.82472	**15**
46	.17550	.38039	.82450	14
47	.17572	.38058	.82428	13
48	.17594	.38077	.82406	12
49	.17616	.38096	.82384	11
50	.17638	.38115	.82362	**10**
51	.17661	.38133	.82339	9
52	.17683	.38152	.82317	8
53	.17705	.38171	.82295	7
54	.17727	.38190	.82273	6
55	.17749	.38209	.82251	**5**
56	.17772	.38227	.82228	4
57	.17794	.38246	.82206	3
58	.17816	.38265	.82184	2
59	.17838	.38284	.82162	1
60	.17861	.38302	.82139	**0**
′	Cos²	Sin · Cos	Sin²	′

114° (294°) — (245°) **65°**

25° (205°) — (334°) **154°**

′	Sin²	Sin · Cos	Cos²	′
0	.17861	.38302	.82139	**60**
1	.17883	.38321	.82117	59
2	.17905	.38340	.82095	58
3	.17928	.38358	.82072	57
4	.17950	.38377	.82050	56
5	.17972	.38396	.82028	**55**
6	.17995	.38414	.82005	54
7	.18017	.38433	.81983	53
8	.18039	.38451	.81961	52
9	.18062	.38470	.81938	51
10	.18084	.38489	.81916	**50**
11	.18106	.38507	.81894	49
12	.18129	.38526	.81871	48
13	.18151	.38544	.81849	47
14	.18174	.38563	.81826	46
15	.18196	.38581	.81804	**45**
16	.18219	.38600	.81781	44
17	.18241	.38618	.81759	43
18	.18263	.38637	.81737	42
19	.18286	.38655	.81714	41
20	.18308	.38674	.81692	**40**
21	.18331	.38692	.81669	39
22	.18353	.38710	.81647	38
23	.18376	.38729	.81624	37
24	.18399	.38747	.81601	36
25	.18421	.38766	.81579	**35**
26	.18444	.38784	.81556	34
27	.18466	.38802	.81534	33
28	.18489	.38821	.81511	32
29	.18511	.38839	.81489	31
30	.18534	.38857	.81466	**30**
31	.18557	.38876	.81443	29
32	.18579	.38894	.81421	28
33	.18602	.38912	.81398	27
34	.18624	.38930	.81376	26
35	.18647	.38949	.81353	**25**
36	.18670	.38967	.81330	24
37	.18692	.38985	.81308	23
38	.18715	.39003	.81285	22
39	.18738	.39022	.81262	21
40	.18761	.39040	.81239	**20**
41	.18783	.39058	.81217	19
42	.18806	.39076	.81194	18
43	.18829	.39094	.81171	17
44	.18852	.39112	.81148	16
45	.18874	.39130	.81126	**15**
46	.18897	.39149	.81103	14
47	.18920	.39167	.81080	13
48	.18943	.39185	.81057	12
49	.18965	.39203	.81035	11
50	.18988	.39221	.81012	**10**
51	.19011	.39239	.80989	9
52	.19034	.39257	.80966	8
53	.19057	.39275	.80943	7
54	.19080	.39293	.80920	6
55	.19102	.39311	.80898	**5**
56	.19125	.39329	.80875	4
57	.19148	.39347	.80852	3
58	.19171	.39365	.80829	2
59	.19194	.39383	.80806	1
60	.19217	.39401	.80783	**0**
′	Cos²	Sin · Cos	Sin²	′

115° (295°) — (244°) **64°**

Sin² x Cos² x Sin x Cos x

26° (206°) (333°) **153°**

′	Sin²	Sin · Cos	Cos²	′
0	.19217	.39401	.80783	**60**
1	.19240	.39418	.80760	59
2	.19263	.39436	.80737	58
3	.19286	.39454	.80714	57
4	.19309	.39472	.80691	56
5	.19332	.39490	.80668	**55**
6	.19355	.39508	.80645	54
7	.19378	.39526	.80622	53
8	.19401	.39543	.80599	52
9	.19424	.39561	.80576	51
10	.19447	.39579	.80553	**50**
11	.19470	.39597	.80530	49
12	.19493	.39614	.80507	48
13	.19516	.39632	.80484	47
14	.19539	.39650	.80461	46
15	.19562	.39668	.80438	**45**
16	.19585	.39685	.80415	44
17	.19608	.39703	.80392	43
18	.19631	.39721	.80369	42
19	.19654	.39738	.80346	41
20	.19677	.39756	.80323	**40**
21	.19701	.39774	.80299	39
22	.19724	.39791	.80276	38
23	.19747	.39809	.80253	37
24	.19770	.39826	.80230	36
25	.19793	.39844	.80207	**35**
26	.19816	.39862	.80184	34
27	.19840	.39879	.80160	33
28	.19863	.39897	.80137	32
29	.19886	.39914	.80114	31
30	.19909	.39932	.80091	**30**
31	.19932	.39949	.80068	29
32	.19956	.39967	.80044	28
33	.19979	.39984	.80021	27
34	.20002	.40002	.79998	26
35	.20026	.40019	.79974	**25**
36	.20049	.40037	.79951	24
37	.20072	.40054	.79928	23
38	.20095	.40071	.79905	22
39	.20119	.40089	.79881	21
40	.20142	.40106	.79858	**20**
41	.20165	.40124	.79835	19
42	.20189	.40141	.79811	18
43	.20212	.40158	.79788	17
44	.20235	.40176	.79765	16
45	.20259	.40193	.79741	**15**
46	.20282	.40210	.79718	14
47	.20306	.40227	.79694	13
48	.20329	.40245	.79671	12
49	.20352	.40262	.79648	11
50	.20376	.40279	.79624	**10**
51	.20399	.40296	.79601	9
52	.20423	.40314	.79577	8
53	.20446	.40331	.79554	7
54	.20470	.40348	.79530	6
55	.20493	.40365	.79507	**5**
56	.20517	.40382	.79483	4
57	.20540	.40399	.79460	3
58	.20564	.40417	.79436	2
59	.20587	.40434	.79413	1
60	.20611	.40451	.79389	**0**
′	Cos²	Sin · Cos	Sin²	′

116° (296°) (243°) **63°**

27° (207°) (332°) **152°**

′	Sin²	Sin · Cos	Cos²	′
0	.20611	.40451	.79389	**60**
1	.20634	.40468	.79366	59
2	.20658	.40485	.79342	58
3	.20681	.40502	.79319	57
4	.20705	.40519	.79295	56
5	.20729	.40536	.79271	**55**
6	.20752	.40553	.79248	54
7	.20776	.40570	.79224	53
8	.20799	.40587	.79201	52
9	.20823	.40604	.79177	51
10	.20847	.40621	.79153	**50**
11	.20870	.40638	.79130	49
12	.20894	.40655	.79106	48
13	.20918	.40672	.79082	47
14	.20941	.40689	.79059	46
15	.20965	.40706	.79035	**45**
16	.20989	.40723	.79011	44
17	.21012	.40740	.78988	43
18	.21036	.40756	.78964	42
19	.21060	.40773	.78940	41
20	.21083	.40790	.78917	**40**
21	.21107	.40807	.78893	39
22	.21131	.40824	.78869	38
23	.21155	.40840	.78845	37
24	.21178	.40857	.78822	36
25	.21202	.40874	.78798	**35**
26	.21226	.40891	.78774	34
27	.21250	.40907	.78750	33
28	.21274	.40924	.78726	32
29	.21297	.40941	.78703	31
30	.21321	.40958	.78679	**30**
31	.21345	.40974	.78655	29
32	.21369	.40991	.78631	28
33	.21393	.41008	.78607	27
34	.21417	.41024	.78583	26
35	.21440	.41041	.78560	**25**
36	.21464	.41057	.78536	24
37	.21488	.41074	.78512	23
38	.21512	.41091	.78488	22
39	.21536	.41107	.78464	21
40	.21560	.41124	.78440	**20**
41	.21584	.41140	.78416	19
42	.21608	.41157	.78392	18
43	.21632	.41173	.78368	17
44	.21656	.41190	.78344	16
45	.21680	.41206	.78320	**15**
46	.21704	.41223	.78296	14
47	.21728	.41239	.78272	13
48	.21752	.41256	.78248	12
49	.21776	.41272	.78224	11
50	.21800	.41289	.78200	**10**
51	.21824	.41305	.78176	9
52	.21848	.41321	.78152	8
53	.21872	.41338	.78128	7
54	.21896	.41354	.78104	6
55	.21920	.41370	.78080	**5**
56	.21944	.41387	.78056	4
57	.21968	.41403	.78032	3
58	.21992	.41419	.78008	2
59	.22016	.41436	.77984	1
60	.22040	.41452	.77960	**0**
′	Cos²	Sin · Cos	Sin²	′

117° (297°) (242°) **62°**

Sin² x Cos² x Sin x Cos x

28° (208°) (331°) **151°**

′	Sin²	Sin · Cos	Cos²	′
0	.22040	.41452	.77960	**60**
1	.22064	.41468	.77936	59
2	.22089	.41484	.77911	58
3	.22113	.41501	.77887	57
4	.22137	.41517	.77863	56
5	.22161	.41533	.77839	**55**
6	.22185	.41549	.77815	54
7	.22209	.41565	.77791	53
8	.22234	.41582	.77766	52
9	.22258	.41598	.77742	51
10	.22282	.41614	.77718	**50**
11	.22306	.41630	.77694	49
12	.22330	.41646	.77670	48
13	.22355	.41662	.77645	47
14	.22379	.41678	.77621	46
15	.22403	.41694	.77597	**45**
16	.22427	.41710	.77573	44
17	.22452	.41726	.77548	43
18	.22476	.41742	.77524	42
19	.22500	.41758	.77500	41
20	.22525	.41774	.77475	**40**
21	.22549	.41790	.77451	39
22	.22573	.41806	.77427	38
23	.22598	.41822	.77402	37
24	.22622	.41838	.77378	36
25	.22646	.41854	.77354	**35**
26	.22671	.41870	.77329	34
27	.22695	.41886	.77305	33
28	.22719	.41902	.77281	32
29	.22744	.41918	.77256	31
30	.22768	.41934	.77232	**30**
31	.22792	.41949	.77208	29
32	.22817	.41965	.77183	28
33	.22841	.41981	.77159	27
34	.22866	.41997	.77134	26
35	.22890	.42013	.77110	**25**
36	.22915	.42028	.77085	24
37	.22939	.42044	.77061	23
38	.22964	.42060	.77036	22
39	.22988	.42076	.77012	21
40	.23012	.42091	.76988	**20**
41	.23037	.42107	.76963	19
42	.23061	.42123	.76939	18
43	.23086	.42138	.76914	17
44	.23110	.42154	.76890	16
45	.23135	.42170	.76865	**15**
46	.23160	.42185	.76840	14
47	.23184	.42201	.76816	13
48	.23209	.42216	.76791	12
49	.23233	.42232	.76767	11
50	.23258	.42248	.76742	**10**
51	.23282	.42263	.76718	9
52	.23307	.42279	.76693	8
53	.23332	.42294	.76668	7
54	.23356	.42310	.76644	6
55	.23381	.42325	.76619	**5**
56	.23405	.42341	.76595	4
57	.23430	.42356	.76570	3
58	.23455	.42372	.76545	2
59	.23479	.42387	.76521	1
60	.23504	.42402	.76496	**0**
′	Cos²	Sin · Cos	Sin²	′

118° (298°) (241°) **61°**

29° (209°) (330°) **150°**

′	Sin²	Sin · Cos	Cos²	′
0	.23504	.42402	.76496	**60**
1	.23529	.42418	.76471	59
2	.23553	.42433	.76447	58
3	.23578	.42449	.76422	57
4	.23603	.42464	.76397	56
5	.23627	.42479	.76373	**55**
6	.23652	.42495	.76348	54
7	.23677	.42510	.76323	53
8	.23702	.42525	.76298	52
9	.23726	.42541	.76274	51
10	.23751	.42556	.76249	**50**
11	.23776	.42571	.76224	49
12	.23801	.42586	.76199	48
13	.23825	.42602	.76175	47
14	.23850	.42617	.76150	46
15	.23875	.42632	.76125	**45**
16	.23900	.42647	.76100	44
17	.23925	.42662	.76075	43
18	.23950	.42678	.76050	42
19	.23974	.42693	.76026	41
20	.23999	.42708	.76001	**40**
21	.24024	.42723	.75976	39
22	.24049	.42738	.75951	38
23	.24074	.42753	.75926	37
24	.24099	.42768	.75901	36
25	.24124	.42783	.75876	**35**
26	.24148	.42798	.75852	34
27	.24173	.42813	.75827	33
28	.24198	.42828	.75802	32
29	.24223	.42843	.75777	31
30	.24248	.42858	.75752	**30**
31	.24273	.42873	.75727	29
32	.24298	.42888	.75702	28
33	.24323	.42903	.75677	27
34	.24348	.42918	.75652	26
35	.24373	.42933	.75627	**25**
36	.24398	.42948	.75602	24
37	.24423	.42963	.75577	23
38	.24448	.42978	.75552	22
39	.24473	.42993	.75527	21
40	.24498	.43007	.75502	**20**
41	.24523	.43022	.75477	19
42	.24548	.43037	.75452	18
43	.24573	.43052	.75427	17
44	.24598	.43067	.75402	16
45	.24623	.43081	.75377	**15**
46	.24648	.43096	.75352	14
47	.24673	.43111	.75327	13
48	.24698	.43126	.75302	12
49	.24723	.43140	.75277	11
50	.24749	.43155	.75251	**10**
51	.24774	.43170	.75226	9
52	.24799	.43184	.75201	8
53	.24824	.43199	.75176	7
54	.24849	.43214	.75151	6
55	.24874	.43228	.75126	**5**
56	.24899	.43243	.75101	4
57	.24924	.43258	.75076	3
58	.24950	.43272	.75050	2
59	.24975	.43287	.75025	1
60	.25000	.43301	.75000	**0**
′	Cos²	Sin · Cos	Sin²	′

119° (299°) (240°) **60°**

Sin^2 x Cos^2 x Sin x Cos x

30° (210°) (329°) **149°**

′	Sin^2	Sin · Cos	Cos^2	′
0	.25000	.43301	.75000	**60**
1	.25025	.43316	.74975	59
2	.25050	.43330	.74950	58
3	.25076	.43345	.74924	57
4	.25101	.43359	.74899	56
5	.25126	.43374	.74874	**55**
6	.25151	.43388	.74849	54
7	.25177	.43403	.74823	53
8	.25202	.43417	.74798	52
9	.25227	.43432	.74773	51
10	.25252	.43446	.74748	**50**
11	.25278	.43460	.74722	49
12	.25303	.43475	.74697	48
13	.25328	.43489	.74672	47
14	.25354	.43503	.74646	46
15	.25379	.43518	.74621	**45**
16	.25404	.43532	.74596	44
17	.25429	.43546	.74571	43
18	.25455	.43561	.74545	42
19	.25480	.43575	.74520	41
20	.25506	.43589	.74494	**40**
21	.25531	.43603	.74469	39
22	.25556	.43618	.74444	38
23	.25582	.43632	.74418	37
24	.25607	.43646	.74393	36
25	.25632	.43660	.74368	**35**
26	.25658	.43674	.74342	34
27	.25683	.43689	.74317	33
28	.25709	.43703	.74291	32
29	.25734	.43717	.74266	31
30	.25760	.43731	.74240	**30**
31	.25785	.43745	.74215	29
32	.25810	.43759	.74190	28
33	.25836	.43773	.74164	27
34	.25861	.43787	.74139	26
35	.25887	.43801	.74113	**25**
36	.25912	.43815	.74088	24
37	.25938	.43829	.74062	23
38	.25963	.43843	.74037	22
39	.25989	.43857	.74011	21
40	.26014	.43871	.73986	**20**
41	.26040	.43885	.73960	19
42	.26065	.43899	.73935	18
43	.26091	.43913	.73909	17
44	.26117	.43927	.73883	16
45	.26142	.43941	.73858	**15**
46	.26168	.43955	.73832	14
47	.26193	.43969	.73807	13
48	.26219	.43982	.73781	12
49	.26244	.43996	.73756	11
50	.26270	.44010	.73730	**10**
51	.26296	.44024	.73704	9
52	.26321	.44038	.73679	8
53	.26347	.44051	.73653	7
54	.26372	.44065	.73628	6
55	.26398	.44079	.73602	**5**
56	.26424	.44093	.73576	4
57	.26449	.44106	.73551	3
58	.26475	.44120	.73525	2
59	.26501	.44134	.73499	1
60	.26526	.44147	.73474	**0**
′	Cos^2	Sin · Cos	Sin^2	′

120° (300°) (239°) **59°**

31° (211°) (328°) **148°**

′	Sin^2	Sin · Cos	Cos^2	′
0	.26526	.44147	.73474	**60**
1	.26552	.44161	.73448	59
2	.26578	.44175	.73422	58
3	.26604	.44188	.73396	57
4	.26629	.44202	.73371	56
5	.26655	.44215	.73345	**55**
6	.26681	.44229	.73319	54
7	.26706	.44243	.73294	53
8	.26732	.44256	.73268	52
9	.26758	.44270	.73242	51
10	.26784	.44283	.73216	**50**
11	.26809	.44297	.73191	49
12	.26835	.44310	.73165	48
13	.26861	.44324	.73139	47
14	.26887	.44337	.73113	46
15	.26913	.44351	.73087	**45**
16	.26938	.44364	.73062	44
17	.26964	.44377	.73036	43
18	.26990	.44391	.73010	42
19	.27016	.44404	.72984	41
20	.27042	.44418	.72958	**40**
21	.27068	.44431	.72932	39
22	.27093	.44444	.72907	38
23	.27119	.44458	.72881	37
24	.27145	.44471	.72855	36
25	.27171	.44484	.72829	**35**
26	.27197	.44497	.72803	34
27	.27223	.44511	.72777	33
28	.27249	.44524	.72751	32
29	.27275	.44537	.72725	31
30	.27300	.44550	.72700	**30**
31	.27326	.44564	.72674	29
32	.27352	.44577	.72648	28
33	.27378	.44590	.72622	27
34	.27404	.44603	.72596	26
35	.27430	.44616	.72570	**25**
36	.27456	.44629	.72544	24
37	.27482	.44642	.72518	23
38	.27508	.44655	.72492	22
39	.27534	.44669	.72466	21
40	.27560	.44682	.72440	**20**
41	.27586	.44695	.72414	19
42	.27612	.44708	.72388	18
43	.27638	.44721	.72362	17
44	.27664	.44734	.72336	16
45	.27690	.44747	.72310	**15**
46	.27716	.44760	.72284	14
47	.27742	.44773	.72258	13
48	.27768	.44786	.72232	12
49	.27794	.44799	.72206	11
50	.27820	.44811	.72180	**10**
51	.27846	.44824	.72154	9
52	.27873	.44837	.72127	8
53	.27899	.44850	.72101	7
54	.27925	.44863	.72075	6
55	.27951	.44876	.72049	**5**
56	.27977	.44889	.72023	4
57	.28003	.44901	.71997	3
58	.28029	.44914	.71971	2
59	.28055	.44927	.71945	1
60	.28081	.44940	.71919	**0**
′	Cos^2	Sin · Cos	Sin^2	′

121° (301°) (238°) **58°**

$\sin^2 x$ $\cos^2 x$ $\sin x \cos x$

32° (212°) — (327°) **147°**

′	Sin²	Sin · Cos	Cos²	′
0	.28081	.44940	.71919	**60**
1	.28108	.44952	.71892	59
2	.28134	.44965	.71866	58
3	.28160	.44978	.71840	57
4	.28186	.44991	.71814	56
5	.28212	.45003	.71788	**55**
6	.28238	.45016	.71762	54
7	.28265	.45029	.71735	53
8	.28291	.45041	.71709	52
9	.28317	.45054	.71683	51
10	.28343	.45066	.71657	**50**
11	.28369	.45079	.71631	49
12	.28396	.45092	.71604	48
13	.28422	.45104	.71578	47
14	.28448	.45117	.71552	46
15	.28474	.45129	.71526	**45**
16	.28501	.45142	.71499	44
17	.28527	.45154	.71473	43
18	.28553	.45167	.71447	42
19	.28580	.45179	.71420	41
20	.28606	.45192	.71394	**40**
21	.28632	.45204	.71368	39
22	.28658	.45217	.71342	38
23	.28685	.45229	.71315	37
24	.28711	.45241	.71289	36
25	.28737	.45254	.71263	**35**
26	.28764	.45266	.71236	34
27	.28790	.45278	.71210	33
28	.28816	.45291	.71184	32
29	.28843	.45303	.71157	31
30	.28869	.45315	.71131	**30**
31	.28895	.45328	.71105	29
32	.28922	.45340	.71078	28
33	.28948	.45352	.71052	27
34	.28975	.45364	.71025	26
35	.29001	.45377	.70999	**25**
36	.29027	.45389	.70973	24
37	.29054	.45401	.70946	23
38	.29080	.45413	.70920	22
39	.29107	.45425	.70893	21
40	.29133	.45438	.70867	**20**
41	.29160	.45450	.70840	19
42	.29186	.45462	.70814	18
43	.29212	.45474	.70788	17
44	.29239	.45486	.70761	16
45	.29265	.45498	.70735	**15**
46	.29292	.45510	.70708	14
47	.29318	.45522	.70682	13
48	.29345	.45534	.70655	12
49	.29371	.45546	.70629	11
50	.29398	.45558	.70602	**10**
51	.29424	.45570	.70576	9
52	.29451	.45582	.70549	8
53	.29477	.45594	.70523	7
54	.29504	.45606	.70496	6
55	.29530	.45618	.70470	**5**
56	.29557	.45630	.70443	4
57	.29583	.45642	.70417	3
58	.29610	.45654	.70390	2
59	.29637	.45665	.70363	1
60	.29663	.45677	.70337	**0**
′	Cos²	Sin · Cos	Sin²	′

122° (302°) — (237°) **57°**

33° (213°) — (326°) **146°**

′	Sin²	Sin · Cos	Cos²	′
0	.29663	.45677	.70337	**60**
1	.29690	.45689	.70310	59
2	.29716	.45701	.70284	58
3	.29743	.45713	.70257	57
4	.29770	.45724	.70230	56
5	.29796	.45736	.70204	**55**
6	.29823	.45748	.70177	54
7	.29849	.45760	.70151	53
8	.29876	.45771	.70124	52
9	.29903	.45783	.70097	51
10	.29929	.45795	.70071	**50**
11	.29956	.45806	.70044	49
12	.29983	.45818	.70017	48
13	.30009	.45830	.69991	47
14	.30036	.45841	.69964	46
15	.30063	.45853	.69937	**45**
16	.30089	.45865	.69911	44
17	.30116	.45876	.69884	43
18	.30143	.45888	.69857	42
19	.30169	.45899	.69831	41
20	.30196	.45911	.69804	**40**
21	.30223	.45922	.69777	39
22	.30249	.45934	.69751	38
23	.30276	.45945	.69724	37
24	.30303	.45957	.69697	36
25	.30330	.45968	.69670	**35**
26	.30356	.45980	.69644	34
27	.30383	.45991	.69617	33
28	.30410	.46002	.69590	32
29	.30437	.46014	.69563	31
30	.30463	.46025	.69537	**30**
31	.30490	.46037	.69510	29
32	.30517	.46048	.69483	28
33	.30544	.46059	.69456	27
34	.30571	.46071	.69429	26
35	.30597	.46082	.69403	**25**
36	.30624	.46093	.69376	24
37	.30651	.46104	.69349	23
38	.30678	.46116	.69322	22
39	.30705	.46127	.69295	21
40	.30732	.46138	.69268	**20**
41	.30758	.46149	.69242	19
42	.30785	.46161	.69215	18
43	.30812	.46172	.69188	17
44	.30839	.46183	.69161	16
45	.30866	.46194	.69134	**15**
46	.30893	.46205	.69107	14
47	.30920	.46216	.69080	13
48	.30946	.46227	.69054	12
49	.30973	.46238	.69027	11
50	.31000	.46249	.69000	**10**
51	.31027	.46260	.68973	9
52	.31054	.46272	.68946	8
53	.31081	.46283	.68919	7
54	.31108	.46294	.68892	6
55	.31135	.46305	.68865	**5**
56	.31162	.46315	.68838	4
57	.31189	.46326	.68811	3
58	.31216	.46337	.68784	2
59	.31243	.46348	.68757	1
60	.31270	.46359	.68730	**0**
′	Cos²	Sin · Cos	Sin²	′

123° (303°) — (236°) **56°**

Sin^2 x Cos^2 x Sin x Cos x

34° (214°) (325°) **145°**

′	Sin²	Sin · Cos	Cos²	′
0	.31270	.46359	.68730	**60**
1	.31297	.46370	.68703	59
2	.31324	.46381	.68676	58
3	.31351	.46392	.68649	57
4	.31378	.46403	.68622	56
5	.31405	.46413	.68595	**55**
6	.31432	.46424	.68568	54
7	.31459	.46435	.68541	53
8	.31486	.46446	.68514	52
9	.31513	.46457	.68487	51
10	.31540	.46467	.68460	**50**
11	.31567	.46478	.68433	49
12	.31594	.46489	.68406	48
13	.31621	.46500	.68379	47
14	.31648	.46510	.68352	46
15	.31675	.46521	.68325	**45**
16	.31702	.46532	.68298	44
17	.31729	.46542	.68271	43
18	.31756	.46553	.68244	42
19	.31783	.46563	.68217	41
20	.31810	.46574	.68190	**40**
21	.31837	.46585	.68163	39
22	.31865	.46595	.68135	38
23	.31892	.46606	.68108	37
24	.31919	.46616	.68081	36
25	.31946	.46627	.68054	**35**
26	.31973	.46637	.68027	34
27	.32000	.46648	.68000	33
28	.32027	.46658	.67973	32
29	.32054	.46669	.67946	31
30	.32082	.46679	.67918	**30**
31	.32109	.46689	.67891	29
32	.32136	.46700	.67864	28
33	.32163	.46710	.67837	27
34	.32190	.46721	.67810	26
35	.32217	.46731	.67783	**25**
36	.32245	.46741	.67755	24
37	.32272	.46752	.67728	23
38	.32299	.46762	.67701	22
39	.32326	.46772	.67674	21
40	.32353	.46782	.67647	**20**
41	.32381	.46793	.67619	19
42	.32408	.46803	.67592	18
43	.32435	.46813	.67565	17
44	.32462	.46823	.67538	16
45	.32490	.46834	.67510	**15**
46	.32517	.46844	.67483	14
47	.32544	.46854	.67456	13
48	.32571	.46864	.67429	12
49	.32599	.46874	.67401	11
50	.32626	.46884	.67374	**10**
51	.32653	.46894	.67347	9
52	.32681	.46905	.67319	8
53	.32708	.46915	.67292	7
54	.32735	.46925	.67265	6
55	.32762	.46935	.67238	**5**
56	.32790	.46945	.67210	4
57	.32817	.46955	.67183	3
58	.32844	.46965	.67156	2
59	.32872	.46975	.67128	1
60	.32899	.46985	.67101	**0**
′	Cos²	Sin · Cos	Sin²	′

124° (304°) (235°) **55°**

35° (215°) (324°) **144°**

′	Sin²	Sin · Cos	Cos²	′
0	.32899	.46985	.67101	**60**
1	.32926	.46995	.67074	59
2	.32954	.47004	.67046	58
3	.32981	.47014	.67019	57
4	.33008	.47024	.66992	56
5	.33036	.47034	.66964	**55**
6	.33063	.47044	.66937	54
7	.33090	.47054	.66910	53
8	.33118	.47064	.66882	52
9	.33145	.47074	.66855	51
10	.33173	.47083	.66827	**50**
11	.33200	.47093	.66800	49
12	.33227	.47103	.66773	48
13	.33255	.47113	.66745	47
14	.33282	.47122	.66718	46
15	.33310	.47132	.66690	**45**
16	.33337	.47142	.66663	44
17	.33365	.47151	.66635	43
18	.33392	.47161	.66608	42
19	.33419	.47171	.66581	41
20	.33447	.47180	.66553	**40**
21	.33474	.47190	.66526	39
22	.33502	.47200	.66498	38
23	.33529	.47209	.66471	37
24	.33557	.47219	.66443	36
25	.33584	.47228	.66416	**35**
26	.33612	.47238	.66388	34
27	.33639	.47247	.66361	33
28	.33667	.47257	.66333	32
29	.33694	.47266	.66306	31
30	.33722	.47276	.66278	**30**
31	.33749	.47285	.66251	29
32	.33777	.47295	.66223	28
33	.33804	.47304	.66196	27
34	.33832	.47314	.66168	26
35	.33859	.47323	.66141	**25**
36	.33887	.47332	.66113	24
37	.33914	.47342	.66086	23
38	.33942	.47351	.66058	22
39	.33969	.47361	.66031	21
40	.33997	.47370	.66003	**20**
41	.34024	.47379	.65976	19
42	.34052	.47388	.65948	18
43	.34080	.47398	.65920	17
44	.34107	.47407	.65893	16
45	.34135	.47416	.65865	**15**
46	.34162	.47425	.65838	14
47	.34190	.47435	.65810	13
48	.34218	.47444	.65782	12
49	.34245	.47453	.65755	11
50	.34273	.47462	.65727	**10**
51	.34300	.47471	.65700	9
52	.34328	.47480	.65672	8
53	.34356	.47490	.65644	7
54	.34383	.47499	.65617	6
55	.34411	.47508	.65589	**5**
56	.34439	.47517	.65561	4
57	.34466	.47526	.65534	3
58	.34494	.47535	.65506	2
59	.34521	.47544	.65479	1
60	.34549	.47553	.65451	**0**
′	Cos²	Sin · Cos	Sin²	′

125° (305°) (234°) **54°**

Sin² x Cos² x Sin x Cos x

36° (216°) (323°) **143°**

′	Sin²	Sin · Cos	Cos²	′
0	.34549	.47553	.65451	**60**
1	.34577	.47562	.65423	59
2	.34604	.47571	.65396	58
3	.34632	.47580	.65368	57
4	.34660	.47589	.65340	56
5	.34688	.47598	.65312	**55**
6	.34715	.47606	.65285	54
7	.34743	.47615	.65257	53
8	.34771	.47624	.65229	52
9	.34798	.47633	.65202	51
10	.34826	.47642	.65174	**50**
11	.34854	.47651	.65146	49
12	.34882	.47660	.65118	48
13	.34909	.47668	.65091	47
14	.34937	.47677	.65063	46
15	.34965	.47686	.65035	**45**
16	.34992	.47695	.65008	44
17	.35020	.47703	.64980	43
18	.35048	.47712	.64952	42
19	.35076	.47721	.64924	41
20	.35103	.47729	.64897	**40**
21	.35131	.47738	.64869	39
22	.35159	.47747	.64841	38
23	.35187	.47755	.64813	37
24	.35215	.47764	.64785	36
25	.35242	.47773	.64758	**35**
26	.35270	.47781	.64730	34
27	.35298	.47790	.64702	33
28	.35326	.47798	.64674	32
29	.35354	.47807	.64646	31
30	.35381	.47815	.64619	**30**
31	.35409	.47824	.64591	29
32	.35437	.47832	.64563	28
33	.35465	.47841	.64535	27
34	.35493	.47849	.64507	26
35	.35521	.47858	.64479	**25**
36	.35548	.47866	.64452	24
37	.35576	.47874	.64424	23
38	.35604	.47883	.64396	22
39	.35632	.47891	.64368	21
40	.35660	.47899	.64340	**20**
41	.35688	.47908	.64312	19
42	.35716	.47916	.64284	18
43	.35743	.47924	.64257	17
44	.35771	.47933	.64229	16
45	.35799	.47941	.64201	**15**
46	.35827	.47949	.64173	14
47	.35855	.47957	.64145	13
48	.35883	.47966	.64117	12
49	.35911	.47974	.64089	11
50	.35939	.47982	.64061	**10**
51	.35967	.47990	.64033	9
52	.35995	.47998	.64005	8
53	.36023	.48007	.63977	7
54	.36050	.48015	.63950	6
55	.36078	.48023	.63922	**5**
56	.36106	.48031	.63894	4
57	.36134	.48039	.63866	3
58	.36162	.48047	.63838	2
59	.36190	.48055	.63810	1
60	.36218	.48063	.63782	**0**
′	Cos²	Sin · Cos	Sin²	′

126° (306°) (233°) **53°**

37° (217°) (322°) **142°**

′	Sin²	Sin · Cos	Cos²	′
0	.36218	.48063	.63782	**60**
1	.36246	.48071	.63754	59
2	.36274	.48079	.63726	58
3	.36302	.48087	.63698	57
4	.36330	.48095	.63670	56
5	.36358	.48103	.63642	**55**
6	.36386	.48111	.63614	54
7	.36414	.48119	.63586	53
8	.36442	.48127	.63558	52
9	.36470	.48135	.63530	51
10	.36498	.48142	.63502	**50**
11	.36526	.48150	.63474	49
12	.36554	.48158	.63446	48
13	.36582	.48166	.63418	47
14	.36610	.48174	.63390	46
15	.36638	.48182	.63362	**45**
16	.36666	.48189	.63334	44
17	.36694	.48197	.63306	43
18	.36722	.48205	.63278	42
19	.36750	.48212	.63250	41
20	.36778	.48220	.63222	**40**
21	.36806	.48228	.63194	39
22	.36834	.48236	.63166	38
23	.36862	.48243	.63138	37
24	.36891	.48251	.63109	36
25	.36919	.48258	.63081	**35**
26	.36947	.48266	.63053	34
27	.36975	.48274	.63025	33
28	.37003	.48281	.62997	32
29	.37031	.48289	.62969	31
30	.37059	.48296	.62941	**30**
31	.37087	.48304	.62913	29
32	.37115	.48311	.62885	28
33	.37143	.48319	.62857	27
34	.37171	.48326	.62829	26
35	.37200	.48334	.62800	**25**
36	.37228	.48341	.62772	24
37	.37256	.48349	.62744	23
38	.37284	.48356	.62716	22
39	.37312	.48363	.62688	21
40	.37340	.48371	.62660	**20**
41	.37368	.48378	.62632	19
42	.37397	.48385	.62603	18
43	.37425	.48393	.62575	17
44	.37453	.48400	.62547	16
45	.37481	.48407	.62519	**15**
46	.37509	.48415	.62491	14
47	.37537	.48422	.62463	13
48	.37566	.48429	.62434	12
49	.37594	.48436	.62406	11
50	.37622	.48444	.62378	**10**
51	.37650	.48451	.62350	9
52	.37678	.48458	.62322	8
53	.37706	.48465	.62294	7
54	.37735	.48472	.62265	6
55	.37763	.48479	.62237	**5**
56	.37791	.48487	.62209	4
57	.37819	.48494	.62181	3
58	.37847	.48501	.62153	2
59	.37876	.48508	.62124	1
60	.37904	.48515	.62096	**0**
′	Cos²	Sin · Cos	Sin²	′

127° (307°) (232°) **52°**

Sin² x Cos² x Sin x Cos x

38° (218°) (321°) **141°**

′	Sin²	Sin · Cos	Cos²	′
0	.37904	.48515	.62096	**60**
1	.37932	.48522	.62068	59
2	.37960	.48529	.62040	58
3	.37989	.48536	.62011	57
4	.38017	.48543	.61983	56
5	.38045	.48550	.61955	**55**
6	.38073	.48557	.61927	54
7	.38102	.48564	.61898	53
8	.38130	.48571	.61870	52
9	.38158	.48577	.61842	51
10	.38186	.48584	.61814	**50**
11	.38215	.48591	.61785	49
12	.38243	.48598	.61757	48
13	.38271	.48605	.61729	47
14	.38299	.48612	.61701	46
15	.38328	.48618	.61672	**45**
16	.38356	.48625	.61644	44
17	.38384	.48632	.61616	43
18	.38413	.48639	.61587	42
19	.38441	.48646	.61559	41
20	.38469	.48652	.61531	**40**
21	.38498	.48659	.61502	39
22	.38526	.48666	.61474	38
23	.38554	.48672	.61446	37
24	.38582	.48679	.61418	36
25	.38611	.48686	.61389	**35**
26	.38639	.48692	.61361	34
27	.38667	.48699	.61333	33
28	.38696	.48705	.61304	32
29	.38724	.48712	.61276	31
30	.38752	.48719	.61248	**30**
31	.38781	.48725	.61219	29
32	.38809	.48732	.61191	28
33	.38837	.48738	.61163	27
34	.38866	.48745	.61134	26
35	.38894	.48751	.61106	**25**
36	.38923	.48757	.61077	24
37	.38951	.48764	.61049	23
38	.38979	.48770	.61021	22
39	.39008	.48777	.60992	21
40	.39036	.48783	.60964	**20**
41	.39064	.48789	.60936	19
42	.39093	.48796	.60907	18
43	.39121	.48802	.60879	17
44	.39150	.48808	.60850	16
45	.39178	.48815	.60822	**15**
46	.39206	.48821	.60794	14
47	.39235	.48827	.60765	13
48	.39263	.48834	.60737	12
49	.39292	.48840	.60708	11
50	.39320	.48846	.60680	**10**
51	.39348	.48852	.60652	9
52	.39377	.48858	.60623	8
53	.39405	.48865	.60595	7
54	.39434	.48871	.60566	6
55	.39462	.48877	.60538	**5**
56	.39491	.48883	.60509	4
57	.39519	.48889	.60481	3
58	.39548	.48895	.60452	2
59	.39576	.48901	.60424	1
60	.39604	.48907	.60396	**0**
′	Cos²	Sin · Cos	Sin²	′

128° (308°) (231°) **51°**

39° (219°) (320°) **140°**

′	Sin²	Sin · Cos	Cos²	′
0	.39604	.48907	.60396	**60**
1	.39633	.48913	.60367	59
2	.39661	.48919	.60339	58
3	.39690	.48925	.60310	57
4	.39718	.48931	.60282	56
5	.39747	.48937	.60253	**55**
6	.39775	.48943	.60225	54
7	.39804	.48949	.60196	53
8	.39832	.48955	.60168	52
9	.39861	.48961	.60139	51
10	.39889	.48967	.60111	**50**
11	.39918	.48973	.60082	49
12	.39946	.48979	.60054	48
13	.39975	.48985	.60025	47
14	.40003	.48990	.59997	46
15	.40032	.48996	.59968	**45**
16	.40060	.49002	.59940	44
17	.40089	.49008	.59911	43
18	.40117	.49014	.59883	42
19	.40146	.49019	.59854	41
20	.40174	.49025	.59826	**40**
21	.40203	.49031	.59797	39
22	.40231	.49036	.59769	38
23	.40260	.49042	.59740	37
24	.40288	.49048	.59712	36
25	.40317	.49053	.59683	**35**
26	.40345	.49059	.59655	34
27	.40374	.49065	.59626	33
28	.40402	.49070	.59598	32
29	.40431	.49076	.59569	31
30	.40460	.49081	.59540	**30**
31	.40488	.49087	.59512	29
32	.40517	.49092	.59483	28
33	.40545	.49098	.59455	27
34	.40574	.49103	.59426	26
35	.40602	.49109	.59398	**25**
36	.40631	.49114	.59369	24
37	.40660	.49120	.59340	23
38	.40688	.49125	.59312	22
39	.40717	.49131	.59283	21
40	.40745	.49136	.59255	**20**
41	.40774	.49141	.59226	19
42	.40802	.49147	.59198	18
43	.40831	.49152	.59169	17
44	.40860	.49157	.59140	16
45	.40888	.49163	.59112	**15**
46	.40917	.49168	.59083	14
47	.40945	.49173	.59055	13
48	.40974	.49179	.59026	12
49	.41003	.49184	.58997	11
50	.41031	.49189	.58969	**10**
51	.41060	.49194	.58940	9
52	.41089	.49199	.58911	8
53	.41117	.49205	.58883	7
54	.41146	.49210	.58854	6
55	.41174	.49215	.58826	**5**
56	.41203	.49220	.58797	4
57	.41232	.49225	.58768	3
58	.41260	.49230	.58740	2
59	.41289	.49235	.58711	1
60	.41318	.49240	.58682	**0**
′	Cos²	Sin · Cos	Sin²	′

129° (309°) (230°) **50°**

Sin² x Cos² x Sin x Cos x

40° (220°) (319°) **139°**

′	Sin²	Sin · Cos	Cos²	′
0	.41318	.49240	.58682	**60**
1	.41346	.49245	.58654	59
2	.41375	.49250	.58625	58
3	.41404	.49255	.58596	57
4	.41432	.49260	.58568	56
5	.41461	.49265	.58539	**55**
6	.41490	.49270	.58510	54
7	.41518	.49275	.58482	53
8	.41547	.49280	.58453	52
9	.41576	.49285	.58424	51
10	.41604	.49290	.58396	**50**
11	.41633	.49295	.58367	49
12	.41662	.49300	.58338	48
13	.41690	.49305	.58310	47
14	.41719	.49309	.58281	46
15	.41748	.49314	.58252	**45**
16	.41776	.49319	.58224	44
17	.41805	.49324	.58195	43
18	.41834	.49329	.58166	42
19	.41862	.49333	.58138	41
20	.41891	.49338	.58109	**40**
21	.41920	.49343	.58080	39
22	.41949	.49347	.58051	38
23	.41977	.49352	.58023	37
24	.42006	.49357	.57994	36
25	.42035	.49361	.57965	**35**
26	.42063	.49366	.57937	34
27	.42092	.49371	.57908	33
28	.42121	.49375	.57879	32
29	.42150	.49380	.57850	31
30	.42178	.49384	.57822	**30**
31	.42207	.49389	.57793	29
32	.42236	.49393	.57764	28
33	.42264	.49398	.57736	27
34	.42293	.49402	.57707	26
35	.42322	.49407	.57678	**25**
36	.42351	.49411	.57649	24
37	.42379	.49416	.57621	23
38	.42408	.49420	.57592	22
39	.42437	.49425	.57563	21
40	.42466	.49429	.57534	**20**
41	.42494	.49433	.57506	19
42	.42523	.49438	.57477	18
43	.42552	.49442	.57448	17
44	.42581	.49446	.57419	16
45	.42610	.49451	.57390	**15**
46	.42638	.49455	.57362	14
47	.42667	.49459	.57333	13
48	.42696	.49464	.57304	12
49	.42725	.49468	.57275	11
50	.42753	.49472	.57247	**10**
51	.42782	.49476	.57218	9
52	.42811	.49480	.57189	8
53	.42840	.49485	.57160	7
54	.42869	.49489	.57131	6
55	.42897	.49493	.57103	**5**
56	.42926	.49497	.57074	4
57	.42955	.49501	.57045	3
58	.42984	.49505	.57016	2
59	.43013	.49509	.56987	1
60	.43041	.49513	.56959	**0**
′	Cos²	Sin · Cos	Sin²	′

130°(310°) (229°) **49°**

41° (221°) (318°) **138°**

′	Sin²	Sin · Cos	Cos²	′
0	.43041	.49513	.56959	**60**
1	.43070	.49517	.56930	59
2	.43099	.49521	.56901	58
3	.43128	.49525	.56872	57
4	.43157	.49529	.56843	56
5	.43185	.49533	.56815	**55**
6	.43214	.49537	.56786	54
7	.43243	.49541	.56757	53
8	.43272	.49545	.56728	52
9	.43301	.49549	.56699	51
10	.43330	.49553	.56670	**50**
11	.43358	.49557	.56642	49
12	.43387	.49561	.56613	48
13	.43416	.49565	.56584	47
14	.43445	.49568	.56555	46
15	.43474	.49572	.56526	**45**
16	.43503	.49576	.56497	44
17	.43531	.49580	.56469	43
18	.43560	.49584	.56440	42
19	.43589	.49587	.56411	41
20	.43618	.49591	.56382	**40**
21	.43647	.49595	.56353	39
22	.43676	.49598	.56324	38
23	.43704	.49602	.56296	37
24	.43733	.49606	.56267	36
25	.43762	.49609	.56238	**35**
26	.43791	.49613	.56209	34
27	.43820	.49617	.56180	33
28	.43849	.49620	.56151	32
29	.43878	.49624	.56122	31
30	.43907	.49627	.56093	**30**
31	.43935	.49631	.56065	29
32	.43964	.49634	.56036	28
33	.43993	.49638	.56007	27
34	.44022	.49641	.55978	26
35	.44051	.49645	.55949	**25**
36	.44080	.49648	.55920	24
37	.44109	.49652	.55891	23
38	.44138	.49655	.55862	22
39	.44166	.49659	.55834	21
40	.44195	.49662	.55805	**20**
41	.44224	.49665	.55776	19
42	.44253	.49669	.55747	18
43	.44282	.49672	.55718	17
44	.44311	.49675	.55689	16
45	.44340	.49679	.55660	**15**
46	.44369	.49682	.55631	14
47	.44398	.49685	.55602	13
48	.44427	.49688	.55573	12
49	.44455	.49692	.55545	11
50	.44484	.49695	.55516	**10**
51	.44513	.49698	.55487	9
52	.44542	.49701	.55458	8
53	.44571	.49704	.55429	7
54	.44600	.49708	.55400	6
55	.44629	.49711	.55371	**5**
56	.44658	.49714	.55342	4
57	.44687	.49717	.55313	3
58	.44716	.49720	.55284	2
59	.44745	.49723	.55255	1
60	.44774	.49726	.55226	**0**
′	Cos²	Sin · Cos	Sin²	′

131° (311°) (228°) **48°**

42° (222°) (317°) **137°**

′	Sin^2	Sin · Cos	Cos^2	′
0	.44774	.49726	.55226	**60**
1	.44803	.49729	.55197	59
2	.44831	.49732	.55169	58
3	.44860	.49735	.55140	57
4	.44889	.49738	.55111	56
5	.44918	.49741	.55082	**55**
6	.44947	.49744	.55053	54
7	.44976	.49747	.55024	53
8	.45005	.49750	.54995	52
9	.45034	.49753	.54966	51
10	.45063	.49756	.54937	**50**
11	.45092	.49759	.54908	49
12	.45121	.49761	.54879	48
13	.45150	.49764	.54850	47
14	.45179	.49767	.54821	46
15	.45208	.49770	.54792	**45**
16	.45237	.49773	.54763	44
17	.45266	.49775	.54734	43
18	.45295	.49778	.54705	42
19	.45324	.49781	.54676	41
20	.45353	.49784	.54647	**40**
21	.45381	.49786	.54619	39
22	.45410	.49789	.54590	38
23	.45439	.49792	.54561	37
24	.45468	.49794	.54532	36
25	.45497	.49797	.54503	**35**
26	.45526	.49799	.54474	34
27	.45555	.49802	.54445	33
28	.45584	.49805	.54416	32
29	.45613	.49807	.54387	31
30	.45642	.49810	.54358	**30**
31	.45671	.49812	.54329	29
32	.45700	.49815	.54300	28
33	.45729	.49817	.54271	27
34	.45758	.49820	.54242	26
35	.45787	.49822	.54213	**25**
36	.45816	.49825	.54184	24
37	.45845	.49827	.54155	23
38	.45874	.49829	.54126	22
39	.45903	.49832	.54097	21
40	.45932	.49834	.54068	**20**
41	.45961	.49837	.54039	19
42	.45990	.49839	.54010	18
43	.46019	.49841	.53981	17
44	.46048	.49844	.53952	16
45	.46077	.49846	.53923	**15**
46	.46106	.49848	.53894	14
47	.46135	.49850	.53865	13
48	.46164	.49853	.53836	12
49	.46193	.49855	.53807	11
50	.46222	.49857	.53778	**10**
51	.46251	.49859	.53749	9
52	.46280	.49861	.53720	8
53	.46309	.49864	.53691	7
54	.46338	.49866	.53662	6
55	.46367	.49868	.53633	**5**
56	.46396	.49870	.53604	4
57	.46425	.49872	.53575	3
58	.46454	.49874	.53546	2
59	.46483	.49876	.53517	1
60	.46512	.49878	.53488	**0**
′	Cos^2	Sin · Cos	Sin^2	′

132° (312°) (227°) **47°**

43° (223°) (316°) **136°**

′	Sin^2	Sin · Cos	Cos^2	′
0	.46512	.49878	.53488	**60**
1	.46541	.49880	.53459	59
2	.46570	.49882	.53430	58
3	.46599	.49884	.53401	57
4	.46628	.49886	.53372	56
5	.46657	.49888	.53343	**55**
6	.46686	.49890	.53314	54
7	.46715	.49892	.53285	53
8	.46744	.49894	.53256	52
9	.46773	.49896	.53227	51
10	.46802	.49898	.53198	**50**
11	.46831	.49900	.53169	49
12	.46860	.49901	.53140	48
13	.46890	.49903	.53110	47
14	.46919	.49905	.53081	46
15	.46948	.49907	.53052	**45**
16	.46977	.49909	.53023	44
17	.47006	.49910	.52994	43
18	.47035	.49912	.52965	42
19	.47064	.49914	.52936	41
20	.47093	.49915	.52907	**40**
21	.47122	.49917	.52878	39
22	.47151	.49919	.52849	38
23	.47180	.49920	.52820	37
24	.47209	.49922	.52791	36
25	.47238	.49924	.52762	**35**
26	.47267	.49925	.52733	34
27	.47296	.49927	.52704	33
28	.47325	.49928	.52675	32
29	.47354	.49930	.52646	31
30	.47383	.49931	.52617	**30**
31	.47412	.49933	.52588	29
32	.47441	.49934	.52559	28
33	.47470	.49936	.52530	27
34	.47499	.49937	.52501	26
35	.47528	.49939	.52472	**25**
36	.47558	.49940	.52442	24
37	.47587	.49942	.52413	23
38	.47616	.49943	.52384	22
39	.47645	.49944	.52355	21
40	.47674	.49946	.52326	**20**
41	.47703	.49947	.52297	19
42	.47732	.49949	.52268	18
43	.47761	.49950	.52239	17
44	.47790	.49951	.52210	16
45	.47819	.49952	.52181	**15**
46	.47848	.49954	.52152	14
47	.47877	.49955	.52123	13
48	.47906	.49956	.52094	12
49	.47935	.49957	.52065	11
50	.47964	.49959	.52036	**10**
51	.47993	.49960	.52007	9
52	.48022	.49961	.51978	8
53	.48052	.49962	.51948	7
54	.48081	.49963	.51919	6
55	.48110	.49964	.51890	**5**
56	.48139	.49965	.51861	4
57	.48168	.49966	.51832	3
58	.48197	.49967	.51803	2
59	.48226	.49969	.51774	1
60	.48255	.49970	.51745	**0**
′	Cos^2	Sin · Cos	Sin^2	′

133° (313°) (226°) **46°**

44° (224°) (315°) 135°

′	Sin²	Sin · Cos	Cos²	′
0	.48255	.49970	.51745	**60**
1	.48284	.49971	.51716	59
2	.48313	.49972	.51687	58
3	.48342	.49973	.51658	57
4	.48371	.49973	.51629	56
5	.48400	.49974	.51600	**55**
6	.48429	.49975	.51571	54
7	.48459	.49976	.51541	53
8	.48488	.49977	.51512	52
9	.48517	.49978	.51483	51
10	.48546	.49979	.51454	**50**
11	.48575	.49980	.51425	49
12	.48604	.49981	.51396	48
13	.48633	.49981	.51367	47
14	.48662	.49982	.51338	46
15	.48691	.49983	.51309	**45**
16	.48720	.49984	.51280	44
17	.48749	.49984	.51251	43
18	.48778	.49985	.51222	42
19	.48807	.49986	.51193	41
20	.48837	.49986	.51163	**40**
21	.48866	.49987	.51134	39
22	.48895	.49988	.51105	38
23	.48924	.49988	.51076	37
24	.48953	.49989	.51047	36
25	.48982	.49990	.51018	**35**
26	.49011	.49990	.50989	34
27	.49040	.49991	.50960	33
28	.49069	.49991	.50931	32
29	.49098	.49992	.50902	31
30	.49127	.49992	.50873	**30**
31	.49156	.49993	.50844	29
32	.49186	.49993	.50814	28
33	.49215	.49994	.50785	27
34	.49244	.49994	.50756	26
35	.49273	.49995	.50727	**25**
36	.49302	.49995	.50698	24
37	.49331	.49996	.50669	23
38	.49360	.49996	.50640	22
39	.49389	.49996	.50611	21
40	.49418	.49997	.50582	**20**
41	.49447	.49997	.50553	19
42	.49476	.49997	.50524	18
43	.49505	.49998	.50495	17
44	.49535	.49998	.50465	16
45	.49564	.49998	.50436	**15**
46	.49593	.49998	.50407	14
47	.49622	.49999	.50378	13
48	.49651	.49999	.50349	12
49	.49680	.49999	.50320	11
50	.49709	.49999	.50291	**10**
51	.49738	.49999	.50262	9
52	.49767	.49999	.50233	8
53	.49796	.50000	.50204	7
54	.49825	.50000	.50175	6
55	.49855	.50000	.50145	**5**
56	.49884	.50000	.50116	4
57	.49913	.50000	.50087	3
58	.49942	.50000	.50058	2
59	.49971	.50000	.50029	1
60	.50000	.50000	.50000	**0**
′	Cos²	Sin · Cos	Sin²	′

134° (314°) (225°) 45°

NATURAL OR NAPERIAN LOGARITHMS

0.000–0.499

N	0	1	2	3	4	5	6	7	8	9
0.00	− ∞	−6† .90776	−6 .21461	−5 .80914	−5 .52146	−5 .29832	−5 .11600	−4 .96185	−4 .82831	−4 .71053
.01	−4.60517	.50986	.42285	.34281	.26870	.19971	.13517	.07454	.01738	*.96332
.02	−3.91202	.86323	.81671	.77226	.72970	.68888	.64966	.61192	.57555	.54046
.03	.50656	.47377	.44202	.41125	.38139	.35241	.32424	.29684	.27017	.24419
.04	.21888	.19418	.17009	.14656	.12357	.10109	.07911	.05761	.03655	.01593
.05	−2.99573	.97593	.95651	.93746	.91877	.90042	.88240	.86470	.84731	.83022
.06	.81341	.79688	.78062	.76462	.74887	.73337	.71810	.70306	.68825	.67365
.07	.65926	.64508	.63109	.61730	.60369	.59027	.57702	.56395	.55105	.53831
.08	.52573	.51331	.50104	.48891	.47694	.46510	.45341	.44185	.43042	.41912
.09	.40795	.39690	.38597	.37516	.36446	.35388	.34341	.33304	.32279	.31264
0.10	−2.30259	.29263	.28278	.27303	.26336	.25379	.24432	.23493	.22562	.21641
.11	.20727	.19823	.18926	.18037	.17156	.16282	.15417	.14558	.13707	.12863
.12	.12026	.11196	.10373	.09557	.08747	.07944	.07147	.06357	.05573	.04794
.13	.04022	.03256	.02495	.01741	.00992	.00248	*.99510	*.98777	*.98050	*.97328
.14	−1.96611	.95900	.95193	.94491	.93794	.93102	.92415	.91732	.91054	.90381
.15	.89712	.89048	.88387	.87732	.87080	.86433	.85790	.85151	.84516	.83885
.16	.83258	.82635	.82016	.81401	.80789	.80181	.79577	.78976	.78379	.77786
.17	.77196	.76609	.76026	.75446	.74870	.74297	.73727	.73161	.72597	.72037
.18	.71480	.70926	.70375	.69827	.69282	.68740	.68201	.67665	.67131	.66601
.19	.66073	.65548	.65026	.64507	.63990	.63476	.62964	.62455	.61949	.61445
0.20	−1.60944	.60445	.59949	.59455	.58964	.58475	.57988	.57504	.57022	.56542
.21	.56065	.55590	.55117	.54646	.54178	.53712	.53248	.52786	.52326	.51868
.22	.51413	.50959	.50508	.50058	.49611	.49165	.48722	.48281	.47841	.47403
.23	.46968	.46534	.46102	.45672	.45243	.44817	.44392	.43970	.43548	.43129
.24	.42712	.42296	.41882	.41469	.41059	.40650	.40242	.39837	.39433	.39030
.25	.38629	.38230	.37833	.37437	.37042	.36649	.36258	.35868	.35480	.35093
.26	.34707	.34323	.33941	.33560	.33181	.32803	.32426	.32051	.31677	.31304
.27	.30933	.30564	.30195	.29828	.29463	.29098	.28735	.28374	.28013	.27654
.28	.27297	.26940	.26585	.26231	.25878	.25527	.25176	.24827	.24479	.24133
.29	.23787	.23443	.23100	.22758	.22418	.22078	.21740	.21402	.21066	.20731
0.30	−1.20397	.20065	.19733	.19402	.19073	.18744	.18417	.18091	.17766	.17441
.31	.17118	.16796	.16475	.16155	.15836	.15518	.15201	.14885	.14570	.14256
.32	.13943	.13631	.13320	.13010	.12701	.12393	.12086	.11780	.11474	.11170
.33	.10866	.10564	.10262	.09961	.09661	.09362	.09064	.08767	.08471	.08176
.34	.07881	.07587	.07294	.07002	.06711	.06421	.06132	.05843	.05555	.05268
.35	−1.04982	.04697	.04412	.04129	.03846	.03564	.03282	.03002	.02722	.02443
.36	.02165	.01888	.01611	.01335	.01060	.00786	.00512	.00239	*.99967	*.99696
.37	−0.99425	.99155	.98886	.98618	.98350	.98083	.97817	.97551	.97286	.97022
.38	.96758	.96496	.96233	.95972	.95711	.95451	.95192	.94933	.94675	.94418
.39	.94161	.93905	.93649	.93395	.93140	.92887	.92634	.92382	.92130	.91879
0.40	−0.91629	.91379	.91130	.90882	.90634	.90387	.90140	.89894	.89649	.89404
.41	.89160	.88916	.88673	.88431	.88189	.87948	.87707	.87467	.87227	.86988
.42	.86750	.86512	.86275	.86038	.85802	.85567	.85332	.85097	.84863	.84630
.43	.84397	.84165	.83933	.83702	.83471	.83241	.83011	.82782	.82554	.82326
.44	.82098	.81871	.81645	.81419	.81193	.80968	.80744	.80520	.80296	.80073
.45	.79851	.79629	.79407	.79186	.78966	.78746	.78526	.78307	.78089	.77871
.46	.77653	.77436	.77219	.77003	.76787	.76572	.76357	.76143	.75929	.75715
.47	.75502	.75290	.75078	.74866	.74655	.74444	.74234	.74024	.73814	.73605
.48	.73397	.73189	.72981	.72774	.72567	.72361	.72155	.71949	.71744	.71539
.49	.71335	.71131	.70928	.70725	.70522	.70320	.70118	.69917	.69716	.69515

† Note that the characteristics are given *above* the mantissa for the first line. In the second and following lines they are given at the left.

0.500–0.999

N	0	1	2	3	4	5	6	7	8	9
0.50	−0.69315	.69115	.68916	.68717	.68518	.68320	.68122	.67924	.67727	.67531
.51	.67334	.67139	.66943	.66748	.66553	.66359	.66165	.65971	.65778	.65585
.52	.65393	.65201	.65009	.64817	.64626	.64436	.64245	.64055	.63866	.63677
.53	.63488	.63299	.63111	.62923	.62736	.62549	.62362	.62176	.61990	.61804
.54	.61619	.61434	.61249	.61065	.60881	.60697	.60514	.60331	.60148	.59966
.55	.59784	.59602	.59421	.59240	.59059	.58879	.58699	.58519	.58340	.58161
.56	.57982	.57803	.57625	.57448	.57270	.57093	.56916	.56740	.56563	.56387
.57	.56212	.56037	.55862	.55687	.55513	.55339	.55165	.54991	.54818	.54645
.58	.54473	.54300	.54128	.53957	.53785	.53614	.53444	.53273	.53103	.52933
.59	.52763	.52594	.52425	.52256	.52088	.51919	.51751	.51584	.51416	.51249
0.60	−0.51083	.50916	.50750	.50584	.50418	.50253	.50088	.49923	.49758	.49594
.61	.49430	.49266	.49102	.48939	.48776	.48613	.48451	.48289	.48127	.47965
.62	.47804	.47642	.47482	.47321	.47160	.47000	.46840	.46681	.46522	.46362
.63	.46204	.46045	.45887	.45728	.45571	.45413	.45256	.45099	.44942	.44785
.64	.44629	.44473	.44317	.44161	.44006	.43850	.43696	.43541	.43386	.43232
.65	.43078	.42925	.42771	.42618	.42465	.42312	.42159	.42007	.41855	.41703
.66	.41552	.41400	.41249	.41098	.40947	.40797	.40647	.40497	.40347	.40197
.67	.40048	.39899	.39750	.39601	.39453	.39304	.39156	.39008	.38861	.38713
.68	.38566	.38419	.38273	.38126	.37980	.37834	.37688	.37542	.37397	.37251
.69	.37106	.36962	.36817	.36673	.36528	.36384	.36241	.36097	.35954	.35810
0.70	−0.35667	.35525	.35382	.35240	.35098	.34956	.34814	.34672	.34531	.34390
.71	.34249	.34108	.33968	.33827	.33687	.33547	.33408	.33268	.33129	.32989
.72	.32850	.32712	.32573	.32435	.32296	.32158	.32021	.31883	.31745	.31608
.73	.31471	.31334	.31197	.31061	.30925	.30788	.30653	.30517	.30381	.30246
.74	.30111	.29975	.29841	.29706	.29571	.29437	.29303	.29169	.29035	.28902
.75	.28768	.28635	.28502	.28369	.28236	.28104	.27971	.27839	.27707	.27575
.76	.27444	.27312	.27181	.27050	.26919	.26788	.26657	.26527	.26397	.26266
.77	.26136	.26007	.25877	.25748	.25618	.25489	.25360	.25231	.25103	.24974
.78	.24846	.24718	.24590	.24462	.24335	.24207	.24080	.23953	.23826	.23699
.79	.23572	.23446	.23319	.23193	.23067	.22941	.22816	.22690	.22565	.22439
0.80	−0.22314	.22189	.22065	.21940	.21816	.21691	.21567	.21443	.21319	.21196
.81	.21072	.20949	.20825	.20702	.20579	.20457	.20334	.20212	.20089	.19967
.82	.19845	.19723	.19601	.19480	.19358	.19237	.19116	.18995	.18874	.18754
.83	.18633	.18513	.18392	.18272	.18152	.18032	.17913	.17793	.17674	.17554
.84	.17435	.17316	.17198	.17079	.16960	.16842	.16724	.16605	.16487	.16370
.85	−0.16252	.16134	.16017	.15900	.15782	.15665	.15548	.15432	.15315	.15199
.86	.15032	.14966	.14850	.14734	.14618	.14503	.14387	.14272	.14156	.14041
.87	.13926	.13811	.13697	.13582	.13467	.13353	.13239	.13125	.13011	.12897
.88	.12783	.12670	.12556	.12443	.12330	.12217	.12104	.11991	.11878	.11766
.89	.11653	.11541	.11429	.11317	.11205	.11093	.10981	.10870	.10759	.10647
0.90	−0.10536	.10425	.10314	.10203	.10093	.09982	.09872	.09761	.09651	.09541
.91	.09431	.09321	.09212	.09102	.08992	.08883	.08774	.08665	.08556	.08447
.92	.08338	.08230	.08121	.08013	.07904	.07796	.07688	.07580	.07472	.07365
.93	.07257	.07150	.07042	.06935	.06828	.06721	.06614	.06507	.06401	.06294
.94	.06188	.06081	.05975	.05869	.05763	.05657	.05551	.05446	.05340	.05235
.95	.05129	.05024	.04919	.04814	.04709	.04604	.04500	.04395	.04291	.04186
.96	.04082	.03978	.03874	.03770	.03666	.03563	.03459	.03356	.03252	.03149
.97	.03046	.02943	.02840	.02737	.02634	.02532	.02429	.02327	.02225	.02122
.98	.02020	.01918	.01816	.01715	.01613	.01511	.01410	.01309	.01207	.01106
.99	.01005	.00904	.00803	.00702	.00602	.00501	.00401	.00300	.00200	.00100

NATURAL OR NAPERIAN LOGARITHMS (Continued)

To find the natural logarithm of a number which is $\frac{1}{10}$, $\frac{1}{100}$, $\frac{1}{1000}$, etc. of a number whose logarithm is given, subtract from the given logarithm $\log_e 10$, $2 \log_e 10$, $3 \log_e 10$, etc.

To find the natural logarithm of a number which is 10, 100, 1000, etc. times a number whose logarithm is given, add to the given logarithm $\log_e 10$, $2 \log_e 10$, $3 \log_e 10$, etc.

$\log_e 10 =$ 2.30258 50930	$6 \log_e 10 =$ 13.81551 05580
$2 \log_e 10 =$ 4.60517 01860	$7 \log_e 10 =$ 16.11809 56510
$3 \log_e 10 =$ 6.90775 52790	$8 \log_e 10 =$ 18.42068 07440
$4 \log_e 10 =$ 9.21034 03720	$9 \log_e 10 =$ 20.72326 58369
$5 \log_e 10 =$ 11.51292 54650	$10 \log_e 10 =$ 23.02585 09299

See preceding table for logarithms for numbers between 0.000 and 0.999.

1.00–4.99

N	0	1	2	3	4	5	6	7	8	9
1.0	0.00000	.00995	.01980	.02956	.03922	.04879	.05827	.06766	.07696	.08618
.1	.09531	.10436	.11333	.12222	.13103	.13976	.14842	.15700	.16551	.17395
.2	.18232	.19062	.19885	.20701	.21511	.22314	.23111	.23902	.24686	.25464
.3	.26236	.27003	.27763	.28518	.29267	.30010	.30748	.31481	.32208	.32930
.4	.33647	.34359	.35066	.35767	.36464	.37156	.37844	.38526	.39204	.39878
.5	.40547	.41211	.41871	.42527	.43178	.43825	.44469	.45108	.45742	.46373
.6	.47000	.47623	.48243	.48858	.49470	.50078	.50682	.51282	.51879	.52473
.7	.53063	.53649	.54232	.54812	.55389	.55962	.56531	.57098	.57661	.58222
.8	.58779	.59333	.59884	.60432	.60977	.61519	.62058	.62594	.63127	.63658
.9	.64185	.64710	.65233	.65752	.66269	.66783	.67294	.67803	.68310	.68813
2.0	0.69315	.69813	.70310	.70804	.71295	.71784	.72271	.72755	.73237	.73716
.1	.74194	.74669	.75142	.75612	.76081	.76547	.77011	.77473	.77932	.78390
.2	.78846	.79299	.79751	.80200	.80648	.81093	.81536	.81978	.82418	.82855
.3	.83291	.83725	.84157	.84587	.85015	.85442	.85866	.86289	.86710	.87129
.4	.87547	.87963	.88377	.88789	.89200	.89609	.90016	.90422	.90826	.91228
.5	.91629	.92028	.92426	.92822	.93216	.93609	.94001	.94391	.94779	.95166
.6	.95551	.95935	.96317	.96698	.97078	.97456	.97833	.98208	.98582	.98954
.7	.99325	.99695	*.00063	*.00430	*.00796	*.01160	*.01523	*.01885	*.02245	*.02604
.8	1.02962	.03318	.03674	.04028	.04380	.04732	.05082	.05431	.05779	.06126
.9	.06471	.06815	.07158	.07500	.07841	.08181	.08519	.0885[illegible]	.09192	.09527
3.0	1.09861	.10194	.10526	.10856	.11186	.11514	.11841	.12168	.12493	.12817
.1	.13140	.13462	.13783	.14103	.14422	.14740	.15057	.15373	.15688	.16002
.2	.16315	.16627	.16938	.17248	.17557	.17865	.18173	.18479	.18784	.19089
.3	.19392	.19695	.19996	.20297	.20597	.20896	.21194	.21491	.21788	.22083
.4	.22378	.22671	.22964	.23256	.23547	.23837	.24127	.24415	.24703	.24990
.5	.25276	.25562	.25846	.26130	.26413	.26695	.26976	.27257	.27536	.27815
.6	.28093	.28371	.28647	.28923	.29198	.29473	.29746	.30019	.30291	.30563
.7	.30833	.31103	.31372	.31641	.31909	.32176	.32442	.32708	.32972	.33237
.8	.33500	.33763	.34025	.34286	.34547	.34807	.35067	.35325	.35584	.35841
.9	.36098	.36354	.36609	.36864	.37118	.37372	.37624	.37877	.38128	.38379
4.0	1.38629	.38879	.39128	.39377	.39624	.39872	.40118	.40364	.40610	.40854
.1	.41099	.41342	.41585	.41828	.42070	.42311	.42552	.42792	.43031	.43270
.2	.43508	.43746	.43984	.44220	.44456	.44692	.44927	.45161	.45395	.45629
.3	.45862	.46094	.46326	.46557	.46787	.47018	.47247	.47476	.47705	.47933
.4	.48160	.48387	.48614	.48840	.49065	.49290	.49515	.49739	.49962	.50185
.5	.50408	.50630	.50851	.51072	.51293	.51513	.51732	.51951	.52170	.52388
.6	.52606	.52823	.53039	.53256	.53471	.53687	.53902	.54116	.54330	.54543
.7	.54756	.54969	.55181	.55393	.55604	.55814	.56025	.56235	.56444	.56653
.8	.56862	.57070	.57277	.57485	.57691	.57898	.58104	.58309	.58515	.58719
.9	.58924	.59127	.59331	.59534	.59737	.59939	.60141	.60342	.60543	.60744

NATURAL OR NAPERIAN LOGARITHMS (Continued)

5.00–9.99

N	0	1	2	3	4	5	6	7	8	9
5.0	1.60944	.61144	.61343	.61542	.61741	.61939	.62137	.62334	.62531	.62728
.1	.62924	.63120	.63315	.63511	.63705	.63900	.64094	.64287	.64481	.64673
.2	.64866	.65058	.65250	.65441	.65632	.65823	.66013	.66203	.66393	.66582
.3	.66771	.66959	.67147	.67335	.67523	.67710	.67896	.68083	.68269	.68455
.4	.68640	.68825	.69010	.69194	.69378	.69562	.69745	.69928	.70111	.70293
.5	.70475	.70656	.70838	.71019	.71199	.71380	.71560	.71740	.71919	.72098
.6	.72277	.72455	.72633	.72811	.72988	.73166	.73342	.73519	.73695	.73871
.7	.74047	.74222	.74397	.74572	.74746	.74920	.75094	.75267	.75440	.75613
.8	.75786	.75958	.76130	.76302	.76473	.76644	.76815	.76985	.77156	.77326
.9	.77495	.77665	.77834	.78002	.78171	.78339	.78507	.78675	.78842	.79009
6.0	1.79176	.79342	.79509	.79675	.79840	.80006	.80171	.80336	.80500	.80665
.1	.80829	.80993	.81156	.81319	.81482	.81645	.81808	.81970	.82132	.82294
.2	.82455	.82616	.82777	.82938	.83098	.83258	.83418	.83578	.83737	.83896
.3	.84055	.84214	.84372	.84530	.84688	.84845	.85003	.85160	.85317	.85473
.4	.85630	.85786	.85942	.86097	.86253	.86408	.86563	.86718	.86872	.87026
.5	.87180	.87334	.87487	.87641	.87794	.87947	.88099	.88251	.88403	.88555
.6	.88707	.88858	.89010	.89160	.89311	.89462	.89612	.89762	.89912	.90061
.7	.90211	.90360	.90509	.90658	.90806	.90954	.91102	.91250	.91398	.91545
.8	.91692	.91839	.91986	.92132	.92279	.92425	.92571	.92716	.92862	.93007
.9	.93152	.93297	.93442	.93586	.93730	.93874	.94018	.94162	.94305	.94448
7.0	1.94591	.94734	.94876	.95019	.95161	.95303	.95445	.95586	.95727	.95869
.1	.96009	.96150	.96291	.96431	.96571	.96711	.96851	.96991	.97130	.97269
.2	.97408	.97547	.97685	.97824	.97962	.98100	.98238	.98376	.98513	.98650
.3	.98787	.98924	.99061	.99198	.99334	.99470	.99606	.99742	.99877	*.00013
.4	2.00148	.00283	.00418	.00553	.00687	.00821	.00956	.01089	.01223	.01357
.5	.01490	.01624	.01757	.01890	.02022	.02155	.02287	.02419	.02551	.02683
.6	.02815	.02946	.03078	.03209	.03340	.03471	.03601	.03732	.03862	.03992
.7	.04122	.04252	.04381	.04511	.04640	.04769	.04898	.05027	.05156	.05284
.8	.05412	.05540	.05668	.05796	.05924	.06051	.06179	.06306	.06433	.06560
.9	.06686	.06813	.06939	.07065	.07191	.07317	.07443	.07568	.07694	.07819
8.0	2.07944	.08069	.08194	.08318	.08443	.08567	.08691	.08815	.08939	.09063
.1	.09186	.09310	.09433	.09556	.09679	.09802	.09924	.10047	.10169	.10291
.2	.10413	.10535	.10657	.10779	.10900	.11021	.11142	.11263	.11384	.11505
.3	.11626	.11746	.11866	.11986	.12106	.12226	.12346	.12465	.12585	.12704
.4	.12823	.12942	.13061	.13180	.13298	.13417	.13535	.13653	.13771	.13889
.5	.14007	.14124	.14242	.14359	.14476	.14593	.14710	.14827	.14943	.15060
.6	.15176	.15292	.15409	.15524	.15640	.15756	.15871	.15987	.16102	.16217
.7	.16332	.16447	.16562	.16677	.16791	.16905	.17020	.17134	.17248	.17361
.8	.17475	.17589	.17702	.17816	.17929	.18042	.18155	.18267	.18380	.18493
.9	.18605	.18717	.18830	.18942	.19054	.19165	.19277	.19389	.19500	.19611
9.0	2.19722	.19834	.19944	.20055	.20166	.20276	.20387	.20497	.20607	.20717
.1	.20827	.20937	.21047	.21157	.21266	.21375	.21485	.21594	.21703	.21812
.2	.21920	.22029	.22138	.22246	.22354	.22462	.22570	.22678	.22786	.22894
.3	.23001	.23109	.23216	.23324	.23431	.23538	.23645	.23751	.23858	.23965
.4	.24071	.24177	.24284	.24390	.24496	.24601	.24707	.24813	.24918	.25024
.5	.25129	.25234	.25339	.25444	.25549	.25654	.25759	.25863	.25968	.26072
.6	.26176	.26280	.26384	.26488	.26592	.26696	.26799	.26903	.27006	.27109
.7	.27213	.27316	.27419	.27521	.27624	.27727	.27829	.27932	.28034	.28136
.8	.28238	.28340	.28442	.28544	.28646	.28747	.28849	.28950	.29051	.29152
.9	.29253	.29354	.29455	.29556	.29657	.29757	.29858	.29958	.30058	.30158

NATURAL OR NAPERIAN LOGARITHMS (Continued)

Constants

$\log_e 10 = 2.30258\ 50930$	$6 \log_e 10 = 13.81551\ 05580$
$2 \log_e 10 = 4.60517\ 01860$	$7 \log_e 10 = 16.11809\ 56510$
$3 \log_e 10 = 6.90775\ 52790$	$8 \log_e 10 = 18.42068\ 07440$
$4 \log_e 10 = 9.21034\ 03720$	$9 \log_e 10 = 20.72326\ 58369$
$5 \log_e 10 = 11.51292\ 54650$	$10 \log_e 10 = 23.02585\ 09299$

10.0–49.9

N	0	1	2	3	4	5	6	7	8	9
10.	2.30259	.31254	.32239	.33214	.34181	.35138	.36085	.37024	.37955	.38876
11.	.39790	.40695	.41591	.42480	.43361	.44235	.45101	.45959	.46810	.47654
12.	.48491	.49321	.50144	.50960	.51770	.52573	.53370	.54160	.54945	.55723
13.	.56495	.57261	.58022	.58776	.59525	.60269	.61007	.61740	.62467	.63189
14.	.63906	.64617	.65324	.66026	.66723	.67415	.68102	.68785	.69463	.70136
15.	.70805	.71469	.72130	.72785	.73437	.74084	.74727	.75366	.76001	.76632
16.	.77259	.77882	.78501	.79117	.79728	.80336	.80940	.81541	.82138	.82731
17.	.83321	.83908	.84491	.85071	.85647	.86220	.86790	.87356	.87920	.88480
18.	.89037	.89591	.90142	.90690	.91235	.91777	.92316	.92852	.93386	.93916
19.	.94444	.94969	.95491	.96011	.96527	.97041	.97553	.98062	.98568	.99072
20.	2.99573	*.00072	*.00568	*.01062	*.01553	*.02042	*.02529	*.03013	*.03495	*.03975
21.	3.04452	.04927	.05400	.05871	.06339	.06805	.07269	.07731	.08191	.08649
22.	.09104	.09558	.10009	.10459	.10906	.11352	.11795	.12236	.12676	.13114
23.	.13549	.13983	.14415	.14845	.15274	.15700	.16125	.16548	.16969	.17388
24.	.17805	.18221	.18635	.19048	.19458	.19867	.20275	.20680	.21084	.21487
25.	.21888	.22287	.22684	.23080	.23475	.23868	.24259	.24649	.25037	.25424
26.	.25810	.26194	.26576	.26957	.27336	.27714	.28091	.28466	.28840	.29213
27.	.29584	.29953	.30322	.30689	.31054	.31419	.31782	.32143	.32504	.32863
28.	.33220	.33577	.33932	.34286	.34639	.34990	.35341	.35690	.36038	.36384
29.	.36730	.37074	.37417	.37759	.38099	.38439	.38777	.39115	.39451	.39786
30.	3.40120	.40453	.40784	.41115	.41444	.41773	.42100	.42426	.42751	.43076
31.	.43399	.43721	.44042	.44362	.44681	.44999	.45316	.45632	.45947	.46261
32.	.46574	.46886	.47197	.47507	.47816	.48124	.48431	.48738	.49043	.49347
33.	.49651	.49953	.50255	.50556	.50856	.51155	.51453	.51750	.52046	.52342
34.	.52636	.52930	.53223	.53515	.53806	.54096	.54385	.54674	.54962	.55249
35.	.55535	.55820	.56105	.56388	.56671	.56953	.57235	.57515	.57795	.58074
36.	.58352	.58629	.58906	.59182	.59457	.59731	.60005	.60278	.60550	.60821
37.	.61092	.61362	.61631	.61899	.62167	.62434	.62700	.62966	.63231	.63495
38.	.63759	.64021	.64284	.64545	.64806	.65066	.65325	.65584	.65842	.66099
39.	.66356	.66612	.66868	.67122	.67377	.67630	.67883	.68135	.68387	.68638
40.	3.68888	.69138	.69387	.69635	.69883	.70130	.70377	.70623	.70868	.71113
41.	.71357	.71601	.71844	.72086	.72328	.72569	.72810	.73050	.73290	.73529
42.	.73767	.74005	.74242	.74479	.74715	.74950	.75185	.75420	.75654	.75887
43.	.76120	.76352	.76584	.76815	.77046	.77276	.77506	.77735	.77963	.78191
44.	.78419	.78646	.78872	.79098	.79324	.79549	.79773	.79997	.80221	.80444
45.	.80666	.80888	.81110	.81331	.81551	.81771	.81991	.82210	.82428	.82647
46.	.82864	.83081	.83298	.83514	.83730	.83945	.84160	.84374	.84588	.84802
47.	.85015	.85227	.85439	.85651	.85862	.86073	.86283	.86493	.86703	.86912
48.	.87120	.87328	.87536	.87743	.87950	.88156	.88362	.88568	.88773	.88978
49.	.89182	.89386	.89589	.89792	.89995	.90197	.90399	.90600	.90801	.91002

NATURAL OR NAPERIAN LOGARITHMS (Continued)

50.0–99.9

N	0	1	2	3	4	5	6	7	8	9
50.	3.91202	.91402	.91602	.91801	.91999	.92197	.92395	.92593	.92790	.92986
51.	.93183	.93378	.93574	.93769	.93964	.94158	.94352	.94546	.94739	.94932
52.	.95124	.95316	.95508	.95700	.95891	.96081	.96272	.96462	.96651	.96840
53.	.97029	.97218	.97406	.97594	.97781	.97968	.98155	.98341	.98527	.98713
54.	.98898	.99083	.99268	.99452	.99636	.99820	*.00003	*.00186	*.00369	*.00551
55.	4.00733	.00915	.01096	.01277	.01458	.01638	.01818	.01998	.02177	.02356
56.	.02535	.02714	.02892	.03069	.03247	.03424	.03601	.03777	.03954	.04130
57.	.04305	.04480	.04655	.04830	.05004	.05178	.05352	.05526	.05699	.05872
58.	.06044	.06217	.06389	.06560	.06732	.06903	.07073	.07244	.07414	.07584
59.	.07754	.07923	.08092	.08261	.08429	.08598	.08766	.08933	.09101	.09268
60.	4.09434	.09601	.09767	.09933	.10099	.10264	.10429	.10594	.10759	.10923
61.	.11087	.11251	.11415	.11578	.11741	.11904	.12066	.12228	.12390	.12552
62.	.12713	.12875	.13036	.13196	.13357	.13517	.13677	.13836	.13996	.14155
63.	.14313	.14472	.14630	.14789	.14946	.15104	.15261	.15418	.15575	.15732
64.	.15888	.16044	.16200	.16356	.16511	.16667	.16821	.16976	.17131	.17285
65.	.17439	.17592	.17746	.17899	.18052	.18205	.18358	.18510	.18662	.18814
66.	.18965	.19117	.19268	.19419	.19570	.19720	.19870	.20020	.20170	.20320
67.	.20469	.20618	.20767	.20916	.21065	.21213	.21361	.21509	.21656	21804
68.	.21951	.22098	.22244	.22391	.22537	.22683	.22829	.22975	.23120	.23266
69.	.23411	.23555	.23700	.23844	.23989	.24133	.24276	.24420	.24563	.24707
70.	4.24850	.24992	.25135	.25277	.25419	.25561	.25703	.25845	.25986	.26127
71.	.26268	.26409	.26549	.26690	.26830	.26970	.27110	.27249	.27388	.27528
72.	.27667	.27805	.27944	.28082	.28221	.28359	.28496	.28634	.28772	.28909
73.	.29046	.29183	.29320	.29456	.29592	.29729	.29865	.30000	.30136	.30271
74.	.30407	.30542	.30676	.30811	.30946	.31080	.31214	.31348	.31482	.31615
75.	.31749	.31882	.32015	.32149	.32281	.32413	.32546	.32678	.32810	.32942
76.	.33073	.33205	.33336	.33467	.33598	.33729	.33860	.33990	.34120	.34251
77.	.34381	.34510	.34640	.34769	.34899	.35028	.35157	.35286	.35414	.35543
78.	.35671	.35800	.35927	.36055	.36182	.36310	.36437	.36564	.36691	.36818
79.	.36945	.37071	.37198	.37324	.37450	.37576	.37701	.37827	.37952	.38078
80.	4.38203	.38328	.38452	.38577	.38701	.38826	.38950	.39074	.39198	.39321
81.	.39445	.39568	.39692	.39815	.39938	.40060	.40183	.40305	.40428	.40550
82.	.40672	.40794	.40916	.41037	.41159	.41280	.41401	.41522	.41643	41764
83.	.41884	.42004	.42125	.42245	.42365	.42485	.42604	.42724	.42843	.42963
84.	.43082	.43201	.43319	.43438	.43557	.43675	.43793	.43912	.44030	.44147
85.	.44265	.44383	.44500	.44617	.44735	.44852	.44969	.45085	.45202	.45318
86.	.45435	.45551	.45667	.45783	.45899	.46014	.46130	.46245	.46361	.46476
87.	.46591	.46706	.46820	.46935	.47050	.47164	.47278	.47392	.47506	.47620
88.	.47734	.47847	.47961	.48074	.48187	.48300	.48413	.48526	.48639	.48751
89.	.48864	.48976	.49088	.49200	.49312	.49424	.49536	.49647	.49758	.49870
90.	4.49981	.50092	.50203	.50314	.50424	.50535	.50645	.50756	.50866	.50976
91.	.51086	.51196	.51305	.51415	.51525	.51634	.51743	.51852	.51961	.52070
92.	.52179	.52287	.52396	.52504	.52613	.52721	.52829	.52937	.53045	.53152
93.	.53260	.53367	.53475	.53582	.53689	.53796	.53903	.54010	.54116	.54223
94.	.54329	.54436	.54542	.54648	.54754	.54860	.54966	.55071	.55177	.55282
95.	.55388	.55493	.55598	.55703	.55808	.55913	.56017	.56122	.56226	.56331
96.	.56435	.56539	.56643	.56747	.56851	.56954	.57058	.57161	.57265	.57368
97.	.57471	.57574	.57677	.57780	.57883	.57985	.58088	.58190	.58292	.58395
98.	.58497	.58599	.58701	.58802	.58904	.59006	.59107	.59208	.59310	.59411
99.	.59512	.59613	.59714	.59815	.59915	.60016	.60116	.60217	.60317	.60417

NATURAL OR NAPERIAN LOGARITHMS (Continued)

0–499

N	0	1	2	3	4	5	6	7	8	9
0	∞	0.00000	0.69315	1.09861	.38629	.60944	.79176	.94591	*.07944	*.19722
1	2.30259	.39790	.48491	.56495	.63906	.70805	.77259	.83321	.89037	.94444
2	.99573	*.04452	*.09104	*.13549	*.17805	*.21888	*.25810	*.29584	*.33220	*.36730
3	3.40120	.43399	.46574	.49651	.52636	.55535	.58352	.61092	.63759	.66356
4	.68888	.71357	.73767	.76120	.78419	.80666	.82864	.85015	.87120	.89182
5	.91202	.93183	.95124	.97029	.98898	*.00733	*.02535	*.04305	*.06044	*.07754
6	4.09434	.11087	.12713	.14313	.15888	.17439	.18965	.20469	.21951	.23411
7	.24850	.26268	.27667	.29046	.30407	.31749	.33073	.34381	.35671	.36945
8	.38203	.39445	.40672	.41884	.43082	.44265	.45435	.46591	.47734	.48864
9	.49981	.51086	.52179	.53260	.54329	.55388	.56435	.57471	.58497	.59512
10	4.60517	.61512	.62497	.63473	.64439	.65396	.66344	.67283	.68213	.69135
11	.70048	.70953	.71850	.72739	.73620	.74493	.75359	.76217	.77068	.77912
12	.78749	.79579	.80402	.81218	.82028	.82831	.83628	.84419	.85203	.85981
13	.86753	.87520	.88280	.89035	.89784	.90527	.91265	.91998	.92725	.93447
14	.94164	.94876	.95583	.96284	.96981	.97673	.98361	.99043	.99721	*.00395
15	5.01064	.01728	.02388	.03044	.03695	.04343	.04986	.05625	.06260	.06890
16	.07517	.08140	.08760	.09375	.09987	.10595	.11199	.11799	.12396	.12990
17	.13580	.14166	.14749	.15329	.15906	.16479	.17048	.17615	.18178	.18739
18	.19296	.19850	.20401	.20949	.21494	.22036	.22575	.23111	.23644	.24175
19	.24702	.25227	.25750	.26269	.26786	.27300	.27811	.28320	.28827	.29330
20	5.29832	.30330	.30827	.31321	.31812	.32301	.32788	.33272	.33754	.34233
21	.34711	.35186	.35659	.36129	.36598	.37064	.37528	.37990	.38450	.38907
22	.39363	.39816	.40268	.40717	.41165	.41610	.42053	.42495	.42935	.43372
23	.43808	.44242	.44674	.45104	.45532	.45959	.46383	.46806	.47227	.47646
24	.48064	.48480	.48894	.49306	.49717	.50126	.50533	.50939	.51343	.51745
25	.52146	.52545	.52943	.53339	.53733	.54126	.54518	.54908	.55296	.55683
26	.56068	.56452	.56834	.57215	.57595	.57973	.58350	.58725	.59099	.59471
27	.59842	.60212	.60580	.60947	.61313	.61677	.62040	.62402	.62762	.63121
28	.63479	.63835	.64191	.64545	.64897	.65249	.65599	.65948	.66296	.66643
29	.66988	.67332	.67675	.68017	.68358	.68698	.69036	.69373	.69709	.70044
30	5.70378	.70711	.71043	.71373	.71703	.72031	.72359	.72685	.73010	.73334
31	.73657	.73979	.74300	.74620	.74939	.75257	.75574	.75890	.76205	.76519
32	.76832	.77144	.77455	.77765	.78074	.78383	.78690	.78996	.79301	.79606
33	.79909	.80212	.80513	.80814	.81114	.81413	.81711	.82008	.82305	.82600
34	.82895	.83188	.83481	.83773	.84064	.84354	.84644	.84932	.85220	.85507
35	.85793	.86079	.86363	.86647	.86930	.87212	.87493	.87774	.88053	.88332
36	.88610	.88888	.89164	.89440	.89715	.89990	.90263	.90536	.90808	.91080
37	.91350	.91620	.91889	.92158	.92426	.92693	.92959	.93225	.93489	.93754
38	.94017	.94280	.94542	.94803	.95064	.95324	.95584	.95842	.96101	.96358
39	.96615	.96871	.97126	.97381	.97635	.97889	.98141	.98394	.98645	.98896
40	5.99146	.99396	.99645	.99894	*.00141	*.00389	*.00635	*.00881	*.01127	*.01372
41	6.01616	.01859	.02102	.02345	.02587	.02828	.03069	.03309	.03548	.03787
42	.04025	.04263	.04501	.04737	.04973	.05209	.05444	.05678	.05912	.06146
43	.06379	.06611	.06843	.07074	.07304	.07535	.07764	.07993	.08222	.08450
44	.08677	.08904	.09131	.09357	.09582	.09807	.10032	.10256	.10479	.10702
45	.10925	.11147	.11368	.11589	.11810	.12030	.12249	.12468	.12687	.12905
46	.13123	.13340	.13556	.13773	.13988	.14204	.14419	.14633	.14847	.15060
47	.15273	.15486	.15698	.15910	.16121	.16331	.16542	.16752	.16961	.17170
48	.17379	.17587	.17794	.18002	.18208	.18415	.18621	.18826	.19032	.19236
49	.19441	.19644	.19848	.20051	.20254	.20456	.20658	.20859	.21060	.21261

NATURAL OR NAPERIAN LOGARITHMS (Continued)

500-999

N	0	1	2	3	4	5	6	7	8	9
50	6.21461	.21661	.21860	.22059	.22258	.22456	.22654	.22851	.23048	.23245
51	.23441	.23637	.23832	.24028	.24222	.24417	.24611	.24804	.24998	.25190
52	.25383	.25575	.25767	.25958	.26149	.26340	.26530	.26720	.26910	.27099
53	.27288	.27476	.27664	.27852	.28040	.28227	.28413	.28600	.28786	.28972
54	.29157	.29342	.29527	.29711	.29895	.30079	.30262	.30445	.30628	.30810
55	.30992	.31173	.31355	.31536	.31716	.31897	.32077	.32257	.32436	.32615
56	.32794	.32972	.33150	.33328	.33505	.33683	.33859	.34036	.34212	.34388
57	.34564	.34739	.34914	.35089	.35263	.35437	.35611	.35784	.35957	.36130
58	.36303	.36475	.36647	.36819	.36990	.37161	.37332	.37502	.37673	.37843
59	.38012	.38182	.38351	.38519	.38688	.38856	.39024	.39192	.39359	.39526
60	6.39693	.39859	.40026	.40192	.40357	.40523	.40688	.40853	.41017	.41182
61	.41346	.41510	.41673	.41836	.41999	.42162	.42325	.42487	.42649	.42811
62	.42972	.43133	.43294	.43455	.43615	.43775	.43935	.44095	.44254	.44413
63	.44572	.44731	.44889	.45047	.45205	.45362	.45520	.45677	.45834	.45990
64	.46147	.46303	.46459	.46614	.46770	.46925	.47080	.47235	.47389	.47543
65	.47697	.47851	.48004	.48158	.48311	.48464	.48616	.48768	.48920	.49072
66	.49224	.49375	.49527	.49677	.49828	.49979	.50129	.50279	.50429	.50578
67	.50728	.50877	.51026	.51175	.51323	.51471	.51619	.51767	.51915	.52062
68	.52209	.52356	.52503	.52649	.52796	.52942	.53088	.53233	.53379	.53524
69	.53669	.53814	.53959	.54103	.54247	.54391	54535	.54679	.54822	.54965
70	6.55108	.55251	.55393	.55536	.55678	.55820	.55962	.56103	.56244	.56386
71	.56526	.56667	.56808	.56948	.57088	.57228	.57368	.57508	.57647	.57786
72	.57925	.58064	.58203	.58341	.58479	.58617	.58755	.58893	.59030	.59167
73	.59304	.59441	.59578	.59715	.59851	.59987	.60123	.60259	.60394	.60530
74	.60665	.60800	.60935	.61070	.61204	.61338	.61473	.61607	.61740	.61874
75	.62007	.62141	.62274	.62407	.62539	.62672	.62804	.62936	.63068	.63200
76	.63332	.63463	.63595	.63726	.63857	.63988	.64118	.64249	.64379	.64509
77	.64639	.64769	.64898	65028	.65157	.65286	.65415	.65544	.65673	.65801
78	.65929	.66058	.66185	.66313	.66441	.66568	.66696	.66823	.66950	.67077
79	.67203	.67330	.67456	.67582	.67708	.67834	.67960	.68085	.68211	.68336
80	6.68461	.68586	.68711	.63835	.68960	.69084	.69208	.69332	.69456	.69580
81	.69703	.69827	.69950	.70073	.70196	.70319	.70441	.70564	.70686	.70808
82	.70930	.71052	.71174	.71296	.71417	.71538	.71659	.71780	.71901	.72022
83	.72143	.72263	.72383	.72503	.72623	.72743	.72863	.72982	.73102	.73221
84	.73340	.73459	.73578	.73697	.73815	.73934	.74052	.74170	.74288	.74406
85	.74524	.74641	.74759	.74876	.74993	.75110	.75227	.75344	.75460	.75577
86	.75693	.75809	.75926	.76041	.76157	.76273	.76388	.76504	.76619	.76734
87	.76849	.76964	.77079	.77194	.77308	.77422	.77537	.77651	.77765	.77878
88	.77992	.78106	.78219	.78333	.78446	.78559	.78672	.78784	.78897	.79010
89	.79122	.79234	.79347	.79459	.79571	.79682	.79794	.79906	.80017	.80128
90	6.80239	.80351	.80461	.80572	.80683	.80793	.80904	.81014	.81124	.81235
91	.81344	.81454	.81564	.81674	.81783	.81892	.82002	.82111	.82220	.82329
92	.82437	.82546	.82655	.82763	.82871	.82979	.83087	.83195	.83303	.83411
93	.83518	.83626	.83733	.83841	.83948	.84055	.84162	.84268	.84375	.84482
94	.84588	.84694	.84801	.84907	.85013	.85118	.85224	.85330	.85435	.85541
95	.85646	.85751	.85857	.85961	.86066	.86171	.86276	.86380	.86485	.86589
96	.86693	.86797	.86901	.87005	.87109	.87213	.87316	.87420	.87523	.87626
97	.87730	.87833	.87936	.88038	.88141	.88244	.88346	.88449	.88551	.88653
98	.88755	.88857	.88959	.89061	.89163	.89264	.89366	.89467	.89568	.89669
99	.89770	.89871	.89972	.90073	.90174	.90274	.90375	.90475	.90575	.90675

EXPONENTIAL FUNCTIONS

x	e^x	$\text{Log}_{10}(e^x)$	e^{-x}	x	e^x	$\text{Log}_{10}(e^x)$	e^{-x}
0.00	1.0000	0.00000	1.000000	**0.50**	1.6487	0.21715	0.606531
0.01	1.0101	.00434	0.990050	0.51	1.6653	.22149	.600496
0.02	1.0202	.00869	.980199	0.52	1.6820	.22583	.594521
0.03	1.0305	.01303	.970446	0.53	1.6989	.23018	.588605
0.04	1.0408	.01737	.960789	0.54	1.7160	.23452	.582748
0.05	1.0513	0.02171	0.951229	**0.55**	1.7333	0.23886	0.576950
0.06	1.0618	.02606	.941765	0.56	1.7507	.24320	.571209
0.07	1.0725	.03040	.932394	0.57	1.7683	.24755	.565525
0.08	1.0833	.03474	.923116	0.58	1.7860	.25189	.559898
0.09	1.0942	.03909	.913931	0.59	1.8040	.25623	.554327
0.10	1.1052	0.04343	0.904837	**0.60**	1.8221	0.26058	0.548812
0.11	1.1163	.04777	.895834	0.61	1.8404	.26492	.543351
0.12	1.1275	.05212	.886920	0.62	1.8589	.26926	.537944
0.13	1.1388	.05646	.878095	0.63	1.8776	.27361	.532592
0.14	1.1503	.06080	.869358	0.64	1.8965	.27795	.527292
0.15	1.1618	0.06514	0.860708	**0.65**	1.9155	0.28229	0.522046
0.16	1.1735	.06949	.852144	0.66	1.9348	.28663	.516851
0.17	1.1853	.07383	.843665	0.67	1.9542	.29098	.511709
0.18	1.1972	.07817	.835270	0.68	1.9739	.29532	.506617
0.19	1.2092	.08252	.826959	0.69	1.9937	.29966	.501576
0.20	1.2214	0.08686	0.818731	**0.70**	2.0138	0.30401	0.496585
0.21	1.2337	.09120	.810584	0.71	2.0340	.30835	.491644
0.22	1.2461	.09554	.802519	0.72	2.0544	.31269	.486752
0.23	1.2586	.09989	.794534	0.73	2.0751	.31703	.481909
0.24	1.2712	.10423	.786628	0.74	2.0959	.32138	.477114
0.25	1.2840	0.10857	0.778801	**0.75**	2.1170	0.32572	0.472367
0.26	1.2969	.11292	.771052	0.76	2.1383	.33006	.467666
0.27	1.3100	.11726	.763379	0.77	2.1598	.33441	.463013
0.28	1.3231	.12160	.755784	0.78	2.1815	.33875	.458406
0.29	1.3364	.12595	.748264	0.79	2.2034	.34309	.453845
0.30	1.3499	0.13029	0.740818	**0.80**	2.2255	0.34744	0.449329
0.31	1.3634	.13463	.733447	0.81	2.2479	.35178	.444858
0.32	1.3771	.13897	.726149	0.82	2.2705	.35612	.440432
0.33	1.3910	.14332	.718924	0.83	2.2933	.36046	.436049
0.34	1.4049	.14766	.711770	0.84	2.3164	.36481	.431711
0.35	1.4191	0.15200	0.704688	**0.85**	2.3396	0.36915	0.427415
0.36	1.4333	.15635	.697676	0.86	2.3632	.37349	.423162
0.37	1.4477	.16069	.690734	0.87	2.3869	.37784	.418952
0.38	1.4623	.16503	.683861	0.88	2.4109	.38218	.414783
0.39	1.4770	.16937	.677057	0.89	2.4351	.38652	.410656
0.40	1.4918	0.17372	0.670320	**0.90**	2.4596	0.39087	0.406570
0.41	1.5068	.17806	.663650	0.91	2.4843	.39521	.402524
0.42	1.5220	.18240	.657047	0.92	2.5093	.39955	.398519
0.43	1.5373	.18675	.650509	0.93	2.5345	.40389	.394554
0.44	1.5527	.19109	.644036	0.94	2.5600	.40824	.390628
0.45	1.5683	0.19543	0.637628	**0.95**	2.5857	0.41258	0.386741
0.46	1.5841	.19978	.631284	0.96	2.6117	.41692	.382893
0.47	1.6000	.20412	.625002	0.97	2.6379	.42127	.379083
0.48	1.6161	.20846	.618783	0.98	2.6645	.42561	.375311
0.49	1.6323	.21280	.612626	0.99	2.6912	.42995	.371577
0.50	1.6487	0.21715	0.606531	**1.00**	2.7183	0.43429	0.367879

EXPONENTIAL FUNCTIONS (Continued)

x	e^x	$\mathrm{Log}_{10}(e^x)$	e^{-x}	x	e^x	$\mathrm{Log}_{10}(e^x)$	e^{-x}
1.00	2.7183	0.43429	0.367879	**1.50**	4.4817	0.65144	0.223130
1.01	2.7456	.43864	.364219	1.51	4.5267	.65578	.220910
1.02	2.7732	.44298	.360595	1.52	4.5722	.66013	.218712
1.03	2.8011	.44732	.357007	1.53	4.6182	.66447	.216536
1.04	2.8292	.45167	.353455	1.54	4.6646	.66881	.214381
1.05	2.8577	0.45601	0.349938	**1.55**	4.7115	0.67316	0.212248
1.06	2.8864	.46035	.346456	1.56	4.7588	.67750	.210136
1.07	2.9154	.46470	.343009	1.57	4.8066	.68184	.208045
1.08	2.9447	.46904	.339596	1.58	4.8550	.68619	.205975
1.09	2.9743	.47338	.336216	1.59	4.9037	.69053	.203926
1.10	3.0042	0.47772	0.332871	**1.60**	4.9530	0.69487	0.201897
1.11	3.0344	.48207	.329559	1.61	5.0028	.69921	.199888
1.12	3.0649	.48641	.326280	1.62	5.0531	.70356	.197899
1.13	3.0957	.49075	.323033	1.63	5.1039	.70790	.195930
1.14	3.1268	.49510	.319819	1.64	5.1552	.71224	.193980
1.15	3.1582	0.49944	0.316637	**1.65**	5.2070	0.71659	0.192050
1.16	3.1899	.50378	.313486	1.66	5.2593	.72093	.190139
1.17	3.2220	.50812	.310367	1.67	5.3122	.72527	.188247
1.18	3.2544	.51247	.307279	1.68	5.3656	.72961	.186374
1.19	3.2871	.51681	.304221	1.69	5.4195	.73396	.184520
1.20	3.3201	0.52115	0.301194	**1.70**	5.4739	0.73830	0.182684
1.21	3.3535	.52550	.298197	1.71	5.5290	.74264	.180866
1.22	3.3872	.52984	.295230	1.72	5.5845	.74699	.179066
1.23	3.4212	.53418	.292293	1.73	5.6407	.75133	.177284
1.24	3.4556	.53853	.289384	1.74	5.6973	.75567	.175520
1.25	3.4903	0.54287	0.286505	**1.75**	5.7546	0.76002	0.173774
1.26	3.5254	.54721	.283654	1.76	5.8124	.76436	.172045
1.27	3.5609	.55155	.280832	1.77	5.8709	.76870	.170333
1.28	3.5966	.55590	.278037	1.78	5.9299	.77304	.168638
1.29	3.6328	.56024	.275271	1.79	5.9895	.77739	.166960
1.30	3.6693	0.56458	0.272532	**1.80**	6.0496	0.78173	0.165299
1.31	3.7062	.56893	.269820	1.81	6.1104	.78607	.163654
1.32	3.7434	.57327	.267135	1.82	6.1719	.79042	.162026
1.33	3.7810	.57761	.264477	1.83	6.2339	.79476	.160414
1.34	3.8190	.58195	.261846	1.84	6.2965	.79910	.158817
1.35	3.8574	0.58630	0.259240	**1.85**	6.3598	0.80344	0.157237
1.36	3.8962	.59064	.256661	1.86	6.4237	.80779	.155673
1.37	3.9354	.59498	.254107	1.87	6.4883	.81213	.154124
1.38	3.9749	.59933	.251579	1.88	6.5535	.81647	.152590
1.39	4.0149	.60367	.249075	1.89	6.6194	.82082	.151072
1.40	4.0552	0.60801	0.246597	**1.90**	6.6859	0.82516	0.149569
1.41	4.0960	.61236	.244143	1.91	6.7531	.82950	.148080
1.42	4.1371	.61670	.241714	1.92	6.8210	.83385	.146607
1.43	4.1787	.62104	.239309	1.93	6.8895	.83819	.145148
1.44	4.2207	.62538	.236928	1.94	6.9588	.84253	.143704
1.45	4.2631	0.62973	0.234570	**1.95**	7.0287	0.84687	0.142274
1.46	4.3060	.63407	.232236	1.96	7.0993	.85122	.140858
1.47	4.3492	.63841	.229925	1.97	7.1707	.85556	.139457
1.48	4.3929	.64276	.227638	1.98	7.2427	.85990	.138069
1.49	4.4371	.64710	.225373	1.99	7.3155	.86425	.136695
1.50	4.4817	0.65144	0.223130	**2.00**	7.3891	0.86859	0.135335

EXPONENTIAL FUNCTIONS (Continued)

x	e^x	$\text{Log}_{10}(e^x)$	e^{-x}	x	e^x	$\text{Log}_{10}(e^x)$	e^{-x}
2.00	7.3891	0.86859	0.135335	**2.50**	12.182	1.08574	0.082085
2.01	7.4633	.87293	.133989	2.51	12.305	1.09008	.081268
2.02	7.5383	.87727	.132655	2.52	12.429	1.09442	.080460
2.03	7.6141	.88162	.131336	2.53	12.554	1.09877	.079659
2.04	7.6906	.88596	.130029	2.54	12.680	1.10311	.078866
2.05	7.7679	0.89030	0.128735	**2.55**	12.807	1.10745	0.078082
2.06	7.8460	.89465	.127454	2.56	12.936	1.11179	.077305
2.07	7.9248	.89899	.126186	2.57	13.066	1.11614	.076536
2.08	8.0045	.90333	.124930	2.58	13.197	1.12048	.075774
2.09	8.0849	.90768	.123687	2.59	13.330	1.12482	.075020
2.10	8.1662	0.91202	0.122456	**2.60**	13.464	1.12917	0.074274
2.11	8.2482	.91636	.121238	2.61	13.599	1.13351	.073535
2.12	8.3311	.92070	.120032	2.62	13.736	1.13785	.072803
2.13	8.4149	.92505	.118837	2.63	13.874	1.14219	.072078
2.14	8.4994	.92939	.117655	2.64	14.013	1.14654	.071361
2.15	8.5849	0.93373	0.116484	**2.65**	14.154	1.15088	0.070651
2.16	8.6711	.93808	.115325	2.66	14.296	1.15522	.069948
2.17	8.7583	.94242	.114178	2.67	14.440	1.15957	.069252
2.18	8.8463	.94676	.113042	2.68	14.585	1.16391	.068563
2.19	8.9352	.95110	.111917	2.69	14.732	1.16825	.067881
2.20	9.0250	0.95545	0.110803	**2.70**	14.880	1.17260	0.067206
2.21	9.1157	.95979	.109701	2.71	15.029	1.17694	.066537
2.22	9.2073	.96413	.108609	2.72	15.180	1.18128	.065875
2.23	9.2999	.96848	.107528	2.73	15.333	1.18562	.065219
2.24	9.3933	.97282	.106459	2.74	15.487	1.18997	.064570
2.25	9.4877	0.97716	0.105399	**2.75**	15.643	1.19431	0.063928
2.26	9.5831	.98151	.104350	2.76	15.800	1.19865	.063292
2.27	9.6794	.98585	.103312	2.77	15.959	1.20300	.062662
2.28	9.7767	.99019	.102284	2.78	16.119	1.20734	.062039
2.29	9.8749	.99453	.101266	2.79	16.281	1.21168	.061421
2.30	9.9742	0.99888	0.100259	**2.80**	16.445	1.21602	0.060810
2.31	10.074	1.00322	.099261	2.81	16.610	1.22037	.060205
2.32	10.176	1.00756	.098274	2.82	16.777	1.22471	.059606
2.33	10.278	1.01191	.097296	2.83	16.945	1.22905	.059013
2.34	10.381	1.01625	.096328	2.84	17.116	1.23340	.058426
2.35	10.486	1.02059	0.095369	**2.85**	17.288	1.23774	0.057844
2.36	10.591	1.02493	.094420	2.86	17.462	1.24208	.057269
2.37	10.697	1.02928	.093481	2.87	17.637	1.24643	.056699
2.38	10.805	1.03362	.092551	2.88	17.814	1.25077	.056135
2.39	10.913	1.03796	.091630	2.89	17.993	1.25511	.055576
2.40	11.023	1.04231	0.090718	**2.90**	18.174	1.25945	0.055023
2.41	11.134	1.04665	.089815	2.91	18.357	1.26380	.054476
2.42	11.246	1.05099	.088922	2.92	18.541	1.26814	.053934
2.43	11.359	1.05534	.088037	2.93	18.728	1.27248	.053397
2.44	11.473	1.05968	.087161	2.94	18.916	1.27683	.052866
2.45	11.588	1.06402	0.086294	**2.95**	19.106	1.28117	0.052340
2.46	11.705	1.06836	.085435	2.96	19.298	1.28551	.051819
2.47	11.822	1.07271	.084585	2.97	19.492	1.28985	.051303
2.48	11.941	1.07705	.083743	2.98	19.688	1.29420	.050793
2.49	12.061	1.08139	.082910	2.99	19.886	1.29854	.050287
2.50	12.182	1.08574	0.082085	**3.00**	20.086	1.30288	0.049787

EXPONENTIAL FUNCTIONS (Continued)

x	e^x	$\text{Log}_{10}(e^x)$	e^{-x}	x	e^x	$\text{Log}_{10}(e^x)$	e^{-x}
3.00	20.086	1.30288	0.049787	**3.50**	33.115	1.52003	0.030197
3.01	20.287	1.30723	.049292	3.51	33.448	1.52437	.029897
3.02	20.491	1.31157	.048801	3.52	33.784	1.52872	.029599
3.03	20.697	1.31591	.048316	3.53	34.124	1.53306	.029305
3.04	20.905	1.32026	.047835	3.54	34.467	1.53740	.029013
3.05	21.115	1.32460	0.047359	**3.55**	34.813	1.54175	0.028725
3.06	21.328	1.32894	.046888	3.56	35.163	1.54609	.028439
3.07	21.542	1.33328	.046421	3.57	35.517	1.55043	.028156
3.08	21.758	1.33763	.045959	3.58	35.874	1.55477	.027876
3.09	21.977	1.34197	.045502	3.59	36.234	1.55912	.027598
3.10	22.198	1.34631	0.045049	**3.60**	36.598	1.56346	0.027324
3.11	22.421	1.35066	.044601	3.61	36.966	1.56780	.027052
3.12	22.646	1.35500	.044157	3.62	37.338	1.57215	.026783
3.13	22.874	1.35934	.043718	3.63	37.713	1.57649	.026516
3.14	23.104	1.36368	.043283	3.64	38.092	1.58083	.026252
3.15	23.336	1.36803	0.042852	**3.65**	38.475	1.58517	0.025991
3.16	23.571	1.37237	.042426	3.66	38.861	1.58952	.025733
3.17	23.807	1.37671	.042004	3.67	39.252	1.59386	.025476
3.18	24.047	1.38106	.041586	3.68	39.646	1.59820	.025223
3.19	24.288	1.38540	.041172	3.69	40.045	1.60255	.024972
3.20	24.533	1.38974	0 040762	**3.70**	40.447	1.60689	0.024724
3.21	24.779	1.39409	.040357	3.71	40.854	1.61123	.024478
3.22	25.028	1.39843	.039955	3.72	41.264	1.61558	.024234
3.23	25.280	1.40277	.039557	3.73	41.679	1.61992	.023993
3.24	25.534	1.40711	.039164	3.74	42.098	1.62426	.023754
3.25	25.790	1.41146	0.038774	**3.75**	42.521	1.62860	0.023518
3.26	26.050	1.41580	.038388	3.76	42.948	1.63295	.023284
3.27	26.311	1.42014	.038006	3.77	43.380	1.63729	.023052
3.28	26.576	1.42449	.037628	3.78	43.816	1.64163	.022823
3.29	26.843	1.42883	.037254	3.79	44.256	1.64598	.022596
3.30	27.113	1.43317	0.036883	**3.80**	44.701	1.65032	0.022371
3.31	27.385	1.43751	.036516	3.81	45.150	1.65466	.022148
3.32	27.660	1.44186	.036153	3.82	45.604	1.65900	.021928
3.33	27.938	1.44620	.035793	3.83	46.063	1.66335	.021710
3.34	28.219	1.45054	.035437	3.84	46.525	1.66769	.021494
3.35	28.503	1.45489	0.035084	**3.85**	46.993	1.67203	0.021280
3.36	28.789	1.45923	.034735	3.86	47.465	1.67638	.021068
3.37	29.079	1.46357	.034390	3.87	47.942	1.68072	.020858
3.38	29.371	1.46792	.034047	3.88	48.424	1.68506	.020651
3.39	29.666	1.47226	.033709	3.89	48.911	1.68941	.020445
3.40	29.964	1.47660	0.033373	**3.90**	49.402	1.69375	0.020242
3.41	30.265	1.48094	.033041	3.91	49.899	1.69809	.020041
3.42	30.569	1.48529	.032712	3.92	50.400	1.70243	.019841
3.43	30.877	1.48963	.032387	3.93	50.907	1.70678	.019644
3.44	31.187	1.49397	.032065	3.94	51.419	1.71112	.019448
3.45	31.500	1.49832	0.031746	**3.95**	51.935	1.71546	0.019255
3.46	31.817	1.50266	.031430	3.96	52.457	1.71981	.019063
3.47	32.137	1.50700	.031117	3.97	52.985	1.72415	.018873
3.48	32.460	1.51134	.030807	3.98	53.517	1.72849	.018686
3.49	32.786	1.51569	.030501	3.99	54.055	1.73283	.018500
3.50	33.115	1.52003	0.030197	**4.00**	54.598	1.73718	0.018316

EXPONENTIAL FUNCTIONS (Continued)

x	e^x	$\text{Log}_{10}(e^x)$	e^{-x}	x	e^x	$\text{Log}_{10}(e^x)$	e^{-x}
4.00	54.598	1.73718	0.018316	**4.50**	90.017	1.95433	0.011109
4.01	55.147	1.74152	.018133	4.51	90.922	1.95867	.010998
4.02	55.701	1.74586	.017953	4.52	91.836	1.96301	.010889
4.03	56.261	1.75021	.017774	4.53	92.759	1.96735	.010781
4.04	56.826	1.75455	.017597	4.54	93.691	1.97170	.010673
4.05	57.397	1.75889	0.017422	**4.55**	94.632	1.97604	0.010567
4.06	57.974	1.76324	.017249	4.56	95.583	1.98038	.010462
4.07	58.557	1.76758	.017077	4.57	96.544	1.98473	.010358
4.08	59.145	1.77192	.016907	4.58	97.514	1.98907	.010255
4.09	59.740	1.77626	.016739	4.59	98.494	1.99341	.010153
4.10	60.340	1.78061	0.016573	**4.60**	99.484	1.99775	0.010052
4.11	60.947	1.78495	.016408	4.61	100.48	2.00210	.009952
4.12	61.559	1.78929	.016245	4.62	101.49	2.00644	.009853
4.13	62.178	1.79364	.016083	4.63	102.51	2.01078	.009755
4.14	62.803	1.79798	.015923	4.64	103.54	2.01513	.009658
4.15	63.434	1.80232	0.015764	**4.65**	104.58	2.01947	0.009562
4.16	64.072	1.80667	.015608	4.66	105.64	2.02381	.009466
4.17	64.715	1.81101	.015452	4.67	106.70	2.02816	.009372
4.18	65.366	1.81535	.015299	4.68	107.77	2.03250	.009279
4.19	66.023	1.81969	.015146	4.69	108.85	2.03684	.009187
4.20	66.686	1.82404	0.014996	**4.70**	109.95	2.04118	0.009095
4.21	67.357	1.82838	.014846	4.71	111.05	2.04553	.009005
4.22	68.033	1.83272	.014699	4.72	112.17	2.04987	.008915
4.23	68.717	1.83707	.014552	4.73	113.30	2.05421	.008826
4.24	69.408	1.84141	.014408	4.74	114.43	2.05856	.008739
4.25	70.105	1.84575	0.014264	**4.75**	115.58	2.06290	0.008652
4.26	70.810	1.85009	.014122	4.76	116.75	2.06724	.008566
4.27	71.522	1.85444	.013982	4.77	117.92	2.07158	.008480
4.28	72.240	1.85878	.013843	4.78	119.10	2.07593	.008396
4.29	72.966	1.86312	.013705	4.79	120.30	2.08027	.008312
4.30	73.700	1.86747	0.013569	**4.80**	121.51	2.08461	0.008230
4.31	74.440	1.87181	.013434	4.81	122.73	2.08896	.008148
4.32	75.189	1.87615	.013300	4.82	123.97	2.09330	.008067
4.33	75.944	1.88050	.013168	4.83	125.21	2.09764	.007987
4.34	76.708	1.88484	.013037	4.84	126.47	2.10199	.007907
4.35	77.478	1.88918	0.012907	**4.85**	127.74	2.10633	0.007828
4.36	78.257	1.89352	.012778	4.86	129.02	2.11067	.007750
4.37	79.044	1.89787	.012651	4.87	130.32	2.11501	.007673
4.38	79.838	1.90221	.012525	4.88	131.63	2.11936	.007597
4.39	80.640	1.90655	.012401	4.89	132.95	2.12370	.007521
4.40	81.451	1.91090	0.012277	**4.90**	134.29	2.12804	0.007447
4.41	82.269	1.91524	.012155	4.91	135.64	2.13239	.007372
4.42	83.096	1.91958	.012034	4.92	137.00	2.13673	.007299
4.43	83.931	1.92392	.011914	4.93	138.38	2.14107	.007227
4.44	84.775	1.92827	.011796	4.94	139.77	2.14541	.007155
4.45	85.627	1.93261	0.011679	**4.95**	141.17	2.14976	0.007083
4.46	86.488	1.93695	.011562	4.96	142.59	2.15410	.007013
4.47	87.357	1.94130	.011447	4.97	144.03	2.15844	.006943
4.48	88.235	1.94564	.011333	4.98	145.47	2.16279	.006874
4.49	89.121	1.94998	.011221	4.99	146.94	2.16713	.006806
4.50	90.017	1.95433	0.011109	**5.00**	148.41	2.17147	0.006738

EXPONENTIAL FUNCTIONS (Continued)

x	e^x	$\text{Log}_{10}(e^x)$	e^{-x}	x	e^x	$\text{Log}_{10}(e^x)$	e^{-x}
5.00	148.41	2.17147	0.006738	**5.0**	148.41	2.17147	0.006738
5.01	149.90	2.17582	.006671	5.1	164.02	2.21490	.006097
5.02	151.41	2.18016	.006605	5.2	181.27	2.25833	.005517
5.03	152.93	2.18450	.006539	5.3	200.34	2.30176	.004992
5.04	154.47	2.18884	.006474	5.4	221.41	2.34519	.004517
5.05	156.02	2.19319	0.006409	**5.5**	244.69	2.38862	0.004087
5.06	157.59	2.19753	.006346	5.6	270.43	2.43205	.003698
5.07	159.17	2.20187	.006282	5.7	298.87	2.47548	.003346
5.08	160.77	2.20622	.006220	5.8	330.30	2.51891	.003028
5.09	162.39	2.21056	.006158	5.9	365.04	2.56234	.002739
5.10	164.02	2.21490	0.006097	**6.0**	403.43	2.60577	0.002479
5.11	165.67	2.21924	.006036	6.1	445.86	2.64920	.002243
5.12	167.34	2.22359	.005976	6.2	492.75	2.69263	.002029
5.13	169.02	2.22793	.005917	6.3	544.57	2.73606	.001836
5.14	170.72	2.23227	.005858	6.4	601.85	2.77948	.001662
5.15	172.43	2.23662	0.005799	**6.5**	665.14	2.82291	0.001503
5.16	174.16	2.24096	.005742	6.6	735.10	2.86634	.001360
5.17	175.91	2.24530	.005685	6.7	812.41	2.90977	.001231
5.18	177.68	2.24965	.005628	6.8	897.85	2.95320	.001114
5.19	179.47	2.25399	.005572	6.9	992.27	2.99663	.001008
5.20	181.27	2.25833	0.005517	**7.0**	1096.6	3.04006	0.000912
5.21	183.09	2.26267	.005462	7.1	1212.0	3.08349	.000825
5.22	184.93	2.26702	.005407	7.2	1339.4	3.12692	.000747
5.23	186.79	2.27136	.005354	7.3	1480.3	3.17035	.000676
5.24	188.67	2.27570	.005300	7.4	1636.0	3.21378	.000611
5.25	190.57	2.28005	0.005248	**7.5**	1808.0	3.25721	0.000553
5.26	192.48	2.28439	.005195	7.6	1998.2	3.30064	.000500
5.27	194.42	2.28873	.005144	7.7	2208.3	3.34407	.000453
5.28	196.37	2.29307	.005092	7.8	2440.6	3.38750	.000410
5.29	198.34	2.29742	.005042	7.9	2697.3	3.43093	.000371
5.30	200.34	2.30176	0.004992	**8.0**	2981.0	3.47436	0.000335
5.31	202.35	2.30610	.004942	8.1	3294.5	3.51779	.000304
5.32	204.38	2.31045	.004893	8.2	3641.0	3.56121	.000275
5.33	206.44	2.31479	.004844	8.3	4023.9	3.60464	.000249
5.34	208.51	2.31913	.004796	8.4	4447.1	3.64807	.000225
5.35	210.61	2.32348	0.004748	**8.5**	4914.8	3.69150	0.000203
5.36	212.72	2.32782	.004701	8.6	5431.7	3.73493	.000184
5.37	214.86	2.33216	.004654	8.7	6002.9	3.77836	.000167
5.38	217.02	2.33650	004608	8.8	6634.2	3.82179	.000151
5.39	219.20	2.34085	.004562	8.9	7332.0	3.86522	.000136
5.40	221.41	2.34519	0.004517	**9.0**	8103.1	3.90865	0.000123
5.41	223.63	2.34953	004472	9.1	8955.3	3.95208	.000112
5.42	225.88	2.35388	.004427	9.2	9897.1	3.99551	.000101
5.43	228.15	2.35822	.004383	9.3	10938	4.03894	.000091
5.44	230.44	2.36256	.004339	9.4	12088	4.08237	.000083
5.45	232.76	2.36690	0.004296	**9.5**	13360	4.12580	0.000075
5.46	235.10	2.37125	.004254	9.6	14765	4.16923	.000068
5.47	237.46	2.37559	.004211	9.7	16318	4.21266	.000061
5.48	239.85	2.37993	.004169	9.8	18034	4.25609	.000055
5.49	242.26	2.38428	.004128	9.9	19930	4.29952	.000050
5.50	244.69	2.38862	0.004087	**10.0**	22026	4.34294	0.000045

HYPERBOLIC FUNCTIONS

The logarithms given below show the mantissa only. The proper characteristic must be added.

x	Sinh x		Cosh x		Tanh x		Coth x	
	Value	$\log_{10}$	Value	$\log_{10}$	Value	$\log_{10}$	Value	$\log_{10}$
0.00	0.00000	$-\infty$	1.00000	.00000	0.00000	$-\infty$	∞	∞
0.01	.01000	.00001	1.00005	.00002	.01000	.99999	100.003	.00001
0.02	.02000	.30106	1.00020	.00009	.02000	.30097	50.007	.69903
0.03	.03000	.47719	1.00045	.00020	.02999	.47699	33.343	.52301
0.04	.04001	.60218	1.00080	.00035	.03998	.60183	25.013	.39817
0.05	0.05002	.69915	1.00125	.00054	0.04996	.69861	20.017	.30139
0.06	.06004	.77841	1.00180	.00078	.05993	.77763	16.687	.22237
0.07	.07006	.84545	1.00245	.00106	.06989	.84439	14.309	.15561
0.08	.08009	.90355	1.00320	.00139	.07983	.90216	12.527	.09784
0.09	.09012	.95483	1.00405	.00176	.08976	.95307	11.141	.04693
0.10	0.10017	.00072	1.00500	.00217	0.09967	99856	10.0333	.00144
0.11	.11022	.04227	1.00606	.00262	.10956	.03965	9.1275	.96035
0.12	.12029	.08022	1.00721	.00312	.11943	.07710	8.3733	.92290
0.13	.13037	.11517	1.00846	.00366	.12927	.11151	7.7356	.88849
0.14	.14046	.14755	1.00982	.00424	.13909	.14330	7.1895	.85670
0.15	0.15056	.17772	1.01127	.00487	0.14889	.17285	6.7166	.82715
0.16	.16068	.20597	1.01283	.00554	.15865	.20044	6.3032	.79956
0.17	.17082	.23254	1.01448	.00625	.16838	.22629	5.9389	.77371
0.18	.18097	.25762	1.01624	.00700	.17808	.25062	5.6154	.74938
0 19	.19115	.28136	1.01810	.00779	.18775	.27357	5.3263	.72643
0.20	0.20134	.30392	1.02007	.00863	0.19738	.29529	5.0665	.70471
0.21	.21155	.32541	1.02213	.00951	.20697	.31590	4.8317	.68410
0.22	.22178	.34592	1.02430	.01043	.21652	.33549	4.6186	.66451
0.23	.23203	.36555	1.02657	.01139	.22603	.35416	4.4242	.64584
0.24	.24231	.38437	1.02894	.01239	.23550	.37198	4.2464	.62802
0.25	0.25261	.40245	1.03141	.01343	0.24492	.38902	4.0830	.61098
0.26	.26294	.41986	1.03399	.01452	.25430	.40534	3.9324	.59466
0.27	.27329	.43663	1.03667	.01564	.26362	.42099	3.7933	.57901
0.28	.28367	.45282	1.03946	.01681	.27291	43601	3.6643	.56399
0.29	.29408	.46847	1.04235	.01801	.28213	.45046	3.5444	.54954
0.30	0.30452	.48362	1.04534	.01926	0.29131	.46436	3.4327	.53564
0.31	.31499	.49830	1.04844	.02054	.30044	.47775	3.3285	.52225
0.32	.32549	.51254	1.05164	.02187	.30951	.49067	3.2309	.50933
0.33	.33602	.52637	1.05495	.02323	.31852	.50314	3.1395	.49686
0.34	.34659	.53981	1.05836	.02463	.32748	.51518	3.0536	.48482
0.35	0.35719	.55290	1.06188	.02607	0.33638	.52682	2.9729	.47318
0.36	.36783	.56564	1.06550	.02755	.34521	.53809	2.8968	.46191
0.37	.37850	.57807	1.06923	.02907	.35399	.54899	2.8249	.45101
0.38	.38921	.59019	1.07307	.03063	.36271	.55956	2.7570	.44044
0.39	.39996	.60202	1.07702	.03222	.37136	.56980	2.6928	.43020
0.40	0.41075	.61358	1.08107	.03385	0.37995	.57973	2.6319	.42027
0.41	.42158	.62488	1.08523	.03552	.38847	.58936	2.5742	.41064
0.42	.43246	.63594	1.08950	.03723	.39693	.59871	2.5193	.40129
0.43	.44337	.64677	1.09388	.03897	.40532	.60780	2.4672	.39220
0.44	.45434	.65738	1.09837	.04075	.41364	.61663	2.4175	.38337
0.45	0.46534	.66777	1.10297	.04256	0.42190	.62521	2.3702	.37479
0.46	.47640	.67797	1.10768	.04441	.43008	.63355	2.3251	.36645
0.47	.48750	.68797	1.11250	.04630	.43820	.64167	2.2821	.35833
0.48	.49865	.69779	1.11743	.04822	.44624	.64957	2.2409	.35043
0.49	.50984	.70744	1.12247	.05018	.45422	.65726	2.2016	34274

HYPERBOLIC FUNCTIONS (Continued)

The logarithms given below show the mantissa only. The proper characteristic must be added.

x	Sinh x		Cosh x		Tanh x		Coth x	
	Value	$\log_{10}$	Value	$\log_{10}$	Value	$\log_{10}$	Value	$\log_{10}$
0.50	0.52110	.71692	1.12763	.05217	0.46212	.66475	2.1640	.33525
0.51	.53240	.72624	1.13289	.05419	.46995	.67205	2.1279	.32795
0.52	.54375	.73540	1.13827	.05625	.47770	.67916	2.0934	.32084
0.53	.55516	.74442	1.14377	.05834	.48538	.68608	2.0602	.31392
0.54	.56663	.75330	1.14938	.06046	.49299	.69284	2.0284	.30716
0.55	0.57815	.76204	1.15510	.06262	0.50052	.69942	1.9979	.30058
0.56	.58973	.77065	1.16094	.06481	.50798	.70584	1.9686	.29416
0.57	.60137	.77914	1.16690	.06703	.51536	.71211	1.9404	.28789
0.58	.61307	.78751	1.17297	.06929	.52267	.71822	1.9133	.28178
0.59	.62483	.79576	1.17916	.07157	.52990	.72419	1.8872	.27581
0.60	0.63665	.80390	1.18547	.07389	0.53705	.73001	1.8620	.26999
0.61	.64854	.81194	1.19189	.07624	.54413	.73570	1.8378	.26430
0.62	.66049	.81987	1.19844	.07861	.55113	.74125	1.8145	.25875
0.63	.67251	.82770	1.20510	.08102	.55805	.74667	1.7919	.25333
0.64	.68459	.83543	1.21189	.08346	.56490	.75197	1.7702	.24803
0.65	0.69675	.84308	1.21879	.08593	0.57167	.75715	1.7493	.24285
0.66	.70897	.85063	1.22582	.08843	.57836	.76220	1.7290	.23780
0.67	.72126	.85809	1.23297	.09095	.58498	.76714	1.7095	.23286
0.68	.73363	.86548	1.24025	.09351	.59152	.77197	1.6906	.22803
0.69	.74607	.87278	1.24765	.09609	.59798	.77669	1.6723	.22331
0.70	0.75858	.88000	1.25517	.09870	0.60437	.78130	1.6546	.21870
0.71	.77117	.88715	1.26282	.10134	.61068	.78581	1.6375	.21419
0.72	.78384	.89423	1.27059	.10401	.61691	.79022	1.6210	.20978
0.73	.79659	.90123	1.27849	.10670	.62307	.79453	1.6050	.20547
0.74	.80941	.90817	1.28652	.10942	.62915	.79875	1.5895	.20125
0.75	0.82232	.91504	1.29468	.11216	0.63515	.80288	1.5744	.19712
0.76	.83530	.92185	1.30297	.11493	.64108	.80691	1.5599	.19309
0.77	.84838	.92859	1.31139	.11773	.64693	.81086	1.5458	.18914
0.78	.86153	.93527	1.31994	.12055	.65271	.81472	1.5321	.18528
0.79	.87478	.94190	1.32862	.12340	.65841	.81850	1.5188	.18150
0.80	0.88811	.94846	1.33743	.12627	0.66404	.82219	1.5059	.17781
0.81	.90152	.95498	1.34638	.12917	.66959	.82581	1.4935	.17419
0.82	.91503	.96144	1.35547	.13209	.67507	.82935	1.4813	.17065
0.83	.92863	.96784	1.36468	.13503	.68048	.83281	1.4696	.16719
0.84	.94233	.97420	1.37404	.13800	.68581	.83620	1.4581	.16380
0.85	0.95612	.98051	1.38353	.14099	0.69107	.83952	1.4470	.16048
0.86	.97000	.98677	1.39316	.14400	.69626	.84277	1.4362	.15723
0.87	.98398	.99299	1.40293	.14704	.70137	.84595	1.4258	.15405
0.88	.99806	.99916	1.41284	.15009	.70642	.84906	1.4156	.15094
0.89	1.01224	.00528	1.42289	.15317	.71139	.85211	1.4057	.14789
0.90	1.02652	.01137	1.43309	.15627	0.71630	.85509	1.3961	.14491
0.91	1.04090	.01741	1.44342	.15939	.72113	.85801	1.3867	.14199
0.92	1.05539	.02341	1.45390	.16254	.72590	.86088	1.3776	.13912
0.93	1.06998	.02937	1.46453	.16570	.73059	.86368	1.3687	.13632
0.94	1.08468	.03530	1.47530	.16888	.73522	.86642	1.3601	.13358
0.95	1.09948	.04119	1.48623	.17208	0.73978	.86910	1.3517	.13090
0.96	1.11440	.04704	1.49729	.17531	.74428	.87173	1.3436	.12827
0.97	1.12943	.05286	1.50851	.17855	.74870	.87431	1.3356	.12569
0.98	1.14457	.05864	1.51988	.18181	.75307	.87683	1.3279	.12317
0.99	1.15983	.06439	1.53141	.18509	.75736	.87930	1.3204	.12070

HYPERBOLIC FUNCTIONS (Continued)

The logarithms given below show the mantissa only. The proper characteristic must be added.

x	Sinh x Value	Sinh x log10	Cosh x Value	Cosh x log10	Tanh x Value	Tanh x log10	Coth x Value	Coth x log10
1.00	1.17520	.07011	1.54308	.18839	0 76159	88172	1.3130	.11828
1.01	1.19069	.07580	1.55491	.19171	.76576	.88409	1.3059	.11591
1.02	1.20630	.08146	1.56689	.19504	.76987	.88642	1.2989	.11358
1.03	1.22203	.08708	1.57904	.19839	.77391	.88869	1.2921	.11131
1.04	1.23788	.09268	1.59134	.20176	.77789	.89092	1.2855	.10908
1.05	1.25386	.09825	1.60379	.20515	0.78181	.89310	1.2791	.10690
1.06	1.26996	.10379	1.61641	.20855	.78566	.89524	1.2728	.10476
1.07	1.28619	.10930	1.62919	.21197	.78946	.89733	1.2667	.10267
1.08	1.30254	.11479	1.64214	.21541	.79320	.89938	1.2607	.10062
1.09	1.31903	.12025	1.65525	.21886	.79688	.90139	1.2549	.09861
1.10	1.33565	.12569	1.66852	.22233	0.80050	.90336	1.2492	.09664
1.11	1.35240	.13111	1.68196	.22582	.80406	.90529	1.2437	.09471
1.12	1.36929	.13649	1.69557	.22931	.80757	.90718	1.2383	.09282
1.13	1.38631	.14186	1.70934	.23283	.81102	.90903	1.2330	.09097
1.14	1.40347	.14720	1.72329	.23636	.81441	.91085	1.2279	.08915
1.15	1.42078	.15253	1.73741	.23990	0.81775	.91262	1.2229	.08738
1.16	1.43822	.15783	1.75171	.24346	.82104	.91436	1.2180	.08564
1.17	1.45581	.16311	1.76618	.24703	.82427	.91607	1.2132	.08393
1.18	1.47355	.16836	1.78083	.25062	.82745	.91774	1.2085	.08226
1.19	1.49143	.17360	1.79565	.25422	.83058	.91938	1.2040	.08062
1.20	1.50946	.17882	1.81066	.25784	0.83365	.92099	1.1995	.07901
1.21	1.52764	.18402	1.82584	.26146	.83668	.92256	1.1952	.07744
1.22	1.54598	.18920	1.84121	.26510	.83965	.92410	1.1910	.07590
1.23	1.56447	.19437	1.85676	.26876	.84258	.92561	1.1868	.07439
1.24	1.58311	.19951	1.87250	.27242	.84546	.92709	1.1828	.07291
1.25	1.60192	.20464	1.88842	.27610	0.84828	.92854	1.1789	.07146
1.26	1.62088	.20975	1.90454	.27979	.85106	.92996	1.1750	.07004
1.27	1.64001	.21485	1.92084	.28349	.85380	.93135	1.1712	.06865
1.28	1.65930	.21993	1.93734	.28721	.85648	.93272	1.1676	.06728
1.29	1.67876	.22499	1.95403	.29093	.85913	.93406	1 1640	.06594
1.30	1.69838	.23004	1.97091	.29467	0.86172	.93537	1.1605	.06463
1.31	1.71818	.23507	1.98800	.29842	.86428	.93665	1.1570	.06335
1.32	1.73814	.24009	2.00528	.30217	.86678	.93791	1.1537	.06209
1.33	1.75828	.24509	2.02276	.30594	.86925	.93914	1.1504	.06086
1.34	1.77860	.25008	2.04044	.30972	.87167	.94035	1.1472	.05965
1.35	1.79909	.25505	2.05833	.31352	0.87405	.94154	1.1441	.05846
1.36	1.81977	.26002	2.07643	.31732	.87639	.94270	1 1410	.05730
1.37	1.84062	.26496	2.09473	.32113	.87869	94384	1.1381	.05616
1.38	1.86166	.26990	2.11324	.32495	.88095	.94495	1.1351	.05505
1.39	1.88289	.27482	2.13196	.32878	.88317	.94604	1.1323	.05396
1.40	1.90430	.27974	2.15090	.33262	0.88535	.94712	1.1295	.05288
1.41	1.92591	.28464	2.17005	.33647	.88749	.94817	1.1268	.05183
1.42	1.94770	.28952	2.18942	.34033	.88960	.94919	1.1241	.05081
1.43	1.96970	.29440	2.20900	.34420	.89167	.95020	1.1215	.04980
1.44	1.99188	.29926	2.22881	.34807	.89370	.95119	1.1189	.04881
1.45	2.01427	.30412	2.24884	.35196	0.89569	.95216	1.1165	.04784
1.46	2 03686	.30896	2.26910	.35585	.89765	.95311	1.1140	.04689
1.47	2.05965	.31379	2.28958	.35976	.89958	.95404	1.1116	.04596
1.48	2.08265	.31862	2.31029	.36367	.90147	.95495	1.1093	.04505
1.49	2.10586	.32343	2.33123	.36759	.90332	.95584	1.1070	.04416

HYPERBOLIC FUNCTIONS (Continued)

The logarithms given below show the mantissa only. The proper characteristic must be added.

x	Sinh x		Cosh x		Tanh x		Coth x	
	Value	$\log_{10}$	Value	$\log_{10}$	Value	$\log_{10}$	Value	$\log_{10}$
1.50	2.12928	.32823	2.35241	.37151	0.90515	.95672	1.1048	.04328
1.51	2.15291	.33303	2.37382	.37545	.90694	.95758	1.1026	.04242
1.52	2.17676	.33781	2.39547	.37939	.90870	.95842	1.1005	.04158
1.53	2.20082	.34258	2.41736	.38334	.91042	.95924	1.0984	.04076
1.54	2.22510	.34735	2.43949	.38730	.91212	.96005	1.0963	.03995
1.55	2.24961	.35211	2.46186	.39126	0.91379	.96084	1.0943	.03916
1.56	2.27434	.35686	2.48448	.39524	.91542	.96162	1.0924	.03838
1.57	2.29930	.36160	2.50735	.39921	.91703	.96238	1.0905	.03762
1.58	2.32449	.36633	2.53047	.40320	.91860	.96313	1.0886	.03687
1.59	2.34991	.37105	2.55384	.40719	.92015	.96386	1.0868	.03614
1.60	2.37557	.37577	2.57746	.41119	0.92167	.96457	1.0850	.03543
1.61	2.40146	.38048	2.60135	.41520	.92316	.96528	1.0832	.03472
1.62	2.42760	.38518	2.62549	.41921	.92462	.96597	1.0815	.03403
1.63	2.45397	.38987	2.64990	.42323	.92606	.96664	1.0798	.03336
1.64	2.48059	.39456	2.67457	.42725	.92747	.96730	1.0782	.03270
1.65	2.50746	.39923	2.69951	.43129	0.92886	.96795	1.0766	.03205
1.66	2.53459	.40391	2.72472	.43532	.93022	.96858	1.0750	.03142
1.67	2.56196	.40857	2.75021	.43937	.93155	.96921	1.0735	.03079
1.68	2.58959	.41323	2.77596	.44341	.93286	.96982	1.0720	.03018
1.69	2.61748	.41788	2.80200	.44747	.93415	.97042	1.0705	.02958
1.70	2.64563	.42253	2.82832	.45153	.93541	.97100	1.0691	.02900
1.71	2.67405	.42717	2.85491	.45559	.93665	.97158	1.0676	.02842
1.72	2.70273	.43180	2.88180	.45966	.93786	.97214	1.0663	.02786
1.73	2.73168	.43643	2.90897	.46374	.93906	.97269	1.0649	.02731
1.74	2.76091	.44105	2.93643	.46782	.94023	.97323	1.0636	.02677
1.75	2.79041	.44567	2.96419	.47191	0.94138	.97376	1.0623	.02624
1.76	2.82020	.45028	2.99224	.47600	.94250	.97428	1.0610	.02572
1.77	2.85026	.45488	3.02059	.48009	.94361	.97479	1.0598	.02521
1.78	2.88061	.45948	3.04925	.48419	.94470	.97529	1.0585	.02471
1.79	2.91125	.46408	3.07821	.48830	.94576	.97578	1.0574	.02422
1.80	2.94217	.46867	3.10747	.49241	0.94681	.97626	1.0562	.02374
1.81	2.97340	.47325	3.13705	.49652	.94783	.97673	1.0550	.02327
1.82	3.00492	.47783	3.16694	.50064	.94884	.97719	1.0539	.02281
1.83	3.03674	.48241	3.19715	.50476	.94983	.97764	1.0528	.02236
1.84	3.06886	.48698	3.22768	.50889	.95080	.97809	1.0518	.02191
1.85	3.10129	.49154	3.25853	.51302	0.95175	.97852	1.0507	.02148
1.86	3.13403	.49610	3.28970	.51716	.95268	.97895	1.0497	.02105
1.87	3.16709	.50066	3.32121	.52130	.95359	.97936	1.0487	.02064
1.88	3.20046	.50521	3.35305	.52544	.95449	.97977	1.0477	.02023
1.89	3.23415	.50976	3.38522	.52959	.95537	.98017	1.0467	.01983
1.90	3.26816	.51430	3.41773	.53374	0.95624	.98057	1.0458	.01943
1.91	3.30250	.51884	3.45058	.53789	.95709	.98095	1.0448	.01905
1.92	3.33718	52338	3.48378	.54205	.95792	.98133	1.0439	.01867
1.93	3.37218	.52791	3.51733	.54621	.95873	.98170	1.0430	.01830
1.94	3.40752	.53244	3.55123	.55038	.95953	.98206	1.0422	.01794
1.95	3.44321	.53696	3.58548	.55455	0.96032	.98242	1.0413	.01758
1.96	3.47923	.54148	3.62009	.55872	.96109	.98276	1.0405	.01724
1.97	3.51561	.54600	3.65507	.56290	.96185	.98311	1.0397	.01689
1.98	3.55234	.55051	3.69041	.56707	.96259	.98344	1.0389	.01656
1.99	3.58942	.55502	3.72611	.57126	.96331	.98377	1.0381	.01623

HYPERBOLIC FUNCTIONS (Continued)

The logarithms given below show the mantissa only. The proper characteristic must be added.

x	Sinh x		Cosh x		Tanh x		Coth x	
	Value	$\log_{10}$	Value	$\log_{10}$	Value	$\log_{10}$	Value	$\log_{10}$
2.00	3.62686	.55953	3.76220	.57544	0.96403	.98409	1.0373	.01591
2.01	3.66466	.56403	3.79865	.57963	.96473	.98440	1.0366	.01560
2.02	3.70283	.56853	3.83549	.58382	.96541	.98471	1.0358	.01529
2.03	3.74138	.57303	3.87271	.58802	.96609	.98502	1.0351	.01498
2.04	3.78029	.57753	3.91032	.59221	.96675	.98531	1.0344	.01469
2.05	3.81958	.58202	3.94832	.59641	0.96740	.98560	1.0337	.01440
2.06	3.85[illegible]26	.58650	3.98671	.60061	.96803	.98589	1.0330	.01411
2.07	3.89932	.59099	4.02550	.60482	.96865	.98617	1.0324	.01383
2.08	3.93977	.59547	4.06470	.60903	.96926	.98644	1.0317	.01356
2.09	3.98061	.59995	4.10430	.61324	.96986	.98671	1.0311	.01329
2.10	4.02186	.60443	4.14431	.61745	0.97045	.98697	1.0304	.01303
2.11	4.06350	.60890	4.18474	.62167	.97103	.98723	1.0298	.01277
2.12	4.10555	.61337	4.22558	.62589	.97159	.98748	1.0292	.01252
2.13	4.14801	.61784	4.26685	.63011	.97215	.98773	1.0286	.01227
2.14	4.19089	.62231	4.30855	.63433	.97269	.98798	1.0281	.01202
2.15	4.23419	.62677	4.35067	.63856	0.97323	.98821	1.0275	.01179
2.16	4.27791	.63123	4.39323	.64278	.97375	.98845	1.0270	.01155
2.17	4.32205	.63569	4.43623	.64701	.97426	.98868	1.0264	.01132
2.18	4.36663	.64015	4.47967	.65125	.97477	.98890	1.0259	.01110
2.19	4.41165	.64460	4.52356	.65548	.97526	.98912	1.0254	.01088
2.20	4.45711	.64905	4.56791	.65972	0.97574	.98934	1.0249	.01066
2.21	4.50301	.65350	4.61271	.66396	.97622	.98955	1.0244	.01045
2.22	4.54936	.65795	4.65797	.66820	.97668	.98975	1.0239	.01025
2.23	4.59617	.66240	4.70370	.67244	.97714	.98996	1.0234	.01004
2.24	4.64344	.66684	4.74989	.67668	.97759	.99016	1.0229	.00984
2.25	4.69117	.67128	4.79657	.68093	0.97803	.99035	1.0225	.00965
2.26	4.73937	.67572	4.84372	.68518	.97846	.99054	1.0220	.00946
2.27	4.78804	.68016	4.89136	.68943	.97888	.99073	1.0216	.00927
2.28	4.83720	.68459	4.93948	.69368	.97929	.99091	1.0211	.00909
2.29	4.88684	.68903	4.98810	.69794	.97970	.99109	1.0207	.00891
2.30	4.93696	.69346	5.03722	.70219	0.98010	.99127	1.0203	.00873
2.31	4.98758	.69789	5.08684	.70645	.98049	.99144	1.0199	.00856
2.32	5.03870	.70232	5.13697	.71071	.98087	.99161	1.0195	.00839
2.33	5.09032	.70675	5.18762	.71497	.98124	.99178	1.0191	.00822
2.34	5.14245	.71117	5.23878	.71923	.98161	.99194	1.0187	.00806
2.35	5.19510	.71559	5.29047	.72349	0.98197	.99210	1.0184	.00790
2.36	5.24827	.72002	5.34269	.72776	.98233	.99226	1.0180	.00774
2.37	5.30196	.72444	5.39544	.73203	.98267	.99241	1.0176	.00759
2.38	5.35618	.72885	5.44873	.73630	.98301	.99256	1.0173	.00744
2.39	5.41093	.73327	5.50256	.74056	.98335	.99271	1.0169	.00729
2.40	5.46623	.73769	5.55695	.74484	0.98367	.99285	1.0166	.00715
2.41	5.52207	.74210	5.61189	.74911	.98400	.99299	1.0163	.00701
2.42	5.57847	.74652	5.66739	.75338	.98431	.99313	1.0159	.00687
2.43	5.63542	.75093	5.72346	.75766	.98462	.99327	1.0156	.00673
2.44	5.69294	.75534	5.78010	.76194	.98492	.99340	1.0153	.00660
2.45	5.75103	.75975	5.83732	.76621	0.98522	.99353	1.0150	.00647
2.46	5.80969	.76415	5.89512	.77049	.98551	.99366	1.0147	.00634
2.47	5.86893	.76856	5.95352	.77477	.98579	.99379	1.0144	.00621
2.48	5.92876	.77296	6.01250	.77906	.98607	.99391	1.0141	.00609
2.49	5.98918	.77737	6.07209	.78334	.98635	.99403	1.0138	.00597

HYPERBOLIC FUNCTIONS (Continued)

The logarithms given below show the mantissa only. The proper characteristic must be added.

x	Sinh x		Cosh x		Tanh x		Coth x	
	Value	$\log_{10}$	Value	$\log_{10}$	Value	$\log_{10}$	Value	$\log_{10}$
2.50	6.05020	.78177	6.13229	.78762	0.98661	.99415	1.0136	.00585
2.51	6.11183	.78617	6.19310	.79191	.98688	.99426	1.0133	.00574
2.52	6.17407	.79057	6.25453	.79619	.98714	.99438	1.0130	.00562
2.53	6.23692	.79497	6.31658	.80048	.98739	.99449	1.0128	.00551
2.54	6.30040	.79937	6.37927	.80477	.98764	.99460	1.0125	.00540
2.55	6.36451	.80377	6.44259	.80906	0.98788	.99470	1.0123	.00530
2.56	6.42926	.80816	6.50656	.81335	.98812	.99481	1.0120	.00519
2.57	6.49464	.81256	6.57118	.81764	.98835	.99491	1.0118	.00509
2 58	6.56068	.81695	6.63646	.82194	.98858	.99501	1.0115	.00499
2.59	6.62738	.82134	6.70240	.82623	.98881	.99511	1.0113	.00489
2.60	6.69473	.82573	6.76901	.83052	0.98903	.99521	1.0111	.00479
2.61	6.76276	.83012	6.83629	.83482	.98924	.99530	1.0109	.00470
2.62	6.83146	.83451	6.90426	.83912	.98946	.99540	1.0107	.00460
2.63	6.90085	.83890	6.97292	.84341	.98966	.99549	1.0104	.00451
2.64	6.97092	.84329	7.04228	.84771	.98987	.99558	1.0102	.00442
2.65	7.04169	.84768	7.11234	.85201	0.99007	.99566	1.0100	.00434
2.66	7.11317	.85206	7.18312	.85631	.99026	.99575	1.0098	.00425
2.67	7.18536	.85645	7.25461	.86061	.99045	.99583	1.0096	.00417
2.68	7.25827	.86083	7.32683	.86492	.99064	.99592	1.0094	.00408
2.69	7.33190	.86522	7.39978	.86922	.99083	.99600	1.0093	.00400
2.70	7.40626	.86960	7.47347	.87352	0.99101	.99608	1.0091	.00392
2.71	7.48137	.87398	7.54791	.87783	.99118	.99615	1.0089	.00385
2.72	7.55722	.87836	7.62310	.88213	.99136	.99623	1.0087	.00377
2.73	7.63383	.88274	7.69905	.88644	.99153	.99631	1.0085	.00369
2.74	7.71121	.88712	7.77578	.89074	.99170	.99638	1.0084	.00362
2.75	7.78935	.89150	7.85328	.89505	0.99186	.99645	1.0082	.00355
2.76	7.86828	.89588	7.93157	.89936	.99202	.99652	1.0080	.00348
2.77	7.94799	.90026	8.01065	.90367	.99218	.99659	1.0079	.00341
2.78	8.02849	.90463	8.09053	.90798	.99233	.99666	1.0077	.00334
2.79	8.10980	.90901	8.17122	.91229	.99248	.99672	1.0076	.00328
2.80	8.19192	.91339	8.25273	.91660	0.99263	.99679	1.0074	.00321
2.81	8.27486	.91776	8.33506	.92091	.99278	.99685	1.0073	.00315
2.82	8.35862	.92213	8.41823	.92522	.99292	.99691	1.0071	.00309
2.83	8.44322	.92651	8.50224	.92953	.99306	.99698	1.0070	.00302
2.84	8.52867	.93088	8.58710	.93385	.99320	.99704	1.0069	.00296
2.85	8.61497	.93525	8.67281	.93816	0.99333	.99709	1.0067	.00291
2.86	8.70213	.93963	8.75940	.94247	.99346	.99715	1.0066	.00285
2.87	8.79016	.94400	8.84686	.94679	.99359	.99721	1.0065	.00279
2.88	8.87907	.94837	8.93520	.95110	.99372	.99726	1.0063	.00274
2.89	8.96887	.95274	9.02444	.95542	.99384	.99732	1.0062	.00268
2.90	9.05956	.95711	9.11458	.95974	0.99396	.99737	1.0061	.00263
2.91	9 15116	.96148	9.20564	.96405	.99408	.99742	1.0060	.00258
2.92	9.24368	.96584	9.29761	.96837	.99420	.99747	1.0058	.00253
2.93	9.33712	.97021	9.39051	.97269	.99431	.99752	1.0057	.00248
2.94	9.43149	.97458	9.48436	.97701	.99443	.99757	1.0056	.00243
2.95	9.52681	.97895	9.57915	.98133	0.99454	.99762	1.0055	.00238
2.96	9.62308	.98331	9.67490	.98565	.99464	.99767	1.0054	.00233
2.97	9.72031	.98768	9.77161	.98997	.99475	.99771	1.0053	.00229
2.98	9.81851	.99205	9.86930	.99429	.99485	.99776	1.0052	.00224
2.99	9.91770	.99641	9.96798	.99861	.99496	.99780	1.0051	.00220
3.00	10.01787	.00078	10.06766	.00293	0.99505	.99785	1.0050	.00215

HYPERBOLIC FUNCTIONS (Continued)

The logarithms given below show the mantissa only. The proper characteristic must be added.

x	Sinh x		Cosh x		Tanh x		Coth x	
	Value	$\log_{10}$	Value	$\log_{10}$	Value	$\log_{10}$	Value	$\log_{10}$
3.0	10.0179	.00078	10.0677	.00293	0.99505	.99785	1.0050	.00215
3.1	11.0765	.04440	11.1215	.04616	.99595	.99824	1.0041	.00176
3.2	12.2459	.08799	12.2866	.08943	.99668	.99856	1.0033	.00144
3.3	13.5379	.13155	13.5748	.13273	.99728	.99882	1.0027	.00118
3.4	14.9654	.17509	14.9987	.17605	.99777	.99903	1.0022	.00097
3.5	16.5426	.21860	16.5728	.21940	0.99818	.99921	1.0018	.00079
3.6	18.2855	.26211	18.3128	.26275	.99851	.99935	1.0015	.00065
3.7	20.2113	.30559	20.2360	.30612	.99878	.99947	1.0012	.00053
3.8	22.3394	.34907	22.3618	.34951	.99900	.99957	1.0010	.00043
3.9	24.6911	.39254	24.7113	.39290	.99918	.99964	1.0008	.00036
4.0	27.2899	.43600	27.3082	.43629	0.99933	.99971	1.0007	.00029
4.1	30.1619	.47946	30.1784	.47970	.99945	.99976	1.0005	.00024
4.2	33.3357	.52291	33.3507	.52310	.99955	.99980	1.0004	.00020
4.3	36.8431	.56636	36.8567	.56652	.99963	.99984	1.0004	.00016
4.4	40.7193	.60980	40.7316	.60993	.99970	.99987	1.0003	.00013
4.5	45.0030	.65324	45.0141	.65335	0.99975	.99989	1.0002	.00011
4.6	49.7371	.69668	49.7472	.69677	.99980	.99991	1.0002	.00009
4.7	54.9690	.74012	54.9781	.74019	.99983	.99993	1.0002	.00007
4.8	60.7511	.78355	60.7593	.78361	.99986	.99994	1.0001	00006
4.9	67.1412	.82699	67.1486	.82704	.99989	.99995	1.0001	.00005
5.0	74.2032	.87042	74.2099	.87046	0.99991	.99996	1.0001	.00004

FACTORIALS, EXACT VALUES AND RECIPROCALS

n	$n!$	n	$n!$	n	$1/n!$	n	$1/n!$
1	1	11	39916800	1	1.	11	$.25052 \times 10^{-7}$
2	2	12	479001600	2	0.5	12	$.20877 \times 10^{-8}$
3	6	13	6227020800	3	.16667	13	$.16059 \times 10^{-9}$
4	24	14	87178291200	4	$.41667 \times 10^{-1}$	14	$.11471 \times 10^{-10}$
5	120	15	1307674368000	5	$.83333 \times 10^{-2}$	15	$.76472 \times 10^{-12}$
6	720	16	20922789888000	6	$.13889 \times 10^{-2}$	16	$.47795 \times 10^{-13}$
7	5040	17	355687428096000	7	$.19841 \times 10^{-3}$	17	$.28115 \times 10^{-14}$
8	40320	18	6402373705728000	8	$.24802 \times 10^{-4}$	18	$.15619 \times 10^{-15}$
9	362880	19	121645100408832000	9	$.27557 \times 10^{-5}$	19	$.82206 \times 10^{-17}$
10	3628800	20	2432902008176640000	10	$.27557 \times 10^{-6}$	20	$.41103 \times 10^{-18}$

DEGREES—RADIANS

1 radian = 57° 17′ 44″.80625

	log
1 radian = 57.29577 95131 degrees	1.75812 26324
1 radian = 3437.74677 07849 minutes	3.53627 38828
1 radian = 206264.80625 seconds	5.31442 51332
1 degree = 0.01745 32925 19943 radians	8.24187 73676–10
1 minute = 0.00029 08882 08666 radians	6.46372 61172–10
1 second = 0.00000 48481 36811 radians	4.68557 48668–10

DEGREES—RADIANS

The table gives in radians the angle which is expressed in degrees and minutes at the side and top. Angles expressed to the nearest minute and second can readily be converted to radians by adding to the equivalent of the whole number of degrees the equivalents of the minutes and seconds found on the third page of this table.

°	00′	10	20	30	40	50
0	0.00000	0.00291	0.00582	0.00873	0.01164	0.01454
1	0.01745	0.02036	0.02327	0.02618	0.02909	0.03200
2	0.03491	0.03782	0.04072	0.04363	0.04654	0.04945
3	0.05236	0.05527	0.05818	0.06109	0.06400	0.06690
4	0.06981	0.07272	0.07563	0.07854	0.08145	0.08436
5	0.08727	0.09018	0.09308	0.09599	0.09890	0.10181
6	0.10472	0.10763	0.11054	0.11345	0.11636	0.11926
7	0.12217	0.12508	0.12799	0.13090	0.13381	0.13672
8	0.13963	0.14254	0.14544	0.14835	0.15126	0.15417
9	0.15708	0.15999	0.16290	0.16581	0.16872	0.17162
10	0.17453	0.17744	0.18035	0.18326	0.18617	0.18908
11	0.19199	0.19490	0.19780	0.20071	0.20362	0.20653
12	0.20944	0.21235	0.21526	0.21817	0.22108	0.22398
13	0.22689	0.22980	0.23271	0.23562	0.23853	0.24144
14	0.24435	0.24725	0.25016	0.25307	0.25598	0.25889
15	0.26180	0.26471	0.26762	0.27053	0.27343	0.27634
16	0.27925	0.28216	0.28507	0.28798	0.29089	0.29380
17	0.29671	0.29961	0.30252	0.30543	0.30834	0.31125
18	0.31416	0.31707	0.31998	0.32289	0.32579	0.32870
19	0.33161	0.33452	0.33743	0.34034	0.34325	0.34616
20	0.34907	0.35197	0.35488	0.35779	0.36070	0.36361
21	0.36652	0.36943	0.37234	0.37525	0.37815	0.38106
22	0.38397	0.38688	0.38979	0.39270	0.39561	0.39852
23	0.40143	0.40433	0.40724	0.41015	0.41306	0.41597
24	0.41888	0.42179	0.42470	0.42761	0.43051	0.43342
25	0.43633	0.43924	0.44215	0.44506	0.44797	0.45088
26	0.45379	0.45669	0.45960	0.46251	0.46542	0.46833
27	0.47124	0.47415	0.47706	0.47997	0.48287	0.48578
28	0.48869	0.49160	0.49451	0.49742	0.50033	0.50324
29	0.50615	0.50905	0.51196	0.51487	0.51778	0.52069
30	0.52360	0.52651	0.52942	0.53233	0.53523	0.53814
31	0.54105	0.54396	0.54687	0.54978	0.55269	0.55560
32	0.55851	0.56141	0.56432	0.56723	0.57014	0.57305
33	0.57596	0.57887	0.58178	0.58469	0.58759	0.59050
34	0.59341	0.59632	0.59923	0.60214	0.60505	0.60796
35	0.61087	0.61377	0.61668	0.61959	0.62250	0.62541
36	0.62832	0.63123	0.63414	0.63705	0.63995	0.64286
37	0.64577	0.64868	0.65159	0.65450	0.65741	0.66032
38	0.66323	0.66613	0.66904	0.67195	0.67486	0.67777
39	0.68068	0.68359	0.68650	0.68941	0.69231	0.69522
40	0.69813	0.70104	0.70395	0.70686	0.70977	0.71268
41	0.71558	0.71849	0.72140	0.72431	0.72722	0.73013
42	0.73304	0.73595	0.73886	0.74176	0.74467	0.74758
43	0.75049	0.75340	0.75631	0.75922	0.76213	0.76504
44	0.76794	0.77085	0.77376	0.77667	0.77958	0.78249
45	0.78540	0.78831	0.79122	0.79412	0.79703	0.79994
46	0.80285	0.80576	0.80867	0.81158	0.81449	0.81740
47	0.82030	0.82321	0.82612	0.82903	0.83194	0.83485
48	0.83776	0.84067	0.84358	0.84648	0.84939	0.85230
49	0.85521	0.85812	0.86103	0.86394	0.86685	0.86976
50	0.87266	0.87557	0.87848	0.88139	0.88430	0.88721

DEGREES—RADIANS (Continued)

°	00′	10	20	30	40	50
50	0.87266	0.87557	0.87848	0.88139	0.88430	0.88721
51	0.89012	0.89303	0.89594	0.89884	0.90175	0.90466
52	0.90757	0.91048	0.91339	0.91630	0.91921	0.92212
53	0.92502	0.92793	0.93084	0.93375	0.93666	0.93957
54	0.94248	0.94539	0.94830	0.95120	0.95411	0.95702
55	0.95993	0.96284	0.96575	0.96866	0.97157	0.97448
56	0.97738	0.98029	0.98320	0.98611	0.98902	0.99193
57	0.99484	0.99775	1.00066	1.00356	1.00647	1.00938
58	1.01229	1.01520	1.01811	1.02102	1.02393	1.02684
59	1.02974	1.03265	1.03556	1.03847	1.04138	1.04429
60	1.04720	1.05011	1.05302	1.05592	1.05883	1.06174
61	1.06465	1.06756	1.07047	1.07338	1.07629	1.07920
62	1.08210	1.08501	1.08792	1.09083	1.09374	1.09665
63	1.09956	1.10247	1.10538	1.10828	1.11119	1.11410
64	1.11701	1.11992	1.12283	1.12574	1.12865	1.13156
65	1.13446	1.13737	1.14028	1.14319	1.14610	1.14901
66	1.15192	1.15483	1.15774	1.16064	1.16355	1.16646
67	1.16937	1.17228	1.17519	1.17810	1.18101	1.18392
68	1.18682	1.18973	1.19264	1.19555	1.19846	1.20137
69	1.20428	1.20719	1.21009	1.21300	1.21591	1.21882
70	1.22173	1.22464	1.22755	1.23046	1.23337	1.23627
71	1.23918	1.24209	1.24500	1.24791	1.25082	1.25373
72	1.25664	1.25955	1.26245	1.26536	1.26827	1.27118
73	1.27409	1.27700	1.27991	1.28282	1.28573	1.28863
74	1.29154	1.29445	1.29736	1.30027	1.30318	1.30609
75	1.30900	1.31191	1.31481	1.31772	1.32063	1.32354
76	1.32645	1.32936	1.33227	1.33518	1.33809	1.34099
77	1.34390	1.34681	1.34972	1.35263	1.35554	1.35845
78	1.36136	1.36427	1.36717	1.37008	1.37299	1.37590
79	1.37881	1.38172	1.38463	1.38754	1.39045	1.39335
80	1.39626	1.39917	1.40208	1.40499	1.40790	1.41081
81	1.41372	1.41663	1.41953	1.42244	1.42535	1.42826
82	1.43117	1.43408	1.43699	1.43990	1.44281	1.44571
83	1.44862	1.45153	1.45444	1.45735	1.46026	1.46317
84	1.46608	1.46899	1.47189	1.47480	1.47771	1.48062
85	1.48353	1.48644	1.48935	1.49226	1.49517	1.49807
86	1.50098	1.50389	1.50680	1.50971	1.51262	1.51553
87	1.51844	1.52135	1.52425	1.52716	1.53007	1.53298
88	1.53589	1.53880	1.54171	1.54462	1.54753	1.55043
89	1.55334	1.55625	1.55916	1.56207	1.56498	1.56789
90	1.57080	1.57371	1.57661	1.57952	1.58243	1.58534
91	1.58825	1.59116	1.59407	1.59698	1.59989	1.60279
92	1.60570	1.60861	1.61152	1.61443	1.61734	1.62025
93	1.62316	1.62607	1.62897	1.63188	1.63479	1.63770
94	1.64061	1.64352	1.64643	1.64934	1.65225	1.65515
95	1.65806	1.66097	1.66388	1.66679	1.66970	1.67261
96	1.67552	1.67842	1.68133	1.68424	1.68715	1.69006
97	1.69297	1.69588	1.69879	1.70170	1.70460	1.70751
98	1.71042	1.71333	1.71624	1.71915	1.72206	1.72497
99	1.72788	1.73078	1.73369	1.73660	1.73951	1.74242
100	1.74533	1.74824	1.75115	1.75406	1.75696	1.75987
101	1.76278	1.76569	1.76860	1.77151	1.77442	1.77733
102	1.78024	1.78314	1.78605	1.78896	1.79187	1.79478
103	1.79769	1.80060	1.80351	1.80642	1.80932	1.81223
104	1.81514	1.81805	1.82096	1.82387	1.82678	1.82969
105	1.83260	1.83550	1.83841	1.84132	1.84423	1.84714
106	1.85004	1.85296	1.85587	1.85878	1.86168	1.86459
107	1.86750	1.87041	1.87332	1.87623	1.87914	1.88205
108	1.88496	1.88786	1.89077	1.89368	1.89659	1.89950
109	1.90241	1.90532	1.90823	1.91114	1.91404	1.91695
110	1.91986	1.92277	1.92568	1.92859	1.93150	1.93441

DEGREES—RADIANS (Concluded)

Deg.	Radians	Deg.	Radians	Min.	Radians	Sec.	Radians
90	1.57080	**150**	2.61799	**0**	0.00000	**0**	0.00000
91	1.58825	151	2.63545	1	0.00029	1	0.00000
92	1.60570	152	2.65290	2	0.00058	2	0.00001
93	1.62316	153	2.67035	3	0.00087	3	0.00001
94	1.64061	154	2.68781	4	0.00116	4	0.00002
95	1.65806	**155**	2.70526	**5**	0.00145	**5**	0.00002
96	1.67552	156	2.72271	6	0.00175	6	0.00003
97	1.69297	157	2.74017	7	0.00204	7	0.00003
98	1.71042	158	2.75762	8	0.00233	8	0.00004
99	1.72788	159	2.77507	9	0.00262	9	0.00004
100	1.74533	**160**	2.79253	**10**	0.00291	**10**	0.00005
101	1.76278	161	2.80998	11	0.00320	11	0.00005
102	1.78024	162	2.82743	12	0.00349	12	0.00006
103	1.79769	163	2.84489	13	0.00378	13	0.00006
104	1.81514	164	2.86234	14	0.00407	14	0.00007
105	1.83260	**165**	2.87979	**15**	0.00436	**15**	0.00007
106	1.85005	166	2.89725	16	0.00465	16	0.00008
107	1.86750	167	2.91470	17	0.00495	17	0.00008
108	1.88496	168	2.93215	18	0.00524	18	0.00009
109	1.90241	169	2.94961	19	0.00553	19	0.00009
110	1.91986	**170**	2.96706	**20**	0.00582	**20**	0.00010
111	1.93732	171	2.98451	21	0.00611	21	0.00010
112	1.95477	172	3.00197	22	0.00640	22	0.00011
113	1.97222	173	3.01942	23	0.00669	23	0.00011
114	1.98968	174	3.03687	24	0.00698	24	0.00012
115	2.00713	**175**	3.05433	**25**	0.00727	**25**	0.00012
116	2.02458	176	3.07178	26	0.00756	26	0.00013
117	2.04204	177	3.08923	27	0.00785	27	0.00013
118	2.05949	178	3.10669	28	0.00814	28	0.00014
119	2.07694	179	3.12414	29	0.00844	29	0.00014
120	2.09440	**180**	3.14159	**30**	0.00873	**30**	0.00015
121	2.11185	190	3.31613	31	0.00902	31	0.00015
122	2.12930	200	3.49066	32	0.00931	32	0.00016
123	2.14676	210	3.66519	33	0.00960	33	0.00016
124	2.16421	220	3.83972	34	0.00989	34	0.00016
125	2.18166	**230**	4.01426	**35**	0.01018	**35**	0.00017
126	2.19911	240	4.18879	36	0.01047	36	0.00017
127	2.21657	250	4.36332	37	0.01076	37	0.00018
128	2.23402	260	4.53786	38	0.01105	38	0.00018
129	2.25147	270	4.71239	39	0.01134	39	0.00019
130	2.26893	**280**	4.88692	**40**	0.01164	**40**	0.00019
131	2.28638	290	5.06145	41	0.01193	41	0.00020
132	2.30383	300	5.23599	42	0.01222	42	0.00020
133	2.32129	310	5.41052	43	0.01251	43	0.00021
134	2.33874	320	5.58505	44	0.01280	44	0.00021
135	2.35619	**330**	5.75959	**45**	0.01309	**45**	0.00022
136	2.37365	340	5.93412	46	0.01338	46	0.00022
137	2.39110	350	6.10865	47	0.01367	47	0.00023
138	2.40855	360	6.28319	48	0.01396	48	0.00023
139	2.42601	370	6.45772	49	0.01425	49	0.00024
140	2.44346	**380**	6.63225	**50**	0.01454	**50**	0.00024
141	2.46091	390	6.80678	51	0.01484	51	0.00025
142	2.47837	400	6.98132	52	0.01513	52	0.00025
143	2.49582	410	7.15585	53	0.01542	53	0.00026
144	2.51327	420	7.33038	54	0.01571	54	0.00026
145	2.53073	**430**	7.50492	**55**	0.01600	**55**	0.00027
146	2.54818	440	7.67945	56	0.01629	56	0.00027
147	2.56563	450	7.85398	57	0.01658	57	0.00028
148	2.58309	460	8.02851	58	0.01687	58	0.00028
149	2.60054	470	8.20305	59	0.01716	59	0.00029
150	2.61799	**480**	8.37758	**60**	0.01745	**60**	0.00029

DEGREES AND DECIMAL FRACTIONS TO RADIANS

The table below facilitates conversion of an angle expressed in degrees and decimal fractions into radians. To convert 25.78 into radians, find the equivalents, successively, of 20°, 5°, 0°.7, 0°.08 and add.

Deg.	Radians	Deg.	Radians	Deg.	Radians	Deg.	Radians	Deg.	Radians
10	0.174533	1	0.017453	0.1	0.001745	0.01	0.000175	0.001	0.000017
20	0.349066	2	.034907	.2	.003491	.02	.000349	.002	.000035
30	0.523599	3	.052360	.3	.005236	.03	.000524	.003	.000052
40	0.698132	4	.069813	.4	.006981	.04	.000698	.004	.000070
50	0.872665	5	.087266	.5	.008727	.05	.000873	.005	.000087
60	1.047198	6	.104720	.6	.010472	.06	.001047	.006	.000105
70	1.221730	7	.122173	.7	.012217	.07	.001222	.007	.000122
80	1.396263	8	.139626	.8	.013963	.08	.001396	.008	.000140
90	1.570796	9	.157080	.9	.015708	.09	.001571	.009	.000157

RADIANS—DEGREES

Radians	Degrees	Radians	Degrees	Radians	Degrees	Radians	Degrees
1	57.2958	0.1	5.7296	0.01	0.5730	0.001	0.0573
2	114.5916	.2	11.4592	.02	1.1459	.002	.1146
3	171.8873	.3	17.1887	.03	1.7189	.003	.1719
4	229.1831	.4	22.9183	.04	2.2918	.004	.2292
5	286.4789	.5	28.6479	.05	2.8648	.005	.2865
6	343.7747	.6	34.3775	.06	3.4377	.006	.3438
7	401.0705	.7	40.1070	.07	4.0107	.007	.4011
8	458.3662	.8	45.8366	.08	4.5837	.008	.4584
9	515.6620	.9	51.5662	.09	5.1566	.009	.5157
10	572.9578	1.0	57.2958	.10	5.7296	.010	.5730

RADIANS—DEGREES

Multiples and Fractions of π Radians

Radians	Radians	Deg.	Radians	Radians	Deg.	Radians	Radians	Deg.
π	3.1416	180	$\pi/2$	1.5708	90	$2\pi/3$	2.0944	120
2π	6.2832	360	$\pi/3$	1.0472	60	$3\pi/4$	2.3562	135
3π	9.4248	540	$\pi/4$	0.7854	45	$5\pi/6$	2.6180	150
4π	12.5664	720	$\pi/5$	0.6283	36	$7\pi/6$	3.6652	210
5π	15.7080	900	$\pi/6$	0.5236	30	$5\pi/4$	3.9270	225
6π	18.8496	1080	$\pi/7$	0.4488	25.714	$4\pi/3$	4.1888	240
7π	21.9911	1260	$\pi/8$	0.3927	22.5	$3\pi/2$	4.7124	270
8π	25.1327	1440	$\pi/9$	0.3491	20	$5\pi/3$	5.2360	300
9π	28.2743	1620	$\pi/10$	0.3142	18	$7\pi/4$	5.4978	315
10π	31.4159	1800	$\pi/12$	0.2618	15	$11\pi/6$	5.7596	330

CONVERSION OF ANGLES FROM ARC TO TIME

Arc	Time	Arc	Time	Arc	Time	Arc	Time
°	h m	°	h m	″	s	″	s
′	m s	′	m s				
0	0 00	20	1 20	0	0.00	8	0.53
1	0 04	30	2 00	1	0.07	9	0.60
2	0 08	40	2 40	2	0.13	10	0.67
3	0 12	50	3 20	3	0.20	20	1.33
4	0 16	60	4 00	4	0.27	30	2.00
5	0 20	70	4 40	5	0.33	40	2.67
6	0 24	80	5 20	6	0.40	50	3.33
7	0 28	90	6 00	7	0.47	60	4.00
8	0 32	100	6 40				
9	0 36	200	13 20				
10	0 40	300	20 00				

MINUTES AND SECONDS TO DECIMAL PARTS OF A DEGREE

MINUTES AND SECONDS TO DECIMAL PARTS OF A DEG.				DECIMAL PARTS OF A DEGREE TO MINUTES AND SECONDS					
Min.	Degrees	Sec.	Degrees	Deg.	′	″	Deg.	′	″
0	0.00000	**0**	0.00000	**0.00**	0	00	**0.60**	36	
1	.01667	1	.00028	.01	0	36	.61	36	36
2	.03333	2	.00056	.02	1	12	.62	37	12
3	.05	3	.00083	.03	1	48	.63	37	48
4	.06667	4	.00111	.04	2	24	.64	38	24
5	.08333	5	.00139	.05	3		.65	39	
6	.10	6	.00167	.06	3	36	.66	39	36
7	.11667	7	.00194	.07	4	12	.67	40	12
8	.13333	8	.00222	.08	4	48	.68	40	48
9	.15	9	.0025	.09	5	24	.69	41	24
10	0.16667	**10**	0.00278	**0.10**	6		**0.70**	42	
11	.18333	11	.00306	.11	6	36	.71	42	36
12	.20	12	.00333	.12	7	12	.72	43	12
13	.21667	13	.00361	.13	7	48	.73	43	48
14	.23333	14	.00389	.14	8	24	.74	44	24
15	.25	15	.00417	.15	9		.75	45	
16	.26667	16	.00444	.16	9	36	.76	45	36
17	.28333	17	.00472	.17	10	12	.77	46	12
18	.30	18	.005	.18	10	48	.78	46	48
19	.31667	19	.00528	.19	11	24	.79	47	24
20	0.33333	**20**	0.00556	**0.20**	12		**0.80**	48	
21	.35	21	.00583	.21	12	36	.81	48	36
22	.36667	22	.00611	.22	13	12	.82	49	12
23	.38333	23	.00639	.23	13	48	.83	49	48
24	.40	24	.00667	.24	14	24	.84	50	24
25	.41667	25	.00694	.25	15		.85	51	
26	.43333	26	.00722	.26	15	36	.86	51	36
27	.45	27	.0075	.27	16	12	.87	52	12
28	.46667	28	.00778	.28	16	48	.88	52	48
29	.48333	29	.00806	.29	17	24	.89	53	24
30	0.50	**30**	0.00833	**0.30**	18		**0.90**	54	
31	.51667	31	.00861	.31	18	36	.91	54	36
32	.53333	32	.00889	.32	19	12	.92	55	12
33	.55	33	.00917	.33	19	48	.93	55	48
34	.56667	34	.00944	.34	20	24	.94	56	24
35	.58333	35	.00972	.35	21		.95	57	
36	.60	36	.01	.36	21	36	.96	57	36
37	.61667	37	.01028	.37	22	12	.97	58	12
38	.63333	38	.01056	.38	22	48	.98	58	48
39	.65	39	.01083	.39	23	24	.99	59	24
40	0.66667	**40**	0.01111	**0.40**	24		**1.00**	60	
41	.68333	41	.01139	.41	24	36			
42	.70	42	.01167	.42	25	12			
43	.71667	43	.01194	.43	25	48			
44	.73333	44	.01222	.44	26	24			
45	.75	45	.0125	.45	27				
46	.76667	46	.01278	.46	27	36			
47	.78333	47	.01306	.47	28	12			
48	.80	48	.01333	.48	28	48			
49	.81667	49	.01361	.49	29	24			
50	0.83333	**50**	0.01389	**0.50**	30				
51	.85	51	.01417	.51	30	36			
52	.86667	52	.01444	.52	31	12			
53	.88333	53	.01472	.53	31	48			
54	.90	54	.015	.54	32	24			
55	.91667	55	.01528	.55	33				
56	.93333	56	.01556	.56	33	36			
57	.95	57	.01583	.57	34	12			
58	.96667	58	.01611	.58	34	48			
59	.98333	59	.01639	.59	35	24			
60	1.00	**60**	0.01667	**0.60**	36				

Deg.	Sec.
0.000	0.0
.001	3.6
.002	7.2
.003	10.8
.004	14.4
.005	18.
.006	21.6
.007	25.2
.008	28.8
.009	32.4
0.010	36.

NUMERICAL TABLES
Reciprocals, Circumference and Area of Circles

As a matter of convenience, the values of 1000 × $(1/n)$ are given in the table. To obtain the actual value of the reciprocal, shift the decimal point three places to the left.

Circumferences and areas of circles are given for the values of n as the diameter.

n	$1000\frac{1}{n}$	Circumference πn	Area $\frac{\pi n^2}{4}$	n	$1000\frac{1}{n}$	Circumference πn	Area $\frac{\pi n^2}{4}$
0	∞	0.000000	.0000000	**50**	20.00000	157.0796	1963.495
1	1000.000	3.141593	.7853982	51	19.60784	160.2212	2042.821
2	500.0000	6.283185	3.141593	52	19.23077	163.3628	2123.717
3	333.3333	9.424778	7.068583	53	18.86792	166.5044	2206.183
4	250.0000	12.56637	12.56637	54	18.51852	169.6460	2290.221
5	200.0000	15.70796	19.63495	55	18.18182	172.7876	2375.829
6	166.6667	18.84956	28.27433	56	17.85714	175.9292	2463.009
7	142.8571	21.99115	38.48451	57	17.54386	179.0708	2551.759
8	125.0000	25.13274	50.26548	58	17.24138	182.2124	2642.079
9	111.1111	28.27433	63.61725	59	16.94915	185.3540	2733.971
10	100.0000	31.41593	78.53982	**60**	16.66667	188.4956	2827.433
11	90.90909	34.55752	95.03318	61	16.39344	191.6372	2922.467
12	83.33333	37.69911	113.0973	62	16.12903	194.7787	3019.071
13	76.92308	40.84070	132.7323	63	15.87302	197.9203	3117.245
14	71.42857	43.98230	153.9380	64	15.62500	201.0619	3216.991
15	66.66667	47.12389	176.7146	65	15.38462	204.2035	3318.307
16	62.50000	50.26548	201.0619	66	15.15152	207.3451	3421.194
17	58.82353	53.40708	226.9801	67	14.92537	210.4867	3525.652
18	55.55556	56.54867	254.4690	68	14.70588	213.6283	3631.681
19	52.63158	59.69026	283.5287	69	14.49275	216.7699	3739.281
20	50.00000	62.83185	314.1593	**70**	14.28571	219.9115	3848.451
21	47.61905	65.97345	346.3606	71	14.08451	223.0531	3959.192
22	45.45455	69.11504	380.1327	72	13.88889	226.1947	4071.504
23	43.47826	72.25663	415.4756	73	13.69863	229.3363	4185.387
24	41.66667	75.39822	452.3893	74	13.51351	232.4779	4300.840
25	40.00000	78.53982	490.8739	75	13.33333	235.6194	4417.865
26	38.46154	81.68141	530.9292	76	13.15789	238.7610	4536.460
27	37.03704	84.82300	572.5553	77	12.98701	241.9026	4656.626
28	35.71429	87.96459	615.7522	78	12.82051	245.0442	4778.362
29	34.48276	91.10619	660.5199	79	12.65823	248.1858	4901.670
30	33.33333	94.24778	706.8583	**80**	12.50000	251.3274	5026.548
31	32.25806	97.38937	754.7676	81	12.34568	254.4690	5152.997
32	31.25000	100.5310	804.2477	82	12.19512	257.6106	5281.017
33	30.30303	103.6726	855.2986	83	12.04819	260.7522	5410.608
34	29.41176	106.8142	907.9203	84	11.90476	263.8938	5541.769
35	28.57143	109.9557	962.1128	85	11.76471	267.0354	5674.502
36	27.77778	113.0973	1017.876	86	11.62791	270.1770	5808.805
37	27.02703	116.2389	1075.210	87	11.49425	273.3186	5944.679
38	26.31579	119.3805	1134.115	88	11.36364	276.4602	6082.123
39	25.64103	122.5221	1194.591	89	11.23596	279.6017	6221.139
40	25.00000	125.6637	1256.637	**90**	11.11111	282.7433	6361.725
41	24.39024	128.8053	1320.254	91	10.98901	285.8849	6503.882
42	23.80952	131.9469	1385.442	92	10.86957	289.0265	6647.610
43	23.25581	135.0885	1452.201	93	10.75269	292.1681	6792.909
44	22.72727	138.2301	1520.531	94	10.63830	295.3097	6939.778
45	22.22222	141.3717	1590.431	95	10.52632	298.4513	7088.218
46	21.73913	144.5133	1661.903	96	10.41667	301.5929	7238.229
47	21.27660	147.6549	1734.945	97	10.30928	304.7345	7389.811
48	20.83333	150.7964	1809.557	98	10.20408	307.8761	7542.964
49	20.40816	153.9380	1885.741	99	10.10101	311.0177	7697.687
50	20.00000	157.0796	1963.495	**100**	10.00000	314.1593	7853.982

RECIPROCALS, CIRCUMFERENCE AND AREA OF CIRCLES (Continued)

n	$1000\frac{1}{n}$	Circumference πn	Area $\frac{\pi n^2}{4}$	n	$1000\frac{1}{n}$	Circumference πn	Area $\frac{\pi n^2}{4}$
100	10.00000	314.1593	7853.982	**150**	6.666 667	471.2389	17671.46
101	9.900 990	317.3009	8011.847	151	6.622 517	474.3805	17907.86
102	9.803 922	320.4425	8171.282	152	6.578 947	477.5221	18145.84
103	9.708 738	323.5840	8332.289	153	6.535 948	480.6637	18385.39
104	9.615 385	326.7256	8494.867	154	6.493 506	483.8053	18626.50
105	9.523 810	329.8672	8659.015	155	6.451 613	486.9469	18869.19
106	9.433 962	333.0088	8824.734	156	6.410 256	490.0885	19113.45
107	9.345 794	336.1504	8992.024	157	6.369 427	493.2300	19359.28
108	9.259 259	339.2920	9160.884	158	6.329 114	496.3716	19606.68
109	9.174 312	342.4336	9331.316	159	6.289 308	499.5132	19855.65
110	9.090 909	345.5752	9503.318	**160**	6.250 000	502.6548	20106.19
111	9.009 009	348.7168	9676.891	161	6.211 180	505.7964	20358.31
112	8.928 571	351.8584	9852.035	162	6.172 840	508.9380	20611.99
113	8.849 558	355.0000	10028.75	163	6.134 969	512.0796	20867.24
114	8.771 930	358.1416	10207.03	164	6.097 561	515.2212	21124.07
115	8.695 652	361.2832	10386.89	165	6.060 606	518.3628	21382.46
116	8.620 690	364.4247	10568.32	166	6.024 096	521.5044	21642.43
117	8.547 009	367.5663	10751.32	167	5.988 024	524.6460	21903.97
118	8.474 576	370.7079	10935.88	168	5.952 381	527.7876	22167.08
119	8.403 361	373.8495	11122.02	169	5.917 160	530.9292	22431.76
120	8.333 333	376.9911	11309.73	**170**	5.882 353	534.0708	22698.01
121	8.264 463	380.1327	11499.01	171	5.847 953	537.2123	22965.83
122	8.196 721	383.2743	11689.87	172	5.813 953	540.3539	23235.22
123	8.130 081	386.4159	11882.29	173	5.780 347	543.4955	23506.18
124	8.064 516	389.5575	12076.28	174	5.747 126	546.6371	23778.71
125	8.000 000	392.6991	12271.85	175	5.714 286	549.7787	24052.82
126	7.936 508	395.8407	12468.98	176	5.681 818	552.9203	24328.49
127	7.874 016	398.9823	12667.69	177	5.649 718	556.0619	24605.74
128	7.812 500	402.1239	12867.96	178	5.617 978	559.2035	24884.56
129	7.751 938	405.2655	13069.81	179	5.586 592	562.3451	25164.94
130	7.692 308	408.4070	13273.23	**180**	5.555 556	565.4867	25446.90
131	7.633 588	411.5486	13478.22	181	5.524 862	568.6283	25730.43
132	7.575 758	414.6902	13684.78	182	5.494 505	571.7699	26015.53
133	7.518 797	417.8318	13892.91	183	5.464 481	574.9115	26302.20
134	7.462 687	420.9734	14102.61	184	5.434 783	578.0530	26590.44
135	7.407 407	424.1150	14313.88	185	5.405 405	581.1946	26880.25
136	7.352 941	427.2566	14526.72	186	5.376 344	584.3362	27171.63
137	7.299 270	430.3982	14741.14	187	5.347 594	587.4778	27464.59
138	7.246 377	433.5398	14957.12	188	5.319 149	590.6194	27759.11
139	7.194 245	436.6814	15174.68	189	5.291 005	593.7610	28055.21
140	7.142 857	439.8230	15393.80	**190**	5.263 158	596.9026	28352.87
141	7.092 199	442.9646	15614.50	191	5.235 602	600.0442	28652.11
142	7.042 254	446.1062	15836.77	192	5.208 333	603.1858	28952.92
143	6.993 007	449.2477	16060.61	193	5.181 347	606.3274	29255.30
144	6.944 444	452.3893	16286.02	194	5.154 639	609.4690	29559.25
145	6.896 552	455.5309	16513.00	195	5.128 205	612.6106	29864.77
146	6.849 315	458.6725	16741.55	196	5.102 041	615.7522	30171.86
147	6.802 721	461.8141	16971.67	197	5.076 142	618.8938	30480.52
148	6.756 757	464.9557	17203.36	198	5.050 505	622.0353	30790.75
149	6.711 409	468.0973	17436.62	199	5.025 126	625.1769	31102.55
150	6.666 667	471.2389	17671.46	**200**	5.000 000	628.3185	31415.93

RECIPROCALS, CIRCUMFERENCE AND AREA OF CIRCLES
(Continued)

n	$1000\frac{1}{n}$	Circumference πn	Area $\frac{\pi n^2}{4}$	n	$1000\frac{1}{n}$	Circumference πn	Area $\frac{\pi n^2}{4}$
200	5.000 000	628.3185	31415.93	**250**	4.000 000	785.3982	49087.39
201	4.975 124	631.4601	31730.87	251	3.984 064	788.5398	49480.87
202	4.950 495	634.6017	32047.39	252	3.968 254	791.6813	49875.92
203	4.926 108	637.7433	32365.47	253	3.952 569	794.8229	50272.55
204	4.901 961	640.8849	32685.13	254	3.937 008	797.9645	50670.75
205	4.878 049	644.0265	33006.36	255	3.921 569	801.1061	51070.52
206	4.854 369	647.1681	33329.16	256	3.906 250	804.2477	51471.85
207	4.830 918	650.3097	33653.53	257	3.891 051	807.3893	51874.76
208	4.807 692	653.4513	33979.47	258	3.875 969	810.5309	52279.24
209	4.784 689	656.5929	34306.98	259	3.861 004	813.6725	52685.29
210	4.761 905	659.7345	34636.06	**260**	3.846 154	816.8141	53092.92
211	4.739 336	662.8760	34966.71	261	3.831 418	819.9557	53502.11
212	4.716 981	666.0176	35298.94	262	3.816 794	823.0973	53912.87
213	4.694 836	669.1592	35632.73	263	3.802 281	826.2389	54325.21
214	4.672 897	672.3008	35968.09	264	3.787 879	829.3805	54739.11
215	4.651 163	675.4424	36305.03	265	3.773 585	832.5221	55154.59
216	4.629 630	678.5840	36643.54	266	3.759 398	835.6636	55571.63
217	4.608 295	681.7256	36983.61	267	3.745 318	838.8052	55990.25
218	4.587 156	684.8672	37325.26	268	3.731 343	841.9468	56410.44
219	4.566 210	688.0088	37668.48	269	3.717 472	845.0884	56832.20
220	4.545 455	691.1504	38013.27	**270**	3.703 704	848.2300	57255.53
221	4.524 887	694.2920	38359.63	271	3.690 037	851.3716	57680.43
222	4.504 505	697.4336	38707.56	272	3.676 471	854.5132	58106.90
223	4.484 305	700.5752	39057.07	273	3.663 004	857.6548	58534.94
224	4.464 286	703.7168	39408.14	274	3.649 635	860.7964	58964.55
225	4.444 444	706.8583	39760.78	275	3.636 364	863.9380	59395.74
226	4.424 779	709.9999	40115.00	276	3.623 188	867.0796	59828.49
227	4.405 286	713.1415	40470.78	277	3.610 108	870.2212	60262.82
228	4.385 965	716.2831	40828.14	278	3.597 122	873.3628	60698.71
229	4.366 812	719.4247	41187.07	279	3.584 229	876.5044	61136.18
230	4.347 826	722.5663	41547.56	**280**	3.571 429	879.6459	61575.22
231	4.329 004	725.7079	41909.63	281	3.558 719	882.7875	62015.82
232	4.310 345	728.8495	42273.27	282	3.546 099	885.9291	62458.00
233	4.291 845	731.9911	42638.48	283	3.533 569	889.0707	62901.75
234	4.273 504	735.1327	43005.26	284	3.521 127	892.2123	63347.07
235	4.255 319	738.2743	43373.61	285	3.508 772	895.3539	63793.97
236	4.237 288	741.4159	43743.54	286	3.496 503	898.4955	64242.43
237	4.219 409	744.5575	44115.03	287	3.484 321	901.6371	64692.46
238	4.201 681	747.6991	44488.09	288	3.472 222	904.7787	65144.07
239	4.184 100	750.8406	44862.73	289	3.460 208	907.9203	65597.24
240	4.166 667	753.9822	45238.93	**290**	3.448 276	911.0619	66051.99
241	4.149 378	757.1238	45616.71	291	3.436 426	914.2035	66508.30
242	4.132 231	760.2654	45996.06	292	3.424 658	917.3451	66966.19
243	4.115 226	763.4070	46376.98	293	3.412 969	920.4866	67425.65
244	4.098 361	766.5486	46759.47	294	3.401 361	923.6282	67886.68
245	4.081 633	769.6902	47143.52	295	3.389 831	926.7698	68349.28
246	4.065 041	772.8318	47529.16	296	3.378 378	929.9114	68813.45
247	4.048 583	775.9734	47916.36	297	3.367 003	933.0530	69279.19
248	4.032 258	779.1150	48305.13	298	3.355 705	936.1946	69746.50
249	4.016 064	782.2566	48695.47	299	3.344 482	939.3362	70215.38
250	4.000 000	785.3982	49087.39	**300**	3.333 333	942.4778	70685.83

RECIPROCALS, CIRCUMFERENCE AND AREA OF CIRCLES (Continued)

n	$1000\frac{1}{n}$	Circumference πn	Area $\frac{\pi n^2}{4}$	n	$1000\frac{1}{n}$	Circumference πn	Area $\frac{\pi n^2}{4}$
300	3.333 333	942 4778	70685.83	**350**	2.857 143	1099.557	96211.28
301	3.322 259	945.6194	71157.86	351	2.849 003	1102.699	96761.84
302	3.311 258	948.7610	71631.45	352	2.840 909	1105.841	97313.97
303	3.300 330	951 9026	72106.62	353	2.832 861	1108 982	97867.68
304	3.289 474	955.0442	72583.36	354	2.824 859	1112.124	98422.96
305	3.278 689	958.1858	73061.66	355	2.816 901	1115.265	98979.80
306	3.267 974	961.3274	73541.54	356	2.808 989	1118 407	99538.22
307	3.257 329	964.4689	74022.99	357	2.801 120	1121.549	100 098.2
308	3 246 753	967.6105	74506.01	358	2.793 296	1124.690	100 659.8
309	3.236 246	970.7521	74990.60	359	2.785 515	1127.832	101 222.9
310	3.225 806	973.8937	75476.76	**360**	2.777 778	1130.973	101 787.6
311	3.215 434	977.0353	75964.50	361	2.770 083	1134.115	102 353.9
312	3.205 128	980.1769	76453.80	362	2.762 431	1137.257	102 921.7
313	3.194 888	983 3185	76944.67	363	2.754 821	1140.398	103 491.1
314	3.184 713	986.4601	77437.12	364	2.747 253	1143.540	104 062.1
315	3.174 603	989.6017	77931.13	365	2.739 726	1146.681	104 634.7
316	3.164 557	992.7433	78426.72	366	2.732 240	1149.823	105 208.8
317	3.154 574	995.8849	78923.88	367	2.724 796	1152.965	105 784.5
318	3.144 654	999.0265	79422.60	368	2.717 391	1156.106	106 361.8
319	3.134 796	1002.168	79922.90	369	2.710 027	1159.248	106 940.6
320	3.125 000	1005.310	80424.77	**370**	2.702 703	1162.389	107 521.0
321	3.115 265	1008.451	80928.21	371	2.695 418	1165.531	108 103.0
322	3.105 590	1011.593	81433.22	372	2.688 172	1168.672	108 686.5
323	3.095 975	1014.734	81939.80	373	2.680 965	1171.814	109 271.7
324	3.086 420	1017.876	82447.96	374	2.673 797	1174.956	109 858.4
325	3.076 923	1021.018	82957.68	375	2.666 667	1178.097	110 446.6
326	3.067 485	1024.159	83468.98	376	2.659 574	1181.239	111 036.5
327	3.058 104	1027.301	83981.84	377	2.652 520	1184.380	111 627.9
328	3.048.780	1030.442	84496.28	378	2.645 503	1187.522	112 220.8
329	3.039 514	1033.584	85012.28	379	2.638 522	1190.664	112 815.4
330	3.030 303	1036.726	85529.86	**380**	2.631 579	1193.805	113 411.5
331	3.021 148	1039.867	86049.01	381	2.624 672	1196.947	114 009.2
332	3.012 048	1043.009	86569.73	382	2.617 801	1200.088	114 608.4
333	3.003 003	1046.150	87092.02	383	2.610 966	1203.230	115 209.3
334	2.994 012	1049.292	87615.88	384	2.604 167	1206.372	115 811.7
335	2.985 075	1052.434	88141.31	385	2.597 403	1209.513	116 415.6
336	2.976 190	1055.575	88668.31	386	2.590 674	1212 655	117 021.2
337	2.967 359	1058.717	89196.88	387	2.583 979	1215.796	117 628.3
338	2.958 580	1061.858	89727.03	388	2.577.320	1218.938	118 237.0
339	2.949 853	1065.000	90258.74	389	2.570 694	1222.080	118 847.2
340	2.941 176	1068.142	90792.03	**390**	2.564 103	1225.221	119 459.1
341	2.932 551	1071.283	91326.88	391	2.557 545	1228.363	120 072.5
342	2.923 977	1074.425	91863.31	392	2.551 020	1231.504	120 687.4
343	2.915 452	1077.566	92401.31	393	2.544 529	1234.646	121 304.0
344	2.906 977	1080.708	92940.88	394	2.538.071	1237.788	121 922.1
345	2.898 551	1083.849	93482.02	395	2.531 646	1240.929	122 541.7
346	2.890 173	1086.991	94024.73	396	2.525.253	1244.071	123 163.0
347	2.881 844	1090.133	94569.01	397	2.518.892	1247.212	123 785.8
348	2.873 563	1093.274	95114.86	398	2.512 563	1250.354	124 410.2
349	2.865 330	1096.416	95662.28	399	2.506 266	1253.495	125 036.2
350	2.857 143	1099.557	96211.28	**400**	2.500 000	1256.637	125 663.7

RECIPROCALS, CIRCUMFERENCE AND AREA OF CIRCLES (Continued)

n	$1000\frac{1}{n}$	Circumference πn	Area $\frac{\pi n^2}{4}$	n	$1000\frac{1}{n}$	Circumference πn	Area $\frac{\pi n^2}{4}$
400	2.500 000	1256.637	125 663.7	**450**	2.222 222	1413.717	159 043.1
401	2.493 766	1259.779	126 292.8	451	2.217 295	1416.858	159 750.8
402	2.487 562	1262.920	126 923.5	452	2.212 389	1420.000	160 460.0
403	2.481 390	1266.062	127 555.7	453	2.207 506	1423.141	161 170.8
404	2.475 248	1269.203	128 189.5	454	2.202 643	1426.283	161 883.1
405	2.469 136	1272.345	128 824.9	455	2.197 802	1429.425	162 597.1
406	2.463 054	1275.487	129 461.9	456	2.192 982	1432.566	163 312.6
407	2.457 002	1278.628	130 100.4	457	2.188 184	1435.708	164 029.6
408	2.450 980	1281.770	130 740.5	458	2.183 406	1438.849	164 748.3
409	2.444 988	1284.911	131 382.2	459	2.178 649	1441.991	165 468.5
410	2.439 024	1288.053	132 025.4	**460**	2.173 913	1445.133	166 190.3
411	2.433 090	1291.195	132 670.2	461	2.169 197	1448.274	166 913.6
412	2.427 184	1294.336	133 316.6	462	2.164 502	1451.416	167 638.5
413	2.421 308	1297.478	133 964.6	463	2.159 827	1454.557	168 365.0
414	2.415 459	1300.619	134 614.1	464	2.155 172	1457.699	169 093.1
415	2.409 639	1303.761	135 265.2	465	2.150 538	1460.841	169 822.7
416	2.403 846	1306.903	135 917.9	466	2.145 923	1463.982	170 553.9
417	2.398 082	1310.044	136 572.1	467	2.141 328	1467.124	171 286.7
418	2.392 344	1313.186	137 227.9	468	2.136 752	1470.265	172 021.0
419	2.386 635	1316.327	137 885.3	469	2.132 196	1473.407	172 757.0
420	2.380 952	1319.469	138 544.2	**470**	2.127 660	1476.549	173 494.5
421	2.375 297	1322.611	139 204.8	471	2.123 142	1479.690	174 233.5
422	2.369 668	1325.752	139 866.8	472	2.118 644	1482.832	174 974.1
423	2.364 066	1328.894	140 530.5	473	2.114 165	1485.973	175 716.3
424	2.358 491	1332.035	141 195.7	474	2.109 705	1489.115	176 460.1
425	2.352 941	1335.177	141 862.5	475	2.105 263	1492.257	177 205.5
426	2.347 418	1338.318	142 530.9	476	2.100 840	1495.398	177 952.4
427	2.341 920	1341.460	143 200.9	477	2.096 436	1498.540	178 700.9
428	2.336 449	1344.602	143 872.4	478	2.092 050	1501.681	179 450.9
429	2.331 002	1347.743	144 545.5	479	2.087 683	1504.823	180 202.5
430	2.325 581	1350.885	145 220.1	**480**	2.083 333	1507.964	180 955.7
431	2.320 186	1354.026	145 896.3	481	2.079 002	1511.106	181 710.5
432	2.314 815	1357.168	146 574 1	482	2.074 689	1514.248	182 466.8
433	2.309 469	1360.310	147 253.5	483	2.070 393	1517.389	183 224.8
434	2.304 147	1363.451	147 934.5	484	2.066 116	1520.531	183 984.2
435	2.298 851	1366.593	148 617.0	485	2.061 856	1523.672	184 745.3
436	2.293 578	1369.734	149 301.0	486	2.057 613	1526.814	185 507.9
437	2.288 330	1372.876	149 986.7	487	2.053 388	1529.956	186 272.1
438	2.283 105	1376.018	150 673.9	488	2.049 180	1533.097	187 037.9
439	2.277 904	1379.159	151 362.7	489	2.044 990	1536.239	187 805.2
440	2.272 727	1382.301	152 053.1	**490**	2.040 816	1539.380	188 574.1
441	2.267 574	1385.442	152 745.0	491	2.036 660	1542.522	189 344.6
442	2.262 443	1388.584	153 438.5	492	2.032 520	1545.664	190 116.6
443	2.257 336	1391.726	154 133.6	493	2.028 398	1548.805	190 890.2
444	2.252 252	1394.867	154 830.3	494	2.024 291	1551.947	191 665.4
445	2.247 191	1398.009	155 528.5	495	2.020 202	1555.088	192 442.2
446	2.242 152	1401.150	156 228.3	496	2.016 129	1558.230	193 220.5
447	2.237 136	1404.292	156 929.6	497	2.012 072	1561.372	194 000.4
448	2.232 143	1407.434	157 632.6	498	2.008 032	1564.513	194 781.9
449	2.227 171	1410.575	158 337.1	499	2.004 008	1567.655	195 564.9
450	2.222 222	1413.717	159 043.1	**500**	2.000 000	1570.796	196 349.5

RECIPROCALS, CIRCUMFERENCE AND AREA OF CIRCLES (Continued)

n	$1000\frac{1}{n}$	Circumference πn	Area $\frac{\pi n^2}{4}$	n	$1000\frac{1}{n}$	Circumference πn	Area $\frac{\pi n^2}{4}$
500	2.000 000	1570.796	196 349.5	**550**	1.818 182	1727.876	237 582.9
501	1.996 008	1573.938	197 135.7	551	1.814 882	1731.018	238 447.7
502	1.992 032	1577.080	197 923.5	552	1.811 594	1734.159	239 314.0
503	1.988 072	1580.221	198 712.8	553	1.808 318	1737.301	240 181.8
504	1.984 127	1583.363	199 503.7	554	1.805 054	1740.442	241 051.3
505	1.980 198	1586.504	200 296.2	555	1.801 802	1743.584	241 922.3
506	1.976 285	1589.646	201 090.2	556	1.798 561	1746.726	242 794.8
507	1.972 387	1592.787	201 885.8	557	1.795 332	1749.867	243 669.0
508	1.968 504	1595.929	202 683.0	558	1.792 115	1753.009	244 544.7
509	1.964 637	1599.071	203 481.7	559	1.788 909	1756.150	245 422.0
510	1.960 784	1602.212	204 282.1	**560**	1.785 714	1759.292	246 300.9
511	1.956 947	1605.354	205 084.0	561	1.782 531	1762.433	247 181.3
512	1.953 125	1608.495	205 887.4	562	1.779 359	1765.575	248 063.3
513	1.949 318	1611.637	206 692.4	563	1.776 199	1768.717	248 946.9
514	1.945 525	1614.779	207 499.1	564	1.773 050	1771.858	249 832.0
515	1.941 748	1617.920	208 307.2	565	1.769 912	1775.000	250 718.7
516	1.937 984	1621.062	209 117.0	566	1.766 784	1778.141	251 607.0
517	1.934 236	1624.203	209 928.3	567	1.763 668	1781.283	252 496.9
518	1.930 502	1627.345	210 741.2	568	1.760 563	1784.425	253 388.3
519	1.926 782	1630.487	211 555.6	569	1.757 469	1787.566	254 281.3
520	1.923 077	1633.628	212 371.7	**570**	1.754 386	1790.708	255 175.9
521	1.919 386	1636.770	213 189.3	571	1.751 313	1793.849	256 072.0
522	1.915 709	1639.911	214 008.4	572	1.748 252	1796.991	256 969.7
523	1.912 046	1643.053	214 829.2	573	1.745 201	1800.133	257 869.0
524	1.908 397	1646.195	215 651.5	574	1.742 160	1803.274	258 769.8
525	1.904 762	1649.336	216 475.4	575	1.739 130	1806.416	259 672.3
526	1.901 141	1652.478	217 300.8	576	1.736 111	1809.557	260 576.3
527	1.897 533	1655.619	218 127.8	577	1.733 102	1812.699	261 481.8
528	1.893 939	1658.761	218 956.4	578	1.730 104	1815.841	262 389.0
529	1.890 359	1661.903	219 786.6	579	1.727 116	1818.982	263 297.7
530	1.886 792	1665.044	220 618.3	**580**	1.724 138	1822.124	264 207.9
531	1.883 239	1668.186	221 451.7	581	1.721 170	1825.265	265 119.8
532	1.879 699	1671.327	222 286.5	582	1.718 213	1828.407	266 033.2
533	1.876 173	1674.469	223 123.0	583	1.715 266	1831.549	266 948.2
534	1.872 659	1677.610	223 961.0	584	1.712 329	1834.690	267 864.8
535	1.869 159	1680.752	224 800.6	585	1.709 402	1837.832	268 782.9
536	1.865 672	1683.894	225 641.8	586	1.706 485	1840.973	269 702.6
537	1.862 197	1687.035	226 484.5	587	1.703 578	1844.115	270 623.9
538	1.858 736	1690.177	227 328.8	588	1.700 680	1847.256	271 546.7
539	1.855 288	1693.318	228 174.7	589	1.697 793	1850.398	272 471.1
540	1.851 852	1696.460	229 022.1	**590**	1.694 915	1853.540	273 397.1
541	1.848 429	1699.602	229 871.1	591	1.692 047	1856.681	274 324.7
542	1.845 018	1702.743	230 721.7	592	1.689 189	1859.823	275 253.8
543	1.841 621	1705.885	231 573.9	593	1.686 341	1862.964	276 184.5
544	1.838 235	1709.026	232 427.6	594	1.683 502	1866.106	277 116.7
545	1.834 862	1712.168	233 282.9	595	1.680 672	1869.248	278 050.6
546	1.831 502	1715.310	234 139.8	596	1.677 852	1872.389	278 986.0
547	1.828 154	1718.451	234 998.2	597	1.675 042	1875.531	279 923.0
548	1.824 818	1721.593	235.858.2	598	1.672 241	1878.672	280 861.5
549	1.821 494	1724.734	236 719.8	599	1.669 449	1881.814	281 801.6
550	1.818 182	1727.876	237.582.9	**600**	1.666 667	1884.956	282 743.3

RECIPROCALS, CIRCUMFERENCE AND AREA OF CIRCLES (Continued)

n	$1000\frac{1}{n}$	Circumference πn	Area $\frac{\pi n^2}{4}$	n	$1000\frac{1}{n}$	Circumference πn	Area $\frac{\pi n^2}{4}$
600	1.666 667	1884.956	282 743.3	**650**	1.538 462	2042.035	331 830.7
601	1.663 894	1888.097	283 686.6	651	1.536 098	2045.177	332 852.5
602	1.661 130	1891.239	284 631.4	652	1.533 742	2048.318	333 875.9
603	1.658 375	1894.380	285 577.8	653	1.531 394	2051.460	334 900.8
604	1.655 629	1897.522	286 525.8	654	1.529 052	2054.602	335 927.4
605	1.652 893	1900.664	287 475.4	655	1.526 718	2057.743	336 955.4
606	1.650 165	1903.805	288 426.5	656	1.524 390	2060.885	337 985.1
607	1.647 446	1906.947	289 379.2	657	1.522 070	2064.026	339 016.3
608	1.644 737	1910.088	290 333.4	658	1.519 757	2067.168	340 049.1
609	1.642 036	1913.230	291 289.3	659	1.517 451	2070.310	341 083.5
610	1.639 344	1916.372	292 246.7	**660**	1.515 152	2073.451	342 119.4
611	1.636 661	1919.513	293 205.6	661	1.512 859	2076.593	343 157.0
612	1.633 987	1922.655	294 166.2	662	1.510 574	2079.734	344 196.0
613	1.631 321	1925.796	295 128.3	663	1.508 296	2082.876	345 236.7
614	1.628 664	1928.938	296 092.0	664	1.506 024	2086.018	346 278.9
615	1.626 016	1932.079	297 057.2	665	1.503 759	2089.159	347 322.7
616	1.623 377	1935.221	298 024.0	666	1.501 502	2092.301	348 368.1
617	1.620 746	1938.363	298 992.4	667	1.499 250	2095.442	349 415.0
618	1.618 123	1941.504	299 962.4	668	1.497 006	2098.584	350 463.5
619	1.615 509	1944.646	300 933.9	669	1.494 768	2101.725	351 513.6
620	1.612 903	1947.787	301 907.1	**670**	1.492 537	2104.867	352 565.2
621	1.610 306	1950.929	302 881.7	671	1.490 313	2108.009	353 618.5
622	1.607 717	1954.071	303 858.0	672	1.488 095	2111.150	354 673.2
623	1.605 136	1957.212	304 835.8	673	1.485 884	2114.292	355 729.6
624	1.602 564	1960.354	305 815.2	674	1.483 680	2117.433	356 787.5
625	1.600 000	1963.495	306 796.2	675	1.481 481	2120.575	357 847.0
626	1.597 444	1966.637	307 778.7	676	1.479 290	2123.717	358 908.1
627	1.594 896	1969.779	308 762.8	677	1.477 105	2126.858	359 970.8
628	1.592 357	1972.920	309 748.5	678	1.474 926	2130.000	361 035.0
629	1.589 825	1976.062	310 735.7	679	1.472 754	2133.141	362 100.8
630	1.587 302	1979.203	311 724.5	**680**	1.470 588	2136.283	363 168.1
631	1.584 786	1982.345	312 714.9	681	1.468 429	2139.425	364 237.0
632	1.582 278	1985.487	313 706.9	682	1.466 276	2142.566	365 307.5
633	1.579 779	1988.628	314 700.4	683	1.464 129	2145.708	366 379.6
634	1.577 287	1991.770	315 695.5	684	1.461 988	2148.849	367 453.2
635	1.574 803	1994.911	316 692.2	685	1.459 854	2151.991	368 528.5
636	1.572 327	1998.053	317 690.4	686	1.457 726	2155.133	369 605.2
637	1.569 859	2001.195	318 690.2	687	1.455 604	2158.274	370 683.6
638	1.567 398	2004.336	319 691.6	688	1.453 488	2161.416	371 763.5
639	1.564 945	2007.478	320 694.6	689	1.451 379	2164.557	372 845.0
640	1.562 500	2010.619	321 699.1	**690**	1.449 275	2167.699	373 928.1
641	1.560 062	2013.761	322 705.2	691	1.447 178	2170.841	375 012.7
642	1.557 632	2016.902	323 712.8	692	1.445 087	2173.982	376 098.9
643	1.555 210	2020.044	324 722.1	693	1.443 001	2177.124	377 186.7
644	1.552 795	2023.186	325 732.9	694	1.440 922	2180.265	378 276.0
645	1.550 388	2026.327	326 745.3	695	1.438 849	2183.407	379 366.9
646	1.547 988	2029.469	327 759.2	696	1.436 782	2186.548	380 459.4
647	1.545 595	2032.610	328 774.7	697	1.434 720	2189.690	381 553.5
648	1.543 210	2035.752	329 791.8	698	1.432 665	2192.832	382 649.1
649	1.540 832	2038.894	330 810.5	699	1.430 615	2195.973	383 746.3
650	1.538 462	2042.035	331 830.7	**700**	1.428 571	2199.115	384 845.1

RECIPROCALS, CIRCUMFERENCE AND AREA OF CIRCLES (Continued)

n	$1000\frac{1}{n}$	Circumference πn	Area $\frac{\pi n^2}{4}$	n	$1000\frac{1}{n}$	Circumference πn	Area $\frac{\pi n^2}{4}$
700	1.428 571	2199.115	384 845.1	**750**	1.333 333	2356.194	441 786.5
701	1.426 534	2202.256	385 945.4	751	1.331 558	2359.336	442 965.3
702	1.424 501	2205.398	387 047.4	752	1.329 787	2362.478	444 145.8
703	1.422 475	2208.540	388 150.8	753	1.328 021	2365.619	445 327.8
704	1.420 455	2211.681	389 255.9	754	1.326 260	2368.761	446 511.4
705	1.418 440	2214.823	390 362.5	755	1.324 503	2371.902	447 696.6
706	1.416 431	2217.964	391 470.7	756	1.322 751	2375.044	448 883.3
707	1.414 427	2221.106	392 580.5	757	1.321 004	2378.186	450 071.6
708	1.412 429	2224.248	393 691.8	758	1.319 261	2381.327	451 261.5
709	1.410 437	2227.389	394 804.7	759	1.317 523	2384.469	452 453.0
710	1.408 451	2230.531	395 919.2	**760**	1.315 789	2387.610	453 646.0
711	1.406 470	2233.672	397 035.3	761	1.314 060	2390.752	454 840.6
712	1.404 494	2236.814	398 152.9	762	1.312 336	2393.894	456 036.7
713	1.402 525	2239.956	399 272.1	763	1.310 616	2397.035	457 234.5
714	1.400 560	2243.097	400 392.8	764	1.308 901	2400.177	458 433.8
715	1.398 601	2246.239	401 515.2	765	1.307 190	2403.318	459 634.6
716	1.396 648	2249.380	402 639.1	766	1.305 483	2406.460	460 837.1
717	1.394 700	2252.522	403 764.6	767	1.303 781	2409.602	462 041.1
718	1.392 758	2255.664	404 891.6	768	1.302 083	2412.743	463 246.7
719	1.390 821	2258.805	406 020.2	769	1.300 390	2415.885	464 453.8
720	1.388 889	2261.947	407 150.4	**770**	1.298 701	2419.026	465 662.6
721	1.386 963	2265.088	408 282.2	771	1.297 017	2422.168	466 872.9
722	1.385 042	2268.230	409 415.5	772	1.295 337	2425.310	468 084.7
723	1.383 126	2271.371	410 550.4	773	1.293 661	2428.451	469 298.2
724	1.381 215	2274.513	411 686.9	774	1.291 990	2431.593	470 513.2
725	1.379 310	2277.655	412 824.9	775	1.290 323	2434.734	471 729.8
726	1.377 410	2280.796	413 964.5	776	1.288 660	2437.876	472 947.9
727	1.375 516	2283.938	415 105.7	777	1.287 001	2441.017	474 167.6
728	1.373 626	2287.079	416 248.5	778	1.285 347	2444.159	475 388.9
729	1.371 742	2290.221	417 392.8	779	1.283 697	2447.301	476 611.8
730	1.369 863	2293.363	418 538.7	**780**	1.282 051	2450.442	477 836.2
731	1.367 989	2296.504	419 686.1	781	1.280 410	2453.584	479 062.2
732	1.366 120	2299.646	420 835.2	782	1.278 772	2456.725	480 289.8
733	1.364 256	2302.787	421 985.8	783	1.277 139	2459.867	481 519.0
734	1.362 398	2305.929	423 138.0	784	1.275 510	2463.009	482 749.7
735	1.360 544	2309.071	424 291.7	785	1.273 885	2466.150	483 982.0
736	1.358 696	2312.212	425 447.0	786	1.272 265	2469.292	485 215.8
737	1.356 852	2315.354	426 603.9	787	1.270 648	2472.433	486 451.3
738	1.355 014	2318.495	427 762.4	788	1.269 036	2475.575	487 688.3
739	1.353 180	2321.637	428 922.4	789	1.267 427	2478.717	488 926.9
740	1.351 351	2324.779	430 084.0	**790**	1.265 823	2481.858	490 167.0
741	1.349 528	2327.920	431 247.2	791	1.264 223	2485.000	491 408.7
742	1.347 709	2331.062	432 412.0	792	1.262 626	2488.141	492 652.0
743	1.345 895	2334.203	433 578.3	793	1.261 034	2491.283	493 896.8
744	1.344 086	2337.345	434 746.2	794	1.259 446	2494.425	495 143.3
745	1.342 282	2340.487	435 915.6	795	1.257 862	2497.566	496 391.3
746	1.340 483	2343.628	437 086.6	796	1.256 281	2500.708	497 640.8
747	1.338 688	2346.770	438 259.2	797	1.254 705	2503.849	498 892.0
748	1.336 898	2349.911	439 433.4	798	1.253 133	2506.991	500 144.7
749	1.335 113	2353.053	440 609.2	799	1.251 564	2510.133	501 399.0
750	1.333 333	2356.194	441 786.5	**800**	1.250 000	2513.274	502 654.8

n	$1000\frac{1}{n}$	Circumference πn	Area $\frac{\pi n^2}{4}$	n	$1000\frac{1}{n}$	Circumference πn	Area $\frac{\pi n^2}{4}$
800	1.250 000	2513.274	502 654.8	**850**	1.176 471	2670.354	567 450.2
801	1.248 439	2516.416	503 912.2	851	1.175 088	2673.495	568 786.1
802	1.246 883	2519.557	505 171.2	852	1.173 709	2676.637	570 123.7
803	1.245 330	2522.699	506 431.8	853	1.172 333	2679.779	571 462.8
804	1.243 781	2525.840	507 693.9	854	1.170 960	2682.920	572 803.4
805	1.242 236	2528.982	508 957.6	855	1.169 591	2686.062	574 145.7
806	1.240 695	2532.124	510 222.9	856	1.168 224	2689.203	575 489.5
807	1.239 157	2535.265	511 489.8	857	1.166 861	2692.345	576 834.9
808	1.237 624	2538.407	512 758.2	858	1.165 501	2695.486	578 181.9
809	1.236 094	2541.548	514 028.2	859	1.164 144	2698.628	579 530.4
810	1.234 568	2544.690	515 299.7	**860**	1.162 791	2701.770	580 880.5
811	1.233 046	2547.832	516 572.9	861	1.161 440	2704.911	582 232.2
812	1.231 527	2550.973	517 847.6	862	1.160 093	2708.053	583 585.4
813	1.230 012	2554.115	519 123.8	863	1.158 749	2711.194	584 940.2
814	1.228 501	2557.256	520 401.7	864	1.157 407	2714.336	586 296.6
815	1.226 994	2560.398	521 681.1	865	1.156 069	2717.478	587 654.5
816	1.225 490	2563.540	522 962.1	866	1.154 734	2720.619	589 014.1
817	1.223 990	2566.681	524 244.6	867	1.153 403	2723.761	590 375.2
818	1.222 494	2569.823	525 528.8	868	1.152 074	2726.902	591 737.8
819	1.221 001	2572.964	526 814.5	869	1.150 748	2730.044	593 102.1
820	1.219 512	2576.106	528 101.7	**870**	1.149 425	2733.186	594 467.9
821	1.218 027	2579.248	529 390.6	871	1.148 106	2736.327	595 835.2
822	1.216 545	2582.389	530 681.0	872	1.146 789	2739.469	597 204.2
823	1.215 067	2585.531	531 973.0	873	1.145 475	2742.610	598 574.7
824	1.213 592	2588.672	533 266.5	874	1.144 165	2745.752	599 946.8
825	1.212 121	2591.814	534 561.6	875	1.142 857	2748.894	601 320.5
826	1.210 654	2594.956	535 858.3	876	1.141 553	2752.035	602 695.7
827	1.209 190	2598.097	537 156.6	877	1.140 251	2755.177	604 072.5
828	1.207 729	2601.239	538 456.4	878	1.138 952	2758.318	605 450.9
829	1.206 273	2604.380	539 757.8	879	1.137 656	2761.460	606 830.8
830	1.204 819	2607.522	541 060.8	**880**	1.136 364	2764.602	608 212.3
831	1.203 369	2610.663	542 365.3	881	1.135 074	2767.743	609 595.4
832	1.201 923	2613.805	543 671.5	882	1.133 787	2770.885	610 980.1
833	1.200 480	2616.947	544 979.1	883	1.132 503	2774.026	612 366.3
834	1.199 041	2620.088	546 288.4	884	1.131 222	2777.168	613 754.1
835	1.197 605	2623.230	547 599.2	885	1.129 944	2780.309	615 143.5
836	1.196 172	2626.371	548 911.6	886	1.128 668	2783.451	616 534.4
837	1.194 743	2629.513	550 225.6	887	1.127 396	2786.593	617 926.9
838	1.193 317	2632.655	551 541.1	888	1.126 126	2789.734	619 321.0
839	1.191 895	2635.796	552 858.3	889	1.124 859	2792.876	620 716.7
840	1.190 476	2638.938	554 176.9	**890**	1.123 596	2796.017	622 113.9
841	1.189 061	2642.079	555 497.2	891	1.122 334	2799.159	623 512.7
842	1.187 648	2645.221	556 819.0	892	1.121 076	2802.301	624 913.0
843	1.186 240	2648.363	558 142.4	893	1.119 821	2805.442	626 315.0
844	1.184 834	2651.504	559 467.4	894	1.118 568	2808.584	627 718.5
845	1.183 432	2654.646	560 793.9	895	1.117 318	2811.725	629 123.6
846	1.182 033	2657.787	562 122.0	896	1.116 071	2814.867	630 530.2
847	1.180 638	2660.929	563 451.7	897	1.114 827	2818.009	631 938.4
848	1.179 245	2664.071	564 783.0	898	1.113 586	2821.150	633 348.2
849	1.177 856	2667.212	566 115.8	899	1.112 347	2824.292	634 759.6
850	1.176 471	2670.354	567 450.2	**900**	1.111 111	2827.433	636 172.5

ECIPROCALS, CIRCUMFERENCE AND AREA OF CIRCLES (Continued)

	$1000\frac{1}{n}$	Circumference πn	Area $\frac{\pi n^2}{4}$	n	$1000\frac{1}{n}$	Circumference πn	Area $\frac{\pi n^2}{4}$
0	1.111 111	2827.433	636 172.5	**950**	1.052 632	2984.513	708 821.8
1	1.109 878	2830.575	637 587.0	951	1.051 525	2987.655	710 314.9
2	1.108 647	2833.717	639 003.1	952	1.050 420	2990.796	711 809.5
3	1.107 420	2836.858	640 420.7	953	1.049 318	2993.938	713 305.7
4	1.106 195	2840.000	641 839.9	954	1.048 218	2997.079	714 803.4
5	1.104 972	2843.141	643 260.7	955	1.047 120	3000.221	716 302.8
6	1.103 753	2846.283	644 683.1	956	1.046 025	3003.363	717 803.7
7	1.102 536	2849.425	646 107.0	957	1.044 932	3006.504	719 306.1
8	1.101 322	2852.566	647 532.5	958	1.043 841	3009.646	720 810.2
9	1.100 110	2855.708	648 959.6	959	1.042 753	3012.787	722 315.8
0	1.098 901	2858.849	650 388.2	**960**	1.041 667	3015.929	723 822.9
1	1.097 695	2861.991	651 818.4	961	1.040 583	3019.071	725 331.7
2	1.096 491	2865.133	653 250.2	962	1.039 501	3022.212	726 842.0
3	1.095 290	2868.274	654 683.6	963	1.038 422	3025.354	728 353.9
4	1.094 092	2871.416	656 118.5	964	1.037 344	3028.495	729 867.4
5	1.092 896	2874.557	657 555.0	965	1.036 269	3031.637	731 382.4
6	1.091 703	2877.699	658 993.0	966	1.035 197	3034.779	732 899.0
7	1.090 513	2880.840	660 432.7	967	1.034 126	3037.920	734 417.2
8	1.089 325	2883.982	661 873.9	968	1.033 058	3041.062	735 936.9
9	1.088 139	2887.124	663 316.7	969	1.031 992	3044.203	737 458.2
0	1.086 957	2890.265	664 761.0	**970**	1.030 928	3047.345	738 981.1
1	1.085 776	2893.407	666 206.9	971	1.029 866	3050.486	740 505.6
2	1.084 599	2896.548	667 654.4	972	1.028 807	3053.628	742 031.6
3	1.083 424	2899.690	669 103.5	973	1.027 749	3056.770	743 559.2
4	1.082 251	2902.832	670 554.1	974	1.026 694	3059.911	745 088.4
5	1.081 081	2905.973	672 006.3	975	1.025 641	3063.053	746 619.1
6	1.079 914	2909.115	673 460.1	976	1.024 590	3066.194	748 151.4
7	1.078 749	2912.256	674 915.4	977	1.023 541	3069.336	749 685.3
8	1.077 586	2915.398	676 372.3	978	1.022 495	3072.478	751 220.8
9	1.076 426	2918.540	677 830.8	979	1.021 450	3075.619	752 757.8
0	1.075 269	2921.681	679 290.9	**980**	1.020 408	3078.761	754 296.4
1	1.074 114	2924.823	680 752.5	981	1.019 368	3081.902	755 836.6
2	1.072 961	2927.964	682 215.7	982	1.018 330	3085.044	757 378.3
3	1.071 811	2931.106	683 680.5	983	1.017 294	3088.186	758 921.6
4	1.070 664	2934.248	685 146.8	984	1.016 260	3091.327	760 466.5
5	1.069 519	2937.389	686 614.7	985	1.015 228	3094.469	762 012.9
6	1.068 376	2940.531	688 084.2	986	1.014 199	3097.610	763 561.0
7	1.067 236	2943.672	689 555.2	987	1.013 171	3100.752	765 110.5
8	1.066 098	2946.814	691 027.9	988	1.012 146	3103.894	766 661.7
9	1.064 963	2949.956	692 502.1	989	1.011 122	3107.035	768 214.4
0	1.063 830	2953.097	693 977.8	**990**	1.010 101	3110.177	769 768.7
1	1.062 699	2956.239	695 455.2	991	1.009 082	3113.318	771 324.6
2	1.061 571	2959.380	696 934.1	992	1.008 065	3116.460	772 882.1
3	1.060 445	2962.522	698 414.5	993	1.007 049	3119.602	774 441.1
4	1.059 322	2965.663	699 896.6	994	1.006 036	3122.743	776 001.7
5	1.058 201	2968.805	701 380.2	995	1.005 025	3125.885	777 563.8
6	1.057 082	2971.947	702 865.4	996	1.004 016	3129.026	779 127.5
7	1.055 966	2975.088	704 352.1	997	1.003 009	3132.168	780 692.8
8	1.054 852	2978.230	705 840.5	998	1.002 004	3135.309	782 259.7
9	1.053 741	2981.371	707 330.4	999	1.001 001	3138.451	783 828.2
0	1.052 632	2984.513	708 821.8	**1000**	1.000 000	3141.593	785 398.2

Squares, Cubes and Roots

Roots of numbers other than those given directly may be found by the following relations

$\sqrt{100n} = 10\sqrt{n}$; $\sqrt{1000n} = 10\sqrt{10n}$; $\sqrt{\frac{1}{10}n} = \frac{1}{10}\sqrt{10n}$; $\sqrt{\frac{1}{100}n} = \frac{1}{10}\sqrt{n}$
$\sqrt{\frac{1}{1000}n} = \frac{1}{100}\sqrt{10n}$; $\sqrt[3]{1000n} = 10\sqrt[3]{n}$; $\sqrt[3]{10{,}000n} = 10\sqrt[3]{10n}$; $\sqrt[3]{100{,}000n} =$
$10\sqrt[3]{100n}$; $\sqrt[3]{\frac{1}{10}n} = \frac{1}{10}\sqrt[3]{100n}$; $\sqrt[3]{\frac{1}{100}n} = \frac{1}{10}\sqrt[3]{10n}$; $\sqrt[3]{\frac{1}{1000}n} = \frac{1}{10}\sqrt[3]{n}$.

n	n^2	$\sqrt{n}$	$\sqrt{10n}$	n^3	$\sqrt[3]{n}$	$\sqrt[3]{10n}$	$\sqrt[3]{100n}$
1	1	1.000 000	3.162 278	1	1.000 000	2.154 435	4.641 58
2	4	1.414 214	4.472 136	8	1.259 921	2.714 418	5.848 03
3	9	1.732 051	5.477 226	27	1.442 250	3.107 233	6.694 33
4	16	2.000 000	6.324 555	64	1.587 401	3.419 952	7.368 06
5	25	2.236 068	7.071 068	125	1.709 976	3.684 031	7.937 00
6	36	2.449 490	7.745 967	216	1.817 121	3.914 868	8.434 32
7	49	2.645 751	8.366 600	343	1.912 931	4.121 285	8.879 04
8	64	2.828 427	8.944 272	512	2.000 000	4.308 869	9.283 17
9	81	3.000 000	9.486 833	729	2.080 084	4.481 405	9.654 89
10	100	3.162 278	10.00000	1 000	2.154 435	4.641 589	10.00000
11	121	3.316 625	10.48809	1 331	2.223 980	4.791 420	10.32280
12	144	3.464 102	10.95445	1 728	2.289 428	4.932 424	10.62659
13	169	3.605 551	11.40175	2 197	2.351 335	5.065 797	10.91393
14	196	3.741 657	11.83216	2 744	2.410 142	5.192 494	11.18689
15	225	3.872 983	12.24745	3 375	2.466 212	5.313 293	11.44714
16	256	4.000 000	12.64911	4 096	2.519 842	5.428 835	11.69607
17	289	4.123 106	13.03840	4 913	2.571 282	5.539 658	11.93483
18	324	4.242 641	13.41641	5 832	2.620 741	5.646 216	12.16440
19	361	4.358 899	13.78405	6 859	2.668 402	5.748 897	12.38562
20	400	4.472 136	14.14214	8 000	2.714 418	5.848 035	12.59921
21	441	4.582 576	14.49138	9 261	2.758 924	5.943 922	12.80579
22	484	4.690 416	14.83240	10 648	2.802 039	6.036 811	13.00591
23	529	4.795 832	15.16575	12 167	2.843 867	6.126 926	13.20006
24	576	4.898 979	15.49193	13 824	2.884 499	6.214 465	13.38866
25	625	5.000 000	15.81139	15 625	2.924 018	6.299 605	13.57209
26	676	5.099 020	16.12452	17 576	2.962 496	6.382 504	13.75069
27	729	5.196 152	16.43168	19 683	3.000 000	6.463 304	13.92477
28	784	5.291 503	16.73320	21 952	3.036 589	6.542 133	14.09460
29	841	5.385 165	17.02939	24 389	3.072 317	6.619 106	14.26043
30	900	5.477 226	17.32051	27 000	3.107 233	6.694 330	14.42250
31	961	5.567 764	17.60682	29 791	3.141 381	6.767 899	14.58100
32	1 024	5.656 854	17.88854	32 768	3.174 802	6.839 904	14.73613
33	1 089	5.744 563	18.16590	35 937	3.207 534	6.910 423	14.88806
34	1 156	5.830 952	18.43909	39 304	3.239 612	6.979 532	15.03695
35	1 225	5.916 080	18.70829	42 875	3.271 066	7.047 299	15.18294
36	1 296	6.000 000	18.97367	46 656	3.301 927	7.113 787	15.32619
37	1 369	6.082 763	19.23538	50 653	3.332 222	7.179 054	15.46680
38	1 444	6.164 414	19.49359	54 872	3.361 975	7.243 156	15.60491
39	1 521	6.244 998	19.74842	59 319	3.391 211	7.306 144	15.74061
40	1 600	6.324 555	20.00000	64 000	3.419 952	7.368 063	15.87401
41	1 681	6.403 124	20.24846	68 921	3.448 217	7.428 959	16.00521
42	1 764	6.480 741	20.49390	74 088	3.476 027	7.488 872	16.13429
43	1 849	6.557 439	20.73644	79 507	3.503 398	7.547 842	16.26133
44	1 936	6.633 250	20.97618	85 184	3.530 348	7.605 905	16.38643
45	2 025	6.708 204	21.21320	91 125	3.556 893	7.663 094	16.50964
46	2 116	6.782 330	21.44761	97 336	3.583 048	7.719 443	16.63103
47	2 209	6.855 655	21.67948	103 823	3.608 826	7.774 980	16.75069
48	2 304	6.928 203	21.90890	110 592	3.634 241	7.829 735	16.86865
49	2 401	7.000 000	22.13594	117 649	3.659 306	7.883 735	16.98499
50	2 500	7.071 068	22.36068	125 000	3.684 031	7.937 005	17.09976

SQUARES, CUBES AND ROOTS (Continued)

n	n^2	$\sqrt{n}$	$\sqrt{10n}$	n^3	$\sqrt[3]{n}$	$\sqrt[3]{10n}$	$\sqrt[3]{100n}$
50	2 500	7.071 068	22.36068	125 000	3.684 031	7.937 005	17.09976
51	2 601	7.141 428	22.58318	132 651	3.708 430	7.989 570	17.21301
52	2 704	7.211 103	22.80351	140 608	3.732 511	8.041 452	17.32478
53	2 809	7.280 110	23.02173	148 877	3.756 286	8.092 672	17.43513
54	2 916	7.348 469	23.23790	157 464	3.779 763	8.143 253	17.54411
55	3 025	7.416 198	23.45208	166 375	3.802 952	8.193 213	17.65174
56	3 136	7.483 315	23.66432	175 616	3.825 862	8.242 571	17.75808
57	3 249	7.549 834	23.87467	185 193	3.848 501	8.291 344	17.86316
58	3 364	7.615 773	24.08319	195 112	3.870 877	8.339 551	17.96702
59	3 481	7.681 146	24.28992	205 379	3.892 996	8.387 207	18.06969
60	3 600	7.745 967	24.49490	216 000	3.914 868	8.434 327	18.17121
61	3 721	7.810 250	24.69818	226 981	3.936 497	8.480 926	18.27160
62	3 844	7.874 008	24.89980	238 328	3.957 892	8.527 019	18.37091
63	3 969	7.937 254	25.09980	250 047	3.979 057	8.572 619	18.46915
64	4 096	8.000 000	25.29822	262 144	4.000 000	8.617 739	18.56636
65	4 225	8.062 258	25.49510	274 625	4.020 726	8.662 391	18.66256
66	4 356	8.124 038	25.69047	287 496	4.041 240	8.706 588	18.75777
67	4 489	8.185 353	25.88436	300 763	4.061 548	8.750 340	18.85204
68	4 624	8.246 211	26.07681	314 432	4.081 655	8.793 659	18.94536
69	4 761	8.306 624	26.26785	328 509	4.101 566	8.836 556	19.03778
70	4 900	8.366 600	26.45751	343 000	4.121 285	8.879 040	19.12931
71	5 041	8.426 150	26.64583	357 911	4.140 818	8.921 121	19.21997
72	5 184	8.485 281	26.83282	373 248	4.160 168	8.962 809	19.30979
73	5 329	8.544 004	27.01851	389 017	4.179 339	9.004 113	19.39877
74	5 476	8.602 325	27.20294	405 224	4.198 336	9.045 042	19.48695
75	5 625	8.660 254	27.38613	421 875	4.217 163	9.085 603	19.57434
76	5 776	8.717 798	27.56810	438 976	4.235 824	9.125 805	19.66095
77	5 929	8.774 964	27.74887	456 533	4.254 321	9.165 656	19.74681
78	6 084	8.831 761	27.92848	474 552	4.272 659	9.205 164	19.83192
79	6 241	8.888 194	28.10694	493 039	4.290 840	9.244 335	19.91632
80	6 400	8.944 272	28.28427	512 000	4.308 869	9.283 178	20.00000
81	6 561	9 000 000	28.46050	531 441	4.326 749	9.321 698	20.08299
82	6 724	9.055 385	28.63564	551 368	4.344 481	9.359 902	20.16530
83	6 889	9.110 434	28.80972	571 787	4.362 071	9.397 796	20.24694
84	7 056	9.165 151	28.98275	592 704	4.379 519	9.435 388	20.32793
85	7 225	9.219 544	29.15476	614 125	4.396 830	9.472 682	20.40828
86	7 396	9.273 618	29.32576	636 056	4.414 005	9.509 685	20.48800
87	7 569	9.327 379	29.49576	658 503	4.431 048	9.546 403	20.56710
88	7 744	9.380 832	29.66479	681 472	4.447 960	9.582 840	20.64560
89	7 921	9.433 981	29.83287	704 969	4.464 745	9.619 002	20.72351
90	8 100	9.486 833	30.00000	729 000	4.481 405	9.654 894	20.80084
91	8 281	9.539 392	30.16621	753 571	4.497 941	9.690 521	20.87759
92	8 464	9.591 663	30.33150	778 688	4.514 357	9.725 888	20.95379
93	8 649	9.643 651	30.49590	804 357	4.530 655	9.761 000	21.02944
94	8 836	9.695 360	30.65942	830 584	4.546 836	9.795 861	21.10454
95	9 025	9.746 794	30.82207	857 375	4.562 903	9.830 476	21.17912
96	9 216	9.797 959	30.98387	884 736	4.578 857	9.864 848	21.25317
97	9 409	9.848 858	31.14482	912 673	4.594 701	9.898 983	21.32671
98	9 604	9.899 495	31.30495	941 192	4.610 436	9.932 884	21.39975
99	9 801	9.949 874	31.46427	970 299	4.626 065	9.966 555	21.47229
100	10 000	10.00000	31.62278	1 000 000	4.641 589	10.00000	21.54435

n	n^2	$\sqrt{n}$	$\sqrt{10n}$	n^3	$\sqrt[3]{n}$	$\sqrt[3]{10n}$	$\sqrt[3]{100n}$
100	10 000	10.00000	31.62278	1 000 000	4.641 589	10.00000	21.54435
101	10 201	10.04988	31.78050	1 030 301	4.657 010	10.03322	21.61592
102	10 404	10.09950	31.93744	1 061 208	4.672 329	10.06623	21.68703
103	10 609	10.14889	32.09361	1 092 727	4.687 548	10.09902	21.75767
104	10 816	10.19804	32.24903	1 124 864	4.702 669	10.13159	21.82786
105	11 025	10.24695	32.40370	1 157 625	4.717 694	10.16396	21.89760
106	11 236	10.29563	32.55764	1 191 016	4.732 623	10.19613	21.96689
107	11 449	10.34408	32.71085	1 225 043	4.747 459	10.22809	22.03575
108	11 664	10.39230	32.86335	1 259 712	4.762 203	10.25986	22.10419
109	11 881	10.44031	33.01515	1 295 029	4.776 856	10.29142	22.17220
110	12 100	10.48809	33.16625	1 331 000	4.791 420	10.32280	22.23980
111	12 321	10.53565	33.31666	1 367 631	4.805 896	10.35399	22.30699
112	12 544	10.58301	33.46640	1 404 928	4.820 285	10.38499	22.37378
113	12 769	10.63015	33.61547	1 442 897	4.834 588	10.41580	22.44017
114	12 996	10.67708	33.76389	1 481 544	4.848 808	10.44644	22.50617
115	13 225	10.72381	33.91165	1 520 875	4.862 944	10.47690	22.57179
116	13 456	10.77033	34.05877	1 560 896	4.876 999	10.50718	22.63702
117	13 689	10.81665	34.20526	1 601 613	4.890 973	10.53728	22.70189
118	13 924	10.86278	34.35113	1 643 032	4.904 868	10.56722	22.76638
119	14 161	10.90871	34.49638	1 685 159	4.918 685	10.59699	22.83051
120	14 400	10.95445	34.64102	1 728 000	4.932 424	10.62659	22.89428
121	14 641	11.00000	34.78505	1 771 561	4.946 087	10.65602	22.95770
122	14 884	11.04536	34.92850	1 815 848	4.959 676	10.68530	23.02078
123	15 129	11.09054	35.07136	1 860 867	4.973 190	10.71441	23.08350
124	15 376	11.13553	35.21363	1 906 624	4.986 631	10.74337	23.14589
125	15 625	11.18034	35.35534	1 953 125	5.000 000	10.77217	23.20794
126	15 876	11.22497	35.49648	2 000 376	5.013 298	10.80082	23.26967
127	16 129	11.26943	35.63706	2 048 383	5.026 526	10.82932	23.33107
128	16 384	11.31371	35.77709	2 097 152	5.039 684	10.85767	23.39214
129	16 641	11.35782	35.91657	2 146 689	5.052 774	10.88587	23.45290
130	16 900	11.40175	36.05551	2 197 000	5.065 797	10.91393	23.51335
131	17 161	11.44552	36.19392	2 248 091	5.078 753	10.94184	23.57348
132	17 424	11.48913	36.33180	2 299 968	5.091 643	10.96961	23.63332
133	17 689	11.53256	36.46917	2 352 637	5.104 469	10.99724	23.69285
134	17 956	11.57584	36.60601	2 406 104	5.117 230	11.02474	23.75208
135	18 225	11.61895	36.74235	2 460 375	5.129 928	11.05209	23.81102
136	18 496	11.66190	36.87818	2 515 456	5.142 563	11.07932	23.86966
137	18 769	11.70470	37.01351	2 571 353	5.155 137	11.10641	23.92803
138	19 044	11.74734	37.14835	2 628 072	5.167 649	11.13336	23.98610
139	19 321	11.78983	37.28270	2 685 619	5.180 101	11.16019	24.04390
140	19 600	11.83216	37.41657	2 744 000	5.192 494	11.18689	24.10142
141	19 881	11.87434	37.54997	2 803 221	5.204 828	11.21346	24.15867
142	20 164	11.91638	37.68289	2 863 288	5.217 103	11.23991	24.21565
143	20 449	11.95826	37.81534	2 924 207	5.229 322	11.26623	24.27236
144	20 736	12.00000	37.94733	2 985 984	5.241 483	11.29243	24.32881
145	21 025	12.04159	38.07887	3 048 625	5.253 588	11.31851	24.38499
146	21 316	12.08305	38.20995	3 112 136	5.265 637	11.34447	24.44092
147	21 609	12.12436	38.34058	3 176 523	5.277 632	11.37031	24.49660
148	21 904	12.16553	38.47077	3 241 792	5.289 572	11.39604	24.55202
149	22 201	12.20656	38.60052	3 307 949	5.301 459	11.42165	24.60719
150	22 500	12.24745	38.72983	3 375 000	5.313 293	11.44714	24.66212

n	n^2	$\sqrt{n}$	$\sqrt{10n}$	n^3	$\sqrt[3]{n}$	$\sqrt[3]{10n}$	$\sqrt[3]{100n}$
150	22 500	12.24745	38.72983	3 375 000	5.313 293	11.44714	24.66212
151	22 801	12.28821	38.85872	3 442 951	5.325 074	11.47252	24.71680
152	23 104	12.32883	38.98718	3 511 808	5.336 803	11.49779	24.77125
153	23 409	12.36932	39.11521	3 581 577	5.348 481	11.52295	24.82545
154	23 716	12.40967	39.24283	3 652 264	5.360 108	11.54800	24.87942
155	24 025	12.44990	39.37004	3 723 875	5.371 685	11 57295	24.93315
156	24 336	12.49000	39.49684	3 796 416	5.383 213	11.59778	24.98666
157	24 649	12.52996	39.62323	3 869 893	5.394 691	11.62251	25.03994
158	24 964	12.56981	39.74921	3 944 312	5.406 120	11.64713	25.09299
159	25 281	12.60952	39.87480	4 019 679	5.417 502	11.67165	25.14581
160	25 600	12.64911	40.00000	4 096 000	5.428 835	11.69607	25.19842
161	25 921	12.68858	40.12481	4 173 281	5.440 122	11.72039	25.25081
162	26 244	12.72792	40.24922	4 251 528	5.451 362	11.74460	25.30298
163	26 569	12.76715	40.37326	4 330 747	5.462 556	11.76872	25.35494
164	26 896	12.80625	40.49691	4 410 944	5.473 704	11.79274	25.40668
165	27 225	12.84523	40.62019	4 492 125	5.484 807	11.81666	25.45822
166	27 556	12.88410	40.74310	4 574 296	5.495 865	11.84048	25.50954
167	27 889	12.92285	40.86563	4 657 463	5.506 878	11.86421	25.56067
168	28 224	12.96148	40.98780	4 741 632	5.517 848	11.88784	25.61158
169	28 561	13.00000	41.10961	4 826 809	5.528 775	11.91138	25.66230
170	28 900	13.03840	41.23106	4 913 000	5.539 658	11.93483	25.71282
171	29 241	13.07670	41.35215	5 000 211	5.550 499	11.95819	25.76313
172	29 584	13.11488	41.47288	5 088 448	5.561 298	11.98145	25.81326
173	29 929	13.15295	41.59327	5 177 717	5.572 055	12.00463	25.86319
174	30 276	13.19091	41.71331	5 268 024	5.582 770	12.02771	25.91292
175	30 625	13.22876	41.83300	5 359 375	5.593 445	12.05071	25.96247
176	30 976	13.26650	41.95235	5 451 776	5.604 079	12.07362	26.01183
177	31 329	13.30413	42.07137	5 545 233	5.614 672	12.09645	26.06100
178	31 684	13.34166	42.19005	5 639 752	5.625 226	12.11918	26.10999
179	32 041	13.37909	42.30839	5 735 339	5.635 741	12.14184	26.15879
180	32 400	13.41641	42.42641	5 832 000	5.646 216	12.16440	26.20741
181	32 761	13.45362	42.54409	5 929 741	5.656 653	12.18689	26.25586
182	33 124	13.49074	42.66146	6 028 568	5.667 051	12.20929	26.30412
183	33 489	13.52775	42.77850	6 128 487	5.677 411	12.23161	26.35221
184	33 856	13.56466	42.89522	6 229 504	5.687 734	12.25385	26.40012
185	34 225	13.60147	43.01163	6 331 625	5.698 019	12.27601	26.44786
186	34 596	13.63818	43.12772	6 434 856	5.708 267	12.29809	26.49543
187	34 969	13.67479	43.24350	6 539 203	5.718 479	12.32009	26.54283
188	35 344	13.71131	43.35897	6 644 672	5.728 654	12.34201	26.59006
189	35 721	13.74773	43.47413	6 751 269	5.738 794	12.36386	26.63712
190	36 100	13.78405	43.58899	6 859 000	5.748 897	12.38562	26.68402
191	36 481	13.82027	43.70355	6 967 871	5.758 965	12.40731	26.73075
192	36 864	13.85641	43.81780	7 077 888	5.768 998	12.42893	26.77732
193	37 249	13.89244	43.93177	7 189 057	5.778 997	12.45047	26.82373
194	37 636	13.92839	44.04543	7 301 384	5.788 960	12.47194	26.86997
195	38 025	13.96424	44.15880	7 414 875	5.798 890	12.49333	26.91606
196	38 416	14.00000	44.27189	7 529 536	5.808 786	12.51465	26.96199
197	38 809	14.03567	44.38468	7 645 373	5.818 648	12.53590	27.00777
198	39 204	14.07125	44.49719	7 762 392	5.828 477	12.55707	27.05339
199	39 601	14.10674	44.60942	7 880 599	5.838 272	12.57818	27.09886
200	40 000	14.14214	44.72136	8 000 000	5.848 035	12.59921	27.14418

n	n^2	$\sqrt{n}$	$\sqrt{10n}$	n^3	$\sqrt[3]{n}$	$\sqrt[3]{10n}$	$\sqrt[3]{100n}$
200	40 000	14.14214	44.72136	8 000 000	5.848 035	12.59921	27.14418
201	40 401	14.17745	44.83302	8 120 601	5.857 766	12.62017	27.18934
202	40 804	14.21267	44.94441	8 242 408	5.867 464	12.64107	27.23436
203	41 209	14.24781	45.05552	8 365 427	5.877 131	12.66189	27.27922
204	41 616	14.28286	45.16636	8 489 664	5.886 765	12.68265	27.32394
205	42 025	14.31782	45.27693	8 615 125	5.896 369	12.70334	27.36852
206	42 436	14.35270	45.38722	8 741 816	5.905 941	12.72396	27.41295
207	42 849	14.38749	45.49725	8 869 743	5.915 482	12.74452	27.45723
208	43 264	14.42221	45.60702	8 998 912	5.924 992	12.76501	27.50138
209	43 681	14.45683	45.71652	9 129 329	5.934 472	12.78543	27.54538
210	44 100	14.49138	45.82576	9 261 000	5.943 922	12.80579	27.58924
211	44 521	14.52584	45.93474	9 393 931	5.953 342	12.82609	27.63296
212	44 944	14.56022	46.04346	9 528 128	5.962 732	12.84632	27.67655
213	45 369	14.59452	46.15192	9 663 597	5.972 093	12.86648	27.72000
214	45 796	14.62874	46.26013	9 800 344	5.981 424	12.88659	27.76331
215	46 225	14.66288	46.36809	9 938 375	5.990 726	12.90663	27.80649
216	46 656	14.69694	46.47580	10 077 696	6.000 000	12.92661	27.84953
217	47 089	14.73092	46.58326	10 218 313	6.009 245	12.94653	27.89244
218	47 524	14.76482	46.69047	10 360 232	6.018 462	12.96638	27.93522
219	47 961	14.79865	46.79744	10 503 459	6.027 650	12.98618	27.97787
220	48 400	14.83240	46.90416	10 648 000	6.036 811	13.00591	28.02039
221	48 841	14.86607	47.01064	10 793 861	6.045 944	13.02559	28.06278
222	49 284	14.89966	47.11688	10 941 048	6.055 049	13.04521	28.10505
223	49 729	14.93318	47.22288	11 089 567	6.064 127	13.06477	28.14718
224	50 176	14.96663	47.32864	11 239 424	6.073 178	13.08427	28.18919
225	50 625	15.00000	47.43416	11 390 625	6.082 202	13.10371	28.23108
226	51 076	15.03330	47.53946	11 543 176	6.091 199	13.12309	28.27284
227	51 529	15.06652	47.64452	11 697 083	6.100 170	13.14242	28.31448
228	51 984	15.09967	47.74935	11 852 352	6.109 115	13.16169	28.35600
229	52 441	15.13275	47.85394	12 008 989	6.118 033	13.18090	28.39739
230	52 900	15.16575	47.95832	12 167 000	6.126 926	13.20006	28.43867
231	53 361	15.19868	48.06246	12 326 391	6.135 792	13.21916	28.47983
232	53 824	15.23155	48.16638	12 487 168	6.144 634	13.23821	28.52086
233	54 289	15.26434	48.27007	12 649 337	6.153 449	13.25721	28.56178
234	54 756	15.29706	48.37355	12 812 904	6.162 240	13.27614	28.60259
235	55 225	15.32971	48.47680	12 977 875	6.171 006	13.29503	28.64327
236	55 696	15.36229	48.57983	13 144 256	6.179 747	13.31386	28.68384
237	56 169	15.39480	48.68265	13 312 053	6.188 463	13.33264	28.72430
238	56 644	15.42725	48.78524	13 481 272	6.197 154	13.35136	28.76464
239	57 121	15.45962	48.88763	13 651 919	6.205 822	13.37004	28.80487
240	57 600	15.49193	48.98979	13 824 000	6.214 465	13.38866	28.84499
241	58 081	15.52417	49.09175	13 997 521	6.223 084	13.40723	28.88500
242	58 564	15.55635	49.19350	14 172 488	6.231 680	13.42575	28.92489
243	59 049	15.58846	49.29503	14 348 907	6.240 251	13.44421	28.96468
244	59 536	15.62050	49.39636	14 526 784	6.248 800	13.46263	29.00436
245	60 025	15.65248	49.49747	14 706 125	6.257 325	13.48100	29.04393
246	60 516	15.68439	49.59839	14 886 936	6.265 827	13.49931	29.08339
247	61 009	15.71623	49.69909	15 069 223	6.274 305	13.51758	29.12275
248	61 504	15.74802	49.79960	15 252 992	6.282 761	13.53580	29.16199
249	62 001	15.77973	49.89990	15 438 249	6.291 195	13.55397	29.20114
250	62 500	15.81139	50.00000	15 625 000	6.299 605	13.57209	29.24018

SQUARES, CUBES AND ROOTS (Continued)

n	n^2	$\sqrt{n}$	$\sqrt{10n}$	n^3	$\sqrt[3]{n}$	$\sqrt[3]{10n}$	$\sqrt[3]{100n}$
250	62 500	15.81139	50.00000	15 625 000	6.299 605	13.57209	29.24018
251	63 001	15.84298	50.09990	15 813 251	6.307 994	13.59016	29.27911
252	63 504	15.87451	50.19960	16 003 008	6.316 360	13.60818	29.31794
253	64 009	15.90597	50.29911	16 194 277	6.324 704	13.62616	29.35667
254	64 516	15.93738	50.39841	16 387 064	6.333 026	13.64409	29.39530
255	65 025	15.96872	50.49752	16 581 375	6.341 326	13.66197	29.43383
256	65 536	16.00000	50.59644	16 777 216	6.349 604	13.67981	29.47225
257	66 049	16.03122	50.69517	16 974 593	6.357 861	13.69760	29.51058
258	66 564	16.06238	50.79370	17 173 512	6.366 097	13.71534	29.54880
259	67 081	16.09348	50.89204	17 373 979	6.374 311	13.73304	29.58693
260	67 600	16.12452	50.99020	17 576 000	6.382 504	13.75069	29.62496
261	68 121	16.15549	51.08816	17 779 581	6.390 677	13.76830	29.66289
262	68 644	16.18641	51.18594	17 984 728	6.398 828	13.78586	29.70073
263	69 169	16.21727	51.28353	18 191 447	6.406 959	13.80337	29.73847
264	69 696	16.24808	51.38093	18 399 744	6.415 069	13.82085	29.77611
265	70 225	16.27882	51.47815	18 609 625	6.423 158	13.83828	29.81366
266	70 756	16.30951	51.57519	18 821 096	6.431 228	13.85566	29.85111
267	71 289	16 34013	51.67204	19 034 163	6.439 277	13.87300	29.88847
268	71 824	16.37071	51.76872	19 248 832	6.447 306	13.89030	29.92574
269	72 361	16.40122	51.86521	19 465 109	6.455 315	13.90755	29.96292
270	72 900	16.43168	51.96152	19 683 000	6.463 304	13.92477	30.00000
271	73 441	16.46208	52.05766	19 902 511	6.471 274	13.94194	30.03699
272	73 984	16.49242	52.15362	20 123 648	6.479 224	13.95906	30.07389
273	74 529	16.52271	52.24940	20 346 417	6.487 154	13.97615	30.11070
274	75 076	16.55295	52.34501	20 570 824	6.495 065	13.99319	30.14742
275	75 625	16.58312	52.44044	20 796 875	6.502 957	14.01020	30.18405
276	76 176	16.61325	52.53570	21 024 576	6.510 830	14.02716	30.22060
277	76 729	16.64332	52.63079	21 253 933	6.518 684	14.04408	30.25705
278	77 284	16.67333	52.72571	21 484 952	6.526 519	14.06096	30.29342
279	77 841	16.70329	52.82045	21 717 639	6.534 335	14.07780	30.32970
280	78 400	16.73320	52.91503	21 952 000	6.542 133	14.09460	30.36589
281	78 961	16.76305	53.00943	22 188 041	6.549 912	14.11136	30.40200
282	79 524	16.79286	53.10367	22 425 768	6.557 672	14.12808	30.43802
283	80 089	16.82260	53.19774	22 665 187	6.565 414	14.14476	30.47395
284	80 656	16.85230	53.29165	22 906 304	6.573 138	14.16140	30.50981
285	81 225	16.88194	53.38539	23 149 125	6.580 844	14.17800	30.54557
286	81 796	16.91153	53.47897	23 393 656	6.588 532	14.19456	30.58126
287	82 369	16.94107	53.57238	23 639 903	6.596 202	14.21109	30.61686
288	82 944	16.97056	53.66563	23 887 872	6.603 854	14.22757	30.65238
289	83 521	17.00000	53.75872	24 137 569	6.611 489	14.24402	30.68781
290	84 100	17 02939	53.85165	24 389 000	6.619 106	14.26043	30.72317
291	84 681	17.05872	53.94442	24 642 171	6.626 705	14.27680	30.75844
292	85 264	17.08801	54.03702	24 897 088	6.634 287	14.29314	30.79363
293	85 849	17.11724	54.12947	25 153 757	6.641 852	14.30944	30.82875
294	86 436	17.14643	54.22177	25 412 184	6.649 400	14.32570	30.86378
295	87 025	17.17556	54.31390	25 672 375	6.656 930	14.34192	30.89873
296	87 616	17.20465	54.40588	25 934 336	6.664 444	14.35811	30.93361
297	88 209	17.23369	54.49771	26 198 073	6.671 940	14.37426	30.96840
298	88 804	17.26268	54.58938	26 463 592	6.679 420	14.39037	31.00312
299	89 401	17.29162	54.68089	26 730 899	6.686 883	14.40645	31.03776
300	90 000	17.32051	54.77226	27 000 000	6.694 330	14.42250	31.07233

SQUARES, CUBES AND ROOTS (Continued)

n	n^2	$\sqrt{n}$	$\sqrt{10n}$	n^3	$\sqrt[3]{n}$	$\sqrt[3]{10n}$	$\sqrt[3]{100n}$
300	90 000	17.32051	54.77226	27 000 000	6.694 330	14.42250	31.07233
301	90 601	17.34935	54.86347	27 270 901	6.701 759	14.43850	31.10681
302	91 204	17.37815	54.95453	27 543 608	6.709 173	14.45447	31.14122
303	91 809	17.40690	55.04544	27 818 127	6.716 570	14.47041	31.17556
304	92 416	17.43560	55.13620	28 094 464	6.723 951	14.48631	31.20982
305	93 025	17.46425	55.22681	28 372 625	6.731 315	14.50218	31.24400
306	93 636	17.49286	55.31727	28 652 616	6.738 664	14.51801	31.27811
307	94 249	17.52142	55.40758	28 934 443	6.745 997	14.53381	31.31214
308	94 864	17.54993	55.49775	29 218 112	6.753 313	14.54957	31.34610
309	95 481	17.57840	55.58777	29 503 629	6.760 614	14.56530	31.37999
310	96 100	17.60682	55.67764	29 791 000	6.767 899	14.58100	31.41381
311	96 721	17.63519	55.76737	30 080 231	6.775 169	14.59666	31.44755
312	97 344	17.66352	55.85696	30 371 328	6.782 423	14.61229	31.48122
313	97 969	17.69181	55.94640	30 664 297	6.789 661	14.62788	31.51482
314	98 596	17.72005	56.03570	30 959 144	6.796 884	14.64344	31.54834
315	99 225	17.74824	56.12486	31 255 875	6.804 092	14.65897	31.58180
316	99 856	17.77639	56.21388	31 554 496	6.811 285	14.67447	31.61518
317	100 489	17.80449	56.30275	31 855 013	6.818 462	14.68993	31.64850
318	101 124	17.83255	56.39149	32 157 432	6.825 624	14.70536	31.68174
319	101 761	17.86057	56.48008	32 461 759	6.832 771	14.72076	31.71492
320	102 400	17.88854	56.56854	32 768 000	6.839 904	14.73613	31.74802
321	103 041	17.91647	56.65686	33 076 161	6.847 021	14.75146	31.78106
322	103 684	17.94436	56.74504	33 386 248	6.854 124	14.76676	31.81403
323	104 329	17.97220	56.83309	33 698 267	6.861 212	14.78203	31.84693
324	104 976	18.00000	56.92100	34 012 224	6.868 285	14.79727	31.87976
325	105 625	18.02776	57.00877	34 328 125	6.875 344	14.81248	31.91252
326	106 276	18.05547	57.09641	34 645 976	6.882 389	14.82766	31.94522
327	106 929	18.08314	57.18391	34 965 783	6.889 419	14.84280	31.97785
328	107 584	18.11077	57.27128	35 287 552	6.896 434	14.85792	32.01041
329	108 241	18.13836	57.35852	35 611 289	6.903 436	14.87300	32.04291
330	108 900	18.16590	57.44563	35 937 000	6.910 423	14.88806	32.07534
331	109 561	18.19341	57.53260	36 264 691	6.917 396	14.90308	32.10771
332	110 224	18.22087	57.61944	36 594 368	6.924 356	14.91807	32.14001
333	110 889	18.24829	57.70615	36 926 037	6.931 301	14.93303	32.17225
334	111 556	18.27567	57.79273	37 259 704	6.938 232	14.94797	32.20442
335	112 225	18.30301	57.87918	37 595 375	6.945 150	14.96287	32.23653
336	112 896	18.33030	57.96551	37 933 056	6.952 053	14.97774	32.26857
337	113 569	18.35756	58.05170	38 272 753	6.958 943	14.99259	32.30055
338	114 244	18.38478	58.13777	38 614 472	6.965 820	15.00740	32.33247
339	114 921	18.41195	58.22371	38 958 219	6.972 683	15.02219	32.36433
340	115 600	18.43909	58.30952	39 304 000	6.979 532	15.03695	32.39612
341	116 281	18.46619	58.39521	39 651 821	6.986 368	15.05167	32.42785
342	116 964	18.49324	58.48077	40 001 688	6.993 191	15.06637	32.45952
343	117 649	18.52026	58.56620	40 353 607	7.000 000	15.08104	32.49112
344	118 336	18.54724	58.65151	40 707 584	7.006 796	15.09568	32.52267
345	119 025	18.57418	58.73670	41 063 625	7.013 579	15.11030	32.55415
346	119 716	18.60108	58.82176	41 421 736	7.020 349	15.12488	32.58557
347	120 409	18.62794	58.90671	41 781 923	7.027 106	15.13944	32.61694
348	121 104	18.65476	58.99152	42 144 192	7.033 850	15.15397	32.64824
349	121 801	18.68154	59.07622	42 508 549	7.040 581	15.16847	32.67948
350	122 500	18.70829	59.16080	42 875 000	7.047 299	15.18294	32.71066

SQUARES, CUBES AND ROOTS (Continued)

n	n^2	$\sqrt{n}$	$\sqrt{10n}$	n^3	$\sqrt[3]{n}$	$\sqrt[3]{10n}$	$\sqrt[3]{100n}$
350	122 500	18.70829	59.16080	42 875 000	7.047 299	15.18294	32.71066
351	123 201	18.73499	59.24525	43 243 551	7.054 004	15.19739	32.74179
352	123 904	18.76166	59.32959	43 614 208	7.060 697	15.21181	32.77285
353	124 609	18.78829	59.41380	43 986 977	7.067 377	15.22620	32.80386
354	125 316	18.81489	59.49790	44 361 864	7.074 044	15.24057	32.83480
355	126 025	18.84144	59.58188	44 738 875	7.080 699	15.25490	32.86569
356	126 736	18.86796	59.66574	45 118 016	7.087 341	15.26921	32.89652
357	127 449	18.89444	59.74948	45 499 293	7.093 971	15.28350	32.92730
358	128 164	18.92089	59.83310	45 882 712	7.100 588	15.29775	32.95801
359	128 881	18.94730	59.91661	46 268 279	7.107 194	15.31198	32.98867
360	129 600	18.97367	60.00000	46 656 000	7.113 787	15.32619	33.01927
361	130 321	19.00000	60.08328	47 045 881	7.120 367	15.34037	33.04982
362	131 044	19.02630	60.16644	47 437 928	7.126 936	15.35452	33.08031
363	131 769	19.05256	60.24948	47 832 147	7.133 492	15.36864	33.11074
364	132 496	19.07878	60.33241	48 228 544	7.140 037	15.38274	33.14112
365	133 225	19.10497	60.41523	48 627 125	7.146 569	15.39682	33.17144
366	133 956	19.13113	60.49793	49 027 896	7.153 090	15.41087	33.20170
367	134 689	19.15724	60.58052	49 430 863	7.159 599	15.42489	33.23191
368	135 424	19.18333	60.66300	49 836 032	7.166 096	15.43889	33.26207
369	136 161	19.20937	60.74537	50 243 409	7.172 581	15.45286	33.29217
370	136 900	19.23538	60.82763	50 653 000	7.179 054	15.46680	33.32222
371	137 641	19.26136	60.90977	51 064 811	7.185 516	15.48073	33.35221
372	138 384	19.28730	60.99180	51 478 848	7.191 966	15.49462	33.38215
373	139 129	19.31321	61.07373	51 895 117	7.198 405	15.50849	33.41204
374	139 876	19.33908	61.15554	52 313 624	7.204 832	15.52234	33.44187
375	140 625	19.36492	61.23724	52 734 375	7.211 248	15.53616	33.47165
376	141 376	19.39072	61.31884	53 157 376	7.217 652	15.54996	33.50137
377	142 129	19.41649	61.40033	53 582 633	7.224 045	15.56373	33.53105
378	142 884	19.44222	61.48170	54 010 152	7.230 427	15.57748	33.56067
379	143 641	19.46792	61.56298	54 439 939	7.236 797	15.59121	33.59024
380	144 400	19.49359	61.64414	54 872 000	7.243 156	15.60491	33.61975
381	145 161	19.51922	61.72520	55 306 341	7.249 505	15.61858	33.64922
382	145 924	19.54482	61.80615	55 742 968	7.255 842	15.63224	33.67863
383	146 689	19.57039	61.88699	56 181 887	7.262 167	15.64587	33.70800
384	147 456	19.59592	61.96773	56 623 104	7.268 482	15.65947	33.73731
385	148 225	19.62142	62.04837	57 066 625	7.274 786	15.67305	33.76657
386	148 996	19.64688	62.12890	57 512 456	7.281 079	15.68661	33.79578
387	149 769	19.67232	62.20932	57 960 603	7.287 362	15.70014	33.82494
388	150 544	19.69772	62.28965	58 411 072	7.293 633	15.71366	33.85405
389	151 321	19.72308	62.36986	58 863 869	7.299 894	15.72714	33.88310
390	152 100	19.74842	62.44998	59 319 000	7.306 144	15.74061	33.91211
391	152 881	19.77372	62.52999	59 776 471	7.312 383	15.75405	33.94107
392	153 664	19.79899	62.60990	60 236 288	7.318 611	15.76747	33.96999
393	154 449	19.82423	62.68971	60 698 457	7.324 829	15.78087	33.99885
394	155 236	19.84943	62.76942	61 162 984	7.331 037	15.79424	34.02766
395	156 025	19.87461	62.84903	61 629 875	7.337 234	15.80759	34.05642
396	156 816	19.89975	62.92853	62 099 136	7.343 420	15.82092	34.08514
397	157 609	19.92486	63.00794	62 570 773	7.349 597	15.83423	34.11381
398	158 404	19.94994	63.08724	63 044 792	7.355 762	15.84751	34.14242
399	159 201	19.97498	63.16645	63 521 199	7.361 918	15.86077	34.17100
400	160 000	20.00000	63.24555	64 000 000	7.368 063	15.87401	34.19952

n	n^2	$\sqrt{n}$	$\sqrt{10n}$	n^3	$\sqrt[3]{n}$	$\sqrt[3]{10n}$	$\sqrt[3]{100n}$
400	160 000	20.00000	63.24555	64 000 000	7.368 063	15.87401	34.19952
401	160 801	20.02498	63.32456	64 481 201	7.374 198	15.88723	34.22799
402	161 604	20.04994	63.40347	64 964 808	7.380 323	15.90042	34.25642
403	162 409	20.07486	63.48228	65 450 827	7.386 437	15.91360	34.28480
404	163 216	20.09975	63.56099	65 939 264	7.392 542	15.92675	34.31314
405	164 025	20.12461	63.63961	66 430 125	7.398 636	15.93988	34.34143
406	164 836	20.14944	63.71813	66 923 416	7.404 721	15.95299	34.36967
407	165 649	20.17424	63.79655	67 419 143	7.410 795	15.96607	34.39786
408	166 464	20.19901	63.87488	67 917 312	7.416 860	15.97914	34.42601
409	167 281	20.22375	63.95311	68 417 929	7.422 914	15.99218	34.45412
410	168 100	20.24846	64.03124	68 921 000	7.428 959	16.00521	34.48217
411	168 921	20.27313	64.10928	69 426 531	7.434 994	16.01821	34.51018
412	169 744	20.29778	64.18723	69 934 528	7.441 019	16.03119	34.53815
413	170 569	20.32240	64.26508	70 444 997	7.447 034	16.04415	34.56607
414	171 396	20.34699	64.34283	70 957 944	7.453 040	16.05709	34.59395
415	172 225	20.37155	64.42049	71 473 375	7.459 036	16.07001	34.62178
416	173 056	20.39608	64.49806	71 991 296	7.465 022	16.08290	34.64956
417	173 889	20.42058	64.57554	72 511 713	7.470 999	16.09578	34.67731
418	174 724	20.44505	64.65292	73 034 632	7.476 966	16.10864	34.70500
419	175 561	20.46949	64.73021	73 560 059	7.482 924	16.12147	34.73266
420	176 400	20.49390	64.80741	74 088 000	7.488 872	16.13429	34.76027
421	177 241	20.51828	64.88451	74 618 461	7.494 811	16.14708	34.78783
422	178 084	20.54264	64.96153	75 151 448	7.500 741	16.15986	34.81535
423	178 929	20.56696	65.03845	75 686 967	7.506 661	16.17261	34.84283
424	179 776	20.59126	65.11528	76 225 024	7.512 572	16.18534	34.87027
425	180 625	20.61553	65.19202	76 765 625	7.518 473	16.19806	34.89766
426	181 476	20.63977	65.26868	77 308 776	7.524 365	16.21075	34.92501
427	182 329	20.66398	65.34524	77 854 483	7.530 248	16.22343	34.95232
428	183 184	20.68816	65.42171	78 402 752	7.536 122	16.23608	34.97958
429	184 041	20.71232	65.49809	78 953 589	7.541 987	16.24872	35.00680
430	184 900	20.73644	65.57439	79 507 000	7.547 842	16.26133	35.03398
431	185 761	20.76054	65.65059	80 062 991	7.553 689	16.27393	35.06112
432	186 624	20.78461	65.72671	80 621 568	7.559 526	16.28651	35.08821
433	187 489	20.80865	65.80274	81 182 737	7.565 355	16.29906	35.11527
434	188 356	20.83267	65.87868	81 746 504	7.571 174	16.31160	35.14228
435	189 225	20.85665	65.95453	82 312 875	7.576 985	16.32412	35.16925
436	190 096	20.88061	66.03030	82 881 856	7.582 787	16.33662	35.19618
437	190 969	20.90454	66.10598	83 453 453	7.588 579	16.34910	35.22307
438	191 844	20.92845	66.18157	84 027 672	7.594 363	16.36156	35.24991
439	192 721	20.95233	66.25708	84 604 519	7.600 139	16.37400	35.27672
440	193 600	20.97618	66.33250	85 184 000	7.605 905	16.38643	35.30348
441	194 481	21.00000	66.40783	85 766 121	7.611 663	16.39883	35.33021
442	195 364	21.02380	66.48308	86 350 888	7.617 412	16.41122	35.35689
443	196 249	21.04757	66.55825	86 938 307	7.623 152	16.42358	35.38354
444	197 136	21.07131	66.63332	87 528 384	7.628 884	16.43593	35.41014
445	198 025	21.09502	66.70832	88 121 125	7.634 607	16.44826	35.43671
446	198 916	21.11871	66.78323	88 716 536	7.640 321	16.46057	35.46323
447	199 809	21.14237	66.85806	89 314 623	7.646 027	16.47287	35.48971
448	200 704	21.16601	66.93280	89 915 392	7.651 725	16.48514	35.51616
449	201 601	21.18962	67.00746	90 518 849	7.657 414	16.49740	35.54257
450	202 500	21.21320	67.08204	91 125 000	7.663 094	16.50964	35.56893

SQUARES, CUBES AND ROOTS (Continued)

n	n^2	$\sqrt{n}$	$\sqrt{10n}$	n^3	$\sqrt[3]{n}$	$\sqrt[3]{10n}$	$\sqrt[3]{100n}$
450	202 500	21.21320	67.08204	91 125 000	7.663 094	16.50964	35.56893
451	203 401	21.23676	67.15653	91 733 851	7.668 766	16.52186	35.59526
452	204 304	21.26029	67.23095	92 345 408	7.674 430	16.53406	35.62155
453	205 209	21.28380	67.30527	92 959 677	7.680 086	16.54624	35.64780
454	206 116	21.30728	67.37952	93 576 664	7.685 733	16.55841	35.67401
455	207 025	21.33073	67.45369	94 196 375	7.691 372	16.57056	35.70018
456	207 936	21.35416	67.52777	94 818 816	7.697 002	16.58269	35.72632
457	208 849	21.37756	67.60178	95 443 993	7.702 625	16.59480	35.75242
458	209 764	21.40093	67.67570	96 071 912	7.708 239	16.60690	35.77848
459	210 681	21.42429	67.74954	96 702 579	7.713 845	16.61897	35.80450
460	211 600	21.44761	67.82330	97 336 000	7.719 443	16.63103	35.83048
461	212 521	21.47091	67.89698	97 972 181	7.725 032	16.64308	35.85642
462	213 444	21.49419	67.97058	98 611 128	7.730 614	16.65510	35.88233
463	214 369	21.51743	68.04410	99 252 847	7.736 188	16.66711	35.90820
464	215 296	21.54066	68.11755	99 897 344	7.741 753	16.67910	35.93404
465	216 225	21.56386	68.19091	100 544 625	7.747 311	16.69108	35.95983
466	217 156	21.58703	68.26419	101 194 696	7.752 861	16.70303	35.98559
467	218 089	21.61018	68.33740	101 847 563	7.758 402	16.71497	36.01131
468	219 024	21.63331	68.41053	102 503 232	7.763 936	16.72689	36.03700
469	219 961	21.65641	68.48357	103 161 709	7.769 462	16.73880	36.06265
470	220 900	21.67948	68.55655	103 823 000	7.774 980	16.75069	36.08826
471	221 841	21.70253	68.62944	104 487 111	7.780 490	16.76256	36.11384
472	222 784	21.72556	68.70226	105 154 048	7.785 993	16.77441	36.13938
473	223 729	21.74856	68.77500	105 823 817	7.791 488	16.78625	36.16488
474	224 676	21.77154	68.84766	106 496 424	7.796 975	16.79807	36.19035
475	225 625	21.79449	68.92024	107 171 875	7.802 454	16.80988	36.21578
476	226 576	21.81742	68.99275	107 850 176	7.807 925	16.82167	36.24118
477	227 529	21.84033	69.06519	108 531 333	7.813 389	16.83344	36.26654
478	228 484	21.86321	69.13754	109 215 352	7.818 846	16.84519	36.29187
479	229 441	21.88607	69.20983	109 902 239	7.824 294	16.85693	36.31716
480	230 400	21.90890	69.28203	110 592 000	7.829 735	16.86865	36.34241
481	231 361	21.93171	69.35416	111 284 641	7.835 169	16.88036	36.36763
482	232 324	21.95450	69.42622	111 980 168	7.840 595	16.89205	36.39282
483	233 289	21.97726	69.49820	112 678 587	7.846 013	16.90372	36.41797
484	234 256	22.00000	69.57011	113 379 904	7.851 424	16.91538	36.44308
485	235 225	22.02272	69.64194	114 084 125	7.856 828	16.92702	36.46817
486	236 196	22.04541	69.71370	114 791 256	7.862 224	16.93865	36.49321
487	237 169	22.06808	69.78539	115 501 303	7.867 613	16.95026	36.51822
488	238 144	22.09072	69.85700	116 214 272	7.872 994	16.96185	36.54320
489	239 121	22.11334	69.92853	116 930 169	7.878 368	16.97343	36.56815
490	240 100	22.13594	70.00000	117 649 000	7.883 735	16.98499	36.59306
491	241 081	22.15852	70.07139	118 370 771	7.889 095	16.99654	36.61793
492	242 064	22.18107	70.14271	119 095 488	7.894 447	17.00807	36.64278
493	243 049	22.20360	70.21396	119 823 157	7.899 792	17.01959	36.66758
494	244 036	22.22611	70.28513	120 553 784	7.905 129	17.03108	36.69236
495	245 025	22.24860	70.35624	121 287 375	7.910 460	17.04257	36.71710
496	246 016	22.27106	70.42727	122 023 936	7.915 783	17.05404	36.74181
497	247 009	22.29350	70.49823	122 763 473	7.921 099	17.06549	36.76649
498	248 004	22.31591	70.56912	123 505 992	7.926 408	17.07693	36.79113
499	249 001	22.33831	70.63993	124 251 499	7.931 710	17.08835	36.81574
500	250 000	22.36068	70.71068	125 000 000	7.937 005	17.09976	36.84031

SQUARES, CUBES AND ROOTS (Continued)

n	n^2	$\sqrt{n}$	$\sqrt{10n}$	n^3	$\sqrt[3]{n}$	$\sqrt[3]{10n}$	$\sqrt[3]{100n}$
500	250 000	22.36068	70.71068	125 000 000	7.937 005	17.09976	36.84031
501	251 001	22.38303	70.78135	125 751 501	7.942 293	17.11115	36.86486
502	252 004	22.40536	70.85196	126 506 008	7.947 574	17.12253	36.88937
503	253 009	22.42766	70.92249	127 263 527	7.952 848	17.13389	36.91385
504	254 016	22.44994	70.99296	128 024 064	7.958 114	17.14524	36.93830
505	255 025	22.47221	71.06335	128 787 625	7.963 374	17.15657	36.96271
506	256 036	22.49444	71.13368	129 554 216	7.968 627	17.16789	36.98709
507	257 049	22.51666	71.20393	130 323 843	7.973 873	17.17919	37.01144
508	258 064	22.53886	71.27412	131 096 512	7.979 112	17.19048	37.03576
509	259 081	22.56103	71.34424	131 872 229	7.984 344	17.20175	37.06004
510	260 100	22.58318	71.41428	132 651 000	7.989 570	17.21301	37.08430
511	261 121	22.60531	71.48426	133 432 831	7.994 788	17.22425	37.10852
512	262 144	22.62742	71.55418	134 217 728	8.000 000	17.23548	37.13271
513	263 169	22.64950	71.62402	135 005 697	8.005 205	17.24669	37.15687
514	264 196	22.67157	71.69379	135 796 744	8.010 403	17.25789	37.18100
515	265 225	22.69361	71.76350	136 590 875	8.015 595	17.26908	37.20509
516	266 256	22.71563	71.83314	137 388 096	8.020 779	17.28025	37.22916
517	267 289	22.73763	71.90271	138 188 413	8.025 957	17.29140	37.25319
518	268 324	22.75961	71.97222	138 991 832	8.031 129	17.30254	37.27720
519	269 361	22.78157	72.04165	139 798 359	8.036 293	17.31367	37.30117
520	270 400	22.80351	72.11103	140 608 000	8.041 452	17.32478	37.32511
521	271 441	22.82542	72.18033	141 420 761	8.046 603	17.33588	37.34902
522	272 484	22.84732	72.24957	142 236 648	8.051 748	17.34696	37.37290
523	273 529	22.86919	72.31874	143 055 667	8.056 886	17.35804	37.39675
524	274 576	22.89105	72.38784	143 877 824	8.062 018	17.36909	37.42057
525	275 625	22.91288	72.45688	144 703 125	8.067 143	17.38013	37.44436
526	276 676	22.93469	72.52586	145 531 576	8.072 262	17.39116	37.46812
527	277 729	22.95648	72.59477	146 363 183	8.077 374	17.40218	37.49185
528	278 784	22.97825	72.66361	147 197 952	8.082 480	17.41318	37.51555
529	279 841	23.00000	72.73239	148 035 889	8.087 579	17.42416	37.53922
530	280 900	23.02173	72.80110	148 877 000	8.092 672	17.43513	37.56286
531	281 961	23.04344	72.86975	149 721 291	8.097 759	17.44609	37.58647
532	283 024	23.06513	72.93833	150 568 768	8.102 839	17.45704	37.61005
533	284 089	23.08679	73.00685	151 419 437	8.107 913	17.46797	37.63360
534	285 156	23.10844	73.07530	152 273 304	8.112 980	17.47889	37.65712
535	286 225	23.13007	73.14369	153 130 375	8.118 041	17.48979	37.68061
536	287 296	23.15167	73.21202	153 990 656	8.123 096	17.50068	37.70407
537	288 369	23.17326	73.28028	154 854 153	8.128 145	17.51156	37.72751
538	289 444	23.19483	73.34848	155 720 872	8.133 187	17.52242	37.75091
539	290 521	23.21637	73.41662	156 590 819	8.138 223	17.53327	37.77429
540	291 600	23.23790	73.48469	157 464 000	8.143 253	17.54411	37.79763
541	292 681	23.25941	73.55270	158 340 421	8.148 276	17.55493	37.82095
542	293 764	23.28089	73.62065	159 220 088	8.153 294	17.56574	37.84424
543	294 849	23.30236	73.68853	160 103 007	8.158 305	17.57654	37.86750
544	295 936	23.32381	73.75636	160 989 184	8.163 310	17.58732	37.89073
545	297 025	23.34524	73.82412	161 878 625	8.168 309	17.59809	37.91393
546	298 116	23.36664	73.89181	162 771 336	8.173 302	17.60885	37.93711
547	299 209	23.38803	73.95945	163 667 323	8.178 289	17.61959	37.96025
548	300 304	23.40940	74.02702	164 566 592	8.183 269	17.63032	37.98337
549	301 401	23.43075	74.09453	165 469 149	8.188 244	17.64104	38.00646
550	302 500	23.45208	74.16198	166 375 000	8.193 213	17.65174	38.02952

n	n^2	$\sqrt{n}$	$\sqrt{10n}$	n^3	$\sqrt[3]{n}$	$\sqrt[3]{10n}$	$\sqrt[3]{100n}$
550	302 500	23.45208	74.16198	166 375 000	8.193 213	17.65174	38.02952
551	303 601	23.47339	74.22937	167 284 151	8.198 175	17.66243	38.05256
552	304 704	23.49468	74.29670	168 196 608	8.203 132	17.67311	38.07557
553	305 809	23.51595	74.36397	169 112 377	8.208 082	17.68378	38.09854
554	306 916	23.53720	74.43118	170 031 464	8.213 027	17.69443	38.12149
555	308 025	23.55844	74.49832	170 953 875	8.217 966	17.70507	38.14442
556	309 136	23.57965	74.56541	171 879 616	8.222 899	17.71570	38.16731
557	310 249	23.60085	74.63243	172 808 693	8.227 825	17.72631	38.19018
558	311 364	23.62202	74.69940	173 741 112	8.232 746	17.73691	38.21302
559	312 481	23.64318	74.76630	174 676 879	8.237 661	17.74750	38.23584
560	313 600	23.66432	74.83315	175 616 000	8.242 571	17.75808	38.25862
561	314 721	23.68544	74.89993	176 558 481	8.247 474	17.76864	38.28138
562	315 844	23.70654	74.96666	177 504 328	8.252 372	17.77920	38.30412
563	316 969	23.72762	75.03333	178 453 547	8.257 263	17.78973	38.32682
564	318 096	23.74868	75.09993	179 406 144	8.262 149	17.80026	38.34950
565	319 225	23.76973	75.16648	180 362 125	8.267 029	17.81077	38.37215
566	320 356	23.79075	75.23297	181 321 496	8.271 904	17.82128	38.39478
567	321 489	23.81176	75.29940	182 284 263	8.276 773	17.83177	38.41737
568	322 624	23.83275	75.36577	183 250 432	8.281 635	17.84224	38.43995
569	323 761	23.85372	75.43209	184 220 009	8.286 493	17.85271	38.46249
570	324 900	23.87467	75.49834	185 193 000	8.291 344	17.86316	38.48501
571	326 041	23.89561	75.56454	186 169 411	8.296 190	17.87360	38.50750
572	327 184	23.91652	75.63068	187 149 248	8.301 031	17.88403	38.52997
573	328 329	23.93742	75.69676	188 132 517	8.305 865	17.89444	38.55241
574	329 476	23.95830	75.76279	189 119 224	8.310 694	17.90485	38.57482
575	330 625	23.97916	75.82875	190 109 375	8.315 517	17.91524	38.59721
576	331 776	24.00000	75.89466	191 102 976	8.320 335	17.92562	38.61958
577	332 929	24.02082	75.96052	192 100 033	8.325 148	17.93599	38.64191
578	334 084	24.04163	76.02631	193 100 552	8.329 954	17.94634	38.66422
579	335 241	24.06242	76.09205	194 104 539	8.334 755	17.95669	38.68651
580	336 400	24.08319	76.15773	195 112 000	8.339 551	17.96702	38.70877
581	337 561	24.10394	76.22336	196 122 941	8.344 341	17.97734	38.73100
582	338 724	24.12468	76.28892	197 137 368	8.349 126	17.98765	38.75321
583	339 889	24.14539	76.35444	198 155 287	8.353 905	17.99794	38.77539
584	341 056	24.16609	76.41989	199 176 704	8.358 678	18.00823	38.79755
585	342 225	24.18677	76.48529	200 201 625	8.363 447	18.01850	38.81968
586	343 396	24.20744	76.55064	201 230 056	8.368 209	18.02876	38.84179
587	344 569	24.22808	76.61593	202 262 003	8.372 967	18.03901	38.86387
588	345 744	24.24871	76.68116	203 297 472	8.377 719	18.04925	38.88593
589	346 921	24.26932	76.74634	204 336 469	8.382 465	18.05947	38.90796
590	348 100	24.28992	76.81146	205 379 000	8.387 207	18.06969	38.92996
591	349 281	24.31049	76.87652	206 425 071	8.391 942	18.07989	38.95195
592	350 464	24.33105	76.94154	207 474 688	8.396 673	18.09008	38.97390
593	351 649	24.35159	77.00649	208 527 857	8.401 398	18.10026	38.99584
594	352 836	24.37212	77.07140	209 584 584	8.406 118	18.11043	39.01774
595	354 025	24.39262	77.13624	210 644 875	8.410 833	18.12059	39.03963
596	355 216	24.41311	77.20104	211 708 736	8.415 542	18.13074	39.06149
597	356 409	24.43358	77.26578	212 776 173	8.420 246	18.14087	39.08332
598	357 604	24.45404	77.33046	213 847 192	8.424 945	18.15099	39.10513
599	358 801	24.47448	77.39509	214 921 799	8.429 638	18 16111	39.12692
600	360 000	24.49490	77.45967	216 000 000	8.434 327	18.17121	39.14868

n	n^2	$\sqrt{n}$	$\sqrt{10n}$	n^3	$\sqrt[3]{n}$	$\sqrt[3]{10n}$	$\sqrt[3]{100n}$
600	360 000	24.49490	77.45967	216 000 000	8.434 327	18.17121	39.14868
601	361 201	24.51530	77.52419	217 081 801	8.439 010	18.18130	39.17041
602	362 404	24.53569	77.58866	218 167 208	8.443 688	18.19137	39.19213
603	363 609	24.55606	77.65307	219 256 227	8.448 361	18.20144	39.21382
604	364 816	24.57641	77.71744	220 348 864	8.453 028	18.21150	39.23548
605	366 025	24.59675	77.78175	221 445 125	8.457 691	18.22154	39.25712
606	367 236	24.61707	77.84600	222 545 016	8.462 348	18.23158	39.27874
607	368 449	24.63737	77.91020	223 648 543	8.467 000	18.24160	39.30033
608	369 664	24.65766	77.97435	224 755 712	8.471 647	18.25161	39.32190
609	370 881	24.67793	78.03845	225 866 529	8.476 289	18.26161	39.34345
610	372 100	24.69818	78.10250	226 981 000	8.480 926	18.27160	39.36497
611	373 321	24.71841	78.16649	228 099 131	8.485 558	18.28158	39.38647
612	374 544	24.73863	78.23043	229 220 928	8.490 185	18.29155	39.40795
613	375 769	24.75884	78.29432	230 346 397	8.494 807	18.30151	39.42940
614	376 996	24.77902	78.35815	231 475 544	8.499 423	18.31145	39.45083
615	378 225	24.79919	78.42194	232 608 375	8.504 035	18.32139	39.47223
616	379 456	24.81935	78.48567	233 744 896	8.508 642	18.33131	39.49362
617	380 689	24.83948	78.54935	234 885 113	8.513 243	18.34123	39.51498
618	381 924	24.85961	78.61298	236 029 032	8.517 840	18.35113	39.53631
619	383 161	24.87971	78.67655	237 176 659	8.522 432	18.36102	39.55763
620	384 400	24.89980	78.74008	238 328 000	8.527 019	18.37091	39.57892
621	385 641	24.91987	78.80355	239 483 061	8.531 601	18.38078	39.60018
622	386 884	24.93993	78.86698	240 641 848	8.536 178	18.39064	39.62143
623	388 129	24.95997	78.93035	241 804 367	8.540 750	18.40049	39.64265
624	389 376	24.97999	78.99367	242 970 624	8.545 317	18.41033	39.66385
625	390 625	25.00000	79.05694	244 140 625	8.549 880	18.42016	39.68503
626	391 876	25.01999	79.12016	245 314 376	8.554 437	18.42998	39.70618
627	393 129	25.03997	79.18333	246 491 883	8.558 990	18.43978	39.72731
628	394 384	25.05993	79.24645	247 673 152	8.563 538	18.44958	39.74842
629	395 641	25.07987	79.30952	248 858 189	8.568 081	18.45937	39.76951
630	396 900	25.09980	79.37254	250 047 000	8.572 619	18.46915	39.79057
631	398 161	25.11971	79.43551	251 239 591	8.577 152	18.47891	39.81161
632	399 424	25.13961	79.49843	252 435 968	8.581 681	18.48867	39.83263
633	400 689	25.15949	79.56130	253 636 137	8.586 205	18.49842	39.85363
634	401 956	25.17936	79.62412	254 840 104	8.590 724	18.50815	39.87461
635	403 225	25.19921	79.68689	256 047 875	8.595 238	18.51788	39.89556
636	404 496	25.21904	79.74961	257 259 456	8.599 748	18.52759	39.91649
637	405 769	25.23886	79.81228	258 474 853	8.604 252	18.53730	39.93740
638	407 044	25.25866	79.87490	259 694 072	8.608 753	18.54700	39.95829
639	408 321	25.27845	79.93748	260 917 119	8.613 248	18.55668	39.97916
640	409 600	25.29822	80.00000	262 144 000	8.617 739	18.56636	40.00000
641	410 881	25.31798	80.06248	263 374 721	8.622 225	18.57602	40.02082
642	412 164	25.33772	80.12490	264 609 288	8.626 706	18.58568	40.04162
643	413 449	25.35744	80.18728	265 847 707	8.631 183	18.59532	40.06240
644	414 736	25.37716	80.24961	267 089 984	8.635 655	18.60495	40.08316
645	416 025	25.39685	80.31189	268 336 125	8.640 123	18.61458	40.10390
646	417 316	25.41653	80.37413	269 586 136	8.644 585	18.62419	40.12461
647	418 609	25.43619	80.43631	270 840 023	8.649 044	18.63380	40.14530
648	419 904	25.45584	80.49845	272 097 792	8.653 497	18.64340	40.16598
649	421 201	25.47548	80.56054	273 359 449	8.657 947	18.65298	40.18663
650	422 500	25.49510	80.62258	274 625 000	8.662 391	18.66256	40.20726

SQUARES, CUBES AND ROOTS (Continued)

n	n^2	$\sqrt{n}$	$\sqrt{10n}$	n^3	$\sqrt[3]{n}$	$\sqrt[3]{10n}$	$\sqrt[3]{100n}$
650	422 500	25.49510	80.62258	274 625 000	8.662 391	18.66256	40.20726
651	423 801	25.51470	80.68457	275 894 451	8.666 831	18.67212	40.22787
652	425 104	25.53429	80.74652	277 167 808	8.671 266	18.68168	40.24845
653	426 409	25.55386	80.80842	278 445 077	8.675 697	18.69122	40.26902
654	427 716	25.57342	80.87027	279 726 264	8.680 124	18.70076	40.28957
655	429 025	25.59297	80.93207	281 011 375	8.684 546	18.71029	40.31009
656	430 336	25.61250	80.99383	282 300 416	8.688 963	18.71980	40.33059
657	431 649	25.63201	81.05554	283 593 393	8.693 376	18.72931	40.35108
658	432 964	25.65151	81.11720	284 890 312	8.697 784	18.73881	40.37154
659	434 281	25.67100	81.17881	286 191 179	8.702 188	18.74830	40.39198
660	435 600	25.69047	81.24038	287 496 000	8.706 588	18.75777	40.41240
661	436 921	25.70992	81.30191	288 804 781	8.710 983	18.76724	40.43280
662	438 244	25.72936	81.36338	290 117 528	8.715 373	18.77670	40.45318
663	439 569	25.74879	81.42481	291 434 247	8.719 760	18.78615	40.47354
664	440 896	25.76820	81.48620	292 754 944	8.724 141	18.79559	40.49388
665	442 225	25.78759	81.54753	294 079 625	8.728 519	18.80502	40.51420
666	443 556	25.80698	81.60882	295 408 296	8.732 892	18.81444	40.53449
667	444 889	25.82634	81.67007	296 740 963	8.737 260	13.82386	40.55477
668	446 224	25.84570	81.73127	298 077 632	8.741 625	18.83326	40.57503
669	447 561	25.86503	81.79242	299 418 309	8.745 985	18.84265	40.59526
670	448 900	25.88436	81.85353	300 763 000	8.750 340	18.85204	40.61548
671	450 241	25.90367	81.91459	302 111 711	8.754 691	18.86141	40.63568
672	451 584	25.92296	81.97561	303 464 448	8.759 038	18.87078	40.65585
673	452 929	25.94224	82.03658	304 821 217	8.763 381	18.88013	40.67601
674	454 276	25.96151	82.09750	306 182 024	8.767 719	18.88948	40.69615
675	455 625	25.98076	82.15838	307 546 875	8.772 053	18.89882	40.71626
676	456 976	26.00000	82.21922	308 915 776	8.776 383	18.90814	40.73636
677	458 329	26.01922	82.28001	310 288 733	8.780 708	18.91746	40.75644
678	459 684	26.03843	82.34076	311 665 752	8.785 030	18.92677	40.77650
679	461 041	26.05763	82.40146	313 046 839	8.789 347	18.93607	40.79653
680	462 400	26.07681	82.46211	314 432 000	8.793 659	18.94536	40.81655
681	463 761	26.09598	82.52272	315 821 241	8.797 968	18.95465	40.83655
682	465 124	26.11513	82.58329	317 214 568	8.802 272	18.96392	40.85653
683	466 489	26.13427	82.64381	318 611 987	8.806 572	18.97318	40.87649
684	467 856	26.15339	82.70429	320 013 504	8.810 868	18.98244	40.89643
685	469 225	26.17250	82.76473	321 419 125	8.815 160	18.99169	40.91635
686	470 596	26.19160	82.82512	322 828 856	8.819 447	19.00092	40.93625
687	471 969	26.21068	82.88546	324 242 703	8.823 731	19.01015	40.95613
688	473 344	26.22975	82.94577	325 660 672	8.828 010	19.01937	40.97599
689	474 721	26.24881	83.00602	327 082 769	8.832 285	19.02858	40.99584
690	476 100	26.26785	83.06624	328 509 000	8.836 556	19.03778	41.01566
691	477 481	26.28688	83.12641	329 939 371	8.840 823	19.04698	41.03546
692	478 864	26.30589	83.18654	331 373 888	8.845 085	19.05616	41.05525
693	480 249	26.32489	83.24662	332 812 557	8.849 344	19.06533	41.07502
694	481 636	26.34388	83.30666	334 255 384	8.853 599	19.07450	41.09476
695	483 025	26.36285	83.36666	335 702 375	8.857 849	19.08366	41.11449
696	484 416	26.38181	83.42661	337 153 536	8.862 095	19.09281	41.13420
697	485 809	26.40076	83.48653	338 608 873	8.866 338	19.10195	41.15389
698	487 204	26.41969	83.54639	340 068 392	8.870 576	19.11108	41.17357
699	488 601	26.43861	83.60622	341 532 099	8.874 810	19.12020	41.19322
700	490 000	26.45751	83.66600	343 000 000	8.879 040	19.12931	41.21285

n	n^2	$\sqrt{n}$	$\sqrt{10n}$	n^3	$\sqrt[3]{n}$	$\sqrt[3]{10n}$	$\sqrt[3]{100n}$
700	490 000	26.45751	83.66600	343 000 000	8.879 040	19.12931	41.21285
701	491 401	26.47640	83.72574	344 472 101	8.883 266	19.13842	41.23247
702	492 804	26.49528	83.78544	345 948 408	8.887 488	19.14751	41.25207
703	494 209	26.51415	83.84510	347 428 927	8.891 706	19.15660	41.27164
704	495 616	26.53300	83.90471	348 913 664	8.895 920	19.16568	41.29120
705	497 025	26.55184	83.96428	350 402 625	8.900 130	19.17475	41.31075
706	498 436	26.57066	84.02381	351 895 816	8.904 337	19.18381	41.33027
707	499 849	26.58947	84.08329	353 393 243	8.908 539	19.19286	41.34977
708	501 264	26.60827	84.14274	354 894 912	8.912 737	19.20191	41.36926
709	502 681	26.62705	84.20214	356 400 829	8.916 931	19.21095	41.38873
710	504 100	26.64583	84.26150	357 911 000	8.921 121	19.21997	41.40818
711	505 521	26.66458	84.32082	359 425 431	8.925 308	19.22899	41.42761
712	506 944	26.68333	84.38009	360 944 128	8.929 490	19.23800	41.44702
713	508 369	26.70206	84.43933	362 467 097	8.933 669	19.24701	41.46642
714	509 796	26.72078	84.49852	363 994 344	8.937 843	19.25600	41.48579
715	511 225	26.73948	84.55767	365 525 875	8.942 014	19.26499	41.50515
716	512 656	26.75818	84.61678	367 061 696	8.946 181	19.27396	41.52449
717	514 089	26.77686	84.67585	368 601 813	8.950 344	19.28293	41.54382
718	515 524	26.79552	84.73488	370 146 232	8.954 503	19.29189	41.56312
719	516 961	26.81418	84.79387	371 694 959	8.958 658	19.30084	41.58241
720	518 400	26.83282	84.85281	373 248 000	8.962 809	19.30979	41.60168
721	519 841	26.85144	84.91172	374 805 361	8.966 957	19.31872	41.62093
722	521 284	26.87006	84.97058	376 367 048	8.971 101	19.32765	41.64016
723	522 729	26.88866	85.02941	377 933 067	8.975 241	19.33657	41.65938
724	524 176	26.90725	85.08819	379 503 424	8.979 377	19.34548	41.67857
725	525 625	26.92582	85.14693	381 078 125	8.983 509	19.35438	41.69775
726	527 076	26.94439	85.20563	382 657 176	8.987 637	19.36328	41.71692
727	528 529	26.96294	85.26429	384 240 583	8.991 762	19.37216	41.73606
728	529 984	26.98148	85.32292	385 828 352	8.995 883	19.38104	41.75519
729	531 441	27.00000	85.38150	387 420 489	9.000 000	19.38991	41.77430
730	532 900	27.01851	85.44004	389 017 000	9.004 113	19.39877	41.79339
731	534 361	27.03701	85.49854	390 617 891	9.008 223	19.40763	41.81247
732	535 824	27.05550	85.55700	392 223 168	9.012 329	19.41647	41.83152
733	537 289	27.07397	85.61542	393 832 837	9.016 431	19.42531	41.85056
734	538 756	27.09243	85.67380	395 446 904	9.020 529	19.43414	41.86959
735	540 225	27.11088	85.73214	397 065 375	9.024 624	19.44296	41.88859
736	541 696	27.12932	85.79044	398 688 256	9.028 715	19.45178	41.90758
737	543 169	27.14774	85.84870	400 315 553	9.032 802	19.46058	41.92655
738	544 644	27.16616	85.90693	401 947 272	9.036 886	19.46938	41.94551
739	546 121	27.18455	85.96511	403 583 419	9.040 966	19.47817	41.96444
740	547 600	27.20294	86.02325	405 224 000	9.045 042	19.48695	41.98336
741	549 081	27.22132	86.08136	406 869 021	9.049 114	19.49573	42.00227
742	550 564	27.23968	86.13942	408 518 488	9.053 183	19.50449	42.02115
743	552 049	27.25803	86.19745	410 172 407	9.057 248	19.51325	42.04002
744	553 536	27.27636	86.25543	411 830 784	9.061 310	19.52200	42.05887
745	555 025	27.29469	86.31338	413 493 625	9.065 368	19.53074	42.07771
746	556 516	27.31300	86.37129	415 160 936	9.069 422	19.53948	42.09653
747	558 009	27.33130	86.42916	416 832 723	9.073 473	19.54820	42.11533
748	559 504	27.34959	86.48699	418 508 992	9.077 520	19.55692	42.13411
749	561 001	27.36786	86.54479	420 189 749	9.081 563	19.56563	42.15288
750	562 500	27.38613	86.60254	421 875 000	9.085 603	19.57434	42.17163

SQUARES, CUBES AND ROOTS (Continued)

n	n^2	$\sqrt{n}$	$\sqrt{10n}$	n^3	$\sqrt[3]{n}$	$\sqrt[3]{10n}$	$\sqrt[3]{100n}$
750	562 500	27.38613	86.60254	421 875 000	9.085 603	19.57434	42.17163
751	564 001	27.40438	86.66026	423 564 751	9.089 639	19.58303	42.19037
752	565 504	27.42262	86.71793	425 259 008	9.093 672	19.59172	42.20909
753	567 009	27.44085	86.77557	426 957 777	9.097 701	19.60040	42 22779
754	568 516	27.45906	86.83317	428 661 064	9.101 727	19.60908	42.24647
755	570 025	27.47726	86.89074	430 368 875	9.105 748	19.61774	42.26514
756	571 536	27.49545	86.94826	432 081 216	9.109 767	19.62640	42.28379
757	573 049	27.51363	87.00575	433 798 093	9.113 782	19.63505	42.30243
758	574 564	27.53180	87.06320	435 519 512	9.117 793	19.64369	42.32105
759	576 081	27.54995	87.12061	437 245 479	9.121 801	19.65232	42.33965
760	577 600	27.56810	87.17798	438 976 000	9.125 805	19.66095	42.35824
761	579 121	27.58623	87.23531	440 711 081	9.129 806	19.66957	42.37681
762	580 644	27.60435	87.29261	442 450 728	9.133 803	19.67818	42.39536
763	582 169	27.62245	87.34987	444 194 947	9.137 797	19.68679	42.41390
764	583 696	27.64055	87.40709	445 943 744	9.141 787	19.69538	42.43242
765	585 225	27.65863	87.46428	447 697 125	9.145 774	19.70397	42.45092
766	586 756	27.67671	87.52143	449 455 096	9.149 758	19.71256	42.46941
767	588 289	27.69476	87.57854	451 217 663	9.153 738	19.72113	42.48789
768	589 824	27.71281	87.63561	452 984 832	9.157 714	19.72970	42.50634
769	591 361	27.73085	87.69265	454 756 609	9.161 687	19.73826	42.52478
770	592 900	27.74887	87.74964	456 533 000	9.165 656	19.74681	42.54321
771	594 441	27.76689	87.80661	458 314 011	9.169 623	19.75535	42.56162
772	595 984	27.78489	87.86353	460 099 648	9.173 585	19.76389	42.58001
773	597 529	27.80288	87.92042	461 889 917	9.177 544	19.77242	42.59839
774	599 076	27.82086	87.97727	463 684 824	9.181 500	19.78094	42.61675
775	600 625	27.83882	88.03408	465 484 375	9.185 453	19.78946	42.63509
776	602 176	27.85678	88.09086	467 288 576	9.189 402	19.79797	42.65342
777	603 729	27.87472	88.14760	469 097 433	9.193 347	19.80647	42.67174
778	605 284	27.89265	88.20431	470 910 952	9.197 290	19.81496	42.69004
779	606 841	27.91057	88.26098	472 729 139	9.201 229	19.82345	42.70832
780	608 400	27.92848	88.31761	474 552 000	9.205 164	19.83192	42.72659
781	609 961	27.94638	88.37420	476 379 541	9.209 096	19.84040	42.74484
782	611 524	27.96426	88.43076	478 211 768	9.213 025	19.84886	42.76307
783	613 089	27.98214	88.48729	480 048 687	9.216 950	19.85732	42.78129
784	614 656	28.00000	88.54377	481 890 304	9.220 873	19.86577	42.79950
785	616 225	28.01785	88.60023	483 736 625	9.224 791	19.87421	42.81769
786	617 796	28.03569	88.65664	485 587 656	9.228 707	19.88265	42.83586
787	619 369	28.05352	88.71302	487 443 403	9.232 619	19.89107	42.85402
788	620 944	28.07134	88.76936	489 303 872	9.236 528	19.89950	42.87216
789	622 521	28.08914	88.82567	491 169 069	9.240 433	19.90791	42.89029
790	624 100	28.10694	88.88194	493 039 000	9.244 335	19.91632	42.90840
791	625 681	28.12472	88.93818	494 913 671	9.248 234	19.92472	42.92650
792	627 264	28.14249	88.99438	496 793 088	9.252 130	19.93311	42.94458
793	628 849	28.16026	89.05055	498 677 257	9.256 022	19.94150	42.96265
794	630 436	28.17801	89.10668	500 566 184	9.259 911	19.94987	42.98070
795	632 025	28.19574	89.16277	502 459 875	9.263 797	19.95825	42.99874
796	633 616	28.21347	89.21883	504 358 336	9.267 680	19.96661	43.01676
797	635 209	28.23119	89.27486	506 261 573	9.271 559	19.97497	43.03477
798	636 804	28.24889	89.33085	508 169 592	9.275 435	19.98332	43.05276
799	638 401	28.26659	89.38680	510 082 399	9.279 308	19.99166	43.07073
800	640 000	28.28427	89.44272	512 000 000	9.283 178	20.00000	43.08869

SQUARES, CUBES AND ROOTS (Continued)

n	n^2	$\sqrt{n}$	$\sqrt{10n}$	n^3	$\sqrt[3]{n}$	$\sqrt[3]{10n}$	$\sqrt[3]{100n}$
800	640 000	28.28427	89.44272	512 000 000	9.283 178	20.00000	43.08869
801	641 601	28.30194	89.49860	513 922 401	9.287 044	20.00833	43.10664
802	643 204	28.31960	89.55445	515 849 608	9.290 907	20.01665	43.12457
803	644 809	28.33725	89.61027	517 781 627	9.294 767	20.02497	43.14249
804	646 416	28.35489	89.66605	519 718 464	9.298 624	20.03328	43.16039
805	648 025	28.37252	89.72179	521 660 125	9.302 477	20.04158	43.17828
806	649 636	28.39014	89.77750	523 606 616	9.306 328	20.04988	43.19615
807	651 249	28.40775	89.83318	525 557 943	9.310 175	20.05816	43.21400
808	652 864	28.42534	89.88882	527 514 112	9.314 019	20.06645	43.23185
809	654 481	28.44293	89.94443	529 475 129	9.317 860	20.07472	43.24967
810	656 100	28.46050	90.00000	531 441 000	9.321 698	20.08299	43.26749
811	657 721	28.47806	90.05554	533 411 731	9.325 532	20.09125	43.28529
812	659 344	28.49561	90.11104	535 387 328	9.329 363	20.09950	43.30307
813	660 969	28.51315	90.16651	537 367 797	9.333 192	20.10775	43.32084
814	662 596	28.53069	90.22195	539 353 144	9.337 017	20.11599	43.33859
815	664 225	28.54820	90.27735	541 343 375	9.340 839	20.12423	43.35633
816	665 856	28.56571	90.33272	543 338 496	9.344 657	20.13245	43.37406
817	667 489	28.58321	90.38805	545 338 513	9.348 473	20.14067	43.39177
818	669 124	28.60070	90.44335	547 343 432	9.352 286	20.14889	43.40947
819	670 761	28.61818	90.49862	549 353 259	9.356 095	20.15710	43.42715
820	672 400	28.63564	90.55385	551 368 000	9.359 902	20.16530	43.44481
821	674 041	28.65310	90.60905	553 387 661	9.363 705	20.17349	43.46247
822	675 684	28.67054	90.66422	555 412 248	9.367 505	20.18168	43.48011
823	677 329	28.68798	90.71935	557 441 767	9.371 302	20.18986	43.49773
824	678 976	28.70540	90.77445	559 476 224	9.375 096	20.19803	43.51534
825	680 625	28.72281	90.82951	561 515 625	9.378 887	20.20620	43.53294
826	682 276	28.74022	90.88454	563 559 976	9.382 675	20.21436	43.55052
827	683 929	28.75761	90.93954	565 609 283	9.386 460	20.22252	43.56809
828	685 584	28.77499	90.99451	567 663 552	9.390 242	20.23066	43.58564
829	687 241	28.79236	91.04944	569 722 789	9.394 021	20.23880	43.60318
830	688 900	28.80972	91.10434	571 787 000	9.397 796	20.24694	43.62071
831	690 561	28.82707	91.15920	573 856 191	9.401 569	20.25507	43.63822
832	692 224	28.84441	91.21403	575 930 368	9.405 339	20.26319	43.65572
833	693 889	28.86174	91.26883	578 009 537	9.409 105	20.27130	43.67320
834	695 556	28.87906	91.32360	580 093 704	9.412 869	20.27941	43.69067
835	697 225	28.89637	91.37833	582 182 875	9.416 630	20.28751	43.70812
836	698 896	28.91366	91.43304	584 277 056	9.420 387	20.29561	43.72556
837	700 569	28.93095	91.48770	586 376 253	9.424 142	20.30370	43.74299
838	702 244	28.94823	91.54234	588 480 472	9.427 894	20.31178	43.76041
839	703 921	28.96550	91.59694	590 589 719	9.431 642	20.31986	43.77781
840	705 600	28.98275	91.65151	592 704 000	9.435 388	20.32793	43.79519
841	707 281	29.00000	91.70605	594 823 321	9.439 131	20.33599	43.81256
842	708 964	29.01724	91.76056	596 947 688	9.442 870	20.34405	43.82992
843	710 649	29.03446	91.81503	599 077 107	9.446 607	20.35210	43.84727
844	712 336	29.05168	91.86947	601 211 584	9.450 341	20.36014	43.86460
845	714 025	29.06888	91.92388	603 351 125	9.454 072	20.36818	43.88191
846	715 716	29.08608	91.97826	605 495 736	9.457 800	20.37621	43.89922
847	717 409	29.10326	92.03260	607 645 423	9.461 525	20.38424	43.91651
848	719 104	29.12044	92.08692	609 800 192	9.465 247	20.39226	43.93378
849	720 801	29.13760	92.14120	611 960 049	9.468 966	20.40027	43.95105
850	722 500	29.15476	92.19544	614 125 000	9.472 682	20.40828	43.96830

n	n^2	$\sqrt{n}$	$\sqrt{10n}$	n^3	$\sqrt[3]{n}$	$\sqrt[3]{10n}$	$\sqrt[3]{100n}$
850	722 500	29.15476	92.19544	614 125 000	9.472 682	20.40828	43.96830
851	724 201	29.17190	92.24966	616 295 051	9.476 396	20.41628	43.98553
852	725 904	29.18904	92.30385	618 470 208	9.480 106	20.42427	44.00275
853	727 609	29.20616	92.35800	620 650 477	9.483 814	20.43226	44.01996
854	729 316	29.22328	92.41212	622 835 864	9.487 518	20.44024	44.03716
855	731 025	29.24038	92.46621	625 026 375	9.491 220	20.44821	44.05434
856	732 736	29.25748	92.52027	627 222 016	9.494 919	20.45618	44.07151
857	734 449	29.27456	92.57429	629 422 793	9.498 615	20.46415	44.08866
858	736 164	29.29164	92.62829	631 628 712	9.502 308	20.47210	44.10581
859	737 881	29.30870	92.68225	633 839 779	9.505 998	20.48005	44.12293
860	739 600	29.32576	92.73618	636 056 000	9.509 685	20.48800	44.14005
861	741 321	29.34280	92.79009	638 277 381	9.513 370	20.49593	44.15715
862	743 044	29.35984	92.84396	640 503 928	9.517 052	20.50387	44.17424
863	744 769	29.37686	92.89779	642 735 647	9.520 730	20.51179	44.19132
864	746 496	29.39388	92.95160	644 972 544	9.524 406	20.51971	44.20838
865	748 225	29.41088	93.00538	647 214 625	9.528 079	20.52762	44.22543
866	749 956	29.42788	93.05912	649 461 896	9.531 750	20.53553	44.24246
867	751 689	29.44486	93.11283	651 714 363	9.535 417	20.54343	44.25949
868	753 424	29.46184	93.16652	653 972 032	9.539 082	20.55133	44.27650
869	755 161	29.47881	93.22017	656 234 909	9.542 744	20.55922	44.29349
870	756 900	29.49576	93.27379	658 503 000	9.546 403	20.56710	44.31048
871	758 641	29.51271	93.32738	660 776 311	9.550 059	20.57498	44.32745
872	760 384	29.52965	93.38094	663 054 848	9.553 712	20.58285	44.34440
873	762 129	29.54657	93.43447	665 338 617	9.557 363	20.59071	44.36135
874	763 876	29.56349	93.48797	667 627 624	9.561 011	20.59857	44.37828
875	765 625	29.58040	93.54143	669 921 875	9.564 656	20.60643	44.39520
876	767 376	29.59730	93.59487	672 221 376	9.568 298	20.61427	44.41211
877	769 129	29.61419	93.64828	674 526 133	9.571 938	20.62211	44.42900
878	770 884	29.63106	93.70165	676 836 152	9.575 574	20.62995	44.44588
879	772 641	29.64793	93.75500	679 151 439	9.579 208	20.63778	44.46275
880	774 400	29.66479	93.80832	681 472 000	9.582 840	20.64560	44.47960
881	776 161	29.68164	93.86160	683 797 841	9.586 468	20.65342	44.49644
882	777 924	29.69848	93.91486	686 128 968	9.590 094	20.66123	44.51327
883	779 689	29.71532	93.96808	688 465 387	9.593 717	20.66904	44.53009
884	781 456	29.73214	94.02127	690 807 104	9.597 337	20.67684	44.54689
885	783 225	29.74895	94.07444	693 154 125	9.600 955	20.68463	44.56368
886	784 996	29.76575	94.12757	695 506 456	9.604 570	20.69242	44.58046
887	786 769	29.78255	94.18068	697 864 103	9.608 182	20.70020	44.59723
888	788 544	29.79933	94.23375	700 227 072	9.611 791	20.70798	44.61398
889	790 321	29.81610	94.28680	702 595 369	9.615 398	20.71575	44.63072
890	792 100	29.83287	94.33981	704 969 000	9.619 002	20.72351	44.64745
891	793 881	29.84962	94.39280	707 347 971	9.622 603	20.73127	44.66417
892	795 664	29.86637	94.44575	709 732 288	9.626 202	20.73902	44.68087
893	797 449	29.88311	94.49868	712 121 957	9.629 797	20.74677	44.69756
894	799 236	29.89983	94.55157	714 516 984	9.633 391	20.75451	44.71424
895	801 025	29.91655	94.60444	716 917 375	9.636 981	20.76225	44.73090
896	802 816	29.93326	94.65728	719 323 136	9.640 569	20.76998	44.74756
897	804 609	29.94996	94.71008	721 734 273	9.644 154	20.77770	44.76420
898	806 404	29.96665	94.76286	724 150 792	9.647 737	20.78542	44.78083
899	808 201	29.98333	94.81561	726 572 699	9.651 317	20.79313	44.79744
900	810 000	30.00000	94.86833	729 000 000	9.654 894	20.80084	44.81405

SQUARES, CUBES AND ROOTS (Continued)

n	n^2	$\sqrt{n}$	$\sqrt{10n}$	n^3	$\sqrt[3]{n}$	$\sqrt[3]{10n}$	$\sqrt[3]{100n}$
900	810 000	30.00000	94.86833	729 000 000	9.654 894	20.80084	44.81405
901	811 801	30.01666	94.92102	731 432 701	9.658 468	20.80854	44.83064
902	813 604	30.03331	94.97368	733 870 808	9.662 040	20.81623	44.84722
903	815 409	30.04996	95.02631	736 314 327	9.665 610	20.82392	44.86379
904	817 216	30.06659	95.07891	738 763 264	9.669 176	20.83161	44.88034
905	819 025	30.08322	95.13149	741 217 625	9.672 740	20.83929	44.89688
906	820 836	30.09983	95.18403	743 677 416	9.676 302	20.84696	44.91341
907	822 649	30.11644	95.23655	746 142 643	9.679 860	20.85463	44.92993
908	824 464	30.13304	95.28903	748 613 312	9.683 417	20.86229	44.94644
909	826 281	30.14963	95.34149	751 089 429	9.686 970	20.86994	44.96293
910	828 100	30.16621	95.39392	753 571 000	9.690 521	20.87759	44.97941
911	829 921	30.18278	95.44632	756 058 031	9.694 069	20.88524	44.99588
912	831 744	30.19934	95.49869	758 550 528	9.697 615	20.89288	45.01234
913	833 569	30.21589	95.55103	761 048 497	9.701 158	20.90051	45.02879
914	835 396	30.23243	95.60335	763 551 944	9.704 699	20.90814	45.04522
915	837 225	30.24897	95.65563	766 060 875	9.708 237	20.91576	45.06164
916	839 056	30.26549	95.70789	768 575 296	9.711 772	20.92338	45.07805
917	840 889	30.28201	95.76012	771 095 213	9.715 305	20.93099	45.09445
918	842 724	30.29851	95.81232	773 620 632	9.718 835	20.93860	45 11084
919	844 561	30.31501	95.86449	776 151 559	9.722 363	20.94620	45.12721
920	846 400	30.33150	95.91663	778 688 000	9.725 888	20.95379	45.14357
921	848 241	30.34798	95.96874	781 229 961	9.729 411	20.96138	45.15992
922	850 084	30.36445	96.02083	783 777 448	9.732 931	20.96896	45.17626
923	851 929	30.38092	96.07289	786 330 467	9.736 448	20.97654	45.19259
924	853 776	30.39737	96.12492	788 889 024	9.739 963	20.98411	45.20891
925	855 625	30.41381	96.17692	791 453 125	9.743 476	20.99168	45.22521
926	857 476	30.43025	96.22889	794 022 776	9.746 986	20.99924	45.24150
927	859 329	30.44667	96.28084	796 597 983	9.750 493	21.00680	45.25778
928	861 184	30.46309	96.33276	799 178 752	9.753 998	21.01435	45.27405
929	863 041	30.47950	96.38465	801 765 089	9.757 500	21.02190	45.29030
930	864 900	30.49590	96.43651	804 357 000	9.761 000	21.02944	45.30655
931	866 761	30.51229	96.48834	806 954 491	9.764 497	21.03697	45.32278
932	868 624	30.52868	96.54015	809 557 568	9.767 992	21.04450	45.33900
933	870 489	30.54505	96.59193	812 166 237	9.771 485	21.05203	45.35521
934	872 356	30.56141	96.64368	814 780 504	9.774 974	21.05954	45.37141
935	874 225	30.57777	96.69540	817 400 375	9.778 462	21.06706	45.38760
936	876 096	30.59412	96.74709	820 025 856	9.781 946	21.07456	45.40377
937	877 969	30.61046	96.79876	822 656 953	9.785 429	21.08207	45.41994
938	879 844	30.62679	96.85040	825 293 672	9.788 909	21.08956	45.43609
939	881 721	30.64311	96.90201	827 936 019	9.792 386	21.09706	45.45223
940	883 600	30.65942	96.95360	830 584 000	9.795 861	21.10454	45.46836
941	885 481	30.67572	97.00515	833 237 621	9.799 334	21.11202	45.48448
942	887 364	30.69202	97.05668	835 896 888	9.802 804	21.11950	45.50058
943	889 249	30.70831	97.10819	838 561 807	9.806 271	21.12697	45.51668
944	891 136	30.72458	97.15966	841 232 384	9.809 736	21.13444	45.53276
945	893 025	30.74085	97.21111	843 908 625	9.813 199	21.14190	45.54883
946	894 916	30.75711	97.26253	846 590 536	9.816 659	21.14935	45.56490
947	896 809	30.77337	97.31393	849 278 123	9.820 117	21.15680	45.58095
948	898 704	30.78961	97.36529	851 971 392	9.823 572	21.16424	45.59698
949	900 601	30.80584	97.41663	854 670 349	9.827 025	21.17168	45.61301
950	902 500	30.82207	97.46794	857 375 000	9.830 476	21.17912	45.62903

SQUARES, CUBES AND ROOTS (Continued)

n	n^2	$\sqrt{n}$	$\sqrt{10n}$	n^3	$\sqrt[3]{n}$	$\sqrt[3]{10n}$	$\sqrt[3]{100n}$
950	902 500	30.82207	97.46794	857 375 000	9.830 476	21.17912	45.62903
951	904 401	30.83829	97.51923	860 085 351	9.833 924	21.18655	45.64503
952	906 304	30.85450	97.57049	862 801 408	9.837 369	21.19397	45.66102
953	908 209	30.87070	97.62172	865 523 177	9.840 813	21.20139	45.67701
954	910 116	30.88689	97.67292	868 250 664	9.844 254	21.20880	45.69298
955	912 025	30.90307	97.72410	870 983 875	9.847 692	21.21621	45.70894
956	913 936	30.91925	97.77525	873 722 816	9.851 128	21.22361	45.72489
957	915 849	30.93542	97.82638	876 467 493	9.854 562	21.23101	45.74082
958	917 764	30.95158	97.87747	879 217 912	9.857 993	21.23840	45.75675
959	919 681	30.96773	97.92855	881 974 079	9.861 422	21.24579	45.77267
960	921 600	30.98387	97.97959	884 736 000	9.864 848	21.25317	45.78857
961	923 521	31.00000	98.03061	887 503 681	9.868 272	21.26055	45.80446
962	925 444	31.01612	98.08160	890 277 128	9.871 694	21.26792	45.82035
963	927 369	31.03224	98.13256	893 056 347	9.875 113	21.27529	45.83622
964	929 296	31.04835	98.18350	895 841 344	9.878 530	21.28265	45.85208
965	931 225	31.06445	98.23441	898 632 125	9.881 945	21.29001	45.86793
966	933 156	31.08054	98.28530	901 428 696	9.885 357	21.29736	45.88376
967	935 089	31.09662	98.33616	904 231 063	9.888 767	21.30470	45.89959
968	937 024	31.11270	98.38699	907 039 232	9.892 175	21.31204	45.91541
969	938 961	31.12876	98.43780	909 853 209	9.895 580	21.31938	45.93121
970	940 900	31.14482	98.48858	912 673 000	9.898 983	21.32671	45.94701
971	942 841	31.16087	98.53933	915 498 611	9.902 384	21.33404	45.96279
972	944 784	31.17691	98.59006	918 330 048	9.905 782	21.34136	45.97857
973	946 729	31.19295	98.64076	921 167 317	9.909 178	21.34868	45.99433
974	948 676	31.20897	98.69144	924 010 424	9.912 571	21.35599	46.01008
975	950 625	31.22499	98.74209	926 859 375	9.915 962	21.36329	46.02582
976	952 576	31.24100	98.79271	929 714 176	9.919 351	21.37059	46.04155
977	954 529	31.25700	98.84331	932 574 833	9.922 738	21.37789	46.05727
978	956 484	31.27299	98.89388	935 441 352	9.926 122	21.38518	46.07298
979	958 441	31.28898	98.94443	938 313 739	9.929 504	21.39247	46.08868
980	960 400	31.30495	98.99495	941 192 000	9.932 884	21.39975	46.10436
981	962 361	31.32092	99.04544	944 076 141	9.936 261	21.40703	46.12004
982	964 324	31.33688	99.09591	946 966 168	9.939 636	21.41430	46.13571
983	966 289	31.35283	99.14636	949 862 087	9.943 009	21.42156	46.15136
984	968 256	31.36877	99.19677	952 763 904	9.946 380	21.42883	46.16700
985	970 225	31.38471	99.24717	955 671 625	9.949 748	21.43608	46.18264
986	972 196	31.40064	99.29753	958 585 256	9.953 114	21.44333	46.19826
987	974 169	31.41656	99.34787	961 504 803	9.956 478	21.45058	46.21387
988	976 144	31.43247	99.39819	964 430 272	9.959 839	21.45782	46.22948
989	978 121	31.44837	99.44848	967 361 669	9.963 198	21.46506	46.24507
990	980 100	31.46427	99.49874	970 299 000	9.966 555	21.47229	46.26065
991	982 081	31.48015	99.54898	973 242 271	9.969 910	21.47952	46.27622
992	984 064	31.49603	99.59920	976 191 488	9.973 262	21.48674	46.29178
993	986 049	31.51190	99.64939	979 146 657	9.976 612	21.49396	46.30733
994	988 036	31.52777	99.69955	982 107 784	9.979 960	21.50117	46.32287
995	990 025	31.54362	99.74969	985 074 875	9.983 305	21.50838	46.33840
996	992 016	31.55947	99.79980	988 047 936	9.986 649	21.51558	46.35392
997	994 009	31.57531	99.84989	991 026 973	9.989 990	21.52278	46.36943
998	996 004	31.59114	99.89995	994 011 992	9.993 329	21.52997	46.38492
999	998 001	31.60696	99.94999	997 002 999	9.996 666	21.53716	46.40041
1000	1 000 000	31.62278	100.00000	1 000 000 000	10.000 000	21.54435	46.41589

POWERS OF NUMBERS

n	n^4	n^5	n^6	n^7	n^8
1	1	1	1	1	1
2	16	32	64	128	256
3	81	243	729	2187	6561
4	256	1024	4096	16384	65536
5	625	3125	15625	78125	390625
6	1296	7776	46656	279936	1679616
7	2401	16807	117649	823543	5764801
8	4096	32768	262144	2097152	16777216
9	6561	59049	531441	4782969	43046721
					$\times 10^8$
10	10000	100000	1000000	10000000	1.000000
11	14641	161051	1771561	19487171	2.143589
12	20736	248832	2985984	35831808	4.299817
13	28561	371293	4826809	62748517	8.157307
14	38416	537824	7529536	105413504	14.757891
15	50625	759375	11390625	170859375	25.628906
16	65536	1048576	16777216	268435456	42.949673
17	83521	1419857	24137569	410338673	69.757574
18	104976	1889568	34012224	612220032	110.199606
19	130321	2476099	47045881	893871739	169.835630
				$\times 10^9$	$\times 10^{10}$
20	160000	3200000	64000000	1.280000	2.560000
21	194481	4084101	85766121	1.801089	3.782286
22	234256	5153632	113379904	2.494358	5.487587
23	279841	6436343	148035889	3.404825	7.831099
24	331776	7962624	191102976	4.586471	11.007531
25	390625	9765625	244140625	6.103516	15.258789
26	456976	11881376	308915776	8.031810	20.882706
27	531441	14348907	387420489	10.460353	28.242954
28	614656	17210368	481890304	13.492929	37.780200
29	707281	20511149	594823321	17.249876	50.024641
			$\times 10^8$	$\times 10^{10}$	$\times 10^{11}$
30	810000	24300000	7.290000	2.187000	6.561000
31	923521	28629151	8.875037	2.751261	8.528910
32	1048576	33554432	10.737418	3.435974	10.995116
33	1185921	39135393	12.914680	4.261844	14.064086
34	1336336	45435424	15.448044	5.252335	17.857939
35	1500625	52521875	18.382656	6.433930	22.518754
36	1679616	60466176	21.767823	7.836416	28.211099
37	1874161	69343957	25.657264	9.493188	35.124795
38	2085136	79235168	30.109364	11.441558	43.477921
39	2313441	90224199	35.187438	13.723101	53.520093
			$\times 10^9$	$\times 10^{10}$	$\times 10^{12}$
40	2560000	102400000	4.096000	16.384000	6.553600
41	2825761	115856201	4.750104	19.475427	7.984925
42	3111696	130691232	5.489032	23.053933	9.682652
43	3418801	147008443	6.321363	27.181861	11.688200
44	3748096	164916224	7.256314	31.927781	14.048224
45	4100625	184528125	8.303766	37.366945	16.815125
46	4477456	205962976	9.474297	43.581766	20.047612
47	4879681	229345007	10.779215	50.662312	23.811287
48	5308416	254803968	12.230590	58.706834	28.179280
49	5764801	282475249	13.841287	67.822307	33.232931
50	6250000	312500000	15.625000	78.125000	39.062500

POWERS OF NUMBERS (Continued)

n	n^4	n^5	n^6	n^7	n^8
			$\times 10^9$	$\times 10^{11}$	$\times 10^{13}$
50	6250000	312500000	15.625000	7.812500	3.906250
51	6765201	345025251	17.596288	8.974107	4.576794
52	7311616	380204032	19.770610	10.280717	5.345973
53	7890481	418195493	22.164361	11.747111	6.225969
54	8503056	459165024	24.794911	13.389252	7.230196
55	9150625	503284375	27.680641	15.224352	8.373394
56	9834496	550731776	30.840979	17.270948	9.671731
57	10556001	601692057	34.296447	19.548975	11.142916
58	11316496	656356768	38.068693	22.079842	12.806308
59	12117361	714924299	42.180534	24.886515	14.683044
		$\times 10^8$	$\times 10^{10}$	$\times 10^{11}$	$\times 10^{13}$
60	12960000	7.776000	4.665600	27.993600	16.796160
61	13845841	8.445963	5.152037	31.427428	19.170731
62	14776336	9.161328	5.680024	35.216146	21.834011
63	15752961	9.924365	6.252350	39.389806	24.815578
64	16777216	10.737418	6.871948	43.980465	28.147498
65	17850625	11.602906	7.541889	49.022279	31.864481
66	18974736	12.523326	8.265395	54.551607	36.004061
67	20151121	13.501251	9.045838	60.607116	40.606768
68	21381376	14.539336	9.886748	67.229888	45.716324
69	22667121	15.640313	10.791816	74.463533	51.379837
		$\times 10^8$	$\times 10^{10}$	$\times 10^{12}$	$\times 10^{14}$
70	24010000	16.807000	11.764900	8.235430	5.764801
71	25411681	18.042294	12.810028	9.095120	6.457535
72	26873856	19.349176	13.931407	10.030613	7.222041
73	28398241	20.730716	15.133423	11.047399	8.064601
74	29986576	22.190066	16.420649	12.151280	8.991947
75	31640625	23.730469	17.797852	13.348389	10.011292
76	33362176	25.355254	19.269993	14.645195	11.130348
77	35153041	27.067842	20.842238	16.048523	12.357363
78	37015056	28.871744	22.519960	17.565569	13.701144
79	38950081	30.770564	24.308746	19.203909	15.171088
		$\times 10^8$	$\times 10^{10}$	$\times 10^{12}$	$\times 10^{14}$
80	40960000	32.768000	26.214400	20.971520	16.777216
81	43046721	34.867844	28.242954	22.876792	18.530202
82	45212176	37.073984	30.400667	24.928547	20.441409
83	47458321	39.390406	32.694037	27.136051	22.522922
84	49787136	41.821194	35.129803	29.509035	24.787589
85	52200625	44.370531	37.714952	32.057709	27.249053
86	54700816	47.042702	40.456724	34.792782	29.921793
87	57289761	49.842092	43.362620	37.725479	32.821167
88	59969536	52.773192	46.440409	40.867560	35.963452
89	62742241	55.840594	49.698129	44.231335	39.365888
		$\times 10^9$	$\times 10^{11}$	$\times 10^{13}$	$\times 10^{15}$
90	65610000	5.904900	5.314410	4.782969	4.304672
91	68574961	6.240321	5.678693	5.167610	4.702525
92	71639296	6.590815	6.063550	5.578466	5.132189
93	74805201	6.956884	6.469902	6.017009	5.595818
94	78074896	7.339040	6.898698	6.484776	6.095689
95	81450625	7.737809	7.350919	6.983373	6.634204
96	84934656	8.153727	7.827578	7.514475	7.213896
97	88529281	8.587340	8.329720	8.079828	7.837434
98	92236816	9.039208	8.858424	8.681255	8.507630
99	96059601	9.509900	9.414801	9.320653	9.227447
100	100000000	10.000000	10.000000	10.000000	10.000000

POWERS OF TWO

n	2^n	n	2^n
1	2	41	21990 23255 552
2	4	42	43980 46511 104
3	8	43	87960 93022 208
4	16	44	17592 18604 4416
5	32	45	35184 37208 8832
6	64	46	70368 74417 7664
7	128	47	14073 74883 55328
8	256	48	28147 49767 10656
9	512	49	56294 99534 21312
10	1024	50	11258 99906 84262 4
11	2048	51	22517 99813 68524 8
12	4096	52	45035 99627 37049 6
13	8192	53	90071 99254 74099 2
14	16384	54	18014 39850 94819 84
15	32768	55	36028 79701 89639 68
16	65536	56	72057 59403 79279 36
17	13107 2	57	14411 51880 75855 872
18	26214 4	58	28823 03761 51711 744
19	52428 8	59	57646 07523 03423 488
20	10485 76	60	11529 21504 60684 6976
21	20971 52	61	23058 43009 21369 3952
22	41943 04	62	46116 86018 42738 7904
23	83886 08	63	92233 72036 85477 5808
24	16777 216	64	18446 74407 37095 51616
25	33554 432	65	36893 48814 74191 03232
26	67108 864	66	73786 97629 48382 06464
27	13421 7728	67	14757 39525 89676 41292 8
28	26843 5456	68	29514 79051 79352 82585 6
29	53687 0912	69	59029 58103 58705 65171 2
30	10737 41824	70	11805 91620 71741 13034 24
31	21474 83648	71	23611 83241 43482 26068 48
32	42949 67296	72	47223 66482 86964 52136 96
33	85899 34592	73	94447 32965 73929 04273 92
34	17179 86918 4	74	18889 46593 14785 80854 784
35	34359 73836 8	75	37778 93186 29571 61709 568
36	68719 47673 6	76	75557 86372 59143 23419 136
37	13743 89534 72	77	15111 57274 51828 64683 8272
38	27487 79069 44	78	30223 14549 03657 29367 6544
39	54975 58138 88	79	60446 29098 07314 58735 3088
40	10995 11627 776	80	12089 25819 61462 91747 06176

n	2^n
81	24178 51639 22925 83494 12352
82	48357 03278 45851 66988 24704
83	96714 06556 91703 33976 49408
84	19342 81311 38340 66795 29881 6
85	38685 62622 76681 33590 59763 2
86	77371 25245 53362 67181 19526 4
87	15474 25049 10672 53436 23905 28
88	30948 50098 21345 06872 47810 56
89	61897 00196 42690 13744 95621 12
90	12379 40039 28538 02748 99124 224
91	24758 80078 57076 05497 98248 448
92	49517 60157 14152 10995 96496 896
93	99035 20314 28304 21991 92993 792
94	19807 04062 85660 84398 38598 7584
95	39614 08125 71321 68796 77197 5168
96	79228 16251 42643 37593 54395 0336
97	15845 63250 28528 67518 70879 00672
98	31691 26500 57057 35037 41758 01344
99	63382 53001 14114 70074 83516 02688
100	12676 50600 22822 94014 96703 20537 6
101	25353 01200 45645 88029 93406 41075 2

FACTORIALS AND THEIR LOGARITHMS

n	$n!$	$\log n!$	n	$n!$	$\log n!$
			50	3.0414×10^{64}	64.48307
1	1.0000	0.00000	51	1.5511×10^{66}	66.19065
2	2.0000	0.30103	52	8.0658×10^{67}	67.90665
3	6.0000	0.77815	53	4.2749×10^{69}	69.63092
4	2.4000×10	1.38021	54	2.3084×10^{71}	71.36332
5	1.2000×10^{2}	2.07918	**55**	1.2696×10^{73}	73.10368
6	7.2000×10^{2}	2.85733	56	7.1100×10^{74}	74.85187
7	5.0400×10^{3}	3.70243	57	4.0527×10^{76}	76.60774
8	4.0320×10^{4}	4.60552	58	2.3506×10^{78}	78.37117
9	3.6288×10^{5}	5.55976	59	1.3868×10^{80}	80.14202
10	3.6288×10^{6}	6.55976	**60**	8.3210×10^{81}	81.92017
11	3.9917×10^{7}	7.60116	61	5.0758×10^{83}	83.70550
12	4.7900×10^{8}	8.68034	62	3.1470×10^{85}	85.49790
13	6.2270×10^{9}	9.79428	63	1.9826×10^{87}	87.29724
14	8.7178×10^{10}	10.94041	64	1.2689×10^{89}	89.10342
15	1.3077×10^{12}	12.11650	**65**	8.2477×10^{90}	90.91633
16	2.0923×10^{13}	13.32062	66	5.4435×10^{92}	92.73587
17	3.5569×10^{14}	14.55107	67	3.6471×10^{94}	94.56195
18	6.4024×10^{15}	15.80634	68	2.4800×10^{96}	96.39446
19	1.2165×10^{17}	17.08509	69	1.7112×10^{98}	98.23331
20	2.4329×10^{18}	18.38612	**70**	1.1979×10^{100}	100.07841
21	5.1091×10^{19}	19.70834	71	8.5048×10^{101}	101.92966
22	1.1240×10^{21}	21.05077	72	6.1234×10^{103}	103.78700
23	2.5852×10^{22}	22.41249	73	4.4701×10^{105}	105.65032
24	6.2045×10^{23}	23.79271	74	3.3079×10^{107}	107.51955
25	1.5511×10^{25}	25.19065	**75**	2.4809×10^{109}	109.39461
26	4.0329×10^{26}	26.60562	76	1.8855×10^{111}	111.27543
27	1.0889×10^{28}	28.03698	77	1.4518×10^{113}	113.16192
28	3.0489×10^{29}	29.48414	78	1.1324×10^{115}	115.05401
29	8.8418×10^{30}	30.94654	79	8.9462×10^{116}	116.95164
30	2.6525×10^{32}	32.42366	**80**	7.1569×10^{118}	118.85473
31	8.2228×10^{33}	33.91502	81	5.7971×10^{120}	120.76321
32	2.6313×10^{35}	35.42017	82	4.7536×10^{122}	122.67703
33	8.6833×10^{36}	36.93869	83	3.9455×10^{124}	124.59610
34	2.9523×10^{38}	38.47016	84	3.3142×10^{126}	126.52038
35	1.0333×10^{40}	40.01423	**85**	2.8171×10^{128}	128.44980
36	3.7199×10^{41}	41.57054	86	2.4227×10^{130}	130.38430
37	1.3764×10^{43}	43.13874	87	2.1078×10^{132}	132.32382
38	5.2302×10^{44}	44.71852	88	1.8548×10^{134}	134.26830
39	2.0398×10^{46}	46.30959	89	1.6508×10^{136}	136.21769
40	8.1592×10^{47}	47.91165	**90**	1.4857×10^{138}	138.17194
41	3.3453×10^{49}	49.52443	91	1.3520×10^{140}	140.13098
42	1.4050×10^{51}	51.14768	92	1.2438×10^{142}	142.09477
43	6.0415×10^{52}	52.78115	93	1.1568×10^{144}	144.06325
44	2.6583×10^{54}	54.42460	94	1.0874×10^{146}	146.03638
45	1.1962×10^{56}	56.07781	**95**	1.0330×10^{148}	148.01410
46	5.5026×10^{57}	57.74057	96	9.9168×10^{149}	149.99637
47	2.5862×10^{59}	59.41267	97	9.6193×10^{151}	151.98314
48	1.2414×10^{61}	61.09391	98	9.4269×10^{153}	153.97437
49	6.0828×10^{62}	62.78410	99	9.3326×10^{155}	155.97000
50	3.0414×10^{64}	64.48307	**100**	9.3326×10^{157}	157.97000

FACTORS FOR COMPUTING PROBABLE ERRORS

n	$\frac{1}{\sqrt{n}}$	$\frac{1}{\sqrt{n(n-1)}}$	$\frac{.6745}{\sqrt{n-1}}$	$\frac{.6745}{\sqrt{n(n-1)}}$	$\frac{.8453}{n\sqrt{n-1}}$	$\frac{.8453}{\sqrt{n(n-1)}}$
2	.707107	.707107	.6745	.4769	.4227	.5978
3	.577350	.408248	.4769	.2754	.1993	.3451
4	.500000	.288675	.3894	.1947	.1220	.2440
5	.447214	.223607	.3372	.1508	.0845	.1890
6	.408248	.182574	.3016	.1231	.0630	.1543
7	.377964	.154303	.2754	.1041	.0493	.1304
8	.353553	.133631	.2549	.0901	.0399	.1130
9	.333333	.117851	.2385	.0795	.0332	.0996
10	.316228	.105409	.2248	.0711	.0282	.0891
11	.301511	.095346	.2133	.0643	.0243	.0806
12	.288675	.087039	.2034	.0587	.0212	.0736
13	.277350	.080064	.1947	.0540	.0188	.0677
14	.267261	.074125	.1871	.0500	.0167	.0627
15	.258199	.069007	.1803	.0465	.0151	.0583
16	.250000	.064550	.1742	.0435	.0136	.0546
17	.242536	.060634	.1686	.0409	.0124	.0513
18	.235702	.057166	.1636	.0386	.0114	.0483
19	.229416	.054074	.1590	.0365	.0105	.0457
20	.223607	.051299	.1547	.0346	.0097	.0434
21	.218218	.048795	.1508	.0329	.0090	.0412
22	.213201	.046524	.1472	.0314	.0084	.0393
23	.208514	.044455	.1438	.0300	.0078	.0376
24	.204124	.042563	.1406	.0287	.0073	.0360
25	.200000	.040825	.1377	.0275	.0069	.0345
26	.196116	.039223	.1349	.0265	.0065	.0332
27	.192450	.037743	.1323	.0255	.0061	.0319
28	.188982	.036370	.1298	.0245	.0058	.0307
29	.185695	.035093	.1275	.0237	.0055	.0297
30	.182574	.033903	.1252	.0229	.0052	.0287
31	.179605	.032791	.1231	.0221	.0050	.0277
32	.176777	.031750	.1211	.0214	.0047	.0268
33	.174078	.030773	.1192	.0208	.0045	.0260
34	.171499	.029854	.1174	.0201	.0043	.0252
35	.169031	.028989	.1157	.0196	.0041	.0245
36	.166667	.028172	.1140	.0190	.0040	.0238
37	.164399	.027400	.1124	.0185	.0038	.0232
38	.162221	.026669	.1109	.0180	.0037	.0225
39	.160128	.025976	.1094	.0175	.0035	.0220
40	.158114	.025318	.1080	.0171	.0034	.0214
41	.156174	.024693	.1066	.0167	.0033	.0209
42	.154303	.024098	.1053	.0163	.0031	.0204
43	.152499	.023531	.1041	.0159	.0030	.0199
44	.150756	.022990	.1029	.0155	.0029	.0194
45	.149071	.022473	.1017	.0152	.0028	.0190
46	.147442	.021979	.1005	.0148	.0027	.0186
47	.145865	.021507	.0994	.0145	.0027	.0182
48	.144338	.021054	.0984	.0142	.0026	.0178
49	.142857	.020620	.0974	.0139	.0025	.0174
50	.141421	.020203	.0964	.0136	.0024	.0171

FACTORS FOR COMPUTING PROBABLE ERRORS
(Continued)

n	$\frac{1}{\sqrt{n}}$	$\frac{1}{\sqrt{n(n-1)}}$	$\frac{.6745}{\sqrt{n-1}}$	$\frac{.6745}{\sqrt{n(n-1)}}$	$\frac{.8453}{n\sqrt{n-1}}$	$\frac{.8453}{\sqrt{n(n-1)}}$
50	.141421	.020203	.0964	.0136	.0024	.0171
51	.140028	.019803	.0954	.0134	.0023	.0167
52	.138675	.019418	.0945	.0131	.0023	.0164
53	.137361	.019048	.0935	.0129	.0022	.0161
54	.136083	.018692	.0927	.0126	.0022	.0158
55	.134840	.018349	.0918	.0124	.0021	.0155
56	.133631	.018019	.0910	.0122	.0020	.0152
57	.132453	.017700	.0901	.0119	.0020	.0150
58	.131306	.017392	.0893	.0117	.0019	.0147
59	.130189	.017095	.0886	.0115	.0019	.0145
60	.129099	.016807	.0878	.0113	.0018	.0142
61	.128037	.016529	.0871	.0112	.0018	.0140
62	.127000	.016261	.0864	.0110	.0018	.0138
63	.125988	.016001	.0857	.0108	.0017	.0135
64	.125000	.015749	.0850	.0106	.0017	.0133
65	.124035	.015504	.0843	.0105	.0016	.0131
66	.123091	.015268	.0837	.0103	.0016	.0129
67	.122169	.015038	.0830	.0101	.0016	.0127
68	.121268	.014815	.0824	.0100	.0015	.0125
69	.120386	.014599	.0818	.0099	.0015	.0123
70	.119523	.014389	.0812	.0097	.0015	.0122
71	.118678	.014185	.0806	.0096	.0014	.0120
72	.117851	.013986	.0801	.0094	.0014	.0118
73	.117041	.013793	.0795	.0093	.0014	.0117
74	.116248	.013606	.0789	.0092	.0013	.0115
75	.115470	.013423	.0784	.0091	.0013	.0113
76	.114708	.013245	.0779	.0089	.0013	.0112
77	.113961	.013072	.0773	.0088	.0013	.0111
78	.113228	.012904	.0769	.0087	.0012	.0109
79	.112509	.012739	.0764	.0086	.0012	.0108
80	.111803	.012579	.0759	.0085	.0012	.0106
81	.111111	.012423	.0754	.0084	.0012	.0105
82	.110432	.012270	.0749	.0083	.0012	.0104
83	.109764	.012121	.0745	.0082	.0011	.0103
84	.109109	.011976	.0740	.0081	.0011	.0101
85	.108465	.011835	.0736	.0080	.0011	.0100
86	.107833	.011696	.0732	.0079	.0011	.0099
87	.107211	.011561	.0727	.0078	.0011	.0098
88	.106600	.011429	.0723	.0077	.0010	.0097
89	.106000	.011300	.0719	.0076	.0010	.0096
90	.105409	.011173	.0715	.0075	.0010	.0094
91	.104828	.011050	.0711	.0075	.0010	.0093
92	.104257	.010929	.0707	.0074	.0010	.0092
93	.103695	.010811	.0703	.0073	.0010	.0091
94	.103142	.010695	.0699	.0072	.0009	.0090
95	.102598	.010582	.0696	.0071	.0009	.0089
96	.102062	.010471	.0692	.0071	.0009	.0089
97	.101535	.010363	.0688	.0070	.0009	.0088
98	.101015	.010257	.0685	.0069	.0009	.0087
99	.100504	.010152	.0681	.0069	.0009	.0086
100	.100000	.010050	.0678	.0068	.0008	.0085

PROBABILITY OF OCCURRENCE OF DEVIATIONS

Valid for thirty or more samples.

Probability of occurrence, expressed as per cent, and odds against a deviation as great or greater than that designated is given for various ratios of the deviation to the probable error and to the standard deviation.

(From Pearl, Medical Biometry and Statistics, W. B. Saunders Company, publishers, by permission.)

Ratio dev. to P.E.	Probable occurrence %	Odds against, to 1	Ratio dev. to std. dev.	Probable occurrence %	Odds against, to 1
1.0	50.00	1.00	0.67449	50.00	1.00
1.1	45.81	1.18	0.7	48.39	1.07
1.2	41.83	1.39	0.8	42.37	1.36
1.3	38.06	1.63	0.9	36.81	1.72
1.4	34.50	1.90	1.0	31.73	2.15
1.5	31.17	2.21	1.1	27.13	2.69
1.6	28.05	2.57	1.2	23.01	3.35
1.7	25.15	2.98	1.3	19.36	4.17
1.8	22.47	3.45	1.4	16.15	5.19
1.9	20.00	4.00	1.5	13.36	6.48
2.0	17.73	4.64	1.6	10.96	8.12
2.1	15.67	5.38	1.7	8.91	10.22
2.2	13.78	6.25	1.8	7.19	12.92
2.3	12.08	7.28	1.9	5.74	16.41
2.4	10.55	8.48	2.0	4.55	20.98
2.5	9.18	9.90	2.1	3.57	26.99
2.6	7.95	11.58	2.2	2.78	34.96
2.7	6.86	13.58	2.3	2.14	45.62
2.8	5.89	15.96	2.4	1.64	59.99
2.9	5.05	18.82	2.5	1.24	79.52
3.0	4.30	22.24	2.6	.932	106.3
3.1	3.65	26.37	2.7	.693	143.2
3.2	3.09	31.36	2.8	.511	194.7
3.3	2.60	37.42	2.9	373	267.0
3.4	2.18	44.80	3.0	.270	369.4
3.5	1.82	53.82	3.1	.194	515.7
3.6	1.52	64.89	3.2	.137	726.7
3.7	1.26	78.53	3.3	.0967	1,033.
3.8	1.04	95.38	3.4	.0674	1,483.
3.9	.853	116.3	3.5	.0465	2,149.
4.0	.698	142.3	3.6	.0318	3,142.
4.1	.569	174.9	3.7	.0216	4,637.
4.2	.461	215.8	3.8	.0145	6,915.
4.3	.373	267.2	3.9	.00962	10,394.
4.4	.300	332.4	4.0	.00634	15,772.
4.5	.240	415.0	5.0	5.73×10^{-5}	1.744×10^{6}
4.6	.192	520.4	6.0	2.0×10^{-7}	5.0×10^{8}
4.7	.152	655.3	7.0	2.6×10^{-10}	3.9×10^{11}
4.8	.121	828.3			
4.9	.0950	1,052.			
5.0	.0745	1,341.			
6.0	.0052	19,300.			
7.0	.00023	4.27×10^{5}			
8.0	6.8×10^{-6}	1.47×10^{7}			
9.0	1.3×10^{-7}	7.30×10^{8}			
10.0	1.5×10^{-9}	6.5×10^{10}			

AREAS, ORDINATES AND DERIVATIVES OF THE NORMAL CURVE OF ERROR

The following table gives values of the area under the curve from the ordinate at $t = 0$ to the ordinate for the values of t given in the column at the left. Values of the ordinate and of the second, third and fourth derivatives are also given.

t	Area	Ordinate	Second derivative	Third derivative	Fourth derivative	t	Area	Ordinate	Second derivative	Third derivative	Fourth derivative
.00	.0000	.3989	−.3989	.0000	1.1968	**.50**	.1915	.3521	−.2641	.4841	.5501
.01	.0040	.3989	−.3989	.0120	1.1965	.51	.1950	.3503	−.2592	.4895	.5279
.02	.0080	.3989	−.3987	.0239	1.1956	.52	.1985	.3485	−.2543	.4947	.5056
.03	.0120	.3988	−.3984	.0359	1.1941	.53	.2019	.3467	−.2493	.4996	.4831
.04	.0160	.3986	−.3980	.0478	1.1920	.54	.2054	.3448	−.2443	.5043	.4605
.05	.0199	.3984	−.3975	.0597	1.1894	**.55**	.2088	.3429	−.2392	.5088	.4378
.06	.0239	.3982	−.3968	.0716	1.1861	.56	.2123	.3411	−.2341	.5131	.4150
.07	.0279	.3980	−.3960	.0834	1.1822	.57	.2157	.3391	−.2289	.5171	.3921
.08	.0319	.3977	−.3951	.0952	1.1778	.58	.2190	.3372	−.2238	.5209	.3691
.09	.0359	.3973	−.3941	.1070	1.1727	.59	.2224	.3352	−.2185	.5245	.3461
.10	.0398	.3970	−.3930	.1187	1.1671	**.60**	.2258	.3332	−.2133	.5278	.3231
.11	.0438	.3965	−.3917	.1303	1.1609	.61	.2291	.3312	−.2080	.5309	.3000
.12	.0478	.3961	−.3904	.1419	1.1541	.62	.2324	.3292	−.2027	.5338	.2770
.13	.0517	.3956	−.3889	.1534	1.1468	.63	.2357	.3271	−.1973	.5365	.2539
.14	.0557	.3951	−.3873	.1648	1.1389	.64	.2389	.3251	−.1919	.5389	.2309
.15	.0596	.3945	−.3856	.1762	1.1304	**.65**	.2422	.3230	−.1865	.5411	.2078
.16	.0636	.3939	−.3838	.1874	1.1214	.66	.2454	.3209	−.1811	.5431	.1849
.17	.0675	.3932	−.3819	.1986	1.1118	.67	.2486	.3187	−.1757	.5448	.1620
.18	.0714	.3925	−.3798	.2097	1.1017	.68	.2518	.3166	−.1702	.5463	.1391
.19	.0754	.3918	−.3777	.2206	1.0911	.69	.2549	.3144	−.1647	.5476	.1164
.20	.0793	.3910	−.3754	.2315	1.0799	**.70**	.2580	.3123	−.1593	.5486	.0937
.21	.0832	.3902	−.3730	.2422	1.0682	.71	.2612	.3101	−.1538	.5495	.0712
.22	.0871	.3894	−.3706	.2529	1.0560	.72	.2642	.3079	−.1483	.5501	.0487
.23	.0910	.3885	−.3680	.2634	1.0434	.73	.2673	.3056	−.1428	.5504	.0265
.24	.0948	.3876	−.3653	.2737	1.0302	.74	.2704	.3034	−.1373	.5506	.0043
.25	.0987	.3867	−.3625	.2840	1.0165	**.75**	.2734	.3011	−.1318	.5505	−.0176
.26	.1026	.3857	−.3596	.2941	1.0024	.76	.2764	.2989	−.1262	.5502	−.0394
.27	.1064	.3847	−.3566	.3040	0.9878	.77	.2794	.2966	−.1207	.5497	−.0611
.28	.1103	.3836	−.3535	.3138	0.9727	.78	.2823	.2943	−.1153	.5490	−.0825
.29	.1141	.3825	−.3504	.3235	0.9572	.79	.2852	.2920	−.1098	.5481	−.1037
.30	.1179	.3814	−.3471	.3330	0.9413	**.80**	.2881	.2897	−.1043	.5469	−.1247
.31	.1217	.3802	−.3437	.3423	0.9250	.81	.2910	.2874	−.0988	.5456	−.1455
.32	.1255	.3790	−.3402	.3515	0.9082	.82	.2939	.2850	−.0934	.5440	−.1660
.33	.1293	.3778	−.3367	.3605	0.8910	.83	.2967	.2827	−.0880	.5423	−.1862
.34	.1331	.3765	−.3330	.3693	0.8735	.84	.2996	.2803	−.0825	.5403	−.2063
.35	.1368	.3752	−.3293	.3779	0.8556	**.85**	.3023	.2780	−.0771	.5381	−.2260
.36	.1406	.3739	−.3255	.3864	0.8373	.86	.3051	.2756	−.0718	.5358	−.2455
.37	.1443	.3726	−.3216	.3947	0.8186	.87	.3079	.2732	−.0664	.5332	−.2646
.38	.1480	.3712	−.3176	.4028	0.7996	.88	.3106	.2709	−.0611	.5305	−.2835
.39	.1517	.3697	−.3135	.4107	0.7803	.89	.3133	.2685	−.0558	.5276	−.3021
.40	.1554	.3683	−.3094	.4184	0.7607	**.90**	.3159	.2661	−.0506	.5245	−.3203
.41	.1591	.3668	−.3051	.4259	0.7408	.91	.3186	.2637	−.0453	.5212	−.3383
42	.1628	.3653	−.3008	.4332	0.7206	.92	.3212	.2613	−.0401	.5177	−.3559
.43	.1664	.3637	−.2965	.4403	0.7001	.93	.3238	.2589	−.0350	.5140	−.3731
.44	.1700	.3621	−.2920	.4472	0.6793	.94	.3264	.2565	−.0299	.5102	−.3901
.45	1736	.3605	−.2875	.4539	0.6583	**.95**	.3289	.2541	−.0248	.5062	−.4066
.46	.1772	.3589	−.2830	.4603	0.6371	.96	.3315	.2516	−.0197	.5021	−.4228
.47	.1808	.3572	−.2783	.4666	0.6156	.97	.3340	.2492	−.0147	.4978	−.4387
.48	.1844	.3555	−.2736	.4727	0.5940	.98	.3365	.2468	−.0098	.4933	−.4541
.49	.1879	.3538	−.2689	.4785	0.5721	.99	.3389	.2444	−.0049	.4887	−.4692
.50	.1915	.3521	−.2641	.4841	0.5501	**1.00**	.3413	.2420	.0000	.4839	−.4839

AREAS ORDINATES AND DERIVATIVES OF THE NORMAL CURVE OF ERROR (Continued)

t	Area	Ordinate	Second derivative	Third derivative	Fourth derivative	t	Area	Ordinate	Second derivative	Third derivative	Fourth derivative
1.00	.3413	.2420	.0000	.4839	−.4839	**1.50**	.4332	.1295	.1619	.1457	−.7043
1.01	.3438	.2396	.0048	.4790	−.4983	1.51	.4345	.1276	.1633	.1387	−.6994
1.02	.3461	.2371	.0096	.4740	−.5122	1.52	.4357	.1257	.1647	.1317	−.6942
1.03	.3485	.2347	.0143	.4688	−.5257	1.53	.4370	.1238	.1660	.1248	−.6888
1.04	.3508	.2323	.0190	.4635	−.5389	1.54	.4382	.1219	.1672	.1180	−.6831
1.05	.3531	.2299	.0236	.4580	−.5516	**1.55**	.4394	.1200	.1683	.1111	−.6772
1.06	.3554	.2275	.0281	.4524	−.5639	1.56	.4406	.1182	.1694	.1044	−.6710
1.07	.3577	.2251	.0326	.4467	−.5758	1.57	.4418	.1163	.1704	.0977	−.6646
1.08	.3599	.2227	.0371	.4409	−.5873	1.58	.4430	.1145	.1714	.0911	−.6580
1.09	.3621	.2203	.0414	.4350	−.5984	1.59	.4441	.1127	.1722	.0846	−.6511
1.10	.3643	.2179	.0458	.4290	−.6091	**1.60**	.4452	.1109	.1730	.0781	−.6441
1.11	.3665	.2155	.0500	.4228	−.6193	1.61	.4463	.1092	.1738	.0717	−.6368
1.12	.3686	.2131	.0542	.4166	−.6292	1.62	.4474	.1074	.1745	.0654	−.6293
1.13	.3708	.2107	.0583	.4102	−.6386	1.63	.4485	.1057	.1751	.0591	−.6216
1.14	.3729	.2083	.0624	.4038	−.6476	1.64	.4495	.1040	.1757	.0529	−.6138
1.15	.3749	.2059	.0664	.3973	−.6561	**1.65**	.4505	.1023	.1762	.0468	−.6057
1.16	.3770	.2036	.0704	.3907	−.6643	1.66	.4515	.1006	.1766	.0408	−.5975
1.17	.3790	.2012	.0742	.3840	−.6720	1.67	.4525	.0989	.1770	.0349	−.5891
1.18	.3810	.1989	.0780	.3772	−.6792	1.68	.4535	.0973	.1773	.0290	−.5806
1.19	.3830	.1965	.0818	.3704	−.6861	1.69	.4545	.0957	.1776	.0233	−.5720
1.20	.3849	.1942	.0854	.3635	−.6926	**1.70**	.4554	.0941	.1778	.0176	−.5632
1.21	.3869	.1919	.0890	.3566	−.6986	1.71	.4564	.0925	.1779	.0120	−.5542
1.22	.3888	.1895	.0926	.3496	−.7042	1.72	.4573	.0909	.1780	.0065	−.5452
1.23	.3907	.1872	.0960	.3425	−.7094	1.73	.4582	.0893	.1780	.0011	−.5360
1.24	.3925	.1849	.0994	.3354	−.7141	1.74	.4591	.0878	.1780	−.0042	−.5267
1.25	.3944	.1827	.1027	.3282	−.7185	**1.75**	.4599	.0863	.1780	−.0094	−.5173
1.26	.3962	.1804	.1060	.3210	−.7224	1.76	.4608	.0848	.1778	−.0146	−.5079
1.27	.3980	.1781	.1092	.3138	−.7259	1.77	.4616	.0833	.1777	−.0196	−.4983
1.28	.3997	.1759	.1123	.3065	−.7291	1.78	.4625	.0818	.1774	−.0245	−.4887
1.29	.4015	.1736	.1153	.2992	−.7318	1.79	.4633	.0804	.1772	−.0294	−.4789
1.30	.4032	.1714	.1182	.2918	−.7341	**1.80**	.4641	.0790	.1769	−.0341	−.4692
1.31	.4049	.1692	.1211	.2845	−.7361	1.81	.4649	.0775	.1765	−.0388	−.4593
1.32	.4066	.1669	.1239	.2771	−.7376	1.82	.4656	.0761	.1761	−.0433	−.4494
1.33	.4082	.1647	.1267	.2697	−.7388	1.83	.4664	.0748	.1756	−.0477	−.4395
1.34	.4099	.1626	.1293	.2624	−.7395	1.84	.4671	.0734	.1751	−.0521	−.4295
1.35	.4115	.1604	.1319	.2550	−.7399	**1.85**	.4678	.0721	.1746	−.0563	−.4195
1.36	.4131	.1582	.1344	.2476	−.7400	1.86	.4686	.0707	.1740	−.0605	−.4095
1.37	.4147	.1561	.1369	.2402	−.7396	1.87	.4693	.0694	.1734	−.0645	−.3995
1.38	.4162	.1540	.1392	.2328	−.7389	1.88	.4700	.0681	.1727	−.0685	−.3894
1.39	.4177	.1518	.1415	.2254	−.7378	1.89	.4706	.0669	.1720	−.0723	−.3793
1.40	.4192	.1497	.1437	.2180	−.7364	**1.90**	.4713	.0656	.1713	−.0761	−.3693
1.41	.4207	.1476	.1459	.2107	−.7347	1.91	.4719	.0644	.1705	−.0797	−.3592
1.42	.4222	.1456	.1480	.2033	−.7326	1.92	.4726	.0632	.1697	−.0832	−.3492
1.43	.4236	.1435	.1500	.1960	−.7301	1.93	.4732	.0620	.1688	−.0867	−.3392
1.44	.4251	.1415	.1519	.1887	−.7274	1.94	.4738	.0608	.1679	−.0900	−.3292
1.45	.4265	.1394	.1537	.1815	−.7243	**1.95**	.4744	.0596	.1670	−.0933	−.3192
1.46	.4279	.1374	.1555	.1742	−.7209	1.96	.4750	.0584	.1661	−.0964	−.3093
1.47	.4292	.1354	.1572	.1670	−.7172	1.97	.4756	.0573	.1651	−.0994	−.2994
1.48	.4306	.1334	.1588	.1599	−.7132	1.98	.4762	.0562	.1641	−.1024	−.2895
1.49	.4319	.1315	.1604	.1528	−.7089	1.99	.4767	.0551	.1630	−.1052	−.2797
1.50	.4332	.1295	.1619	.1457	−.7043	**2.00**	.4773	.0540	.1620	−.1080	−.2700

AREAS, ORDINATES AND DERIVATIVES OF THE NORMAL CURVE OF ERROR (Continued)

t	Area	Ordinate	Second derivative	Third derivative	Fourth derivative	t	Area	Ordinate	Second derivative	Third derivative	Fourth derivative
2.00	.4773	.0540	.1620	−.1080	−.2700	**2.50**	.4938	.0175	.0920	−.1424	.0800
2.01	.4778	.0529	.1609	−.1106	−.2603	2.51	.4940	.0171	.0906	−.1416	.0836
2.02	.4783	.0519	.1598	−.1132	−.2506	2.52	.4941	.0167	.0892	−.1408	.0871
2.03	.4788	.0508	.1586	−.1157	−.2411	2.53	.4943	.0163	.0878	−.1399	.0905
2.04	.4793	.0498	.1575	−.1180	−.2316	2.54	.4945	.0159	.0864	−.1389	.0937
2.05	.4798	.0488	.1563	−.1203	−.2222	**2.55**	.4946	.0155	.0850	−.1380	.0968
2.06	.4803	.0478	.1550	−.1225	−.2129	2.56	.4948	.0151	.0836	−.1370	.0998
2.07	.4808	.0468	.1538	−.1245	−.2036	2.57	.4949	.0147	.0823	−.1360	.1027
2.08	.4812	.0459	.1526	−.1265	−.1945	2.58	.4951	.0143	.0809	−.1350	.1054
2.09	.4817	.0449	.1513	−.1284	−.1854	2.59	.4952	.0139	.0796	−.1339	.1080
2.10	.4821	.0440	.1500	−.1302	−.1765	**2.60**	.4953	.0136	.0782	−.1328	.1105
2.11	.4826	.0431	.1487	−.1320	−.1676	2.61	.4955	.0132	.0769	−.1317	.1129
2.12	.4830	.0422	.1474	−.1336	−.1588	2.62	.4956	.0129	.0756	−.1305	.1152
2.13	.4834	.0413	.1460	−.1351	−.1502	2.63	.4957	.0126	.0743	−.1294	.1173
2.14	.4838	.0404	.1446	−.1366	−.1416	2.64	.4959	.0122	.0730	−.1282	.1194
2.15	.4842	.0396	.1433	−.1380	−.1332	**2.65**	.4960	.0119	.0717	−.1270	.1213
2.16	.4846	.0387	.1419	−.1393	−.1249	2.66	.4961	.0116	.0705	−.1258	.1231
2.17	.4850	.0379	.1405	−.1405	−.1167	2.67	.4962	.0113	.0692	−.1245	.1248
2.18	.4854	.0371	.1391	−.1416	−.1086	2.68	.4963	.0110	.0680	−.1233	.1264
2.19	.4857	.0363	.1377	−.1426	−.1006	2.69	.4964	.0107	.0668	−.1220	.1279
2.20	.4861	.0355	.1362	−.1436	−.0927	**2.70**	.4965	.0104	.0656	−.1207	.1293
2.21	.4865	.0347	.1348	−.1445	−.0850	2.71	.4966	.0101	.0644	−.1194	.1306
2.22	.4868	.0339	.1333	−.1453	−.0774	2.72	.4967	.0099	.0632	−.1181	1317
2.23	.4871	.0332	.1319	−.1460	−.0700	2.73	.4968	.0096	.0620	−.1168	.1328
2.24	.4875	.0325	.1304	−.1467	−.0626	2.74	.4969	.0094	.0608	−.1154	.1338
2.25	.4878	.0317	.1289	−.1473	−.0554	**2.75**	.4970	.0091	.0597	−.1141	.1347
2.26	.4881	.0310	.1275	−.1478	−.0484	2.76	.4971	.0089	.0585	−.1127	.1356
2.27	.4884	.0303	.1260	−.1483	−.0414	2.77	.4972	.0086	.0574	−.1114	.1363
2.28	.4887	.0297	.1245	−.1486	−.0346	2.78	.4973	.0084	.0563	−.1100	.1369
2.29	.4890	.0290	.1230	−.1490	−.0279	2.79	.4974	.0081	.0552	−.1087	.1375
2.30	.4893	.0283	.1215	−.1492	−.0214	**2.80**	.4974	.0079	.0541	−.1073	.1379
2.31	.4896	.0277	.1200	−.1494	−.0150	2.81	.4975	.0077	.0531	−.1059	.1383
2.32	.4898	.0271	.1185	−.1495	−.0088	2.82	.4976	.0075	.0520	−.1045	.1386
2.33	.4901	.0264	.1170	−.1496	−.0027	2.83	.4977	.0073	.0510	−.1031	.1389
2.34	.4904	.0258	.1155	−.1496	.0033	2.84	.4977	.0071	.0500	−.1017	.1390
2.35	.4906	.0252	.1141	−.1495	.0092	**2.85**	.4978	.0069	.0490	−.1003	.1391
2.36	.4909	.0246	.1126	−.1494	.0149	2.86	.4979	.0067	.0480	−.0990	.1391
2.37	.4911	.0241	.1111	−.1492	.0204	2.87	.4980	.0065	.0470	−.0976	.1391
2.38	.4913	.0235	.1096	−.1490	.0258	2.88	.4980	.0063	.0460	−.0962	.1389
2.39	.4916	.0229	.1081	−.1487	.0311	2.89	.4981	.0061	.0451	−.0948	.1388
2.40	.4918	.0224	.1066	−.1483	.0362	**2.90**	.4981	.0060	.0441	−.0934	.1385
2.41	.4920	.0219	.1051	−.1480	.0412	2.91	.4982	.0058	.0432	−.0920	.1382
2.42	.4922	.0213	.1036	−.1475	.0461	2.92	.4983	.0056	.0423	−.0906	.1378
2.43	.4925	.0208	.1022	−.1470	.0508	2.93	.4983	.0055	.0414	−.0893	.1374
2.44	.4927	.0203	.1007	−.1465	.0554	2.94	.4984	.0053	.0405	−.0879	.1369
2.45	.4929	.0198	.0992	−.1459	.0598	**2.95**	.4984	.0051	.0396	−.0865	.1364
2.46	.4931	.0194	.0978	−.1453	.0641	2.96	.4985	.0050	.0388	−.0852	.1358
2.47	.4932	.0189	.0963	−.1446	.0683	2.97	.4985	.0049	.0379	−.0838	.1352
2.48	.4934	.0184	.0949	−.1439	.0723	2.98	.4986	.0047	.0371	−.0825	.1345
2.49	.4936	.0180	.0935	−.1432	.0762	2.99	.4986	.0046	.0363	−.0811	.1337
2.50	.4938	.0175	.0920	−.1424	.0800	**3.00**	.4987	.0044	.0355	−.0798	.1330

AREAS, ORDINATES AND DERIVATIVES OF THE NORMAL CURVE OF ERROR (Continued)

t	Area	Ordinate	Second derivative	Third derivative	Fourth derivative	t	Area	Ordinate	Second derivative	Third derivative	Fourth derivative
3.00	.4987	.0044	.0355	−.0798	.1330	**3.50**	.4998	.0009	.0098	−.0283	.0694
3.01	.4987	.0043	.0347	−.0785	.1321	3.51	.4998	.0008	.0095	−.0276	.0681
3.02	.4987	.0042	.0339	−.0771	.1313	3.52	.4998	.0008	.0093	−.0269	.0669
3.03	.4988	.0041	.0331	−.0758	.1304	3.53	.4998	.0008	.0090	−.0262	.0656
3.04	.4988	.0039	.0324	−.0745	.1294	3.54	.4998	.0008	.0087	−.0256	.0643
3.05	.4989	.0038	.0316	−.0732	.1285	**3.55**	.4998	.0007	.0085	−.0249	.0631
3.06	.4989	.0037	.0309	−.0720	.1275	3.56	.4998	.0007	.0082	−.0243	.0618
3.07	.4989	.0036	.0302	−.0707	.1264	3.57	.4998	.0007	.0080	−.0237	.0606
3.08	.4990	.0035	.0295	−.0694	.1254	3.58	.4998	.0007	.0078	−.0231	.0594
3.09	.4990	.0034	.0288	−.0682	.1243	3.59	.4998	.0006	.0075	−.0225	.0582
3.10	.4990	.0033	.0281	−.0669	.1231	**3.60**	.4998	.0006	.0073	−.0219	.0570
3.11	.4991	.0032	.0275	−.0657	.1220	3.61	.4999	.0006	.0071	−.0214	.0559
3.12	.4991	.0031	.0268	−.0645	.1208	3.62	.4999	.0006	.0069	−.0208	.0547
3.13	.4991	.0030	.0262	−.0633	.1196	3.63	.4999	.0006	.0067	−.0203	.0536
3.14	.4992	.0029	.0256	−.0621	.1184	3.64	.4999	.0005	.0065	−.0198	.0524
3.15	.4992	.0028	.0249	−.0609	.1171	**3.65**	.4999	.0005	.0063	−.0192	.0513
3.16	.4992	.0027	.0243	−.0598	.1159	3.66	.4999	.0005	.0061	−.0187	.0502
3.17	.4992	.0026	.0237	−.0586	.1146	3.67	.4999	.0005	.0059	−.0182	.0492
3.18	.4993	.0025	.0232	−.0575	.1133	3.68	.4999	.0005	.0057	−.0177	.0481
3.19	.4993	.0025	.0226	−.0564	.1120	3.69	.4999	.0004	.0056	−.0173	.0470
3.20	.4993	.0024	.0220	−.0552	.1107	**3.70**	.4999	.0004	.0054	−.0168	.0460
3.21	.4993	.0023	.0215	−.0541	.1093	3.71	.4999	.0004	.0052	−.0164	.0450
3.22	.4994	.0022	.0210	−.0531	.1080	3.72	.4999	.0004	.0051	−.0159	.0440
3.23	.4994	.0022	.0204	−.0520	.1066	3.73	.4999	.0004	.0049	−.0155	.0430
3.24	.4994	.0021	.0199	−.0509	.1053	3.74	.4999	.0004	.0048	−.0150	.0420
3.25	.4994	.0020	.0194	−.0499	.1039	**3.75**	.4999	.0004	.0046	−.0146	.0410
3.26	.4994	.0020	.0189	−.0488	.1025	3.76	.4999	.0003	.0045	−.0142	.0401
3.27	.4995	.0019	.0184	−.0478	.1011	3.77	.4999	.0003	.0043	−.0138	.0392
3.28	.4995	.0018	.0180	−.0468	.0997	3.78	.4999	.0003	.0042	−.0134	.0382
3.29	.4995	.0018	.0175	−.0458	.0983	3.79	.4999	.0003	.0041	−.0131	.0373
3.30	.4995	.0017	.0170	−.0449	.0969	**3.80**	.4999	.0003	.0039	−.0127	.0365
3.31	.4995	.0017	.0166	−.0439	.0955	3.81	.4999	.0003	.0038	−.0123	.0356
3.32	.4996	.0016	.0162	−.0429	.0941	3.82	.4999	.0003	.0037	−.0120	.0347
3.33	.4996	.0016	.0157	−.0420	.0927	3.83	.4999	.0003	.0036	−.0116	.0339
3.34	.4996	.0015	.0153	−.0411	.0913	3.84	.4999	.0003	.0034	−.0113	.0331
3.35	.4996	.0015	.0149	−.0402	.0899	**3.85**	.4999	.0002	.0033	−.0110	.0323
3.36	.4996	.0014	.0145	−.0393	.0885	3.86	.4999	.0002	.0032	−.0107	.0315
3.37	.4996	.0014	.0141	−.0384	.0871	3.87	.5000	.0002	.0031	−.0104	.0307
3.38	.4996	.0013	.0138	−.0376	.0857	3.88	.5000	.0002	.0030	−.0100	.0299
3.39	.4997	.0013	.0134	−.0367	.0843	3.89	.5000	.0002	.0029	−.0098	.0292
3.40	.4997	.0012	.0130	−.0359	.0829	**3.90**	.5000	.0002	.0028	−.0095	.0284
3.41	.4997	.0012	.0127	−.0350	.0815	3.91	.5000	.0002	.0027	−.0092	.0277
3.42	.4997	.0012	.0123	−.0342	.0801	3.92	.5000	.0002	.0026	−.0089	.0270
3.43	.4997	.0011	.0120	−.0334	.0788	3.93	.5000	.0002	.0026	−.0086	.0263
3.44	.4997	.0011	.0116	−.0327	.0774	3.94	.5000	.0002	.0025	−.0084	.0256
3.45	.4997	.0010	.0113	−.0319	.0761	**3.95**	.5000	.0002	.0024	−.0081	.0250
3.46	.4997	.0010	.0110	−.0311	.0747	3.96	.5000	.0002	.0023	−.0079	.0243
3.47	.4997	.0010	.0107	−.0304	.0734	3.97	.5000	.0002	.0022	−.0076	.0237
3.48	.4998	.0009	.0104	−.0297	.0721	3.98	.5000	.0001	.0022	−.0074	.0230
3.49	.4998	.0009	.0101	−.0290	.0707	3.99	.5000	.0001	.0021	−.0072	.0224
3.50	.4998	.0009	.0098	−.0283	.0694	**4.00**	.5000	.0001	.0020	−.0070	.0218

AREAS, ORDINATES AND DERIVATIVES OF THE NORMAL CURVE OF ERROR (Continued)

t	Area	Ordinate	Second derivative	Third derivative	Fourth derivative	t	Area	Ordinate	Second derivative	Third derivative	Fourth derivative
4.00	.5000	.0001	.0020	−.0070	.0218	**4.50**	.5000	.0000	.0003	−.0012	.0047
4.01	.5000	.0001	.0019	−.0067	.0212	4.51	.5000	.0000	.0003	−.0012	.0045
4.02	.5000	.0001	.0019	−.0065	.0207	4.52	.5000	.0000	.0003	−.0012	.0044
4.03	.5000	.0001	.0018	−.0063	.0201	4.53	.5000	.0000	.0003	−.0011	.0042
4.04	.5000	.0001	.0018	−.0061	.0195	4.54	.5000	.0000	.0003	−.0011	.0041
4.05	.5000	.0001	.0017	−.0059	.0190	**4.55**	.5000	.0000	.0003	−.0010	.0039
4.06	.5000	.0001	.0016	−.0058	.0185	4.56	.5000	.0000	.0002	−.0010	.0038
4.07	.5000	.0001	.0016	−.0056	.0180	4.57	.5000	.0000	.0002	−.0010	.0037
4.08	.5000	.0001	.0015	−.0054	.0175	4.58	.5000	.0000	.0002	−.0009	.0035
4.09	.5000	.0001	.0015	−.0052	.0170	4.59	.5000	.0000	.0002	−.0009	.0034
4.10	.5000	.0001	.0014	−.0051	.0165	**4.60**	.5000	.0000	.0002	−.0009	.0033
4.11	.5000	.0001	.0014	−.0049	.0160	4.61	.5000	.0000	.0002	−.0008	.0032
4.12	.5000	.0001	.0013	−.0047	.0156	4.62	.5000	.0000	.0002	−.0008	.0031
4.13	.5000	.0001	.0013	−.0046	.0151	4.63	.5000	.0000	.0002	−.0008	.0030
4.14	.5000	.0001	.0012	−.0044	.0147	4.64	.5000	.0000	.0002	−.0007	.0028
4.15	.5000	.0001	.0012	−.0043	.0143	**4.65**	.5000	.0000	.0002	−.0007	.0027
4.16	.5000	.0001	.0011	−.0042	.0138	4.66	.5000	.0000	.0002	−.0007	.0026
4.17	.5000	.0001	.0011	−.0040	.0134	4.67	.5000	.0000	.0002	−.0006	.0026
4.18	.5000	.0001	.0011	−.0039	.0130	4.68	.5000	.0000	.0002	−.0006	.0025
4.19	.5000	.0001	.0010	−.0038	.0127	4.69	.5000	.0000	.0001	−.0006	.0024
4.20	.5000	.0001	.0010	−.0036	.0123	**4.70**	.5000	.0000	.0001	−.0006	.0023
4.21	.5000	.0001	.0009	−.0035	.0119	4.71	.5000	.0000	.0001	−.0006	.0022
4.22	.5000	.0001	.0009	−.0034	.0116	4.72	.5000	.0000	.0001	−.0005	.0021
4.23	.5000	.0001	.0009	−.0033	.0112	4.73	.5000	.0000	.0001	−.0005	.0020
4.24	.5000	.0001	.0009	−.0032	.0109	4.74	.5000	.0000	.0001	−.0005	.0020
4.25	.5000	.0001	.0008	−.0031	.0105	**4.75**	.5000	.0000	.0001	−.0005	.0019
4.26	.5000	.0001	.0008	−.0030	.0102	4.76	.5000	.0000	.0001	−.0005	.0018
4.27	.5000	.0000	.0008	−.0029	.0099	4.77	.5000	.0000	.0001	−.0004	.0018
4.28	.5000	.0000	.0007	−.0028	.0096	4.78	.5000	.0000	.0001	−.0004	.0017
4.29	.5000	.0000	.0007	−.0027	.0093	4.79	.5000	.0000	.0001	−.0004	.0016
4.30	.5000	.0000	.0007	−.0026	.0090	**4.80**	.5000	.0000	.0001	−.0004	.0016
4.31	.5000	.0000	.0007	−.0025	.0087	4.81	.5000	.0000	.0001	−.0004	.0015
4.32	.5000	.0000	.0006	−.0024	.0085	4.82	.5000	.0000	.0001	−.0004	.0015
4.33	.5000	.0000	.0006	−.0023	.0082	4.83	.5000	.0000	.0001	−.0003	.0014
4.34	.5000	.0000	.0006	−.0022	.0079	4.84	.5000	.0000	.0001	−.0003	.0013
4.35	.5000	.0000	.0006	−.0022	.0077	**4.85**	.5000	.0000	.0001	−.0003	.0013
4.36	.5000	.0000	.0005	−.0021	.0074	4.86	.5000	.0000	.0001	−.0003	.0012
4.37	.5000	.0000	.0005	−.0020	.0072	4.87	.5000	.0000	.0001	−.0003	.0012
4.38	.5000	.0000	.0005	−.0019	.0070	4.88	.5000	.0000	.0001	−.0003	.0012
4.39	.5000	.0000	.0005	−.0019	.0067	4.89	.5000	.0000	.0001	−.0003	.0011
4.40	.5000	.0000	.0005	−.0018	.0065	**4.90**	.5000	.0000	.0001	−.0003	.0011
4.41	.5000	.0000	.0004	−.0017	.0063	4.91	.5000	.0000	.0001	−.0002	.0010
4.42	.5000	.0000	.0004	−.0017	.0061	4.92	.5000	.0000	.0001	−.0002	.0010
4.43	.5000	.0000	.0004	−.0016	.0059	4.93	.5000	.0000	.0001	−.0002	.0009
4.44	.5000	.0000	.0004	−.0016	.0057	4.94	.5000	.0000	.0001	−.0002	.0009
4.45	.5000	.0000	.0004	−.0015	.0055	**4.95**	.5000	.0000	.0000	−.0002	.0009
4.46	.5000	.0000	.0004	−.0014	.0053	4.96	.5000	.0000	.0000	−.0002	.0008
4.47	.5000	.0000	.0004	−.0014	.0052	4.97	.5000	.0000	.0000	−.0002	.0008
4.48	.5000	.0000	.0003	−.0013	.0050	4.98	.5000	.0000	.0000	−.0002	.0008
4.49	.5000	.0000	.0003	−.0013	.0048	4.99	.5000	.0000	.0000	−.0002	.0007
4.50	.5000	.0000	.0003	−.0012	.0047						

COMPLETE ELLIPTIC INTEGRALS

$$K = \int_0^{\pi/2} \frac{d\phi}{\sqrt{1 - k^2 \sin^2 \phi}}. \qquad E = \int_0^{\pi/2} \sqrt{1 - k^2 \sin^2 \phi} \cdot d\phi.$$

$\sin^{-1} k$	K	$\log K$	$\sin^{-1} k$	K	$\log K$
0°	1.5708	0.196120	**40°**	1.7868	0.252068
1	1.5709	0.196153	41	1.7992	0.255085
2	1.5713	0.196252	42	1.8122	0.258197
3	1.5719	0.196418	43	1.8256	0.261406
4	1.5727	0.196649	44	1.8396	0.264716
5	1.5738	0.196947	**45**	1.8541	0.268127
6	1.5751	0.197312	46	1.8691	0.271644
7	1.5767	0.197743	47	1.8848	0.275267
8	1.5785	0.198241	48	1.9011	0.279001
9	1.5805	0.198806	49	1.9180	0.282848
10	1.5828	0.199438	**50**	1.9356	0.286811
11	1.5854	0.200137	51	1.9539	0.290895
12	1.5882	0.200904	52	1.9729	0.295101
13	1.5913	0.201740	53	1.9927	0.299435
14	1.5946	0.202643	54	2.0133	0.303901
15	1.5981	0.203615	**55**	2.0347	0.308504
16	1.6020	0.204657	56	2.0571	0.313247
17	1.6061	0.205768	57	2.0804	0.318138
18	1.6105	0.206948	58	2.1047	0.323182
19	1.6151	0.208200	59	2.1300	0.328384
20	1.6200	0.209522	**60**	2.1565	0.333753
21	1.6252	0.210916	61	2.1842	0.339295
22	1.6307	0.212382	62	2.2132	0.345020
23	1.6365	0.213921	63	2.2435	0.350936
24	1.6426	0.215533	64	2.2754	0.357053
25	1.6490	0.217219	**65**	2.3088	0.363384
26	1.6557	0.218981	66	2.3439	0.369940
27	1.6627	0.220818	67	2.3809	0.376736
28	1.6701	0.222732	68	2.4198	0.383787
29	1.6777	0.224723	69	2.4610	0.391112
30	1.6858	0.226793	**70**	2.5046	0.398730
31	1.6941	0.228943	71	2.5507	0.406665
32	1.7028	0.231173	72	2.5998	0.414943
33	1.7119	0.233485	73	2.6521	0.423596
34	1.7214	0.235880	74	2.7081	0.432660
35	1.7312	0.238359	**75**	2.7681	0.442176
36	1.7415	0.240923	76	2.8327	0.452196
37	1.7522	0.243575	77	2.9026	0.462782
38	1.7633	0.246315	78	2.9786	0.474008
39	1.7748	0.249146	79	3.0617	0.485967
40	1.7868	0.252068	**80**	3.1534	0.498777

COMPLETE ELLIPTIC INTEGRALS (Continued)

$\sin^{-1} k$	K	$\log K$	$\sin^{-1} k$	K	$\log K$
80°	3.1534	0.498777	**85°**	3.8317	0.583396
81	3.2553	0.512591	86	4.0528	0.607751
82	3.3699	0.527613	87	4.3387	0.637355
83	3.5004	0.544120	88	4.7427	0.676027
84	3.6519	0.562514	89	5.4349	0.735192
85	3.8317	0.583396	**90**	∞	∞

Values of K for $\sin^{-1} k$ = 85° to 89° by 0.1° and 89° to 90° by minutes.

$\sin^{-1} k$	K	$\log K$	$\sin^{-1} k$	K	$\log K$
85.0°	3.832	0.58343	**89° 0′**	5.435	0.73520
85.1	3.852	0.58569	89 2	5.469	0.73791
85.2	3.872	0.58794	89 4	5.504	0.74068
85.3	3.893	0.59028	89 6	5.540	0.74351
85.4	3.914	0.59262	89 8	5.578	0.74648
85.5	3.936	0.59506	**89 10**	5.617	0.74950
85.6	3.958	0.59748	89 12	5.658	0.75266
85.7	3.981	0.59999	89 14	5.700	0.75587
85.8	4.004	0.60249	89 16	5.745	0.75929
85.9	4.028	0.60509	89 18	5.791	0.76275
86.0	4.053	0.60778	**89 20**	5.840	0.76641
86.1	4.078	0.61045	89 22	5.891	0.77019
86.2	4.104	0.61321	89 24	5.946	0.77422
86.3	4.130	0.61595	89 26	6.003	0.77837
86.4	4.157	0.61878	89 28	6.063	0.78269
86.5	4.185	0.62170	**89 30**	6.128	0.78732
86.6	4.214	0.62469	89 32	6.197	0.79218
86.7	4.244	0.62778	89 34	6.271	0.79734
86.8	4.274	0.63083	89 36	6.351	0.80284
86.9	4.306	0.63407	89 38	6.438	0.80875
87.0	4.339	0.63739	**89 40**	6.533	0.81511
87.1	4.372	0.64068	89 41	6.584	0.81849
87.2	4.407	0.64414	89 42	6.639	0.82210
87.3	4.444	0.64777	89 43	6.696	0.82582
87.4	4.481	0.65137	89 44	6.756	0.82969
87.5	4.520	0.65514	**89 45**	6.821	0.83385
87.6	4.562	0.65916	89 46	6.890	0.83822
87.7	4.603	0.66304	89 47	6.964	0.84286
87.8	4.648	0.66727	89 48	7.044	0.84782
87.9	4.694	0.67154	89 49	7.131	0.85315
88.0	4.743	0.67605	**89 50**	7.226	0.85890
88.1	4.794	0.68070	89 51	7.332	0.86522
88.2	4.848	0.68556	89 52	7.449	0.87210
88.3	4.905	0.69064	89 53	7.583	0.87984
88.4	4.965	0.69592	89 54	7.737	0.88857
88.5	5.030	0.70157	**89 55**	7.919	0.89867
88.6	5.099	0.70749	89 56	8.143	0.91078
88.7	5.173	0.71374	89 57	8.430	0.92583
88.8	5.253	0.72041	89 58	8.836	0.94626
88.9	5.340	0.72754	89 59	9.529	0.97905
89.0	5.435	0.73520	**90 0**	∞	∞

COMPLETE ELLIPTIC INTEGRALS (Continued)

$\sin^{-1} k$	E	$\log E$	$\sin^{-1} k$	E	$\log E$
0°	1.5708	0.196120	**45°**	1.3506	0.130541
1	1.5707	0.196087	46	1.3418	0.127690
2	1.5703	0.195988	47	1.3329	0.124788
3	1.5697	0.195822	48	1.3238	0.121836
4	1.5689	0.195591	49	1.3147	0.118836
5	1.5678	0.195293	**50**	1.3055	0.115790
6	1.5665	0.194930	51	1.2963	0.112698
7	1.5649	0.194500	52	1.2870	0.109563
8	1.5632	0.194004	53	1.2776	0.106386
9	1.5611	0.193442	54	1.2681	0.103169
10	1.5589	0.192815	**55**	1.2587	0.099915
11	1.5564	0.192121	56	1.2492	0.096626
12	1.5537	0.191362	57	1.2397	0.093303
13	1.5507	0.190537	58	1.2301	0.089950
14	1.5476	0.189646	59	1.2206	0.086569
15	1.5442	0.188690	**60**	1.2111	0.083164
16	1.5405	0.187668	61	1.2015	0.079738
17	1.5367	0.186581	62	1.1920	0.076293
18	1.5326	0.185428	63	1.1826	0.072834
19	1.5283	0.184210	64	1.1732	0.069364
20	1.5238	0.182928	**65**	1.1638	0.065889
21	1.5191	0.181580	66	1.1545	0.062412
22	1.5141	0.180168	67	1.1453	0.058937
23	1.5090	0.178691	68	1.1362	0.055472
24	1.5037	0.177150	69	1.1272	0.052020
25	1.4981	0.175545	**70**	1.1184	0.048589
26	1.4924	0.173876	71	1.1096	0.045183
27	1.4864	0.172144	72	1.1011	0.041812
28	1.4803	0.170348	73	1.0927	0.038481
29	1.4740	0.168489	74	1.0844	0.035200
30	1.4675	0.166567	**75**	1.0764	0.031976
31	1.4608	0.164583	76	1.0686	0.028819
32	1.4539	0.162537	77	1.0611	0.025740
33	1.4469	0.160429	78	1.0538	0.022749
34	1.4397	0.158261	79	1.0468	0.019858
35	1.4323	0.156031	**80**	1.0401	0.017081
36	1.4248	0.153742	81	1.0338	0.014432
37	1.4171	0.151393	82	1.0278	0.011927
38	1.4092	0.148985	83	1.0223	0.009584
39	1.4013	0.146519	84	1.0172	0.007422
40	1.3931	0.143995	**85**	1.0127	0.005465
41	1.3849	0.141414	86	1.0086	0.003740
42	1.3765	0.138778	87	1.0053	0.002278
43	1.3680	0.136086	88	1.0026	0.001121
44	1.3594	0.133340	89	1.0008	0.000326
45	1.3506	0.130541	**90**	1.0000	0.000000

FACTORS AND PRIMES

FACTORS AND PRIMES

If n is prime the mantissa of its logarithm is given.

n	0	1	2	3	4
0	....	**0000000**	**3010300**	**4771213**	2^2
1	$2 \cdot 5$	**0413927**	$2^2 \cdot 3$	**1139434**	$2 \cdot 7$
2	$2^2 \cdot 5$	$3 \cdot 7$	$2 \cdot 11$	**3617278**	$2^3 \cdot 3$
3	$2 \cdot 3 \cdot 5$	**4913617**	2^5	$3 \cdot 11$	$2 \cdot 17$
4	$2^3 \cdot 5$	**6127839**	$2 \cdot 3 \cdot 7$	**6334685**	$2^2 \cdot 11$
5	$2 \cdot 5^2$	$3 \cdot 17$	$2^2 \cdot 13$	**7242759**	$2 \cdot 3^3$
6	$2^2 \cdot 3 \cdot 5$	**7853298**	$2 \cdot 31$	$3^2 \cdot 7$	2^6
7	$2 \cdot 5 \cdot 7$	**8512583**	$2^3 \cdot 3^2$	**8633229**	$2 \cdot 37$
8	$2^4 \cdot 5$	3^4	$2 \cdot 41$	**9190781**	$2^2 \cdot 3 \cdot 7$
9	$2 \cdot 3^2 \cdot 5$	$7 \cdot 13$	$2^2 \cdot 23$	$3 \cdot 31$	$2 \cdot 47$
10	$2^2 \cdot 5^2$	**0043214**	$2 \cdot 3 \cdot 17$	**0128372**	$2^3 \cdot 13$
11	$2 \cdot 5 \cdot 11$	$3 \cdot 37$	$2^4 \cdot 7$	**0530784**	$2 \cdot 3 \cdot 19$
12	$2^3 \cdot 3 \cdot 5$	11^2	$2 \cdot 61$	$3 \cdot 41$	$2^2 \cdot 31$
13	$2 \cdot 5 \cdot 13$	**1172713**	$2^2 \cdot 3 \cdot 11$	$7 \cdot 19$	$2 \cdot 67$
14	$2^2 \cdot 5 \cdot 7$	$3 \cdot 47$	$2 \cdot 71$	$11 \cdot 13$	$2^4 \cdot 3^2$
15	$2 \cdot 3 \cdot 5^2$	**1789769**	$2^3 \cdot 19$	$3^2 \cdot 17$	$2 \cdot 7 \cdot 11$
16	$2^5 \cdot 5$	$7 \cdot 23$	$2 \cdot 3^4$	**2121876**	$2^2 \cdot 41$
17	$2 \cdot 5 \cdot 17$	$3^2 \cdot 19$	$2^2 \cdot 43$	**2380461**	$2 \cdot 3 \cdot 29$
18	$2^2 \cdot 3^2 \cdot 5$	**2576786**	$2 \cdot 7 \cdot 13$	$3 \cdot 61$	$2^3 \cdot 23$
19	$2 \cdot 5 \cdot 19$	**2810334**	$2^6 \cdot 3$	**2855573**	$2 \cdot 97$
20	$2^3 \cdot 5^2$	$3 \cdot 67$	$2 \cdot 101$	$7 \cdot 29$	$2^2 \cdot 3 \cdot 17$
21	$2 \cdot 3 \cdot 5 \cdot 7$	**3242825**	$2^2 \cdot 53$	$3 \cdot 71$	$2 \cdot 107$
22	$2^2 \cdot 5 \cdot 11$	$13 \cdot 17$	$2 \cdot 3 \cdot 37$	**3483049**	$2^5 \cdot 7$
23	$2 \cdot 5 \cdot 23$	$3 \cdot 7 \cdot 11$	$2^3 \cdot 29$	**3673559**	$2 \cdot 3^2 \cdot 13$
24	$2^4 \cdot 3 \cdot 5$	**3820170**	$2 \cdot 11^2$	3^5	$2^2 \cdot 61$
25	$2 \cdot 5^3$	**3996737**	$2^2 \cdot 3^2 \cdot 7$	$11 \cdot 23$	$2 \cdot 127$
26	$2^2 \cdot 5 \cdot 13$	$3^2 \cdot 29$	$2 \cdot 131$	**4199557**	$2^3 \cdot 3 \cdot 11$
27	$2 \cdot 3^3 \cdot 5$	**4329693**	$2^4 \cdot 17$	$3 \cdot 7 \cdot 13$	$2 \cdot 137$
28	$2^3 \cdot 5 \cdot 7$	**4487063**	$2 \cdot 3 \cdot 47$	**4517864**	$2^2 \cdot 71$
29	$2 \cdot 5 \cdot 29$	$3 \cdot 97$	$2^2 \cdot 73$	**4668676**	$2 \cdot 3 \cdot 7^2$
30	$2^2 \cdot 3 \cdot 5^2$	$7 \cdot 43$	$2 \cdot 151$	$3 \cdot 101$	$2^4 \cdot 19$
31	$2 \cdot 5 \cdot 31$	**4927604**	$2^3 \cdot 3 \cdot 13$	**4955443**	$2 \cdot 157$
32	$2^6 \cdot 5$	$3 \cdot 107$	$2 \cdot 7 \cdot 23$	$17 \cdot 19$	$2^2 \cdot 3^4$
33	$2 \cdot 3 \cdot 5 \cdot 11$	**5198280**	$2^2 \cdot 83$	$3^2 \cdot 37$	$2 \cdot 167$
34	$2^2 \cdot 5 \cdot 17$	$11 \cdot 31$	$2 \cdot 3^2 \cdot 19$	7^3	$2^3 \cdot 43$
35	$2 \cdot 5^2 \cdot 7$	$3^3 \cdot 13$	$2^5 \cdot 11$	**5477747**	$2 \cdot 3 \cdot 59$
36	$2^3 \cdot 3^2 \cdot 5$	19^2	$2 \cdot 181$	$3 \cdot 11^2$	$2^2 \cdot 7 \cdot 13$
37	$2 \cdot 5 \cdot 37$	$7 \cdot 53$	$2^2 \cdot 3 \cdot 31$	**5717088**	$2 \cdot 11 \cdot 17$
38	$2^2 \cdot 5 \cdot 19$	$3 \cdot 127$	$2 \cdot 191$	**5831988**	$2^7 \cdot 3$
39	$2 \cdot 3 \cdot 5 \cdot 13$	$17 \cdot 23$	$2^3 \cdot 7^2$	$3 \cdot 131$	$2 \cdot 197$
40	$2^4 \cdot 5^2$	**6031444**	$2 \cdot 3 \cdot 67$	$13 \cdot 31$	$2^2 \cdot 101$
41	$2 \cdot 5 \cdot 41$	$3 \cdot 137$	$2^2 \cdot 103$	$7 \cdot 59$	$2 \cdot 3^2 \cdot 23$
42	$2^2 \cdot 3 \cdot 5 \cdot 7$	**6242821**	$2 \cdot 211$	$3^2 \cdot 47$	$2^3 \cdot 53$
43	$2 \cdot 5 \cdot 43$	**6344773**	$2^4 \cdot 3^3$	**6364879**	$2 \cdot 7 \cdot 31$
44	$2^3 \cdot 5 \cdot 11$	$3^2 \cdot 7^2$	$2 \cdot 13 \cdot 17$	**6464037**	$2^2 \cdot 3 \cdot 37$
45	$2 \cdot 3^2 \cdot 5^2$	$11 \cdot 41$	$2^2 \cdot 113$	$3 \cdot 151$	$2 \cdot 227$
46	$2^2 \cdot 5 \cdot 23$	**6637009**	$2 \cdot 3 \cdot 7 \cdot 11$	**6655810**	$2^4 \cdot 29$
47	$2 \cdot 5 \cdot 47$	$3 \cdot 157$	$2^3 \cdot 59$	$11 \cdot 43$	$2 \cdot 3 \cdot 79$
48	$2^5 \cdot 3 \cdot 5$	$13 \cdot 37$	$2 \cdot 241$	$3 \cdot 7 \cdot 23$	$2^2 \cdot 11^2$
49	$2 \cdot 5 \cdot 7^2$	**6910815**	$2^2 \cdot 3 \cdot 41$	$17 \cdot 29$	$2 \cdot 13 \cdot 19$
50	$2^2 \cdot 5^3$	$3 \cdot 167$	$2 \cdot 251$	**7015680**	$2^3 \cdot 3^2 \cdot 7$

FACTORS AND PRIMES (Continued)

If n is not prime its prime factors are given.

n	5	6	7	8	9
0	**6989700**	$2 \cdot 3$	**8450980**	2^3	3^2
1	$3 \cdot 5$	2^4	**2304489**	$2 \cdot 3^2$	**2787536**
2	5^2	$2 \cdot 13$	3^3	$2^2 \cdot 7$	**4623980**
3	$5 \cdot 7$	$2^2 \cdot 3^2$	**5682017**	$2 \cdot 19$	$3 \cdot 13$
4	$3^2 \cdot 5$	$2 \cdot 23$	**6720979**	$2^4 \cdot 3$	7^2
5	$5 \cdot 11$	$2^3 \cdot 7$	$3 \cdot 19$	$2 \cdot 29$	**7708520**
6	$5 \cdot 13$	$2 \cdot 3 \cdot 11$	**8260748**	$2^2 \cdot 17$	$3 \cdot 23$
7	$3 \cdot 5^2$	$2^2 \cdot 19$	$7 \cdot 11$	$2 \cdot 3 \cdot 13$	**8976271**
8	$5 \cdot 17$	$2 \cdot 43$	$3 \cdot 29$	$2^3 \cdot 11$	**9493900**
9	$5 \cdot 19$	$2^5 \cdot 3$	**9867717**	$2 \cdot 7^2$	$3^2 \cdot 11$
10	$3 \cdot 5 \cdot 7$	$2 \cdot 53$	**0293838**	$2^2 \cdot 3^3$	**0374265**
11	$5 \cdot 23$	$2^2 \cdot 29$	$3^2 \cdot 13$	$2 \cdot 59$	$7 \cdot 17$
12	5^3	$2 \cdot 3^2 \cdot 7$	**1038037**	2^7	$3 \cdot 43$
13	$3^3 \cdot 5$	$2^3 \cdot 17$	**1367206**	$2 \cdot 3 \cdot 23$	**1430148**
14	$5 \cdot 29$	$2 \cdot 73$	$3 \cdot 7^2$	$2^2 \cdot 37$	**1731863**
15	$5 \cdot 31$	$2^2 \cdot 3 \cdot 13$	**1958997**	$2 \cdot 79$	$3 \cdot 53$
16	$3 \cdot 5 \cdot 11$	$2 \cdot 83$	**2227165**	$2^3 \cdot 3 \cdot 7$	13^2
17	$5^2 \cdot 7$	$2^4 \cdot 11$	$3 \cdot 59$	$2 \cdot 89$	**2528530**
18	$5 \cdot 37$	$2 \cdot 3 \cdot 31$	$11 \cdot 17$	$2^2 \cdot 47$	$3^3 \cdot 7$
19	$3 \cdot 5 \cdot 13$	$2^2 \cdot 7^2$	**2944662**	$2 \cdot 3^2 \cdot 11$	**2988531**
20	$5 \cdot 41$	$2 \cdot 103$	$3^2 \cdot 23$	$2^4 \cdot 13$	$11 \cdot 19$
21	$5 \cdot 43$	$2^3 \cdot 3^3$	$7 \cdot 31$	$2 \cdot 109$	$3 \cdot 73$
22	$3^2 \cdot 5^2$	$2 \cdot 113$	**3560259**	$2^2 \cdot 3 \cdot 19$	**3598355**
23	$5 \cdot 47$	$2^2 \cdot 59$	$3 \cdot 79$	$2 \cdot 7 \cdot 17$	**3783979**
24	$5 \cdot 7^2$	$2 \cdot 3 \cdot 41$	$13 \cdot 19$	$2^3 \cdot 31$	$3 \cdot 83$
25	$3 \cdot 5 \cdot 17$	2^8	**4099331**	$2 \cdot 3 \cdot 43$	$7 \cdot 37$
26	$5 \cdot 53$	$2 \cdot 7 \cdot 19$	$3 \cdot 89$	$2^2 \cdot 67$	**4297523**
27	$5^2 \cdot 11$	$2^2 \cdot 3 \cdot 23$	**4424798**	$2 \cdot 139$	$3^2 \cdot 31$
28	$3 \cdot 5 \cdot 19$	$2 \cdot 11 \cdot 13$	$7 \cdot 41$	$2^5 \cdot 3^2$	17^2
29	$5 \cdot 59$	$2^3 \cdot 37$	$3^3 \cdot 11$	$2 \cdot 149$	$13 \cdot 23$
30	$5 \cdot 61$	$2 \cdot 3^2 \cdot 17$	**4871384**	$2^2 \cdot 7 \cdot 11$	$3 \cdot 103$
31	$3^2 \cdot 5 \cdot 7$	$2^2 \cdot 79$	**5010593**	$2 \cdot 3 \cdot 53$	$11 \cdot 29$
32	$5^2 \cdot 13$	$2 \cdot 163$	$3 \cdot 109$	$2^3 \cdot 41$	$7 \cdot 47$
33	$5 \cdot 67$	$2^4 \cdot 3 \cdot 7$	**5276299**	$2 \cdot 13^2$	$3 \cdot 113$
34	$3 \cdot 5 \cdot 23$	$2 \cdot 173$	**5403295**	$2^2 \cdot 3 \cdot 29$	**5428254**
35	$5 \cdot 71$	$2^2 \cdot 89$	$3 \cdot 7 \cdot 17$	$2 \cdot 179$	**5550944**
36	$5 \cdot 73$	$2 \cdot 3 \cdot 61$	**5646661**	$2^4 \cdot 23$	$3^2 \cdot 41$
37	$3 \cdot 5^3$	$2^3 \cdot 47$	$13 \cdot 29$	$2 \cdot 3^3 \cdot 7$	**5786392**
38	$5 \cdot 7 \cdot 11$	$2 \cdot 193$	$3^2 \cdot 43$	$2^2 \cdot 97$	**5899496**
39	$5 \cdot 79$	$2^2 \cdot 3^2 \cdot 11$	**5987905**	$2 \cdot 199$	$3 \cdot 7 \cdot 19$
40	$3^4 \cdot 5$	$2 \cdot 7 \cdot 29$	$11 \cdot 37$	$2^3 \cdot 3 \cdot 17$	**6117233**
41	$5\ 83$	$2^5 \cdot 13$	$3 \cdot 139$	$2 \cdot 11 \cdot 19$	**6222140**
42	$5^2 \cdot 17$	$2 \cdot 3 \cdot 71$	$7 \cdot 61$	$2^2 \cdot 107$	$3 \cdot 11 \cdot 13$
43	$3 \cdot 5 \cdot 29$	$2^2 \cdot 109$	$19 \cdot 23$	$2 \cdot 3 \cdot 73$	**6424645**
44	$5 \cdot 89$	$2 \cdot 223$	$3 \cdot 149$	$2^6 \cdot 7$	**6522463**
45	$5 \cdot 7 \cdot 13$	$2^3 \cdot 3 \cdot 19$	**6599162**	$2 \cdot 229$	$3^3 \cdot 17$
46	$3 \cdot 5 \cdot 31$	$2 \cdot 233$	**6693169**	$2^2 \cdot 3^2 \cdot 13$	$7 \cdot 67$
47	$5^2 \cdot 19$	$2^2 \cdot 7 \cdot 17$	$3^2 \cdot 53$	$2 \cdot 239$	**6803355**
48	$5 \cdot 97$	$2 \cdot 3^5$	**6875290**	$2^3 \cdot 61$	$3 \cdot 163$
49	$3^2 \cdot 5 \cdot 11$	$2^4 \cdot 31$	$7 \cdot 71$	$2 \cdot 3 \cdot 83$	**6981005**
50	$5 \cdot 101$	$2 \cdot 11 \cdot 23$	$3 \cdot 13^2$	$2^2 \cdot 127$	**7067178**

FACTORS AND PRIMES (Continued)

n	0	1	2	3	4
50	$2^2 \cdot 5^3$	$3 \cdot 167$	$2 \cdot 251$	**7015680**	$2^3 \cdot 3^2 \cdot 7$
51	$2 \cdot 3 \cdot 5 \cdot 17$	$7 \cdot 73$	2^9	$3^3 \cdot 19$	$2 \cdot 257$
52	$2^3 \cdot 5 \cdot 13$	**7168377**	$2 \cdot 3^2 \cdot 29$	**7185017**	$2^2 \cdot 131$
53	$2 \cdot 5 \cdot 53$	$3^2 \cdot 59$	$2^2 \cdot 7 \cdot 19$	$13 \cdot 41$	$2 \cdot 3 \cdot 89$
54	$2^2 \cdot 3^3 \cdot 5$	**7331973**	$2 \cdot 271$	$3 \cdot 181$	$2^5 \cdot 17$
55	$2 \cdot 5^2 \cdot 11$	$19 \cdot 29$	$2^3 \cdot 3 \cdot 23$	$7 \cdot 79$	$2 \cdot 277$
56	$2^4 \cdot 5 \cdot 7$	$3 \cdot 11 \cdot 17$	$2 \cdot 281$	**7505084**	$2^2 \cdot 3 \cdot 47$
57	$2 \cdot 3 \cdot 5 \cdot 19$	**7566361**	$2^2 \cdot 11 \cdot 13$	$3 \cdot 191$	$2 \cdot 7 \cdot 41$
58	$2^2 \cdot 5 \cdot 29$	$7 \cdot 83$	$2 \cdot 3 \cdot 97$	$11 \cdot 53$	$2^3 \cdot 73$
59	$2 \cdot 5 \cdot 59$	$3 \cdot 197$	$2^4 \cdot 37$	**7730547**	$2 \cdot 3^3 \cdot 11$
60	$2^3 \cdot 3 \cdot 5^2$	**7788745**	$2 \cdot 7 \cdot 43$	$3^2 \cdot 67$	$2^2 \cdot 151$
61	$2 \cdot 5 \cdot 61$	$13 \cdot 47$	$2^2 \cdot 3^2 \cdot 17$	**7874605**	$2 \cdot 307$
62	$2^2 \cdot 5 \cdot 31$	$3^3 \cdot 23$	$2 \cdot 311$	$7 \cdot 89$	$2^4 \cdot 3 \cdot 13$
63	$2 \cdot 3^2 \cdot 5 \cdot 7$	**8000294**	$2^3 \cdot 79$	$3 \cdot 211$	$2 \cdot 317$
64	$2^7 \cdot 5$	**8068580**	$2 \cdot 3 \cdot 107$	**8082110**	$2^2 \cdot 7 \cdot 23$
65	$2 \cdot 5^2 \cdot 13$	$3 \cdot 7 \cdot 31$	$2^2 \cdot 163$	**8149132**	$2 \cdot 3 \cdot 109$
66	$2^2 \cdot 3 \cdot 5 \cdot 11$	**8202015**	$2 \cdot 331$	$3 \cdot 13 \cdot 17$	$2^3 \cdot 83$
67	$2 \cdot 5 \cdot 67$	$11 \cdot 61$	$2^5 \cdot 3 \cdot 7$	**8280151**	$2 \cdot 337$
68	$2^3 \cdot 5 \cdot 17$	$3 \cdot 227$	$2 \cdot 11 \cdot 31$	**8344207**	$2^2 \cdot 3^2 \cdot 19$
69	$2 \cdot 3 \cdot 5 \cdot 23$	**8394780**	$2^2 \cdot 173$	$3^2 \cdot 7 \cdot 11$	$2 \cdot 347$
70	$2^2 \cdot 5^2 \cdot 7$	**8457180**	$2 \cdot 3^3 \cdot 13$	$19 \cdot 37$	$2^6 \cdot 11$
71	$2 \cdot 5 \cdot 71$	$3^2 \cdot 79$	$2^3 \cdot 89$	$23 \cdot 31$	$2 \cdot 3 \cdot 7 \cdot 17$
72	$2^4 \cdot 3^2 \cdot 5$	$7 \cdot 103$	$2 \cdot 19^2$	$3 \cdot 241$	$2^2 \cdot 181$
73	$2 \cdot 5 \cdot 73$	$17 \cdot 43$	$2^2 \cdot 3 \cdot 61$	**8651040**	$2 \cdot 367$
74	$2^2 \cdot 5 \cdot 37$	$3 \cdot 13 \cdot 19$	$2 \cdot 7 \cdot 53$	**8709888**	$2^3 \cdot 3 \cdot 31$
75	$2 \cdot 3 \cdot 5^3$	**8756399**	$2^4 \cdot 47$	$3 \cdot 251$	$2 \cdot 13 \cdot 29$
76	$2^3 \cdot 5 \cdot 19$	**8813847**	$2 \cdot 3 \cdot 127$	$7 \cdot 109$	$2^2 \cdot 191$
77	$2 \cdot 5 \cdot 7 \cdot 11$	$3 \cdot 257$	$2^2 \cdot 193$	**8881795**	$2 \cdot 3^2 \cdot 43$
78	$2^2 \cdot 3 \cdot 5 \cdot 13$	$11 \cdot 71$	$2 \cdot 17 \cdot 23$	$3^3 \cdot 29$	$2^4 \cdot 7^2$
79	$2 \cdot 5 \cdot 79$	$7 \cdot 113$	$2^3 \cdot 3^2 \cdot 11$	$13 \cdot 61$	$2 \cdot 397$
80	$2^5 \cdot 5^2$	$3^2 \cdot 89$	$2 \cdot 401$	$11 \cdot 73$	$2^2 \cdot 3 \cdot 67$
81	$2 \cdot 3^4 \cdot 5$	**9090209**	$2^2 \cdot 7 \cdot 29$	$3 \cdot 271$	$2 \cdot 11 \cdot 37$
82	$2^2 \cdot 5 \cdot 41$	**9143432**	$2 \cdot 3 \cdot 137$	**9153998**	$2^3 \cdot 103$
83	$2 \cdot 5 \cdot 83$	$3 \cdot 277$	$2^6 \cdot 13$	$7^2 \cdot 17$	$2 \cdot 3 \cdot 139$
84	$2^3 \cdot 3 \cdot 5 \cdot 7$	29^2	$2 \cdot 421$	$3 \cdot 281$	$2^2 \cdot 211$
85	$2 \cdot 5^2 \cdot 17$	$23 \cdot 37$	$2^2 \cdot 3 \cdot 71$	**9309490**	$2 \cdot 7 \cdot 61$
86	$2^2 \cdot 5 \cdot 43$	$3 \cdot 7 \cdot 41$	$2 \cdot 431$	**9360108**	$2^5 \cdot 3^3$
87	$2 \cdot 3 \cdot 5 \cdot 29$	$13 \cdot 67$	$2^3 \cdot 109$	$3^2 \cdot 97$	$2 \cdot 19 \cdot 23$
88	$2^4 \cdot 5 \cdot 11$	**9449759**	$2 \cdot 3^2 \cdot 7^2$	**9459607**	$2^2 \cdot 13 \cdot 17$
89	$2 \cdot 5 \cdot 89$	$3^4 \cdot 11$	$2^2 \cdot 223$	$19 \cdot 47$	$2 \cdot 3 \cdot 149$
90	$2^2 \cdot 3^2 \cdot 5^2$	$17 \cdot 53$	$2 \cdot 11 \cdot 41$	$3 \cdot 7 \cdot 43$	$2^3 \cdot 113$
91	$2 \cdot 5 \cdot 7 \cdot 13$	**9595184**	$2^4 \cdot 3 \cdot 19$	$11 \cdot 83$	$2 \cdot 457$
92	$2^3 \cdot 5 \cdot 23$	$3 \cdot 307$	$2 \cdot 461$	$13 \cdot 71$	$2^2 \cdot 3 \cdot 7 \cdot 11$
93	$2 \cdot 3 \cdot 5 \cdot 31$	$7^2 \cdot 19$	$2^2 \cdot 233$	$3 \cdot 311$	$2 \cdot 467$
94	$2^2 \cdot 5 \cdot 47$	**9735896**	$2 \cdot 3 \cdot 157$	$23 \cdot 41$	$2^4 \cdot 59$
95	$2 \cdot 5^2 \cdot 19$	$3 \cdot 317$	$2^3 \cdot 7 \cdot 17$	**9790929**	$2 \cdot 3^2 \cdot 53$
96	$2^6 \cdot 3 \cdot 5$	31^2	$2 \cdot 13 \cdot 37$	$3^2 \cdot 107$	$2^2 \cdot 241$
97	$2 \cdot 5 \cdot 97$	**9872192**	$2^2 \cdot 3^5$	$7 \cdot 139$	$2 \cdot 487$
98	$2^2 \cdot 5 \cdot 7^2$	$3^2 \cdot 109$	$2 \cdot 491$	**9925535**	$2^3 \cdot 3 \cdot 41$
99	$2 \cdot 3^2 \cdot 5 \cdot 11$	**9960737**	$2^5 \cdot 31$	$3 \cdot 331$	$2 \cdot 7 \cdot 71$
100	$2^3 \cdot 5^3$	$7 \cdot 11 \cdot 13$	$2 \cdot 3 \cdot 167$	$17 \cdot 59$	$2^2 \cdot 251$

FACTORS AND PRIMES (Continued)

n	5	6	7	8	9
50	$5 \cdot 101$	$2 \cdot 11 \cdot 23$	$3 \cdot 13^2$	$2^2 \cdot 127$	**7067178**
51	$5 \cdot 103$	$2^2 \cdot 3 \cdot 43$	$11 \cdot 47$	$2 \cdot 7 \cdot 37$	$3 \cdot 173$
52	$3 \cdot 5^2 \cdot 7$	$2 \cdot 263$	$17 \cdot 31$	$2^4 \cdot 3 \cdot 11$	23^2
53	$5 \cdot 107$	$2^3 \cdot 67$	$3 \cdot 179$	$2 \cdot 269$	$7^2 \cdot 11$
54	$5 \cdot 109$	$2 \cdot 3 \cdot 7 \cdot 13$	**7379873**	$2^2 \cdot 137$	$3^2 \cdot 61$
55	$3 \cdot 5 \cdot 37$	$2^2 \cdot 139$	**7458552**	$2 \cdot 3^2 \cdot 31$	$13 \cdot 43$
56	$5 \cdot 113$	$2 \cdot 283$	$3^4 \cdot 7$	$2^3 \cdot 71$	**7551123**
57	$5^2 \cdot 23$	$2^6 \cdot 3^2$	**7611758**	$2 \cdot 17^2$	$3 \cdot 193$
58	$3^2 \cdot 5 \cdot 13$	$2 \cdot 293$	**7686381**	$2^2 \cdot 3 \cdot 7^2$	$19 \cdot 31$
59	$5 \cdot 7 \cdot 17$	$2^2 \cdot 149$	$3 \cdot 199$	$2 \cdot 13 \cdot 23$	**7774268**
60	$5 \cdot 11^2$	$2 \cdot 3 \cdot 101$	**7831887**	$2^5 \cdot 19$	$3 \cdot 7 \cdot 29$
61	$3 \cdot 5 \cdot 41$	$2^3 \cdot 7 \cdot 11$	**7902852**	$2 \cdot 3 \cdot 103$	**7916906**
62	5^4	$2 \cdot 313$	$3 \cdot 11 \cdot 19$	$2^2 \cdot 157$	$17 \cdot 37$
63	$5 \cdot 127$	$2^2 \cdot 3 \cdot 53$	$7^2 \cdot 13$	$2 \cdot 11 \cdot 29$	$3^2 \cdot 71$
64	$3 \cdot 5 \cdot 43$	$2 \cdot 17 \cdot 19$	**8109043**	$2^3 \cdot 3^4$	$11 \cdot 59$
65	$5 \cdot 131$	$2^4 \cdot 41$	$3^2 \cdot 73$	$2 \cdot 7 \cdot 47$	**8188854**
66	$5 \cdot 7 \cdot 19$	$2 \cdot 3^2 \cdot 37$	$23 \cdot 29$	$2^2 \cdot 167$	$3 \cdot 223$
67	$3^3 \cdot 5^2$	$2^2 \cdot 13^2$	**8305887**	$2 \cdot 3 \cdot 113$	$7 \cdot 97$
68	$5 \cdot 137$	$2 \cdot 7^3$	$3 \cdot 229$	$2^4 \cdot 43$	$13 \cdot 53$
69	$5 \cdot 139$	$2^3 \cdot 3 \cdot 29$	$17 \cdot 41$	$2 \cdot 349$	$3 \cdot 233$
70	$3 \cdot 5 \cdot 47$	$2 \cdot 353$	$7 \cdot 101$	$2^2 \cdot 3 \cdot 59$	**8506462**
71	$5 \cdot 11 \cdot 13$	$2^2 \cdot 179$	$3 \cdot 239$	$2 \cdot 359$	**8567289**
72	$5^2 \cdot 29$	$2 \cdot 3 \cdot 11^2$	**8615344**	$2^3 \cdot 7 \cdot 13$	3^6
73	$3 \cdot 5 \cdot 7^2$	$2^5 \cdot 23$	$11 \cdot 67$	$2 \cdot 3^2 \cdot 41$	**8686444**
74	$5 \cdot 149$	$2 \cdot 373$	$3^2 \cdot 83$	$2^2 \cdot 11 \cdot 17$	$7 \cdot 107$
75	$5 \cdot 151$	$2^2 \cdot 3^3 \cdot 7$	**8790959**	$2 \cdot 379$	$3 \cdot 11 \cdot 23$
76	$3^2 \cdot 5 \cdot 17$	$2 \cdot 383$	$13 \cdot 59$	$2^8 \cdot 3$	**8859263**
77	$5^2 \cdot 31$	$2^3 \cdot 97$	$3 \cdot 7 \cdot 37$	$2 \cdot 389$	$19 \cdot 41$
78	$5 \cdot 157$	$2 \cdot 3 \cdot 131$	**8959747**	$2^2 \cdot 197$	$3 \cdot 263$
79	$3 \cdot 5 \cdot 53$	$2^2 \cdot 199$	**9014583**	$2 \cdot 3 \cdot 7 \cdot 19$	$17 \cdot 47$
80	$5 \cdot 7 \cdot 23$	$2 \cdot 13 \cdot 31$	$3 \cdot 269$	$2^3 \cdot 101$	**9079485**
81	$5 \cdot 163$	$2^4 \cdot 3 \cdot 17$	$19 \cdot 43$	$2 \cdot 409$	$3^2 \cdot 7 \cdot 13$
82	$3 \cdot 5^2 \cdot 11$	$2 \cdot 7 \cdot 59$	**9175055**	$2^2 \cdot 3^2 \cdot 23$	**9185545**
83	$5 \cdot 167$	$2^2 \cdot 11 \cdot 19$	$3^3 \cdot 31$	$2 \cdot 419$	**9237620**
84	$5 \cdot 13^2$	$2 \cdot 3^2 \cdot 47$	$7 \cdot 11^2$	$2^4 \cdot 53$	$3 \cdot 283$
85	$3^2 \cdot 5 \cdot 19$	$2^3 \cdot 107$	**9329808**	$2 \cdot 3 \cdot 11 \cdot 13$	**9339932**
86	$5 \cdot 173$	$2 \cdot 433$	$3 \cdot 17^2$	$2^2 \cdot 7 \cdot 31$	$11 \cdot 79$
87	$5^3 \cdot 7$	$2^2 \cdot 3 \cdot 73$	**9429996**	$2 \cdot 439$	$3 \cdot 293$
88	$3 \cdot 5 \cdot 59$	$2 \cdot 443$	**9479236**	$2^3 \cdot 3 \cdot 37$	$7 \cdot 127$
89	$5 \cdot 179$	$2^7 \cdot 7$	$3 \cdot 13 \cdot 23$	$2 \cdot 449$	$29 \cdot 31$
90	$5 \cdot 181$	$2 \cdot 3 \cdot 151$	**9576073**	$2^2 \cdot 227$	$3^2 \cdot 101$
91	$3 \cdot 5 \cdot 61$	$2^2 \cdot 229$	$7 \cdot 131$	$2 \cdot 3^3 \cdot 17$	**9633155**
92	$5^2 \cdot 37$	$2 \cdot 463$	$3^2 \cdot 103$	$2^5 \cdot 29$	**9680157**
93	$5 \cdot 11 \cdot 17$	$2^3 \cdot 3^2 \cdot 13$	**9717396**	$2 \cdot 7 \cdot 67$	$3 \cdot 313$
94	$3^3 \cdot 5 \cdot 7$	$2 \cdot 11 \cdot 43$	**9763500**	$2^2 \cdot 3 \cdot 79$	$13 \cdot 73$
95	$5 \cdot 191$	$2^2 \cdot 239$	$3 \cdot 11 \cdot 29$	$2 \cdot 479$	$7 \cdot 137$
96	$5 \cdot 193$	$2 \cdot 3 \cdot 7 \cdot 23$	**9854265**	$2^3 \cdot 11^2$	$3 \cdot 17 \cdot 19$
97	$3 \cdot 5^2 \cdot 13$	$2^4 \cdot 61$	**9898946**	$2 \cdot 3 \cdot 163$	$11 \cdot 89$
98	$5 \cdot 197$	$2 \cdot 17 \cdot 29$	$3 \cdot 7 \cdot 47$	$2^2 \cdot 13 \cdot 19$	$23 \cdot 43$
99	$5 \cdot 199$	$2^2 \cdot 3 \cdot 83$	**9986952**	$2 \cdot 499$	$3^3 \cdot 37$
100	$3 \cdot 5 \cdot 67$	$2 \cdot 503$	$19 \cdot 53$	$2^4 \cdot 3^2 \cdot 7$	**0038912**

FACTORS AND PRIMES (Continued)

n	0	1	2	3	4
100	$2^3 \cdot 5^3$	$7 \cdot 11 \cdot 13$	$2 \cdot 3 \cdot 167$	$17 \cdot 59$	$2^2 \cdot 251$
101	$2 \cdot 5 \cdot 101$	$3 \cdot 337$	$2^2 \cdot 11 \cdot 23$	**0056094**	$2 \cdot 3 \cdot 13^2$
102	$2^2 \cdot 3 \cdot 5 \cdot 17$	**0090257**	$2 \cdot 7 \cdot 73$	$3 \cdot 11 \cdot 31$	2^{10}
103	$2 \cdot 5 \cdot 103$	**0132587**	$2^3 \cdot 3 \cdot 43$	**0141003**	$2 \cdot 11 \cdot 47$
104	$2^4 \cdot 5 \cdot 13$	$3 \cdot 347$	$2 \cdot 521$	$7 \cdot 149$	$2^2 \cdot 3^2 \cdot 29$
105	$2 \cdot 3 \cdot 5^2 \cdot 7$	**0216027**	$2^2 \cdot 263$	$3^4 \cdot 13$	$2 \cdot 17 \cdot 31$
106	$2^2 \cdot 5 \cdot 53$	**0257154**	$2 \cdot 3^2 \cdot 59$	**0265333**	$2^3 \cdot 7 \cdot 19$
107	$2 \cdot 5 \cdot 107$	$3^2 \cdot 7 \cdot 17$	$2^4 \cdot 67$	$29 \cdot 37$	$2 \cdot 3 \cdot 179$
108	$2^3 \cdot 3^3 \cdot 5$	$23 \cdot 47$	$2 \cdot 541$	$3 \cdot 19^2$	$2^2 \cdot 271$
109	$2 \cdot 5 \cdot 109$	**0378248**	$2^2 \cdot 3 \cdot 7 \cdot 13$	**0386202**	$2 \cdot 547$
110	$2^2 \cdot 5^2 \cdot 11$	$3 \cdot 367$	$2 \cdot 19 \cdot 29$	**0425755**	$2^4 \cdot 3 \cdot 23$
111	$2 \cdot 3 \cdot 5 \cdot 37$	$11 \cdot 101$	$2^3 \cdot 139$	$3 \cdot 7 \cdot 53$	$2 \cdot 557$
112	$2^5 \cdot 5 \cdot 7$	$19 \cdot 59$	$2 \cdot 3 \cdot 11 \cdot 17$	**0503798**	$2^2 \cdot 281$
113	$2 \cdot 5 \cdot 113$	$3 \cdot 13 \cdot 29$	$2^2 \cdot 283$	$11 \cdot 103$	$2 \cdot 3^4 \cdot 7$
114	$2^2 \cdot 3 \cdot 5 \cdot 19$	$7 \cdot 163$	$2 \cdot 571$	$3^2 \cdot 127$	$2^3 \cdot 11 \cdot 13$
115	$2 \cdot 5^2 \cdot 23$	**0610753**	$2^7 \cdot 3^2$	**0618293**	$2 \cdot 577$
116	$2^3 \cdot 5 \cdot 29$	$3^3 \cdot 43$	$2 \cdot 7 \cdot 83$	**0655797**	$2^2 \cdot 3 \cdot 97$
117	$2 \cdot 3^2 \cdot 5 \cdot 13$	**0685569**	$2^2 \cdot 293$	$3 \cdot 17 \cdot 23$	$2 \cdot 587$
118	$2^2 \cdot 5 \cdot 59$	**0722499**	$2 \cdot 3 \cdot 197$	$7 \cdot 13^2$	$2^5 \cdot 37$
119	$2 \cdot 5 \cdot 7 \cdot 17$	$3 \cdot 397$	$2^3 \cdot 149$	**0766404**	$2 \cdot 3 \cdot 199$
120	$2^4 \cdot 3 \cdot 5^2$	**0795430**	$2 \cdot 601$	$3 \cdot 401$	$2^2 \cdot 7 \cdot 43$
121	$2 \cdot 5 \cdot 11^2$	$7 \cdot 173$	$2^2 \cdot 3 \cdot 101$	**0838608**	$2 \cdot 607$
122	$2^2 \cdot 5 \cdot 61$	$3 \cdot 11 \cdot 37$	$2 \cdot 13 \cdot 47$	**0874265**	$2^3 \cdot 3^2 \cdot 17$
123	$2 \cdot 3 \cdot 5 \cdot 41$	**0902581**	$2^4 \cdot 7 \cdot 11$	$3^2 \cdot 137$	$2 \cdot 617$
124	$2^3 \cdot 5 \cdot 31$	$17 \cdot 73$	$2 \cdot 3^3 \cdot 23$	$11 \cdot 113$	$2^2 \cdot 311$
125	$2 \cdot 5^4$	$3^2 \cdot 139$	$2^2 \cdot 313$	$7 \cdot 179$	$2 \cdot 3 \cdot 11 \cdot 19$
126	$2^2 \cdot 3^2 \cdot 5 \cdot 7$	$13 \cdot 97$	$2 \cdot 631$	$3 \cdot 421$	$2^4 \cdot 79$
127	$2 \cdot 5 \cdot 127$	$31 \cdot 41$	$2^3 \cdot 3 \cdot 53$	$19 \cdot 67$	$2 \cdot 7^2 \cdot 13$
128	$2^8 \cdot 5$	$3 \cdot 7 \cdot 61$	$2 \cdot 641$	**1082267**	$2^2 \cdot 3 \cdot 107$
129	$2 \cdot 3 \cdot 5 \cdot 43$	**1109262**	$2^2 \cdot 17 \cdot 19$	$3 \cdot 431$	$2 \cdot 647$
130	$2^2 \cdot 5^2 \cdot 13$	**1142773**	$2 \cdot 3 \cdot 7 \cdot 31$	**1149444**	$2^3 \cdot 163$
131	$2 \cdot 5 \cdot 131$	$3 \cdot 19 \cdot 23$	$2^5 \cdot 41$	$13 \cdot 101$	$2 \cdot 3^2 \cdot 73$
132	$2^3 \cdot 3 \cdot 5 \cdot 11$	**1209028**	$2 \cdot 661$	$3^3 \cdot 7^2$	$2^2 \cdot 331$
133	$2 \cdot 5 \cdot 7 \cdot 19$	11^3	$2^2 \cdot 3^2 \cdot 37$	$31 \cdot 43$	$2 \cdot 23 \cdot 29$
134	$2^2 \cdot 5 \cdot 67$	$3^2 \cdot 149$	$2 \cdot 11 \cdot 61$	$17 \cdot 79$	$2^6 \cdot 3 \cdot 7$
135	$2 \cdot 3^3 \cdot 5^2$	$7 \cdot 193$	$2^3 \cdot 13^2$	$3 \cdot 11 \cdot 41$	$2 \cdot 677$
136	$2^4 \cdot 5 \cdot 17$	**1338581**	$2 \cdot 3 \cdot 227$	$29 \cdot 47$	$2^2 \cdot 11 \cdot 31$
137	$2 \cdot 5 \cdot 137$	$3 \cdot 457$	$2^2 \cdot 7^3$	**1376705**	$2 \cdot 3 \cdot 229$
138	$2^2 \cdot 3 \cdot 5 \cdot 23$	**1401937**	$2 \cdot 691$	$3 \cdot 461$	$2^3 \cdot 173$
139	$2 \cdot 5 \cdot 139$	$13 \cdot 107$	$2^4 \cdot 3 \cdot 29$	$7 \cdot 199$	$2 \cdot 17 \cdot 41$
140	$2^3 \cdot 5^2 \cdot 7$	$3 \cdot 467$	$2 \cdot 701$	$23 \cdot 61$	$2^2 \cdot 3^3 \cdot 13$
141	$2 \cdot 3 \cdot 5 \cdot 47$	$17 \cdot 83$	$2^2 \cdot 353$	$3^2 \cdot 157$	$2 \cdot 7 \cdot 101$
142	$2^2 \cdot 5 \cdot 71$	$7^2 \cdot 29$	$2 \cdot 3^2 \cdot 79$	**1532049**	$2^4 \cdot 89$
143	$2 \cdot 5 \cdot 11 \cdot 13$	$3^3 \cdot 53$	$2^3 \cdot 179$	**1562462**	$2 \cdot 3 \cdot 239$
144	$2^5 \cdot 3^2 \cdot 5$	$11 \cdot 131$	$2 \cdot 7 \cdot 103$	$3 \cdot 13 \cdot 37$	$2^2 \cdot 19^2$
145	$2 \cdot 5^2 \cdot 29$	**1616674**	$2^2 \cdot 3 \cdot 11^2$	**1622656**	$2 \cdot 727$
146	$2^2 \cdot 5 \cdot 73$	$3 \cdot 487$	$2 \cdot 17 \cdot 43$	$7 \cdot 11 \cdot 19$	$2^3 \cdot 3 \cdot 61$
147	$2 \cdot 3 \cdot 5 \cdot 7^2$	**1676127**	$2^6 \cdot 23$	$3 \cdot 491$	$2 \cdot 11 \cdot 67$
148	$2^3 \cdot 5 \cdot 37$	**1705551**	$2 \cdot 3 \cdot 13 \cdot 19$	**1711412**	$2^2 \cdot 7 \cdot 53$
149	$2 \cdot 5 \cdot 149$	$3 \cdot 7 \cdot 71$	$2^2 \cdot 373$	**1740598**	$2 \cdot 3^2 \cdot 83$
150	$2^2 \cdot 3 \cdot 5^3$	$19 \cdot 79$	$2 \cdot 751$	$3^2 \cdot 167$	$2^5 \cdot 47$

FACTORS AND PRIMES (Continued)

n	5	6	7	8	9
100	$3 \cdot 5 \cdot 67$	$2 \cdot 503$	$19 \cdot 53$	$2^4 \cdot 3^2 \cdot 7$	**0038912**
101	$5 \cdot 7 \cdot 29$	$2^3 \cdot 127$	$3^2 \cdot 113$	$2 \cdot 509$	**0081742**
102	$5^2 \cdot 41$	$2 \cdot 3^3 \cdot 19$	$13 \cdot 79$	$2^2 \cdot 257$	$3 \cdot 7^3$
103	$3^2 \cdot 5 \cdot 23$	$2^2 \cdot 7 \cdot 37$	$17 \cdot 61$	$2 \cdot 3 \cdot 173$	**0166155**
104	$5 \cdot 11 \cdot 19$	$2 \cdot 523$	$3 \cdot 349$	$2^3 \cdot 131$	**0207755**
105	$5 \cdot 211$	$2^5 \cdot 3 \cdot 11$	$7 \cdot 151$	$2 \cdot 23^2$	$3 \cdot 353$
106	$3 \cdot 5 \cdot 71$	$2 \cdot 13 \cdot 41$	$11 \cdot 97$	$2^2 \cdot 3 \cdot 89$	**0289777**
107	$5^2 \cdot 43$	$2^2 \cdot 269$	$3 \cdot 359$	$2 \cdot 7^2 \cdot 11$	$13 \cdot 83$
108	$5 \cdot 7 \cdot 31$	$2 \cdot 3 \cdot 181$	**0362295**	$2^6 \cdot 17$	$3^2 \cdot 11^2$
109	$3 \cdot 5 \cdot 73$	$2^3 \cdot 137$	**0402066**	$2 \cdot 3^2 \cdot 61$	$7 \cdot 157$
110	$5 \cdot 13 \cdot 17$	$2 \cdot 7 \cdot 79$	$3^3 \cdot 41$	$2^2 \cdot 277$	**0449315**
111	$5 \cdot 223$	$2^2 \cdot 3^2 \cdot 31$	**0480532**	$2 \cdot 13 \cdot 43$	$3 \cdot 373$
112	$3^2 \cdot 5^3$	$2 \cdot 563$	$7^2 \cdot 23$	$2^3 \cdot 3 \cdot 47$	**0526939**
113	$5 \cdot 227$	$2^4 \cdot 71$	$3 \cdot 379$	$2 \cdot 569$	$17 \cdot 67$
114	$5 \cdot 229$	$2 \cdot 3 \cdot 191$	$31 \cdot 37$	$2^2 \cdot 7 \cdot 41$	$3 \cdot 383$
115	$3 \cdot 5 \cdot 7 \cdot 11$	$2^2 \cdot 17^2$	$13 \cdot 89$	$2 \cdot 3 \cdot 193$	$19 \cdot 61$
116	$5 \cdot 233$	$2 \cdot 11 \cdot 53$	$3 \cdot 389$	$2^4 \cdot 73$	$7 \cdot 167$
117	$5^2 \cdot 47$	$2^3 \cdot 3 \cdot 7^2$	$11 \cdot 107$	$2 \cdot 19 \cdot 31$	$3^2 \cdot 131$
118	$3 \cdot 5 \cdot 79$	$2 \cdot 593$	**0744507**	$2^2 \cdot 3^3 \cdot 11$	$29 \cdot 41$
119	$5 \cdot 239$	$2^2 \cdot 13 \cdot 23$	$3^2 \cdot 7 \cdot 19$	$2 \cdot 599$	$11 \cdot 109$
120	$5 \cdot 241$	$2 \cdot 3^2 \cdot 67$	$17 \cdot 71$	$2^3 \cdot 151$	$3 \cdot 13 \cdot 31$
121	$3^5 \cdot 5$	$2^6 \cdot 19$	**0852906**	$2 \cdot 3 \cdot 7 \cdot 29$	$23 \cdot 53$
122	$5^2 \cdot 7^2$	$2 \cdot 613$	$3 \cdot 409$	$2^2 \cdot 307$	**0895519**
123	$5 \cdot 13 \cdot 19$	$2^2 \cdot 3 \cdot 103$	**0923697**	$2 \cdot 619$	$3 \cdot 7 \cdot 59$
124	$3 \cdot 5 \cdot 83$	$2 \cdot 7 \cdot 89$	$29 \cdot 43$	$2^5 \cdot 3 \cdot 13$	**0965624**
125	$5 \cdot 251$	$2^3 \cdot 157$	$3 \cdot 419$	$2 \cdot 17 \cdot 37$	**1000257**
126	$5 \cdot 11 \cdot 23$	$2 \cdot 3 \cdot 211$	$7 \cdot 181$	$2^2 \cdot 317$	$3^3 \cdot 47$
127	$3 \cdot 5^2 \cdot 17$	$2^2 \cdot 11 \cdot 29$	**1061909**	$2 \cdot 3^2 \cdot 71$	**1068705**
128	$5 \cdot 257$	$2 \cdot 643$	$3^2 \cdot 11 \cdot 13$	$2^3 \cdot 7 \cdot 23$	**1102529**
129	$5 \cdot 7 \cdot 37$	$2^4 \cdot 3^4$	**1129400**	$2 \cdot 11 \cdot 59$	$3 \cdot 433$
130	$3^2 \cdot 5 \cdot 29$	$2 \cdot 653$	**1162756**	$2^2 \cdot 3 \cdot 109$	$7 \cdot 11 \cdot 17$
131	$5 \cdot 263$	$2^2 \cdot 7 \cdot 47$	$3 \cdot 439$	$2 \cdot 659$	**1202448**
132	$5^2 \cdot 53$	$2 \cdot 3 \cdot 13 \cdot 17$	**1228709**	$2^4 \cdot 83$	$3 \cdot 443$
133	$3 \cdot 5 \cdot 89$	$2^3 \cdot 167$	$7 \cdot 191$	$2 \cdot 3 \cdot 223$	$13 \cdot 103$
134	$5 \cdot 269$	$2 \cdot 673$	$3 \cdot 449$	$2^2 \cdot 337$	$19 \cdot 71$
135	$5 \cdot 271$	$2^2 \cdot 3 \cdot 113$	$23 \cdot 59$	$2 \cdot 7 \cdot 97$	$3^2 \cdot 151$
136	$3 \cdot 5 \cdot 7 \cdot 13$	$2 \cdot 683$	**1357685**	$2^3 \cdot 3^2 \cdot 19$	37^2
137	$5^3 \cdot 11$	$2^5 \cdot 43$	$3^4 \cdot 17$	$2 \cdot 13 \cdot 53$	$7 \cdot 197$
138	$5 \cdot 277$	$2 \cdot 3^2 \cdot 7 \cdot 11$	$19 \cdot 73$	$2^2 \cdot 347$	$3 \cdot 463$
139	$3^2 \cdot 5 \cdot 31$	$2^2 \cdot 349$	$11 \cdot 127$	$2 \cdot 3 \cdot 233$	**1458177**
140	$5 \cdot 281$	$2 \cdot 19 \cdot 37$	$3 \cdot 7 \cdot 67$	$2^7 \cdot 11$	**1489110**
141	$5 \cdot 283$	$2^3 \cdot 3 \cdot 59$	$13 \cdot 109$	$2 \cdot 709$	$3 \cdot 11 \cdot 43$
142	$3 \cdot 5^2 \cdot 19$	$2 \cdot 23 \cdot 31$	**1544240**	$2^2 \cdot 3 \cdot 7 \cdot 17$	**1550322**
143	$5 \cdot 7 \cdot 41$	$2^2 \cdot 359$	$3 \cdot 479$	$2 \cdot 719$	**1580608**
144	$5 \cdot 17^2$	$2 \cdot 3 \cdot 241$	**1604685**	$2^3 \cdot 181$	$3^2 \cdot 7 \cdot 23$
145	$3 \cdot 5 \cdot 97$	$2^4 \cdot 7 \cdot 13$	$31 \cdot 47$	$2 \cdot 3^6$	**1640553**
146	$5 \cdot 293$	$2 \cdot 733$	$3^2 \cdot 163$	$2^2 \cdot 367$	$13 \cdot 113$
147	$5^2 \cdot 59$	$2^2 \cdot 3^2 \cdot 41$	$7 \cdot 211$	$2 \cdot 739$	$3 \cdot 17 \cdot 29$
148	$3^3 \cdot 5 \cdot 11$	$2 \cdot 743$	**1723110**	$2^4 \cdot 3 \cdot 31$	**1728947**
149	$5 \cdot 13 \cdot 23$	$2^3 \cdot 11 \cdot 17$	$3 \cdot 499$	$2 \cdot 7 \cdot 107$	**1758016**
150	$5 \cdot 7 \cdot 43$	$2 \cdot 3 \cdot 251$	$11 \cdot 137$	$2^2 \cdot 13 \cdot 29$	$3 \cdot 503$

FACTORS AND PRIMES (Continued)

n	0	1	2	3	4
150	$2^2 \cdot 3 \cdot 5^3$	$19 \cdot 79$	$2 \cdot 751$	$3^2 \cdot 167$	$2^5 \cdot 47$
151	$2 \cdot 5 \cdot 151$	**1792645**	$2^3 \cdot 3^3 \cdot 7$	$17 \cdot 89$	$2 \cdot 757$
152	$2^4 \cdot 5 \cdot 19$	$3^2 \cdot 13^2$	$2 \cdot 761$	**1826999**	$2^2 \cdot 3 \cdot 127$
153	$2 \cdot 3^2 \cdot 5 \cdot 17$	**1849752**	$2^2 \cdot 383$	$3 \cdot 7 \cdot 73$	$2 \cdot 13 \cdot 59$
154	$2^2 \cdot 5 \cdot 7 \cdot 11$	$23 \cdot 67$	$2 \cdot 3 \cdot 257$	**1883659**	$2^3 \cdot 193$
155	$2 \cdot 5^2 \cdot 31$	$3 \cdot 11 \cdot 47$	$2^4 \cdot 97$	**1911715**	$2 \cdot 3 \cdot 7 \cdot 37$
156	$2^3 \cdot 3 \cdot 5 \cdot 13$	$7 \cdot 223$	$2 \cdot 11 \cdot 71$	$3 \cdot 521$	$2^2 \cdot 17 \cdot 23$
157	$2 \cdot 5 \cdot 157$	**1961762**	$2^2 \cdot 3 \cdot 131$	$11^2 \cdot 13$	$2 \cdot 787$
158	$2^2 \cdot 5 \cdot 79$	$3 \cdot 17 \cdot 31$	$2 \cdot 7 \cdot 113$	**1994809**	$2^4 \cdot 3^2 \cdot 11$
159	$2 \cdot 3 \cdot 5 \cdot 53$	$37 \cdot 43$	$2^3 \cdot 199$	$3^3 \cdot 59$	$2 \cdot 797$
160	$2^6 \cdot 5^2$	**2043913**	$2 \cdot 3^2 \cdot 89$	$7 \cdot 229$	$2^2 \cdot 401$
161	$2 \cdot 5 \cdot 7 \cdot 23$	$3^2 \cdot 179$	$2^2 \cdot 13 \cdot 31$	**2076344**	$2 \cdot 3 \cdot 269$
162	$2^2 \cdot 3^4 \cdot 5$	**2097830**	$2 \cdot 811$	$3 \cdot 541$	$2^3 \cdot 7 \cdot 29$
163	$2 \cdot 5 \cdot 163$	$7 \cdot 233$	$2^5 \cdot 3 \cdot 17$	$23 \cdot 71$	$2 \cdot 19 \cdot 43$
164	$2^3 \cdot 5 \cdot 41$	$3 \cdot 547$	$2 \cdot 821$	$31 \cdot 53$	$2^2 \cdot 3 \cdot 137$
165	$2 \cdot 3 \cdot 5^2 \cdot 11$	$13 \cdot 127$	$2^2 \cdot 7 \cdot 59$	$3 \cdot 19 \cdot 29$	$2 \cdot 827$
166	$2^2 \cdot 5 \cdot 83$	$11 \cdot 151$	$2 \cdot 3 \cdot 277$	**2208922**	$2^7 \cdot 13$
167	$2 \cdot 5 \cdot 167$	$3 \cdot 557$	$2^3 \cdot 11 \cdot 19$	$7 \cdot 239$	$2 \cdot 3^3 \cdot 31$
168	$2^4 \cdot 3 \cdot 5 \cdot 7$	41^2	$2 \cdot 29^2$	$3^2 \cdot 11 \cdot 17$	$2^2 \cdot 421$
169	$2 \cdot 5 \cdot 13^2$	$19 \cdot 89$	$2^2 \cdot 3^2 \cdot 47$	**2286570**	$2 \cdot 7 \cdot 11^2$
170	$2^2 \cdot 5^2 \cdot 17$	$3^5 \cdot 7$	$2 \cdot 23 \cdot 37$	$13 \cdot 131$	$2^3 \cdot 3 \cdot 71$
171	$2 \cdot 3^2 \cdot 5 \cdot 19$	$29 \cdot 59$	$2^4 \cdot 107$	$3 \cdot 571$	$2 \cdot 857$
172	$2^3 \cdot 5 \cdot 43$	**2357809**	$2 \cdot 3 \cdot 7 \cdot 41$	**2362853**	$2^2 \cdot 431$
173	$2 \cdot 5 \cdot 173$	$3 \cdot 577$	$2^2 \cdot 433$	**2387986**	$2 \cdot 3 \cdot 17^2$
174	$2^2 \cdot 3 \cdot 5 \cdot 29$	**2407988**	$2 \cdot 13 \cdot 67$	$3 \cdot 7 \cdot 83$	$2^4 \cdot 109$
175	$2 \cdot 5^3 \cdot 7$	$17 \cdot 103$	$2^3 \cdot 3 \cdot 73$	**2437819**	$2 \cdot 877$
176	$2^5 \cdot 5 \cdot 11$	$3 \cdot 587$	$2 \cdot 881$	$41 \cdot 43$	$2^2 \cdot 3^2 \cdot 7^2$
177	$2 \cdot 3 \cdot 5 \cdot 59$	$7 \cdot 11 \cdot 23$	$2^2 \cdot 443$	$3^2 \cdot 197$	$2 \cdot 887$
178	$2^2 \cdot 5 \cdot 89$	$13 \cdot 137$	$2 \cdot 3^4 \cdot 11$	**2511513**	$2^3 \cdot 223$
179	$2 \cdot 5 \cdot 179$	$3^2 \cdot 199$	$2^8 \cdot 7$	$11 \cdot 163$	$2 \cdot 3 \cdot 13 \cdot 23$
180	$2^3 \cdot 3^2 \cdot 5^2$	**2555137**	$2 \cdot 17 \cdot 53$	$3 \cdot 601$	$2^2 \cdot 11 \cdot 41$
181	$2 \cdot 5 \cdot 181$	**2579185**	$2^2 \cdot 3 \cdot 151$	$7^2 \cdot 37$	$2 \cdot 907$
182	$2^2 \cdot 5 \cdot 7 \cdot 13$	$3 \cdot 607$	$2 \cdot 911$	**2607867**	$2^5 \cdot 3 \cdot 19$
183	$2 \cdot 3 \cdot 5 \cdot 61$	**2626883**	$2^3 \cdot 229$	$3 \cdot 13 \cdot 47$	$2 \cdot 7 \cdot 131$
184	$2^4 \cdot 5 \cdot 23$	$7 \cdot 263$	$2 \cdot 3 \cdot 307$	$19 \cdot 97$	$2^2 \cdot 461$
185	$2 \cdot 5^2 \cdot 37$	$3 \cdot 617$	$2^2 \cdot 463$	$17 \cdot 109$	$2 \cdot 3^2 \cdot 103$
186	$2^2 \cdot 3 \cdot 5 \cdot 31$	**2697464**	$2 \cdot 7^2 \cdot 19$	$3^4 \cdot 23$	$2^3 \cdot 233$
187	$2 \cdot 5 \cdot 11 \cdot 17$	**2720738**	$2^4 \cdot 3^2 \cdot 13$	**2725378**	$2 \cdot 937$
188	$2^3 \cdot 5 \cdot 47$	$3^2 \cdot 11 \cdot 19$	$2 \cdot 941$	$7 \cdot 269$	$2^2 \cdot 3 \cdot 157$
189	$2 \cdot 3^3 \cdot 5 \cdot 7$	$31 \cdot 61$	$2^2 \cdot 11 \cdot 43$	$3 \cdot 631$	$2 \cdot 947$
190	$2^2 \cdot 5^2 \cdot 19$	**2789821**	$2 \cdot 3 \cdot 317$	$11 \cdot 173$	$2^4 \cdot 7 \cdot 17$
191	$2 \cdot 5 \cdot 191$	$3 \cdot 7^2 \cdot 13$	$2^3 \cdot 239$	**2817150**	$2 \cdot 3 \cdot 11 \cdot 29$
192	$2^7 \cdot 3 \cdot 5$	$17 \cdot 113$	$2 \cdot 31^2$	$3 \cdot 641$	$2^2 \cdot 13 \cdot 37$
193	$2 \cdot 5 \cdot 193$	**2857823**	$2^2 \cdot 3 \cdot 7 \cdot 23$	**2862319**	$2 \cdot 967$
194	$2^2 \cdot 5 \cdot 97$	$3 \cdot 647$	$2 \cdot 971$	$29 \cdot 67$	$2^3 \cdot 3^5$
195	$2 \cdot 3 \cdot 5^2 \cdot 13$	**2902573**	$2^5 \cdot 61$	$3^2 \cdot 7 \cdot 31$	$2 \cdot 977$
196	$2^3 \cdot 5 \cdot 7^2$	$37 \cdot 53$	$2 \cdot 3^2 \cdot 109$	$13 \cdot 151$	$2^2 \cdot 491$
197	$2 \cdot 5 \cdot 197$	$3^3 \cdot 73$	$2^2 \cdot 17 \cdot 29$	**2951271**	$2 \cdot 3 \cdot 7 \cdot 47$
198	$2^2 \cdot 3^2 \cdot 5 \cdot 11$	$7 \cdot 283$	$2 \cdot 991$	$3 \cdot 661$	$2^6 \cdot 31$
199	$2 \cdot 5 \cdot 199$	$11 \cdot 181$	$2^3 \cdot 3 \cdot 83$	**2995073**	$2 \cdot 997$
200	$2^4 \cdot 5^3$	$3 \cdot 23 \cdot 29$	$2 \cdot 7 \cdot 11 \cdot 13$	**3016809**	$2^2 \cdot 3 \cdot 167$

FACTORS AND PRIMES (Continued)

n	5	6	**7**	8	9
150	$5 \cdot 7 \cdot 43$	$2 \cdot 3 \cdot 251$	$11 \cdot 137$	$2^2 \cdot 13 \cdot 29$	$3 \cdot 503$
151	$3 \cdot 5 \cdot 101$	$2^2 \cdot 379$	$37 \cdot 41$	$2 \cdot 3 \cdot 11 \cdot 23$	$7^2 \cdot 31$
152	$5^2 \cdot 61$	$2 \cdot 7 \cdot 109$	$3 \cdot 509$	$2^3 \cdot 191$	$11 \cdot 139$
153	$5 \cdot 307$	$2^9 \cdot 3$	$29 \cdot 53$	$2 \cdot 769$	$3^4 \cdot 19$
154	$3 \cdot 5 \cdot 103$	$2 \cdot 773$	$7 \cdot 13 \cdot 17$	$2^2 \cdot 3^2 \cdot 43$	**1900514**
155	$5 \cdot 311$	$2^2 \cdot 389$	$3^2 \cdot 173$	$2 \cdot 19 \cdot 41$	**1928461**
156	$5 \cdot 313$	$2 \cdot 3^3 \cdot 29$	**1950690**	$2^5 \cdot 7^2$	$3 \cdot 523$
157	$3^2 \cdot 5^2 \cdot 7$	$2^3 \cdot 197$	$19 \cdot 83$	$2 \cdot 3 \cdot 263$	**1983821**
158	$5 \cdot 317$	$2 \cdot 13 \cdot 61$	$3 \cdot 23^2$	$2^2 \cdot 397$	$7 \cdot 227$
159	$5 \cdot 11 \cdot 29$	$2^2 \cdot 3 \cdot 7 \cdot 19$	**2033049**	$2 \cdot 17 \cdot 47$	$3 \cdot 13 \cdot 41$
160	$3 \cdot 5 \cdot 107$	$2 \cdot 11 \cdot 73$	**2060159**	$2^3 \cdot 3 \cdot 67$	**2065560**
161	$5 \cdot 17 \cdot 19$	$2^4 \cdot 101$	$3 \cdot 7^2 \cdot 11$	$2 \cdot 809$	**2092468**
162	$5^3 \cdot 13$	$2 \cdot 3 \cdot 271$	**2113876**	$2^2 \cdot 11 \cdot 37$	$3^2 \cdot 181$
163	$3 \cdot 5 \cdot 109$	$2^2 \cdot 409$	**2140487**	$2 \cdot 3^2 \cdot 7 \cdot 13$	$11 \cdot 149$
164	$5 \cdot 7 \cdot 47$	$2 \cdot 823$	$3^3 \cdot 61$	$2^4 \cdot 103$	$17 \cdot 97$
165	$5 \cdot 331$	$2^3 \cdot 3^2 \cdot 23$	**2193225**	$2 \cdot 829$	$3 \cdot 7 \cdot 79$
166	$3^2 \cdot 5 \cdot 37$	$2 \cdot 7^2 \cdot 17$	**2219356**	$2^2 \cdot 3 \cdot 139$	**2224563**
167	$5^2 \cdot 67$	$2^2 \cdot 419$	$3 \cdot 13 \cdot 43$	$2 \cdot 839$	$23 \cdot 73$
168	$5 \cdot 337$	$2 \cdot 3 \cdot 281$	$7 \cdot 241$	$2^3 \cdot 211$	$3 \cdot 563$
169	$3 \cdot 5 \cdot 113$	$2^5 \cdot 53$	**2296818**	$2 \cdot 3 \cdot 283$	**2301934**
170	$5 \cdot 11 \cdot 31$	$2 \cdot 853$	$3 \cdot 569$	$2^2 \cdot 7 \cdot 61$	**2327421**
171	$5 \cdot 7^3$	$2^2 \cdot 3 \cdot 11 \cdot 13$	$17 \cdot 101$	$2 \cdot 859$	$3^2 \cdot 191$
172	$3 \cdot 5^2 \cdot 23$	$2 \cdot 863$	$11 \cdot 157$	$2^6 \cdot 3^3$	$7 \cdot 13 \cdot 19$
173	$5 \cdot 347$	$2^3 \cdot 7 \cdot 31$	$3^2 \cdot 193$	$2 \cdot 11 \cdot 79$	$37 \cdot 47$
174	$5 \cdot 349$	$2 \cdot 3^2 \cdot 97$	**2422929**	$2^2 \cdot 19 \cdot 23$	$3 \cdot 11 \cdot 53$
175	$3^3 \cdot 5 \cdot 13$	$2^2 \cdot 439$	$7 \cdot 251$	$2 \cdot 3 \cdot 293$	**2452658**
176	$5 \cdot 353$	$2 \cdot 883$	$3 \cdot 19 \cdot 31$	$2^3 \cdot 13 \cdot 17$	$29 \cdot 61$
177	$5^2 \cdot 71$	$2^4 \cdot 3 \cdot 37$	**2496874**	$2 \cdot 7 \cdot 127$	$3 \cdot 593$
178	$3 \cdot 5 \cdot 7 \cdot 17$	$2 \cdot 19 \cdot 47$	**2521246**	$2^2 \cdot 3 \cdot 149$	**2526103**
179	$5 \cdot 359$	$2^2 \cdot 449$	$3 \cdot 599$	$2 \cdot 29 \cdot 31$	$7 \cdot 257$
180	$5 \cdot 19^2$	$2 \cdot 3 \cdot 7 \cdot 43$	$13 \cdot 139$	$2^4 \cdot 113$	$3^3 \cdot 67$
181	$3 \cdot 5 \cdot 11^2$	$2^3 \cdot 227$	$23 \cdot 79$	$2 \cdot 3^2 \cdot 101$	$17 \cdot 107$
182	$5^2 \cdot 73$	$2 \cdot 11 \cdot 83$	$3^2 \cdot 7 \cdot 29$	$2^2 \cdot 457$	$31 \cdot 59$
183	$5 \cdot 367$	$2^2 \cdot 3^3 \cdot 17$	$11 \cdot 167$	$2 \cdot 919$	$3 \cdot 613$
184	$3^2 \cdot 5 \cdot 41$	$2 \cdot 13 \cdot 71$	**2664669**	$2^3 \cdot 3 \cdot 7 \cdot 11$	43^2
185	$5 \cdot 7 \cdot 53$	$2^6 \cdot 29$	$3 \cdot 619$	$2 \cdot 929$	$11 \cdot 13^2$
186	$5 \cdot 373$	$2 \cdot 3 \cdot 311$	**2711443**	$2^2 \cdot 467$	$3 \cdot 7 \cdot 89$
187	$3 \cdot 5^4$	$2^2 \cdot 7 \cdot 67$	**2734643**	$2 \cdot 3 \cdot 313$	**2739268**
188	$5 \cdot 13 \cdot 29$	$2 \cdot 23 \cdot 41$	$3 \cdot 17 \cdot 37$	$2^5 \cdot 59$	**2762320**
189	$5 \cdot 379$	$2^3 \cdot 3 \cdot 79$	$7 \cdot 271$	$2 \cdot 13 \cdot 73$	$3^2 \cdot 211$
190	$3 \cdot 5 \cdot 127$	$2 \cdot 953$	**2803507**	$2^2 \cdot 3^2 \cdot 53$	$23 \cdot 83$
191	$5 \cdot 383$	$2^2 \cdot 479$	$3^3 \cdot 71$	$2 \cdot 7 \cdot 137$	$19 \cdot 101$
192	$5^2 \cdot 7 \cdot 11$	$2 \cdot 3^2 \cdot 107$	$41 \cdot 47$	$2^3 \cdot 241$	$3 \cdot 643$
193	$3^2 \cdot 5 \cdot 43$	$2^4 \cdot 11^2$	$13 \cdot 149$	$2 \cdot 3 \cdot 17 \cdot 19$	$7 \cdot 277$
194	$5 \cdot 389$	$2 \cdot 7 \cdot 139$	$3 \cdot 11 \cdot 59$	$2^2 \cdot 487$	**2898118**
195	$5 \cdot 17 \cdot 23$	$2^2 \cdot 3 \cdot 163$	$19 \cdot 103$	$2 \cdot 11 \cdot 89$	$3 \cdot 653$
196	$3 \cdot 5 \cdot 131$	$2 \cdot 983$	$7 \cdot 281$	$2^4 \cdot 3 \cdot 41$	$11 \cdot 179$
197	$5^2 \cdot 79$	$2^3 \cdot 13 \cdot 19$	$3 \cdot 659$	$2 \cdot 23 \cdot 43$	**2964458**
198	$5 \cdot 397$	$2 \cdot 3 \cdot 331$	**2981979**	$2^2 \cdot 7 \cdot 71$	$3^2 \cdot 13 \cdot 17$
199	$3 \cdot 5 \cdot 7 \cdot 19$	$2^2 \cdot 499$	**3003781**	$2 \cdot 3^3 \cdot 37$	**3008128**
200	$5 \cdot 401$	$2 \cdot 17 \cdot 59$	$3^2 \cdot 223$	$2^3 \cdot 251$	$7^2 \cdot 41$

CALCULUS

DIFFERENTIALS

$d\,ax = a\,dx$

$d(u + v) = du + dv$

$d\,uv = u\,dv + v\,du$

$d\frac{u}{v} = \frac{v\,du - u\,dv}{v^2}$

$d\,x^n = n\,x^{n-1}dx$

$dx^y = yx^{y-1}dx + x^y \log_e x\,dy$

$d\,e^x = e^x\,dx$

$d\,e^{ax} = a\,e^{ax}dx$

$d\,a^x = a^x \log_e a\,dx$

$d \log_e x = x^{-1}dx$

$d \log_a x = x^{-1} \log_a e\,dx$

$d\,x^x = x^x (1 + \log_e x)\,dx$

$d \sin x = \cos x\,dx$

$d \cos x = -\sin x\,dx$

$d \tan x = \sec^2 x\,dx$

$d \cot x = -\csc^2 x\,dx$

$d \sec x = \tan x \sec x\,dx$

$d \csc x = -\cot x \cdot \csc x\,dx$

$d\,\mathrm{vers}\,x = \sin x\,dx$

$d \sin^{-1}x = (1 - x^2)^{-\frac{1}{2}}dx$

$d \cos^{-1}x = -(1 - x^2)^{-\frac{1}{2}}dx$

$d \tan^{-1}x = (1 + x^2)^{-1}dx$

$d \cot^{-1}x = -(1 + x^2)^{-1}dx$

$d \sec^{-1}x = x^{-1}(x^2 - 1)^{-\frac{1}{2}}dx$

$d \csc^{-1}x = -x^{-1}(x^2 - 1)^{-\frac{1}{2}}dx$

$d\,\mathrm{vers}^{-1}\,x = (2x - x^2)^{-\frac{1}{2}}\,dx$

$d \sinh x = \cosh x\,dx$

$d \cosh x = \sinh x\,dx$

$d \tanh x = \mathrm{sech}^2\,x\,dx$

$d \coth x = -\mathrm{csch}^2\,x\,dx$

$d\,\mathrm{sech}\,x = -\mathrm{sech}\,x \tanh x\,dx$

$d\,\mathrm{csch}\,x = -\mathrm{csch}\,x \coth x\,dx$

$d \sinh^{-1} x = (x^2 + 1)^{-\frac{1}{2}}dx$

$d \cosh^{-1} x = (x^2 - 1)^{-\frac{1}{2}}dx$

$d \tanh^{-1} x = (1 - x^2)^{-1}dx$

$d \coth^{-1} x = -(x^2 - 1)^{-1}dx$

$d\,\mathrm{sech}^{-1}\,x = -x^{-1}(1 - x^2)^{-\frac{1}{2}}dx$

$d\,\mathrm{csch}^{-1}\,x = -x^{-1}(x^2 + 1)^{-\frac{1}{2}}dx$

INTEGRALS

Elementary Forms

1. $\int a\,dx = ax.$
2. $\int a \cdot f(x)dx = a \int f(x)dx.$
3. $\int \phi(y)dx = \int \frac{\phi(y)}{y'}\,dy,$ where $y' = dy/dx.$
4. $\int (u + v)\,dx = \int u\,dx + \int v\,dx,$ where u and v are any functions of x.
5. $\int u\,dv = uv - \int v\,du.$
6. $\int u \frac{dv}{dx}\,dx = uv - \int v \frac{du}{dx}\,dx.$
7. $\int x^n\,dx = \frac{x^{n+1}}{n+1},$ except $n = -1.$
8. $\int \frac{f'(x)\,dx}{f(x)} = \log f(x),$ $[d\,f(x) = f'(x)\,dx]$
9. $\int \frac{dx}{x} = \log x,$ or $\log(-x).$
10. $\int \frac{f'(x)\,dx}{2\sqrt{f(x)}} = \sqrt{f(x)}.$ $[d\,f(x) = f'(x)\,dx].$
11. $\int e^x\,dx = e^x.$
12. $\int e^{ax}\,dx = e^{ax}/a.$
13. $\int b^{ax}dx = \frac{b^{ax}}{a \log b}.$
14. $\int \log x\,dx = x \log x - x.$
15. $\int a^x \log a\,dx = a^x.$
16. $\int \frac{dx}{a^2 + x^2} = \frac{1}{a}\tan^{-1}\left(\frac{x}{a}\right),$ or $-\frac{1}{a}\cot^{-1}\left(\frac{x}{a}\right).$
17. $\int \frac{dx}{a^2 - x^2} = \frac{1}{a}\tanh^{-1}\left(\frac{x}{a}\right),$ or $\frac{1}{2a}\log\frac{a+x}{a-x}.$
18. $\int \frac{dx}{x^2 - a^2} = -\frac{1}{a}\coth^{-1}\left(\frac{x}{a}\right),$ or $\frac{1}{2a}\log\frac{x-a}{x+a}.$
19. $\int \frac{dx}{\sqrt{a^2 - x^2}} = \sin^{-1}\left(\frac{x}{a}\right),$ or $-\cos^{-1}\left(\frac{x}{a}\right).$
20. $\int \frac{dx}{\sqrt{x^2 \pm a^2}} = \log\left(x + \sqrt{x^2 \pm a^2}\right).$
21. $\int \frac{dx}{x\sqrt{x^2 - a^2}} = \frac{1}{a}\cos^{-1}\left(\frac{a}{x}\right).$
22. $\int \frac{dx}{x\sqrt{a^2 \pm x^2}} = -\frac{1}{a}\log\left(\frac{a + \sqrt{a^2 \pm x^2}}{x}\right).$

23. $\int \frac{dx}{x\sqrt{a+bx}} = \frac{2}{\sqrt{-a}} \tan^{-1}\sqrt{\frac{a+bx}{-a}}$, or

$$\frac{-2}{\sqrt{a}} \tanh^{-1}\sqrt{\frac{a+bx}{a}}.$$

Forms Containing $(a + bx)$

24. $\int (a+bx)^n dx = \frac{(a+bx)^{n+1}}{(n+1)b}$, except $n = -1$.

25. $\int x\,(a+bx)^n dx = \frac{1}{b^2(n+2)}(a+bx)^{n+2} - \frac{a}{b^2(n+1)}(a+bx)^{n+1}$, except $n = -1$ or -2.

26. $\int x^2 (a+bx)^n\,dx = \frac{1}{b^3}\left[\frac{(a+bx)^{n+3}}{n+3} - 2a\frac{(a+bx)^{n+2}}{n+2} + a^2\frac{(a+bx)^{n+1}}{n+1}\right].$

27. $\int x^m (a+bx)^n\,dx = \frac{x^{m+1}(a+bx)^n}{m+n+1} + \frac{an}{m+n+1}\int x^m (a+bx)^{n-1}\,dx.$

28. $\int \frac{dx}{a+bx} = \frac{1}{b}\log(a+bx).$

29. $\int \frac{dx}{(a+bx)^2} = -\frac{1}{b(a+bx)}.$

30. $\int \frac{dx}{(a+bx)^3} = -\frac{1}{2b(a+bx)^2}.$

31. $\int \frac{xdx}{a+bx} = \frac{1}{b^2}[a+bx-a\log(a+bx)].$

32. $\int \frac{xdx}{(a+bx)^2} = \frac{1}{b^2}\left[\log(a+bx) + \frac{a}{a+bx}\right].$

33. $\int \frac{xdx}{(a+bx)^3} = \frac{1}{b^2}\left[-\frac{1}{a+bx} + \frac{a}{2(a+bx)^2}\right].$

34. $\int \frac{x^2\,dx}{a+bx} = \frac{1}{b^3}\left[\frac{1}{2}(a+bx)^2 - 2a(a+bx) + a^2\log(a+bx)\right]$

35. $\int \frac{x^2\,dx}{(a+bx)^2} = \frac{1}{b^3}\left[a+bx - 2a\log(a+bx) - \frac{a^2}{a+bx}\right]$

36. $\int \frac{x^2\,dx}{(a+bx)^3} = \frac{1}{b^3}\left[\log(a+bx) + \frac{2a}{a+bx} - \frac{a^2}{2(a+bx)^2}\right]$

37. $\int \frac{dx}{x(a + bx)} = -\frac{1}{a} \log \frac{a + bx}{x}.$

38. $\int \frac{dx}{x(a + bx)^2} = \frac{1}{a(a + bx)} - \frac{1}{a^2} \log \frac{a + bx}{x}.$

39. $\int \frac{dx}{x^2(a + bx)} = -\frac{1}{ax} + \frac{b}{a^2} \log \frac{a + bx}{x}$

40. $\int \frac{dx}{x^2 (a + bx)^2} = -\frac{a + 2\,bx}{a^2x\,(a + bx)} + \frac{2b}{a^3} \log \frac{a + bx}{x}.$

FORMS CONTAINING $c^2 \pm x^2$, $x^2 - c^2$

41. $\int \frac{dx}{c^2 + x^2} = \frac{1}{c} \tan^{-1} \frac{x}{c}$, or $\frac{1}{c} \sin^{-1} \frac{x}{\sqrt{c^2 + x^2}}.$

42. $\int \frac{dx}{c^2 - x^2} = \frac{1}{2\,c} \log \frac{c + x}{c - x}$, or $\frac{1}{c} \tanh^{-1} \left(\frac{x}{c}\right).$

43. $\int \frac{dx}{x^2 - c^2} = \frac{1}{2\,c} \log \frac{x - c}{x + c}$, or $-\frac{1}{c} \coth^{-1} \left(\frac{x}{c}\right).$

FORMS CONTAINING $a + bx$ AND $a' + b'x$

44. $\int \frac{dx}{(a + bx)(a' + b'x)} = \frac{1}{ab' - a'b} \cdot \log \left(\frac{a' + b'x}{a + bx}\right).$

45. $\int \frac{x\,dx}{(a + bx)(a' + b'x)} = \frac{1}{ab' - a'b} \left[\frac{a}{b} \log (a + bx) - \frac{a'}{b'} \log (a' + b'x)\right].$

46. $\int \frac{dx}{(a + bx)^2(a' + b'x)} = \frac{1}{ab' - a'b} \left(\frac{1}{a + bx} + \frac{b'}{ab' - a'b} \log \frac{a' + b'x}{a + bx}\right).$

47. $\int \frac{x\,dx}{(a + bx)^2(a' + b'x)} = \frac{-a}{b(ab' - a'b)(a + bx)} - \frac{a'}{(ab' - a'b)^2} \log \frac{a' + b'x}{a + bx}.$

48. $\int \frac{x^2\,dx}{(a + bx)^2(a' + b'x)} = \frac{a^2}{b^2(ab' - a'b)(a + bx)} + \frac{1}{(ab' - a'b)^2}\left[\frac{a'^2}{b'} \log (a' + b'x) + \frac{a(ab' - 2\,a'b)}{b^2} \log (a + bx)\right].$

49. $\int \frac{dx}{(a + bx)^n(a' + b'x)^m} = \frac{1}{(m - 1)(ab' - a'b)} \left(\frac{-1}{(a + bx)^{n-1}(a' + b'x)^{m-1}} - (m + n - 2)b \int \frac{dx}{(a + bx)^n(a' + b'x)^{m-1}}\right).$

Forms Containing $\sqrt{a+bx}$ and $\sqrt{a'+b'x}$ $\quad u = a + bx \quad v = a' + b'x \quad k = ab' - a'b$

50. $\int \sqrt{uv}\,dx = \frac{k + 2bv}{4bb'}\sqrt{uv} - \frac{k^2}{8bb'}\int \frac{dx}{\sqrt{uv}}.$

51. $\int \frac{dx}{v\sqrt{u}} = \frac{1}{\sqrt{kb'}} \log \frac{b'\sqrt{u} - \sqrt{kb'}}{b'\sqrt{u} + \sqrt{kb'}} = \frac{2}{\sqrt{-kb'}} \tan^{-1} \frac{b'\sqrt{u}}{\sqrt{-kb'}}.$

52. $\int \frac{dx}{\sqrt{uv}} = \frac{2}{\sqrt{bb'}} \log (\sqrt{bb'u} + b\sqrt{v}) = \frac{2}{\sqrt{-bb'}} \tan^{-1} \sqrt{\frac{-b'u}{bv}},$

or $\frac{2}{\sqrt{bb'}} \tanh^{-1} \sqrt{\frac{b'u}{bv}} = \frac{1}{\sqrt{-bb'}} \sin^{-1} \frac{2bb'x + a'b + ab'}{k}.$

53. $\int \frac{xdx}{\sqrt{uv}} = \frac{\sqrt{uv}}{bb'} - \frac{ab' + a'b}{2bb'} \int \frac{dx}{\sqrt{uv}}.$

54. $\int \frac{dx}{v\sqrt{uv}} = -\frac{2\sqrt{u}}{k\sqrt{v}}.$

55. $\int \frac{\sqrt{v}\,dx}{\sqrt{u}} = \frac{1}{b}\sqrt{uv} - \frac{k}{2b}\int \frac{dx}{\sqrt{uv}}.$

56. $\int v^m \sqrt{u}\,dx = \frac{1}{(2m+3)b'}\left(2v^{m+1}\sqrt{u} + k\int \frac{v^m dx}{\sqrt{u}}\right).$

57. $\int \frac{dx}{v^m\sqrt{u}} = -\frac{1}{(m-1)k}\left(\frac{\sqrt{u}}{v^{m-1}} + \left(m - \frac{3}{2}\right)b \int \frac{dx}{v^{m-1}\sqrt{u}}\right).$

Forms Containing $(a + bx^n)$

58. $\int \frac{dx}{a + bx^2} = \frac{1}{\sqrt{ab}} \tan^{-1} \frac{x\sqrt{ab}}{a}.$

59. $\int \frac{dx}{a + bx^2} = \frac{1}{2\sqrt{-ab}} \log \frac{a + x\sqrt{-ab}}{a - x\sqrt{-ab}}$, or $\frac{1}{\sqrt{-ab}} \tanh^{-1} \frac{x\sqrt{-ab}}{a}.$

60. $\int \frac{xdx}{a + bx^2} = \frac{1}{2b} \log \left(x^2 + \frac{a}{b}\right).$

61. $\int \frac{x^2\,dx}{a + bx^2} = \frac{x}{b} - \frac{a}{b}\int \frac{dx}{a + bx^2}.$

62. $\int \frac{dx}{(a+bx^2)^2} = \frac{x}{2a(a+bx^2)} + \frac{1}{2a}\int \frac{dx}{a+bx^2}.$

63. $\int \frac{dx}{(a+bx^2)^{m+1}} = \frac{1}{2\,ma}\frac{x}{(a+bx^2)^m} + \frac{2m-1}{2\,ma}\int \frac{dx}{(a+bx^2)^m}.$

64. $\int \frac{xdx}{(a+bx^2)^{m+1}} = \frac{1}{2}\int \frac{dz}{(a+bz)^{m+1}},$ $[z = x^2].$

65. $\int \frac{x^2dx}{(a+bx^2)^{m+1}} = \frac{-x}{2\,mb(a+bx^2)^m} + \frac{1}{2\,mb}\int \frac{dx}{(a+bx^2)^m}.$

66. $\int \frac{dx}{x^2(a+bx^2)^{m+1}} = \frac{1}{a}\int \frac{dx}{x^2(a+bx^2)^m} - \frac{b}{a}\int \frac{dx}{(a+bx^2)^{m+1}}.$

67. $\int \frac{dx}{x(a+bx^2)} = \frac{1}{2\,a}\log \frac{x^2}{a+bx^2}.$

68. $\int \frac{dx}{x^2(a+bx^2)} = -\frac{1}{ax} - \frac{b}{a}\int \frac{dx}{a+bx^2}.$

69. $\int \frac{dx}{a+bx^3} = \frac{k}{3\,a}\left[\frac{1}{2}\log \frac{(k+x)^2}{k^2-kx+x^2} + \sqrt{3}\tan^{-1}\frac{2\,x-k}{k\sqrt{3}}\right],$ $[bk^3 = a].$

70. $\int \frac{xdx}{a+bx^3} = \frac{1}{3bk}\left[\frac{1}{2}\log \frac{k^2-kx+x^2}{(k+x)^2} + \sqrt{3}\tan^{-1}\frac{2x-k}{k\sqrt{3}}\right],$ $[bk^3 = a].$

71. $\int \frac{dx}{x(a+bx^n)} = \frac{1}{an}\log \frac{x^n}{a+bx^n}.$

72. $\int \frac{dx}{(a+bx^n)^{m+1}} = \frac{1}{a}\int \frac{dx}{(a+bx^n)^m} - \frac{b}{a}\int \frac{x^ndx}{(a+bx^n)^{m+1}}.$

73. $\int \frac{x^mdx}{(a+bx^n)^{p+1}} = \frac{1}{b}\int \frac{x^{m-n}dx}{(a+bx^n)^p} - \frac{a}{b}\int \frac{x^{m-n}dx}{(a+bx^n)^{p+1}}.$

74. $\int \frac{dx}{x^m(a+bx^n)^{p+1}} = \frac{1}{a}\int \frac{dx}{x^m(a+bx^n)^p} - \frac{b}{a}\int \frac{dx}{x^{m-n}(a+bx^n)^{p+1}}$

75. $\int x^m(a+bx^n)^p dx = \frac{x^{m-n+1}(a+bx^n)^{p+1}}{b(np+m+1)} - \frac{a(m-n+1)}{b(np+m+1)}\int x^{m-n}(a+bx^n)^p\, dx.$

76. $\int x^m(a+bx^n)^p\,dx = \dfrac{x^{m+1}(a+bx^n)^p}{np+m+1} + \dfrac{anp}{np+m+1}\int x^m(a+bx^n)^{p-1}\,dx.$

77. $\int x^{m-1}(a+bx^n)^p\,dx = \dfrac{1}{b(m+np)}[x^{m-n}(a+bx^n)^{p+1} - (m-n)\,a\int x^{m-n-1}(a+bx^n)^p\,dx].$

78. $\int x^{m-1}(a+bx^n)^p\,dx = \dfrac{1}{m+np}[x^m(a+bx^n)^p + npa\int x^{m-1}(a+bx^n)^{p-1}\,dx].$

79. $\int x^{m-1}(a+bx^n)^p\,dx = \dfrac{1}{ma}[x^m(a+bx^n)^{p+1} - (m+np+n)b\int x^{m+n-1}(a+bx^n)^p\,dx].$

80. $\int x^{m-1}(a+bx^n)^p\,dx = \dfrac{1}{an(p+1)}[-x^m(a+bx^n)^{p+1} + (m+np+n)\int x^{m-1}(a+bx^n)^{p+1}\,dx].$

Forms Containing $(a + bx + cx^2)$

$X = a + bx + cx^2$ and $q = 4\,ac - b^2$

81. $\int \dfrac{dx}{X} = \dfrac{2}{\sqrt{q}}\tan^{-1}\dfrac{2\,cx+b}{\sqrt{q}}.$

82. $\int \dfrac{dx}{X} = \dfrac{-2}{\sqrt{-q}}\tanh^{-1}\dfrac{2\,cx+b}{\sqrt{-q}}.$

83. $\int \dfrac{dx}{X} = \dfrac{1}{\sqrt{-q}}\log\dfrac{2\,cx+b-\sqrt{-q}}{2\,cx+b+\sqrt{-q}}.$

84. $\int \dfrac{dx}{X^2} = \dfrac{2\,cx+b}{qX} + \dfrac{2\,c}{q}\int\dfrac{dx}{X}.$

85. $\int \dfrac{dx}{X^3} = \dfrac{2\,cx+b}{q}\left(\dfrac{1}{2\,X^2}+\dfrac{3\,c}{qX}\right) + \dfrac{6\,c^2}{q^2}\int\dfrac{dx}{X}.$

86. $\int \dfrac{dx}{X^{n+1}} = \dfrac{2\,cx+b}{nqX^n} + \dfrac{2\,(2\,n-1)\,c}{qn}\int\dfrac{dx}{X^n}.$

87. $\int \dfrac{xdx}{X} = \dfrac{1}{2\,c}\log X - \dfrac{b}{2\,c}\int\dfrac{dx}{X}.$

88. $\int \dfrac{xdx}{X^2} = -\dfrac{bx+2a}{qX} - \dfrac{b}{q}\int\dfrac{dx}{X}.$

89. $\int \dfrac{xdx}{X^{n+1}} = -\dfrac{2\,a+bx}{nqX^n} - \dfrac{b\,(2\,n-1)}{nq}\int\dfrac{dx}{X^n}.$

90. $\int \dfrac{x^2}{X}\,dx = \dfrac{x}{c} - \dfrac{b}{2\,c^2}\log X + \dfrac{b^2-2\,ac}{2\,c^2}\int\dfrac{dx}{X}.$

91. $\int \dfrac{x^2}{X^2}\,dx = \dfrac{(b^2-2\,ac)x+ab}{cqX} + \dfrac{2\,a}{q}\int\dfrac{dx}{X}.$

92. $\int \frac{x^m\,dx}{X^{n+1}} = -\frac{x^{m-1}}{(2n-m+1)cX^n} - \frac{n-m+1}{2n-m+1}\cdot\frac{b}{c}\int \frac{x^{m-1}\,dx}{X^{n+1}} + \frac{m-1}{2n-m+1}\cdot\frac{a}{c}\int\frac{x^{m-2}\,dx}{X^{n+1}}.$

93. $\int \frac{dx}{xX} = \frac{1}{2a}\log\frac{x^2}{X} - \frac{b}{2a}\int\frac{dx}{X}.$

94. $\int \frac{dx}{x^2X} = \frac{b}{2a^2}\log\frac{X}{x^2} - \frac{1}{ax} + \left(\frac{b^2}{2a^2} - \frac{c}{a}\right)\int\frac{dx}{X}.$

95. $\int \frac{dx}{xX^n} = \frac{1}{2a(n-1)X^{n-1}} - \frac{b}{2a}\int\frac{dx}{X^n} + \frac{1}{a}\int\frac{dx}{xX^{n-1}}.$

96. $\int \frac{dx}{x^mX^{n+1}} = -\frac{1}{(m-1)ax^{m-1}X^n} - \frac{n+m-1}{m-1}\cdot\frac{b}{a}\int\frac{dx}{x^{m-1}X^{n+1}} - \frac{2n+m-1}{m-1}\cdot\frac{c}{a}\int\frac{dx}{x^{m-2}X^{n+1}}.$

Forms Containing $\sqrt{a+bx}$

97. $\int \sqrt{a+bx}\,dx = \frac{2}{3b}\sqrt{(a+bx)^3}.$

98. $\int x\sqrt{a+bx}\,dx = -\frac{2(2a-3bx)\sqrt{(a+bx)^3}}{15b^2}.$

99. $\int x^2\sqrt{a+bx}\,dx = \frac{2(8a^2-12abx+15b^2x^2)\sqrt{(a+bx)^3}}{105b^3}.$

100. $\int \frac{\sqrt{a+bx}}{x}dx = 2\sqrt{a+bx} + a\int\frac{dx}{x\sqrt{a+bx}}.$

101. $\int \frac{dx}{\sqrt{a+bx}} = \frac{2\sqrt{a+bx}}{b}.$

102. $\int \frac{xdx}{\sqrt{a+bx}} = -\frac{2(2a-bx)}{3b^2}\sqrt{a+bx}.$

103. $\int \frac{x^2dx}{\sqrt{a+bx}} = \frac{2(8a^2-4abx+3b^2x^2)}{15b^3}\sqrt{a+bx}.$

104. $\int \frac{x^mdx}{\sqrt{a+bx}} = \frac{2x^m\sqrt{a+bx}}{(2m+1)b} - \frac{2ma}{(2m+1)b}\int\frac{x^{m-1}dx}{\sqrt{a+bx}}.$

105. $\int \frac{dx}{x\sqrt{a+bx}} = \frac{1}{\sqrt{a}}\log\left(\frac{\sqrt{a+bx}-\sqrt{a}}{\sqrt{a+bx}+\sqrt{a}}\right).$

106. $\int \frac{dx}{x\sqrt{a+bx}} = \frac{-2}{\sqrt{a}}\tanh^{-1}\sqrt{\frac{a+bx}{a}}.$

107. $\int \frac{dx}{x^2\sqrt{a+bx}} = -\frac{\sqrt{a+bx}}{ax} - \frac{b}{2a}\int \frac{dx}{x\sqrt{a+bx}}.$

108. $\int \frac{dx}{x^n\sqrt{a+bx}} = -\frac{\sqrt{a+bx}}{(n-1)ax^{n-1}} - \frac{(2n-3)b}{(2n-2)a} \int \frac{dx}{x^{n-1}\sqrt{a+bx}}.$

109. $\int (a+bx)^{\pm n/2}dx = \frac{2(a+bx)^{\frac{2\pm n}{2}}}{b(2\pm n)}.$

110. $\int x(a+bx)^{\pm n/2}dx = \frac{2}{b^2}\left[\frac{(a+bx)^{\frac{4\pm n}{2}}}{4\pm n} - \frac{a(a+bx)^{\frac{2\pm n}{2}}}{2\pm n}\right].$

111. $\int \frac{dx}{x(a+bx)^{m/2}} = \frac{1}{a}\int \frac{dx}{x(a+bx)^{\frac{m-2}{2}}} - \frac{b}{a}\int \frac{dx}{(a+bx)^{m/2}}.$

112. $\int \frac{(a+bx)^{n/2}dx}{x} = b\int (a+bx)^{\frac{n-2}{2}}dx + a \int \frac{(a+bx)^{\frac{n-2}{2}}}{x}dx.$

Forms Containing $\sqrt{x^2 \pm a^2}$

113. $\int \sqrt{x^2 \pm a^2}\,dx = \tfrac{1}{2}[x\sqrt{x^2 \pm a^2} \pm a^2 \log (x + \sqrt{x^2 \pm a^2})].$

114. $\int \frac{dx}{\sqrt{x^2 \pm a^2}} = \log (x + \sqrt{x^2 \pm a^2}).$

115. $\int \frac{dx}{x\sqrt{x^2 - a^2}} = \frac{1}{a}\cos^{-1}\left(\frac{a}{x}\right), \text{ or } \frac{1}{a}\sec^{-1}\left(\frac{x}{a}\right).$

116. $\int \frac{dx}{x\sqrt{x^2 + a^2}} = -\frac{1}{a}\log\left(\frac{a + \sqrt{x^2 + a^2}}{x}\right).$

117. $\int \frac{\sqrt{x^2 + a^2}}{x}dx = \sqrt{x^2 + a^2} - a\log\left(\frac{a + \sqrt{x^2 + a^2}}{x}\right).$

118. $\int \frac{\sqrt{x^2 - a^2}}{x}dx = \sqrt{x^2 - a^2} - a\cos^{-1}\frac{a}{x}.$

119. $\int \frac{x\,dx}{\sqrt{x^2 \pm a^2}} = \sqrt{x^2 \pm a^2}.$

120. $\int x\sqrt{x^2 \pm a^2}dx = \tfrac{1}{3}\sqrt{(x^2 \pm a^2)^3}.$

INTEGRALS (Continued)

121. $\int \sqrt{(x^2 \pm a^2)^3}\,dx = \frac{1}{4}\Big[x\sqrt{(x^2 \pm a^2)^3} \pm \frac{3\,a^2x}{2}$
$\sqrt{x^2 \pm a^2} + \frac{3\,a^4}{2}\log\left(x + \sqrt{x^2 \pm a^2}\right)\Big].$

122. $\int \frac{dx}{\sqrt{(x^2 \pm a^2)^3}} = \frac{\pm x}{a^2\sqrt{x^2 \pm a^2}}.$

123. $\int \frac{x\,dx}{\sqrt{(x^2 \pm a^2)^3}} = \frac{-1}{\sqrt{x^2 \pm a^2}}.$

124. $\int x\sqrt{(x^2 \pm a^2)^3}\,dx = \frac{1}{5}\sqrt{(x^2 \pm a^2)^5}.$

125. $\int x^2\sqrt{x^2 \pm a^2}\,dx = \frac{x}{4}\sqrt{(x^2 \pm a^2)^3} \mp \frac{a^2}{8}x\sqrt{x^2 \pm a^2} -$
$\frac{a^4}{8}\log\left(x + \sqrt{x^2 \pm a^2}\right).$

126. $\int \frac{x^2\,dx}{\sqrt{x^2 \pm a^2}} = \frac{x}{2}\sqrt{x^2 \pm a^2} \mp \frac{a^2}{2}\log\left(x + \sqrt{x^2 \pm a^2}\right).$

127. $\int \frac{dx}{x^2\sqrt{x^2 \pm a^2}} = \mp\frac{\sqrt{x^2 \pm a^2}}{a^2x}.$

128. $\int \frac{\sqrt{x^2 \pm a^2}\,dx}{x^2} = -\frac{\sqrt{x^2 \pm a^2}}{x} + \log\left(x + \sqrt{x^2 \pm a^2}\right).$

129. $\int \frac{x^2\,dx}{\sqrt{(x^2 \pm a^2)^3}} = \frac{-x}{\sqrt{x^2 \pm a^2}} + \log\left(x + \sqrt{x^2 \pm a^2}\right).$

Forms Containing $\sqrt{a^2 - x^2}$

130. $\int \sqrt{a^2 - x^2}\,dx = \frac{1}{2}\left[x\sqrt{a^2 - x^2} + a^2\sin^{-1}\left(\frac{x}{a}\right)\right].$

131. $\int \frac{dx}{\sqrt{a^2 - x^2}} = \sin^{-1}\left(\frac{x}{a}\right)$, or $-\cos^{-1}\left(\frac{x}{a}\right).$

132. $\int \frac{dx}{x\sqrt{a^2 - x^2}} = -\frac{1}{a}\log\left(\frac{a + \sqrt{a^2 - x^2}}{x}\right).$

133. $\int \frac{\sqrt{a^2 - x^2}}{x}\,dx = \sqrt{a^2 - x^2} - a\log\left(\frac{a + \sqrt{a^2 - x^2}}{x}\right).$

134. $\int \frac{x\,dx}{\sqrt{a^2 - x^2}} = -\sqrt{a^2 - x^2}.$

135. $\int x\sqrt{a^2 - x^2}\,dx = -\frac{1}{3}\sqrt{(a^2 - x^2)^3}.$

136. $\int \sqrt{(a^2 - x^2)^3}\,dx = \frac{1}{4}\Big[x\sqrt{(a^2 - x^2)^3} + \frac{3\,a^2x}{2}$
$\sqrt{a^2 - x^2} + \frac{3\,a^4}{2}\sin^{-1}\frac{x}{a}\Big].$

137. $\int \frac{dx}{\sqrt{(a^2 - x^2)^3}} = \frac{x}{a^2\sqrt{a^2 - x^2}}.$

138. $\int \frac{x\,dx}{\sqrt{(a^2 - x^2)^3}} = \frac{1}{\sqrt{a^2 - x^2}}.$

139. $\int x\sqrt{(a^2 - x^2)^3}\,dx = -\frac{1}{5}\sqrt{(a^2 - x^2)^5}.$

140. $\int x^2\sqrt{a^2 - x^2}\,dx = -\frac{x}{4}\sqrt{(a^2 - x^2)^3} + \frac{a^2}{8}\left(x\sqrt{a^2 - x^2} + a^2 \sin^{-1}\frac{x}{a}\right).$

141. $\int \frac{x^2\,dx}{\sqrt{a^2 - x^2}} = -\frac{x}{2}\sqrt{a^2 - x^2} + \frac{a^2}{2}\sin^{-1}\frac{x}{a}.$

142. $\int \frac{dx}{x^2\sqrt{a^2 - x^2}} = -\frac{\sqrt{a^2 - x^2}}{a^2x}.$

143. $\int \frac{\sqrt{a^2 - x^2}}{x^2}\,dx = -\frac{\sqrt{a^2 - x^2}}{x} - \sin^{-1}\frac{x}{a}.$

144. $\int \frac{x^2\,dx}{\sqrt{(a^2 - x^2)^3}} = \frac{x}{\sqrt{a^2 - x^2}} - \sin^{-1}\frac{x}{a}.$

Forms Containing $\sqrt{a + bx + cx^2}$

$X = a + bx + cx^2$, $q = 4\,ac - b^2$, and $k = \frac{4\,c}{q}.$

145. $\int \frac{dx}{\sqrt{X}} = \frac{1}{\sqrt{c}}\log\left(\sqrt{X} + x\sqrt{c} + \frac{b}{2\sqrt{c}}\right).$

146. $\int \frac{dx}{\sqrt{X}} = \frac{1}{\sqrt{c}}\sinh^{-1}\left(\frac{2cx + b}{\sqrt{4\,ac - b^2}}\right),$ if $c > 0$.

147. $\int \frac{dx}{\sqrt{X}} = \frac{1}{\sqrt{-c}}\sin^{-1}\left(\frac{-2\,cx - b}{\sqrt{b^2 - 4\,ac}}\right),$ if $c < 0$.

148. $\int \frac{dx}{X\sqrt{X}} = \frac{2\,(2\,cx + b)}{q\sqrt{X}}.$

149. $\int \frac{dx}{X^2\sqrt{X}} = \frac{2(2\,cx + b)}{3q\sqrt{X}}\left(\frac{1}{X} + 2\,k\right).$

150. $\int \frac{dx}{X^n\sqrt{X}} = \frac{2\,(2\,cx + b)\sqrt{X}}{(2\,n - 1)qX^n} + \frac{2k\,(n - 1)}{2n - 1}\int \frac{dx}{X^{n-1}\sqrt{X}}$

151. $\int \sqrt{X}\,dx = \frac{(2\,cx + b)\sqrt{X}}{4\,c} + \frac{1}{2\,k}\int \frac{dx}{\sqrt{X}}.$

152. $\int X\sqrt{X}\,dx = \frac{(2cx+b)\sqrt{X}}{8c}\left(X + \frac{3}{2k}\right) + \frac{3}{8k^2}\int \frac{dx}{\sqrt{X}}.$

153. $\int X^2\sqrt{X}\,dx = \frac{(2cx+b)\sqrt{X}}{12c}\left(X^2 + \frac{5X}{4k} + \frac{15}{8k^2}\right) + \frac{5}{16k^3}\int \frac{dx}{\sqrt{X}}.$

154. $\int X^n\sqrt{X}\,dx = \frac{(2cx+b)X^n\sqrt{X}}{4(n+1)c} + \frac{2n+1}{2(n+1)k}\int \frac{X^n\,dx}{\sqrt{X}}.$

155. $\int \frac{x\,dx}{\sqrt{X}} = \frac{\sqrt{X}}{c} - \frac{b}{2c}\int \frac{dx}{\sqrt{X}}.$

156. $\int \frac{x\,dx}{X\sqrt{X}} = -\frac{2(bx+2a)}{q\sqrt{X}}.$

157. $\int \frac{x\,dx}{X^n\sqrt{X}} = -\frac{\sqrt{X}}{(2n-1)cX^n} - \frac{b}{2c}\int \frac{dx}{X^n\sqrt{X}}.$

158. $\int \frac{x^2\,dx}{\sqrt{X}} = \left(\frac{x}{2c} - \frac{3b}{4c^2}\right)\sqrt{X} + \frac{3b^2-4ac}{8c^2}\int \frac{dx}{\sqrt{X}}.$

159. $\int \frac{x^2\,dx}{X\sqrt{X}} = \frac{(2b^2-4ac)x+2ab}{cq\sqrt{X}} + \frac{1}{c}\int \frac{dx}{\sqrt{X}}.$

160. $\int \frac{x^2\,dx}{X^n\sqrt{X}} = \frac{(2b^2-4ac)x+2ab}{(2n-1)cq\,X^{n-1}\sqrt{X}} + \frac{4ac+(2n-3)b^2}{(2n-1)cq}\int \frac{dx}{X^{n-1}\sqrt{X}}.$

161. $\int \frac{x^3\,dx}{\sqrt{X}} = \left(\frac{x^2}{3c} - \frac{5bx}{12c^2} + \frac{5b^2}{8c^3} - \frac{2a}{3c^2}\right)\sqrt{X} + \left(\frac{3ab}{4c^2} - \frac{5b^3}{16c^3}\right)\int \frac{dx}{\sqrt{X}}.$

162. $\int x\sqrt{X}\,dx = \frac{X\sqrt{X}}{3c} - \frac{b}{2c}\int \sqrt{X}\,dx.$

163. $\int xX\sqrt{X}\,dx = \frac{X^2\sqrt{X}}{5c} - \frac{b}{2c}\int X\sqrt{X}\,dx.$

164. $\int \frac{xX^n\,dx}{\sqrt{X}} = \frac{X^n\sqrt{X}}{(2n+1)c} - \frac{b}{2c}\int \frac{X^n dx}{\sqrt{X}}.$

165. $\int x^2 \sqrt{X} dx = \left(x - \frac{5\,b}{6\,c}\right) \frac{X\sqrt{X}}{4\,c} +$

$$\frac{5\,b^2 - 4\,ac}{16\,c^2} \int \sqrt{X}\, dx.$$

166. $\int \frac{dx}{x\sqrt{X}} = -\frac{1}{\sqrt{a}} \log\left(\frac{\sqrt{X} + \sqrt{a}}{x} + \frac{b}{2\sqrt{a}}\right),$ if $a > 0$.

167. $\int \frac{dx}{x\sqrt{X}} = \frac{1}{\sqrt{-a}} \sin^{-1}\left(\frac{bx + 2\,a}{x\sqrt{b^2 - 4\,ac}}\right),$ if $a < 0$.

168. $\int \frac{dx}{x\sqrt{X}} = -\frac{2\sqrt{X}}{bx},$ if $a = 0$.

169. $\int \frac{dx}{x^2\sqrt{X}} = -\frac{\sqrt{X}}{ax} - \frac{b}{2\,a} \int \frac{dx}{x\sqrt{X}}.$

170. $\int \frac{\sqrt{X}\, dx}{x} = \sqrt{X} + \frac{b}{2} \int \frac{dx}{\sqrt{X}} + a \int \frac{dx}{x\sqrt{X}}.$

171. $\int \frac{\sqrt{X}\, dx}{x^2} = -\frac{\sqrt{X}}{x} + \frac{b}{2} \int \frac{dx}{x\sqrt{X}} + c \int \frac{dx}{\sqrt{X}}.$

Miscellaneous Algebraic Forms

172. $\int \sqrt{2\,ax - x^2}\, dx = \frac{1}{2}\left[(x - a)\sqrt{2\,ax - x^2} + a^2 \sin^{-1} (x - a)/a\right].$

173. $\int \sqrt{ax^2 + c}\, dx = \frac{x}{2}\sqrt{ax^2 + c} + \frac{c}{2\sqrt{a}} \log\left(x\sqrt{a} + \sqrt{ax^2 + c}\right),$ $[a > 0]$.

$$= \frac{x}{2}\sqrt{ax^2 + c} + \frac{c}{2\sqrt{-a}} \sin^{-1}\left(x\sqrt{\frac{-a}{c}}\right), \quad [a < 0].$$

174. $\int \frac{dx}{\sqrt{2\,ax - x^2}} = \cos^{-1}\left(\frac{a - x}{a}\right).$

175. $\int \frac{dx}{\sqrt{a + bx} \cdot \sqrt{a' + b'x}} = \frac{2}{\sqrt{-bb'}} \tan^{-1} \sqrt{\frac{-b'(a + bx)}{b(a' + b'x)}}.$

176. $\int \sqrt{\frac{1 + x}{1 - x}}\, dx = \sin^{-1} x - \sqrt{1 - x^2}.$

177. $\int \frac{dx}{\sqrt{a \pm 2bx + cx^2}} = \frac{1}{\sqrt{c}} \log\left(\pm b + cx + \sqrt{c}\sqrt{a \pm 2bx + cx^2}\right)$

178. $\int \frac{dx}{\sqrt{a \pm 2bx - cx^2}} = \frac{1}{\sqrt{c}} \sin^{-1} \frac{cx \mp b}{\sqrt{b^2 + ac}}.$

179. $\int \frac{xdx}{\sqrt{a \pm 2bx + cx^2}} = \frac{1}{c}\sqrt{a \pm 2bx + cx^2} -$

$\frac{b}{\sqrt{c^3}} \log (\pm b + cx + \sqrt{c}\sqrt{a \pm 2bx + cx^2}).$

180. $\int \frac{xdx}{\sqrt{a \pm 2bx - cx^2}} = -\frac{1}{c}\sqrt{a \pm 2bx - cx^2} \pm$

$\frac{b}{\sqrt{c^3}} \sin^{-1} \frac{cx \mp b}{\sqrt{b^2 + ac}}.$

Trigonometric Forms

181. $\int \sin x \, dx = -\cos x$, or versin x.
182. $\int \cos x \, dx = \sin x$, or $-$ coversin x.
183. $\int \tan x \, dx = -\log \cos x$, or $\log \sec x$.
184. $\int \cot x \, dx = \log \sin x$.

185. $\int \sec x \, dx = \log \tan \left(\frac{\pi}{4} + \frac{x}{2}\right).$

186. $\int \csc x \, dx = \log \tan \frac{1}{2} x$.
187. $\int \sin^2 x \, dx = -\frac{1}{2} \cos x \sin x + \frac{1}{2} x = \frac{1}{2} x - \frac{1}{4} \sin 2x$.
188. $\int \sin^3 x \, dx = -\frac{1}{3} \cos x (\sin^2 x + 2)$.

189. $\int \sin^n x \, dx = -\frac{\sin^{n-1} x \cos x}{n} + \frac{n-1}{n} \int \sin^{n-2} x \, dx.$

190. $\int \cos^2 x \, dx = \frac{1}{2} \sin x \cos x + \frac{1}{2} x = \frac{1}{2} x + \frac{1}{4} \sin 2x$.
191. $\int \cos^3 x \, dx = \frac{1}{3} \sin x (\cos^2 x + 2)$.

192. $\int \cos^n x \, dx = \frac{1}{n} \cos^{n-1} x \sin x + \frac{n-1}{n} \int \cos^{n-2} x \, dx.$

193. $\int \sin \frac{x}{a} \, dx = -a \cos \frac{x}{a}.$

194. $\int \cos \frac{x}{a} \, dx = a \sin \frac{x}{a}.$

195. $\int \sin (a + bx) \, dx = -\frac{1}{b} \cos (a + bx).$

196. $\int \cos (a + bx) \, dx = \frac{1}{b} \sin (a + bx).$

197. $\int \frac{dx}{\sin x} = -\frac{1}{2} \log \frac{1 + \cos x}{1 - \cos x} = \log \tan \frac{x}{2}.$

198. $\int \frac{dx}{\cos x} = \log \tan \left(\frac{\pi}{4} + \frac{x}{2}\right) = \frac{1}{2} \log \left(\frac{1 + \sin x}{1 - \sin x}\right).$

199. $\int \frac{dx}{\cos^2 x} = \tan x.$

200. $\int \frac{dx}{\cos^n x} = \frac{1}{n-1} \cdot \frac{\sin x}{\cos^{n-1} x} + \frac{n-2}{n-1} \int \frac{dx}{\cos^{n-2} x}.$

201. $\int \frac{dx}{1 \pm \sin x} = \mp \tan\left(\frac{\pi}{4} \mp \frac{x}{2}\right).$

202. $\int \frac{dx}{1 + \cos x} = \tan \frac{x}{2}.$

203. $\int \frac{dx}{1 - \cos x} = -\cot \frac{x}{2}.$

204. $\int \frac{dx}{a + b \sin x} = \frac{2}{\sqrt{a^2 - b^2}} \tan^{-1} \frac{a \tan \frac{1}{2} x + b}{\sqrt{a^2 - b^2}},$

$$= \frac{1}{\sqrt{b^2 - a^2}} \log \frac{a \tan \frac{1}{2} x + b - \sqrt{b^2 - a^2}}{a \tan \frac{1}{2} x + b + \sqrt{b^2 - a^2}}.$$

205. $\int \frac{dx}{a + b \cos x} = \frac{2}{\sqrt{a^2 - b^2}} \tan^{-1} \frac{\sqrt{a^2 - b^2} \tan \frac{1}{2} x}{a + b},$

$$= \frac{1}{\sqrt{b^2 - a^2}} \log \left(\frac{\sqrt{b^2 - a^2} \tan \frac{1}{2} x + a + b}{\sqrt{b^2 - a^2} \tan \frac{1}{2} x - a - b}\right).$$

206. $\int \sin mx \sin nx \, dx = \frac{\sin (m - n) x}{2(m - n)} - \frac{\sin (m + n) x}{2(m + n)},$

$[m^2 \neq n^2].$

207. $\int x \sin^2 x \, dx = \frac{x^2}{4} - \frac{x \sin 2x}{4} - \frac{\cos 2x}{8}.$

208. $\int x^2 \sin^2 x \, dx = \frac{x^3}{6} - \left(\frac{x^2}{4} - \frac{1}{8}\right) \sin 2x - \frac{x \cos 2x}{4}.$

209. $\int x \sin^3 x \, dx = \frac{x \cos 3x}{12} - \frac{\sin 3x}{36} - \frac{3}{4} x \cos x + \frac{3}{4} \sin x.$

210. $\int \sin^4 x \, dx = \frac{3x}{8} - \frac{\sin 2x}{4} + \frac{\sin 4x}{32}.$

211. $\int \cos mx \cos nx \, dx = \frac{\sin (m - n)x}{2(m - n)} + \frac{\sin (m + n)x}{2(m + n)},$

$[m^2 \neq n^2].$

212. $\int x \cos^2 x \, dx = \frac{x^2}{4} + \frac{x \sin 2x}{4} + \frac{\cos 2x}{8}.$

213. $\int x^2 \cos^2 x \, dx = \frac{x^3}{6} + \left(\frac{x^2}{4} - \frac{1}{8}\right) \sin 2x + \frac{x \cos 2x}{4}.$

214. $\int x \cos^3 x \, dx = \frac{x \sin 3x}{12} + \frac{\cos 3x}{36} + \frac{3}{4} x \sin x + \frac{3}{4} \cos x.$

215. $\int \cos^4 x \, dx = \frac{3x}{8} + \frac{\sin 2x}{4} + \frac{\sin 4x}{32}.$

216. $\int \frac{\sin x\, dx}{x^m} = -\frac{\sin x}{(m-1)\, x^{m-1}} + \frac{1}{m-1} \int \frac{\cos x\, dx}{x^{m-1}}.$

217. $\int \frac{\cos x\, dx}{x^m} = -\frac{\cos x}{(m-1)x^{m-1}} - \frac{1}{m-1} \int \frac{\sin x\, dx}{x^{m-1}}.$

218. $\int \tan^3 x\, dx = \frac{1}{2} \tan^2 x + \log \cos x.$

219. $\int \tan^4 x\, dx = \frac{1}{3} \tan^3 x - \tan x + x.$

220. $\int \cot^3 x\, dx = -\frac{1}{2} \cot^2 x - \log \sin x.$

221. $\int \cot^4 x\, dx = -\frac{1}{3} \cot^3 x + \cot x + x.$

222. $\int \cot^n x\, dx = -\frac{\cot^{n-1} x}{n-1} - \int \cot^{n-2} x\, dx, \; [n \neq 1].$

223. $\int \sin x \cos x\, dx = \frac{1}{2} \sin^2 x$

224. $\int \sin mx \cos nx\, dx = -\frac{\cos (m-n)x}{2(m-n)} - \frac{\cos (m+n)x}{2(m+n)}.$

225. $\int \sin^2 x \cos^2 x\, dx = -\frac{1}{8}(\frac{1}{4} \sin 4\, x - x).$

226. $\int \sin x \cos^m x\, dx = -\frac{\cos^{m+1} x}{m+1}.$

227. $\int \sin^m x \cos x\, dx = \frac{\sin^{m+1} x}{m+1}.$

228. $\int \cos^m x \sin^n x\, dx = \frac{\cos^{m-1} x \sin^{n+1} x}{m+n} + \frac{m-1}{m+n} \int \cos^{m-2} x \sin^n x\, dx.$

229. $\int \cos^m x \sin^n x\, dx = -\frac{\sin^{n-1} x \cos^{m+1} x}{m+n} + \frac{n-1}{m+n} \int \cos^m x \sin^{n-2} x\, dx.$

230. $\int \frac{\cos^m x\, dx}{\sin^n x} = -\frac{\cos^{m+1} x}{(n-1) \sin^{n-1} x} - \frac{m-n+2}{n-1} \int \frac{\cos^m x\, dx}{\sin^{n-2} x}.$

231. $\int \frac{\cos^m x\, dx}{\sin^n x} = \frac{\cos^{m-1} x}{(m-n) \sin^{n-1} x} + \frac{m-1}{m-n} \int \frac{\cos^{m-2} x\, dx}{\sin^n x}.$

232. $\int \frac{\sin^m x\, dx}{\cos^n x} = -\int \frac{\cos^m \left(\frac{\pi}{2} - x\right) d\left(\frac{\pi}{2} - x\right)}{\sin^n \left(\frac{\pi}{2} - x\right)}.$

233. $\int \frac{\sin x\, dx}{\cos^2 x} = \frac{1}{\cos x} = \sec x.$

234. $\int \frac{\sin^2 x\, dx}{\cos x} = -\sin x + \log \tan\left(\frac{\pi}{4} + \frac{x}{2}\right).$

235. $\int \frac{\cos x\, dx}{\sin^2 x} = \frac{-1}{\sin x} = -\operatorname{cosec} x.$

236. $\int \frac{dx}{\sin x \cos x} = \log \tan x.$

237. $\int \frac{dx}{\sin x \cos^2 x} = \frac{1}{\cos x} + \log \tan \frac{x}{2}.$

238. $\int \frac{dx}{\sin x \cos^n x} = \frac{1}{(n-1)\cos^{n-1} x} + \int \frac{dx}{\sin x \cos^{n-2} x},$ $[n \neq 1].$

239. $\int \frac{dx}{\sin^2 x \cos x} = -\frac{1}{\sin x} + \log \tan\left(\frac{\pi}{4} + \frac{x}{2}\right).$

240. $\int \frac{dx}{\sin^2 x \cos^2 x} = -2 \cot 2x.$

241. $\int \frac{dx}{\sin^m x \cos^n x} = -\frac{1}{m-1} \cdot \frac{1}{\sin^{m-1} x \cdot \cos^{n-1} x} + \frac{m+n-2}{m-1} \int \frac{dx}{\sin^{m-2} x \cdot \cos^n x}.$

242. $\int \frac{dx}{\sin^m x} = -\frac{1}{m-1} \cdot \frac{\cos x}{\sin^{m-1} x} + \frac{m-2}{m-1} \int \frac{dx}{\sin^{m-2} x}.$

243. $\int \frac{dx}{\sin^2 x} = -\cot x.$

---

244. $\int \tan^2 x\, dx = \tan x - x.$

245. $\int \tan^n x\, dx = \frac{\tan^{n-1} x}{n-1} - \int \tan^{n-2} x\, dx.$

246. $\int \cot^2 x\, dx = -\cot x - x.$

247. $\int \cot^n x\, dx = -\frac{\cot^{n-1} x}{n-1} - \int \cot^{n-2} x\, dx.$

248. $\int \sec^2 x\, dx = \tan x.$

249. $\int \sec^n x\, dx = \int \frac{dx}{\cos^n x}.$

250. $\int \csc^2 x\, dx = -\cot x.$

251. $\int \csc^n x\, dx = \int \frac{dx}{\sin^n x}.$

---

252. $\int x \sin x\, dx = \sin x - x \cos x.$

253. $\int x^2 \sin x\, dx = 2x \sin x - (x^2 - 2) \cos x.$

254. $\int x^3 \sin x\, dx = (3x^2 - 6) \sin x - (x^3 - 6x) \cos x.$

255. $\int x^m \sin x\, dx = -x^m \cos x + m \int x^{m-1} \cos x\, dx.$

256. $\int x \cos x \, dx = \cos x + x \sin x.$

257. $\int x^2 \cos x \, dx = 2\,x \cos x + (x^2 - 2) \sin x.$

258. $\int x^3 \cos x \, dx = (3\,x^2 - 6) \cos x + (x^3 - 6\,x) \sin x.$

259. $\int x^m \cos x \, dx = x^m \sin x - m \int x^{m-1} \sin x \, dx.$

260. $\int \frac{\sin x}{x} dx = x - \frac{x^3}{3 \cdot 3!} + \frac{x^5}{5 \cdot 5!} - \frac{x^7}{7 \cdot 7!} + \frac{x^9}{9 \cdot 9!} \cdots$

261. $\int \frac{\cos x}{x} dx = \log x - \frac{x^2}{2 \cdot 2!} + \frac{x^4}{4 \cdot 4!} - \frac{x^6}{6 \cdot 6!} + \frac{x^8}{8 \cdot 8!} \cdots$

---

262. $\int \sin^{-1} x \, dx = x \sin^{-1} x + \sqrt{1 - x^2}.$

263. $\int \cos^{-1} x \, dx = x \cos^{-1} x - \sqrt{1 - x^2}.$

264. $\int \tan^{-1} x \, dx = x \tan^{-1} x - \frac{1}{2} \log (1 + x^2).$

265. $\int \cot^{-1} x \, dx = x \cot^{-1} x + \frac{1}{2} \log (1 + x^2).$

266. $\int \sec^{-1} x \, dx = x \sec^{-1} x - \log (x + \sqrt{x^2 - 1}).$

267. $\int \csc^{-1} x \, dx = x \csc^{-1} x + \log (x + \sqrt{x^2 - 1}).$

268. $\int \text{vers}^{-1} x \, dx = (x - 1) \text{vers}^{-1} x + \sqrt{2x - x^2}.$

269. $\int \sin^{-1} \frac{x}{a} dx = x \sin^{-1} \frac{x}{a} + \sqrt{a^2 - x^2}.$

270. $\int \cos^{-1} \frac{x}{a} dx = x \cos^{-1} \frac{x}{a} - \sqrt{a^2 - x^2}.$

271. $\int \tan^{-1} \frac{x}{a} dx = x \tan^{-1} \frac{x}{a} - \frac{a}{2} \log (a^2 + x^2).$

272. $\int \cot^{-1} \frac{x}{a} dx = x \cot^{-1} \frac{x}{a} + \frac{a}{2} \log (a^2 + x^2).$

273. $\int (\sin^{-1} x)^2 \, dx = x(\sin^{-1} x)^2 - 2x + 2\sqrt{1 - x^2}\,(\sin^{-1} x).$

274. $\int (\cos^{-1} x)^2 \, dx = x(\cos^{-1} x)^2 - 2x - 2\sqrt{1 - x^2}\,(\cos^{-1} x).$

275. $\int x \cdot \sin^{-1} x \, dx = \frac{1}{4} [(2\,x^2 - 1) \sin^{-1} x + x \sqrt{1 - x^2}].$

276. $\int x^n \sin^{-1} x \, dx = \frac{x^{n+1} \sin^{-1} x}{n + 1} - \frac{1}{n + 1} \int \frac{x^{n+1} \, dx}{\sqrt{1 - x^2}}.$

277. $\int x^n \cos^{-1} x \, dx = \frac{x^{n+1} \cos^{-1} x}{n + 1} + \frac{1}{n + 1} \int \frac{x^{n+1} \, dx}{\sqrt{1 - x^2}}.$

278. $\int x^n \tan^{-1} x \, dx = \frac{x^{n+1} \tan^{-1} x}{n + 1} - \frac{1}{n + 1} \int \frac{x^{n+1} \, dx}{1 + x^2}.$

279. $\int \frac{\sin^{-1} x \, dx}{x^2} = \log \left(\frac{1 - \sqrt{1 - x^2}}{x}\right) - \frac{\sin^{-1} x}{x}.$

280. $\int \frac{\tan^{-1} x \, dx}{x^2} = \log x - \frac{1}{2} \log (1 + x^2) - \frac{\tan^{-1} x}{x}.$

Logarithmic Forms

281. $\int \log x \, dx = x \log x - x.$

282. $\int x \log x \, dx = \frac{x^2}{2} \log x - \frac{x^2}{4}.$

283. $\int x^2 \log x \, dx = \frac{x^3}{3} \log x - \frac{x^3}{9}.$

284. $\int x^p \log (ax) \, dx = \frac{x^{p+1}}{p+1} \log (ax) - \frac{x^{p+1}}{(p+1)^2} \; [p \neq -1].$

285. $\int (\log x)^2 \, dx = x (\log x)^2 - 2x \log x + 2x.$

286. $\int (\log x)^n \, dx = x (\log x)^n - n \int (\log x)^{n-1} \, dx,$ $[n \neq -1].$

287. $\int \frac{(\log x)^n}{x} \, dx = \frac{1}{n+1} (\log x)^{n+1}.$

288. $\int \frac{dx}{\log x} = \log (\log x) + \log x + \frac{(\log x)^2}{2 \cdot 2!} + \frac{(\log x)^3}{3 \cdot 3!} + \cdots$

289. $\int \frac{dx}{x \log x} = \log (\log x)$

290. $\int \frac{dx}{x (\log x)^n} = -\frac{1}{(n-1)(\log x)^{n-1}}.$

291. $\int \frac{x^m \, dx}{(\log x)^n} = -\frac{x^{m+1}}{(n-1)(\log x)^{n-1}} + \frac{m+1}{n-1} \int \frac{x^m \, dx}{(\log x)^{n-1}}.$

292. $\int x^m \log x \, dx = x^{m+1} \left[\frac{\log x}{m+1} - \frac{1}{(m+1)^2} \right].$

293. $\int x^m (\log x)^n \, dx = \frac{x^{m+1} (\log x)^n}{m+1} - \frac{n}{m+1} \int x^m (\log x)^{n-1} \, dx,$ $[m, n \neq -1].$

294. $\int \sin \log x \, dx = \frac{1}{2} x \sin \log x - \frac{1}{2} x \cos \log x.$

295. $\int \cos \log x \, dx = \frac{1}{2} x \sin \log x + \frac{1}{2} x \cos \log x.$

Exponential Forms

296. $\int e^x \, dx = e^x.$

297. $\int e^{-x} \, dx = -e^{-x}.$

298. $\int e^{ax} \, dx = \frac{e^{ax}}{a}.$

299. $\int x e^{ax} \, dx = \frac{e^{ax}}{a^2} (ax - 1).$

300. $\int x^m e^{ax} \, dx = \frac{x^m e^{ax}}{a} - \frac{m}{a} \int x^{m-1} e^{ax} \, dx.$

301. $\int \frac{e^{ax} \, dx}{x} = \log x + \frac{ax}{1!} + \frac{a^2 x^2}{2 \cdot 2!} + \frac{a^3 x^3}{3 \cdot 3!} + \cdots$

302. $\int \frac{e^{ax}}{x^m} \, dx = -\frac{1}{m-1} \frac{e^{ax}}{x^{m-1}} + \frac{a}{m-1} \int \frac{e^{ax}}{x^{m-1}} \, dx.$

303. $\int e^{ax} \log x\, dx = \dfrac{e^{ax} \log x}{a} - \dfrac{1}{a} \int \dfrac{e^{ax}}{x}\, dx.$

304. $\int e^{ax} \cdot \sin px\, dx = \dfrac{e^{ax}(a \sin px - p \cos px)}{a^2 + p^2}.$

305. $\int e^{ax} \cdot \cos px\, dx = \dfrac{e^{ax}(a \cos px + p \sin px)}{a^2 + p^2}.$

306. $\int \dfrac{dx}{1 + e^x} = x - \log (1 + e^x) = \log \dfrac{e^x}{1 + e^x}.$

307. $\int \dfrac{dx}{a + be^{px}} = \dfrac{x}{a} - \dfrac{1}{ap} \log (a + be^{px}).$

308. $\int \dfrac{dx}{ae^{mx} + be^{-mx}} = \dfrac{1}{m\sqrt{ab}} \tan^{-1} \left(e^{mx}\sqrt{\dfrac{a}{b}}\right).$

311. $\int e^{ax} \sin^n bx\, dx = \dfrac{1}{a^2 + n^2b^2}\Big((a \sin bx - nb \cos bx)$

$e^{ax} \sin^{n-1} bx + n(n - 1)b^2 \int e^{ax} \sin^{n-2} bx \cdot dx\Big).$

312. $\int e^{ax} \cos^n bx\, dx = \dfrac{1}{a^2 + n^2b^2}\Big((a \cos bx + nb \sin bx)$

$e^{ax} \cos^{n-1} bx + n(n - 1)b^2 \int e^{ax} \cos^{n-2} bx\, dx\Big).$

---

313. $\int \sinh x\, dx = \cosh x.$
314. $\int \cosh x\, dx = \sinh x.$
315. $\int \tanh x\, dx = \log \cosh x.$
316. $\int \coth x\, dx = \log \sinh x.$
317. $\int \operatorname{sech} x\, dx = 2 \tan^{-1} (e^x).$

318. $\int \operatorname{csch} x\, dx = \log \tanh \left(\dfrac{x}{2}\right).$

319. $\int x \sinh x\, dx = x \cosh x - \sinh x.$
320. $\int x \cosh x\, dx = x \sinh x - \cosh x.$
321. $\int \operatorname{sech} x \tanh x\, dx = -\operatorname{sech} x.$
322. $\int \operatorname{csch} x \coth x\, dx = -\operatorname{csch} x.$

DEFINITE INTEGRALS

323. $\int_0^\infty x^{n-1} e^{-x}\, dx = \int_0^1 \left(\log \dfrac{1}{x}\right)^{n-1} dx = \Gamma(n).$

324. $\Gamma(n)$, the gamma function is finite if $n > 0$.

325. $\Gamma(n + 1) = n\Gamma(n).$

326. $\Gamma(n) \cdot \Gamma(1-n) = \dfrac{\pi}{\sin n\pi}.$

327. $\Gamma(n) = (n-1)!$ if $n =$ integer > 0.

328. $\Gamma(\frac{1}{2}) = \sqrt{\pi}.$

(See values of $\Gamma(n)$ at end of integral table.)

329. $\displaystyle\int_0^1 x^{m-1}(1-x)^{n-1}\,dx = \int_0^\infty \frac{x^{m-1}\,dx}{(1+x)^{m+n}} = \frac{\Gamma(m)\,\Gamma(n)}{\Gamma(m+n)}.$

330. $\displaystyle\int_1^\infty \frac{dx}{x^m} = \frac{1}{m-1},$ $[m > 1]$.

331. $\displaystyle\int_0^\infty \frac{dx}{(1+x)x^p} = \pi \csc p\pi,$ $[p < 1]$.

332. $\displaystyle\int_0^\infty \frac{dx}{(1-x)x^p} = -\pi \cot p\pi,$ $[p < 1]$.

333. $\displaystyle\int_0^\infty \frac{x^{p-1}\,dx}{1+x} = \frac{\pi}{\sin p\pi},$ $[0 < p < 1]$.

334. $\displaystyle\int_0^\infty \frac{x^{m-1}\,dx}{1+x^n} = \frac{\pi}{n \sin \frac{m\pi}{n}},$ $[0 < m < n]$.

335. $\displaystyle\int_0^\infty \frac{dx}{(1+x)\sqrt{x}} = \pi.$

336. $\displaystyle\int_0^\infty \frac{a\,dx}{a^2+x^2} = \frac{\pi}{2},$ if $a > 0$; 0, if $a = 0$; $-\frac{\pi}{2}$, if $a < 0$.

337. $\displaystyle\int_0^{\pi/2} \sin^n x\,dx = \int_0^{\pi/2} \cos^n x\,dx$

$\displaystyle = \frac{1 \cdot 3 \cdot 5 \cdots (n-1)}{2 \cdot 4 \cdot 6 \cdots (n)} \cdot \frac{\pi}{2},$ [n an even integer],

$\displaystyle = \frac{2 \cdot 4 \cdot 6 \cdots (n-1)}{1 \cdot 3 \cdot 5 \cdot 7 \cdots n},$ [n an odd integer],

$\displaystyle = \frac{1}{2}\sqrt{\pi}\,\frac{\Gamma\left(\frac{n+1}{2}\right)}{\Gamma\left(\frac{n}{2}+1\right)},$ $[n > -1]$.

338. $\displaystyle\int_0^\infty \frac{\sin mx\,dx}{x} = \frac{\pi}{2},$ if $m > 0$; 0, if $m = 0$; $-\frac{\pi}{2}$, if $m < 0$.

339. $\displaystyle\int_0^\infty \frac{\cos x\,dx}{x} = \infty.$

340. $\displaystyle\int_0^\infty \frac{\tan x\,dx}{x} = \frac{\pi}{2}.$

341. $\int_0^{\pi} \sin kx \cdot \sin mx \, dx = \int_0^{\pi} \cos kx \cdot \cos mx \, dx = 0,$

$[k \neq m;\ m, k = \text{integers}].$

342. $\int_0^{\infty} \frac{\sin x \cos mx \, dx}{x} = 0,\ m < -1 \text{ or } m > 1,$

$= \frac{\pi}{4},\ \text{if } m = \pm 1;\ = \frac{\pi}{2},\ \text{if } m^2 < 1.$

343. $\int_0^{\pi} \sin^2 mx \, dx = \int_0^{\pi} \cos^2 mx \, dx = \frac{\pi}{2}.$

344. $\int_0^{\infty} \frac{\sin^2 x \, dx}{x^2} = \frac{\pi}{2}.$

345. $\int_0^{\infty} \frac{\cos mx}{1 + x^2} dx = \frac{\pi}{2} e^{-m},$ $[m > 0],$

$= \frac{\pi}{2} e^{m},$ $[m < 0].$

346. $\int_0^{\infty} \cos(x^2) \, dx = \int_0^{\infty} \sin(x^2) \, dx = \frac{1}{2}\sqrt{\frac{\pi}{2}}.$

347. $\int_0^{\infty} \frac{\sin x \, dx}{\sqrt{x}} = \int_0^{\infty} \frac{\cos x \, dx}{\sqrt{x}} = \sqrt{\frac{\pi}{2}}.$

348. $\int_0^{\pi/2} \frac{dx}{1 + a \cos x} = \frac{\cos^{-1} a}{\sqrt{1 - a^2}},$ $[a < 1].$

349. $\int_0^{2\pi} \frac{dx}{1 + a \cos x} = \frac{2\pi}{\sqrt{1 - a^2}},$ $[a^2 < 1].$

350. $\int_0^{\infty} e^{-ax} \, dx = \frac{1}{a}.$ $[a > 0].$

351. $\int_0^{\infty} x^n e^{-ax} \, dx = \frac{\Gamma(n + 1)}{a^{n+1}},$ $[n > -1, a > 0],$

$= \frac{n!}{a^{n+1}},$ $[n \text{ pos. integ.}, a > 0].$

352. $\int_0^{\infty} e^{-a^2x^2} \, dx = \frac{1}{2a}\sqrt{\pi} = \frac{1}{2a}\Gamma\left(\frac{1}{2}\right),$ $[a > 0].$

353. $\int_0^{\infty} x e^{-x^2} \, dx = \frac{1}{2}.$

354. $\int_0^{\infty} x^2 e^{-x^2} \, dx = \frac{\sqrt{\pi}}{4}.$

355. $\int_0^{\infty} x^{2n} e^{-ax^2} \, dx = \frac{1 \cdot 3 \cdot 5 \cdots (2n - 1)}{2^{n+1} a^n} \sqrt{\frac{\pi}{a}}.$

356. $\int_0^{\infty} e^{(-x^2 - a^2/x^2)} \, dx = \frac{e^{-2a}\sqrt{\pi}}{2}.$

357. $\int_0^\infty e^{-nx}\sqrt{x}\,dx = \frac{1}{2n}\sqrt{\frac{\pi}{n}}.$

358. $\int_0^\infty \frac{e^{-nx}}{\sqrt{x}}\,dx = \sqrt{\frac{\pi}{n}}.$

359. $\int_0^\infty e^{-ax}\cos mx\,dx = \frac{a}{a^2+m^2},\qquad [a>0].$

360. $\int_0^\infty e^{-ax}\sin mx\,dx = \frac{m}{a^2+m^2},\qquad [a>0].$

361. $\int_0^\infty e^{-a^2x^2}\cos bx\,dx = \frac{\sqrt{\pi}\cdot e^{-b^2/4a^2}}{2a},\qquad [a>0].$

362. $\int_0^1 (\log x)^n\,dx = (-1)^n\cdot n!.$

363. $\int_0^1 \left(\log\frac{1}{x}\right)^{\frac{1}{2}}dx = \frac{\sqrt{\pi}}{2}.$

364. $\int_0^1 \left(\log\frac{1}{x}\right)^{-\frac{1}{2}}dx = \sqrt{\pi}.$

365. $\int_0^1 \left(\log\frac{1}{x}\right)^{n}dx = n!.$

366. $\int_0^1 x\log(1-x)\,dx = -\frac{3}{4}.$

367. $\int_0^1 x\log(1+x)\,dx = \frac{1}{4}.$

368. $\int_0^1 \frac{\log x}{1+x}\,dx = -\frac{\pi^2}{12}.$

369. $\int_0^1 \frac{\log x}{1-x}\,dx = -\frac{\pi^2}{6}.$

370. $\int_0^1 \frac{\log x}{1-x^2}\,dx = -\frac{\pi^2}{8}.$

371. $\int_0^1 \log\left(\frac{1+x}{1-x}\right)\cdot\frac{dx}{x} = \frac{\pi^2}{4}.$

372. $\int_0^1 \frac{\log x\,dx}{\sqrt{1-x^2}} = -\frac{\pi}{2}\log 2.$

373. $\int_0^1 x^m\left(\log\frac{1}{x}\right)^n dx = \frac{\Gamma(n+1)}{(m+1)^{n+1}},$ if $m+1>0$, $n+1>0$.

374. $\int_0^1 \frac{(x^p-x^q)dx}{\log x} = \log\left(\frac{p+1}{q+1}\right),\qquad [p+1>0, q+1>0].$

375. $\int_0^1 \frac{dx}{\sqrt{\log\left(\frac{1}{x}\right)}} = \sqrt{\pi}.$

376. $\int_0^\infty \log\left(\frac{e^x + 1}{e^x - 1}\right) dx = \frac{\pi^2}{4}.$

377. $\int_0^\pi x \cdot \log \sin x \, dx = -\frac{\pi^2}{2} \log 2.$

378. $\int_0^{\pi/2} \log \sin x \, dx = \int_0^{\pi/2} \log \cos x \, dx = -\frac{\pi}{2} \cdot \log 2.$

379. $\int_0^{\pi/2} \sin x \log \sin x \, dx = \log 2 - 1.$

380. $\int_0^{\pi/2} \log \tan x \, dx = 0.$

381. $\int_0^\pi \log (a \pm b \cos x) \, dx = \pi \log \left(\frac{a + \sqrt{a^2 - b^2}}{2}\right), [a \geqq b].$

GAMMA FUNCTION

Values of $\Gamma(n) = \int_0^\infty \epsilon^{-x} x^{n-1} dx$

n	$\Gamma(n)$	n	$\Gamma(n)$	n	$\Gamma(n)$	n	$\Gamma(n)$
1.00	1.00000	1.25	.90640	1.50	.88623	1.75	.91906
1.01	.99433	1.26	.90440	1.51	.88659	1.76	.92137
1.02	.98884	1.27	.90250	1.52	.88704	1.77	.92376
1.03	.98355	1.28	.90072	1.53	.88757	1.78	.92623
1.04	.97844	1.29	.89904	1.54	.88818	1.79	.92877
1.05	.97350	1.30	.89747	1.55	.88887	1.80	.93138
1.06	.96874	1.31	.89600	1.56	.88964	1.81	.93408
1.07	.96415	1.32	.89464	1.57	.89049	1.82	.93685
1.08	.95973	1.33	.89338	1.58	.89142	1.83	.93969
1.09	.95546	1.34	.89222	1.59	.89243	1.84	.94261
1.10	.95135	1.35	.89115	1.60	.89352	1.85	.94561
1.11	.94739	1.36	.89018	1.61	.89468	1.86	.94869
1.12	.94359	1.37	.88931	1.62	.89592	1.87	.95184
1.13	.93993	1.38	.88854	1.63	.89724	1.88	.95507
1.14	.93642	1.39	.88785	1.64	.89864	1.89	.95838
1.15	.93304	1.40	.88726	1.65	.90012	1.90	.96177
1.16	.92980	1.41	.88676	1.66	.90167	1.91	.96523
1.17	.92670	1.42	.88636	1.67	.90330	1.92	.96878
1.18	.92373	1.43	.88604	1.68	.90500	1.93	.97240
1.19	.92088	1.44	.88580	1.69	.90678	1.94	.97610
1.20	.91817	1.45	.88565	1.70	.90864	1.95	.97988
1.21	.91558	1.46	.88560	1.71	.91057	1.96	.98374
1.22	.91311	1.47	.88563	1.72	.91258	1.97	.98768
1.23	.91075	1.48	.88575	1.73	.91466	1.98	.99171
1.24	.90852	1.49	.88595	1.74	.91683	1.99	.99581
						2.00	1.00000

ALGEBRA

Factors and Expansions

$$(a \pm b)^2 = a^2 \pm 2ab + b^2.$$
$$(a \pm b)^3 = a^3 \pm 3a^2b + 3ab^2 \pm b^3.$$
$$(a \pm b)^4 = a^4 \pm 4a^3b + 6a^2b^2 \pm 4ab^3 + b^4.$$
$$a^2 - b^2 = (a - b)(a + b).$$
$$a^2 + b^2 = (a + b\sqrt{-1})(a - b\sqrt{-1}).$$
$$a^3 - b^3 = (a - b)(a^2 + ab + b^2).$$
$$a^3 + b^3 = (a + b)(a^2 - ab + b^2).$$
$$a^4 + b^4 = (a^2 + ab\sqrt{2} + b^2)(a^2 - ab\sqrt{2} + b^2).$$
$$a^n - b^n = (a - b)(a^{n-1} + a^{n-2}b + \ldots . + b^{n-1}).$$
$$a^n - b^n = (a + b)(a^{n-1} - a^{n-2}b + \ldots . - b^{n-1}),$$
for even values of n.
$$a^n + b^n = (a + b)\,(a^{n-1} - a^{n-2}b + \ldots . + b^{n-1}),$$
for odd values of n.
$$a^4 + a^2b^2 + b^4 = (a^2 + ab + b^2)(a^2 - ab + b^2).$$
$$(a + b + c)^2 = a^2 + b^2 + c^2 + 2ab + 2ac + 2bc.$$
$$(a + b + c)^3 = a^3 + b^3 + c^3 + 3a^2(b + c) + 3b^2(a + c) + 3c^2(a + b) + 6abc.$$
$$(a + b + c + d + \ldots)^2 = a^2 + b^2 + c^2 + d^2 + \ldots + 2a(b + c + d + \ldots) + 2b(c + d + \ldots) + 2c(d + \ldots) + \ldots$$

See also under Series

Powers and Roots

$$a^x \times a^y = a^{(x+y)}. \qquad a^0 = 1 \text{ [if } a \neq 0]. \qquad (ab)^x = a^x b^x.$$

$$\frac{a^x}{a^y} = a^{(x-y)}. \qquad a^{-x} = \frac{1}{a^x}. \qquad \left(\frac{a}{b}\right)^x = \frac{a^x}{b^x}.$$

$$(a^x)^y = a^{xy}. \qquad a^{\frac{1}{x}} = \sqrt[x]{a}. \qquad \sqrt[x]{ab} = \sqrt[x]{a}\,\sqrt[x]{b}.$$

$$\sqrt[x]{\sqrt[y]{a}} = \sqrt[xy]{a}. \qquad a^{\frac{x}{y}} = \sqrt[y]{a^x}. \qquad \sqrt[x]{\frac{a}{b}} = \frac{\sqrt[x]{a}}{\sqrt[x]{b}}.$$

Proportion

If $\dfrac{a}{b} = \dfrac{c}{d}$, then $\dfrac{a+b}{b} = \dfrac{c+d}{d}$,

$$\frac{a-b}{b} = \frac{c-d}{d}, \qquad \frac{a-b}{a+b} = \frac{c-d}{c+d}.$$

SUMS OF NUMBERS

The sum of the first n numbers,—

$$\Sigma(n) = 1+2+3+4+5 \ldots\ldots +n = \frac{n(n+1)}{2}$$

The sum of the squares of the first n numbers,

$$\Sigma(n^2) = 1^2+2^2+3^2+4^2+5^2 \ldots +n^2 = \frac{n(n+1)(2n+1)}{6}$$

The sum of the cubes of the first n numbers,

$$\Sigma(n^3) = 1^3+2^3+3^3+4^3+5^3 \ldots\ldots +n^3 = \frac{n^2(n+1)^2}{4}$$

ARITHMETICAL PROGRESSION

If a is the first term; l, the last term; d, the common difference; n, the number of terms and s, the sum of n terms,—

$$l = a + (n-1)d \qquad s = \frac{n}{2}(a+l)$$

$$s = \frac{n}{2}\left\{ 2a + (n-1)d \right\}$$

GEOMETRICAL PROGRESSION

If a is the first term; l, the last term; r, the common ratio; n. the number of terms and s, the sum of n terms,—

$$l = ar^{n-1} \qquad s = a\frac{(1-r^n)}{1-r}$$

$$s = a\frac{(r^n-1)}{r-1} \qquad s = \frac{lr-a}{r-1}$$

If n is infinity and r^2 less than unity,—

$$s = \frac{a}{1-r}$$

FACTORIALS

$$\underline{|n} = n! = e^{-n}n^n\sqrt{2\pi n}, \text{ approximately.}$$

PERMUTATIONS

If M denote the number of permutations of n things taken p at a time,—

$$M = n(n-1)(n-2) \ldots\ldots (n-p+1)$$

COMBINATIONS

If M denote the number of combinations of n things taken p at a time,—

$$M = \frac{n(n-1)(n-2) \ldots\ldots (n-p+1)}{p!}$$

$$M = \frac{n!}{p!(n-p)!}$$

Quadratic Equations

Any quadratic equation may be reduced to the form, —

$$ax^2 + bx + c = 0$$

$$\text{Then} \quad x = \frac{-b \pm \sqrt{b^2 - 4ac}}{2a}.$$

If $b^2 - 4ac$ is positive the roots are real and unequal.
If $b^2 - 4ac$ is zero the roots are real and equal.
If $b^2 - 4ac$ is negative the roots are imaginary and unequal.
If $b^2 - 4ac$ is a perfect square the roots are rational and unequal.

Cubic Equations

A cubic equation, $y^3 + py^2 + qy + r = 0$ may be reduced to the form, —

$$x^3 + ax + b = 0$$

by substituting for y the value, $\left(x - \frac{p}{3}\right)$. Here

$$a = \tfrac{1}{3}(3q - p^2) \text{ and } b = \tfrac{1}{27}(2p^3 - 9pq + 27r).$$

For solution let, —

$$A = \sqrt[3]{-\frac{b}{2} + \sqrt{\frac{b^2}{4} + \frac{a^3}{27}}}, \qquad B = \sqrt[3]{-\frac{b}{2} - \sqrt{\frac{b^2}{4} + \frac{a^3}{27}}},$$

then the values of x will be given by,

$$x = A + B, \quad -\frac{A+B}{2} + \frac{A-B}{2}\sqrt{-3}, \quad -\frac{A+B}{2} - \frac{A-B}{2}\sqrt{-3}$$

If $\frac{b^2}{4} + \frac{a^3}{27} > 0$, there will be one real root and two conjugate imaginary roots.

If $\frac{b^2}{4} + \frac{a^3}{27} = 0$, there will be three real roots of which two at least are equal

If $\frac{b^2}{4} + \frac{a^3}{27} < 0$, there will be three real and unequal roots.

In the last case a trigonometric solution is useful. Compute the value of the angle ϕ in the expression, —

$$\cos \phi = -\frac{b}{2} \div \sqrt{\left(-\frac{a^3}{27}\right)},$$

then x will have the following values:—

$$2\sqrt{-\frac{a}{3}} \cos \frac{\phi}{3}, \qquad 2\sqrt{-\frac{a}{3}} \cos\left(\frac{\phi}{3} + 120°\right),$$

$$2\sqrt{-\frac{a}{3}} \cos\left(\frac{\phi}{3} + 240°\right).$$

APPROXIMATIONS

If a and b are small quantities, the following relations are approximately true,—

$$(1 \pm a)^m = 1 \pm ma,$$

$$(1 \pm a)^m (1 \pm b)^n = 1 \pm ma \pm nb.$$

If n is nearly equal to m,

$$\sqrt{mn} = \frac{n+m}{2}, \text{ approximately.}$$

If θ is a very small angle expressed in radians,—

$$\frac{\sin\theta}{\theta} = 1 \text{ and } \frac{\tan\theta}{\theta} = 1, \text{ approximately.}$$

SERIES

The expression in parentheses following certain of the series indicates the region of convergence. If not otherwise indicated it is to be understood that the series converges for all finite values of x.

Binomial

$$(x+y)^n = x^n + nx^{n-1}y + \frac{n(n-1)}{2!}x^{n-2}y^2 + \frac{n(n-1)(n-2)}{3!}x^{(n-3)}y^3 + \ldots \quad (y^2 < x^2)$$

$$(1 \pm x)^n = 1 \pm nx + \frac{n(n-1)x^2}{2!} \pm \frac{n(n-1)(n-2)x^3}{3!} + \ldots \text{ etc.} \quad (x^2 < 1)$$

$$(1 \pm x)^{-n} = 1 \mp nx + \frac{n(n+1)x^2}{2!} \mp \frac{n(n+1)(n+2)x^3}{3!} + \ldots \text{ etc.} \quad (x^2 < 1)$$

$$(1 \pm x)^{-1} = 1 \mp x + x^2 \mp x^3 + x^4 \mp x^5 + \ldots \quad (x^2 < 1)$$

$$(1 \pm x)^{-2} = 1 \mp 2x + 3x^2 \mp 4x^3 + 5x^4 \mp 6x^5 + \ldots \quad (x^2 < 1)$$

Taylor's Series

$$f(x+h) = f(x) + hf'(x) + \frac{h^2}{2!}f''(x) + \frac{h^3}{3!}f'''(x) + \ldots$$

$$= f(h) + xf'(h) + \frac{x^2}{2!}f''(h) + \frac{x^3}{3!}f'''(h) + \ldots$$

Maclaurin's Series

$$f(x) = f(o) + xf'(o) + \frac{x^2}{2!}f''(o) + \frac{x^3}{3!}f'''(o) + \ldots$$

Exponential

$$e = 1 + \frac{1}{1} + \frac{1}{2!} + \frac{1}{3!} + \frac{1}{4!} + \ldots$$

$$e^x = 1 + x + \frac{x^2}{2!} + \frac{x^3}{3!} + \frac{x^4}{4!} + \ldots$$

$$a^x = 1 + x \log_e a + \frac{(x \log a)^2}{2!} + \frac{(x \log a)^3}{3!} + \ldots$$

LOGARITHMIC

$$\log_e x = \frac{x-1}{x} + \frac{1}{2}\left(\frac{x-1}{x}\right)^2 + \frac{1}{3}\left(\frac{x-1}{x}\right)^3 + \ldots \qquad (x > \tfrac{1}{2})$$

$$\log_e x = (x-1) - \tfrac{1}{2}(x-1)^2 + \tfrac{1}{3}(x-1)^3 - \ldots \qquad (2 > x > 0)$$

$$\log_e x = 2\left[\frac{x-1}{x+1} + \frac{1}{3}\left(\frac{x-1}{x+1}\right)^3 + \frac{1}{5}\left(\frac{x-1}{x+1}\right)^5 + \ldots\right] \qquad (x > 0)$$

$$\log_e(1+x) = x - \tfrac{1}{2}x^2 + \tfrac{1}{3}x^3 - \tfrac{1}{4}x^4 + \ldots \qquad (-1 < x < 1)$$

$$\log_e(n+1) - \log_e(n-1) = 2\left[\frac{1}{n} + \frac{1}{3n^3} + \frac{1}{5n^5} + \ldots\right]$$

$$\log_e(a+x) = \log_e a + 2\left[\frac{x}{2a+x} + \frac{1}{3}\left(\frac{x}{2a+x}\right)^3 + \frac{1}{5}\left(\frac{x}{2a+x}\right)^5 + \ldots\right]$$

$$(a > 0,\ -a < x < +\infty)$$

TRIGONOMETRIC

$$\sin x = x - \frac{x^3}{3!} + \frac{x^5}{5!} - \frac{x^7}{7!} + \ldots$$

$$\cos x = 1 - \frac{x^2}{2!} + \frac{x^4}{4!} - \frac{x^6}{6!} + \ldots$$

$$\tan x = x + \frac{x^3}{3} + \frac{2x^5}{15} + \frac{17x^7}{315} + \frac{62x^9}{2835} + \ldots \qquad \left(x^2 < \frac{\pi^2}{4}\right)$$

$$\sin^{-1} x = x + \frac{x^3}{6} + \frac{1}{2}\cdot\frac{3}{4}\cdot\frac{x^5}{5} + \frac{1}{2}\cdot\frac{3}{4}\cdot\frac{5}{6}\cdot\frac{x^7}{7} + \ldots \qquad (x^2 < 1)$$

$$\tan^{-1} x = x - \tfrac{1}{3}x^3 + \tfrac{1}{5}x^5 - \tfrac{1}{7}x^7 + \ldots \qquad (x^2 < 1)$$

$$= \frac{\pi}{2} - \frac{1}{x} + \frac{1}{3x^3} - \frac{1}{5x^5} + \ldots \qquad (x^2 > 1)$$

$$\log_e \sin x = \log_e x - \frac{x^2}{6} - \frac{x^4}{180} - \frac{x^6}{2835} - \ldots \qquad (x^2 < \pi^2)$$

$$\log_e \cos x = -\frac{x^2}{2} - \frac{x^4}{12} - \frac{x^6}{45} - \frac{17x^8}{2520} - \ldots \qquad \left(x^2 < \frac{\pi^2}{4}\right)$$

$$\log_e \tan x = \log_e x + \frac{x^2}{3} + \frac{7x^4}{90} + \frac{62x^6}{2835} + \ldots \qquad \left(x^2 < \frac{\pi^2}{4}\right)$$

$$e^{\sin x} = 1 + x + \frac{x^2}{2!} - \frac{3x^4}{4!} - \frac{8x^5}{5!} - \frac{3x^6}{6!} + \frac{56x^7}{7!} + \ldots$$

$$e^{\cos x} = e\left(1 - \frac{x^2}{2!} + \frac{4x^4}{4!} - \frac{31x^6}{6!} + \ldots\right)$$

$$e^{\tan x} = 1 + x + \frac{x^2}{2!} + \frac{3x^3}{3!} + \frac{9x^4}{4!} + \frac{37x^5}{5!} + \ldots \qquad \left(x^2 < \frac{\pi^2}{4}\right)$$

MISCELLANEOUS

The Sum (Σ, = Sigma) and Product (Π, = Pi) Notations

Σ denotes the **sum,** and Π, the **product** of all quantities of a given collection. In particular,

$$\sum_{i=m}^{m+n} x_i \text{ means } x_m + x_{m+1} + \dots + x_{m+n}, \ (n + 1 \text{ terms in all}),$$

$$\prod_{i=m}^{m+n} x_i \text{ means } x_m x_{m+1} \dots x_{m+n}, \ (n + 1 \text{ factors in all}).$$

For indicated **range,** R, (such as $m \leqq i \leqq m + n$), one may write $\sum_R x_i$, $\prod_R x_i$, respectively. Where the range is clear from the context one writes Σx_i, Πx_i, or even Σx, Πx, respectively. For c a constant and for x_i and y_i with common range (say of n elements),

$$\Sigma c x_i = c \Sigma x_i, \ \Sigma(x_i + y_i) = \Sigma x_i + \Sigma y_i, \ \Sigma(x_i + c) = nc + \Sigma x_i.$$

Special Numerical Relations

(i) For range, $i = 1, 2, \dots, n$, with $x_i = i$.
$\Sigma x_i = n(n + 1)/2$, $\Sigma(2x_i - 1) = n^2$,
$\Sigma x_i^2 = n(n + 1)(2n + 1)/6$.
$\Sigma x_i^3 = (\Sigma x_i)^2$, $\Sigma x_i^4 = (\Sigma x_i^2)[6(\Sigma x_i) - 1]/5$.
$\Pi(c + 1 - x_i) = c^{(n)}$, $\Pi x_i = n^{(n)} = n!$ (**"factorial n"**).
Hence $n! = n \cdot (n - 1)!$ $0!$ is defined to be 1.
Stirling's formula (used for n large),

$$\sqrt{2n\pi}(n/e)^n < n! < \sqrt{2n\pi}(n/e)^n\left(1 + \frac{1}{12n - 1}\right),$$
$$(\pi = 3.14159 \dots, \ e = 2.71828 \dots).$$

$n!/(n-m)!$ gives the number of **permutations of n distinct things taken m at a time.**

(ii) For range, $i = -\left(\frac{n-1}{2}\right), -\left(\frac{n-1}{2}\right) + 1, \dots, \left(\frac{n-1}{2}\right) - 1, \left(\frac{n-1}{2}\right)$, with $x_i = i$ (whether n is odd or even),

$$\sum x_i = \sum x_i^3 = 0, \ \sum x_i^2 = \frac{n(n^2 - 1)}{12}, \ \sum x_i^4 = \frac{3n^2 - 7}{20} \sum x_i^2.$$

(iii) The Binomial Coefficients, $\binom{n}{m}$.

$\binom{n}{m} = n!/[(n-m)!m!]$, for integers m, n, $0 \leqq m \leqq n$. $\binom{n}{0} = \binom{n}{n} = 1$.

$(x+c)^n = \sum_r \binom{n}{r} x^{n-r} c^r$, $(0 \leqq r \leqq n)$, the **binomial expansion.** $\binom{n}{m}$ gives also the number of **combinations of n distinct things taken m at a time.**

$\binom{n}{m} + \binom{n}{m+1} = \binom{n+1}{m+1}$, **recursion relation** for binomial coefficients.

$$\binom{n}{n-m} = \binom{n}{m}, \quad \sum_r (-1)^r \binom{n}{r} = 0, \quad \sum_r \binom{n}{r}^2 = \binom{2n}{n}, \quad \sum_{s=m}^{n} \binom{s}{m} = \binom{n+1}{m+1}.$$

Table of Binomial Coefficients

n	$\binom{n}{0}$	$\binom{n}{1}$	$\binom{n}{2}$	$\binom{n}{3}$	$\binom{n}{4}$	$\binom{n}{5}$	$\binom{n}{6}$	$\binom{n}{7}$	$\binom{n}{8}$	$\binom{n}{9}$	$\binom{n}{10}$
0	1										
1	1	1									
2	1	2	1								
3	1	3	3	1							
4	1	4	6	4	1						
5	1	5	10	10	5	1					
6	1	6	15	20	15	6	1				
7	1	7	21	35	35	21	7	1			
8	1	8	28	56	70	56	28	8	1		
9	1	9	36	84	126	126	84	36	9	1	
10	1	10	45	120	210	252	210	120	45	10	1
11	1	11	55	165	330	462	462	330	165	55	11
12	1	12	66	220	495	792	924	792	495	220	66
13	1	13	78	286	715	1287	1716	1716	1287	715	286
14	1	14	91	364	1001	2002	3003	3432	3003	2002	1001
15	1	15	105	455	1365	3003	5005	6435	6435	5005	3003
16	1	16	120	560	1820	4368	8008	11440	12870	11440	8008
17	1	17	136	680	2380	6188	12376	19448	24310	24310	19448
18	1	18	153	816	3060	8568	18564	31824	43758	48620	43758
19	1	19	171	969	3876	11628	27132	50388	75582	92378	92378
20	1	20	190	1140	4845	15504	38760	77520	125970	167960	184756

NOTE: $\binom{n}{m} = \dfrac{n(n-1)(n-2)\ldots(n-m+1)}{m(m-1)(m-2)\ldots3.2.1}$: $\binom{n}{0} = 1$; $\binom{n}{1} = n$.

For coefficients missing from the above table, use the relation

$\binom{n}{m} = \binom{n}{n-m}$, e.g. $\binom{20}{11} = \binom{20}{9} = 167960$.

Finite Differences

For equi-spaced arguments x_i, and associated y_i, the successive **advancing y-differences** are, $\Delta^0 y_i = y_i$, $\Delta y_i = y_{i+1} - y_i$, $\Delta^2 y_i = \Delta y_{i+1} - \Delta y_i = y_{i+2} - 2y_{i+1} + y_i, \ldots, \quad \Delta^m y_i = \Delta^{m-1} y_{i+1} - \Delta^{m-1} y_i = \sum_r (-1)^r \binom{m}{r} y_{i+m-r}$. With arbitrary origin A and class-interval length, $x_{i+1} - x_i = h$, using $u_i = (x_i - A)/h$, write $y(u_i)$ for y_i. Then if for some fixed m, for the portion of the table considered, the values of $\Delta^{m+1} y_i$ be zero (or approximately, if these be regarded as negligible) **Newton's formula** gives

$$y(u) = \sum \frac{u^{(r)}}{r!} \Delta^r y(0) = y(0) + u\Delta y(0) + \frac{u(u-1)}{1 \cdot 2} \Delta^2 y(0) + \cdots + \frac{u(u-1)\ldots(u-m+1)}{m!} \Delta^m y(0).$$

This formula reduces to an identity for $u = u_0, u_1, \ldots, u_n$, $(u_i = i)$, and may be used to interpolate for intermediate values.

Example. Given

x	-4,	-2,	0,	2,	4,	6,	8,	$\ldots$
y	10,	14,	30,	64,	122,	210,	334,	$\ldots$

to find a value for y when $x = 10$, and when $x = 1$. Suppose for some reason A has been taken at $x = 2$. The work may be arranged as follows:

u	x	y	Δ	Δ^2	Δ^3	Δ^4
-3	-4	10				
			4			
-2	-2	14		12		
			16		6	
-1	0	30		18		0
			34		6	
0	2	64		24		0
			58		6	
1	4	122		30		0
			88		6	
2	6	210		36		—
			124		—	
3	8	334		—		—
			—		—	
—	—	—		—		—

$$y(u) = 64 + 58u + 30\frac{u(u-1)}{1 \cdot 2} + 6\frac{u(u-1)(u-2)}{1 \cdot 2 \cdot 3}$$
$$= 64 + 58u + 15u(u-1) + u(u-1)(u-2).$$

At $x = 10$, $u = 4$. Substituting $u = 4$, one has $y|_{x=10} = 500$.
At $x = 1$, $u = -\frac{1}{2}$. Substituting $u = -\frac{1}{2}$, one has $y|_{x=1} = 44\frac{3}{8}$.

STATISTICS

Central Measures

Here the range of i is from 1 to n. With each value x_i is associated a weighting factor $f_i \geq 0$ (such as the frequency, the probability, the mass, the reliability, or other multiplier).

N, the **total weight,** $= \Sigma f_i$.

$\bar{x}$, the **arithmetic mean,** $= \Sigma f_i x_i / N = \Sigma f_i x_i / \Sigma f_i$.

GM, the **geometric mean** (available when each x_i is positive), $= \sqrt[N]{\Pi x_i^{f_i}}$. $\text{Log } GM = \Sigma f_i \log x_i / N$.

Mo, the **mode,** = value among $(x_1, \ldots, x_n)$ having maximum associated f_i (usually obtained by interpolating after the data are graduated). For unweighted items, x_i, a mode is a value about which the values of x_i cluster most densely.

RMS, the **root-mean-square,** $= \sqrt{\Sigma f_i x_i^2 / N}$.

Md, the **median** (see below). For unweighted items, the median is the value, equaled or exceeded by exactly half of the values x_i in the given list. In case of a central pair, the median is usually taken as the arithmetic mean of this pair.

Mm, the **mid-mean** (see below). For unweighted items, the mid-mean is the arithmetic mean of the half-list obtained upon dropping out the highest quarter and lowest quarter of the items.

Cum $f|_X$, the value of "cumulative f" at X, $= \sum_{x_i<X} f_i$ (interpolation being used for X if necessary).

The M-Tiles

For **ungrouped data,** X is called the **r**th **m-tile** (or **r**th **m-tile mark**) $(r = 0, 1, \ldots, m)$ if simultaneously, $\sum_{x_i<X} f_i/N \leq r/m$, and $\sum_{x_i>X} f_i/N \leq (m - r)/m$. In particular the zeroth m-tile is **min,** the minimal value among the list $(x_1, \ldots, x_n)$, and the mth m-tile is **max,** the maximal value among the list.

For **grouped data,** the rth m-tile mark, X, is such that

$$\text{Cum } f|_X = Nr/m, \quad (r = 0, 1, 2, \ldots, m).$$

$$\text{Cum } f|_{\min} = 0, \qquad \text{Cum } f|_{\max} = N.$$

In particular, certain intermediate $(0 < r < m)$ m-tile marks are named as follows:

m	$r = 1$	2	3	...
2	Md (median)			
3	T_1 (lower tertile)	T_2 (upper tertile)		
4	Q_1 (lower quartile)	Md	Q_3 (upper quartile)	
10	D_1 (first decile)	D_2	D_3	etc.
100	PC_1 (first percentile)	PC_2	PC_3	etc.

The term "rth m-tile" ($r = 1, \ldots, m$) is also used to denote the class interval extending from the $(r-1)$st to rth m-tile mark as defined above.

Mm, the **mid-mean,** =

$$2 \sum_{Q_1 \leq x_i \leq Q_3} f_i x_i / N = \sum_{Q_1 \leq x_i \leq Q_3} f_i x_i \Big/ \sum_{Q_1 \leq x_i \leq Q_3} f_i.$$

When each x_i is positive, and not all are equal, one always has $0 < \min < GM < \bar{x} < RMS < \max$.

For moderately-skewed distributions, one has approximately $Mo - \bar{x} = 3(Md - \bar{x})$, or $3Md = Mo + 2\bar{x}$.

Measures of Dispersion and Skewness

Here A is an arbitrary reference value, usually a convenient integral measure near $\bar{x}$.

ν_k, kth **moment about** A, $= \Sigma f_i (x_i - A)^k / N$, $(k = 0, 1, \ldots)$.

$\nu_0 = 1$, $\nu_1 = \bar{x} - A$. ν_2 as function of A is minimum for $A = \bar{x}$.

μ_k, kth **moment about** $\bar{x}$, $= \Sigma f_i (x_i - \bar{x})^k / N$, $(k = 0, 1, \ldots)$.

$$\begin{aligned}
\mu_0 &= 1, \\
\mu_1 &= 0, \\
\mu_2 &= \nu_2 - \nu_1^2 \ (\mu_2 = \text{variance}), \\
\mu_3 &= \nu_3 - 3\nu_1\nu_2 + 2\nu_1^3, \\
\mu_4 &= \nu_4 - 4\nu_1\nu_3 + 6\nu_1^2\nu_2 - 3\nu_1^4. \\
\beta_1 &= \mu_3^2/\mu_2^3, \ \beta_2 = \mu_4/\mu_2^2.
\end{aligned}$$

σ, **standard deviation,** $= \sqrt{\mu_2}$.

$\alpha_3/2$, **momental skewness;** $\alpha_3 = \sqrt{\beta_1} = \mu_3/\sigma^3$.

$(\alpha_4 - 3)/2$, **kurtosis;** $\alpha_4 = \beta_2$.

MD, **mean deviation** (from the mean), $= \Sigma f_i |x_i - \bar{x}| / N$

$$= 2\left[\bar{x} \sum_{x_i < \bar{x}} f_i - \sum_{x_i < \bar{x}} f_i x_i\right] \Big/ N.$$

(This latter form is convenient for computation.)

s, **quartile deviation,** $= |Q_3 - Q_1|/2$.

$P.E.$, **probable error,** $= 0.6745\sigma$.

V, **coefficient of variation,** $= 100\sigma/\bar{x}\ \%$.

Pearson's measure of skewness $= (\bar{x} - Mo)/\sigma$. (Usually approximately $\alpha_3/2$.)

Bowley's measure of skewness $= (Q_3 - 2Md + Q_1)/(2s)$.

(Bowley's measure of skewness lies between -1 and $+1$.)

The Class Interval

$$\Delta x_i = x_{i+1} - x_i.$$

For equi-spaced arguments, $\Delta x_i = h$, the **length** of the **class interval,** x_i is the **mid-value** or **class mark.** The interval from $x_i - (h/2)$ to $x_i + (h/2)$ is the **class interval** with these as given **initial** and **terminal end values.**

$$u_i = (x_i - A)/h.$$
$$\bar{u} = \Sigma f_i u_i/N, \ \bar{x} = h\bar{u} + A.$$
$$(\mu_k)_x = h^k(\mu_k)_u, \ (k = 0, 1, \ldots).$$
$$\sigma_u^2 = [\Sigma f_i u_i^2/N] - \bar{u}^2, \ \sigma_x = h\sigma_u.$$
$$(\beta_1)_x = (\beta_1)_u, \ (\beta_2)_x = (\beta_2)_u.$$

Sheppard's corrections (to correct approximately for the error due to treating all elements in a given class interval of length h as though concentrated at the class mark).

For μ_0, μ_1, μ_3, no corrections.

In x-units,

corrected $(\mu_2)_x$ = uncorrected $(\mu_2)_x - h^2/12$,

corrected $(\mu_4)_x$ = uncorrected $(\mu_4)_x - h^2$ uncorrected $(\mu_2)_x/2 + 7h^4/240$.

In u-units, replace h by 1 in the formulae given above.

Least Squares

The **normal equations** for finding coefficients, $a_0, a_1, \ldots, a_m$, in fitting a curve of the form $y = a_0 + a_1x + \ldots + a_mx^m$ to data (X_i, Y_i), $i = 1, \ldots, n$, $(n > m)$, are $m + 1$ in number as follows:

$$\Sigma Y_i = a_0 n + a_1 \Sigma X_i + a_2 \Sigma X_i^2 + \ldots + a_m \Sigma X_i^m,$$
$$\Sigma X_i Y_i = a_0 \Sigma X_i + a_1 \Sigma X_i^2 + a_2 \Sigma X_i^3 + \ldots + a_m \Sigma X_i^{m+1},$$
$$\ldots \ldots \ldots \ldots \ldots \ldots \ldots \ldots$$
$$\Sigma X_i^m Y_i = a_0 \Sigma X_i^m + a_1 \Sigma X_i^{m+1} + a_2 \Sigma X_i^{m+2} + \ldots + a_m \Sigma X_i^{2m}.$$

Deviation from fitted curve,

$$d_i = Y_i - (a_0 + a_1 X_i + \ldots + a_m X_i^m).$$
$$\Sigma d_i^2 = \Sigma Y_i^2 - (a_0 \Sigma Y_i + a_1 \Sigma X_i Y_i + \ldots + a_m \Sigma X_i^m Y_i).$$

For $z = ab^x$, use $y = \log z$, $a_0 = \log a$, $a_1 = \log b$.

For $z = at^p$, use $y = \log z$, $a_0 = \log a$, $a_1 = p$, $x = \log t$.

S_y, **standard error of estimate,** = root-mean-square of the y-deviations about a fitted curve $= \sqrt{\Sigma d_i^2/n}$.

Simple Correlation

Product Moment Method

Given n equi-spaced measurements X_i, $i = 1, 2, \ldots, n$, with $h = X_{i+1} - X_i$, $x_i = X_i - \bar{X}$; and m equi-spaced measurements Y_j, $j = 1, 2, \ldots, m$, with $k = Y_{j+1} - Y_j$, $y_j = Y_j - \bar{Y}$; and a weight (frequency, probability, etc.) e_{ij} (≥ 0), associated with (X_i, Y_j). Here e_{ij} is an entry in the table.

$$f_i = \sum_j e_{ij},\ g_j = \sum_i e_{ij}.$$

$$N = \sum_{ij} e_{ij} = \sum_i f_i = \sum_j g_j. \quad \text{(Check)}$$

$$\bar{x} = \sum_{ij} e_{ij}X_i/N = \sum_i f_i X_i/N;\ \bar{y} = \sum_{ij} e_{ij}Y_j/N = \sum_j g_j Y_j/N.$$

Let A and B be arbitrary reference values, usually convenient integral measures near $\bar{X}$ and $\bar{Y}$, respectively.

$$u_i = (X_i - A)/h,\ v_j = (Y_j - B)/k;$$

$$\bar{u} = \Sigma f_i u_i/N,\ \bar{X} = h\bar{u} + A,\ \bar{v} = \Sigma g_j v_j/N,\ \bar{Y} = k\bar{v} + B.$$

$$\left.\begin{aligned}\sigma_u^2 &= (\mu_2)_u = (\Sigma f_i u_i^2/N) - \bar{u}^2,\ \sigma_x = h\sigma_u.\\ \sigma_v^2 &= (\mu_2)_v = (\Sigma g_j v_j^2/N) - \bar{v}^2,\ \sigma_y = k\sigma_v.\end{aligned}\right\}\text{Apply Sheppard's corrections.}$$

$$U_j = \sum_i e_{ij}u_i,\ V_i = \sum_j e_{ij}v_j,\ P = \sum u_i V_i = \sum v_j U_j. \quad \text{(Check)}$$

$$p_{uv} = \sum_{ij} e_{ij}(u_i - \bar{u})(v_j - \bar{v})/N$$

$$= (P/N) - \bar{u}\bar{v}.$$

$$p_{xy} = hkp_{uv}.$$

$r = p_{uv}/(\sigma_u\sigma_v) = p_{xy}/(\sigma_x\sigma_y)$ **(product-moment) coefficient of correlation.** In every case $-1 \leq r \leq 1$.

$Y - \bar{Y} = r\dfrac{\sigma_y}{\sigma_x}(X - \bar{X})$, or $y = r\dfrac{\sigma_y}{\sigma_x}x$, **regression line of y on x.**

$X - \bar{X} = r\dfrac{\sigma_x}{\sigma_y}(Y - \bar{Y})$, or $x = r\dfrac{\sigma_x}{\sigma_y}y$, **regression line of x on y.**

Example of Computation for Product-Moment Coefficient of Correlation

v_j	u_i / x_i / y_j	-3 / 12	-2 / 16	-1 / 20	0 / 24	1 / 28	2 / 32	g_j	g_jv_j	$g_jv_j^2$	U_j $\left(= \sum_i e_{ij}u_i\right)$	v_jU_j
2	21			1	5	7	1	14	28	56	8	16
1	18		1	3	7	5	2	18	18	18	4	4
0	15		2	3	4	1		10	0	0		0
-1	12		3	1	1			5	-5	5	-7	7
-2	9	2	1					3	-6	12	-8	16
	f_i	2	7	8	17	13	3	50	35	91		43
	f_iu_i	-6	-14	-8	0	13	6	-9				
	$f_iu_i^2$	18	28	8	0	13	12	79				
	$V_i,\left(= \sum_j e_{ij}v_j\right)$	-4	-4	4		19	4					
	u_iV_i	12	8	-4	0	19	8	43				

$A = 24,\ B = 15,$
$h = 4,\ k = 3,$
$N = \Sigma f_i = \Sigma g_j = 50,$
$\Sigma f_i u_i = -9,\ \Sigma g_j v_j = 35,$
$\Sigma f_i u_i^2 = 79,\ \Sigma g_j v_j^2 = 91,$
$P = \Sigma u_i V_i = \Sigma v_j U_j = 43.$

$\bar{u} = -9/50 = -.18 \qquad \bar{v} = 35/50 = .70$

$\sigma_u^2 = (79/50) - (-.18)^2 - .083 = 1.46, \qquad \sigma_u = 1.21$

$\sigma_v^2 = (91/50) - (.70)^2 - .083 = 1.247, \qquad \sigma_v = 1.117$

$p_{uv} = (43/50) - (-.18)(.70) = +0.986$

$r = +0.986/(1.21 \times 1.117) = +.730 \qquad \text{Ans. } r = +.730$

Rank Difference Method

Given n corresponding pairs of measured items (X_i, Y_i), $(i = 1, \ldots, n)$. Let (u_i, v_i) be the corresponding rank numbers. Here $u_i = 1$ for the largest X_i, 2 for the next largest X_i, etc., and similarly $v_i = 1$ for the largest Y_i, 2 for the next largest Y_i, etc. $\rho = 1 - \frac{6\Sigma(u_i - v_i)^2}{n(n^2 - 1)}$, **(rank difference) coefficient of correlation.** In every case $-1 \leq \rho \leq 1$. Check: $\Sigma(u_i - v_i) = 0$.

Example of Computation for Rank-Difference Coefficient of Correlation

X_i	Y_i	u_i	v_i	$u_i - v_i$	$(u_i - v_i)^2$	
76	52	3	1	+2	4	Check: $\Sigma(u_i - v_i) = 0$.
66	34	8	9	−1	1	
63	32	10	10	0	0	
74	45	4	4	0	0	
79	50	1	2	−1	1	$\rho = 1 - \frac{6 \times 62}{10(10^2 - 1)}$
69	37	7	7	0	0	
77	35	2	8	−6	36	$= +0.63$
65	42	9	5	+4	16	
71	40	6	6	0	0	Ans. $\rho = +.63$
73	48	5	3	+2	4	
$N = 10$				0	62	

Probability

If among $a + b$ equi-probable and mutually exclusive events, a are regarded as favorable and b unfavorable, then for a single trial

p, probability of favorable outcome, $= \frac{a}{a + b}$,

q, probability of unfavorable outcome, $= 1 - p = \frac{b}{a + b}$.

The successive terms in the binomial expansion $(p + q)^n = \sum_r \binom{n}{r} p^{n-r} q^r$ give the respective probabilities that in n trials, the event will be favorable exactly $n - r$ times, $r = 0, \ldots, n$.

The mean number of favorable events is np, of unfavorable, nq; the standard deviation is $\sigma = \sqrt{npq}$, $\alpha_3 = (p - q)/\sigma$ (the positive direction being that of increasing unfavorability).

Normal curve (x measured in σ-units from the mean, and with area $= 1$):

$$y = \frac{1}{\sqrt{2\pi}} e^{-x^2/2} = 0.3989 e^{-x^2/2}.$$

MD (mean deviation from the mean) $= \sigma\sqrt{2/\pi} = 0.7979\sigma$.
s (quartile deviation from the mean) $= 0.6745\sigma = 0.845\ MD$.
Percentage areas, under normal curve, for successive class intervals measured from the mean:

Multiples of σ: 34 %, 14 %, 2 %.
Multiples of s: 25 %, 16 %, 7 %, 2 %.

Normal surface (x measured in σ_x-units y in σ_y-units from their means),

$$z = \frac{1}{2\pi\sqrt{1 - r^2}} e^{-(x^2 - 2rxy + y^2)/[2(1-r^2)]}.$$

Goodness of Fit. For a universe of objects falling into n mutually exclusive classes with class marks, $x_i (i = 1, 2, \ldots, n)$, let p_i be the probability for the ith class. Given a sample of N items, with f_i items in the ith class ($\Sigma f_i = N$), the probability that a random sample of N items gives no better fit, expressed in terms of n and χ^2 ("Chi square"), $= \Sigma(f_i - Np_i)^2/(Np_i)$, is given by a table, portions of which are as follows:

Probability that a Random Sample Gives no Better Fit

n \ χ^2	1	2	3	4	6	8	10	15	20
3	.607	.368	.223	.135	.050	.018	.007	.001	.000
4	.801	.572	.392	.261	.112	.046	.019	.002	.000
5	.910	.736	.558	.406	.199	.092	.040	.005	.000
6	.963	.849	.700	.549	.306	.156	.075	.010	.001
7	.986	.920	.809	.677	.423	.238	.125	.020	.003
8	.995	.960	.885	.780	.540	.333	.189	.036	.006
9	.998	.981	.934	.857	.647	.433	.265	.059	.010
10	.999	.991	.964	.911	.740	.534	.350	.091	.018
11	1.000	.996	.981	.947	.815	.629	.440	.132	.029
12	1.000	.998	.991	.970	.873	.713	.530	.182	.045

n \ χ^2	8	10	12	14	16	18	20	25	30
10	.534	.350	.213	.122	.067	.035	.018	.003	.000
11	.629	.440	.285	.173	.100	.055	.029	.005	.001
12	.713	.530	.363	.233	.141	.082	.045	.009	.002
13	.785	.616	.446	.301	.191	.116	.067	.015	.003
14	.844	.694	.528	.374	.249	.158	.095	.023	.005
15	.889	.762	.606	.450	.313	.207	.130	.035	.008
16	.924	.820	.679	.526	.382	.263	.172	.050	.012
17	.949	.867	.744	.599	.453	.324	.220	.070	.018
18	.967	.904	.800	.667	.524	.389	.274	.095	.026
19	.979	.932	.847	.729	.593	.456	.333	.125	.037
20	.987	.953	.886	.784	.657	.522	.395	.161	.052

MENSURATION FORMULÆ

Plane Figures Bounded by Straight Lines

The **area of a triangle** whose base is b and altitude h

$$= \frac{hb}{2}.$$

The area of a **triangle** with angles A, B, and C and sides opposite a, b, and c, respectively

$$= \tfrac{1}{2}ab \sin C.$$

or $$= \sqrt{s(s - a)(s - b)(s - c)},$$
where $s = \frac{1}{2}(a + b + c)$.

A **rectangle** with sides a and b has an area $= ab$.

The area of a **parallelogram** with side b and the perpendicular distance to the parallel side h

$$= bh.$$

The area of a **parallelogram** with sides a and b and the included angle θ

$$= ab \sin \theta.$$

The area of a **rhombus** with diagonals c and d,

$$= \tfrac{1}{2}cd.$$

The area of a **trapezoid** whose parallel sides are a and b and altitude h

$$= \tfrac{1}{2}(a + b)h.$$

The area of any **quadrilateral** with diagonals a and b and the angle between them θ

$$= \tfrac{1}{2}ab \sin \theta.$$

The area of a **regular polygon** with n sides, each of length l,

$$= \tfrac{1}{4}nl^2 \cot \frac{180}{n}.$$

For a regular polygon of n sides, each side of length l, the radius of the **inscribed circle,**

$$= \frac{l}{2} \cot \frac{180}{n}.$$

The radius of the **circumscribed circle,**

$$= \frac{l}{2} \operatorname{cosec} \frac{180}{n}.$$

Area, Radius of Inscribed and Circumscribed Circles for Regular Polygons

l = length of one side.

Name.	Number of sides.	Area.	Radius of inscribed circle.	Radius of circumscribed circle.
Triangle, equilateral	3	$0.43301l^2$	$0.28867l$	$0.57735l$
Square	4	$1.00000l^2$	$0.50000l$	$0.70710l$
Pentagon	5	$1.72048l^2$	$0.68819l$	$0.85065l$
Hexagon	6	$2.59808l^2$	$0.86602l$	$1.0000l$
Heptagon	7	$3.63391l^2$	$1.0383l$	$1.1523l$
Octagon	8	$4.82843l^2$	$1.2071l$	$1.3065l$
Nonagon	9	$6.18182l^2$	$1.3737l$	$1.4619l$
Decagon	10	$7.69421l^2$	$1.5388l$	$1.6180l$
Undecagon	11	$9.36564l^2$	$1.7028l$	$1.7747l$
Dodecagon	12	$11.19615l^2$	$1.8660l$	$1.9318l$

Radius of circle inscribed in any triangle, whose sides are a, b, and c, where $s = \frac{1}{2}(a + b + c)$

$$= \frac{\sqrt{s(s-a)(s-b)(s-c)}}{s}.$$

The radius of the **circumscribed** circle

$$= \frac{abc}{4\sqrt{s(s-a)(s-b)(s-c)}}.$$

The **perimeter of a polygon inscribed in a circle** of radius r, where n is the number of sides,

$$= 2nr \sin \frac{\pi}{n}. \qquad (\pi \text{ radians} = 180°)$$

The area of the **inscribed** polygon,

$$= \tfrac{1}{2}nr^2 \sin \frac{2\pi}{n}.$$

The perimeter of a polygon circumscribed about a circle of radius r, number of sides n

$$= 2nr \tan \frac{\pi}{n}.$$

The area of the **circumscribed** polygon

$$= nr^2 \tan \frac{\pi}{n}.$$

Plane Figures Bounded by Curved Lines

The **circumference of a circle** whose radius is r and diameter $d(d = 2r)$

$$= 2\pi r = \pi d. \qquad (\pi = 3.14159)$$

The **area of a circle**

$$= \pi r^2 = \tfrac{1}{4}\pi d^2 = .7854d^2.$$

The **length of an arc** of a circle for an arc of θ degrees

$$= \frac{\pi r\theta}{180}.$$

NOTE.—In this and following similar formulæ r denotes the radius of the circle, (OC, Fig. 1).

For an arc of θ radians the length

$$= r\theta.$$

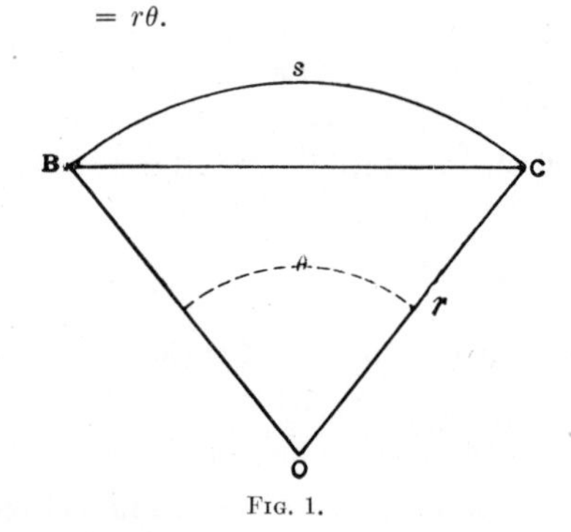

FIG. 1.

The **length of a chord** subtending an angle θ.

$$= 2r \sin \tfrac{1}{2}\theta.$$

The **area of a sector** where θ is the angle between the radii in degrees

$$= \frac{\pi r^2\theta}{360}.$$

If s is the length of the arc, the area of the sector

$$= \frac{sr}{2}.$$

The **area of a segment** where θ is the angle between the two radii in degrees

$$= \frac{\pi r^2\theta}{360} - \frac{r^2 \sin\theta}{2}. \qquad \left[\begin{array}{l}\theta^\circ = 180^\circ - [2x \sin^{-1}(x/r)] \\ x = \perp \text{ dist. center to chord}\end{array}\right]$$

If θ is in radians the area $= \frac{1}{2}r^2(\theta - \sin\theta)$.

The **area of the segment of a circle**

$$= \frac{\pi r^2}{2} - \left[x\sqrt{r^2 - x^2} + r^2 \sin^{-1}\left(\frac{x}{r}\right) \right]$$

where r is the radius of the circle and x the perpendicular distance of the chord from the center. The angle must be expressed in radians.

The **area of the ring** between two circles of radius r_1 and r_2, one of which encloses the other,

$$= \pi(r_1 + r_2)(r_1 - r_2).$$

The two circles are not necessarily concentric.

Area of the sector of an annulus. (Fig. 2.)—If angle $GOH = \theta$ and the lines GO and $JO = r_1$ and r_2 respectively, the area $GHIJ = \frac{1}{2}\theta(r_1 + r_2)(r_1 - r_2)$.

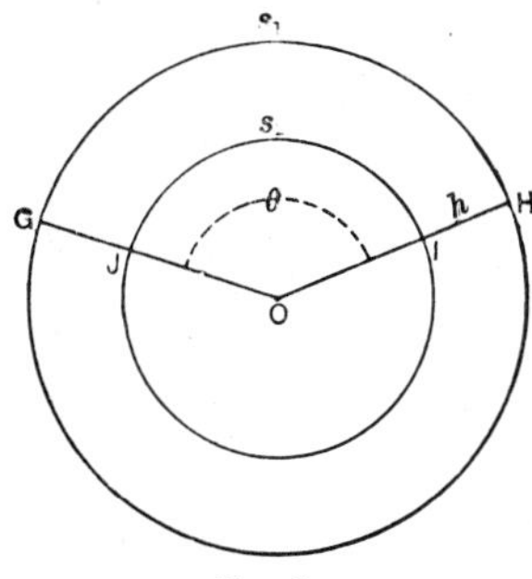

FIG. 2.

If s_1 = the length of the arc GH and s_2 = the arc JI and $h = HI = r_1 - r_2$, the area $GHIJ = \frac{1}{2}h(s_1 + s_2)$.

The **circumference of an ellipse** whose semiaxes are a and b

$= 2\pi\sqrt{\frac{a^2+b^2}{2}}$ (approx.) $= 4aE$ exactly. See tables of elliptic integrals for E, using $k = \sqrt{\frac{a^2-b^2}{a}}$

The **area of an ellipse** $= \pi ab$.

The length of the **arc of a parabola,** as arc SPQ in Fig. 3, where $x = PR$, and $y = QR$

$$\sqrt{4x^2 + y^2} + \frac{y^2}{2x}\log_e \frac{2x + \sqrt{4x^2 + y^2}}{y}$$

The **area of the section of the parabola** $PQRS$, $= \frac{4}{3}xy$.

Solids Bounded by Planes

The **lateral area of a regular prism** = perimeter of a right section × the length.

The **volume of a regular prism** = area of base × the altitude.

The **lateral area of a regular pyramid,** slant height l, length of one side of base a, and a number of sides n,

$$= \tfrac{1}{2}nal.$$

The **volume of a pyramid** = $\frac{1}{3}$ area of base × altitude.

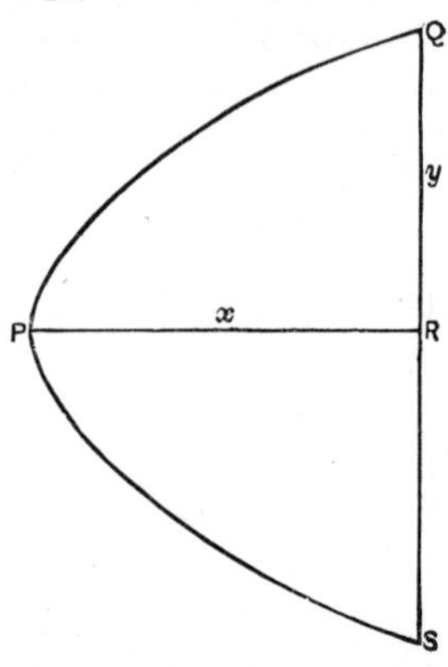

Fig. 3.

Surface and Volume of Regular Polyhedra

Surface and volume of regular polyhedra in terms of the length of one edge l.

Name.	Nature of surface.	Surface.	Volume.
Tetrahedron...	4 equilateral triangles	$1.73205l^2$	$0.11785l^3$
Hexahedron or cube........	6 squares...........	$6.00000l^2$	$1.00000l^3$
Octahedron....	8 equilateral triangles	$3.46410l^2$	$0.47140l^3$
Dodecahedron .	12 pentagons.........	$20.64573l^2$	$7.66312l^3$
Icosahedron...	20 equilateral triangles	$8.66025l^2$	$2.18170l^3$

Solids Bounded by Curved Surfaces

The **surface of a sphere** of radius r and diameter $d(= 2r)$

$$= 4\pi r^2 = \pi d^2 = 12.57r^2.$$

The **volume of a sphere**

$$= \tfrac{4}{3}\pi r^3 = \tfrac{1}{6}\pi d^3 = 4.189r^3.$$

The **area of a lune** on the surface of a sphere of radius r, included between two great circles whose inclination is θ radians.

$$= 2r^2\theta.$$

The **area of a spherical triangle** whose angles are A, B, and C (radians) on a sphere of radius r

$$= (A + B + C - \pi)r^2.$$

The **area of a spherical polygon** of n sides where θ is the sum of its angles in radians

$$= [\theta - (n - 2)\pi]r^2.$$

The area of the curved surface of a **spherical segment** of height h, radius of sphere r

$$= 2\pi\, rh.$$

The **volume of a spherical segment,** data as above

$$= \tfrac{1}{3}\pi h^2 (3r - h).$$

If a = radius of the base of the segment, the volume

$$= \tfrac{1}{6}\pi h(h^2 + 3a^2).$$

The **curved surface of a right cylinder where** r = the radius of the base and h, the altitude,

$$= 2\pi rh.$$

The **volume of a cylinder,** data as above,

$$= \pi r^2 h.$$

The **curved surface of a right cone** whose altitude is h and radius of base r

$$= \pi r \sqrt{r^2 + h^2}.$$

The **volume of a cone,** data as above,

$$= \frac{\pi}{3} r^2 h = 1.047\, r^2 h.$$

The **curved surface of the frustum of a right cone,** radius of base r_1, of top r_2 and altitude h,

$$= \pi(r_1 + r_2) \sqrt{h^2 + (r_1 - r_2)^2}.$$

The **volume of the frustum of a cone,** data as above,

$$= \pi \frac{h}{3} (r_1^2 + r_1 r_2 + r_2^2).$$

The **oblate spheroid** is formed by the rotation of an ellipse about its minor axis. If a and b are the major and minor semi-axes respectively, and e the eccentricity, the surface

$$= 2\pi a^2 + \pi \frac{b^2}{e} \log_\epsilon \frac{1 + e}{1 - e},$$

and volume $= \tfrac{4}{3}\pi a^2 b.$

The prolate spheroid is formed by the rotation of an ellipse about its major axis ($2a$), data as above.

Surface $=2\pi b^2+2\pi \frac{ab}{e}\sin^{-1}e,$

volume $=\frac{4}{3}\pi ab^2.$

SIMPSON'S RULE FOR IRREGULAR AREAS

Divide the area into an even number ($2m$) of panels by means of $2m+1$ parallel lines, drawn at constant distance h apart; and denote the lengths of the intercepted segments by $y_0, y_1, \ldots, y_{2m-1}, y_{2m}$. The first and last of these may be zero. The area will then be

$$A=\tfrac{1}{3}h[(y_0+y_{2m})+4(y_1+y_3+\ldots+y_{2m-1})+2(y_2+y_4+\ldots+y_{2m-2})]$$

While the formula is exact in many simple cases, ordinarily the formula provides only an approximation, for which the accuracy increases with an increase in the number of divisions. Simpson's Rule may be applied to finding volumes, if the measures $y_0, y_1, \ldots, y_{2m}$ be interpreted as the areas of parallel plane sections at constant distance h apart.

PRISMOIDAL FORMULA

As a special case where $m=1$, and H, $(=2h)$ is the distance between two limiting parallel planes, one has for the volume of a solid figure,

$$V=\tfrac{1}{6}H(S_0+4S_1+S_2).$$

Here S_0 and S_2 are the cross-sectional areas in these limiting planes (lower and upper bases, respectively), and S_1 is the cross section of the mid-section. The formula is exact for the cone, sphere, ellipsoid, and prismoid.

TRIGONOMETRIC FUNCTIONS IN A RIGHT-ANGLED TRIANGLE

If A, B, and C are the vertices (C the right angle), and a, b, and h the sides opposite respectively,

$$\text{sine } A = \sin A = \frac{a}{h}, \qquad \text{cosine } A = \cos A = \frac{b}{h},$$

$$\text{tangent } A = \tan A = \frac{a}{b}, \quad \text{cotangent } A = \cot A = \text{ctn } A = \frac{b}{a},$$

$$\text{secant } A = \sec A = \frac{h}{b}, \qquad \text{cosecant } A = \csc A = \frac{h}{a}.$$

exsecant A = exsec A = sec $A - 1$

versine A = vers A = $1 - \cos A$

coversine A = covers A = $1 - \sin A$

haversine A = hav A = $\frac{1}{2}$ vers A

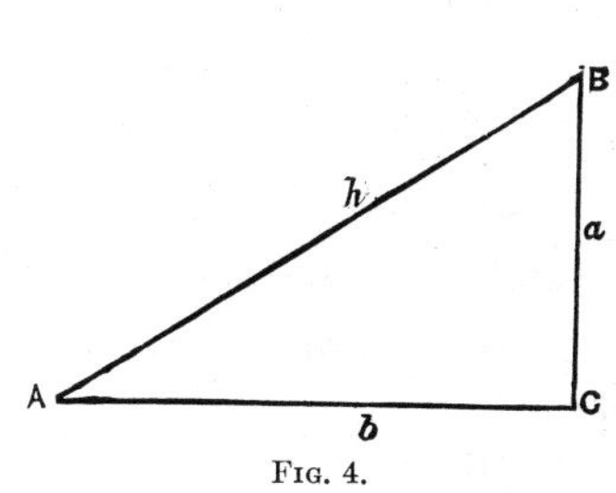

FIG. 4.

SIGNS AND LIMITS OF VALUE ASSUMED BY THE FUNCTIONS

Function.	Quadrant I.		Quadrant II.		Quadrant III.		Quadrant IV.	
	Sign.	Value.	Sign.	Value.	Sign.	Value.	Sign.	Value.
sin.....	+	0 to 1	+	1 to 0	−	0 to 1	−	1 to 0
cos.....	+	1 to 0	−	0 to 1	−	1 to 0	+	0 to 1
tan.....	+	0 to ∞	−	∞ to 0	+	0 to ∞	−	∞ to 0
cot.....	+	∞ to 0	−	0 to ∞	+	∞ to 0	−	0 to ∞
sec.....	+	1 to ∞	−	∞ to 1	−	1 to ∞	+	∞ to 1
cosec...	+	∞ to 1	+	1 to ∞	−	∞ to 1	−	1 to ∞

VALUE OF THE FUNCTIONS OF VARIOUS ANGLES

	0°	30°	45°	60°	90°	180°	270°
sin..........	0	$\frac{1}{2}$	$\frac{1}{2}\sqrt{2}$	$\frac{1}{2}\sqrt{3}$	1	0	−1
cos..........	1	$\frac{1}{2}\sqrt{3}$	$\frac{1}{2}\sqrt{2}$	$\frac{1}{2}$	0	−1	0
tan..........	0	$\frac{1}{3}\sqrt{3}$	1	$\sqrt{3}$	∞	0	∞
cot..........	∞	$\sqrt{3}$	1	$\frac{1}{3}\sqrt{3}$	0	∞	0

RELATIONS OF THE FUNCTIONS

$$\sin x = \frac{1}{\operatorname{cosec} x}. \qquad \operatorname{cosec} x = \frac{1}{\sin x}.$$

$$\cos x = \frac{1}{\sec x}. \qquad \sec x = \frac{1}{\cos x}.$$

$$\tan x = \frac{1}{\cot x} = \frac{\sin x}{\cos x}. \qquad \sin^2 x + \cos^2 x = 1$$

$$1 + \tan^2 x = \sec^2 x$$

$$\cot x = \frac{1}{\tan x} = \frac{\cos x}{\sin x}. \qquad 1 + \cot^2 x = \operatorname{cosec}^2 x$$

$$\sin x = \sqrt{1 - \cos^2 x}. \qquad \cos x = \sqrt{1 - \sin^2 x}.$$

$$\tan x = \sqrt{\sec^2 x - 1}. \qquad \sec x = \sqrt{\tan^2 x + 1}.$$

$$\cot x = \sqrt{\operatorname{cosec}^2 x - 1}. \qquad \operatorname{cosec} x = \sqrt{\cot^2 x + 1}.$$

$$\sin x = \cos (90 - x) = \sin (180 - x).$$

$$\cos x = \sin (90 - x) = -\cos (180 - x).$$

$$\tan x = \cot (90 - x) = -\tan (180 - x).$$

$$\cot x = \tan (90 - x) = -\cot (180 - x).$$

$$\operatorname{cosec} x = \cot \frac{x}{2} - \cot x.$$

FUNCTIONS OF SUMS OF ANGLES

$$\sin (x + y) = \sin x \cos y + \cos x \sin y.$$

$$\sin (x - y) = \sin x \cos y - \cos x \sin y.$$

$$\cos (x + y) = \cos x \cos y - \sin x \sin y.$$

$$\cos (x - y) = \cos x \cos y + \sin x \sin y.$$

$$\tan (x + y) = \frac{\tan x + \tan y}{1 - \tan x \tan y}.$$

$$\tan (x - y) = \frac{\tan x - \tan y}{1 + \tan x \tan y}.$$

FUNCTIONS OF MULTIPLE ANGLES

$\sin 2x = 2 \sin x \cos x.$
$\cos 2x = \cos^2 x - \sin^2 x = 2 \cos^2 x - 1 = 1 - 2 \sin^2 x.$
$\sin 3x = 3 \sin x - 4 \sin^3 x.$
$\cos 3x = 4 \cos^3 x - 3 \cos x.$
$\sin 4x = 8 \cos^3 x \sin x - 4 \cos x \sin x.$
$\cos 4x = 8 \cos^4 x - 8 \cos^2 x + 1.$
$\sin 5x = 5 \sin x - 20 \sin^3 x + 16 \sin^5 x.$
$\cos 5x = 16 \cos^5 x - 20 \cos^3 x + 5 \cos x.$
$\sin 6x = 32 \cos^5 x \sin x - 32 \cos^3 x \sin x + 6 \cos x \sin x.$
$\cos 6x = 32 \cos^6 x - 48 \cos^4 x + 18 \cos^2 x - 1.$

$$\tan 2x = \frac{2 \tan x}{1 - \tan^2 x}.$$

$$\cot 2x = \frac{\cot^2 x - 1}{2 \cot x}.$$

$$\tan 3x = \frac{3 \tan x - \tan^3 x}{1 - 3 \tan^2 x}.$$

$$\sin \tfrac{1}{2}x = \pm \sqrt{\frac{1 - \cos x}{2}}.$$

$$\cos \tfrac{1}{2}x = \pm \sqrt{\frac{1 + \cos x}{2}}$$

$$\tan \tfrac{1}{2}x = \pm \sqrt{\frac{1 - \cos x}{1 + \cos x}} = \frac{1 - \cos x}{\sin x} = \frac{\sin x}{1 + \cos x}.$$

MISCELLANEOUS RELATIONS

$\sin x \pm \sin y = 2 \sin \tfrac{1}{2} (x \pm y) . \cos \tfrac{1}{2} (x \mp y).$
$\cos x + \cos y = 2 \cos \tfrac{1}{2} (x + y) . \cos \tfrac{1}{2} (x - y).$
$\cos x - \cos y = -2 \sin \tfrac{1}{2} (x + y) . \sin \tfrac{1}{2} (x - y).$

$$\tan x \pm \tan y = \frac{\sin (x \pm y)}{\cos x . \cos y}. \quad \cot x \pm \cot y = \frac{\pm \sin (x \pm y)}{\sin x \cdot \sin y}.$$

$$\frac{1 + \tan x}{1 - \tan x} = \tan (45 + x) \qquad \frac{\cot x + 1}{\cot x - 1} = \cot (45 - x)$$

$$\frac{\sin x \pm \sin y}{\cos x + \cos y} = \tan \tfrac{1}{2} (x \pm y).$$

$$\frac{\sin x \pm \sin y}{\cos x - \cos y} = -\cot \tfrac{1}{2} (x \mp y).$$

$$\frac{\sin x + \sin y}{\sin x - \sin y} = \frac{\tan \tfrac{1}{2} (x + y)}{\tan \tfrac{1}{2} (x - y)}.$$

$\sin^2 x - \sin^2 y = \sin (x + y) . \sin (x - y).$
$\cos^2 x - \cos^2 y = -\sin (x + y) \sin (x - y).$
$\cos^2 x - \sin^2 y = \cos (x + y) \cos (x - y).$

RELATIONS BETWEEN SIDES AND ANGLES OF ANY PLANE TRIANGLE

In a triangle with angles A, B, and C and sides opposite a, b. and c respectively,

$$\frac{a}{\sin A}=\frac{b}{\sin B}=\frac{c}{\sin C}=\text{diameter of the circumscribed circle.}$$

$$a^2=b^2+c^2-2bc\cos A.$$

$$a=b\cos C+c\cos B.$$

$$\cos A=\frac{b^2+c^2-a^2}{2bc}.$$

$$\tan\frac{A-B}{2}=\frac{a-b}{a+b}\cot\frac{C}{2}.$$

$$\sin A=\frac{2}{bc}\sqrt{s(s-a)\,(s-b)\,(s-c)},$$

where $s=\frac{1}{2}(a+b+c)$ and $r=\sqrt{\frac{(s-a)\,(s-b)\,(s-c)}{s}}$.

$$\sin\frac{A}{2}=\sqrt{\frac{(s-b)\,(s-c)}{bc}}.$$

$$\cos\frac{A}{2}=\sqrt{\frac{s(s-a)}{bc}}.$$

$$\tan\frac{A}{2}=\sqrt{\frac{(s-b)\,(s-c)}{s(s-a)}}=\frac{r}{s-a}.$$

$$\frac{a+b}{a-b}=\frac{\sin A+\sin B}{\sin A-\sin B}=\frac{\tan\frac{1}{2}(A+B)}{\tan\frac{1}{2}(A-B)}=\frac{\cot\frac{1}{2}C}{\tan\frac{1}{2}(A-B)}.$$

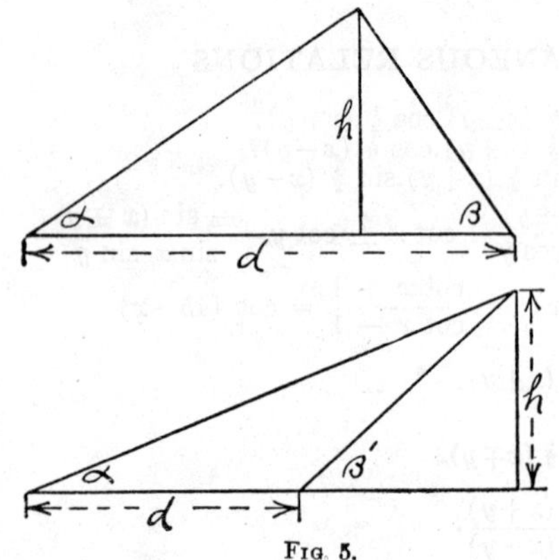

$$h=d\frac{\sin\alpha\sin\beta}{\sin(\alpha+\beta)}=\frac{d}{\cot\alpha+\cot\beta}$$

Similarly

$$h=d\frac{\sin\alpha\sin\beta'}{\sin(\beta'-\alpha)}=\frac{d}{\cot\alpha-\cot\beta'}$$

Fig. 5.

RELATIONS IN ANY SPHERICAL TRIANGLE

If A, B and C be the three angles and a, b, and c the opposite sides,

$$\frac{\sin A}{\sin a}=\frac{\sin B}{\sin b}=\frac{\sin C}{\sin c}.$$

$$\cos a=\cos b\cos c+\sin b\sin c\cos A=\frac{\cos b\cos(c\pm\theta)}{\cos\theta}.$$

where $\tan\theta=\tan b\cos A$.

$$\cos A=-\cos B\cos C+\sin B\sin C\cos a.$$

$$\sin\tfrac{1}{2}A=\sqrt{\frac{\sin(s-b)\sin(s-c)}{\sin b\sin c}}.$$

where $s=\tfrac{1}{2}(a+b+c)$.

$$\cos\tfrac{1}{2}A=\sqrt{\frac{\sin s\sin(s-a)}{\sin b\sin c}}.$$

$$\tan\tfrac{1}{2}A=\frac{r}{\sin(s-a)}.$$

where $r=\sqrt{\dfrac{\sin(s-a)\sin(s-b)\sin(s-c)}{\sin s}}$.

$$\cos\tfrac{1}{2}a=\sqrt{\frac{\cos(S-B)\cos(S-C)}{\sin B\sin C}}.$$

where $S=\tfrac{1}{2}(A+B+C)$.

$$\sin\tfrac{1}{2}a=\sqrt{-\frac{\cos S\cos(S-A)}{\sin B\sin C}}.$$

$$\tan\tfrac{1}{2}a=R\cos(S-A)$$

where $R=\sqrt{\dfrac{-\cos S}{\cos(S-A)\cos(S-B)\cos(S-C)}}$.

$$\frac{\tan\frac{a+b}{2}}{\tan\frac{c}{2}}=\frac{\cos\frac{A-B}{2}}{\cos\frac{A+B}{2}},\qquad\frac{\tan\frac{A+B}{2}}{\cot\frac{C}{2}}=\frac{\cos\frac{a-b}{2}}{\cos\frac{a+b}{2}}.$$

$$\frac{\tan\frac{a-b}{2}}{\tan\frac{c}{2}}=\frac{\sin\frac{A-B}{2}}{\sin\frac{A+B}{2}},\qquad\frac{\tan\frac{A-B}{2}}{\cot\frac{C}{2}}=\frac{\sin\frac{a-b}{2}}{\sin\frac{a+b}{2}}$$

$$\operatorname{hav} a=\operatorname{hav}(b\sim c)+\sin b\sin c\operatorname{hav} A$$

$$\operatorname{hav} A=\frac{\sqrt{\operatorname{hav}[a+(b\sim c)]\operatorname{hav}[a-(b\sim c)]}}{\sin b\sin c}$$

The distance between two points $x_1\ y_1$, and x_2, y_2, —rectangular coördinates:

$$d = \pm\sqrt{(x_2 - x_1)^2 + (y_2 - y_1)^2}$$

For polar coördinates and points r_1, θ_1, and r_2, θ_2:

$$d = \pm\sqrt{r_1^2 + r_2^2 - 2r_1r_2 \cos(\theta_1 - \theta_2)}$$

The area of a triangle whose vertices are x_1, y_1; x_2, y_2, and x_3, y_3:

$$A = \tfrac{1}{2}(x_1y_2 - x_2y_1 + x_2y_3 - x_3y_2 + x_3y_1 - x_1y_3)$$

For polar coördinates and vertices, r_1, θ_1; r_2, θ_2, and r_3, θ_3:

$$A = \tfrac{1}{2}\{(r_1r_2 \sin(\theta_2 - \theta_1) + r_2r_3 \sin(\theta_3 - \theta_2) + r_3r_1 \sin(\theta_1 - \theta_3)\}$$

The equation of a straight line where m is the tangent of the angle of inclination and c, the distance of intersection with the Y axis from the origin:

$$y = mx + c$$

If a line of slope m passes through the point x_1, y_1 its equation is:

$$y - y_1 = m(x - x_1)$$

The equation of a line through the points x_1, y_1, and x_2, y_2 is:

$$\frac{y - y_1}{y_2 - y_1} = \frac{x - x_1}{x_2 - x_1}$$

If the intercepts on the X and Y axes are a and b respectively, the equation is:

$$\frac{x}{a} + \frac{y}{b} = 1$$

If the length of the perpendicular from the origin is p and its angle of inclination θ the equation is:

$$x \cos\theta + y \sin\theta = p$$

General equation of the straight line:

$$Ax + By + C = 0$$

The equation of a circle whose center is at a, b, and whose radius is c:

$$(x - a)^2 + (y - b)^2 = c^2$$

If the origin is at the center:

$$x^2 + y^2 = c^2$$

The polar equation of a circle with the origin on the circumference and its center at point c, α:

$$r = 2c \cos(\theta - \alpha).$$

If the origin is not on the circumference, the radius a and the center at a point, l, α, the equation becomes:

$$a^2 = r^2 + l^2 - 2rl \cos(\theta - \alpha)$$

The equation of a parabola with the origin at the vertex, where f is the distance from the focus to the vertex:

$$y^2=4fx$$

If p is the semi-latus rectum ($=2f$) the equation is:

$$y^2=2px$$

The polar equation where the pole is at the focus and p the semi-latus rectum is:

$$r=\frac{p}{1-\cos\theta}$$

If the pole is at the vertex and p as above:

$$r=\frac{2p\cos\theta}{\sin^2\theta}$$

The equation of the ellipse with the origin at the center and semi-axes a and b:

$$\frac{x^2}{a^2}+\frac{y^2}{b^2}=1$$

Polar equation where the pole is at the center:

$$r^2=\frac{a^2b^2}{a^2\sin^2\theta+b^2\cos^2\theta}$$

The equation of the hyperbola with the origin at the center, semi-axes a and b:

$$\frac{x^2}{a^2}-\frac{y^2}{b^2}=1$$

Polar equation, pole at center:

$$r^2=\frac{a^2b^2}{a^2\sin^2\theta-b^2\cos^2\theta}$$

Definitions

An hyperbolic function represents a relation between the coordinates of a given portion on the arc of a rectangular hyperbola. If O is the center, A the vertex, and P any point of the hyperbola APB,

$$\mathrm{OM} = x, \quad \mathrm{MP} = y, \quad \mathrm{OA} = a.$$

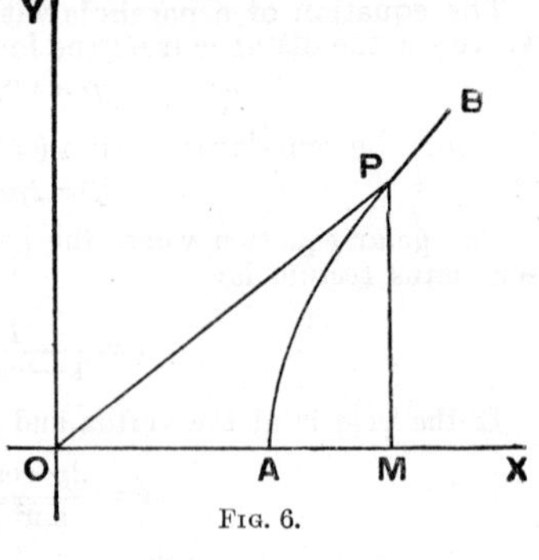

FIG. 6.

The function u may be defined by the following relation,

$$u = \frac{2 \times \text{Area OAP}}{\text{OA}^2}$$

The hyperbolic sine of u = $\sinh u = y/a$.
The hyperbolic cosine of u = $\cosh u = x/a$.

$$\sinh u = \frac{1}{2}(e^u - e^{-u}) = u + \frac{u^3}{3\,!} + \frac{u^5}{5\,!} + \cdots$$

$$\cosh u = \frac{1}{2}(e^u + e^{-u}) = 1 + \frac{u^2}{2\,!} + \frac{u^4}{4\,!} + \cdots$$

$$\tanh u = u - \frac{u^3}{3} + \frac{2u^5}{15} - \frac{17u^7}{315} + \cdots \qquad \left(u^2 < \frac{1}{4}\pi^2\right).$$

$$\sinh^{-1} u = u - \frac{1}{2}\cdot\frac{u^3}{3} + \frac{1\cdot 3}{2\cdot 4}\cdot\frac{u^5}{5} - \frac{1\cdot 3\cdot 5}{2\cdot 4\cdot 6}\cdot\frac{u^7}{7} + \cdots \qquad (u^2 < 1).$$

$$\sinh^{-1} u = \log 2u + \frac{1}{2}\cdot\frac{1}{2u^2} - \frac{1\cdot 3}{2\cdot 4}\cdot\frac{1}{4u^4} + \frac{1\cdot 3\cdot 5}{2\cdot 4\cdot 6}\cdot\frac{1}{6u^6} - \cdots \qquad (u^2 > 1).$$

$$\cosh^{-1} u = \log 2u - \frac{1}{2}\cdot\frac{1}{2u^2} - \frac{1\cdot 3}{2\cdot 4}\cdot\frac{1}{4u^4} - \frac{1\cdot 3\cdot 5}{2\cdot 4\cdot 6}\cdot\frac{1}{6u^6} - \cdots \qquad (u^2 > 1).$$

$$\tanh^{-1} u = u + \frac{u^3}{3} + \frac{u^5}{5} + \frac{u^7}{7} + \cdots \qquad (u^2 < 1).$$

$$\tanh u = \frac{\sinh u}{\cosh u}. \qquad \operatorname{sech} u = \frac{1}{\cosh u}.$$

HYPERBOLIC FUNCTIONS (Continued)

$$\coth u = \frac{1}{\tanh u}. \qquad \operatorname{csch} u = \frac{1}{\sinh u}.$$

Relations of the Functions

$$\sinh x = -\sinh(-x). \qquad \operatorname{sech} x = \operatorname{sech}(-x).$$
$$\cosh x = \cosh(-x). \qquad \operatorname{csch} x = -\operatorname{csch}(-x).$$
$$\tanh x = -\tanh(-x). \qquad \coth x = -\coth(-x).$$

$$\sinh x = \frac{2\tanh\frac{1}{2}x}{1 - \tanh^2\frac{1}{2}x} = \frac{\tanh x}{\sqrt{1 - \tanh^2 x}}.$$

$$\cosh x = \frac{1 + \tanh^2\frac{1}{2}x}{1 - \tanh^2\frac{1}{2}x} = \frac{1}{\sqrt{1 - \tanh^2 x}}.$$

$$\cosh^2 x - \sinh^2 x = 1.$$

$$\tanh x = \sqrt{1 - \operatorname{sech}^2 x}. \qquad \operatorname{sech} x = \sqrt{1 - \tanh^2 x}.$$
$$\coth x = \sqrt{\operatorname{csch}^2 x + 1}. \qquad \operatorname{csch} x = \sqrt{\coth^2 x - 1}.$$

$$\sinh(\tfrac{1}{2}x) = \sqrt{\tfrac{1}{2}(\cosh x - 1)}.$$
$$\cosh(\tfrac{1}{2}x) = \sqrt{\tfrac{1}{2}(\cosh x + 1)}.$$
$$\tanh(\tfrac{1}{2}x) = (\cosh x - 1) \div \sinh x = \sinh x \div (\cosh x + 1).$$
$$\sinh(2x) = 2\sinh x \cosh x.$$
$$\cosh(2x) = \cosh^2 x + \sinh^2 x = 2\cosh^2 x - 1 = 1 + 2\sinh^2 x$$
$$\tanh(2x) = 2\tanh x \div (1 + \tanh^2 x).$$
$$\sinh 3x = 3\sinh x + 4\sinh^3 x.$$
$$\cosh 3x = 4\cosh^3 x - 3\cosh x.$$
$$\tanh 3x = (3\tanh x + \tanh^3 x) \div (1 + 3\tanh^2 x).$$
$$\sinh(x \pm y) = \sinh x \cdot \cosh y \pm \cosh x \cdot \sinh y.$$
$$\cosh(x \pm y) = \cosh x \cdot \cosh y \pm \sinh x \cdot \sinh y.$$
$$\tanh(x \pm y) = (\tanh x \pm \tanh y) \div (1 \pm \tanh x \cdot \tanh y).$$
$$\sinh x + \sinh y = 2\sinh\tfrac{1}{2}(x + y) \cdot \cosh\tfrac{1}{2}(x - y).$$
$$\sinh x - \sinh y = 2\cosh\tfrac{1}{2}(x + y) \cdot \sinh\tfrac{1}{2}(x - y).$$
$$\cosh x + \cosh y = 2\cosh\tfrac{1}{2}(x + y) \cdot \cosh\tfrac{1}{2}(x - y).$$
$$\cosh x - \cosh y = 2\sinh\tfrac{1}{2}(x + y) \cdot \sinh\tfrac{1}{2}(x - y).$$

$$\sinh x + \cosh x = \frac{1 + \tanh\frac{1}{2}x}{1 - \tanh\frac{1}{2}x}$$

$$\tanh x \pm \tanh y = \frac{\sinh(x \pm y)}{\cosh x \cosh y}.$$

$$\coth x \pm \coth y = \pm\frac{\sinh(x \pm y)}{\sinh x \sinh y}.$$

Inverse Functions

$$\sinh^{-1} x = \log(x + \sqrt{x^2 + 1}) = \int\frac{dx}{\sqrt{x^2 + 1}} = \cosh^{-1}\sqrt{x^2 + 1}$$

$$\cosh^{-1} x = \log (x + \sqrt{x^2 - 1}) = \int \frac{dx}{\sqrt{x^2 - 1}} = \sinh^{-1} \sqrt{x^2 - 1}.$$

$$\tanh^{-1} x = \frac{1}{2} \log (1 + x) - \frac{1}{2} \log (1 - x) = \int \frac{dx}{1 - x^2}.$$

$$\coth^{-1} x = \frac{1}{2} \log (1 + x) - \frac{1}{2} \log (x - 1) = \int \frac{dx}{1 - x^2}.$$

$$\operatorname{sech}^{-1} x = \log \left(\frac{1}{x} + \sqrt{\frac{1}{x^2} - 1} \right) = -\int \frac{dx}{x\sqrt{1 - x^2}}.$$

$$\operatorname{csch}^{-1} x = \log \left(\frac{1}{x} + \sqrt{\frac{1}{x^2} + 1} \right) = -\int \frac{dx}{x\sqrt{x^2 + 1}}.$$

Relations to Circular Functions

$$\sinh x = -i \sin ix. \qquad \sinh ix = i \sin x.$$
$$\cosh x = \cos ix. \qquad \cosh ix = \cos x.$$
$$\tanh x = -i \tan ix. \qquad \tanh ix = i \tan x.$$

If $x = \log \tan \left(\frac{\pi}{4} + \frac{\theta}{2} \right) = \log (\sec \theta + \tan \theta)$,

$\theta =$ the **gudermannian** of $x = \operatorname{gd} x$.

$$\sinh x = \tan \operatorname{gd} x. \qquad \tanh x = \sin \operatorname{gd} x.$$
$$\cosh x = \sec \operatorname{gd} x. \qquad \tanh \tfrac{1}{2} x = \tan \tfrac{1}{2} \operatorname{gd} x.$$

$$\frac{d \operatorname{gd} x}{dx} = \operatorname{sech} x.$$

Differentials

$$d \sinh x = \cosh x \cdot dx. \qquad d \coth x = -\operatorname{csch}^2 x \cdot dx.$$
$$d \cosh x = \sinh x \cdot dx. \qquad d \operatorname{sech} x = -\operatorname{sech} x \cdot \tanh x \cdot dx.$$
$$d \tanh x = \operatorname{sech}^2 x \cdot dx. \qquad d \operatorname{csch} x = -\operatorname{csch} x \cdot \coth x \cdot dx.$$

$$d \sinh^{-1} x = \frac{dx}{\sqrt{1 + x^2}}. \qquad d \coth^{-1} x = -\frac{dx}{x^2 - 1}.$$

$$d \cosh^{-1} x = \frac{dx}{\sqrt{x^2 - 1}}. \qquad d \operatorname{sech}^{-1} x = -\frac{dx}{x\sqrt{1 - x^2}}.$$

$$d \tanh^{-1} x = \frac{dx}{1 - x^2}. \qquad d \operatorname{csch}^{-1} x = -\frac{dx}{x\sqrt{x^2 + 1}}.$$

Integrals involving the hyperbolic functions will be found in the table of integrals.

ELLIPTIC FUNCTIONS

$$u = F(k, \phi) = \int_0^{\phi} \frac{d\phi}{\sqrt{1 - k^2 \sin^2 \phi}}, \qquad (k^2 < 1),$$

= elliptic integral of the first kind.

$$u = \int_0^{x} \frac{dx}{\sqrt{(1 - x^2)(1 - k^2x^2)}}, \qquad \text{where } x = \sin \phi.$$

ϕ is called the amplitude of u or am u.
k is called the modulus.

$$k' = \sqrt{1 - k^2} = \text{the complementary modulus.}$$

$\sin \phi = \text{sn } u = x.$ $\qquad \tan \phi = \text{tn } u = \dfrac{x}{\sqrt{1 - x^2}}.$

$\cos \phi = \text{cn } u = \sqrt{1 - x^2}.$ $\qquad \Delta\phi = \text{dn } u = \sqrt{1 - k^2x^2}.$

$\text{am } 0 = 0.$
$\text{sn } 0 = 0.$
$\text{cn } 0 = 1.$
$\text{dn } 0 = 1.$
$\text{am } (-u) = -\text{am } u.$
$\text{sn } (-u) = -\text{sn } u.$
$\text{cn } (-u) = \text{cn } u.$
$\text{dn } (-u) = \text{dn } u.$
$\text{tn } (-u) = -\text{tn } u.$
$\text{sn}^2 u + \text{cn}^2 u = 1.$
$\text{dn}^2 u + k^2 \text{sn}^2 u = 1.$
$\text{dn}^2 u - k^2 \text{cn}^2 u = 1 - k^2 = k'^2.$

$$E(\phi, k) = \int_0^{\phi} \sqrt{1 - k^2 \sin^2 \phi}\, d\phi$$

$$= \int_0^{x} \frac{\sqrt{1 - k^2x^2}}{\sqrt{1 - x^2}}\, dx \qquad \text{where } x = \sin \phi$$

= the elliptic integral of the second kind.

Complete Elliptic Integrals

$$K = \int_0^{\pi/2} \frac{d\phi}{\sqrt{1 - k^2 \sin^2 \phi}}.$$

$$E = \int_0^{\pi/2} \sqrt{1 - k^2 \sin^2 \phi}\, d\phi.$$

See tables of values, page 234–236.

INTEREST TABLES

SIMPLE INTEREST

If P is the principal placed at interest at a rate i (expressed as a decimal), for a period of n years

The **amount,**

$$A = P(1 + ni)$$

Present value,

$$P = \frac{A}{1 + ni}$$

COMPOUND INTEREST

At interest compounded annually the **amount,**—

$$A = P(1 + i)^n$$

At interest compounded q times per year,—

$$A = P\left(1 + \frac{i}{q}\right)^{nq}$$

At interest compounded annually the **present value,**—

$$P = \frac{A}{(1 + i)^n} = A(1 + i)^{-n} = Av^n. \qquad v = \frac{1}{1 + i}$$

At interest compounded q times per year,—

$$P = A\left(1 + \frac{i}{q}\right)^{-nq}$$

The amount of an annuity of 1 per annum,—

$$s_{\overline{n}|} \text{ at } i = \frac{(1 + i)^n - 1}{i}$$

The present value of an annuity,—

$$a_{\overline{n}|} \text{ at } i = \frac{1 - (1 + i)^{-n}}{i}$$

The annuity whose present value is 1,—

$$\frac{1}{a_{\overline{n}|} \text{ at } i} = \frac{1}{s_{\overline{n}|}} + i = \frac{i}{(1 - v^n)}$$

Compound amount of 1 for fractional periods,—$(1 + i)^{1/p}$

Nominal rate convertible p times per year equivalent to effective rate i,—

$$j_p = p[(1 + i)^{1/p} - 1]$$

Amount for year of p **deposits of** $1/p$, p **times per year,**—i/j_p

THE NUMBER OF EACH DAY OF THE YEAR

Day of Mo.	Jan.	Feb.	Mar.	Apr.	May	Jun.	Jul.	Aug.	Sep.	Oct.	Nov.	Dec.	Day of Mo.
1	1	32	60	91	121	152	182	213	244	274	305	335	1
2	2	33	61	92	122	153	183	214	245	275	306	336	2
3	3	34	62	93	123	154	184	215	246	276	307	337	3
4	4	35	63	94	124	155	185	216	247	277	308	338	4
5	5	36	64	95	125	156	186	217	248	278	309	339	5
6	6	37	65	96	126	157	187	218	249	279	310	340	6
7	7	38	66	97	127	158	188	219	250	280	311	341	7
8	8	39	67	98	128	159	189	220	251	281	312	342	8
9	9	40	68	99	129	160	190	221	252	282	313	343	9
10	10	41	69	100	130	161	191	222	253	283	314	344	10
11	11	42	70	101	131	162	192	223	254	284	315	345	11
12	12	43	71	102	132	163	193	224	255	285	316	346	12
13	13	44	72	103	133	164	194	225	256	286	317	347	13
14	14	45	73	104	134	165	195	226	257	287	318	348	14
15	15	46	74	105	135	166	196	227	258	288	319	349	15
16	16	47	75	106	136	167	197	228	259	289	320	350	16
17	17	48	76	107	137	168	198	229	260	290	321	351	17
18	18	49	77	108	138	169	199	230	261	291	322	352	18
19	19	50	78	109	139	170	200	231	262	292	323	353	19
20	20	51	79	110	140	171	201	232	263	293	324	354	20
21	21	52	80	111	141	172	202	233	264	294	325	355	21
22	22	53	81	112	142	173	203	234	265	295	326	356	22
23	23	54	82	113	143	174	204	235	266	296	327	357	23
24	24	55	83	114	144	175	205	236	267	297	328	358	24
25	25	56	84	115	145	176	206	237	268	298	329	359	25
26	26	57	85	116	146	177	207	238	269	299	330	360	26
27	27	58	86	117	147	178	208	239	270	300	331	361	27
28	28	59	87	118	148	179	209	240	271	301	332	362	28
29	29	*	88	119	149	180	210	241	272	302	333	363	29
30	30		89	120	150	181	211	242	273	303	334	364	30
31	31		90		151		212	243		304		365	31

* In leap years, after February 28, add 1 to the tabulated number.

AMOUNT AT COMPOUND INTEREST $(1 + i)^n$

The following table gives the amount after a term of n years on unit original principal at rate of interest i.

Years n	Rate i .0025(¼ %)	.004167(5/12 %)	.005(½ %)	.005833(7/12 %)	.0075(¾ %)
1	1.00250000	1.00416667	1.00500000	1.00583333	1.00750000
2	1.00500625	1.00835069	1.01002500	1.01170069	1.01505625
3	1.00751877	1.01255216	1.01507513	1.01760228	1.02266917
4	1.01003756	1.01677112	1.02015050	1.02353830	1.03033919
5	1.01256266	1.02100767	1.02525125	1.02950894	1.03806673
6	1.01509406	1.02526187	1.03037751	1.03551440	1.04585224
7	1.01763180	1.02953379	1.03552940	1.04155490	1.05369613
8	1.02017588	1.03382352	1.04070704	1.04763064	1.06159885
9	1.02272632	1.03813111	1.04591058	1.05374182	1.06956084
10	1.02528313	1.04245666	1.05114013	1.05988865	1.07758255
11	1.02784634	1.04680023	1.05639583	1.06607133	1.08566441
12	1.03041596	1.05116190	1.06167781	1.07229008	1.09380690
13	1.03299200	1.05554174	1.06698620	1.07854511	1.10201045
14	1.03557448	1.05993983	1.07232113	1.08483662	1.11027553
15	1.03816341	1.06435625	1.07768274	1.09116483	1.11860259
16	1.04075882	1.06879106	1.08307115	1.09752996	1.12699211
17	1.04336072	1.07324436	1.08848651	1.10393222	1.13544455
18	1.04596912	1.07771621	1.09392894	1.11037182	1.14396039
19	1.04858404	1.08220670	1.09939858	1.11684899	1.15254009
20	1.05120550	1.08671589	1.10489558	1.12336395	1.16118414
21	1.05383352	1.09124387	1.11042006	1.12991690	1.16989302
22	1.05646810	1.09579072	1.11597216	1.13650808	1.17866722
23	1.05910927	1.10035652	1.12155202	1.14313771	1.18750723
24	1.06175704	1.10494134	1.12715978	1.14980602	1.19641353
25	1.06441144	1.10954526	1.13279558	1.15651322	1.20538663
26	1.06707247	1.11416836	1.13845955	1.16325955	1.21442703
27	1.06974015	1.11881073	1.14415185	1.17004523	1.22353523
28	1.07241450	1.12347244	1.14987261	1.17687049	1.23271175
29	1.07509553	1.12815358	1.15562197	1.18373557	1.24195709
30	1.07778327	1.13285422	1.16140008	1.19064069	1.25127176
31	1.08047773	1.13757444	1.16720708	1.19758610	1.26065630
32	1.08317892	1.14231434	1.17304312	1.20457202	1.27011122
33	1.08588687	1.14707398	1.17890833	1.21159869	1.27963706
34	1.08860159	1.15185346	1.18480288	1.21866634	1.28923434
35	1.09132309	1.15665284	1.19072689	1.22577523	1.29890359
36	1.09405140	1.16147223	1.19668052	1.23292559	1.30864537
37	1.09678653	1.16631170	1.20266393	1.24011765	1.31846021
38	1.09952850	1.17117133	1.20867725	1.24735167	1.32834866
39	1.10227732	1.17605121	1.21472063	1.25462789	1.33831128
40	1.10503301	1.18095142	1.22079424	1.26194655	1.34834861
41	1.10779559	1.18587206	1.22689821	1.26930791	1.35846123
42	1.11056508	1.19081319	1.23303270	1.27671220	1.36864969
43	1.11334149	1.19577491	1.23919786	1.28415969	1.37891456
44	1.11612485	1.20075731	1.24539385	1.29165062	1.38925642
45	1.11891516	1.20576046	1.25162082	1.29918525	1.39967584
46	1.12171245	1.21078446	1.25787892	1.30676383	1.41017341
47	1.12451673	1.21582940	1.26416832	1.31438662	1.42074971
48	1.12732802	1.22089536	1.27048916	1.32205388	1.43140533
49	1.13014634	1.22598242	1.27684161	1.32976586	1.44214087
50	1.13297171	1.23109068	1.28322581	1.33752283	1.45295693

INTEREST TABLES (Continued)

AMOUNT AT COMPOUND INTEREST $(1 + i)^n$

(Continued)

Years	Rate i				
n	.0025($\frac{1}{4}$ %)	.004167($\frac{5}{12}$ %)	.005($\frac{1}{2}$ %)	.005833($\frac{7}{12}$ %)	.0075($\frac{3}{4}$ %)
50	1.13297171	1.23109068	1.28322581	1.33752283	1.45295693
51	1.13580414	1.23622022	1.28964194	1.34532504	1.46385411
52	1.13864365	1.24137114	1.29609015	1.35317277	1.47483301
53	1.14149026	1.24654352	1.30257060	1.36106628	1.48589426
54	1.14434398	1.25173745	1.30908346	1.36900583	1.49703847
55	1.14720484	1.25695302	1.31562887	1.37699170	1.50826626
56	1.15007285	1.26219033	1.32220702	1.38502415	1.51957825
57	1.15294804	1.26744946	1.32881805	1.39310346	1.53097509
58	1.15583041	1.27273050	1.33546214	1.40122990	1.54245740
59	1.15871998	1.27803354	1.34213946	1.40940374	1.55402583
60	1.16161678	1.28335868	1.34885015	1.41762526	1.56568103
61	1.16452082	1.28870601	1.35559440	1.42589474	1.57742363
62	1.16743213	1.29407561	1.36237238	1.43421246	1.58925431
63	1.17035071	1.29946760	1.36918424	1.44257870	1.60117372
64	1.17327658	1.30488204	1.37603016	1.45099374	1.61318252
65	1.17620977	1.31031905	1.38291031	1.45945787	1.62528139
66	1.17915030	1.31577872	1.38982486	1.46797138	1.63747100
67	1.18209817	1.32126113	1.39677399	1.47653454	1.64975203
68	1.18505342	1.32676638	1.40375785	1.48514766	1.66212517
69	1.18801605	1.33229458	1.41077664	1.49381102	1.67459111
70	1.19098609	1.33784580	1.41783053	1.50252492	1.68715055
71	1.19396356	1.34342016	1.42491968	1.51128965	1.69980418
72	1.19694847	1.34901774	1.43204428	1.52010550	1.71255271
73	1.19994084	1.35463865	1.43920450	1.52897279	1.72539685
74	1.20294069	1.36028298	1.44640052	1.53789179	1.73833733
75	1.20594804	1.36595082	1.45363252	1.54686283	1.75137486
76	1.20896291	1.37164229	1.46090069	1.55588620	1.76451017
77	1.21198532	1.37735746	1.46820519	1.56496220	1.77774400
78	1.21501528	1.38309645	1.47554622	1.57409115	1.79107708
79	1.21805282	1.38885935	1.48292395	1.58327334	1.80451015
80	1.22109795	1.39464627	1.49033857	1.59250910	1.81804398
81	1.22415070	1.40045729	1.49779026	1.60179874	1.83167931
82	1.22721108	1.40629253	1.50527921	1.61114257	1.84541691
83	1.23027910	1.41215209	1.51280561	1.62054090	1.85925753
84	1.23335480	1.41803605	1.52036964	1.62999405	1.87320196
85	1.23643819	1.42394454	1.52797148	1.63950235	1.88725098
86	1.23952928	1.42987764	1.53561134	1.64906612	1.90140536
87	1.24262811	1.43583546	1.54328940	1.65868567	1.91566590
88	1.24573468	1.44181811	1.55100585	1.66836134	1.93003339
89	1.24884901	1.44782568	1.55876087	1.67809344	1.94450865
90	1.25197114	1.45385829	1.56655468	1.68788232	1.95909246
91	1.25510106	1.45991603	1.57438745	1.69772830	1.97378565
92	1.25823882	1.46599902	1.58225939	1.70763172	1.98858905
93	1.26138441	1.47210735	1.59017069	1.71759290	2.00350346
94	1.26453787	1.47824113	1.59812154	1.72761219	2.01852974
95	1.26769922	1.48440047	1.60611215	1.73768993	2.03366871
96	1.27086847	1.49058547	1.61414271	1.74782646	2.04892123
97	1.27404564	1.49679624	1.62221342	1.75802211	2.06428814
98	1.27723075	1.50303289	1.63032449	1.76827724	2.07977030
99	1.28042383	1.50929553	1.63847611	1.77859219	2.09536858
100	1.28362489	1.51558426	1.64666849	1.78896731	2.11108384

AMOUNT AT COMPOUND INTEREST $(1 + i)^n$
(Continued)

Years	Rate i				
n	.01(1 %)	.01125($1\frac{1}{8}$ %)	.0125($1\frac{1}{4}$ %)	.015($1\frac{1}{2}$ %)	.0175($1\frac{3}{4}$ %)
1	1.01000000	1.01125000	1.01250000	1.01500000	1.01750000
2	1.02010000	1.02262656	1.02515625	1.03022500	1.03530625
3	1.03030100	1.03413111	1.03797070	1.04567838	1.05342411
4	1.04060401	1.04576509	1.05094534	1.06136355	1.07185903
5	1.05101005	1.05752994	1.06408215	1.07728400	1.09061656
6	1.06152015	1.06942716	1.07738318	1.09344326	1.10970235
7	1.07213535	1.08145821	1.09085047	1.10984491	1.12912215
8	1.08285671	1.09362462	1.10448610	1.12649259	1.14888178
9	1.09368527	1.10592789	1.11829218	1.14338998	1.16898721
10	1.10462213	1.11836958	1.13227083	1.16054083	1.18944449
11	1.11566835	1.13095124	1.14642422	1.17794894	1.21025977
12	1.12682503	1.14367444	1.16075452	1.19561817	1.23143931
13	1.13809328	1.15654078	1.17526395	1.21355244	1.25298950
14	1.14947421	1.16955186	1.18995475	1.23175573	1.27491682
15	1.16096896	1.18270932	1.20482918	1.25023207	1.29722786
16	1.17257864	1.19601480	1.21988955	1.26898555	1.31992935
17	1.18430443	1.20946997	1.23513817	1.28802033	1.34302811
18	1.19614748	1.22307650	1.25057739	1.30734064	1.36653111
19	1.20810895	1.23683611	1.26620961	1.32695075	1.39044540
20	1.22019004	1.25075052	1.28203723	1.34685501	1.41477820
21	1.23239194	1.26482146	1.29806270	1.36705783	1.43953681
22	1.24471586	1.27905071	1.31428848	1.38756370	1.46472871
23	1.25716302	1.29344003	1.33071709	1.40837715	1.49036146
24	1.26973465	1.30799123	1.34735105	1.42950281	1.51644279
25	1.28243200	1.32270613	1.36419294	1.45094535	1.54298054
26	1.29525631	1.33758657	1.38124535	1.47270953	1.56998269
27	1.30820888	1.35263442	1.39851092	1.49480018	1.59745739
28	1.32129097	1.36785156	1.41599230	1.51722218	1.62541290
29	1.33450388	1.38323989	1.43369221	1.53998051	1.65385762
30	1.34784892	1.39880134	1.45161336	1.56308022	1.68280013
31	1.36132740	1.41453785	1.46975853	1.58652642	1.71224913
32	1.37494068	1.43045140	1.48813051	1.61032432	1.74221349
33	1.38869009	1.44654398	1.50673214	1.63447918	1.77270223
34	1.40257699	1.46281760	1.52556629	1.65899637	1.80372452
35	1.41660276	1.47927430	1.54463587	1.68388132	1.83528970
36	1.43076878	1.49591613	1.56394382	1.70913954	1.86740727
37	1.44507647	1.51274519	1.58349312	1.73477663	1.90008689
38	1.45952724	1.52976357	1.60328678	1.76079828	1.93333841
39	1.47412251	1.54697341	1.62332787	1.78721025	1.96717184
40	1.48886373	1.56437687	1.64361946	1.81401841	2.00159734
41	1.50375237	1.58197611	1.66416471	1.84122868	2.03662530
42	1.51878989	1.59977334	1.68496677	1.86884712	2.07226624
43	1.53397779	1.61777079	1.70602885	1.89687982	2.10853090
44	1.54931757	1.63597071	1.72735421	1.92533302	2.14543019
45	1.56481075	1.65437538	1.74894614	1.95421301	2.18297522
46	1.58045885	1.67298710	1.77080797	1.98352621	2.22117728
47	1.59626344	1.69180821	1.79294306	2.01327910	2.26004789
48	1.61222608	1.71084105	1.81535485	2.04347829	2.29959872
49	1.62834834	1.73008801	1.83804679	2.07413046	2.33984170
50	1.64463182	1.74955150	1.86102237	2.10524242	2.38078893

AMOUNT AT COMPOUND INTEREST $(1+i)^n$ (Continued)

Years	Rate i				
n	.01(1 %)	.01125($1\frac{1}{8}$ %)	.0125($1\frac{1}{4}$ %)	.015($1\frac{1}{2}$ %)	.0175($1\frac{3}{4}$ %)
50	1.64463182	1.74955150	1.86102237	2.10524242	2.38078893
51	1.66107814	1.76923395	1.88428515	2.13682106	2.42245274
52	1.67768892	1.78913784	1.90783872	2.16887337	2.46484566
53	1.69446581	1.80926564	1.93168670	2.20140647	2.50798046
54	1.71141047	1.82961988	1.95583279	2.23442757	2.55187012
55	1.72852457	1.85020310	1.98028070	2.26794398	2.59652785
56	1.74580982	1.87101788	2.00503420	2.30196314	2.64196708
57	1.76326792	1.89206684	2.03009713	2.33649259	2.68820151
58	1.78090060	1.91335259	2.05547335	2.37153998	2.73524503
59	1.79870960	1.93487780	2.08116676	2.40711308	2.78311182
60	1.81669670	1.95664518	2.10718135	2.44321978	2.83181628
61	1.83486367	1.97865744	2.13352111	2.47986807	2.88137306
62	1.85321230	2.00091733	2.16019013	2.51706609	2.93179709
63	1.87174443	2.02342765	2.18719250	2.55482208	2.98310354
64	1.89046187	2.04619121	2.21453241	2.59314442	3.03530785
65	1.90936649	2.06921087	2.24221407	2.63204158	3.08842574
66	1.92846015	2.09248949	2.27024174	2.67152221	3.14247319
67	1.94774475	2.11602999	2.29861976	2.71159504	3.19746647
68	1.96722220	2.13983533	2.32735251	2.75226896	3.25342213
69	1.98689442	2.16390848	2.35644442	2.79355300	3.31035702
70	2.00676337	2.18825245	2.38589997	2.83545629	3.36828827
71	2.02683100	2.21287029	2.41572372	2.87798814	3.42723331
72	2.04709931	2.23776508	2.44592027	2.92115796	3.48720990
73	2.06757031	2.26293994	2.47649427	2.96497533	3.54823607
74	2.08824601	2.28839801	2.50745045	3.00944996	3.61033020
75	2.10912847	2.31414249	2.53879358	3.05459171	3.67351098
76	2.13021975	2.34017659	2.57052850	3.10041059	3.73779742
77	2.15152195	2.36650358	2.60266011	3.14691674	3.80320888
78	2.17303717	2.39312675	2.63519336	3.19412050	3.86976503
79	2.19476754	2.42004942	2.66813327	3.24203230	3.93748592
80	2.21671522	2.44727498	2.70148494	3.29066279	4.00639192
81	2.23888237	2.47480682	2.73525350	3.34002273	4.07650378
82	2.26127119	2.50264840	2.76944417	3.39012307	4.14784260
83	2.28388390	2.53080319	2.80406222	3.44097492	4.22042984
84	2.30672274	2.55927473	2.83911300	3.49258954	4.29428737
85	2.32978997	2.58806657	2.87460191	3.54497838	4.36943740
86	2.35308787	2.61718232	2.91053444	3.59815306	4.44590255
87	2.37661875	2.64662562	2.94691612	3.65212535	4.52370584
88	2.40038494	2.67640016	2.98375257	3.70690723	4.60287070
89	2.42438879	2.70650966	3.02104948	3.76251084	4.68342093
90	2.44863267	2.73695789	3.05881260	3.81894851	4.76538080
91	2.47311900	2.76774867	3.09704775	3.87623273	4.84877496
92	2.49785019	2.79888584	3.13576085	3.93437622	4.93362853
93	2.52282869	2.83037331	3.17495786	3.99339187	5.01996703
94	2.54805698	2.86221501	3.21464483	4.05329275	5.10781645
95	2.57353755	2.89441492	3.25482789	4.11409214	5.19720324
96	2.59927293	2.92697709	3.29551324	4.17580352	5.28815429
97	2.62526565	2.95990559	3.33670716	4.23844057	5.38069699
98	2.65151831	2.99320452	3.37841600	4.30201718	5.47485919
99	2.67803349	3.02687807	3.42064620	4.36654744	5.57066923
100	2.70481383	3.06093045	3.46340427	4.43204565	5.66815594

INTEREST TABLES (Continued)

AMOUNT AT COMPOUND INTEREST $(1 + i)^n$
(Continued)

Years	Rate i				
n	.02(2 %)	.0225($2\frac{1}{4}$ %)	.025($2\frac{1}{2}$ %)	.0275($2\frac{3}{4}$ %)	.03(3 %)
1	1.02000000	1.02250000	1.02500000	1.02750000	1.03000000
2	1.04040000	1.04550625	1.05062500	1.05575625	1.06090000
3	1.06120800	1.06903014	1.07689063	1.08478955	1.09272700
4	1.08243216	1.09308332	1.10381289	1.11462126	1.12550881
5	1.10408080	1.11767769	1.13140821	1.14527334	1.15927407
6	1.12616242	1.14282544	1.15969342	1.17676836	1.19405230
7	1.14868567	1.16853901	1.18868575	1.20912949	1.22987387
8	1.17165938	1.19483114	1.21840290	1.24238055	1.26677008
9	1.19509257	1.22171484	1.24886297	1.27654602	1.30477318
10	1.21899442	1.24920343	1.28008454	1.31165103	1.34391638
11	1.24337431	1.27731050	1.31208666	1.34772144	1.38423387
12	1.26824179	1.30604999	1.34488882	1.38478378	1.42576089
13	1.29360663	1.33543611	1.37851104	1.42286533	1.46853371
14	1.31947876	1.36548343	1.41297382	1.46199413	1.51258972
15	1.34586834	1.39620680	1.44829817	1.50219896	1.55796742
16	1.37278571	1.42762146	1.48450562	1.54350944	1.60470644
17	1.40024142	1.45974294	1.52161826	1.58595595	1.65284763
18	1.42824625	1.49258716	1.55965872	1.62956973	1.70243306
19	1.45681117	1.52617037	1.59865019	1.67438290	1.75350605
20	1.48594740	1.56050920	1.63861644	1.72042843	1.80611123
21	1.51566634	1.59562066	1.67958185	1.76774021	1.86029457
22	1.54597967	1.63152212	1.72157140	1.81635307	1.91610341
23	1.57689926	1.66823137	1.76461068	1.86630278	1.97358651
24	1.60843725	1.70576658	1.80872595	1.91762610	2.03279411
25	1.64060599	1.74414632	1.85394410	1.97036082	2.09377793
26	1.67341811	1.78338962	1.90029270	2.02454575	2.15659127
27	1.70688648	1.82351588	1.94780002	2.08022075	2.22128901
28	1.74102421	1.86454499	1.99649502	2.13742682	2.28792768
29	1.77584469	1.90649725	2.04640739	2.19620606	2.35656551
30	1.81136158	1.94939344	2.09756758	2.25660173	2.42726247
31	1.84758882	1.99325479	2.15000677	2.31865828	2.50008035
32	1.88454059	2.03810303	2.20375694	2.38242138	2.57508276
33	1.92223140	2.08396034	2.25885086	2.44793797	2.65233524
34	1.96067603	2.13084945	2.31532213	2.51525626	2.73190530
35	1.99988955	2.17879356	2.37320519	2.58442581	2.81386245
36	2.03988734	2.22781642	2.43253532	2.65549752	2.89827833
37	2.08068509	2.27794229	2.49334870	2.72852370	2.98522668
38	2.12229879	2.32919599	2.55568242	2.80355810	3.07478348
39	2.16474477	2.38160290	2.61957448	2.88065595	3.16702698
40	2.20803966	2.43518897	2.68506384	2.95987399	3.26203779
41	2.25220046	2.48998072	2.75219043	3.04127052	3.35989893
42	2.29724447	2.54600528	2.82099520	3.12490546	3.46069589
43	2.34318936	2.60329040	2.89152008	3.21084036	3.56451677
44	2.39005314	2.66186444	2.96380808	3.29913847	3.67145227
45	2.43785421	2.72175639	3.03790328	3.38986478	3.78159584
46	2.48661129	2.78299590	3.11385086	3.48308606	3.89504372
47	2.53634352	2.84561331	3.19169713	3.57887093	4.01189503
48	2.58707039	2.90963961	3.27148956	3.67728988	4.13225188
49	2.63881179	2.97510650	3.35327680	3.77841535	4.25621944
50	2.69158803	3.04204640	3.43710872	3.88232177	4.38390602

AMOUNT AT COMPOUND INTEREST $(1 + i)^n$

(Continued)

Years	Rate i				
n	.02(2 %)	.0225(2¼ %)	.025(2½ %)	.0275(2¾ %)	.03(3 %)
50	2.69158803	3.04204640	3.43710872	3.88232177	4.38390602
51	2.74541979	3.11049244	3.52303644	3.98908562	4.51542320
52	2.80032819	3.18047852	3.61111235	4.09878547	4.65088590
53	2.85633475	3.25203929	3.70139016	4.21150208	4.79041247
54	2.91346144	3.32521017	3.79392491	4.32731838	4.93412485
55	2.97173067	3.40002740	3.88877303	4.44631964	5.08214859
56	3.03116529	3.47652802	3.98599236	4.56859343	5.23461305
57	3.09178859	3.55474990	4.08564217	4.69422975	5.39165144
58	3.15362436	3.63473177	4.18778322	4.82332107	5.55340098
59	3.21669685	3.71651324	4.29247780	4.95596239	5.72000301
60	3.28103079	3.80013479	4.39978975	5.09225136	5.89160310
61	3.34665140	3.88563782	4.50978449	5.23228827	6.06835120
62	3.41358443	3.97306467	4.62252910	5.37617620	6.25040173
63	3.48185612	4.06245862	4.73809233	5.52402105	6.43791379
64	3.55149324	4.15386394	4.85654464	5.67593162	6.63105120
65	3.62252311	4.24732588	4.97795826	5.83201974	6.82998273
66	3.69497357	4.34289071	5.10240721	5.99240029	7.03488222
67	3.76887304	4.44060576	5.22996739	6.15719130	7.24592868
68	3.84425050	4.54051939	5.36071658	6.32651406	7.46330654
69	3.92113551	4.64268107	5.49473449	6.50049319	7.68720574
70	3.99955822	4.74714140	5.63210286	6.67925676	7.91782191
71	4.07954939	4.85395208	5.77290543	6.86293632	8.15535657
72	4.16114038	4.96316600	5.91722806	7.05166706	8.40001727
73	4.24436318	5.07483723	6.06515876	7.24558791	8.65201778
74	4.32925045	5.18902107	6.21678773	7.44484158	8.91157832
75	4.41583546	5.30577405	6.37220743	7.64957472	9.17892567
76	4.50415216	5.42515396	6.53151261	7.85993802	9.45429344
77	4.59423521	5.54721993	6.69480043	8.07608632	9.73792224
78	4.68611991	5.67203237	6.86217044	8.29817869	10.0300599
79	4.77984231	5.79965310	7.03372470	8.52637861	10.3309617
80	4.87543916	5.93014530	7.20956782	8.76085402	10.6408906
81	4.97294794	6.06357357	7.38980701	9.00177751	10.9601173
82	5.07240690	6.20000397	7.57455219	9.24932639	11.2889208
83	5.17385504	6.33950406	7.76391599	9.50368286	11.6275884
84	5.27733214	6.48214290	7.95801389	9.76503414	11.9764161
85	5.38287878	6.62799112	8.15696424	10.0335726	12.3357085
86	5.49053636	6.77712092	8.36088834	10.3094958	12.7057798
87	5.60034708	6.92960614	8.56991055	10.5930070	13.0869532
88	5.71235402	7.08552228	8.78415832	10.8843147	13.4795618
89	5.82660110	7.24494653	9.00376228	11.1836333	13.8839487
90	5.94313313	7.40795782	9.22885633	11.4911832	14.3004671
91	6.06199579	7.57463688	9.45957774	11.8071908	14.7294811
92	6.18323570	7.74506621	9.69606718	12.1318885	15.1713656
93	6.30690042	7.91933020	9.93846886	12.4655154	15.6265065
94	6.43303843	8.09751512	10.1869306	12.8083171	16.0953017
95	6.56169920	8.27970921	10.4416038	13.1605458	16.5781608
96	6.69293318	8.46600267	10.7026439	13.5224608	17.0755056
97	6.82679184	8.65648773	10.9702100	13.8943285	17.5877708
98	6.96332768	8.85125871	11.2444653	14.2764226	18.1154039
99	7.10259423	9.05041203	11.5255769	14.6690242	18.6588660
100	7.24464612	9.25404630	11.8137164	15.0724223	19.2186320

AMOUNT AT COMPOUND INTEREST $(1+i)^n$
(Continued)

Years	Rate i				
n	.035($3\frac{1}{2}$ %)	.04(4 %)	.045($4\frac{1}{2}$ %)	.05(5 %)	.055($5\frac{1}{2}$ %)
1	1.03500000	1.04000000	1.04500000	1.05000000	1.05500000
2	1.07122500	1.08160000	1.09202500	1.10250000	1.11302500
3	1.10871788	1.12486400	1.14116613	1.15762500	1.17424138
4	1.14752300	1.16985856	1.19251860	1.21550625	1.23882465
5	1.18768631	1.21665290	1.24618194	1.27628156	1.30696001
6	1.22925533	1.26531902	1.30226012	1.34009564	1.37884281
7	1.27227926	1.31593178	1.36086183	1.40710042	1.45467916
8	1.31680904	1.36856905	1.42210061	1.47745544	1.53468651
9	1.36289735	1.42331181	1.48609514	1.55132822	1.61909427
10	1.41059876	1.48024428	1.55296942	1.62889463	1.70814446
11	1.45996972	1.53945406	1.62285305	1.71033936	1.80209240
12	1.51106866	1.60103222	1.69588143	1.79585633	1.90120749
13	1.56395606	1.66507351	1.77219610	1.88564914	2.00577390
14	1.61869452	1.73167645	1.85194492	1.97993160	2.11609146
15	1.67534883	1.80094351	1.93528244	2.07892818	2.23247649
16	1.73398604	1.87298125	2.02237015	2.18287459	2.35526270
17	1.79467555	1.94790050	2.11337681	2.29201832	2.48480215
18	1.85748920	2.02581652	2.20847877	2.40661923	2.62146627
19	1.92250132	2.10684918	2.30786031	2.52695020	2.76564691
20	1.98978886	2.19112314	2.41171402	2.65329771	2.91775749
21	2.05943147	2.27876807	2.52024116	2.78596259	3.07823415
22	2.13151158	2.36991879	2.63365201	2.92526072	3.24753703
23	2.20611448	2.46471554	2.75216635	3.07152376	3.42615157
24	2.28332849	2.56330416	2.87601383	3.22509994	3.61458990
25	2.36324498	2.66583633	3.00543446	3.38635494	3.81339235
26	2.44595856	2.77246978	3.14067901	3.55567269	4.02312893
27	2.53156711	2.88336858	3.28200956	3.73345632	4.24440102
28	2.62017196	2.99870332	3.42969999	3.92012914	4.47784307
29	2.71187798	3.11865145	3.58403649	4.11613560	4.72412444
30	2.80679370	3.24339751	3.74531813	4.32194238	4.98395129
31	2.90503148	3.37313341	3.91385745	4.53803949	5.25806861
32	3.00670759	3.50805875	4.08998104	4.76494147	5.54726238
33	3.11194235	3.64838110	4.27403018	5.00318854	5.85236181
34	3.22086033	3.79431634	4.46636154	5.25334797	6.17424171
35	3.33359045	3.94608899	4.66734781	5.51601537	6.51382501
36	3.45026611	4.10393255	4.87737846	5.79181614	6.87208538
37	3.57102543	4.26808986	5.09686049	6.08140694	7.25005008
38	3.69601132	4.43881345	5.32621921	6.38547729	7.64880283
39	3.82537171	4.61636599	5.56589908	6.70475115	8.06948699
40	3.95925972	4.80102063	5.81636454	7.03998871	8.51330877
41	4.09783381	4.99306145	6.07810094	7.39198815	8.98154076
42	4.24125799	5.19278391	6.35161548	7.76158756	9.47552550
43	4.38970202	5.40049527	6.63743818	8.14966693	9.99667940
44	4.54334160	5.61651508	6.93612290	8.55715028	10.5464968
45	4.70235855	5.84117568	7.24824843	8.98500779	11.1265541
46	4.86694110	6.07482271	7.57441961	9.43425818	11.7385146
47	5.03728404	6.31781562	7.91526849	9.90597109	12.3841329
48	5.21358898	6.57052824	8.27145557	10.4012696	13.0652602
49	5.39606459	6.83334937	8.64367107	10.9213331	13.7838495
50	5.58492686	7.10668335	9.03263627	11.4673998	14.5419612

AMOUNT AT COMPOUND INTEREST $(1+i)^n$

(Continued)

Years	Rate i				
n	.06(6 %)	.065($6\frac{1}{2}$ %)	.07(7 %)	.075($7\frac{1}{2}$) %	.08(8 %)
1	1.06000000	1.06500000	1.07000000	1.07500000	1.08000000
2	1.12360000	1.13422500	1.14490000	1.15562500	1.16640000
3	1.19101600	1.20794963	1.22504300	1.24229688	1.25971200
4	1.26247696	1.28646635	1.31079601	1.33546914	1.36048896
5	1.33822558	1.37008666	1.40255173	1.43562933	1.46932808
6	1.41851911	1.45914230	1.50073035	1.54330153	1.58687432
7	1.50363026	1.55398655	1.60578148	1.65904914	1.71382427
8	1.59384807	1.65499567	1.71818618	1.78347783	1.85093021
9	1.68947896	1.76257039	1.83845921	1.91723866	1.99900463
10	1.79084770	1.87713747	1.96715136	2.06103156	2.15892500
11	1.89829856	1.99915140	2.10485195	2.21560893	2.33163900
12	2.01219647	2.12909624	2.25219159	2.38177960	2.51817012
13	2.13292826	2.26748750	2.40984500	2.56041307	2.71962373
14	2.26090396	2.41487418	2.57853415	2.75244405	2.93719362
15	2.39655819	2.57184101	2.75903154	2.95887735	3.17216911
16	2.54035168	2.73901067	2.95216375	3.18079315	3.42594264
17	2.69277279	2.91704637	3.15881521	3.41935264	3.70001805
18	2.85433915	3.10665438	3.37993228	3.67580409	3.99601950
19	3.02559950	3.30858691	3.61652754	3.95148940	4.31570106
20	3.20713547	3.52364506	3.86968446	4.24785110	4.66095714
21	3.39956360	3.75268199	4.14056237	4.56643993	5.03383372
22	3.60353742	3.99660632	4.43040174	4.90892293	5.43654041
23	3.81974966	4.25638573	4.74052986	5.27709215	5.87146365
24	4.04893464	4.53305081	5.07236695	5.67287406	6.34118070
25	4.29187072	4.82769911	5.42743264	6.09833961	6.84847520
26	4.54938296	5.14149955	5.80735292	6.55571508	7.39635321
27	4.82234594	5.47569702	6.21386763	7.04739371	7.98806147
28	5.11168670	5.83161733	6.64883836	7.57594824	8.62710639
29	5.41838790	6.21067245	7.11425705	8.14414436	9.31727490
30	5.74349117	6.61436616	7.61225504	8.75495519	10.0626569
31	6.08810064	7.04429996	8.14511290	9.41157683	10.8676694
32	6.45338668	7.50217946	8.71527080	10.1174451	11.7370830
33	6.84058988	7.98982113	9.32533975	10.8762535	12.6760496
34	7.25102528	8.50915950	9.97811354	11.6919725	13.6901336
35	7.68608679	9.06225487	10.6765815	12.5688704	14.7853443
36	8.14725200	9.65130143	11.4239422	13.5115357	15.9681718
37	8.63608712	10.2786360	12.2236181	14.5249009	17.2456256
38	9.15425235	10.9467474	13.0792714	15.6142684	18.6252756
39	9.70350749	11.6582859	13.9948204	16.7853386	20.1152977
40	10.2857179	12.4160745	14.9744578	18.0442390	21.7245215
41	10.9028610	13.2231194	16.0226699	19.3975569	23.4624832
42	11.5570327	14.0826221	17.1442568	20.8523737	25.3394819
43	12.2504546	14.9979926	18.3443548	22.4163017	27.3666404
44	12.9854819	15.9728621	19.6284596	24.0975243	29.5559717
45	13.7646108	17.0110981	21.0024518	25.9048386	31.9204494
46	14.5904875	18.1168195	22.4726234	27.8477015	34.4740853
47	15.4659167	19.2944128	24.0457070	29.9362791	37.2320122
48	16.3938717	20.5485496	25.7289065	32.1815001	40.2105731
49	17.3775040	21.8842053	27.5299300	34.5951126	43.4274190
50	18.4201543	23.3066787	29.4570251	37.1897460	46.9016125

PRESENT VALUE $1/(1+i)^n$

The following table gives the value of unit amount due in n years at rate of interest i, compounded annually, $1/(1+i)^n = v^n$.

Years	Rate i				
n	.0025(¼ %)	.004167($\frac{5}{12}$ %)	.005(½ %)	.005833($\frac{7}{12}$ %)	.0075(¾ %)
1	.99750623	.99585062	.99502488	.99420050	.99255583
2	.99501869	.99171846	.99007450	.98843463	.98516708
3	.99253734	.98760345	.98514876	.98270220	.97783333
4	.99006219	.98350551	.98024752	.97700301	.97055417
5	.98759321	.97942457	.97537067	.97133688	.96332920
6	.98513038	.97536057	.97051808	.96570361	.95615802
7	.98267370	.97131343	.96568963	.96010301	.94904022
8	.98022314	.96728308	.96088520	.95453489	.94197540
9	.97777869	.96326946	.95610468	.94899906	.93496318
10	.97534034	.95927249	.95134794	.94349534	.92800315
11	.97290807	.95529211	.94661487	.93802354	.92109494
12	.97048187	.95132824	.94190534	.93258347	.91423815
13	.96806171	.94738082	.93721924	.92717495	.90743241
14	.96564759	.94344978	.93255646	.92179779	.90067733
15	.96323949	.93953505	.92791688	.91645182	.89397254
16	.96083740	.93563657	.92330037	.91113686	.88731766
17	.95844130	.93175426	.91870684	.90585272	.88071231
18	.95605117	.92788806	.91413616	.90059922	.87415614
19	.95366700	.92403790	.90958822	.89537619	.86764878
20	.95128878	.92020372	.90506290	.89018346	.86118985
21	.94891649	.91638544	.90056010	.88502084	.85477901
22	.94655011	.91258301	.89607971	.87988815	.84841589
23	.94418964	.90879636	.89162160	.87478524	.84210014
24	.94183505	.90502542	.88718567	.86971192	.83583140
25	.93948634	.90127013	.88277181	.86466802	.82960933
26	.93714348	.89753042	.87837991	.85965338	.82343358
27	.93480646	.89380623	.87400986	.85466782	.81730380
28	.93247527	.89009749	.86966155	.84971117	.81121966
29	.93014990	.88640414	.86533488	.84478327	.80518080
30	.92783032	.88272611	.86102973	.83988394	.79918690
31	.92551653	.87906335	.85674600	.83501303	.79323762
32	.92320851	.87541578	.85248358	.83017037	.78733262
33	.92090624	.87178335	.84824237	.82535580	.78147158
34	.91860972	.86816599	.84402226	.82056914	.77565418
35	.91631892	.86456365	.83982314	.81581025	.76988008
36	.91403384	.86097624	.83564492	.81107896	.76414896
37	.91175445	.85740373	.83148748	.80637510	.75846051
38	.90948075	.85384604	.82735073	.80169853	.75281440
39	.90721272	.85030311	.82323455	.79704907	.74721032
40	.90495034	.84677488	.81913886	.79242659	.74164796
41	.90269361	.84326129	.81506354	.78783091	.73612701
42	.90044250	.83976228	.81100850	.78326188	.73064716
43	.89819701	.83627779	.80697363	.77871935	.72520809
44	.89595712	.83280776	.80295884	.77420316	.71980952
45	.89372281	.82935212	.79896402	.76971317	.71445114
46	.89149407	.82591083	.79498907	.76524922	.70913264
47	.88927090	.82248381	.79103390	.76081115	.70385374
48	.88705326	.81907102	.78709841	.75639883	.69861414
49	.88484116	81567238	.78318250	.75201209	.69341353
50	.88263457	.81228785	.77928607	.74765079	.68825165

PRESENT VALUE $1/(1 + i)^n$ (Continued)

Years	Rate i				
n	.0025($\frac{1}{4}$ %)	.004167($\frac{5}{12}$ %)	.005($\frac{1}{2}$ %)	.005833($\frac{7}{12}$ %)	.0075($\frac{3}{4}$ %)
50	.88263457	.81228785	.77928607	.74765079	.68825165
51	.88043349	.80891736	.77540902	.74331479	.68312819
52	.87823790	.80556086	.77155127	.73900393	.67804286
53	.87604778	.80221828	.76771270	.73471808	.67299540
54	.87386312	.79888957	.76389324	.73045708	.66798551
55	.87168391	.79557468	.76009277	.72622079	.66301291
56	.86951013	.79227354	.75631122	.72200907	.65807733
57	.86734178	.78898610	.75254847	.71782178	.65317849
58	.86517883	.78571230	.74880445	.71365877	.64831612
59	.86302128	.78245208	.74507906	.70951990	.64348995
60	.86086911	.77920539	.74137220	.70540504	.63869970
61	.85872230	.77597217	.73768378	.70131404	.63394511
62	.85658085	.77275237	.73401371	.69724677	.62922592
63	.85444474	.76954593	.73036190	.69320308	.62454185
64	.85231395	.76635279	.72672826	.68918285	.61989266
65	.85018848	.76317291	.72311269	.68518593	.61527807
66	.84806831	.76000621	.71951512	.68121219	.61069784
67	.84595343	.75685266	.71593544	.67726150	.60615170
68	.84384382	.75371219	.71237357	.67333372	.60163940
69	.84173947	.75058476	.70882943	.66942872	.59716070
70	.83964037	.74747030	.70530291	.66554637	.59271533
71	.83754650	.74436876	.70179394	.66168653	.58830306
72	.83545786	.74128009	.69830243	.65784908	.58392363
73	.83337442	.73820424	.69482829	.65403388	.57957681
74	.83129618	.73514115	.69137143	.65024081	.57526234
75	.82922312	.73209078	.68793177	.64646973	.57097999
76	.82715523	.72905306	.68450923	.64272053	.56672952
77	.82509250	.72602794	.68110371	.63899306	.56251069
78	.82303491	.72301537	.67771513	.63528723	.55832326
79	.82098246	.72001531	.67434342	.63160288	.55416701
80	.81893512	.71702770	.67098847	.62793989	.55004170
81	.81689289	.71405248	.66765022	.62429816	.54594710
82	.81485575	.71108960	.66432858	.62067754	.54188297
83	.81282369	.70813902	.66102346	.61707792	.53784911
84	.81079670	.70520069	.65773479	.61349917	.53384527
85	.80877476	.70227454	.65446248	.60994118	.52987123
86	.80675787	.69936054	.65120644	60640382	.52592678
87	.80474600	.69645863	.64796661	.60288698	.52201169
88	.80273915	.69356876	.64474290	.59939054	.51812575
89	.80073731	.69069088	.64153522	.59591437	.51426873
90	.79874046	.68782495	.63834350	.59245836	.51044043
91	.79674859	.68497090	.63516766	.58902240	.50664063
92	.79476168	.68212870	.63200763	.58560636	.50286911
93	.79277973	.67929829	.62886331	.58221014	.49912567
94	.79080273	.67647962	.62573464	.57883361	.49541009
95	.78883065	.67367265	.62262153	.57547666	.49172217
96	.78686349	.67087733	.61952391	.57213918	.48806171
97	.78490124	.66809361	.61644170	.56882106	.48442850
98	.78294388	.66532143	.61337483	.56552218	.48082233
99	.78099140	.66256076	.61032321	.56224243	.47724301
100	.77904379	.65981155	.60728678	.55898171	.47369033

PRESENT VALUE $1/(1+i)^n$ (Continued)

Years	Rate i				
n	.01(1 %)	.01125($1\frac{1}{8}$ %)	.0125($1\frac{1}{4}$ %)	.015($1\frac{1}{2}$ %)	.0175($1\frac{3}{4}$ %)
1	.99009901	.98887515	.98765432	.98522167	.98280098
2	.98029605	.97787407	.97546106	.97066175	.96589777
3	.97059015	.96699537	.96341833	.95631699	.94928528
4	.96098034	.95623770	.95152428	.94218423	.93295851
5	.95146569	.94559970	.93977706	.92826033	.91691254
6	.94204524	.93508005	.92817488	.91454219	.90114254
7	.93271805	.92467743	.91671593	.90102679	.88564378
8	.92348322	.91439054	.90539845	.88771112	.87041157
9	.91433982	.90421808	.89422069	.87459224	.85544135
10	.90528695	.89415880	.88318093	.86166723	.84072860
11	.89632372	.88421142	.87227746	.84893323	.82626889
12	.88744923	.87437470	.86150860	.83638742	.81205788
13	.87866260	.86464742	.85087269	.82402702	.79809128
14	.86996297	.85502835	.84036809	.81184928	.78436490
15	.86134947	.84551629	.82999318	.79985150	.77087459
16	.85282126	.83611005	.81974635	.78803104	.75761631
17	.84437749	.82680846	.80962602	.77638526	.74458605
18	.83601731	.81761034	.79963064	.76491159	.73177990
19	.82773992	.80851455	.78975866	.75360747	.71919401
20	.81954447	.79951995	.78000855	.74247042	.70682458
21	.81143017	.79062542	.77037881	.73149795	.69466789
22	.80339621	.78182983	.76086796	.72068763	.68272028
23	.79544179	.77313210	.75147453	.71003708	.67097817
24	.78756613	.76453112	.74219707	.69954392	.65943800
25	.77976844	.75602583	.73303414	.68920583	.64809632
26	.77204796	.74761516	.72398434	.67902052	.63694970
27	.76440392	.73929806	.71504626	.66898574	.62599479
28	.75683557	.73107348	.70621853	.65909925	.61522829
29	.74934215	.72294040	.69749978	.64935887	.60464697
30	.74192292	.71489780	.68888867	.63976243	.59424764
31	.73457715	.70694467	.68038387	.63030781	.58402716
32	.72730411	.69908002	.67198407	.62099292	.57398247
33	.72010307	.69130287	.66368797	.61181568	.56411053
34	.71297334	.68361223	.65549429	.60277407	.55440839
35	.70591420	.67600715	.64740177	.59386608	.54487311
36	.69892495	.66848667	.63940916	.58508974	.53550183
37	.69200490	.66104986	.63151522	.57644309	.52629172
38	.68515337	.65369578	.62371873	.56792423	.51724002
39	.67836967	.64642352	.61601850	.55953126	.50834400
40	.67165314	.63923216	.60841334	.55126232	.49960098
41	.66500311	.63212080	.60090206	.54311559	.49100834
42	.65841892	.62508855	.59348352	.53508925	.48256348
43	.65189992	.61813454	.58615656	.52718153	.47426386
44	.64544546	.61125789	.57892006	.51939067	.46610699
45	.63905492	.60445774	.57177290	.51171494	.45809040
46	.63272764	.59773324	.56471397	.50415265	.45021170
47	.62646301	.59108355	.55774219	.49670212	.44246850
48	.62026041	.58450784	.55085649	.48936170	.43485848
49	.61411921	.57800528	.54405579	.48212975	.42737934
50	.60803882	.57157506	.53733905	.47500468	.42002883

PRESENT VALUE $1/(1+i)^n$ (Continued)

Years	Rate i				
n	.01(1 %)	.01125($1\frac{1}{8}$ %)	.0125($1\frac{1}{4}$ %)	.015($1\frac{1}{2}$ %)	.0175($1\frac{3}{4}$ %)
50	.60803882	.57157506	.53733905	.47500468	.42002883
51	.60201864	.56521637	.53070524	.46798491	.41280475
52	.59605806	.55892843	.52415332	.46106887	.40570492
53	.59015649	.55271044	.51768229	.45425505	.39872719
54	.58431336	.54656162	.51129115	.44754192	.39186947
55	.57852808	.54048120	.50497892	.44092800	.38512970
56	.57280008	.53446843	.49874461	.43441182	.37850585
57	.56712879	.52852256	.49258727	.42799194	.37199592
58	.56151365	.52264282	.48650594	.42166694	.36559796
59	.55595411	.51682850	.48049970	.41543541	.35931003
60	.55044962	.51107887	.47456760	.40929597	.35313025
61	.54499962	.50539319	.46870874	.40324726	.34705676
62	.53960358	.49977077	.46292222	.39728794	.34108772
63	.53426097	.49421090	.45720713	.39141669	.33522135
64	.52897126	.48871288	.45156259	.38563221	.32945587
65	.52373392	.48327602	.44598775	.37993321	.32378956
66	.51854844	.47789965	.44048173	.37431843	.31822069
67	.51341429	.47258309	.43504368	.36878663	.31274761
68	.50833099	.46732568	.42967277	.36333658	.30736866
69	.50329801	.46212675	.42436817	.35796708	.30208222
70	.49831486	.45698566	.41912905	.35267692	.29688670
71	.49338105	.45190177	.41395462	.34746495	.29178054
72	.48849609	.44687443	.40884407	.34233000	.28676221
73	.48365949	.44190302	.40379661	.33727093	.28183018
74	.47887078	.43698692	.39881147	.33228663	.27698298
75	.47412949	.43212551	.39388787	.32737599	.27221914
76	.46943514	.42731818	.38902506	.32253793	.26753724
77	.46478726	.42256433	.38422228	.31777136	.26293586
78	.46018541	.41786337	.37947879	.31307523	.25841362
79	.45562912	.41321470	.37479387	.30844850	.25396916
80	.45111794	.40861775	.37016679	.30389015	.24960114
81	.44665142	.40407194	.36559683	.29939916	.24530825
82	.44222913	.39957670	.36108329	.29497454	.24108919
83	.43785063	.39513148	.35662547	.29061531	.23694269
84	.43351547	.39073570	.35222268	.28632050	.23286751
85	.42922324	.38638882	.34787426	.28208917	.22886242
86	.42497350	.38209031	.34357951	.27792036	.22492621
87	.42076585	.37783961	.33933779	.27381316	.22105770
88	.41659985	.37363621	.33514843	.26976666	.21725572
89	.41247510	.36947956	.33101080	.26577996	.21351914
90	.40839119	.36536916	.32692425	.26185218	.20984682
91	.40434771	.36130448	.32288814	.25798245	.20623766
92	.40034427	.35728503	.31890187	.25416990	.20269057
93	.39638046	.35331029	.31496481	.25041369	.19920450
94	.39245590	.34937976	.31107636	.24671300	.19577837
95	.38857020	.34549297	.30723591	.24306699	.19241118
96	.38472297	.34164941	.30344287	.23947487	.18910190
97	.38091383	.33784861	.29969666	.23593583	.18584953
98	.37714241	.33409010	.29599670	.23244909	.18265310
99	.37340832	.33037340	.29234242	.22901389	.17951165
100	.36971121	.32669805	.28873326	.22562944	.17642422

PRESENT VALUE $1/(1 + i)^n$ (Continued)

Years	Rate i				
n	.02(2 %)	.0225(2¼ %)	.025(2½ %)	.0275(2¾ %)	.03(3 %)
1	.98039216	.97799511	.97560976	.97323601	.97087379
2	.96116878	.95647444	.95181440	.94718833	.94259591
3	.94232233	.93542732	.92859941	.92183779	.91514166
4	.92384543	.91484335	.90595064	.89716573	.88848705
5	.90573081	.89471232	.88385429	.87315400	.86260878
6	.88797138	.87502427	.86229687	.84978491	.83748426
7	.87056018	.85576946	.84126524	.82704128	.81309151
8	.85349037	.83693835	.82074657	.80490635	.78940923
9	.83675527	.81852161	.80072836	.78336385	.76641673
10	.82034830	.80051013	.78119840	.76239791	.74409391
11	.80426304	.78289499	.76214478	.74199310	.72242128
12	.78849318	.76566748	.74355589	.72213440	.70137988
13	.77303253	.74881905	.72542038	.70280720	.68095134
14	.75787502	.73234137	.70772720	.68399728	.66111781
15	.74301473	.71622628	.69046556	.66569078	.64186195
16	.72844581	.70046580	.67362493	.64787424	.62316694
17	.71416256	.68505212	.65719506	.63053454	.60501645
18	.70015937	.66997763	.64116591	.61365892	.58739461
19	.68643076	.65523484	.62552772	.59723496	.57028603
20	.67297133	.64081647	.61027094	.58125057	.55367575
21	.65977582	.62671538	.59538629	.56569398	.53754928
22	.64683904	.61292457	.58086467	.55055375	.52189250
23	.63415592	.59943724	.56669724	.53581874	.50669175
24	.62172149	.58624668	.55287535	.52147809	.49193374
25	.60953087	.57334639	.53939059	.50752126	.47760557
26	.59757928	.56072997	.52623472	.49393796	.46369473
27	.58586204	.54839117	.51339973	.48071821	.45018906
28	.57437455	.53632388	.50087778	.46785227	.43707675
29	.56311231	.52452213	.48866125	.45533068	.42434636
30	.55207089	.51298008	.47674269	.44314421	.41198676
31	.54124597	.50169201	.46511481	.43128391	.39998715
32	.53063330	.49065233	.45377055	.41974103	.38833703
33	.52022873	.47985558	.44270298	.40850708	.37702625
34	.51002817	.46929641	.43190534	.39757380	.36604490
35	.50002761	.45896960	.42137107	.38693314	.35538340
36	.49022315	.44887002	.41109372	.37657727	.34503243
37	.48061093	.43899268	.40106705	.36649856	.33498294
38	.47118719	.42933270	.39128492	.35668959	.32522615
39	.46194822	.41988528	.38174139	.34714316	.31575355
40	.45289042	.41064575	.37243062	.33785222	.30655684
41	.44401021	.40160954	.36334695	.32880995	.29762800
42	.43530413	.39277216	.35448483	.32000968	.28895922
43	.42676875	.38412925	.34583886	.31144495	.28054294
44	.41840074	.37567653	.33740376	.30310944	.27237178
45	.41019680	.36740981	.32917440	.29499702	.26443862
46	.40215373	.35932500	.32114576	.28710172	.25673653
47	.39426836	.35141809	.31331294	.27941773	.24925876
48	.38653761	.34368518	.30567116	.27193940	.24199880
49	.37895844	.33612242	.29821576	.26466122	.23495029
50	.37152788	.32872608	.29094221	.25757783	.22810708

PRESENT VALUE $1/(1 + i)^n$ (Continued)

Years n	Rate i .02(2 %)	.0225($2\frac{1}{4}$ %)	.025($2\frac{1}{2}$ %)	.0275($2\frac{3}{4}$ %)	.03(3 %)
50	.37152788	.32872608	.29094221	.25757783	.22810708
51	.36424302	.32149250	.28384606	.25068402	.22146318
52	.35710100	.31441810	.27692298	.24397471	.21501280
53	.35009902	.30749936	.27016876	.23744497	.20875029
54	.34323433	.30073287	.26357928	.23109000	.20267019
55	.33650425	.29411528	.25715052	.22490511	.19676717
56	.32990613	.28764330	.25087855	.21888575	.19103609
57	.32343738	.28131374	.24475956	.21302749	.18547193
58	.31709547	.27512347	.23878982	.20732603	.18006984
59	.31087791	.26906940	.23296568	.20177716	.17482508
60	.30478227	.26314856	.22728359	.19637679	.16973309
61	.29880614	.25735801	.22174009	.19112097	.16478941
62	.29294720	.25169487	.21633179	.18600581	.15998972
63	.28720314	.24615635	.21105541	.18102755	.15532982
64	.28157170	.24073971	.20590771	.17618253	.15080565
65	.27605069	.23544226	.20088557	.17146718	.14641325
66	.27063793	.23026138	.19598593	.16687804	.14214879
67	.26533130	.22519450	.19120578	.16241172	.13800853
68	.26012873	.22023912	.18654223	.15806493	.13398887
69	.25502817	.21539278	.18199241	.15383448	.13008628
70	.25002761	.21065309	.17755358	.14971726	.12629736
71	.24512511	.20601769	.17322300	.14571023	.12261880
72	.24031874	.20148429	.16899805	.14181044	.11904737
73	.23560661	.19705065	.16487615	.13801503	.11557998
74	.23098687	.19271458	.16085478	.13432119	.11221357
75	.22645771	.18847391	.15693149	.13072622	.10894521
76	.22201737	.18432657	.15310389	.12722747	.10577205
77	.21766408	.18027048	.14936965	.12382235	.10269131
78	.21339616	.17630365	.14572649	.12050837	.09970030
79	.20921192	.17242411	.14217218	.11728309	.09679641
80	.20510973	.16862993	.13870457	.11414412	.09397710
81	.20108797	.16491925	.13532153	.11108917	.09123990
82	.19714507	.16129022	.13202101	.10811598	.08858243
83	.19327948	.15774105	.12880098	.10522237	.08600236
84	.18948968	.15426997	.12565949	.10240620	.08349743
85	.18577420	.15087528	.12259463	.09966540	.08106547
86	.18213157	.14755528	.11960452	.09699795	.07870434
87	.17856036	.14430835	.11668733	.09440190	.07641198
88	.17505918	.14113286	.11384130	.09187533	.07418639
89	.17162665	.13802724	.11106468	.08941638	.07202562
90	.16826142	.13498997	.10835579	.08702324	.06992779
91	.16496217	.13201953	.10571296	.08469415	.06789105
92	.16172762	.12911445	.10313460	.08242740	.06591364
93	.15855649	.12627331	.10061912	.08022131	.06399383
94	.15544754	.12349468	.09816500	.07807427	.06212993
95	.15239955	.12077719	.09577073	.07598469	.06032032
96	.14941132	.11811950	.09343486	.07395104	.05856342
97	.14648169	.11552029	.09115596	.07197181	.05685769
98	.14360950	.11297828	.08893264	.07004556	.05520164
99	.14079363	.11049221	.08676355	.06817086	.05359383
100	.13803297	.10806084	.08464737	.06634634	.05203284

PRESENT VALUE $1/(1+i)^n$ (Continued)

Years	Rate i				
n	.035($3\frac{1}{2}$%)	.04(4%)	.045($4\frac{1}{2}$%)	.05(5%)	.055($5\frac{1}{2}$%)
1	.96618357	.96153846	.95693780	.95238095	.94786730
2	.93351070	.92455621	.91572995	.90702948	.89845242
3	.90194271	.88899636	.87629660	.86383760	.85161366
4	.87144223	.85480419	.83856134	.82270247	.80721674
5	.84197317	.82192711	.80245105	.78352617	.76513435
6	.81350064	.79031453	.76789574	.74621540	.72524583
7	.78599096	.75991781	.73482846	.71068133	.68743681
8	.75941156	.73069021	.70318513	.67683936	.65159887
9	.73373097	.70258674	.67290443	.64460892	.61762926
10	.70891881	.67556417	.64392768	.61391325	.58543058
11	.68494571	.64958093	.61619874	.58467929	.55491050
12	.66178330	.62459705	.58966386	.55683742	.52598152
13	.63940415	.60057409	.56427164	.53032135	.49856068
14	.61778179	.57747508	.53997286	.50506795	.47256937
15	.59689062	.55526450	.51672044	.48101710	.44793305
16	.57670591	.53390818	.49446932	.45811152	.42458109
17	.55720378	.51337325	.47317639	.43629669	.40244653
18	.53836114	.49362812	.45280037	.41552065	.38146590
19	.52015569	.47464242	.43330179	.39573396	.36157906
20	.50256588	.45638695	.41464286	.37688948	.34272896
21	.48557090	.43883360	.39678743	.35894236	.32486158
22	.46915063	.42195539	.37970089	.34184987	.30792567
23	.45328563	.40572633	.36335013	.32557131	.29187267
24	.43795713	.39012147	.34770347	.31006791	.27665656
25	.42314699	.37511680	.33273060	.29530277	.26223370
26	.40883767	.36068923	.31840248	.28124073	.24856275
27	.39501224	.34681657	.30469137	.26784832	.23560450
28	.38165434	.33347747	.29157069	.25509364	.22332181
29	.36874815	.32065141	.27901502	.24294632	.21167944
30	.35627841	.30831867	.26700002	.23137745	.20064402
31	.34423035	.29646026	.25550241	.22035947	.19018390
32	.33258971	.28505794	.24449991	.20986617	.18026910
33	.32134271	.27409417	.23397121	.19987254	.17087119
34	.31047605	.26355209	.22389589	.19035480	.16196321
35	.29997686	.25341547	.21425444	.18129029	.15351963
36	.28983272	.24366872	.20502817	.17265741	.14551624
37	.28003161	.23429685	.19619921	.16443563	.13793008
38	.27056194	.22528543	.18775044	.15660536	.13073941
39	.26141250	.21662061	.17966549	.14914797	.12392362
40	.25257247	.20828904	.17192870	.14204568	.11746314
41	.24403137	.20027793	.16452507	.13528160	.11133947
42	.23577910	.19257493	.15744026	.12883962	.10553504
43	.22780590	.18516820	.15066054	.12270440	.10003322
44	.22010231	.17804635	.14417276	.11686133	.09481822
45	.21265924	.17119841	.13796437	.11129651	.08987509
46	.20546787	.16461386	.13202332	.10599668	.08518965
47	.19851968	.15828256	.12633810	.10094921	.08074849
48	.19180645	.15219476	.12089771	.09614211	.07653885
49	.18532024	.14634112	.11569158	.09156391	.07254867
50	.17905337	.14071262	.11070965	.08720373	.06876652

PRESENT VALUE $1/(1 + i)^n$ (Continued)

Years	Rate i				
n	.06(6 %)	.065(6½ %)	.07(7 %)	.075(7½ %)	.08(8 %)
1	.94339623	.93896714	.93457944	.93023256	.92592593
2	.88999644	.88165928	.87343873	.86533261	.85733882
3	.83961928	.82784909	.81629788	.80496057	.79383224
4	.79209366	.77732309	.76289521	.74880053	.73502985
5	.74725817	.72988084	.71298618	.69655863	.68058320
6	.70496054	.68533412	.66634222	.64796152	.63016963
7	.66505711	.64350621	.62274974	.60275490	.58349040
8	.62741237	.60423119	.58200910	.56070223	.54026888
9	.59189846	.56735323	.54393374	.52158347	.50024897
10	.55839478	.53272604	.50834929	.48519393	.46319349
11	.52678753	.50021224	.47509280	.45134319	.42888286
12	.49696936	.46968285	.44401196	.41985413	.39711376
13	.46883902	.44101676	.41496445	.39056198	.36769792
14	.44230096	.41410025	.38781724	.36331347	.34046104
15	.41726506	.38882652	.36244602	.33796602	.31524170
16	.39364628	.36509533	.33873460	.31438699	.29189047
17	.37136442	.34281251	.31657439	.29245302	.27026895
18	.35034379	.32188969	.29586392	.27204932	.25024903
19	.33051301	.30224384	.27650833	.25306913	.23171206
20	.31180473	.28379703	.25841900	.23541315	.21454821
21	.29415540	.26647608	.24151309	.21898897	.19865575
22	.27750510	.25021228	.22571317	.20371067	.18394051
23	.26179726	.23494111	.21094688	.18949830	.17031528
24	.24697855	.22060198	.19714662	.17627749	.15769934
25	.23299863	.20713801	.18424918	.16397906	.14601790
26	.21981003	.19449579	.17219549	.15253866	.13520176
27	.20736795	.18262515	.16093037	.14189643	.12518682
28	.19563014	.17147902	.15040221	.13199668	.11591372
29	.18455674	.16101316	.14056282	.12278761	.10732752
30	.17411013	.15118607	.13136712	.11422103	.09937733
31	.16425484	.14195875	.12277301	.10625212	.09201605
32	.15495740	.13329460	.11474113	.09883918	.08520005
33	.14618622	.12515925	.10723470	.09194343	.07888893
34	.13791153	.11752042	.10021934	.08552877	.07304531
35	.13010522	.11034781	.09366294	.07956164	.06763454
36	.12274077	.10361297	.08753546	.07401083	.06262458
37	.11579318	.09728917	.08180884	.06884729	.05798572
38	.10923885	.09135134	.07645686	.06404399	.05369048
39	.10305552	.08577590	.07145501	.05957580	.04971341
40	.09722219	.08054075	.06678038	.05541935	.04603093
41	.09171905	.07562512	.06241157	.05155288	.04262123
42	.08652740	.07100950	.05832857	.04795617	.03946411
43	.08162962	.06667559	.05451268	.04461039	.03654084
44	.07700908	.06260619	.05094643	.04149804	.03383411
45	.07265007	.05878515	.04761349	.03860283	.03132788
46	.06853781	.05519733	.04449859	.03590961	.02900730
47	.06465831	.05182848	.04158747	.03340428	.02685861
48	.06099840	.04866524	.03886679	.03107375	.02486908
49	.05754566	.04569506	.03632410	.02890582	.02302693
50	.05428836	.04290616	.03394776	.02688913	.02132123

AMOUNT OF ANNUITY $[(1 + i)^n - 1]/i$

The following table gives the amount of an annuity of unit value per period after a term of n periods at rate of interest of i per period; usually indicated as ($s_{\overline{n|}}$ at i).

Years n	Rate i .0025($\frac{1}{4}$%)	.004167($\frac{5}{12}$%)	.005($\frac{1}{2}$%)	.005833($\frac{7}{12}$%)	.0075($\frac{3}{4}$%)
1	1.00000000	1.00000000	1.00000000	1.00000000	1.00000000
2	2.00250000	2.00416667	2.00500000	2.00583333	2.00750000
3	3.00750625	3.01251736	3.01502500	3.01753403	3.02255625
4	4.01502502	4.02506952	4.03010013	4.03513631	4.04522542
5	5.02506258	5.04184064	5.05025063	5.05867460	5.07556461
6	6.03762523	6.06284831	6.07550188	6.08818354	6.11363135
7	7.05271930	7.08811018	7.10587939	7.12369794	7.15948358
8	8.07035110	8.11764397	8.14140879	8.16525285	8.21317971
9	9.09052697	9.15146749	9.18211583	9.21288349	9.27477856
10	10.1132533	10.1895986	10.2280264	10.2666253	10.3443394
11	11.1385364	11.2320553	11.2791665	11.3265140	11.4219219
12	12.1663828	12.2788555	12.3355624	12.3925853	12.5075864
13	13.1967987	13.3300174	13.3972402	13.4648754	13.6013933
14	14.2297907	14.3855591	14.4642264	14.5434205	14.7034037
15	15.2653652	15.4454990	15.5365475	15.6282571	15.8136792
16	16.3035286	16.5098552	16.6142303	16.7194219	16.9322818
17	17.3442874	17.5786463	17.6973014	17.8169519	18.0592739
18	18.3876481	18.6518906	18.7857879	18.9208841	19.1947185
19	19.4336173	19.7296068	19.8797169	20.0312559	20.3386789
20	20.4822013	20.8118135	20.9791154	21.1481049	21.4912190
21	21.5334068	21.8985294	22.0840110	22.2714689	22.6524031
22	22.5872403	22.9897733	23.1944311	23.4013858	23.8222961
23	23.6437084	24.0855640	24.3104032	24.5378939	25.0009634
24	24.7028177	25.1859205	25.4319552	25.6810316	26.1884706
25	25.7645747	26.2908619	26.5591150	26.8308376	27.3848841
26	26.8289862	27.4004071	27.6919106	27.9873508	28.5902707
27	27.8960587	28.5145755	28.8303701	29.1506104	29.8046978
28	28.9657988	29.6333862	29.9745220	30.3206556	31.0282330
29	30.0382133	30.7568587	31.1243946	31.4975261	32.2609448
30	31.1133088	31.8850122	32.2800166	32.6812616	33.5029018
31	32.1910921	33.0178665	33.4414167	33.8719023	34.7541736
32	33.2715698	34.1554409	34.6086237	35.0694884	36.0148299
33	34.3547488	35.2977552	35.7816669	36.2740604	37.2849411
34	35.4406356	36.4448292	36.9605752	37.4856591	38.5645782
35	36.5292372	37.5966827	38.1453781	38.7043255	39.8538125
36	37.6205603	38.7533355	39.3361050	39.9301007	41.1527161
37	38.7146117	39.9148078	40.5327855	41.1630263	42.4613615
38	39.8113982	41.0811195	41.7354494	42.4031440	43.7798217
39	40.9109267	42.2522908	42.9441267	43.6504956	45.1081704
40	42.0132041	43.4283420	44.1588473	44.9051235	46.4464816
41	43.1182371	44.6092934	45.3796415	46.1670701	47.7948303
42	44.2260327	45.7951655	46.6065397	47.4363780	49.1532915
43	45.3365977	46.9859787	47.8395724	48.7130902	50.5219412
44	46.4499392	48.1817536	49.0787703	49.9972499	51.9008557
45	47.5660641	49.3825109	50.3241642	51.2889005	53.2901121
46	48.6849792	50.5882713	51.5757850	52.5880858	54.6897880
47	49.8066917	51.7990558	52.8336639	53.8948496	56.0999614
48	50.9312084	53.0148852	54.0978322	55.2092362	57.5207111
49	52.0585364	54.2357806	55.3683214	56.5312901	58.9521164
50	53.1886828	55.4617630	56.6451630	57.8610559	60.3942573

INTEREST TABLES (Continued)

AMOUNT OF ANNUITY $[(1+i)^n - 1]/i$ (Continued)

Years	Rate i				
n	.0025($\frac{1}{4}$ %)	.004167($\frac{5}{12}$ %)	.005($\frac{1}{2}$ %)	.005833($\frac{7}{12}$ %)	.0075($\frac{3}{4}$ %)
50	53.1886828	55.4617630	56.6451630	57.8610559	60.3942573
51	54.3216545	56.6928537	57.9283888	59.1985788	61.8472142
52	55.4574586	57.9290739	59.2180307	60.5439038	63.3110684
53	56.5961023	59.1704450	60.5141209	61.8970766	64.7859014
54	57.7375925	60.4169885	61.8166915	63.2581429	66.2717956
55	58.8819365	61.6687260	63.1257750	64.6271487	67.7688341
56	60.0291413	62.9256790	64.4414038	66.0041404	69.2771003
57	61.1792142	64.1878694	65.7636109	67.3891646	70.7966786
58	62.3321622	65.4553188	67.0924289	68.7822680	72.3276537
59	63.4879926	66.7280493	68.4278911	70.1834979	73.8701111
60	64.6467126	68.0060828	69.7700305	71.5929016	75.4241369
61	65.8083294	69.2894415	71.1188807	73.0105269	76.9898180
62	66.9728502	70.5781475	72.4744751	74.4364216	78.5672416
63	68.1402824	71.8722231	73.8368474	75.8706341	80.1564959
64	69.3106331	73.1716907	75.2060317	77.3132128	81.7576696
65	70.4839096	74.4765728	76.5820618	78.7642065	83.3708521
66	71.6601194	75.7868918	77.9649721	80.2236644	84.9961335
67	72.8392697	77.1026706	79.3547970	81.6916358	86.6336045
68	74.0213679	78.4239317	80.7515710	83.1681703	88.2833566
69	75.2064213	79.7506981	82.1553288	84.6533180	89.9454817
70	76.3944374	81.0829926	83.5661055	86.1471290	91.6200729
71	77.5854235	82.4208384	84.9839360	87.6496539	93.3072234
72	78.7793870	83.7642586	86.4088557	89.1609436	95.0070276
73	79.9763355	85.1132763	87.8409000	90.6810491	96.7195803
74	81.1762763	86.4679150	89.2801045	92.2100219	98.4449771
75	82.3792170	87.8281980	90.7265050	93.7479137	100.183314
76	83.5851651	89.1941488	92.1801375	95.2947765	101.934689
77	84.7941280	90.5657911	93.6410382	96.8506627	103.699199
78	86.0061133	91.9431485	95.1092434	98.4156249	105.476943
79	87.2211286	93.3262450	96.5847896	99.9897160	107.268021
80	88.4391814	94.7151044	98.0677136	101.572989	109.072531
81	89.6602793	96.1097506	99.5580521	103.165498	110.890575
82	90.8844300	97.5102079	101.055842	104.767297	112.722254
83	92.1116411	98.9165004	102.561122	106.378440	114.567671
84	93.3419202	100.328653	104.073927	107.998981	116.426928
85	94.5752750	101.746689	105.594297	109.628975	118.300130
86	95.8117132	103.170633	107.122268	111.268477	120.187381
87	97.0512425	104.600511	108.657880	112.917543	122.088787
88	98.2938706	106.036346	110.201169	114.576229	124.004453
89	99.5396053	107.478164	111.752175	116.244590	125.934486
90	100.788454	108.925990	113.310936	117.922684	127.878995
91	102.040425	110.379848	114.877490	119.610566	129.838087
92	103.295526	111.839764	116.451878	121.308294	131.811873
93	104.553765	113.305763	118.034137	123.015926	133.800462
94	105.815150	114.777871	119.624308	124.733519	135.803965
95	107.079688	116.256112	121.222430	126.461131	137.822495
96	108.347387	117.740512	122.828542	128.198821	139.856164
97	109.618255	119.231098	124.442684	129.946647	141.905085
98	110.892301	120.727894	126.064898	131.704670	143.969373
99	112.169532	122.230927	127.695222	133.472947	146.049143
100	113.449955	123.740222	129.333698	135.251539	148.144512

INTEREST TABLES (Continued)

AMOUNT OF ANNUITY $[(1 + i)^n - 1]/i$ (Continued)

Years	Rate i				
n	.01(1%)	.01125(1⅛%)	.0125(1¼%)	.015(1½%)	.0175(1¾%)
1	1.00000000	1.00000000	1.00000000	1.00000000	1.00000000
2	2.01000000	2.01125000	2.01250000	2.01500000	2.01750000
3	3.03010000	3.03387656	3.03765625	3.04522500	3.05280625
4	4.06040100	4.06800767	4.07562695	4.09090338	4.10623036
5	5.10100501	5.11377276	5.12657229	5.15226693	5.17808939
6	6.15201506	6.17130270	6.19065444	6.22955093	6.26870596
7	7.21353521	7.24072986	7.26803762	7.32299419	7.37840831
8	8.28567056	8.32218807	8.35888809	8.43283911	8.50753045
9	9.36852727	9.41581269	9.46337420	9.55933169	9.65641224
10	10.4622125	10.5217406	10.5816664	10.7027217	10.8253995
11	11.5668347	11.6401102	11.7139372	11.8632625	12.0148439
12	12.6825030	12.7710614	12.8603614	13.0412114	13.2251037
13	13.8093280	13.9147358	14.0211159	14.2368296	14.4565430
14	14.9474213	15.0712766	15.1963799	15.4503820	15.7095325
15	16.0968955	16.2408285	16.3863346	16.6821378	16.9844493
16	17.2578645	17.4235378	17.5911638	17.9323698	18.2816772
17	18.4304431	18.6195526	18.8110534	19.2013554	19.6016066
18	19.6147476	19.8290226	20.0461915	20.4893757	20.9446347
19	20.8108950	21.0520991	21.2967689	21.7967164	22.3111658
20	22.0190040	22.2889352	22.5629785	23.1236671	23.7016112
21	23.2391940	23.5396857	23.8450158	24.4705221	25.1163894
22	24.4715860	24.8045072	25.1430785	25.8375799	26.5559262
23	25.7163018	26.0835579	26.4573669	27.2251436	28.0206549
24	26.9734649	27.3769979	27.7880840	28.6335208	29.5110164
25	28.2431995	28.6849891	29.1354351	30.0630236	31.0274592
26	29.5256315	30.0076953	30.4996280	31.5139690	32.5704397
27	30.8208878	31.3452818	31.8808734	32.9866785	34.1404224
28	32.1290967	32.6979162	33.2793843	34.4814787	35.7378798
29	33.4503877	34.0657678	34.6953766	35.9987009	37.3632927
30	34.7848915	35.4490077	36.1290688	37.5386814	39.0171503
31	36.1327404	36.8478090	37.5806822	39.1017616	40.6999504
32	37.4940679	38.2623469	39.0504407	40.6882880	42.4121996
33	38.8690085	39.6927983	40.5385712	42.2986123	44.1544130
34	40.2576986	41.1393423	42.0453033	43.9330915	45.9271153
35	41.6602756	42.6021599	43.5708696	45.5920879	47.7308398
36	43.0768784	44.0814342	45.1155055	47.2759692	49.5661295
37	44.5076471	45.5773503	46.6794493	48.9851087	51.4335368
38	45.9527236	47.0900955	48.2629424	50.7198854	53.3336236
39	47.4122508	48.6198591	49.8662292	52.4806837	55.2669621
40	48.8863734	50.1668325	51.4895571	54.2678939	57.2341339
41	50.3752371	51.7312093	53.1331765	56.0819123	59.2357312
42	51.8789895	53.3131854	54.7973412	57.9231410	61.2723565
43	53.3977794	54.9129588	56.4823080	59.7919881	63.3446228
44	54.9317572	56.5307296	58.1883369	61.6888679	65.4531537
45	56.4810747	58.1667003	59.9156911	63.6142010	67.5985839
46	58.0458855	59.8210757	61.6646372	65.5684140	69.7815591
47	59.6263443	61.4940628	63.4354452	67.5519402	72.0027364
48	61.2226078	63.1858710	65.2283882	69.5652193	74.2627843
49	62.8348338	64.8967120	67.0437431	71.6086976	76.5623830
50	64.4631822	66.6268000	68.8817899	73.6828280	78.9022247

AMOUNT OF ANNUITY $[(1 + i)^n - 1]/i$ (Continued)

Years	Rate i				
n	.01(1 %)	.01125($1\frac{1}{8}$ %)	.0125($1\frac{1}{4}$ %)	.015($1\frac{1}{2}$ %)	.0175($1\frac{3}{4}$ %)
50	64.4631822	66.6268000	68.8817899	73.6828280	78.9022247
51	66.1078140	68.3763515	70.7428123	75.7880705	81.2830136
52	67.7688921	70.1455855	72.6270974	77.9248915	83.7054663
53	69.4465811	71.9347233	74.5349361	80.0937649	86.1703120
54	71.1410469	73.7439890	76.4666228	82.2951714	88.6782925
55	72.8524573	75.5736088	78.4224556	84.5295989	91.2301626
56	74.5809819	77.4238119	80.4027363	86.7975429	93.8266904
57	76.3267917	79.2948298	82.4077705	89.0995061	96.4686575
58	78.0900597	81.1868966	84.4378676	91.4359987	99.1568590
59	79.8709603	83.1002492	86.4933410	93.8075386	101.892104
60	81.6696699	85.0351270	88.5745078	96.2146517	104.675216
61	83.4863666	86.9917722	90.6816891	98.6578715	107.507032
62	85.3212302	88.9704297	92.8152102	101.137740	110.388405
63	87.1744425	90.9713470	94.9754003	103.654806	113.320202
64	89.0461869	92.9947746	97.1625928	106.209628	116.303306
65	90.9366488	95.0409659	99.3771253	108.802772	119.338614
66	92.8460153	97.1101767	101.619339	111.434814	122.427039
67	94.7744755	99.2026662	103.889581	114.106336	125.569513
68	96.7222202	101.318696	106.188201	116.817931	128.766979
69	98.6894424	103.458532	108.515553	119.570200	132.020401
70	100.676337	105.622440	110.871998	122.363753	135.330758
71	102.683100	107.810692	113.257898	125.199209	138.699047
72	104.709931	110.023563	115.673621	128.077197	142.126280
73	106.757031	112.261328	118.119542	130.998355	145.613490
74	108.824601	114.524268	120.596036	133.963331	149.161726
75	110.912847	116.812666	123.103486	136.972781	152.772056
76	113.021975	119.126808	125.642280	140.027372	156.445567
77	115.152195	121.466985	128.212809	143.127783	160.183364
78	117.303717	123.833488	130.815469	146.274700	163.986573
79	119.476754	126.226615	133.450662	149.468820	167.856338
80	121.671522	128.646665	136.118795	152.710852	171.793824
81	123.888237	131.093940	138.820280	156.001515	175.800216
82	126.127119	133.568746	141.555534	159.341538	179.876720
83	128.388390	136.071395	144.324978	162.731661	184.024563
84	130.672274	138.602198	147.129040	166.172636	188.244992
85	132.978997	141.161473	149.968153	169.665226	192.539280
86	135.308787	143.749539	152.842755	173.210204	196.908717
87	137.661875	146.366722	155.753289	176.808357	201.354620
88	140.038494	149.013347	158.700206	180.460482	205.878326
89	142.438879	151.689747	161.683958	184.167390	210.481196
90	144.863267	154.396257	164.705008	187.929900	215.164617
91	147.311900	157.133215	167.763820	191.748849	219.929998
92	149.785019	159.900964	170.860868	195.625082	224.778773
93	152.282869	162.699849	173.996629	199.559458	229.712401
94	154.805698	165.530223	177.171587	203.552850	234.732369
95	157.353755	168.392438	180.386232	207.606142	239.840185
96	159.927293	171.286853	183.641059	211.720235	245.037388
97	162.526565	174.213830	186.936573	215.896038	250.325542
98	165.151831	177.173735	190.273280	220.134479	255.706239
99	167.803349	180.166940	193.651696	224.436496	261.181099
100	170.481383	183.193818	197.072342	228.803043	266.751768

AMOUNT OF ANNUITY $[(1+i)^n - 1]/i$ (Continued)

Years	Rate i				
n	.02(2 %)	.0225($2\frac{1}{4}$ %)	.025($2\frac{1}{2}$ %)	.0275($2\frac{3}{4}$ %)	.03(3 %)
1	1.00000000	1.00000000	1.00000000	1.00000000	1.00000000
2	2.02000000	2.02250000	2.02500000	2.02750000	2.03000000
3	3.06040000	3.06800625	3.07562500	3.08325625	3.09090000
4	4.12160800	4.13703639	4.15251563	4.16804580	4.18362700
5	5.20404016	5.23011971	5.25632852	5.28266706	5.30913581
6	6.30812096	6.34779740	6.38773673	6.42794040	6.46840988
7	7.43428338	7.49062284	7.54743015	7.60470876	7.66246218
8	8.58296905	8.65916186	8.73611590	8.81383825	8.89233605
9	9.75462843	9.85399300	9.95451880	10.0562188	10.1591061
10	10.9497210	11.0757078	11.2033818	11.3327648	11.4638793
11	12.1687154	12.3249113	12.4834663	12.6444159	12.8077957
12	13.4120897	13.6022218	13.7955530	13.9921373	14.1920296
13	14.6803315	14.9082718	15.1404418	15.3769211	15.6177904
14	15.9739382	16.2437079	16.5189528	16.7997864	17.0863242
15	17.2934169	17.6091913	17.9319267	18.2617805	18.5989139
16	18.6392853	19.0053981	19.3802248	19.7639795	20.1568813
17	20.0120710	20.4330196	20.8647304	21.3074889	21.7615877
18	21.4123124	21.8927625	22.3863487	22.8934449	23.4144354
19	22.8405586	23.3853497	23.9460074	24.5230146	25.1168684
20	24.2973698	24.9115200	25.5446576	26.1973975	26.8703745
21	25.7833172	26.4720292	27.1832741	27.9178259	28.6764857
22	27.2989835	28.0676499	28.8628559	29.6855661	30.5367803
23	28.8449632	29.6991720	30.5844273	31.5019192	32.4528837
24	30.4218625	31.3674034	32.3490380	33.3682220	34.4264702
25	32.0302997	33.0731700	34.1577639	35.2858481	36.4592643
26	33.6709057	34.8173163	36.0117080	37.2562089	38.5530423
27	35.3443238	36.6007059	37.9120007	39.2807547	40.7096335
28	37.0512103	38.4242218	39.8598008	41.3609754	42.9309225
29	38.7922345	40.2887668	41.8562958	43.4984022	45.2188502
30	40.5680792	42.1952640	43.9027032	45.6946083	47.5754157
31	42.3794408	44.1446575	46.0002707	47.9512100	50.0026782
32	44.2270296	46.1379123	48.1502775	50.2698683	52.5027585
33	46.1115702	48.1760153	50.3540344	52.6522897	55.0778413
34	48.0338016	50.2599756	52.6128853	55.1002277	57.7301765
35	49.9944776	52.3908251	54.9282074	57.6154839	60.4620818
36	51.9943672	54.5696186	57.3014126	60.1999097	63.2759443
37	54.0342545	56.7974351	59.7339479	62.8554072	66.1742226
38	56.1149396	59.0753774	62.2272966	65.5839309	69.1594493
39	58.2372384	61.4045733	64.7829791	68.3874890	72.2342328
40	60.4019832	63.7861762	67.4025535	71.2681450	75.4012597
41	62.6100228	66.2213652	70.0876174	74.2280190	78.6632975
42	64.8622233	68.7113459	72.8398078	77.2692895	82.0231965
43	67.1594678	71.2573512	75.6608030	80.3941950	85.4838923
44	69.5026571	73.8606416	78.5523231	83.6050353	89.0484091
45	71.8927103	76.5225060	81.5161312	86.9041738	92.7198614
46	74.3305645	79.2442624	84.5540344	90.2940386	96.5014572
47	76.8171758	82.0272583	87.6678853	93.7771246	100.396501
48	79.3535193	84.8728716	90.8595824	97.3559956	104.408396
49	81.9405897	87.7825113	94.1310720	101.033285	108.540648
50	84.5794015	90.7576178	97.4843488	104.811701	112.796867

AMOUNT OF ANNUITY $[(1 + i)^n - 1]/i$ (Continued)

Years	Rate i				
n	.02(2 %)	.0225(2¼ %)	.025(2½ %)	.0275(2¾ %)	.03(3 %)
50	84.5794015	90.7576178	97.4843488	104.811701	112.796867
51	87.2709895	93.7996642	100.921458	108.694023	117.180773
52	90.0164093	96.9101566	104.444494	112.683108	121.696197
53	92.8167375	100.090635	108.055606	116.781894	126.347082
54	95.6730722	103.342674	111.756996	120.993396	131.137495
55	98.5865337	106.667885	115.550921	125.320714	136.071620
56	101.558264	110.067912	119.439694	129.767034	141.153768
57	104.589430	113.544440	123.425687	134.335627	146.388381
58	107.681218	117.099190	127.511329	139.029857	151.780033
59	110.834843	120.733922	131.699112	143.853178	157.333434
60	114.051539	124.450435	135.991590	148.809140	163.053437
61	117.332570	128.250570	140.391380	153.901392	168.945040
62	120.679222	132.136208	144.901164	159.133680	175.013391
63	124.092806	136.109272	149.523693	164.509856	181.263793
64	127.574662	140.171731	154.261786	170.033877	187.701707
65	131.126155	144.325595	159.118330	175.709809	194.332758
66	134.748679	148.572921	164.096289	181.541829	201.162741
67	138.443652	152.915811	169.198696	187.534229	208.197623
68	142.212525	157.356417	174.428663	193.691420	215.443551
69	146.056776	161.896937	179.789380	200.017934	222.906858
70	149.977911	166.539618	185.284114	206.518427	230.594064
71	153.977469	171.286759	190.916217	213.197684	238.511886
72	158.057019	176.140711	196.689122	220.060621	246.667242
73	162.218159	181.103877	202.606351	227.112288	255.067259
74	166.462522	186.178714	208.671509	234.357876	263.719277
75	170.791773	191.367735	214.888297	241.802717	272.630856
76	175.207608	196.673509	221.260504	249.452292	281.809781
77	179.711760	202.098663	227.792017	257.312230	291.264075
78	184.305996	207.645883	234.486818	265.388316	301.001997
79	188.992115	213.317916	241.348988	273.686495	311.032057
80	193.771958	219.117569	248.382713	282.212873	321.363019
81	198.647397	225.047714	255.592280	290.973727	332.003909
82	203.620345	231.111288	262.982087	299.975505	342.964026
83	208.692752	237.311292	270.556640	309.224831	354.252947
84	213.866607	243.650796	278.320556	318.728514	365.880536
85	219.143939	250.132939	286.278570	328.493548	377.856952
86	224.526818	256.760930	294.435534	338.527121	390.192660
87	230.017354	263.538051	302.796422	348.836617	402.898440
88	235.617701	270.467657	311.366333	359.429624	415.985393
89	241.330055	277.553179	320.150491	370.313938	429.464955
90	247.156656	284.798126	329.154253	381.497572	443.348904
91	253.099789	292.206083	338.383110	392.988755	457.649371
92	259.161785	299.780720	347.842687	404.795946	472.378852
93	265.345021	307.525786	357.538755	416.927834	487.550217
94	271.651921	315.445117	367.477223	429.393350	503.176724
95	278.084960	323.542632	377.664154	442.201667	519.272026
96	284.646659	331.822341	388.105758	455.362213	535.850186
97	291.339592	340.288344	398.808402	468.884673	552.925692
98	298.166384	348.944831	409.778612	482.779002	570.513463
99	305.129712	357.796090	421.023077	497.055424	588.628867
100	312.232306	366.846502	432.548654	511.724449	607.287733

AMOUNT OF ANNUITY $[(1+i)^n - 1]/i$ (Continued)

Years n	.035(3½%)	.04(4%)	.045(4½%)	.05(5%)	.055(5½%)
1	1.00000000	1.00000000	1.00000000	1.00000000	1.00000000
2	2.03500000	2.04000000	2.04500000	2.05000000	2.05500000
3	3.10622500	3.12160000	3.13702500	3.15250000	3.16802500
4	4.21494288	4.24646400	4.27819113	4.31012500	4.34226638
5	5.36246588	5.41632256	5.47070973	5.52563125	5.58109103
6	6.55015218	6.63297546	6.71689166	6.80191281	6.88805103
7	7.77940751	7.89829448	8.01915179	8.14200845	8.26689384
8	9.05168677	9.21422626	9.38001362	9.54910888	9.72157300
9	10.3684958	10.5827953	10.8021142	11.0265643	11.2562595
10	11.7313932	12.0061071	12.2882094	12.5778925	12.8753538
11	13.1419919	13.4863514	13.8411788	14.2067872	14.5834982
12	14.6019616	15.0258055	15.4640318	15.9171265	16.3855907
13	16.1130303	16.6268377	17.1599133	17.7129828	18.2867981
14	17.6769864	18.2919112	18.9321094	19.5986320	20.2925720
15	19.2956809	20.0235876	20.7840543	21.5785636	22.4086635
16	20.9710297	21.8245311	22.7193367	23.6574918	24.6411400
17	22.7050157	23.6975124	24.7417069	25.8403664	26.9964027
18	24.4996913	25.6454129	26.8550837	28.1323847	29.4812048
19	26.3571805	27.6712294	29.0635625	30.5390039	32.1026711
20	28.2796818	29.7780786	31.3714228	33.0659541	34.8683180
21	30.2694707	31.9692017	33.7831368	35.7192518	37.7860755
22	32.3289022	34.2479698	36.3033780	38.5052144	40.8643097
23	34.4604137	36.6178886	38.9370300	41.4304751	44.1118467
24	36.6665282	39.0826041	41.6891963	44.5019989	47.5379983
25	38.9498567	41.6459083	44.5652101	47.7270988	51.1525882
26	41.3131017	44.3117446	47.5706446	51.1134538	54.9659805
27	43.7590602	47.0842144	50.7113236	54.6691264	58.9891094
28	46.2906273	49.9675830	53.9933332	58.4025828	63.2335105
29	48.9107993	52.9662863	57.4230332	62.3227119	67.7113535
30	51.6226773	56.0849378	61.0070697	66.4388475	72.4354780
31	54.4294710	59.3283353	64.7523878	70.7607899	77.4194293
32	57.3345025	62.7014687	68.6662452	75.2988294	82.6774979
33	60.3412101	66.2095274	72.7562263	80.0637708	88.2247603
34	63.4531524	69.8579085	77.0302565	85.0669594	94.0771221
35	66.6740127	73.6522249	81.4966180	90.3203074	100.251364
36	70.0076032	77.5983138	86.1639658	95.8363227	106.765189
37	73.4578693	81.7022464	91.0413443	101.628139	113.637274
38	77.0288947	85.9703363	96.1382048	107.709546	120.887324
39	80.7249060	90.4091497	101.464424	114.095023	128.536127
40	84.5502777	95.0255157	107.030323	120.799774	136.605614
41	88.5095375	99.8265363	112.846688	127.839763	145.118923
42	92.6073713	104.819598	118.924789	135.231751	154.100464
43	96.8486293	110.012382	125.276404	142.993339	163.575989
44	101.238331	115.412877	131.913842	151.143006	173.572669
45	105.781673	121.029392	138.849965	159.700156	184.119165
46	110.484031	126.870568	146.098214	168.685164	195.245719
47	115.350973	132.945390	153.672633	178.119422	206.984234
48	120.388257	139.263206	161.587902	188.025393	219.368367
49	125.601846	145.833734	169.859357	198.426663	232.433627
50	130.997910	152.667084	178.503028	209.347996	246.217476

AMOUNT OF ANNUITY $[(1 + i)^n - 1]/i$ (Continued)

Years	Rate i				
n	.06(6 %)	.065(6½ %)	.07(7 %)	.075(7½ %)	.08(8 %)
1	1.00000000	1.00000000	1.00000000	1.00000000	1.00000000
2	2.06000000	2.06500000	2.07000000	2.07500000	2.08000000
3	3.18360000	3.19922500	3.21490000	3.23062500	3.24640000
4	4.37461600	4.40717463	4.43994300	4.47292188	4.50611200
5	5.63709296	5.69364098	5.75073901	5.80839102	5.86660096
6	6.97531854	7.06372764	7.15329074	7.24402034	7.33592904
7	8.39383765	8.52286994	8.65402109	8.78732187	8.92280336
8	9.89746791	10.0768565	10.2598026	10.4463710	10.6366276
9	11.4913160	11.7318522	11.9779887	12.2298488	12.4875578
10	13.1807949	13.4944225	13.8164480	14.1470875	14.4865625
11	14.9716426	15.3715600	15.7835993	16.2081191	16.6454875
12	16.8699412	17.3707114	17.8884513	18.4237280	18.9771265
13	18.8821377	19.4998076	20.1406429	20.8055076	21.4952966
14	21.0150659	21.7672951	22.5504879	23.3659207	24.2149203
15	23.2759699	24.1821693	25.1290220	26.1183647	27.1521139
16	25.6725281	26.7540103	27.8880536	29.0772421	30.3242830
17	28.2128798	29.4930210	30.8402173	32.2580352	33.7502257
18	30.9056525	32.4100674	33.9990325	35.6773879	37.4502437
19	33.7599917	35.5167218	37.3789648	39.3531919	41.4462632
20	36.7855912	38.8253087	40.9954923	43.3046813	45.7619643
21	39.9927267	42.3489537	44.8651768	47.5525324	50.4229214
22	43.3922903	46.1016357	49.0057392	52.1189724	55.4567552
23	46.9958277	50.0982420	53.4361409	57.0278953	60.8932956
24	50.8155774	54.3546278	58.1766708	62.3049874	66.7647592
25	54.8645120	58.8876786	63.2490377	67.9778615	73.1059400
26	59.1563827	63.7153777	68.6764704	74.0762011	79.9544151
27	63.7057657	68.8568772	74.4838233	80.6319162	87.3507684
28	68.5281116	74.3325743	80.6976909	87.6793099	95.3388298
29	73.6397983	80.1641916	87.3465293	95.2552582	103.965936
30	79.0581862	86.3748640	94.4607863	103.399403	113.283211
31	84.8016774	92.9892302	102.073041	112.154358	123.345868
32	90.8897780	100.033530	110.218154	121.565935	134.213537
33	97.3431647	107.535710	118.933425	131.683380	145.950620
34	104.183755	115.525531	128.258765	142.559633	158.626670
35	111.434780	124.034690	138.236878	154.251606	172.316804
36	119.120867	133.096945	148.913460	166.820476	187.102148
37	127.268119	142.748247	160.337402	180.332012	203.070320
38	135.904206	153.026883	172.561020	194.856913	220.315945
39	145.058458	163.973630	185.640292	210.471181	238.941221
40	154.761966	175.631916	199.635112	227.256520	259.056519
41	165.047684	188.047990	214.609570	245.300759	280.781040
42	175.950545	201.271110	230.632240	264.698315	304.243523
43	187.507577	215.353732	247.776496	285.550689	329.583005
44	199.758032	230.351725	266.120851	307.966991	356.949646
45	212.743514	246.324587	285.749311	332.064515	386.505617
46	226.508125	263.335685	306.751763	357.969354	418.426067
47	241.098612	281.452504	329.224386	385.817055	452.900152
48	256.564529	300.746917	353.270093	415.753334	490.132164
49	272.958401	321.295467	378.999000	447.934835	530.342737
50	290.335905	343.179672	406.528929	482.529947	573.770156

PRESENT VALUE OF ANNUITY $[1 - (1 + i)^{-n}]/i$

The following table gives the present value of an annuity of unit value per period for a term of n periods at rate of interest i per period; usually indicated as $a_{\overline{n}|}$ at i.

Years	Rate i				
n	.0025($\frac{1}{4}$%)	.004167($\frac{5}{12}$%)	.005($\frac{1}{2}$%)	.005833($\frac{7}{12}$%)	.0075($\frac{3}{4}$%)
1	0.99750623	0.99585062	0.99502488	0.99420050	0.99255583
2	1.99252492	1.98756908	1.98509938	1.98263513	1.97772291
3	2.98506227	2.97517253	2.97024814	2.96533732	2.95555624
4	3.97512446	3.95867804	3.95049566	3.94234034	3.92611041
5	4.96271766	4.93810261	4.92586633	4.91367722	4.88943961
6	5.94784804	5.91346318	5.89638441	5.87938083	5.84559763
7	6.93052174	6.88477661	6.86207404	6.83948384	6.79463785
8	7.91074487	7.85205970	7.82295924	7.79401874	7.73661325
9	8.88852357	8.81532916	8.77906392	8.74301780	8.67157642
10	9.86386391	9.77460165	9.73041186	9.68651314	9.59957958
11	10.8367720	10.7298938	10.6770267	10.6245367	10.5206745
12	11.8072538	11.6812220	11.6189321	11.5571201	11.4349127
13	12.7753156	12.6286028	12.5561513	12.4842951	12.3423451
14	13.7409631	13.5720526	13.4887078	13.4060929	13.2430224
15	14.7042026	14.5115877	14.4166246	14.3225447	14.1369950
16	15.6650400	15.4472242	15.3399250	15.2336816	15.0243126
17	16.6234813	16.3789785	16.2586319	16.1395343	15.9050249
18	17.5795325	17.3068665	17.1727680	17.0401335	16.7791811
19	18.5331995	18.2309044	18.0823562	17.9355097	17.6468298
20	19.4844883	19.1511082	18.9874191	18.8256931	18.5080197
21	20.4334048	20.0674936	19.8879793	19.7107140	19.3627987
22	21.3799549	20.9800766	20.7840590	20.5906021	20.2112146
23	22.3241445	21.8888730	21.6756806	21.4653874	21.0533147
24	23.2659796	22.7938984	22.5628662	22.3350993	21.8891461
25	24.2054659	23.6951685	23.4456380	23.1997673	22.7187555
26	25.1426094	24.5926989	24.3240179	24.0594207	23.5421891
27	26.0774158	25.4865052	25.1980278	24.9140885	24.3594929
28	27.0098911	26.3766027	26.0676894	25.7637997	25.1707125
29	27.9400410	27.2630068	26.9330242	26.6085830	25.9758933
30	28.8678713	28.1457329	27.7940540	27.4484669	26.7750802
31	29.7933879	29.0247963	28.6508000	28.2834799	27.5683178
32	30.7165964	29.9002120	29.5032835	29.1136503	28.3556504
33	31.6375026	30.7719954	30.3515259	29.9390061	29.1371220
34	32.5561123	31.6401614	31.1955482	30.7595752	29.9127762
35	33.4724313	32.5047250	32.0353713	31.5753855	30.6826563
36	34.3864651	33.3657013	32.8710162	32.3864645	31.4468053
37	35.2982196	34.2231050	33.7025037	33.1928396	32.2052658
38	36.2077003	35.0769511	34.5298544	33.9945381	32.9580802
39	37.1149130	35.9272542	35.3530890	34.7915872	33.7052905
40	38.0198634	36.7740290	36.1722279	35.5840137	34.4469384
41	38.9225570	37.6172903	36.9872914	36.3718446	35.1830654
42	39.8229995	38.4570526	37.7982999	37.1551065	35.9137126
43	40.7211965	39.2933304	38.6052735	37.9338259	36.6389207
44	41.6171536	40.1261382	39.4082324	38.7080290	37.3587302
45	42.5108764	40.9554903	40.2071964	39.4777422	38.0731814
46	43.4023705	41.7814011	41.0021855	40.2429914	38.7823140
47	44.2916414	42.6038849	41.7932194	41.0038026	39.4861677
48	45.1786946	43.4229559	42.5803178	41.7602014	40.1847819
49	46.0635358	44.2386283	43.3635003	42.5122135	40.8781954
50	46.9461704	45.0509162	44.1427864	43.2598643	41.5664471

PRESENT VALUE OF ANNUITY $[1 - (1 + i)^{-n}]/i$ (Continued)

Years	Rate i				
n	.0025($\frac{1}{4}$%)	.004167($\frac{5}{12}$%)	.005($\frac{1}{2}$%)	.005833($\frac{7}{12}$%)	.0075($\frac{3}{4}$%)
50	46.9461704	45.0509162	44.1427864	43.2598643	41.5664471
51	47.8266039	45.8598335	44.9181954	44.0031791	42.2495753
52	48.7048418	46.6653944	45.6897466	44.7421830	42.9276181
53	49.5808895	47.4676127	46.4574593	45.4769011	43.6006135
54	50.4547527	48.2665022	47.2213526	46.2073582	44.2685990
55	51.3264366	49.0620769	47.9814454	46.9335789	44.9316119
56	52.1959467	49.8543505	48.7377566	47.6555880	45.5896893
57	53.0632885	50.6433366	49.4903050	48.3734098	46.2428678
58	53.9284673	51.4290489	50.2391095	49.0870686	46.8911839
59	54.7914886	52.2115009	50.9841886	49.7965885	47.5346738
60	55.6523577	52.9907063	51.7255608	50.5019935	48.1733735
61	56.5110800	53.7666785	52.4632445	51.2033075	48.8073186
62	57.3676608	54.5394309	53.1972582	51.9005543	49.4365445
63	58.2221056	55.3089768	53.9276201	52.5937574	50.0610864
64	59.0744195	56.0753296	54.6543484	53.2829402	50.6809791
65	59.9246080	56.8385025	55.3774611	53.9681262	51.2962571
66	60.7726763	57.5985087	56.0969762	54.6493384	51.9069550
67	61.6186297	58.3553614	56.8129117	55.3265999	52.5131067
68	62.4624736	59.1090736	57.5252852	55.9999336	53.1147461
69	63.3042130	59.8596583	58.2341147	56.6693623	53.7119068
70	64.1438534	60.6071286	58.9394176	57.3349087	54.3046221
71	64.9813999	61.3514974	59.6412115	57.9965952	54.8929252
72	65.8168577	62.0927775	60.3395139	58.6544443	55.4768488
73	66.6502322	62.8309817	61.0343422	59.3084781	56.0564256
74	67.4815283	63.5661229	61.7257137	59.9587190	56.6316879
75	68.3107515	64.2982136	62.4136454	60.6051887	57.2026679
76	69.1379067	65.0272667	63.0981547	61.2479092	57.7693975
77	69.9629992	65.7532946	63.7792584	61.8869023	58.3319081
78	70.7860341	66.4763100	64.4569735	62.5221895	58.8902314
79	71.6070166	67.1963253	65.1313169	63.1537924	59.4443984
80	72.4259517	67.9133530	65.8023054	63.7817323	59.9944401
81	73.2428446	68.6274055	66.4699556	64.4060304	60.5403872
82	74.0577003	69.3384951	67.1342842	65.0267080	61.0822702
83	74.8705240	70.0466341	67.7953076	65.6437859	61.6201193
84	75.6813207	70.7518348	68.4530424	66.2572851	62.1539646
85	76.4900955	71.4541094	69.1075049	66.8672262	62.6838358
86	77.2968533	72.1534699	69.7587114	67.4736301	63.2097626
87	78.1015993	72.8499285	70.4066780	68.0765171	63.7317743
88	78.9043385	73.5434973	71.0514209	68.6759076	64.2499000
89	79.7050758	74.2341882	71.6929561	69.2718220	64.7641688
90	80.5038163	74.9220131	72.3312996	69.8642803	65.2746092
91	81.3005649	75.6069840	72.9664672	70.4533027	65.7812498
92	82.0953265	76.2891127	73.5984749	71.0389091	66.2841189
93	82.8881063	76.9684110	74.2273382	71.6211192	66.7832446
94	83.6789090	77.6448906	74.8530728	72.1999528	67.2786547
95	84.4677397	78.3185633	75.4756943	72.7754295	67.7703768
96	85.2546031	78.9894406	76.0952183	73.3475687	68.2584386
97	86.0395044	79.6575342	76.7116600	73.9163897	68.7428671
98	86.8224483	80.3228557	77.3250348	74.4819119	69.2236894
99	87.6034397	80.9854164	77.9353580	75.0441544	69.7009324
100	88.3824835	81.6452280	78.5426448	75.6031361	70.1746227

PRESENT VALUE OF ANNUITY $[1 - (1 + i)^{-n}]/i$ (Continued)

Years	Rate i				
n	.01(1 %)	.01125(1⅛ %)	.0125(1¼ %)	.015(1½ %)	.0175(1¾ %)
1	0.99009901	0.98887515	0.98765432	0.98522167	0.98280098
2	1.97039506	1.96674923	1.96311538	1.95588342	1.94869875
3	2.94098521	2.93374460	2.92653371	2.91220042	2.89798403
4	3.90196555	3.88998230	3.87805798	3.85438465	3.83094254
5	4.85343124	4.83558200	4.81783504	4.78264497	4.74785508
6	5.79547647	5.77066205	5.74600992	5.69718717	5.64899762
7	6.72819453	6.69533948	6.66272585	6.59821396	6.53464139
8	7.65167775	7.60973002	7.56812429	7.48592508	7.40505297
9	8.56601758	8.51394810	8.46234498	8.36051732	8.26049432
10	9.47130453	9.40810690	9.34552591	9.22218455	9.10122291
11	10.3676282	10.2923183	10.2178034	10.0711178	9.92749181
12	11.2550775	11.1666930	11.0793120	10.9075052	10.7395497
13	12.1337401	12.0313404	11.9301847	11.7315322	11.5376410
14	13.0037030	12.8863688	12.7705527	12.5433815	12.3220059
15	13.8650525	13.7318851	13.6005459	13.3432330	13.0928805
16	14.7178738	14.5679951	14.4202923	14.1312640	13.8504968
17	15.5622513	15.3948036	15.2299183	14.9076493	14.5950828
18	16.3982686	16.2124139	16.0295489	15.6725609	15.3268627
19	17.2260085	17.0209285	16.8193076	16.4261684	16.0460567
20	18.0455530	17.8204485	17.5993161	17.1686388	16.7528813
21	18.8569831	18.6110739	18.3696949	17.9001367	17.4475492
22	19.6603793	19.3929037	19.1305629	18.6208244	18.1302695
23	20.4558211	20.1660358	19.8820374	19.3308614	18.8012476
24	21.2433873	20.9305669	20.6242345	20.0304054	19.4606856
25	22.0231557	21.6865928	21.3572687	20.7196112	20.1087820
26	22.7952037	22.4342079	22.0812530	21.3986317	20.7457317
27	23.5596076	23.1735060	22.7962993	22.0676175	21.3717264
28	24.3164432	23.9045795	23.5025178	22.7267167	21.9869547
29	25.0657853	24.6275199	24.2000176	23.3760756	22.5916017
30	25.8077082	25.3424177	24.8889062	24.0158380	23.1858493
31	26.5422854	26.0493623	25.5692901	24.6461458	23.7698765
32	27.2695895	26.7484424	26.2412742	25.2671387	24.3438590
33	27.9896925	27.4397452	26.9049622	25.8789544	24.9079695
34	28.7026659	28.1233575	27.5604564	26.4817285	25.4623779
35	29.4085801	28.7993646	28.2078582	27.0755946	26.0072510
36	30.1075050	29.4678513	28.8472674	27.6606843	26.5427528
37	30.7995099	30.1289011	29.4787826	28.2371274	27.0690445
38	31.4846633	30.7825969	30.1025013	28.8050516	27.5862846
39	32.1630330	31.4290204	30.7185198	29.3645829	28.0946286
40	32.8346861	32.0682526	31.3269332	29.9158452	28.5942295
41	33.4996892	32.7003734	31.9278352	30.4589608	29.0852379
42	34.1581081	33.3254620	32.5213187	30.9940500	29.5678014
43	34.8100081	33.9435965	33.1074753	31.5212316	30.0420652
44	35.4554535	34.5548544	33.6863954	32.0406222	30.5081722
45	36.0945084	35.1593121	34.2581683	32.5523372	30.9662626
46	36.7272361	35.7570454	34.8228822	33.0564898	31.4164743
47	37.3536991	36.3481289	35.3806244	33.5531920	31.8589428
48	37.9739595	36.9326367	35.9314809	34.0425536	32.2938013
49	38.5880787	37.5106420	36.4755367	34.5246834	32.7211806
50	39.1961175	38.0822171	37.0128758	34.9996881	33.1412095

INTEREST TABLES (Continued)

PRESENT VALUE OF ANNUITY $[1 - (1 + i)^{-n}]/i$ (Continued)

Years n	Rate i .01(1%)	.01125($1\frac{1}{8}$%)	.0125($1\frac{1}{4}$%)	.015($1\frac{1}{2}$%)	.0175($1\frac{3}{4}$%)
50	39.1961175	38.0822171	37.0128758	34.9996881	33.1412095
51	39.7981362	38.6474335	37.5435810	35.4676730	33.5540142
52	40.3941942	39.2063619	38.0677343	35.9287419	33.9597191
53	40.9843507	39.7590723	38.5854166	36.3829969	34.3584463
54	41.5686641	40.3056339	39.0967078	36.8305388	34.7503158
55	42.1471922	40.8461151	39.6016867	37.2714668	35.1354455
56	42.7199922	41.3805836	40.1004313	37.7058786	35.5139513
57	43.2871210	41.9091061	40.5930186	38.1338706	35.8859473
58	43.8486347	42.4317490	41.0795245	38.5555375	36.2515452
59	44.4045888	42.9485775	41.5600242	38.9709729	36.6108553
60	44.9550384	43.4596563	42.0345918	39.3802689	36.9639855
61	45.5000380	43.9650495	42.5033005	39.7835161	37.3110423
62	46.0396416	44.4648203	42.9662228	40.1808041	37.6521300
63	46.5739026	44.9590312	43.4234299	40.5722208	37.9873514
64	47.1028738	45.4477441	43.8749925	40.9578530	38.3168072
65	47.6266078	45.9310201	44.3209802	41.3377862	38.6405968
66	48.1451562	46.4089197	44.7614619	41.7121046	38.9588175
67	48.6585705	46.8815028	45.1965056	42.0808912	39.2715651
68	49.1669015	47.3488285	45.6261784	42.4442278	39.5789337
69	49.6701995	47.8109553	46.0505466	42.8021949	39.8810160
70	50.1685143	48.2679409	46.4696756	43.1548718	40.1779027
71	50.6618954	48.7198427	46.8836302	43.5023368	40.4696832
72	51.1503915	49.1667171	47.2924743	43.8446668	40.7564454
73	51.6340510	49.6086202	47.6962709	44.1819377	41.0382756
74	52.1129218	50.0456071	48.0950824	44.5142243	41.3152586
75	52.5870512	50.4777326	48.4889703	44.8416003	41.5874777
76	53.0564864	50.9050508	48.8779953	45.1641383	41.8550149
77	53.5212736	51.3276151	49.2622176	45.4819096	42.1179508
78	53.9814590	51.7454785	49.6416964	45.7949848	42.3763644
79	54.4370882	52.1586932	50.0164903	46.1034333	42.6303336
80	54.8882061	52.5673109	50.3866571	46.4073235	42.8799347
81	55.3348575	52.9713829	50.7522539	46.7067227	43.1252430
82	55.7770867	53.3709596	51.1133372	47.0016972	43.3663322
83	56.2149373	53.7660910	51.4699626	47.2923125	43.6032749
84	56.6484528	54.1568267	51.8221853	47.5786330	43.8361424
85	57.0776760	54.5432156	52.1700596	47.8607222	44.0650048
86	57.5026495	54.9253059	52.5136391	48.1386425	44.2899310
87	57.9234154	55.3031455	52.8529769	48.4124557	44.5109887
88	58.3400152	55.6767817	53.1881253	48.6822224	44.7282444
89	58.7524903	56.0462613	53.5191361	48.9480023	44.9417636
90	59.1608815	56.4116304	53.8460604	49.2098545	45.1516104
91	59.5652292	56.7729349	54.1689485	49.4678370	45.3578480
92	59.9655735	57.1302199	54.4878504	49.7220069	45.5605386
93	60.3619539	57.4835302	54.8028152	49.9724206	45.7597431
94	60.7544098	57.8329100	55.1138915	50.2191335	45.9555215
95	61.1429800	58.1784029	55.4211274	50.4622005	46.1479327
96	61.5277030	58.5200523	55.7245703	50.7016754	46.3370345
97	61.9086168	58.8579010	56.0242670	50.9376112	46.5228841
98	62.2857592	59.1919911	56.3202637	51.1700603	46.7055372
99	62.6591676	59.5223645	56.6126061	51.3990742	46.8850488
100	63.0288788	59.8490625	56.9013394	51.6247037	47.0614730

PRESENT VALUE OF ANNUITY $[1 - (1 + i)^{-n}]/i$
(Continued)

Years	Rate i				
n	.02(2 %)	.0225(2¼ %)	.025(2½ %)	.0275(2¾ %)	.03(3 %)
1	0.98039216	0.97799511	0.97560976	0.97323601	0.97087379
2	1.94156094	1.93446955	1.92742415	1.92042434	1.91346970
3	2.88388327	2.86989687	2.85602356	2.84226213	2.82861135
4	3.80772870	3.78474021	3.76197421	3.73942787	3.71709840
5	4.71345951	4.67945253	4.64582850	4.61258186	4.57970719
6	5.60143089	5.55447680	5.50812536	5.46236678	5.41719144
7	6.47199107	6.41024626	6.34939060	6.28940806	6.23028296
8	7.32548144	7.24718461	7.17013717	7.09431441	7.01969219
9	8.16223671	8.06570622	7.97086553	7.87767826	7.78610892
10	8.98258501	8.86621635	8.75206393	8.64007616	8.53020284
11	9.78684805	9.64911134	9.51420871	9.38206926	9.25262411
12	10.5753412	10.4147788	10.2577646	10.1042037	9.95400399
13	11.3483737	11.1635979	10.9831850	10.8070109	10.6349553
14	12.1062488	11.8959392	11.6909122	11.4910081	11.2960731
15	12.8492635	12.6121655	12.3813777	12.1566989	11.9379351
16	13.5777093	13.3126313	13.0550027	12.8045732	12.5611020
17	14.2918719	13.9976834	13.7121977	13.4351077	13.1661185
18	14.9920313	14.6676611	14.3533636	14.0487666	13.7535131
19	15.6784620	15.3228959	14.9788913	14.6460016	14.3237991
20	16.3514333	15.9637124	15.5891623	15.2272521	14.8774749
21	17.0112092	16.5904277	16.1845486	15.7929461	15.4150241
22	17.6580482	17.2033523	16.7654132	16.3434999	15.9369166
23	18.2922041	17.8027896	17.3321105	16.8793186	16.4436084
24	18.9139256	18.3890362	17.8849858	17.4007967	16.9355421
25	19.5234565	18.9623826	18.4243764	17.9083180	17.4131477
26	20.1210358	19.5231126	18.9506111	18.4022559	17.8768424
27	20.7068978	20.0715038	19.4640109	18.8829741	18.3270315
28	21.2812724	20.6078276	19.9648887	19.3508264	18.7641082
29	21.8443847	21.1323498	20.4535499	19.8061571	19.1884546
30	22.3964556	21.6453298	20.9302926	20.2493013	19.6004413
31	22.9377015	22.1470219	21.3954074	20.6805852	20.0004285
32	23.4683348	22.6376742	21.8491780	21.1003262	20.3887655
33	23.9885636	23.1175298	22.2918809	21.5088333	20.7657918
34	24.4985917	23.5868262	22.7237863	21.9064071	21.1318367
35	24.9986193	24.0457958	23.1451573	22.2933403	21.4872201
36	25.4888425	24.4946658	23.5562511	22.6699175	21.8322525
37	25.9694534	24.9336585	23.9573181	23.0364161	22.1672354
38	26.4406406	25.3629912	24.3486030	23.3931057	22.4924616
39	26.9025888	25.7828765	24.7303444	23.7402488	22.8082151
40	27.3554792	26.1935222	25.1027751	24.0781011	23.1147720
41	27.7994895	26.5951317	25.4661220	24.4069110	23.4124000
42	28.2347936	26.9879039	25.8206068	24.7269207	23.7013592
43	28.6615623	27.3720332	26.1664457	25.0383656	23.9819021
44	29.0799631	27.7477097	26.5038495	25.3414751	24.2542739
45	29.4901599	28.1151195	26.8330239	25.6364721	24.5187125
46	29.8923136	28.4744445	27.1541696	25.9235738	24.7754491
47	30.2865820	28.8258626	27.4674826	26.2029915	25.0247078
48	30.6731196	29.1695478	27.7731537	26.4749309	25.2667066
49	31.0520780	29.5056702	28.0713695	26.7395922	25.5016569
50	31.4236059	29.8343963	28.3623117	26.9971700	25.7297640

PRESENT VALUE OF ANNUITY $[1-(1+i)^{-n}]/i$ (Continued)

Years n	Rate i .02(2%)	.0225(2¼%)	.025(2½%)	.0275(2¾%)	.03(3%)
50	31.4236059	29.8343963	28.3623117	26.9971700	25.7297640
51	31.7878489	30.1558888	28.6461577	27.2478540	25.9512272
52	32.1449499	30.4703069	28.9230807	27.4918287	26.1662400
53	32.4950489	30.7778062	29.1932495	27.7292737	26.3749903
54	32.8382833	31.0785391	29.4568288	27.9603637	26.5776605
55	33.1747875	31.3726544	29.7139793	28.1852688	26.7744276
56	33.5046936	31.6602977	29.9648578	28.4041545	26.9654637
57	33.8281310	31.9416114	30.2096174	28.6171820	27.1509357
58	34.1452265	32.2167349	30.4484072	28.8245081	27.3310055
59	34.4561044	32.4858043	30.6813729	29.0262852	27.5058306
60	34.7608867	32.7489529	30.9086565	29.2226620	27.6755637
61	35.0596928	33.0063109	31.1303966	29.4137830	27.8403531
62	35.3526400	33.2580057	31.3467284	29.5997888	28.0003428
63	35.6398432	33.5041621	31.5577838	29.7808163	28.1556726
64	35.9214149	33.7449018	31.7636915	29.9569989	28.3064783
65	36.1974655	33.9803440	31.9645771	30.1284661	28.4528915
66	36.4681035	34.2106054	32.1605630	30.2953441	28.5950403
67	36.7334348	34.4357999	32.3517688	30.4577558	28.7330488
68	36.9935635	34.6560391	32.5383110	30.6158207	28.8670377
69	37.2485917	34.8714318	32.7203034	30.7696552	28.9971240
70	37.4986193	35.0820849	32.8978570	30.9193725	29.1234214
71	37.7437444	35.2881026	33.0710800	31.0650827	29.2460401
72	37.9840631	35.4895869	33.2400780	31.2068931	29.3650875
73	38.2196697	35.6866376	33.4049542	31.3449082	29.4806675
74	38.4506566	35.8793521	33.5658089	31.4792294	29.5928811
75	38.6771143	36.0678261	33.7227404	31.6099556	29.7018263
76	38.8991317	36.2521526	33.8758443	31.7371830	29.8075983
77	39.1167958	36.4324231	34.0252140	31.8610054	29.9102896
78	39.3301919	36.6087267	34.1709405	31.9815138	30.0099899
79	39.5394039	36.7811509	34.3131127	32.0987969	30.1067863
80	39.7445136	36.9497808	34.4518172	32.2129410	30.2007634
81	39.9456016	37.1147000	34.5871388	32.3240301	30.2920033
82	40.1427466	37.2759903	34.7191598	32.4321461	30.3805858
83	40.3360261	37.4337313	34.8479607	32.5373685	30.4665881
84	40.5255158	37.5880013	34.9736202	32.6397747	30.5500856
85	40.7112900	37.7388765	35.0962149	32.7394401	30.6311510
86	40.8934216	37.8864318	35.2158194	32.8364380	30.7098554
87	41.0719819	38.0307402	35.3325067	32.9308399	30.7862673
88	41.2470411	38.1718730	35.4463480	33.0227153	30.8604537
89	41.4186677	38.3099003	35.5574127	33.1121317	30.9324794
90	41.5869292	38.4448902	35.6657685	33.1991549	31.0024071
91	41.7518913	38.5769098	35.7714814	33.2838490	31.0702982
92	41.9136190	38.7060242	35.8746160	33.3662764	31.1362118
93	42.0721754	38.8322975	35.9752352	33.4464978	31.2002057
94	42.2276230	38.9557922	36.0734002	33.5245720	31.2623356
95	42.3800225	39.0765694	36.1691709	33.6005567	31.3226559
96	42.5294339	39.1946889	36.2626057	33.6745078	31.3812193
97	42.6759155	39.3102092	36.3537617	33.7464796	31.4380770
98	42.8195250	39.4231875	36.4426943	33.8165251	31.4932787
99	42.9603187	39.5336797	36.5294579	33.8846960	31.5468725
100	43.0983516	39.6417405	36.6141053	33.9510423	31.5989053

PRESENT VALUE OF ANNUITY $[1 - (1 + i)^{-n}]/i$ (Continued)

Years n	Rate i .035(3½%)	.04(4%)	.045(4½%)	.05(5%)	.055(5½%)
1	0.96618357	0.96153846	0.95693780	0.95238095	0.94786730
2	1.89969428	1.88609467	1.87266775	1.85941043	1.84631971
3	2.80163698	2.77509103	2.74896435	2.72324803	2.69793338
4	3.67307921	3.62989522	3.58752570	3.54595050	3.50515012
5	4.51505238	4.45182233	4.38997674	4.32947667	4.27028448
6	5.32855302	5.24213686	5.15787248	5.07569207	4.99553031
7	6.11454398	6.00205467	5.89270094	5.78637340	5.68296712
8	6.87395554	6.73274487	6.59588607	6.46321276	6.33456599
9	7.60768651	7.43533161	7.26879050	7.10782168	6.95219525
10	8.31660532	8.11089578	7.91271818	7.72173493	7.53762583
11	9.00155104	8.76047671	8.52891692	8.30641422	8.09253633
12	9.66333433	9.38507376	9.11858078	8.86325164	8.61851785
13	10.3027385	9.98564785	9.68285242	9.39357299	9.11707853
14	10.9205203	10.5631229	10.2228253	9.89864094	9.58964790
15	11.5174109	11.1183874	10.7395457	10.3796580	10.0375809
16	12.0941168	11.6522956	11.2340150	10.8377696	10.4621620
17	12.6513206	12.1656689	11.7071914	11.2740662	10.8646086
18	13.1896817	12.6592970	12.1599918	11.6895869	11.2460745
19	13.7098374	13.1339394	12.5932936	12.0853209	11.6076535
20	14.2124033	13.5903263	13.0079365	12.4622103	11.9503825
21	14.6979742	14.0291599	13.4047239	12.8211527	12.2752441
22	15.1671248	14.4511153	13.7844248	13.1630026	12.5831697
23	15.6204105	14.8568417	14.1477749	13.4885739	12.8750424
24	16.0583676	15.2469631	14.4954784	13.7986418	13.1516990
25	16.4815146	15.6220799	14.8282090	14.0939446	13.4139327
26	16.8903523	15.9827692	15.1466114	14.3751853	13.6624954
27	17.2853645	16.3295857	15.4513028	14.6430336	13.8980999
28	17.6670188	16.6630632	15.7428735	14.8981273	14.1214217
29	18.0357670	16.9837146	16.0218885	15.1410736	14.3331012
30	18.3920454	17.2920333	16.2888885	15.3724510	14.5337452
31	18.7362758	17.5884936	16.5443910	15.5928105	14.7239291
32	19.0688655	17.8735515	16.7888909	15.8026767	14.9041982
33	19.3902082	18.1476457	17.0228621	16.0025492	15.0750694
34	19.7006842	18.4111978	17.2467580	16.1929040	15.2370326
35	20.0006611	18.6646132	17.4610124	16.3741943	15.3905522
36	20.2904938	18.9082820	17.6660406	16.5468517	15.5360684
37	20.5705254	19.1425788	17.8622398	16.7112873	15.6739985
38	20.8410874	19.3678642	18.0499902	16.8678927	15.8047379
39	21.1024999	19.5844848	18.2296557	17.0170407	15.9286615
40	21.3550723	19.7927739	18.4015844	17.1590864	16.0461247
41	21.5991037	19.9930518	18.5661095	17.2943680	16.1574642
42	21.8348828	20.1856267	18.7235498	17.4232076	16.2629992
43	22.0626887	20.3707949	18.8742103	17.5459120	16.3630324
44	22.2827910	20.5488413	19.0183831	17.6627733	16.4578506
45	22.4954503	20.7200397	19.1563474	17.7740698	16.5477257
46	22.7009181	20.8846536	19.2883707	17.8800665	16.6329154
47	22.8994378	21.0429361	19.4147088	17.9810157	16.7136639
48	23.0912443	21.1951309	19.5356065	18.0771578	16.7902027
49	23.2765645	21.3414720	19.6512981	18.1687217	16.8627514
50	23.4556179	21.4821846	19.7620078	18.2559255	16.9315179

PRESENT VALUE OF ANNUITY $[1 - (1 + i)^{-n}]/i$ (Continued)

Years n	Rate i .06(6 %)	.065($6\frac{1}{2}$ %)	.07(7 %)	.075($7\frac{1}{2}$ %)	.08(8 %)
1	0.94339623	0.93896714	0.93457944	0.93023256	0.92592593
2	1.83339267	1.82062642	1.80801817	1.79556517	1.78326475
3	2.67301195	2.64847551	2.62431604	2.60052574	2.57709699
4	3.46510561	3.42579860	3.38721126	3.34932627	3.31212684
5	4.21236379	4.15567944	4.10019744	4.04588490	3.99271004
6	4.91732433	4.84101356	4.76653966	4.69384642	4.62287966
7	5.58238144	5.48451977	5.38928940	5.29660132	5.20637006
8	6.20979381	6.08875096	5.97129851	5.85730355	5.74663894
9	6.80169227	6.65610419	6.51523225	6.37888703	6.24688791
10	7.36008705	7.18883022	7.02358154	6.86408096	6.71008140
11	7.88687458	7.68904246	7.49867434	7.31542415	7.13896426
12	8.38384394	8.15872532	7.94268630	7.73527827	7.53607802
13	8.85268296	8.59974208	8.35765074	8.12584026	7.90377594
14	9.29498393	9.01384233	8.74546799	8.48915373	8.24423698
15	9.71224899	9.40266885	9.10791401	8.82711975	8.55947869
16	10.1058953	9.76776418	9.44664860	9.14150674	8.85136916
17	10.4772597	10.1105767	9.76322299	9.43395976	9.12163811
18	10.8276035	10.4324664	10.0590869	9.70600908	9.37188714
19	11.1581165	10.7347102	10.3355952	9.95907821	9.60359920
20	11.4699212	11.0185072	10.5940142	10.1944914	9.81814741
21	11.7640766	11.2849833	10.8355273	10.4134803	10.0168032
22	12.0415817	11.5351956	11.0612405	10.6171910	10.2007437
23	12.3033790	11.7701367	11.2721874	10.8066893	10.3710589
24	12.5503575	11.9907387	11.4693340	10.9829668	10.5287583
25	12.7833562	12.1978767	11.6535832	11.1469459	10.6747762
26	13.0031662	12.3923725	11.8257787	11.2994845	10.8099780
27	13.2105341	12.5749977	11.9867090	11.4413810	10.9351648
28	13.4061643	12.7464767	12.1371113	11.5733776	11.0510785
29	13.5907210	12.9074898	12.2776741	11.6961652	11.1584060
30	13.7648312	13.0586759	12.4090412	11.8103863	11.2577833
31	13.9290860	13.2006347	12.5318142	11.9166384	11.3497994
32	14.0840434	13.3339293	12.6465553	12.0154776	11.4349994
33	14.2302296	13.4590885	12.7537900	12.1074210	11.5138884
34	14.3681411	13.5766089	12.8540094	12.1929498	11.5869337
35	14.4982464	13.6869567	12.9476723	12.2725114	11.6545682
36	14.6209871	13.7905697	13.0352078	12.3465222	11.7171928
37	14.7367803	13.8878589	13.1170166	12.4153695	11.7751785
38	14.8460192	13.9792102	13.1934735	12.4794135	11.8288690
39	14.9490747	14.0649861	13.2649285	12.5389893	11.8785824
40	15.0462969	14.1455269	13.3317088	12.5944087	11.9246133
41	15.1380159	14.2211520	13.3941204	12.6459615	11.9672346
42	15.2245433	14.2921615	13.4524490	12.6939177	12.0066987
43	15.3061729	14.3588371	13.5069617	12.7385281	12.0432395
44	15.3831820	14.4214433	13.5579081	12.7800261	12.0770736
45	15.4558321	14.4802284	13.6055216	12.8186290	12.1084015
46	15.5243699	14.5354257	13.6500202	12.8545386	12.1374088
47	15.5890282	14.5872542	13.6916076	12.8879429	12.1642674
48	15.6500266	14.6359195	13.7304744	12.9190166	12.1891365
49	15.7075723	14.6816145	13.7667985	12.9479224	12.2121634
50	15.7618606	14.7245207	13.8007463	12.9748116	12.2334846

ANNUITY WHOSE PRESENT VALUE IS 1

$$\frac{1}{a_{\overline{n|}}} = a_{\overline{n|}}^{-1} = \frac{i}{1-(1+i)^{-n}} = \frac{i}{1-v^n} = s_{\overline{n|}}^{-1} + i$$

Years	Rate i				
n	.0025($\frac{1}{4}$%)	.004167($\frac{5}{12}$%)	.005($\frac{1}{2}$%)	.005833($\frac{7}{12}$%)	.0075($\frac{3}{4}$%)
1	1.00250000	1.00416667	1.00500000	1.00583333	1.00750000
2	0.50187578	0.50312717	0.50375312	0.50437924	0.50563200
3	.33500139	.33611496	.33667221	.33722976	.33834579
4	.25156445	.25260958	.25313279	.25365644	.25470501
5	.20150250	.20250693	.20300997	.20351357	.20452242
6	.16812803	.16910564	.16959546	.17008594	.17106891
7	.14428928	.14524800	.14572854	.14620986	.14717488
8	.12641035	.12735512	.12782886	.12830352	.12925552
9	.11250462	.11343876	.11390736	.11437698	.11531929
10	.10138015	.10230596	.10277057	.10323632	.10417123
11	.09227840	.09319757	.09365903	.09412175	.09505094
12	.08469370	.08560748	.08606643	.08652675	.08745148
13	.07827595	.07918532	.07964224	.08010064	.08102188
14	.07277510	.07368082	.07413609	.07459295	.07551146
15	.06800777	.06891045	.06936436	.06982000	.07073639
16	.06383642	.06473655	.06518937	.06564401	.06655879
17	.06015587	.06105387	.06150579	.06195966	.06287321
18	.05688433	.05778053	.05823173	.05868499	.05959766
19	.05395722	.05485191	.05530253	.05575532	.05666740
20	.05132288	.05221630	.05266645	.05311889	.05403063
21	.04893947	.04983183	.05028163	.05073383	.05164543
22	.04677278	.04766427	.04811380	.04856585	.04947748
23	.04479455	.04568531	.04613465	.04658663	.04749846
24	.04298121	.04387139	.04432061	.04477258	.04568474
25	.04131298	.04220270	.04265186	.04310388	.04401650
26	.03977312	.04066247	.04111163	.04156376	.04247693
27	.03834736	.03923645	.03968565	.04013793	.04105176
28	.03702347	.03791239	.03836167	.03881415	.03972871
29	.03579093	.03667974	.03712914	.03758186	.03849723
30	.03464059	.03552936	.03597892	.03643191	.03734816
31	.03356449	.03445330	.03490304	.03535633	.03627352
32	.03255569	.03344458	.03389453	.03434815	.03526634
33	.03160806	.03249708	.03294727	.03340124	.03432048
34	.03071620	.03160540	.03205586	.03251020	.03343053
35	.02987533	.03076476	.03121550	.03167024	.03259170
36	.02908121	.02997090	.03042194	.03087710	.03179973
37	.02833004	.02922003	.02967139	.03012698	.03105082
38	.02761843	.02850875	.02896045	.02941649	.03034157
39	.02694335	.02783402	.02828607	.02874258	.02966893
40	.02630204	.02719310	.02764552	.02810251	.02903016
41	.02569204	.02658352	.02703631	.02749379	.02842276
42	.02511112	.02600303	.02645622	.02691420	.02784452
43	.02455724	.02544961	.02590320	.02636170	.02729338
44	.02402855	.02492141	.02537541	.02583443	.02676751
45	.02352339	.02441675	.02487117	.02533073	.02626521
46	.02304022	.02393409	.02438894	.02484905	.02578495
47	.02257762	.02347204	.02392733	.02438798	.02532532
48	.02213433	.02302929	.02348503	.02394624	.02488504
49	.02170915	.02260468	.02306087	.02352265	.02446292
50	.02130099	.02219711	.02265376	.02311612	.02405787

ANNUITY WHOSE PRESENT VALUE IS 1

$a_{\overline{n}|}^{-1} = i/(1 - v^n) = s_{\overline{n}|}^{-1} + i$ (Continued)

Years	Rate i				
n	.0025($\frac{1}{4}$%)	.004167($\frac{5}{12}$%)	.005($\frac{1}{2}$%)	.005833($\frac{7}{12}$%)	.0075($\frac{3}{4}$%)
50	.02130099	.02219711	.02265376	.02311612	.02405787
51	.02090886	.02180557	.02226269	.02272563	.02366888
52	.02053184	.02142916	.02188675	.02235027	.02329503
53	.02016906	.02106700	.02152507	.02198919	.02293546
54	.01981974	.02071830	.02117686	.02164157	.02258938
55	.01948314	.02038234	.02084139	.02130671	.02225605
56	.01915858	.02005843	.02051797	.02098390	.02193478
57	.01884542	.01974593	.02020598	.02067251	.02162496
58	.01854308	.01944426	.01990481	.02037196	.02132597
59	.01825101	.01915287	.01961392	.02008170	.02103727
60	.01796869	.01887123	.01933280	.01980120	.02075836
61	.01769564	.01859888	.01906096	.01952999	.02048873
62	.01743142	.01833536	.01879796	.01926762	.02022795
63	.01717561	.01808025	.01854337	.01901366	.01997560
64	.01692780	.01783315	.01829681	.01876773	.01973127
65	.01668764	.01759371	.01805789	.01852946	.01949460
66	.01645476	.01736156	.01782627	.01829848	.01926524
67	.01622886	.01713639	.01760163	.01807449	.01904286
68	.01600961	.01691788	.01738366	.01785716	.01882716
69	.01579674	.01670574	.01717206	.01764622	.01861785
70	.01558996	.01649971	.01696657	.01744138	.01841464
71	.01538902	.01629952	.01676693	.01724239	.01821728
72	.01519368	.01610493	.01657289	.01704901	.01802554
73	.01500370	.01591572	.01638422	.01686100	.01783917
74	.01481887	.01573165	.01620070	.01667814	.01765796
75	.01463898	.01555253	.01602214	.01650024	.01748170
76	.01446385	.01537816	.01584832	.01632709	.01731020
77	.01429327	.01520836	.01567908	.01615851	.01714328
78	.01412708	.01504295	.01551423	.01599432	.01698074
79	.01396511	.01488177	.01535360	.01583436	.01682244
80	.01380721	.01472464	.01519704	.01567847	.01666821
81	.01365321	.01457144	.01504439	.01552650	.01651790
82	.01350298	.01442200	.01489552	.01537830	.01637136
83	.01335639	.01427620	.01475028	.01523373	.01622847
84	.01321330	.01413391	.01460855	.01509268	.01608908
85	.01307359	.01399500	.01447021	.01495501	.01595308
86	.01293714	.01385935	.01433513	.01482060	.01582034
87	.01280384	.01372685	.01420320	.01468935	.01569076
88	.01267357	.01359740	.01407431	.01456115	.01556423
89	.01254625	.01347088	.01394837	.01443588	.01544064
90	.01242177	.01334721	.01382527	.01431347	.01531989
91	.01230004	.01322629	.01370493	.01419380	.01520190
92	.01218096	.01310803	.01358724	.01407679	.01508657
93	.01206446	.01299234	.01347213	.01396236	.01497382
94	.01195044	.01287915	.01335950	.01385042	.01486356
95	.01183884	.01276836	.01324930	.01374090	.01475571
96	.01172957	.01265992	.01314143	.01363372	.01465020
97	.01162257	.01255374	.01303583	.01352880	.01454696
98	.01151776	.01244976	.01293242	.01342608	.01444592
99	.01141508	.01234790	.01283115	.01332549	.01434701
100	.01131446	.01224811	.01273194	.01322696	.01425017

ANNUITY WHOSE PRESENT VALUE IS 1

$$a_{\overline{n}|}^{-1} = i/(1 - v^n) = s_{\overline{n}|}^{-1} + i \text{ (Continued)}$$

Years	Rate i				
n	.01(1%)	.01125(1⅛%)	.0125(1¼%)	.015(1½%)	.0175(1¾%)
1	1.01000000	1.01125000	1.01250000	1.01500000	1.01750000
2	0.50751244	0.50845323	0.50939441	0.51127792	0.51316295
3	.34002211	.34086130	.34170117	.34338296	.34506746
4	.25628109	.25707058	.25786102	.25944479	.26103237
5	.20603980	.20680034	.20756211	.20908932	.21062142
6	.17254837	.17329034	.17403381	.17552521	.17702256
7	.14862828	.14935762	.15008872	.15155616	.15303059
8	.13069029	.13141071	.13213314	.13358402	.13504292
9	.11674036	.11745432	.11817055	.11960982	.12105813
10	.10558208	.10629131	.10700307	.10843418	.10987534
11	.09645408	.09715984	.09786839	.09929384	.10073038
12	.08884879	.08955203	.09025831	.09167999	.09311377
13	.08241482	.08311626	.08382100	.08524036	.08667283
14	.07690117	.07760138	.07830515	.07972332	.08115562
15	.07212378	.07282321	.07352646	.07494436	.07637739
16	.06794460	.06864363	.06934672	.07076508	.07219958
17	.06425806	.06495698	.06566023	.06707966	.06851623
18	.06098205	.06168113	.06238479	.06380578	.06524492
19	.05805175	.05875120	.05945548	.06087847	.06232061
20	.05541531	.05611531	.05682039	.05824574	.05969122
21	.05303075	.05373145	.05443749	.05586550	.05731464
22	.05086372	.05156525	.05227238	.05370332	.05515638
23	.04888584	.04958833	.05029666	.05173075	.05318796
24	.04707347	.04777701	.04848665	.04992410	.05138565
25	.04540675	.04611144	.04682247	.04826345	.04972952
26	.04386888	.04457479	.04528729	.04673196	.04820269
27	.04244553	.04315273	.04386677	.04531527	.04679079
28	.04112444	.04183299	.04254863	.04400108	.04548151
29	.03989502	.04060498	.04132228	.04277878	.04426424
30	.03874811	.03945953	.04017854	.04163919	.04312975
31	.03767573	.03838866	.03910942	.04057430	.04207005
32	.03667089	.03738535	.03810791	.03957710	.04107812
33	.03572744	.03644349	.03716786	.03864144	.04014779
34	.03483997	.03555763	.03628387	.03776189	.03927363
35	.03400368	.03472299	.03545111	.03693363	.03845082
36	.03321431	.03393529	.03466533	.03615240	.03767507
37	.03246805	.03319072	.03392270	.03541437	.03694257
38	.03176150	.03248589	.03321983	.03471613	.03624990
39	.03109160	.03181773	.03255365	.03405463	.03559399
40	.03045560	.03118349	.03192141	.03342710	.03497209
41	.02985102	.03058069	.03132063	.03283106	.03438170
42	.02927563	.03000709	.03074906	.03226426	.03382057
43	.02872737	.02946064	.03020466	.03172465	.03328666
44	.02820441	.02893949	.02968557	.03121038	.03277810
45	.02770505	.02844197	.02919012	.03071976	.03229321
46	.02722775	.02796652	.02871675	.03025125	.03183043
47	.02677111	.02751173	.02826406	.02980342	.03138836
48	.02633384	.02707632	.02783075	.02937500	.03096569
49	.02591474	.02665910	.02741563	.02896478	.03056124
50	.02551273	.02625898	.02701763	.02857168	.03017391

ANNUITY WHOSE PRESENT VALUE IS 1)

$$a_{\overline{n}|}^{-1} = i/(1 - v^n) = s_{\overline{n}|}^{-1} + i \text{ (Continued)}$$

Years n	Rate i .01(1%)	.01125(1⅛%)	.0125(1¼%)	.015(1½%)	.0175(1¾%)
50	.02551273	.02625898	.02701763	.02857168	.03017391
51	.02512680	.02587494	.02663571	.02819469	.02980269
52	.02475603	.02550606	.02626897	.02783287	.02944665
53	.02439956	.02515149	.02591653	.02748537	.02910492
54	.02405658	.02481043	.02557760	.02715138	.02877672
55	.02372637	.02448213	.02525145	.02683018	.02846129
56	.02340824	.02416592	.02493739	.02652106	.02815795
57	.02310156	.02386116	.02463478	.02622341	.02786606
58	.02280573	.02356726	.02434303	.02593661	.02758503
59	.02252020	.02328366	.02406158	.02566012	.02731430
60	.02224445	.02300985	.02378993	.02539343	.02705336
61	.02197800	.02274534	.02352758	.02513604	.02680172
62	.02172041	.02248969	.02327410	.02488751	.02655892
63	.02147125	.02224247	.02302904	.02464741	.02632455
64	.02123013	.02200329	.02279203	.02441534	.02609821
65	.02099667	.02177178	.02256268	.02419094	.02587952
66	.02077052	.02154758	.02234065	.02397386	.02566813
67	.02055136	.02133037	.02212560	.02376376	.02546372
68	.02033889	.02111985	.02191724	.02356033	.02526597
69	.02013280	.02091571	.02171527	.02336329	.02507459
70	.01993282	.02071769	.02151941	.02317235	.02488930
71	.01973870	.02052552	.02132941	.02298727	.02470985
72	.01955019	.02033896	.02114501	.02280779	.02453600
73	.01936706	.02015779	.02096600	.02263368	.02436750
74	.01918910	.01998177	.02079215	.02246473	.02420413
75	.01901609	.01981072	.02062325	.02230072	.02404570
76	.01884784	.01964442	.02045910	.02214146	.02389200
77	.01868416	.01948269	.02029953	.02198676	.02374285
78	.01852488	.01932536	.02014436	.02183645	.02359806
79	.01836983	.01917226	.01999341	.02169036	.02345748
80	.01821885	.01902323	.01984652	.02154832	.02332093
81	.01807179	.01887812	.01970356	.02141019	.02318828
82	.01792851	.01873678	.01956437	.02127583	.02305936
83	.01778887	.01859908	.01942881	.02114509	.02293406
84	.01765273	.01846489	.01929675	.02101784	.02281223
85	.01751998	.01833409	.01916808	.02089396	.02269375
86	.01739050	.01820654	.01904267	.02077333	.02257850
87	.01726418	.01808215	.01892041	.02065584	.02246636
88	.01714089	.01796081	.01880119	.02054138	.02235724
89	.01702056	.01784240	.01868491	.02042984	.02225102
90	.01690306	.01772684	.01857146	.02032113	.02214760
91	.01678832	.01761403	.01846076	.02021516	.02204690
92	.01667624	.01750387	.01835272	.02011182	.02194882
93	.01656673	.01739629	.01824724	.02001104	.02185327
94	.01645971	.01729119	.01814425	.01991273	.02176017
95	.01635511	.01718851	.01804366	.01981681	.02166944
96	.01625284	.01708816	.01794541	.01972321	.02158101
97	.01615284	.01699007	.01784941	.01963186	.02149480
98	.01605503	.01689418	.01775560	.01954268	.02141074
99	.01595936	.01680041	.01766391	.01945560	.02132876
100	.01586574	.01670870	.01757428	.01937057	.02124880

ANNUITY WHOSE PRESENT VALUE IS 1

$a_{\overline{n}|}^{-1} = i/(1 - v^n) = s_{\overline{n}|}^{-1} + i$ (Continued)

Years	Rate i				
n	.02(2 %)	.0225(2¼ %)	.025(2½ %)	.0275(2¾ %)	.03(3 %)
1	1.02000000	1.02250000	1.02500000	1.02750000	1.03000000
2	0.51504950	0.51693758	0.51882716	0.52071825	0.52261084
3	.34675467	.34844458	.35013717	.35183243	.35353036
4	.26262375	.26421893	.26581788	.26742059	.26902705
5	.21215839	.21370021	.21524686	.21679832	.21835457
6	.17852581	.18003496	.18154997	.18307083	.18459750
7	.15451196	.15600025	.15749543	.15899747	.16050635
8	.13650980	.13798462	.13946735	.14095795	.14245639
9	.12251544	.12398170	.12545689	.12694095	.12843386
10	.11132653	.11278768	.11425876	.11573972	.11723051
11	.10217794	.10363649	.10510596	.10658629	.10807745
12	.09455960	.09601740	.09748713	.09896871	.10046209
13	.08811835	.08957686	.09104827	.09253252	.09402954
14	.08260197	.08406230	.08553652	.08702457	.08852634
15	.07782547	.07928852	.08076646	.08225917	.08376658
16	.07365013	.07511663	.07659899	.07809710	.07961085
17	.06996984	.07144039	.07292777	.07443186	.07595253
18	.06670210	.06817720	.06967008	.07118063	.07270870
19	.06378177	.06526182	.06676062	.06827802	.06981388
20	.06115672	.06264207	.06414713	.06567173	.06721571
21	.05878477	.06027572	.06178733	.06331941	.06487178
22	.05663140	.05812821	.05964661	.06118640	.06274739
23	.05466810	.05617097	.05769638	.05924410	.06081390
24	.05287110	.05438023	.05591282	.05746863	.05904742
25	.05122044	.05273599	.05427592	.05583997	.05742787
26	.04969923	.05122134	.05276875	.05434116	.05593829
27	.04829309	.04982188	.05137687	.05295776	.05456421
28	.04698967	.04852525	.05008793	.05167738	.05329323
29	.04577836	.04732081	.04889127	.05048935	.05211467
30	.04464992	.04619934	.04777764	.04938442	.05101926
31	.04359635	.04515280	.04673900	.04835453	.04999893
32	.04261061	.04417415	.04576831	.04739263	.04904662
33	.04168653	.04325722	.04485938	.04649253	.04815612
34	.04081867	.04239655	.04400675	.04564875	.04732196
35	.04000221	.04158731	.04320558	.04485645	.04653929
36	.03923285	.04082522	.04245158	.04411132	.04580379
37	.03850678	.04010643	.04174090	.04340953	.04511162
38	.03782057	.03942753	.04107012	.04274764	.04445934
39	.03717114	.03878543	.04043615	.04212256	.04384385
40	.03655575	.03817738	.03983623	.04153151	.04326238
41	.03597188	.03760087	.03926786	.04097200	.04271241
42	.03541729	.03705364	.03872876	.04044175	.04219167
43	.03488993	.03653364	.03821688	.03993871	.04169811
44	.03438794	.03603901	.03773037	.03946100	.04122985
45	.03390962	.03556805	.03726751	.03900693	.04078518
46	.03345342	.03511921	.03682676	.03857493	.04036254
47	.03301792	.03469107	.03640669	.03816358	.03996051
48	.03260184	.03428233	.03600599	.03777158	.03957777
49	.03220396	.03389179	.03562348	.03739773	.03921314
50	.03182321	.03351836	.03525806	.03704092	.03886549

ANNUITY WHOSE PRESENT VALUE IS 1

$a_{\overline{n}|}^{-1} = i/(1 - v^n) = s_{\overline{n}|}^{-1} + i$ (Continued)

Years	Rate i				
n	.02(2%)	.0225(2¼%)	.025(2½%)	.0275(2¾%)	.03(3%)
50	.03182321	.03351836	.03525806	.03704092	.03886549
51	.03145856	.03316102	.03490870	.03670014	.03853382
52	.03110909	.03281884	.03457446	.03637444	.03821718
53	.03077392	.03249094	.03425449	.03606297	.03791471
54	.03045226	.03217654	.03394799	.03576491	.03762558
55	.03014337	.03187489	.03365419	.03547953	.03734907
56	.02984656	.03158530	.03337243	.03520612	.03708447
57	.02956120	.03130712	.03310204	.03494404	.03683114
58	.02928667	.03103977	.03284244	.03469270	.03658848
59	.02902243	.03078268	.03259307	.03445153	.03635593
60	.02876797	.03053533	.03235340	.03422002	.03613296
61	.02852278	.03029724	.03212294	.03399767	.03591908
62	.02828643	.03006795	.03190126	.03378402	.03571385
63	.02805848	.02984704	.03168790	.03357866	.03551682
64	.02783855	.02963411	.03148249	.03338118	.03532760
65	.02762624	.02942878	.03128463	.03319120	.03514581
66	.02742122	.02923070	.03109398	.03300837	.03497110
67	.02722316	.02903955	.03091021	.03283236	.03480313
68	.02703173	.02885500	.03073300	.03266285	.03464159
69	.02684665	.02867677	.03056206	.03249955	.03448618
70	.02666765	.02850458	.03039712	.03234218	.03433663
71	.02649446	.02833816	.03023790	.03219048	.03419266
72	.02632683	.02817728	.03008417	.03204420	.03405404
73	.02616454	.02802169	.02993568	.03190311	.03392053
74	.02600736	.02787118	.02979222	.03176698	.03379191
75	.02585508	.02772554	.02965358	.03163560	.03366796
76	.02570751	.02758457	.02951956	.03150878	.03354849
77	.02556447	.02744808	.02938997	.03138633	.03343331
78	.02542576	.02731589	.02926463	.03126806	.03332224
79	.02529123	.02718784	.02914338	.03115382	.03321510
80	.02516071	.02706376	.02902605	.03104342	.03311175
81	.02503405	.02694350	.02891248	.03093674	.03301201
82	.02491110	.02682692	.02880254	.03083361	.03291576
83	.02479173	.02671387	.02869608	.03073389	.03282284
84	.02467581	.02660423	.02859298	.03063747	.03273313
85	.02456321	.02649787	.02849310	.03054420	.03264650
86	.02445381	.02639467	.02839633	.03045397	.03256284
87	.02434750	.02629452	.02830255	.03036667	.03248202
88	.02424416	.02619730	.02821165	.03028219	.03240393
89	.02414370	.02610291	.02812353	.03020041	.03232848
90	.02404602	.02601126	.02803809	.03012125	.03225556
91	.02395101	.02592224	.02795523	.03004460	.03218508
92	.02385859	.02583577	.02787486	.02997038	.03211694
93	.02376868	.02575176	.02779690	.02989850	.03205107
94	.02368118	.02567012	.02772126	.02982887	.03198737
95	.02359602	.02559078	.02764786	.02976141	.03192577
96	.02351313	.02551366	.02757662	.02969605	.03186619
97	.02343242	.02543868	.02750747	.02963272	.03180856
98	.02335383	.02536578	.02744034	.02957134	.03175281
99	.02327729	.02529489	.02737517	.02951185	.03169886
100	.02320274	.02522594	.02731188	.02945418	.03164667

ANNUITY WHOSE PRESENT VALUE IS 1

$$a_{\overline{n}|}^{-1} = i/(1 - v^n) = s_{\overline{n}|}^{-1} + i \text{ (Continued)}$$

Years	Rate i				
n	.035(3½%)	.04(4%)	.045(4½%)	.05(5%)	.055(5½%)
1	1.03500000	1.04000000	1.04500000	1.05000000	1.05500000
2	0.52640049	0.53019608	0.53399756	0.53780488	0.54161800
3	.35693418	.36034854	.36377336	.36720856	.37065407
4	.27225114	.27549005	.27874365	.28201183	.28529449
5	.22148137	.22462711	.22779164	.23097480	.23417644
6	.18766821	.19076190	.19387839	.19701747	.20017895
7	.16354449	.16660961	.16970147	.17281982	.17596442
8	.14547665	.14852783	.15160965	.15472181	.15786401
9	.13144601	.13449299	.13757447	.14069008	.14383946
10	.12024137	.12329094	.12637882	.12950457	.13266777
11	.11109197	.11414904	.11724818	.12038889	.12357065
12	.10348395	.10655217	.10966619	.11282541	.11602923
13	.09706157	.10014373	.10327535	.10645577	.10968426
14	.09157073	.09466897	.09782032	.10102397	.10427912
15	.08682507	.08994110	.09311381	.09634229	.09962560
16	.08268483	.08582000	.08901537	.09226991	.09558254
17	.07904313	.08219852	.08541758	.08869914	.09204197
18	.07581684	.07899333	.08223690	.08554622	.08891992
19	.07294033	.07613862	.07940734	.08274501	.08615006
20	.07036108	.07358175	.07687614	.08024259	.08367933
21	.06803659	.07128011	.07460057	.07799611	.08146478
22	.06593207	.06919881	.07254565	.07597051	.07947123
23	.06401880	.06730906	.07068249	.07413682	.07766965
24	.06227283	.06558683	.06898703	.07247090	.07603580
25	.06067404	.06401196	.06743903	.07095246	.07454935
26	.05920540	.06256738	.06602137	.06956432	.07319307
27	.05785241	.06123854	.06471946	.06829186	.07195228
28	.05660265	.06001298	.06352081	.06712253	.07081440
29	.05544538	.05887993	.06241461	.06604551	.06976857
30	.05437133	.05783010	.06139154	.06505144	.06880539
31	.05337240	.05685535	.06044345	.06413212	.06791665
32	.05244150	.05594859	.05956320	.06328042	.06709519
33	.05157242	.05510357	.05874453	.06249004	.06633469
34	.05075966	.05431477	.05798191	.06175545	.06562958
35	.04999835	.05357732	.05727045	.06107171	.06497493
36	.04928416	.05288688	.05660578	.06043446	.06436635
37	.04861325	.05223957	.05598402	.05983979	.06379993
38	.04798214	.05163192	.05540169	.05928423	.06327217
39	.04738775	.05106083	.05485567	.05876462	.06277991
40	.04682728	.05052349	.05434315	.05827816	.06232034
41	.04629822	.05001738	.05386158	.05782229	.06189090
42	.04579828	.04954020	.05340868	.05739471	.06148927
43	.04532539	.04908989	.05298235	.05699333	.06111337
44	.04487768	.04866454	.05258071	.05661625	.06076128
45	.04445343	.04826246	.05220202	.05626173	.06043127
46	.04405108	.04788205	.05184471	.05592820	.06012175
47	.04366919	.04752189	.05150734	.05561421	.05983129
48	.04330646	.04718065	.05118858	.05531843	.05955854
49	.04296167	.04685712	.05088722	.05503965	.05930230
50	.04263371	.04655020	.05060215	.05477674	.05906145

INTEREST TABLES (Continued)

ANNUITY WHOSE PRESENT VALUE IS 1

$$a_{\overline{n}|}^{-1} = i/(1 - v^n) = s_{\overline{n}|}^{-1} + i \text{ (Continued)}$$

Years	Rate i				
n	.06(6 %)	.065(6½ %)	.07(7 %)	.075(7½ %)	.08(8 %)
1	1.06000000	1.06500000	1.07000000	1.07500000	1.08000000
2	0.54543689	0.54926150	0.55309179	0.55692771	0.56076923
3	.37410981	.37757570	.38105167	.38453763	.38803351
4	.28859149	.29190274	.29522812	.29856751	.30192080
5	.23739640	.24063454	.24389069	.24716472	.25045645
6	.20336263	.20656831	.20979580	.21304489	.21631539
7	.17913502	.18233137	.18555322	.18880032	.19207240
8	.16103594	.16423730	.16746776	.17072702	.17401476
9	.14702224	.15023803	.15348647	.15676716	.16007971
10	.13586796	.13910469	.14237750	.14568593	.14902949
11	.12679294	.13005521	.13335690	.13669747	.14007634
12	.11927703	.12256817	.12590199	.12927783	.13269502
13	.11296011	.11628256	.11965085	.12306420	.12652181
14	.10758491	.11094048	.11434494	.11779737	.12129685
15	.10296276	.10635278	.10979462	.11328724	.11682954
16	.09895214	.10237757	.10585765	.10939116	.11297687
17	.09544480	.09890633	.10242519	.10600003	.10962943
18	.09235654	.09585461	.09941260	.10302896	.10670210
19	.08962086	.09315575	.09675301	.10041090	.10412763
20	.08718456	.09075640	.09439293	.09809219	.10185221
21	.08500455	.08861333	.09228900	.09602937	.09983225
22	.08304557	.08669120	.09040577	.09418687	.09803207
23	.08127848	.08496078	.08871393	.09253528	.09642217
24	.07967900	.08339770	.08718902	.09105008	.09497796
25	.07822672	.08198148	.08581052	.08971067	.09367878
26	.07690435	.08069480	.08456103	.08849961	.09250713
27	.07569717	.07952288	.08342573	.08740204	.09144810
28	.07459255	.07845305	.08239193	.08640520	.09048891
29	.07357961	.07747440	.08144865	.08549811	.08961854
30	.07264891	.07657744	.08058640	.08467124	.08882743
31	.07179222	.07575393	.07979691	.08391628	.08810728
32	.07100234	.07499665	.07907292	.08322599	.08745081
33	.07027293	.07429924	.07840807	.08259397	.08685163
34	.06959843	.07365610	.07779674	.08201461	.08630411
35	.06897386	.07306226	.07723396	.08148291	.08580326
36	.06839483	.07251332	.07671531	.08099447	.08534467
37	.06785743	.07200534	.07623685	.08054533	.08492440
38	.06735812	.07153480	.07579505	.08013197	.08453894
39	.06689377	.07109854	.07538676	.07975124	.08418513
40	.06646154	.07069373	.07500914	.07940031	.08386016
41	.06605886	.07031779	.07465962	.07907663	.08356149
42	.06568342	.06996842	.07433591	.07877789	.08328684
43	.06533312	.06964352	.07403590	.07850201	.08303414
44	.06500606	.06934119	.07375769	.07824710	.08280152
45	.06470050	.06905968	.07349957	.07801146	.08258728
46	.06441485	.06879743	.07325996	.07779354	.08238991
47	.06414768	.06855300	.07303744	.07759190	.08220799
48	.06389765	.06832505	.07283070	.07740527	.08204027
49	.06366356	.06811240	.07263853	.07723247	.08188557
50	.06344429	.06791393	.07245985	.07707241	.08174286

COMPOUND AMOUNT OF 1 FOR FRACTIONAL PERIODS $(1+i)^{\frac{1}{p}}$

p	¼%	$\frac{5}{12}$%	½%	$\frac{7}{12}$%	¾%
2	1.0012 492	1.0020 812	1.0024 969	1.0029 124	1.0037 430
3	1.0008 326	1.0013 870	1.0016 639	1.0019 407	1.0024 938
4	1.0006 244	1.0010 400	1.0012 477	1.0014 552	1.0018 697
6	1.0004 162	1.0006 932	1.0008 316	1.0009 699	1.0012 461
12	1.0002 089	1.0003 466	1.0004 157	1.0004 848	1.0006 229
13	1.0001 921	1.0003 199	1.0003 837	1.0004 475	1.0005 749
26	1.0000 960	1.0001 599	1.0001 919	1.0002 237	1.0002 874
52	1.0000 480	1.0000 800	1.0000 959	1.0001 119	1.0001 437
365	1.0000 068	1.0000 114	1.0000 137	1.0000 159	1.0000 205
p	1%	1⅛%	1¼%	1½%	1¾%
2	1.0049 876	1.0056 093	1.0062 306	1.0074 721	1.0087 121
3	1.0033 223	1.0037 360	1.0041 494	1.0049 752	1.0057 996
4	1.0024 907	1.0028 008	1.0031 105	1.0037 291	1.0043 466
6	1.0016 598	1.0018 663	1.0020 726	1.0024 845	1.0028 956
12	1.0008 295	1.0009 327	1.0010 357	1.0012 415	1.0014 468
13	1.0007 657	1.0008 609	1.0009 560	1.0011 459	1.0013 354
26	1.0003 828	1.0004 304	1.0004 779	1.0005 728	1.0006 675
52	1.0001 914	1.0002 152	1.0002 389	1.0002 864	1.0003 337
365	1.0000 273	1.0000 307	1.0000 340	1.0000 408	1.0000 475
p	2%	2¼%	2½%	2¾%	3%
2	1.0099 505	1.0111 874	1.0124 228	1.0136 568	1.0148 892
3	1.0066 227	1.0074 444	1.0082 648	1.0090 839	1.0099 016
4	1.0049 629	1.0055 782	1.0061 922	1.0068 052	1.0074 171
6	1.0033 059	1.0037 153	1.0041 239	1.0045 317	1.0049 386
12	1.0016 516	1.0018 559	1.0020 598	1.0022 633	1.0024 663
13	1.0015 244	1.0017 130	1.0019 012	1.0020 890	1.0022 763
26	1.0007 619	1.0008 562	1.0009 502	1.0010 440	1.0011 375
52	1.0003 809	1.0004 280	1.0004 750	1.0005 218	1.0005 686
365	1.0000 543	1.0000 610	1.0000 676	1.0000 743	1.0000 810
p	3½%	4%	4½%	5%	5½%
2	1.0173 495	1.0198 039	1.0222 524	1.0246 951	1.0271 319
3	1.0115 331	1.0131 594	1.0147 805	1.0163 964	1.0180 071
4	1.0086 374	1.0098 534	1.0110 650	1.0122 722	1.0134 752
6	1.0057 500	1.0065 582	1.0073 631	1.0081 649	1.0089 634
12	1.0028 709	1.0032 737	1.0036 748	1.0040 741	1.0044 717
13	1.0026 498	1.0030 215	1.0033 916	1.0037 601	1.0041 270
26	1.0013 240	1.0015 096	1.0016 944	1.0018 783	1.0020 614
52	1.0006 618	1.0007 545	1.0008 468	1.0009 387	1.0010 302
365	1.0000 942	1.0001 075	1.0001 206	1.0001 337	1.0001 467
p	6%	6½%	7%	7½%	8%
2	1.0295 630	1.0319 884	1.0344 080	1.0368 221	1.0392 305
3	1.0196 128	1.0212 135	1.0228 091	1.0243 998	1.0259 856
4	1.0146 738	1.0158 683	1.0170 585	1.0182 446	1.0194 265
6	1.0097 588	1.0105 511	1.0113 403	1.0121 264	1.0129 095
12	1.0048 676	1.0052 617	1.0056 541	1.0060 449	1.0064 340
13	1.0044 923	1.0048 560	1.0052 181	1.0055 786	1.0059 376
26	1.0022 436	1.0024 250	1.0026 056	1.0027 854	1.0029 644
52	1.0011 212	1.0012 118	1.0013 020	1.0013 918	1.0014 811
365	1.0001 596	1.0001 726	1.0001 854	1.0001 982	1.0002 109

INTEREST TABLES (Continued)

NOMINAL RATES CONVERTIBLE p TIMES PER YEAR EQUIVALENT TO EFFECTIVE RATE i GIVEN IN HEADING, $j_p = p[(1+i)^{\frac{1}{p}} - 1]$

p	$\frac{1}{4}$%	$\frac{5}{12}$%	$\frac{1}{2}$%	$\frac{7}{12}$%	$\frac{3}{4}$%
$\frac{1}{4}$	.0025 094	.0041 928	.0050 376	.0058 846	.0075 848
$\frac{1}{2}$	.0025 032	.0041 754	.0050 125	.0058 504	.0075 281
2	.0024 984	.0041 623	.0049 938	.0058 249	.0074 860
4	.0024 977	.0041 602	.0049 907	.0058 206	.0074 790
6	.0024 974	.0041 595	.0049 896	.0058 192	.0074 767
12	.0024 971	.0041 587	.0049 886	.0058 178	.0074 743
13	.0024 971	.0041 587	.0049 885	.0058 177	.0074 742
52	.0024 969	.0041 582	.0049 878	.0058 167	.0074 725
365	.0024 969	.0041 580	.0049 876	.0058 164	.0074 721
∞	.0024 969	.0041 580	.0049 875	.0058 164	.0074 720
p	**1%**	**$1\frac{1}{8}$%**	**$1\frac{1}{4}$%**	**$1\frac{1}{2}$%**	**$1\frac{3}{4}$%**
$\frac{1}{4}$	.0101 510	.0114 413	.0127 363	.0153 409	.0179 648
$\frac{1}{2}$	.0100 500	.0113 133	.0125 781	.0151 125	.0176 531
2	.0099 751	.0112 185	.0124 612	.0149 442	.0174 241
4	.0099 627	.0112 029	.0124 418	.0149 164	.0173 863
6	.0099 586	.0111 976	.0124 354	.0149 071	.0173 737
12	.0099 545	.0111 924	.0124 290	.0148 979	.0173 612
13	.0099 541	.0111 920	.0124 285	.0148 971	.0173 602
52	.0099 513	.0111 884	.0124 240	.0148 907	.0173 515
365	.0099 505	.0111 874	.0124 227	.0148 889	.0173 490
∞	.0099 503	.0111 872	.0124 225	.0148 886	.0173 486
p	**2%**	**$2\frac{1}{4}$%**	**$2\frac{1}{2}$%**	**$2\frac{3}{4}$%**	**3%**
$\frac{1}{4}$	.0206 080	.0232 708	.0259 532	.0286 553	.0313 772
$\frac{1}{2}$	.0202 000	.0227 531	.0253 125	.0278 781	.0304 500
2	.0199 010	.0223 748	.0248 457	.0273 135	.0297 783
4	.0198 517	.0223 126	.0247 690	.0272 209	.0296 683
6	.0198 353	.0222 919	.0247 435	.0271 901	.0296 317
12	.0198 190	.0222 713	.0247 180	.0271 594	.0295 952
13	.0198 177	.0222 697	.0247 161	.0271 570	.0295 924
52	.0198 064	.0222 554	.0246 985	.0271 358	.0295 672
365	.0198 032	.0222 513	.0246 934	.0271 297	.0295 600
∞	.0198 026	.0222 506	.0246 926	.0271 287	.0295 588
p	**$3\frac{1}{2}$%**	**4%**	**$4\frac{1}{2}$%**	**5%**	**$5\frac{1}{2}$%**
$\frac{1}{4}$	.0368 808	.0424 647	.0481 297	.0538 766	.0597 062
$\frac{1}{2}$	.0356 125	.0408 000	.0460 125	.0512 500	.0565 125
2	.0346 990	.0396 078	.0445 048	.0493 902	.0542 639
4	.0345 498	.0394 136	.0442 600	.0490 889	.0539 007
6	.0345 002	.0393 492	.0441 787	.0489 891	.0537 804
12	.0344 508	.0392 849	.0440 977	.0488 895	.0536 604
13	.0344 470	.0392 799	.0440 915	.0488 818	.0536 512
52	.0344 128	.0392 355	.0440 355	.0488 131	.0535 683
365	.0344 030	.0392 228	.0440 195	.0487 934	.0535 447
∞	.0344 014	.0392 207	.0440 169	.0487 902	.0535 408
p	**6%**	**$6\frac{1}{2}$%**	**7%**	**$7\frac{1}{2}$%**	**8%**
$\frac{1}{4}$	.0656 193	.0716 166	.0776 990	.0838 673	.0901 223
$\frac{1}{2}$	.0618 000	.0671 125	.0724 500	.0778 125	.0832 000
2	.0591 260	.0639 767	.0688 161	.0736 441	.0784 610
4	.0586 954	.0634 731	.0682 341	.0729 784	.0777 062
6	.0585 528	.0633 064	.0680 416	.0727 583	.0774 567
12	.0584 106	.0631 403	.0678 497	.0725 390	.0772 084
13	.0583 997	.0631 276	.0678 350	.0725 222	.0771 893
52	.0583 016	.0630 129	.0677 027	.0723 710	.0770 180
365	.0582 736	.0629 802	.0676 649	.0723 278	.0769 692
∞	.0582 689	.0629 748	.0676 586	.0723 207	.0769 610

AMOUNT FOR YEAR OF p DEPOSITS OF $1/p$, p TIMES PER YEAR, i/j_p

p	$\frac{1}{4}$%	$\frac{5}{12}$%	$\frac{1}{2}$%	$\frac{7}{12}$%	$\frac{3}{4}$%
$\frac{1}{4}$	0.9962 5	0.9937 717	0.9925 312	0 9912 924	0.9888 201
$\frac{1}{2}$	0.9974 8	0.9979 210	0.9975 062	0.9970 918	0.9962 640
2	1.0006 246	1.0010 406	1.0012 484	1.0014 562	1.0018 715
4	1.0009 370	1.0015 611	1.0018 730	1.0021 848	1.0028 081
6	1.0010 412	1.0017 347	1.0020 813	1.0024 278	1.0031 205
12	1.0011 453	1.0019 083	1.0022 896	1.0026 708	1.0034 329
13	1.0011 533	1.0019 216	1.0023 056	1.0026 895	1.0034 569
52	1.0012 254	1.0020 418	1.0024 498	1.0028 577	1.0036 732
365	1.0012 461	1.0020 762	1.0024 911	1.0029 058	1.0037 351
∞	1.0012 495	1.0020 819	1.0024 979	1.0029 138	1.0037 453

p	1%	$1\frac{1}{8}$%	$1\frac{1}{4}$%	$1\frac{1}{2}$%	$1\frac{3}{4}$%
$\frac{1}{4}$	0.9851 244	0.9832 823	0.9814 441	0.9777 791	0.9741 295
$\frac{1}{2}$	0.9950 249	0.9944 065	0.9937 888	0.9925 558	0.9913 259
2	1.0024 938	1.0028 046	1.0031 153	1.0037 360	1.0043 618
4	1.0037 422	1.0042 089	1.0046 754	1.0056 076	1.0065 388
6	1.0041 586	1.0046 773	1.0051 958	1.0062 319	1.0072 671
12	1.0045 751	1.0051 458	1.0057 163	1.0068 565	1.0079 957
13	1.0046 071	1.0051 819	1.0057 564	1.0069 046	1.0080 518
52	1.0048 956	1.0055 063	1.0061 169	1.0073 372	1.0085 564
365	1.0049 780	1.0055 991	1.0062 199	1.0074 608	1.0087 007
∞	1.0049 917	1.0056 145	1.0062 371	1.0074 814	1.0087 247

p	2%	$2\frac{1}{4}$%	$2\frac{1}{2}$%	$2\frac{3}{4}$%	3%
$\frac{1}{4}$	0.9704 950	0.9668 757	0.9632 715	0.9596 824	0.9561 082
$\frac{1}{2}$	0.9900 990	0.9888 752	0.9876 543	0.9864 365	0.9852 217
2	1.0049 752	1.0055 937	1.0062 114	1.0068 284	1.0074 446
4	1.0074 686	1.0083 984	1.0093 268	1.0102 542	1.0111 807
6	1.0083 013	1.0093 344	1.0103 667	1.0113 979	1.0124 282
12	1.0091 339	1.0102 711	1.0114 072	1.0125 424	1.0136 766
13	1.0091 980	1.0103 431	1.0114 873	1.0126 305	1.0137 727
52	1.0097 747	1.0109 919	1.0122 082	1.0134 234	1.0146 376
365	1.0099 396	1.0111 775	1.0124 143	1.0136 502	1.0148 850
∞	1.0099 670	1.0112 083	1.0124 486	1.0136 878	1.0149 261

p	$3\frac{1}{2}$%	4%	$4\frac{1}{2}$%	5%	$5\frac{1}{2}$%
$\frac{1}{4}$	0.9490 046	0.9419 6	0.9349 7	0.9280 5	0.9211 8
$\frac{1}{2}$	0.9828 010	0.9803 922	0.9779 951	0.9756 098	0.9732 360
2	1.0086 748	1.0099 020	1.0111 262	1.0123 475	1.0135 660
4	1.0130 309	1.0148 774	1.0167 203	1.0185 594	1.0203 950
6	1.0144 858	1.0165 396	1.0185 895	1.0206 357	1.0226 781
12	1.0159 420	1.0182 035	1.0204 611	1.0227 148	1.0249 647
13	1.0160 541	1.0183 316	1.0206 051	1.0228 748	1.0251 407
52	1.0170 632	1.0194 847	1.0219 623	1.0243 160	1.0267 259
365	1.0173 517	1.0198 145	1.0222 733	1.0247 282	1.0271 793
∞	1.0173 997	1.0198 693	1.0223 349	1.0247 967	1.0272 546

p	6%	$6\frac{1}{2}$%	7%	$7\frac{1}{2}$%	8%
$\frac{1}{4}$	0.9143 7	0.9076 1	0.9009 1	0.8942 7	0.8876 8
$\frac{1}{2}$	0.9708 738	0.9685 230	0.9661 836	0.9638 554	0.9615 385
2	1.0147 815	1.0159 942	1.0172 040	1.0184 110	1.0196 152
4	1.0222 269	1.0240 552	1.0258 800	1.0277 013	1.0295 190
6	1.0247 168	1.0267 517	1.0287 830	1.0308 106	1.0328 346
12	1.0272 107	1.0294 529	1.0316 914	1.0339 262	1.0361 572
13	1.0274 027	1.0296 609	1.0319 154	1.0341 661	1.0364 131
52	1.0291 319	1.0315 340	1.0339 324	1.0363 270	1.0387 179
365	1.0296 265	1.0320 699	1.0345 095	1.0369 453	1.0393 774
∞	1.0297 087	1.0321 589	1.0346 053	1.0370 480	1.0394 870

AMERICAN EXPERIENCE MORTALITY TABLE

Based on 100,000 living at age 10, giving: l_x, number of living; d_x, number of deaths; p_x, probability of living; q_x, probability of dying for age x from 10 to 95.

x	l_x	d_x	p_x	q_x	x	l_x	d_x	p_x	q_x
10	100000	749	.992510	.007490	**55**	64563	1199	.981429	.018571
11	99251	746	.992484	.007516	56	63364	1260	.980115	.019885
12	98505	743	.992457	.007543	57	62104	1325	.978665	.021335
13	97762	740	.992431	.007569	58	60779	1394	.977064	.022936
14	97022	737	.992404	.007596	59	59385	1468	.975280	.024720
15	96285	735	.992366	.007634	**60**	57917	1546	.973307	.026693
16	95550	732	.992339	.007661	61	56371	1628	.971120	.028880
17	94818	729	.992312	.007688	62	54743	1713	.968708	.031292
18	94089	727	.992273	.007727	63	53030	1800	.966057	.033943
19	93362	725	.992235	.007765	64	51230	1889	.963127	.036873
20	92637	723	.992195	.007805	**65**	49341	1980	.959871	.040129
21	91914	722	.992145	.007855	66	47361	2070	.956293	.043707
22	91192	721	.992094	.007906	67	45291	2158	.952353	.047647
23	90471	720	.992042	.007958	68	43133	2243	.947998	.052002
24	89751	719	.991989	.008011	69	40890	2321	.943238	.056762
25	89032	718	.991935	.008065	**70**	38569	2391	.938007	.061993
26	88314	718	.991870	.008130	71	36178	2448	.932335	.067665
27	87596	718	.991803	.008197	72	33730	2487	.926267	.073733
28	86878	718	.991736	.008264	73	31243	2505	.919822	.080178
29	86160	719	.991655	.008345	74	28738	2501	.912972	.087028
30	85441	720	.991573	.008427	**75**	26237	2476	.905629	.094371
31	84721	721	.991490	.008510	76	23761	2431	.897689	.102311
32	84000	723	.991393	.008607	77	21330	2369	.888936	.111064
33	83277	726	.991282	.008718	78	18961	2291	.879173	.120827
34	82551	729	.991169	.008831	79	16670	2196	.868266	.131734
35	81822	732	.991054	.008946	**80**	14474	2091	.855534	.144466
36	81090	737	.990911	.009089	81	12383	1964	.841395	.158605
37	80353	742	.990766	.009234	82	10419	1816	.825703	.174297
38	79611	749	.990592	.009408	83	8603	1648	.808439	.191561
39	78862	756	.990414	.009586	84	6955	1470	.788641	.211359
40	78106	765	.990206	.009794	**85**	5485	1292	.764448	.235552
41	77341	774	.989992	.010008	86	4193	1114	.734319	.265681
42	76567	785	.989748	.010252	87	3079	933	.696980	.303020
43	75782	797	.989483	.010517	88	2146	744	.653308	.346692
44	74985	812	.989171	.010829	89	1402	555	.604137	.395863
45	74173	828	.988837	.011163	**90**	847	385	.545455	.454545
46	73345	848	.988438	.011562	91	462	246	.467532	.532468
47	72497	870	.988000	.012000	92	216	137	.365741	.634259
48	71627	896	.987491	.012509	93	79	58	.265823	.734177
49	70731	927	.986894	.013106	94	21	18	.142857	.857143
50	69804	962	.986219	.013781	**95**	3	3	.000000	1.000000
51	68842	1001	.985459	.014541					
52	67841	1044	.984611	.015389					
53	66797	1091	.983667	.016333					
54	65706	1143	.982604	.017396					

COMMUTATION COLUMNS 3%

$$\mathbb{N}_x = D_x + D_{x+1} + D_{x+2} \cdot \cdot \cdot \cdot + D_{95}$$
$$M_x = C_x + C_{x+1} + C_{x+2} \cdot \cdot \cdot \cdot + C_{95}$$

$1 + a_x = \mathbb{N}_x/D_x$ $\quad$ $A_x = M_x/D_x$

$D_x = v^x l_x$ $\quad$ $C_x = v^{x+1} d_x$

x	D_x	$\mathbb{N}_x$	C_x	M_x	$1 + a_x$	A_x
10	74409.4	1811 346	541.094	21651.7	24.3430	.290981
11	71701.0	1736 936	523.229	21110.7	24.2247	.294426
12	69089.4	1665 235	505.947	20587.4	24.1026	.297982
13	66571.2	1596 146	489.227	20081.5	23.9765	.301654
14	64143.0	1529 575	473.052	19592.3	23.8463	.305447
15	61801.7	1465 432	458.028	19119.2	23.7118	.309364
16	59543.6	1403 630	442.872	18661.2	23.5731	.313403
17	57366.4	1344 086	428.211	18218.3	23.4298	.317578
18	55267.4	1286 720	414.598	17790.1	23.2817	.321891
19	53243.0	1231 453	401.415	17375.5	23.1289	.326343
20	51290.9	1178 210	388.648	16974.1	22.9711	.330938
21	49408.3	1126 919	376.806	16585.4	22.8083	.335681
22	47592.4	1077 510	365.325	16208.6	22.6404	.340571
23	45840.9	1029 918	354.192	15843.3	22.4672	.345615
24	44151.5	984 077	343.398	15489.1	22.2886	.350817
25	42522.2	939 926	332.933	15145.7	22.1044	.356184
26	40950.7	897 403	323.236	14812.8	21.9142	.361722
27	39434.8	856 453	313.821	14489.5	21.7182	.367431
28	37972.4	817 018	304.681	14175.7	21.5161	.373317
29	36561.7	779 046	296.218	13871.0	21.3077	.379387
30	35200.6	742 484	287.991	13574.8	21.0930	.385642
31	33887.3	707 283	279.991	13286.8	20.8716	.392089
32	32620.3	673 396	272.590	13006.8	20.6435	.398734
33	31397.6	640 776	265.749	12734.2	20.4084	.405580
34	30217.4	609 378	259.074	12468.5	20.1665	.412627
35	29078.2	579 161	252.564	12209.4	19.9174	.419883
36	27978.7	550 082	246.882	11956.9	19.6608	.427356
37	26916.9	522 104	241.318	11710.0	19.3969	.435042
38	25891.6	495 187	236.499	11468.7	19.1254	.442949
39	24901.0	469 295	231.757	11232.2	18.8465	.451073
40	23943.9	444 394	227.685	11000.4	18.5598	.459423
41	23018.8	420 450	223.654	10772.7	18.2655	.467996
42	22124.7	397 432	220.226	10549.1	17.9632	.476799
43	21260.1	375 307	217.080	10328.8	17.6531	.485832
44	20423.8	354 047	214.724	10111.8	17.3350	.495097
45	19614.2	333 623	212.578	9897.03	17.0093	.504585
46	18830.3	314 009	211.371	9684.45	16.6757	.514301
47	18070.5	295 178	210.539	9473.08	16.3348	.524229
48	17333.6	277 108	210.515	9262.54	15.9867	.534368
49	16618.3	259 774	211.455	9052.03	15.6318	.544703
50	15922.8	243 156	213.048	8840.57	15.2709	.555215
51	15246.0	227 233	215.228	8627.53	14.9045	.565889
52	14586.7	211 987	217.935	8412.30	14.5329	.576711
53	13943.9	197 401	221.113	8194.36	14.1568	.587667
54	13316.6	183 457	224.905	7973.25	13.7765	.598743

COMMUTATION COLUMNS 3% (Continued)

x	D_x	N_x	C_x	M_x	$1 + a_x$	A_x
55	12703.9	170140	229.052	7748.34	13.3928	.609920
56	12104.8	157436	233.695	7519.29	13.0061	.621182
57	11518.5	145331	238.593	7285.60	12.6172	.632510
58	10944.5	133813	243.706	7047.00	12.2265	.643888
59	10382.0	122868	249.168	6803.30	11.8348	.655298
60	9830.43	112486	254.764	6554.13	11.4427	.666718
61	9289.34	102656	260.463	6299.37	11.0509	.678128
62	8758.32	93366.6	266.080	6038.90	10.6603	.689505
63	8237.14	84608.2	271.450	5772.82	10.2716	.700828
64	7725.77	76371.1	276.575	5501.37	9.88524	.712080
65	7224.18	68645.3	281.455	5224.80	9.50217	.723238
66	6732.31	61421.2	285.678	4943.34	9.12334	.734272
67	6250.54	54688.8	289.148	4657.67	8.74945	.745162
68	5779.34	48438.3	291.784	4368.52	8.38128	.755885
69	5319.23	42659.0	293.136	4076.73	8.01976	.766415
70	4871.16	37339.7	293.182	3783.60	7.66547	.776734
71	4436.10	32468.6	291.428	3490.42	7.31916	.786820
72	4015.47	28032.5	287.447	3198.99	6.98112	.796666
73	3611.07	24017.0	281.095	2911.54	6.65094	.806283
74	3224.79	20405.9	272.472	2630.45	6.32783	.815694
75	2858.40	17181.1	261.892	2357.97	6.01076	.824929
76	2513.25	14322.7	249.643	2096.08	5.69889	.834013
77	2190.41	11809.5	236.190	1846.44	5.39146	.842967
78	1890.42	9619.09	221.761	1610.25	5.08834	.851796
79	1613.60	7728.67	206.374	1388.49	4.78972	.860494
80	1360.22	6115.07	190.783	1182.12	4.49563	.869059
81	1129.82	4754.85	173.976	991.333	4.20849	.877423
82	922.940	3625.02	156.180	817.357	3.92769	.885601
83	739.878	2702.08	137.604	661.177	3.65207	.893629
84	580.725	1962.21	119.166	523.573	3.37889	.901586
85	444.644	1381.48	101.686	404.407	3.10694	.909507
86	330.007	936.837	85.1229	302.721	2.83884	.917315
87	235.272	606.829	69.2159	217.598	2.57926	.924876
88	159.204	371.557	53.5871	148.382	2.33384	.932024
89	100.980	212.353	38.8099	94.7949	2.10292	.938750
90	59.2288	111.373	26.1381	55.9850	1.88039	.945231
91	31.3657	52.1442	16.2148	29.8469	1.66246	.951579
92	14.2373	20.7785	8.76715	13.6321	1.45944	.957492
93	5.05551	6.54120	3.60354	4.86499	1.29388	.962314
94	1.30473	1.48569	1.08577	1.26146	1.13870	.966834
95	0.180961	0.180961	0.175690	0.175690	1.00000	.970874

COMMUTATION COLUMNS 3½%

$$\mathbb{N}_x = D_x + D_{x+1} + D_{x+2} \cdots + D_{95}$$
$$M_x = C_x + C_{x+1} + C_{x+2} \cdots + C_{95}$$
$$1 + a_x = \mathbb{N}_x/D_x \qquad A_x = M_x/D_x$$

x	D_x	$\mathbb{N}_x$	C_x	M_x	$1 + a_x$	A_x
10	70891.9	1575 535	513.024	17612.9	22.2245	.248447
11	67981.5	1504 643	493.690	17099.9	22.1331	.251537
12	65189.0	1436 662	475.077	16606.2	22.0384	.254739
13	62509.4	1371 473	457.159	16131.1	21.9403	.258059
14	59938.4	1308 963	439.908	15674.0	21.8385	.261501
15	57471.6	1249 025	423.879	15234.1	21.7329	.265071
16	55104.2	1191 553	407.873	14810.2	21.6236	.268766
17	52832.9	1136 449	392.465	14402.3	21.5102	.272601
18	50653.9	1083 616	378.153	14009.8	21.3926	.276580
19	48562.8	1032 962	364.360	13631.7	21.2707	.280702
20	46556.2	984 400	351.068	13267.3	21.1443	.284974
21	44630.8	937 843	338.727	12916.3	21.0134	.289402
22	42782.8	893 213	326.819	12577.5	20.8779	.293986
23	41009.2	850 430	315.329	12250.7	20.7375	.298731
24	39307.1	809 421	304.243	11935.4	20.5922	.303644
25	37673.6	770 114	293.545	11631.1	20.4417	.308734
26	36106.1	732 440	283.619	11337.6	20.2858	.314008
27	34601.5	696 334	274.028	11054.0	20.1244	.319465
28	33157.4	661 732	264.761	10779.9	19.9573	.325115
29	31771.3	628 575	256.164	10515.2	19.7843	.330964
30	30440.8	596 804	247.846	10259.0	19.6054	.337016
31	29163.5	566 363	239.797	10011.2	19.4202	.343277
32	27937.5	537 199	232.331	9771.37	19.2286	.349758
33	26760.5	509 262	225.406	9539.04	19.0304	.356460
34	25630.1	482 501	218.683	9313.64	18.8256	.363387
35	24544.7	456 871	212.158	9094.96	18.6138	.370547
36	23502.5	432 327	206.383	8882.80	18.3949	.377951
37	22501.4	408 824	200.757	8676.41	18.1688	.385595
38	21539.7	386 323	195.798	8475.66	17.9354	.393490
39	20615.5	364 783	190.945	8279.86	17.6946	.401632
40	19727.4	344 167	186.684	8088.91	17.4461	.410034
41	18873.6	324 440	182.493	7902.23	17.1901	.418692
42	18052.9	305 566	178.828	7719.74	16.9262	.427618
43	17263.6	287 513	175.422	7540.91	16.6543	.436810
44	16504.4	270 250	172.679	7365.49	16.3744	.446275
45	15773.6	253 745	170.127	7192.81	16.0867	.456004
46	15070.0	237 972	168.345	7022.68	15.7911	.466003
47	14392.1	222 902	166.872	6854.34	15.4878	.476258
48	13738.5	208 510	166.047	6687.47	15.1770	.486768
49	13107.9	194 771	165.982	6521.42	14.8591	.497519
50	12498.6	181 663	166.424	6355.44	14.5346	.508490
51	11909.6	169 165	167.315	6189.01	14.2041	.519668
52	11339.5	157 255	168.602	6021.70	13.8679	.531037
53	10787.4	145 916	170.234	5853.09	13.5264	.542584
54	10252.4	135 128	172.317	5682.86	13.1801	.554295

COMMUNICATION COLUMNS $3\frac{1}{2}\%$ (Continued)

x	D_x	$\mathbb{N}_x$	C_x	M_x	$1 + a_x$	A_x
55	9733.40	124876	174.646	5510.54	12.8296	.566148
56	9229.60	115142	177.325	5335.90	12.4753	.578129
57	8740.17	105913	180.167	5158.57	12.1179	.590215
58	8264.44	97172.6	183.140	4978.41	11.7579	.602389
59	7801.82	88908.2	186.340	4795.27	11.3958	.614634
60	7351.65	81106.4	189.604	4608.93	11.0324	.626924
61	6913.44	73754.7	192.909	4419.32	10.6683	.639236
62	6486.75	66841.3	196.117	4226.41	10.3043	.651546
63	6071.27	60354.5	199.109	4030.30	9.9410	.663831
64	5666.85	54283.3	201.887	3831.19	9.5791	.676070
65	5273.33	48616.4	204.457	3629.30	9.2193	.688236
66	4890.55	43343.1	206.522	3424.84	8.8626	.700298
67	4518.65	38452.5	208.021	3218.32	8.5097	.712231
68	4157.82	33933.9	208.903	3010.30	8.1615	.724009
69	3808.32	29776.1	208.858	2801.40	7.8187	.735600
70	3470.67	25967.7	207.881	2592.54	7.4820	.746984
71	3145.43	22497.1	205.639	2384.66	7.1523	.758135
72	2833.42	19351.6	201.851	2179.02	6.8298	.769041
73	2535.75	16518.2	196.436	1977.17	6.5141	.779716
74	2253.57	13982.5	189.491	1780.73	6.2046	.790183
75	1987.87	11728.9	181.253	1591.24	5.9002	.800475
76	1739.39	9741.03	171.940	1409.99	5.6002	.810620
77	1508.63	8001.63	161.889	1238.05	5.3039	.820641
78	1295.73	6493.00	151.265	1076.16	5.0111	.830543
79	1100.65	5197.27	140.089	924.894	4.7220	.840318
80	923.338	4096.62	128.880	784.805	4.4368	.849965
81	763.234	3173.29	116.959	655.925	4.1577	.859402
82	620.465	2410.05	104.488	538.966	3.8843	.868648
83	494.995	1789.59	91.6153	434.478	3.6154	.877741
84	386.641	1294.59	78.9564	342.862	3.3483	.886772
85	294.610	907.951	67.0490	263.906	3.0819	.895782
86	217.598	613.342	55.8566	196.857	2.8187	.904682
87	154.383	395.744	45.1992	141.000	2.5634	.913315
88	103.963	241.361	34.8243	95.8011	2.3216	.921492
89	65.6231	137.398	25.0993	60.9768	2.0937	.929197
90	38.3047	71.7747	16.8224	35.8775	1.8738	.936635
91	20.1869	33.4700	10.3854	19.0551	1.6580	.943932
92	9.11888	13.2831	5.58815	8.66969	1.4567	.950741
93	3.22236	4.16421	2.28578	3.08155	1.2923	.956300
94	0.827611	0.941843	0.685392	0.795762	1.1380	.961516
95	0.114232	0.114232	0.110369	0.110369	1.0000	.966184

COMMUTATION COLUMNS 4%

$$\mathbb{N}_x = D_x + D_{x+1} + D_{x+2} \cdots + D_{95}$$
$$M_x = C_x + C_{x+1} + C_{x+2} \cdots + C_{95}$$

$1 + a_x = \mathbb{N}_x / D_x$ $\qquad$ $A_x = M_x / D_x$

x	D_x	$\mathbb{N}_x$	C_x	M_x	$1 + a_x$	A_x
10	67556.4	1379 083	486.536	14514.8	20.4138	.214854
11	64471.6	1311 527	465.949	14028.2	20.3427	.217588
12	61525.9	1247 055	446.227	13562.3	20.2688	.220432
13	58713.3	1185 529	427.332	13116.0	20.1918	.223391
14	56027.8	1126 816	409.230	12688.7	20.1117	.226472
15	53463.6	1070 788	392.423	12279.5	20.0283	.229679
16	51014.9	1017 325	375.789	11887.1	19.9417	.233011
17	48677.0	966 310	359.855	11511.3	19.8515	.236483
18	46445.0	917 633	345.065	11151.4	19.7574	.240099
19	44313.6	871 188	330.881	10806.4	19.6596	.243861
20	42278.3	826 874	317.277	10475.5	19.5579	.247774
21	40335.0	784 596	304.652	10158.2	19.4520	.251846
22	38479.0	744 261	292.529	9853.54	19.3420	.256076
23	36706.5	705 782	280.887	9561.01	19.2277	.260472
24	35013.8	669 075	269.709	9280.12	19.1089	.265042
25	33397.4	634 062	258.975	9010.42	18.9854	.269794
26	31853.9	600 664	249.014	8751.44	18.8568	.274737
27	30379.7	568 810	239.437	8502.43	18.7233	.279872
28	28971.9	538 431	230.228	8262.99	18.5846	.285207
29	27627.3	509 459	221.681	8032.76	18.4404	.290754
30	26343.1	481 831	213.451	7811.08	18.2906	.296514
31	25116.4	455 488	205.527	7597.63	18.1351	.302497
32	23944.9	430 372	198.170	7392.10	17.9735	.308713
33	22825.7	406 427	191.339	7193.93	17.8056	.315168
34	21756.5	383 601	184.740	7002.59	17.6316	.321862
35	20735.0	361 845	178.366	6817.85	17.4510	.328810
36	19759.1	341 110	172.677	6639.49	17.2634	.336022
37	18826.5	321 351	167.162	6466.81	17.0691	.343496
38	17935.2	302 524	162.249	6299.65	16.8676	.351245
39	17083.1	284 589	157.467	6137.40	16.6591	.359267
40	16268.6	267 506	153.213	5979.93	16.4431	.367575
41	15489.7	251 237	149.053	5826.72	16.2196	.376168
42	14744.9	235 748	145.357	5677.67	15.9884	.385060
43	14032.4	221 003	141.903	5532.31	15.7494	.394252
44	13350.8	206 970	139.013	5390.41	15.5025	.403752
45	12698.3	193 619	136.300	5251.40	15.2477	.413551
46	12073.6	180 921	134.224	5115.10	14.9849	.423659
47	11475.0	168 848	132.409	4980.87	14.7144	.434063
48	10901.3	157 373	131.122	4848.46	14.4362	.444762
49	10350.9	146 471	130.441	4717.34	14.1507	.455744
50	9822.30	136 120	130.159	4586.90	13.8583	.466988
51	9314.36	126 298	130.227	4456.74	13.5595	.478481
52	8825.89	116 984	130.597	4326.51	13.2546	.490207
53	8355.84	108 158	131.227	4195.92	12.9440	.502154
54	7903.23	99802.1	132.194	4064.69	12.6280	.514307

COMMUTATION COLUMNS 4% (Continued)

x	D_x	$\mathbb{N}_x$	C_x	M_x	$1 + a_x$	A_x
55	7467.07	91898.8	133.337	3932.50	12.3072	.526645
56	7046.53	84431.8	134.732	3799.16	11.9820	.539153
57	6640.78	77385.2	136.233	3664.43	11.6530	.551806
58	6249.13	70744.5	137.815	3528.19	11.3207	.564589
59	5870.97	64495.3	139.549	3390.38	10.9855	.577482
60	5505.61	58624.4	141.311	3250.83	10.6481	.590457
61	5152.55	53118.7	143.083	3109.52	10.3092	.603492
62	4811.29	47966.2	144.763	2966.44	9.96951	.616557
63	4481.48	43154.9	146.264	2821.67	9.62962	.629630
64	4162.85	38673.4	147.593	2675.41	9.29014	.642687
65	3855.15	34510.6	148.753	2527.82	8.95182	.655699
66	3558.12	30655.4	149.533	2379.06	8.61563	.668630
67	3271.74	27097.3	149.894	2229.53	8.28225	.681452
68	2996.01	23825.6	149.806	2079.64	7.95245	.694137
69	2730.97	20829.6	149.053	1929.83	7.62718	.706647
70	2476.88	18098.6	147.643	1780.78	7.30702	.718961
71	2233.97	15621.7	145.349	1633.13	6.99281	.731046
72	2002.70	13387.8	141.985	1487.79	6.68486	.742890
73	1783.69	11385.1	137.512	1345.80	6.38288	.754505
74	1577.57	9601.37	132.012	1208.29	6.08617	.765917
75	1384.89	8023.80	125.666	1076.28	5.79384	.777160
76	1205.95	6638.91	118.636	950.612	5.50511	.788265
77	1040.94	5432.96	111.164	831.975	5.21931	.799257
78	889.735	4392.02	103.369	720.811	4.93633	.810141
79	752.145	3502.29	95.2720	617.442	4.65640	.820908
80	627.945	2750.14	87.2275	522.170	4.37960	.831554
81	516.565	2122.20	78.7785	434.942	4.10829	.841989
82	417.919	1605.63	70.0404	356.164	3.84197	.852232
83	331.805	1187.72	61.1163	286.124	3.57956	.862325
84	257.927	855.910	52.4184	225.007	3.31842	.872368
85	195.588	597.983	44.2991	172.589	3.05736	.882409
86	143.766	402.395	36.7269	128.290	2.79895	.892348
87	101.510	258.629	29.5766	91.5628	2.54781	.902007
88	68.0293	157.118	22.6781	61.9863	2.30957	.911170
89	42.7347	89.0891	16.2664	39.3082	2.08470	.919819
90	24.8246	46.3544	10.8499	23.0418	1.86728	.928182
91	13.0199	21.5298	6.66604	12.1918	1.65361	.936400
92	5.85311	8.50988	3.56960	5.52580	1.45391	.94408
93	2.05838	2.65677	1.45310	1.95620	1.29071	.95036
94	0.52612	0.59839	0.43362	0.50311	1.1374	.9563
95	0.07227	0.07227	0.06949	0.06949	1.0000	.962

VALUATION COLUMNS $3\frac{1}{2}\%$

$u_x = D_x/D_{x+1}$ $k_x = C_x/D_{x+1}$

x	u_x	k_x	x	u_x	k_x
10	1.042 811	0.007 547	**55**	1.054 585	0.018 922
11	1.042 838	.007 573	56	1.055 999	.020 289
12	1.042 866	.007 600	57	1.057 563	.021 800
13	1.042 894	.007 627	58	1.059 296	.023 474
14	1.042 922	.007 654	59	1.061 234	.025 347
15	1.042 962	0.007 692	**60**	1.063 385	0.027 425
16	1.042 990	.007 720	61	1.065 780	.029 739
17	1.043 019	.007 748	62	1.068 433	.032 302
18	1.043 059	.007 787	63	1.071 365	.035 136
19	1.043 100	.007 826	64	1.074 625	.038 285
20	1.043 141	0.007 866	**65**	1.078 270	0.041 807
21	1.043 194	.007 917	66	1.082 304	.045 704
22	1.043 248	.007 969	67	1.086 782	.050 031
23	1.043 303	.008 022	68	1.091 774	.054 854
24	1.043 358	.008 076	69	1.097 284	.060 178
25	1.043 415	0.008 130	**70**	1.103 403	0.066 090
26	1.043 484	.008 197	71	1.110 117	.072 576
27	1.043 554	.008 264	72	1.117 388	.079 602
28	1.043 625	.008 333	73	1.125 218	.087 167
29	1.043 710	.008 415	74	1.133 660	.095 323
30	1.043 796	0.008 498	**75**	1.142 852	0.104 204
31	1.043 884	.008 583	76	1.152 960	.113 971
32	1.043 986	.008 682	77	1.164 314	.124 941
33	1.044 102	.008 795	78	1.177 243	.137 433
34	1.044 221	.008 910	79	1.192 031	.151 720
35	1.044 343	0.009 027	**80**	1.209 771	0.168 861
36	1.044 493	.009 172	81	1.230 099	.188 502
37	1.044 647	.009 320	82	1.253 477	.211 089
38	1.044 830	.009 498	83	1.280 245	.236 952
39	1.045 018	.009 679	84	1.312 384	.268 004
40	1.045 237	0.009 891	**85**	1.353 917	0.308 133
41	1.045 463	.010 109	86	1.409 469	.361 806
42	1.045 721	.010 359	87	1.484 979	.434 762
43	1.046 001	.010 629	88	1.584 244	.530 670
44	1.046 331	.010 947	89	1.713 188	.655 254
45	1.046 684	0.011 289	**90**	1.897 500	0.833 333
46	1.047 106	.011 697	91	2.213 750	1.138 889
47	1.047 571	.012 146	92	2.829 873	1.734 177
48	1.048 111	.012 668	93	3.893 571	2.761 905
49	1.048 745	.013 280	94	7.245 000	6.000 000
50	1.049 463	0.013 974	**95**	....	....
51	1.050 272	.014 755			
52	1.051 176	.015 629			
53	1.052 185	.016 604			
54	1.053 323	.017 704			

MOMENT OF INERTIA FOR VARIOUS BODIES

The mass of the body is indicated by m.

Body	Axis	Moment of inertia
Uniform thin rod, length l	Normal to the length, at one end	$m\frac{l^2}{3}$
Uniform thin rod, length l	Normal to the length, at the center	$m\frac{l^2}{12}$
Thin rectangular sheet, sides a and b	Through the center parallel to b	$m\frac{a^2}{12}$
Thin rectangular sheet, sides a and b	Through the center perpendicular to the sheet	$m\frac{a^2 + b^2}{12}$
Thin circular sheet of radius r	Normal to the plate through the center	$m\frac{r^2}{2}$
Thin circular sheet of radius r	Along any diameter	$m\frac{r^2}{4}$
Thin circular ring. Radii r_1 and r_2	Through center normal to plane of ring	$m\frac{r_1^2 + r_2^2}{2}$
Thin circular ring. Radii r_1 and r_2	Any diameter	$m\frac{r_1^2 + r_2^2}{4}$
Rectangular parallelopiped, edges a, b, and c	Through center perpendicular to face ab, (parallel to edge c)	$m\frac{a^2 + b^2}{12}$
Sphere, radius r	Any diameter	$m\frac{2}{5}r^2$
Spherical shell, external radius r_1, internal radius r_2	Any diameter	$m\frac{2}{5}\frac{(r_1^5 - r_2^5)}{(r_1^3 - r_2^3)}$
Spherical shell, very thin, mean radius r	Any diameter	$m\frac{2}{3}r^2$
Right circular cylinder of radius r, length l	The longitudinal axis of the solid	$m\frac{r^2}{2}$
Right circular cylinder of radius r, length l	Transverse diameter	$m\left(\frac{r^2}{4} + \frac{l^2}{12}\right)$
Hollow circular cylinder, length l, radii r_1 and r_2	The longitudinal axis of the figure	$m\frac{(r_1^2 + r_2^2)}{2}$
Thin cylindrical shell, length l, mean radius r	The longitudinal axis of the figure	mr^2
Hollow circular cylinder, length l, radii r_1 and r_2	Transverse diameter	$m\left[\frac{r_1^2 + r_2^2}{4} + \frac{l^2}{12}\right]$
Hollow circular cylinder, length l, very thin, mean radius r	Transverse diameter	$m\left(\frac{r^2}{2} + \frac{l^2}{12}\right)$
Elliptic cylinder, length l, transverse semiaxes a and b	Longitudinal axis	$m\left(\frac{a^2 + b^2}{4}\right)$
Right cone, altitude h, radius of base r	Axis of the figure	$m\frac{3}{10}r^2$
Spheroid of revolution, equatorial radius r	Polar axis	$m\frac{2}{5}r^2$
Ellipsoid, axes $2a$, $2b$, $2c$	Axis $2a$	$m\frac{b^2 + c^2}{5}$

MATHEMATICAL SYMBOLS AND ABBREVIATIONS

Symbols and Abbreviations of Commercial Arithmetic

#	Number (if written before a numeral); pounds (weight), lb. (if written after a numeral.)
@	At, as "@ 5¢ per C," for "at 5 cents per hundred."
%	Per cent; per hundred.
¢	Cents (placed after figures)
$	Dollars, (prefixed before figures).
✓	Check mark
&	And, as in "Smith, Jones & Co."
c/o	Care of
A	Acre
a/c	Account
acct.	Account
ad val	(ad valorem), according to value
A.M. *or* a.m.	(ante meridiem) in the morning, between midnight and the following noon. 12:00 A.M. is noon, better 12:00 M, 12:01 A.M. is one minute after midnight.
amt.	Amount
ans.	Answer
ap.	Apothecaries' weight or measure
Apr.	April
a/s	Account sales
Aug.	August
av.	Average
avoir.	Avoirdupois
bal.	Balance
bbl. *or* brl.	Barrel
bk.	Bank, book
bl.	Bale
B/L	Bill of lading
bu.	Bushel
bx.	Box
C	(centum) hundred
cd.	Cord
cg.	Centigram
ch.	Chain
chg.	Charge
c.i.f.	Carriage and insurance free.
ck.	Check
cm.	Centimeter
cml.	Commercial
Co.	Company, county
c.o.d.	Cash on delivery
coll.	Collection
com.	Commission
cr.	Credit, creditor, crate
cs.	Case
c. *or* ct.	Cent
cu.	Cubic
cwt.	Hundredweight
da.	Day
Dec.	December
dept.	Department
dft.	Draft
disc.	Discount
dm.	Decimeter
do.	Ditto
doz.	Dozen
dr.	Dram
Dr.	Debit, debtor, doctor
ea.	Each
e.g.	(exempli gratia) for example
etc.	And so forth
ex.	Example, exercise, express
exch.	Exchange
exp.	Expense
F	Fahrenheit
Feb.	February
f.o.b.	Free on board
Fri.	Friday
frt.	Freight
ft. *or* f.	Foot
gal.	Gallon
gi.	Gill
gr.	Grain
gro.	Gross
gr. gro.	Great gross
guar.	Guarantee
hf.	Half
hhd.	Hogshead
hr.	Hour
i.e.	(id est) that is
in.	Inch, inches
ins.	Insurance
inst.	(instant) the present month
int.	Interest
inv.	Invoice
inv'y	Inventory
Jan.	January
kg.	Keg, kilogram
km.	Kilometer
lb., lbs.	Pound, pounds
lp	List price
ltd.	Limited
L.S.	(locus sigillis) place for the seal
M	(mille) thousand; meridiem as in 12:00 M

Symbols and Abbreviations of Commercial Arithmetic (Continued)

Abbreviation	Meaning
m.	Mill, meter
Mar.	March
mdse.	Merchandise
mi.	Mile
min.	Minute
mm.	Millimeter
mo.	Month
Mon.	Monday
mortg.	Mortgage
N, NE, NW, etc.	North, North-east, North-west, etc.
no. *or* numb.	Number
Nov.	November
Oct.	October
O.K.	Correct
oz.	Ounce
p.	Page
par.	Paragraph
pay't	Payment
pc.	Piece
pd.	Paid
per	By, by the, as in "per C," "per M," "per doz."
pfd.	Preferred
pk.	Peck, pecks
pkg.	Package
P.M. *or* p.m.	(post meridiem) in the after-noon, between noon and the following mid-night. 12:00 P.M. is mid-night, 12:01 P.M. is one minute after noon.
pp.	Pages
pr.	Pair
prox.	(proximo) in the following month
pt.	Pint, point
pwt. (*or* dwt.)	Pennyweight
qr.	Quire
qt.	Quart
rd.	Rod, road
rec'd	Received
rec't	Receipt
rm.	Ream
S, SE, SW, etc.	South, South-east, South-west, etc.
Sat.	Saturday
sec.	Second
sec'y	Secretary
Sept.	September
set.	Settlement
sig.	Signed, signature
sq.	Square
stk.	Stock
Sun.	Sunday
T.	Ton
temp.	Temperature
Thu.	Thursday
treas.	Treasurer, treasury
Tues.	Tuesday
ult.	(ultimo) in the last month
via	By way of
viz.	(videlicet) namely
vol.	Volume
Wed.	Wednesday
wk.	Week
wt.	Weight
yd.	Yard
yr.	Year

Symbols Belonging to Plane Geometry

$\angle$	Angle. Use "rt $\angle$" not "∟" for "right angle." Write out the word "arc" rather than using "⌢." On $\angle$ABC, B is the vertex, A, C, points on the sides of the angle.
$\perp$, $\perp$s	Perpendicular, perpendiculars.
$\parallel$, $\parallel$s	Parallel (to), parallel lines.
▱	Parallelogram (vertices are named in counter-clockwise order, starting at any vertex).
$\triangle$	Triangle
□	Square. Use "rect." not ▭ for "rectangle," and use "trap." not ⏢ for trapezoid.
$\odot$, $\odot$s	Circle, circles. $\odot$ A(B) designates the circle with center at A and passing through the point B. $\odot$ (ABC), designates the circle passing through given distinct points, A, B, C.
$\cong$	(is) congruent (to).
$\sim$	(is) similar (to).

Symbols Belonging to Plane Geometry (Continued)

≈	(is) homothetic (to); (is) similar (to) and similarly placed (with).	$\overrightarrow{AB}$	Directed segment, A to B.
#	(is) homothetically congruent (to); or otherwise stated, (is) congruent (to) and similarly placed (with). In case of line segments, this becomes, (is) parallel (with) and congruent (to).	|(AB)	Line (of infinite length) containing points A and B.
≏	(is) equivalent (to), (in area or volume).	↑(AB)	Directed line (of infinite length) containing points A and B, and in the direction from A to B.
$\overline{AB}$	Length of line segment between A and B.	℞	cross-ratio, anharmonic ratio.
		$\overline{\overline{\wedge}}$, $\overset{P}{\overline{\overline{\wedge}}}$	(is) perspective with, (is) perspective with, from center P.
		$\overline{\wedge}$	(is) projective with.

General Mathematical Symbols and Abbreviations

"Bold-face" type—To indicate vectors. In manuscript and at the blackboard, bold-faced type is variously indicated by wavy underscoring, or enclosure in a circle, or even by wavy overscoring. Some persons use German type.

Half-spaces—In writing numbers with many recorded digits, half-spaces (rather than commas or other marks) may well be used to separate convenient groups of digits. Thus $\pi = 3.14159\ 26536-$.

Superscripts—To indicate: **1.** powers, as in x^2, $(a - x)^n$, etc. In modern practice $a^0 = 1$ always by definition (even for $a = 0$). Also in ∞', ∞^2, etc., indicating number of degrees of freedom. Wherever the context restricts the value of a to non-negative (real) values and n to positive integers, $a^{1/n}$ means the non-negative (real) nth root of a. For complex numbers, x^y is defined as $e^{y\,(\log x)}$, where the principal value of log x is to be taken. In tables 0.0^5314 may be used to indicate 0.00000314. Note special use of $\sin^n x$ for $(\sin x)^n$ except for $n = -1$, also for $\cos^n x$, etc. **2.** symbolic powers, or order of iteration, as in T^n or in D^n $(= d^n/dx^n)$, or in inverse functions as in $\sin^{-1}$, $\cos^{-1}$, $\sinh^{-1}$, etc. **3.** order of differentiation, as in y' ("y prime"), y'' ("y second," or "y double prime"), $\cdots$, $y^{(N)}$, $\cdots$. **4.** feet and inches, as in 3′4″. **5.** degrees, minutes, seconds, as in 34°5′17″. Do not omit ° for common angles. Write 0°, 30°, 45°, 60°, etc., not 0, 30, 45, 60, etc. Do not use superscript, ^{r}, for radians. Write $180° = \pi$ rad, but write $\cos(\pi/3)$ for cos 60°. **6.** days, hours, minutes, seconds, as in $10^d3^h27^m5.3^s$. **7.** degrees of temperature as in 104°. Where C (for Centigrade) or F (for Fahrenheit) is given, recent usage approves the omission of the °, thus 100C = 212F, and −40C = −40F. **8.** For use with integral sign ∫, and with vertical bar |, see these symbols.

Dot-accents—To indicate derivatives with respect to time, (Newton's notation), as in $\dot{x}$ for x-component of velocity, and $\ddot{x}$ for x-component of acceleration.

Subscripts—To indicate: **1.** position in a sequence, set, or matrix, as in a_1, a_2, a_3, $\cdots a_n$, $\cdots$, or $a_0x^n + a_1x^{n-1} + \cdots + a_rx^{n-r} + \cdots a_n$ or in

$\begin{pmatrix} a_{11}a_{12}a_{13} \\ a_{21}a_{22}a_{23} \end{pmatrix}$. **2.** general distinguishing mark. Two subscripts may be written adjacently without commas as a_{11} and to be read "a sub one one," not "a sub eleven." A subscript is sometimes enclosed in parentheses as in $F_{(0)1}$ where such distinction seems demanded. For special uses see associated symbols.

Juxtaposition—To indicate: **1.** the algebraic product, as in $2bxy$. **2.** the logical product as in AB where A and B are given classes, and in symbolic logic. Also written with centrally placed dot as $A \cdot B$. **3.** the group product, as in ST (the result of performing first S, then T, or in aH, the co-set consisting for given a of all operations ah, where h is in H. **4.** general operational or functional combination as in dy/dx, $\sin x$, $\log x$, $\max y$, $\lim x_n$, etc. **5.** sequence of points or other elements determining a geometric figure, as line AB, parallelogram $ABCD$, $\angle ABC$, etc. **6.** sum of products (in tensor notation) when index appears as subscript for one factor and superscript for another. Thus a_ix^i means $\Sigma_i a_i x^i$, in tensor notation.

( )—Parentheses ("round brackets") to indicate: **1.** aggregation, as in $(a + b) \cdot (a - b) = a^2 - b^2$. **2.** argument of function, as in $f(x)$, $g(x,y)$, etc. **3.** sequence or set, as in $a = (a_i)$, $x = (x_{ij})$, (x,y,z), etc. **4.** matrix, as in $\begin{pmatrix} a_{11}a_{12}a_{13} \\ a_{21}a_{22}a_{23} \end{pmatrix}$ also written as $\begin{Vmatrix} a_{11}a_{12}a_{13} \\ a_{21}a_{22}a_{23} \end{Vmatrix}$. **5.** permutation (or substitution) in group theory as in $\begin{pmatrix} a_1a_2a_3 \\ b_1b_2b_3 \end{pmatrix}$ where a_i is replaced by $b_i (i = 1,2,3)$. **6.** binomial coefficient, as in $\binom{n}{r} = n!/[r!(n - r)!]$. This is also designated by $C_{n,r}$ or ${}_nC_r$. For n,r, positive integers, $\binom{-n}{r} = (-1)^r\binom{n + r - 1}{r}$, $\binom{n}{-r} = 0$, by definition. **7.** cycle or cylic permutation (in group theory) as in (a_1, a_2, a_3) for $\begin{pmatrix} a_1a_2a_3 \\ a_2a_3a_1 \end{pmatrix}$. **8.** greatest common divisor, as in $(30,42) = 6$, $(7,5) = 1$. **9.** inner product as in (ab), $= \Sigma_i a_i b_i$. **10.** segment or open interval, as in (a,b), for system of values of x, where $a < x < b$.

Superscript $^{(\ )}$—To indicate: **1.** general index as distinguished from exponent. **2.** index of order of derivative as in $y, y', \cdots, y^{(n)}, \cdots$. **3.** "factorial," as in $x^{(r)} = x(x - 1) \cdots (x - r + 1)$. By definition $x^{(-r)} = 1/[(x + 1) \cdot (x + 2) \cdots (x + r)]$.

[ ]—Brackets ("square brackets"), to indicate: **1.** aggregation. **2.** argument of function as with ( ). **3.** greatest integer in, as $[2] = 2$, $[-7/3] = -3$. **4.** inner product (for coefficients in normal equations in the method of least squares), as in $[aa]$, $[XY]$, etc. **5.** outer product of vectors. Other notations are $V\, \mathbf{ab}$ and $\mathbf{a} \times \mathbf{b}$. **6.** divided difference (in formal interpolation). $[x_i] = y_i$, $[x_i, x_{i+1}] = (y_{i+1} - y_i)/(x_{i+1} - x_i)$, $\cdots [x_i, x_{i+1}, \cdots, x_{i+r}] = ([x_{i+1}, \cdots, x_{i+r}] - [x_i, \cdots, x_{i+r-1}])/(x_{i+r} - x_i)$. **7.** range of points (in projective geometry) as in $[P]$. **8.** base (basis) of Abelian group, as in $[a,b, \cdots, k]$. **9.** module or ideal, as $[2] = [0, \pm 2, \pm 4, \cdots, \pm 2n, \cdots]$. **10.** Christoffel symbol, as in $\begin{bmatrix} mn \\ p \end{bmatrix} = \frac{1}{2}\left(\frac{\partial g_{pm}}{\partial x^n} + \frac{\partial g_{pn}}{\partial x^m} = \frac{\partial g_{mn}}{\partial x^p}\right)$. **11.** closed interval, as in $[a,b]$ for system of values of x where $a \leqq x \leqq b$.

Subscript—Note. The use of adjacent subscripts, rather than of indices placed directly below is recommended on account of its availability for running text, and its economy of space and of expense in type setting. Thus use

$\sum_i$ rather than $\sum\limits_i$, $\int_a^b$ rather than $\int\limits_a^b$, etc.

$\{\ \}$—Braces ("curly brackets") to indicate: **1.** aggregation, as in $\{(x - a)(x - b)\}^2$. **2.** class of (in theory of aggregates), where the general element only is mentioned, as in $\{a_i\} = [a_1, a_2, a_3]$, $(i = 1,2,3)$. **3.** Christoffel symbol, as in $\left\{\begin{matrix} m & n \\ & p \end{matrix}\right\} = g^{rp}\left[\begin{matrix} m & n \\ & p \end{matrix}\right]$.

$<\ >$—Angle brackets to indicate: **1.** aggregation. **2.** closed interval as with $[\ ]$.

$|\ |$—Vertical bars, to indicate: **1.** absolute value (modulus of complex number), as $|a + ib|^2 = a^2 + b^2$. **2.** magnitude of (for vectors) as $a = |\mathbf{a}|$. **3.** determinant, as in $\begin{vmatrix} a & b \\ c & d \end{vmatrix} = ad - bc$. The use of the notation $|a_{ij}|$ for the determinant of the maxtrix (a_{ij}), is common but is ambiguous. The notation det (a_{ij}) may be used for this determinant.

$\|\ \|$—Double bars, to indicate: **1.** matrix as in $\begin{Vmatrix} a_{11}a_{12}a_{13} \\ a_{21}a_{22}a_{23} \end{Vmatrix}$ or in $\|a_{ij}\|$. **2.** generalized length (for metrical spaces), as in $\|f\|^2 = \int f^2(x)dx$.

$(]$, $[)$.—For intervals, as $(a,b]$, for system of values of x for which $a < x \leqq b$, and $[a,b)$, for system of values of x for which $a \leqq x < b$. Similarly $(a,b >$, and $< a,b)$ are sometimes used for these respectively.

$\supset$—**1.** contains (or containing) as proper sub-class. **2.** implies (or implying).

$\supseteq$—contains (or containing) as sub-class. (Some writers use, $\supset$, for this.)

$\subset$—(is) contained as proper sub-class within.

$\subseteq$—(is) contained as sub-class within. (Some writers use, $\subset$, for this.)

$\equiv$—**1.** (is) identical with. $\equiv_x$ indicates (is) identical with for all values of x for which both members are defined. **2.** (is) congruent to (with respect to indicated modulus) as in $a \equiv b \pmod{m}$. **3.** (is) equivalent to (in formal logic).

$=$—(is) equal (to).

$<$—(is) less than.

$>$—(is) greater than.

$\leqq$ *or* $\leq$—(is) less than or equal to. Sometimes read (in the case of real numbers) as "(is) not greater than."

$\geqq$ *or* $\geq$—(is) greater than or equal to. Sometimes read (in the case of real numbers) as "(is) not less than.".

$\not\equiv$—**1.** (is) not identically equal (to). (Not "identically unequal to"), is unequal to for at least one value. **2.** (is) not congruent (to).

$\neq$—(is) not equal (to).

$\lessgtr$—**1.** (is) not equal (to), (for real quantities). **2.** (Sometimes when explained by context) less than or greater than respectively.

$\sim$—**1.** (is) formally, asymptotically, or approximately equal to. (The context should make the meaning specific.) Do not use $\doteq$ for "approximately equal to." **2.** (is) similar (to). **3.** not (in some works on formal logic).

$\rightarrow$—**1.** approaches (as a limit), as in $\lim_{x\rightarrow a} f(x) = b$, $f(x) \rightarrow b$, as $x \rightarrow a$, etc. (Do not use $\doteq$). Not usually employed with long expressions. **2.** leads to, validates, implies (in logic). **3.** corresponds to.
$\leftrightarrow$—**1.** mutually implies (in logic). **2.** in one-to-one correspondence with, corresponds reciprocally to.

Superscript $\rightarrow$—directed line as $\overrightarrow{AB}$.
|—Vertical bar, to indicate: **1.** value at, as in $f(x)|_a = f(a)$, or $f(x)|_{x=a} = f(a)$. **2.** value between as in $f(x)|_a^b = f(b) - f(a)$. **3.** is a divisor of, divides (in number theory) as $3|6$, or $(x - a)|(x^2 - a^2)$. **4.** inner product (with parentheses) as $(a|b) = \sum_i a_i b_i$.

\ or /—Stroke, mark of cancellation as in $\overset{2}{\not 3}x = \not 6$, $x + \not 3 = \overset{4}{\not 7}$.
/—Solidus, or oblique rule, to indicate: **1.** actual or symbolic division, as in $3/7$, $(x - a)/(x - b)$, d/dx, dy/dx, d^2y/dx^2. Do not write ambiguously $a - b/c - d$, but $(a - b)/(c - d)$ or $a - (b/c) - d$, as may be intended. Do not write a/bc but $(a/b)c$ or $a/(bc)$ as intended. Write a proportion as $a/b = c/d$ not $a:b::c:d$. Where A, B, C, D designate displayed expressions, write the proportion as $\frac{A}{B} = \frac{C}{D}$. In commercial typing in place of $8\frac{5}{12}$, it is usual to write 8-5/12. The solidus form a/b, adapted to running text should be used where conveniently possible, rather than the displayed form $\frac{a}{b}$. **2.** quotient or factor group (in group theory) as G/H, (where H is a normal subgroup of G). **3.** per, as in ft/sec. **4.** discount symbol, as in Cash 6, 4/5, 2/30, n/90 indicating 6% discount for immediate payment, 4% discount if paid within 5 days, 2% discount if paid within 30 days, no discount thereafter, but face amount of bill is due (net) not later than the 90th day. **5.** shilling, (in British currency) as 3/6d, or 10/ –.
Superscript $\overline{}$—Vinculum. This may be regarded as obsolescent for general use as a mark of aggregation due to its unsuitability for monotype setting. In conjunction with the radical sign it is widely used, but may often be avoided. There is little logical or historical basis for using $\sqrt{2}$ rather than $\surd 2$. For a longer expression, one may write $\surd(x^2 + a^2)$ rather than $\sqrt{x^2 + a^2}$. Instead of $\sqrt{x - a}\,(x - b)$, one might write $(x - b)\surd(x - a)$. In geometry, the vinculum may be used for line segments as in $\overline{AB}$.
Superscript $\overline{}$—Bar. To indicate: **1.** complex conjugate of, as $\bar{z}$. This is somewhat inconvenient for "upper extended" letters and capitals as, $\bar{b}$, $\bar{h}$, $\bar{X}$, etc. Also indicated by *conj*, as $conj\ (x + iy) = x - iy$ or by use of a "star" as in z^*. **2.** arithmetic mean value of, as in $\bar{x}, = \sum_i x_i/n$. **3.** closure of (in topology), as in $\bar{E}$ (the closure of E). **4.** "least upper," as in $\overline{\lim}$, and $\bar{B}$ for least upper limit and least upper bound, respectively. See "sup."
Subscript ____—To indicate: **1.** italics (in manuscript). **2.** "greatest lower," as in $\underline{\lim}$, and $\underline{B}$, for greatest lower limit, and greatest lower bound respectively. See "inf."

——— —horizontal rule, sign of division, as in $\frac{x - a}{x + a}$. Ordinarily the solidus form, adapted to running text, is preferred, as in $(x - a)/(x + a)$. When numerator and denominator are both complicated, the displayed form using horizontal rule may be avoided by writing "A/B, where $A = \cdots$, and $B = \cdots$."

$-$ (centrally placed)—Minus sign. To indicate: **1.** subtraction as in $7 - 2 = 5$, $a^2 - b^2 = (a - b)(a + b)$. **2.** overestimate, as in 3.5−. **3.** approach through negative values as in $-\infty$ and -0. **4.** region where variable indicated by context is negative (in graphs). **5.** logical difference (in theory of classes). **6.** in $(-)^n$, the sign expressed by $(-1)^n$.

. (on line)—**1.** decimal point. In the decimal representation of a number between 0 and 1, the cipher, 0, should (except in tables) appear before the decimal point. Thus 0.314 not .314. Notation by powers of 10, ("scientific notation") is recommended, especially when recording approximate values; thus to four significant figures, 3.140×10^9 and 3.140×10^{-6}. **2.** (sometimes used in quoting bond prices) as in 95.17 for $95\frac{17}{32}$. **3.** (sometimes used in recording mental age) as in 12.3 for 12 yr. 3 mo. **4.** (in symbolic logic) as mark of punctuation separating terms, also as, "and."

:—Colon. To indicate: **1.** hours, in recording time, as in 4:10 p.m. **2.** ratio (an obsolescent form) as in $a:b$. The form a/b is preferred. **3.** (in symbolic logic) as mark of punctuation separating groups of terms, as in $p \cdot p \supset q : \supset : q$.

$\cdot$ (centrally placed)—**1.** mark of algebraic multiplication, particularly where mere juxtaposition would be ambiguous, as in $\overline{AB} \cdot \overline{CD}$. **2.** (for vectors), the mark of inner or dot multiplication as in $\boldsymbol{a} \cdot \boldsymbol{b} = ab \cos < \boldsymbol{ab}$. Other notations are $(\boldsymbol{ab})$ and $S\,\boldsymbol{ab}$.

$\cdots$ (preferably centrally placed)—"three dots" meaning "and so forth," or "and so forth up to." Particularly in relation to the sequence of natural numbers, as in $1, 2 \cdots, n, \cdots$; or $a_0, a_1, \cdots, a_n, \cdots$, or $1, \cdots, m$.

$\therefore$—hence, therefore.

:., ::, ::., etc.—(in symbolic logic), marks of punctuation stronger than $\cdot$ and :

"— ditto.

$+$ plus sign. To indicate: **1.** addition, as in $2 + 3$, $a + b$, 10^{a+1}. **2.** underestimate, as in 3.5+. **3.** continued fraction as in $a_0 + \frac{1}{a_1+}\,\frac{1}{a_2+}\cdots$ for $a_0 + \cfrac{1}{a_1 + \cfrac{1}{a_2+}}\cdot$ **4.** approach through positive values as in $+\infty$, and in $+0$. **5.** region where variable indicated by the context is positive, (in graphs). **6.** logical addition (in theory of classes). **7.** " . . or . . or both," (in formal logic). . Note: In writing series indicate sign before and after dots of omission, as $a_0 + a_1 + \cdots + a_n$, or $1 - \frac{1}{2} + \frac{1}{3} + \cdots + (-1)^{n-1}\frac{1}{n}$. **8.** in abstract group theory a group or co-set may be expressed as the sum of its elements.

$\pm$—**1.** "plus or minus." The repeated appearance of $\pm$ as in $\pm a \pm b \pm c$ is ambiguous. In many cases the sign $\pm$ before a term which appears repeatedly is intended to indicate the systematic use of the positive determination or of the negative determination throughout. Thus one may write $(a \pm b)^3 = a^3 \pm 3a^2b + 3ab^2 \pm b^3$. Where the context restricts the value of a to non-negative (real) values, $\sqrt{a}$ means the non-negative (real) square root of a. Hence when both signs are desired, write $\pm$ before the radical. For roots of a quadratic equation $ax^2 + bx + c = 0$, use $\pm$ as in $(-b \pm \sqrt{b^2 - 4ac})/(2a)$. **2.** (in theory of observation), "with a probable error of." As in 17.2 ± 0.5 cm.

$\mp$—"minus or plus respectively." Used in context where $\pm$ has appeared previously, as in $(a \pm b)(a^2 \mp ab + b^2) = a^3 \pm b^3$. Here upper signs are to be taken throughout, or else lower signs. The notation $\pm a \mp b \pm c$ is ambiguous, meaning perhaps one of the four values $\pm(a - b) \pm c$, or one of the two values $\pm(a - b + c)$.

$\times$—**1.** times, (sign of algebraic multiplication). Used chiefly in arithmetic, as in $2 \times 2 = 4$, 7.3×10^4. **2.** (for vectors) the sign of outer or cross multiplication. **3.** (for classes) the Cartesian product. Thus $A \times B$ is the class of all ordered pairs (a,b) where a is an element of A, and b of B.

$\div$—sign of division. Used chiefly in arithmetic. Should be replaced by solidus, /, where convenient.

$\sqrt{\ }\ \sqrt[n]{\ }$—square root of, nth root of. (See discussion under "superscript," and under "vinculum"). By custom, for a positive, $\sqrt{(-a)}$ means usually $i\sqrt{a}$, rather than $-i\sqrt{a}$, but the latter unambiguous forms are preferred.

!—"factorial," as in $3! = 1 \cdot 2 \cdot 3 = 6$. $0! = 1$, (by definition). The elementary arithmetic definition of factorial n, may be replaced in favor of the definition as a special case of the Gamma function $\Gamma(x)$. For n a natural number, $n! = \Gamma(n + 1), = \int_0^\infty x^n e^{-x} dx$. For n a large natural number, Stirling's asymptotic formula (extended) yields $n! \sim \sqrt{2n\pi}(n/e)^n\left(1 + \frac{1}{12n} + \frac{1}{288n^2} - \frac{139}{51840n^3} - \cdots\right)$. Note: Do not use the obsolescent form $\underline{|n}$ for $n!$

$\int, \int_a^b, \int_a^x, \int\int, \int_c$—Integral signs. (use preferably bold-face type)

$$\int_a^b \int_c^d f(x,y)dxdy \text{ denotes } \int_a^b \left(\int_c^d f(x,y)dx\right)dy, = \int_a^b dy \int_c^d dx f(x,y).$$

$\oint$—curvilinear integral over closed path free from singularities. (Use preferably bold-face type.)

§—section, or article.

P or ¶—paragraph.

$\propto$— varies as. Instead of $y \propto x$ one may write $y = kx$, k being the constant factor of proportionality.

∇—nabla—To indicate: **1.** linear vector operator $\left(\frac{\partial}{\partial x}, \frac{\partial}{\partial y}, \frac{\partial}{\partial z}\right)$ as used also in divergence, gradient, and curl (or rotation). **2.** backward difference (in interpolation theory) $\nabla a_n = a_n - a_{n-1}$.

∇^2—Laplace operator.

$\square$—D'Alembertian operator.

$^\circ$, $'$, $''$, $'''$, . . . , (N) . . . , (superscript)—superscript numbers. See "superscripts."

∞—infinity. Use $+\infty$ or $-\infty$ respectively, where direction of approach along real numbers is to be indicated. Otherwise use ∞ rather than $\pm\infty$. Note: "$n \to \infty$," may be read "as n increases without bound."

$\aleph$—Aleph (initial Hebrew letter) transfinite cardinal number, in particular that of all real numbers. $\aleph_0$ (aleph null) first transfinite cardinal.

α—Alpha. To indicate: **1.** (in analytic geometry of 3 dimensions), direction angle with X-axis. **2.** angular acceleration. **3.** (in statistics) $\alpha_0 = 1$, $\alpha_1 = 0$, $\alpha_2 = 1$, $\alpha_3 = \mu_3/\sigma^3$, $\alpha_4 = \mu_4/\sigma^4 = \mu_4/\mu_2^2$. **4.** (in mathematical astronomy), right ascension (also indicated by R.A.) **5.** angle of triangle at A, opposite side a. **6.** root of algebraic equation as in $a(x - \alpha)(x - \beta)(x - \gamma) = 0$.

B—(Greek Beta)—$\mathrm{B}(m,n) = \Gamma(m)\Gamma(n)/\Gamma(m + n)$, (Eulerian Beta-function).

β—Beta. To indicate: **1.** (in analytic geometry of 3 dimensions), direction angle with Y-axis. **2.** (in statistics), $\beta_1 = \alpha_3^2 = \mu_3^2/\mu_2^3$, $\beta_2 = \alpha_4 = \mu_4/\mu_2^2$. **3.** angle of triangle at B, opposite side b. **4.** root of algebraic equation. See α.

Γ—$\Gamma(x)$ Gamma-function. See "!" Among numerous definitions equivalent for positive real values of x, are the two following: (i) $\Gamma(x) = \lim\limits_{n\to\infty} \dfrac{1 \cdot 2 \cdots n}{x(x+1) \cdots (x+n-1)} n^{x-1}$, $x > 0$. (ii) $\Gamma(x) = \int_0^\infty e^{-t}t^{x-1}dt$, $R(x) > 0$.

γ—Gamma. To indicate: **1.** (in analytic geometry of 3 dimensions) direction angle with Z-axis. **2.** Euler or Mascheroni constant. (Also indicated by C.) $\gamma = \lim\limits_{n\to\infty} \left(\frac{1}{1} + \frac{1}{2} + \cdots + \frac{1}{n} - \log n\right) = 0.57721\ 56649\ 01532\ 86060\ 65120 \cdots$ **3.** angle of triangle at C, opposite side c. **4.** radius of geodesic curvative. **5.** universal constant of gravitation $= 6.670 \times 10^{-8}$ $\mathrm{cm}^3/(\mathrm{gm.\ sec}^2)$. **6.** root of algebraic equation, see α.

Δ—Delta. To indicate: **1.** triangle (in plane geometry). (For right triangle, write rtΔ, not $\mathit{\Delta}$). Also area of triangle. **2.** increment, as in Δx, Δf, $f(x + \Delta x)$, etc. **3.** forward difference (interpolation theory). $\Delta a_n = a_{n+1} - a_n$. **4.** Laplacian operator $\frac{\partial^2}{\partial x^2} + \frac{\partial^2}{\partial y^2}$, or $\frac{\partial^2}{\partial x^2} + \frac{\partial^2}{\partial y^2} + \frac{\partial^2}{\partial z^2}$ also designated by ∇^2. **5.** selected square root of the discriminant of a given polynomial, as in $\Delta^2 = b^2 - 4ac$ for the polynomial $ax^2 + bx + c$. **6.** triangular number, (of form $(n^2 - n)/2$). **7.** Legendre's radical, $\Delta(\varphi)^2 = 1 - k^2 \sin^2 \varphi$.

δ—Delta. To indicate: **1.** positive constant dependent upon ϵ that may be chosen initially as near to zero as desired. (In theory of limits, of continuity, etc.) **2.** variation of. **3.** (in interpolational theory) central difference $\delta y_{c+i+\frac{1}{2}} = y_{c+i+1} - y_{c+i}$ **4.** (in mathematical astronomy) apparent declination. **5.** number of double points, or nodes (Plücker number). **6.** (in statistics) deviation. **7.** force of interest, $e^\delta = 1 + i$, (in mathematics of finance). **8.** Kronecker Delta, $\delta_{ij} = 0$ for $i \neq j$, $= 1$ for $i = j$. In tensor notation, also δ_i^j. One has $\delta_{ij} = \binom{0}{i-j}$ or $C_{0,i-j}$. **9.** unit elongation (in strength of materials).

∂—curly d. To indicate: **1.** partial differentiation as in $\partial f(x,y)/\partial x$. **2.** The Jacobian operator, as in $\partial(u,v,w)/\partial(x,y,z)$. This is variously represented, sometimes as $J\left(\frac{u,v,w}{x,y,z}\right)$ etc. **3.** a specified square root of the discriminant D. (also sometimes as Δ.)

ϵ—Epsilon. To indicate: **1.** positive constant, that may be chosen initially independently as near to zero as desired. (In theory of limits, of continuity, etc.) **2.** primitive root of unity. **3.** (is) member of, (relation of element to containing class). **4.** eccentricity of conic section, usually better designated by e. **5.** (in mathematical astronomy) obliquity of ecliptic. **6.** an ϵ-number is a transfinite ordinal of a certain limiting type. Note: Do not use ϵ or ε for Napierian base except in engineering. See e.

$\notin$—(is not a member of.)

ζ—Zeta. To indicate: **1.** Riemann Zeta-function $\zeta(s) = \Sigma_{n=1}^{\infty} n^{-s}$ (for $s > 1$). **2.** (in statistics) a test of linearity. $\zeta = \eta^2 - r^2$.

η—Eta. To indicate: **1.** general variable or unknown constant, analogous to y as in case of moving system of coordinates, etc. Used in ordered set (ξ,η,ζ). **2.** a confocal coordinate. See ξ. **3.** (in statistics), correlation ratio. **4.** order-type of the aggregate of all rational numbers.

Θ—Theta. To indicate: **1.** Theta-function. See ϑ. **2.** absolute temperature (where t is used for time).

θ—Theta. To indicate: **1.** general angular displacement, (in trigonometry and analytic geometry). **2.** (in plane polar coordinates (r,θ)) angle from initial ray to radius vector, $x = r \cos \theta$, $y = r \sin \theta$. **3.** (in cylindrical coordinates (r,θ,z)) angle from initial radial half-plane to radial half-plane containing radius vector. **4.** (in spherical coordinates (r,θ,φ)) co-latitude (measured from zenith) and (in astronomy) zenith distance. This notation is traditional in mathematical physics. In texts on analytic geometry, usage varies, θ being employed frequently for the longitude. See φ. **5.** Theta-function. See ϑ. **6.** (in formal theory of operations), a displacement operator. **7.** ordinary temperature (when t is used for time).

ϑ—Theta-function. Definitions and notations vary widely. For elliptic Theta-functions the notation here given is that followed by Whittaker and Watson. Here θ_i designates the value of $\vartheta_i(o,q)$, ϑ_i', the value of $d\vartheta_i(z,q)/dz$. $(i = 1,2,3,4)$. These are defined by $\vartheta_1(z,q) = 2q^{\frac{1}{4}} \sin Z - 2q^{\frac{9}{4}} \sin 3z + 2q^{\frac{25}{4}} \sin 5z - \cdots$ $\vartheta_2(z,q) = 2q^{\frac{1}{4}} \sin z + 2q^{\frac{9}{4}} \sin 3z + 2q^{\frac{25}{4}} \sin 5z + \cdots$ $\vartheta_3(z,q) = 1 + 2q \cos 2z + 2q^4 \cos 4z + 2q^9 \cos 6z + \cdots$ $\vartheta_4(z,q) = 1 - 2q \cos 2z + 2q^4 \cos 4z - 2q^9 \cos 6z + \cdots$.

ι—Iota, number of inflexions (a Plücker number).

ι—inverted Iota, (in formal logic) the unique element fulfilling description stated.

κ—Kappa, number of cusps. (A Plücker number).

Λ—Lambda, sometimes used for null-class.

λ—Lambda. To indicate: **1.** general linear parameter (e.g., in a pencil), as in $F + \lambda G$. **2.** running index, as in $x_\lambda(\lambda = 1, 2, \cdots)$. **3.** longitude (in mathematical astronomy). **4.** characteristic value (as in λ_i) in theory of linear differential equations of second order, linear integral equations, etc. **5.** order-type of the aggregate of all real numbers.

μ—Mu. To indicate: **1.** running index, usually used with λ, as in $x_\lambda y_\mu$. **2.** general linear parameter, when used with λ, as in $\lambda F + \mu G$. **3.** (in statistics) moment, about the arithmetic mean, as in $\mu_k = \Sigma_i f_i(x_i - \bar{x})^k$, $\mu_2 = \sigma^2 =$ variance. **4.** μ_x, force of mortality $= -d\,(\log_e l_x)/dx$. **5.** (in number theory) inversion function of Moebius and Mertens.

ν—Nu. To indicate: **1.** running index, usually with λ and μ. **2.** (in statistics) moment about arbitrary origin A (in "short method") as in $\nu_k = \Sigma_i f_i(x_i - A)^k$.

ξ—Xi. To indicate: **1.** general variable, or unknown constant analogous to x, as in moving systems of coordinates, etc. **2.** a confocal coordinate as in (i) confocal ellipses and hyperbolas, $\frac{x^2}{a^2 - \lambda} + \frac{y^2}{b^2 - \lambda} = 1$, $-\infty < \xi < b^2 < \eta < a^2$. (ii) confocal ellipsoids and hyperboloids of revolution, $\frac{x^2}{a^2 - \lambda} + \frac{y^2 + z^2}{b^2 - \lambda} = 1$, $-\infty < \xi < b^2 < \eta < a^2$. (iii) confocal parabolas, $y^2 + 2\lambda \cdot (x - \lambda) = 0$, $-\infty < \xi < 0 < \eta < +\infty$. (iv) confocal paraboloids of revolution, $y^2 + z^2 + 2\lambda(x - \lambda) = 0$, $-\infty < \xi < 0 < \eta < +\infty$. (v) confocal ellipsoids and hyperboloids, $\frac{x^2}{a^2 - \lambda} + \frac{y^2}{b^2 - \lambda} + \frac{z^2}{c^2 - \lambda} = 1$, $-\infty < \xi < c^2 < \eta < b^2 < \zeta < a^2$. (vi) confocal paraboloids, $\frac{x^2}{a^2 - \lambda} + \frac{y^2}{b^2 - \lambda} = 2z - \lambda$, $-\infty < \xi < b^2 < \eta < a^2 < \zeta < +\infty$.

Π, $\Pi_i \Pi_{i=m}^n$, $\Pi_{(R)}$ or $\underset{(R)}{\Pi}$—**1.** product of terms with index i, or j, etc. ranging from m to n, or over R. Do not use $\underset{i}{\Pi}$, $\overset{n}{\underset{i=m}{\Pi}}$, etc. (Bold-faced type preferred.) **2.** (in some formal logical treatments) "for every."

Π_{ij}, Π_{ijk}, $\cdots$—$\Pi_i \Pi_j$, $\Pi_i \Pi_j \Pi_k$, etc.

π—Pi. **1.** the ratio of the length of circumference of a circle, to the diameter. $\pi = 3.14159\ 26535\ 89793\ 23846 \cdots$ **2.** general notation for plane, projectivity, projective, period, etc.

ρ—Rho. **1.** radius of geodesic curvature. **2.** proportionality factor, as in $\rho X_i = \Sigma_j a_{ij} x_j$.

$\sum$, $\sum_i$, $\sum_{i=m}^n$, $\sum_{(R)}$ or $\underset{(R)}{\sum}$—Sigma. **1.** summation, sum of terms of index i, or j, etc., ranging from m to n, or over range R. Do not use $\sum\limits_i$, $\sum\limits_{i=m}^n$, etc. (bold-faced type preferred). **2.** (on some formal logical treatments) "for at least one." **3.** (in number theory) $\Sigma_{d/n}$ summation extended over all divisors of n. **4.** (in mathematical astronomy) Σ-pt is the intersection of the meridian with the equator.

Σ_{ij}, Σ_{ijk} $\cdots$—$\Sigma_i \Sigma_j$, $\Sigma_i \Sigma_j \Sigma_k$, etc.

σ—Sigma. To indicate: **1.** radius of torsion. **2.** (in statistics) standard deviation $\sigma^2 N = \Sigma_i (x_i - \bar{x})^2 f_i$. **3.** (in number theory), $\sigma_k(n)$ = sum of kth powers of divisors of n. **4.** any one of several analogous Sigma-functions. The simplest elliptic Sigma-function $\sigma(x)$ is related to the Weierstrassian $\wp$ function by $\wp u = -d^2 \log \sigma u / du^2$. One has $\sigma u = u \left\{ 1 - \frac{g_2}{2} \frac{u^4}{5!} - 6 g_3 \frac{u^6}{7!} - \frac{9}{4} g_2{}^2 \frac{u^8}{9!} - 18 g_2 g_3 \frac{u^{10}}{11!} - \cdots \right\}$ **5.** proportionality factor, usually used with ρ.

τ—Tau. To indicate: **1.** number of bitangents (a Plücker number). **2.** time (when t is used for temperature). **3.** torsion (of curve in space).

Υ—Upsilon. (In mathematical astronomy) vernal equinox.

φ—Phi. To indicate: **1.** general functional symbol, especially for polynomials. **2.** (in spherical coordinates, (r,θ,φ), longitude from x to y in right-handed system. In some astronomical work the z-axis points to the zenith, θ is the zenith-distance, and φ is the west azimuth. In some works on analytic geometry the roles of θ and φ are interchanged, although the system given is traditional mathematical physics. $x = r \sin \theta \cos \varphi$, $y = r \sin \theta \sin \varphi$, $z = r \cos \theta$. **3.** (in geocentric coordinates, $(r,\varphi,\lambda)\varphi$ = latitude (not co-latitude as with spherical coordinates). **4.** (in plane polar coordinates (r,φ).) Used chiefly as specialized case of spherical coordinates $(r,\pi/2,\varphi)$. See θ. **5.** inclination of plane curve, $\tan \varphi = dy/dx = m$. **6.** (in number theory.) Euler's function or indicatrix. $\varphi(n)$ is the number of positive integers not exceeding n and prime to n. **7.** $\varphi_i(x)$, characteristic function, see λ_i. **8.** argument in Legendre's elliptic integrals. $E(\varphi,k) = \int_0^\varphi \Delta(\varphi)d\varphi$, $F(\varphi_1k) = \int_0^\varphi d\varphi/\Delta(\varphi)$. **9.** the normal probability function of Laplace and Gauss in the form $\varphi(t) = \frac{1}{\sqrt{2\pi}}e^{-t^2}$. **10.** $\varphi_n(x)$, sometimes used for Bernoulli polynomial. See $B_n(x)$.

χ—Chi. (In statistical theory) χ^2 is a measure of goodness of fit, devised by Karl Pearson. $\chi^2 = \Sigma(f_i - Np_i)^2/(Np_i)$ for N items, with p_i the probability of appearances and f_i the frequency for items in an ith class.

ψ—Psi. To indicate: **1.** general functional symbol (usually with φ). **2.** angle from radius vector to tangent of plane curve. **3.** (with geocentric coordinates in mathematical astronomy), co-latitude. See φ.

Ω—Omega. To indicate: **1.** a certain annihilator in the theory of binary concomitants. **2.** (with subscript) transfinite ordinals of certain minimal type. **3.** (in geometry of the triangle) Ω, Ω', the Brocard points.

ω—Omega. To indicate: **1.** angular velocity. **2.** first transfinite ordinal, order-type of the aggregate of all natural numbers. **3.** imaginary cube root of unity, related to i, by $\omega = (-1 + i\sqrt{3})/2$. **4.** ω_1, ω_2, ω_3, half-periods of Weierstrassian $\wp$-function.

A—**1.** A vertex, and the associated angle of ΔABC. See α. **2.** A_{ij}, algebraic complement of a_{ij} in determinant, D. $A_{ij} = dD/da_{ij}$. **3.** (in astronomy) azimuth. **4.** (in astronomy) astronomical unit, mean geocentric distance to the sun. **5.** acres. **6.** area.

AM—arithmetic mean. See also superscript $^{-}$.

Ans.—answer.

AP—arithmetic progression.

Ax—axiom.

a—**1.** (in elementray algebra) initial term in arithmetic or geometric progression. **2.** (with subscript) coefficient in Fourier series, $(a_0/2) + \Sigma_{n=1}^{\infty}(a_n \cos nx + b_n \sin nx)$. **3.** (with two indices) element in matrix or determinant, as in $\begin{pmatrix} a_{11} & a_{12} & a_{13} \\ a_{21} & a_{22} & a_{23} \end{pmatrix}$ or $\begin{vmatrix} a_{11} & a_{12} \\ a_{21} & a_{22} \end{vmatrix}$. **4.** (in elementary geometry) apothegm. **5.** (in geometry of triangle) first side-line, also length of first side of the triangle. **6.** (in elementary analytic geometry) x-intercept. **7.** (in elementary analytic geometry) semi-major axis of ellipse or semi-transverse axis of hyperbola, etc. (When equations are in normal form.) For central conics and quadrics the a is usually associated with x, as in $(x^2/a^2) + (y^2/b^2) = 1$, even when a may be less than b, or as in $-(x^2/a^2) + (y^2/b^2) = 1$, where a is the semi-conjugate axis.

abs—absolute value of.

acc—acceleration.

am—amplitude function. $\varphi = \text{am } u$, where $u = F = \int_0^\varphi d\varphi/\Delta(\varphi)$.

amp—amplitude of vibration.

approx—approximate(ly).

arc (in "arc sin" etc.)—inverse. Also written $\sin^{-1}$ etc. Do not use "arc" for inverse of hyperbolic functions. Write $\sinh^{-1}$, etc.

arg—argument. For r and θ real, θ is the argument of $re^{i\theta}$.

av—average.

B—**1.** (With subscripts) Bernoulli numbers and polynomials. To indicate what usage among many is being followed in any given case, authors would do well to list the values of the first few Bernoulli numbers as for example, $B_1 = \frac{1}{2}$, $B_2 = \frac{1}{6}$, $B_3 = 0$, $B_4 = -\frac{1}{30}$, etc. The Bernoulli polynomials, are defined as $B_n(x) = \Sigma_{r=0}^{n} \binom{n}{r} B_r x^{n-r}$, and satisfy $B_n(x + 1) - B_n(x) = nx^{n-1}$ with the choice of notation for Bernoulli numbers given above. (Also designated by $\varphi_n(x)$.) **2.** bound (general symbol). $\bar{B}$, $\underline{B}$ designate least upper, and greatest lower bound respectively. Preferred notations are "sup" and "inf" respectively. **3.** a vertex and the associated angle of ΔABC. See β. **4.** (in elementary solid geometry), area of base of a solid.

b—**1.** (in elementary geometry) length of base of plane figure. b,b', parallel bases of trapezoid. **2.** (in elementary analytic geometry) y-intercept. **3.** (in elementary analytic geometry) semi-axis. See a. **4.** (in geometry of the triangle) second side-line, also length of second side of the triangle.

bei(z)—Thomson-Bessel function, $\text{bei}(z) = \frac{(\frac{1}{2}z)^2}{(2!)^2} = \frac{(\frac{1}{2}z)^6}{(6!)^2} + \frac{(\frac{1}{2}z)^{10}}{(10!)^2} = \cdots$ $\text{ber}(z) \pm i\,\text{bei}(z) = J_0(zi\sqrt{\pm i}) = I_0(z\sqrt{\pm i})$.

ber(z)—Thomson-Bessel function. (See bei(z).) $\text{ber}(z) = 1 - \frac{(\frac{1}{2}z)^4}{(4!)^2} + \frac{(\frac{1}{2}z)^8}{(8!)^2} - \cdots$.

C—**1.** arbitrary constant of integration. **2.** (in elementary geometry) circumference of circle; also, circle. **3.** general symbol for curve. **4.** (with subscripts) combination, as in $C_{n,r}$ or ${}_nC_r$, the number of combinations of n things taken r at a time (without repetitions). The form ${}_nC_r$ or even ${}^nC_r$ is widely used but the notation $C_{n,r}$ or $C(n,r)$ or $\binom{n}{r}$ is to be preferred. **5.** Roman numeral for "hundred." **6.** Euler or Mascheroni constant. Also designated by γ. (See γ.) **7.** (chiefly as subscript) contour of integration. **8.** Centigrade, degree Centigrade, as −52C.

Ci—cosine integral function, $Ci(x) = \int_\infty^x (\cos u/u)du$.

CF—(in elementary differential equations) complementary function.

c—**1.** (in geometry of triangle) third side-line, also length of third side of triangle. **2.** (in elementary analytic geometry), *z*-intercept. **3.** (in elementary analytic geometry) semi-axis. (See *a*.)
cis—$\text{cis}\ \theta = \cos\theta + i \sin\theta = e^{i\theta} = exp(i\theta)$. The latter forms preferred.
cls—class, set, or aggregate.
cn—cosine amplitude function. (Jacobian elliptic function.)
colog—cologarithm (of).
conj—(complex) conjugate (of). See superscript $^{-}$.
cos—cosine (of).
$\cos^{-1}$—inverse cosine (of). Also written arc cos.
cosh—hyperbolic cosine (of). Do not write Cos nor $\mathfrak{Cof}$ (in German letters).
$\cosh^{-1}$—inverse hyperbolic cosine of. Do not write arc cosh.
csc—cosecant (of).
$\csc^{-1}$—inverse cosecant (of). Also written arc csc.
ctn—cotangent (of).
ctn^{-1}—inverse cotangent (of). Also written arc ctn.
ctnh—hyperbolic cotangent (of). Do not write Ctn, nor $\mathfrak{Ctn}$ (in German letters).
ctnh^{-1}—inverse hyperbolic cotangent of. Do not write arc ctnh.
cu—cubic.
cum—cumulative
cvrs—coversed sine (of) $\text{cvrs}\ x = 1 - \sin x$.
D—**1.** differential operator, as in $Dy = y'$, $d_x f(x,y) = \partial f/\partial x$. **2.** Roman numeral for "five hundred." **3.** general symbol for denominator, or for determinant. **4.** discriminant of binary form, or of polynomial. **5.** (in statistical theory), (with subscripts 0, 1, $\cdots$, 10), decile marks. **6.** $D(a_1, a_2, \cdots, a_n)$ sometimes designates the Vandermonde determinant

$$\begin{vmatrix} 1 a_1 & \cdots & a_1^{n-1} \\ \cdot\ \cdot & \cdot\ \cdot\ \cdot & \cdot\ \cdot \\ 1 a_n & \cdots & a_n^{n-1} \end{vmatrix}$$

Def—definition.
Dem—demonstration, proof.
d—**1.** (in elementary algebra), common difference in arithmetic progression. **2.** differential operator, as in d^2y/dx^2. **3.** (in elementary geometry) diameter. **4.** (as superscript) days, as in $2^d 3^h 17^m$. **5.** (British currency) pence.
deg—degree, degrees.
det—determinant of, as in det (a_{ij}).
div—divergence of, also indicated by ∇.
dn—dn(z), a Jacobian elliptic function.
$\exists$—(there) exists.
$\exists|$—there exist uniquely.
E—**1.** *E,F,G* fundamental differential quantities of first order for surfaces. **2.** $E(\varphi,k)$, Legendre's normal elliptic integral, of the second kind, $E = \int_0^{\varphi} \Delta(\varphi) d\varphi$. **3.** east. **4.** (in Euler's polyhedral formula) number of edges of polyhedron. **5.** displacement operator, $E(f(x)) = f(x + 1)$. **6.** (in mathematical astronomy) equation of time.

Ei—exponential integral function $Ei(x) = \int_x^\infty du/(ue^u)$.

Eq—equation.

Ex—exercise.

e—**1.** base of natural (or Napierian) logarithms. In place of e^A one may write exp A. $e = 2.71828\ 18284\ 59045\ 23536 \cdots \log_{10} e = M = 0.43429\ 44819\ 03251\ 82765 \cdots \log_e 10 = 1/M = 2.30258\ 50929\ 94045\ 68402$. In some engineering work, where e is used otherwise, the base of natural logarithms is designated by ϵ. **2.** eccentricity of a conic. **3.** $e_1 = \wp(\omega_1)$, $e_2 = \wp(\omega_2)$, $e_3 = \wp(\omega_3)$, for Weierstrassian elliptic functions. **4.** (in mathematical astronomy) eccentricity of earth's orbit. **5.** (in elementary solid geometry) length of lateral edge (of right pyramid, prism, etc.).

erf—error function, $\text{erf}(x) = (\sqrt{2/\pi})\int_x^\infty e^{-\frac{1}{2}t^2}dt$.

exp—exponential function of, as in $\exp(a^2 + b^2)$ for $e^{a^2+b^2}$. One could also write this "e^u where $u = a^2 + b^2$."

exsec—exsecant function, exsec $\theta = \sec\theta - 1$.

F—Force.

F—**1.** general symbol for function or functional. **2.** the second fundamental differential quantity of first order for surfaces. See E. **3.** (in Euler's polyhedral formula) number of faces of polyhedron. **4.** $F(\varphi, k)$, Legendre's normal elliptic integral of the first kind, $F = \int_0^\varphi d\varphi/\Delta(\varphi)$. See Δ and E. φ is here the amplitude of F, $\varphi = \text{am}\, F$. **5.** $F(a, b; c: x)$, hypergeometric function. **6.** Fahrenheit, degree Fahrenheit, as in 70F.

FS—Fourier series.

Fig.—figure.

Fr—frontier set of.

f—**1.** general symbol for function or functional. **2.** f_i, frequency of X_i in univariate table. **3.** frequency of vibration. **4.** feet as in f/s, feet per second. Preferable ft/sec.

ft—feet. See also f and $'$.

G—**1.** general symbol for group. **2.** the third fundamental differential quantity of first order for surfaces. **3.** $G(x_1, \cdots, x_n; \xi_1, \cdots, \xi_n)$ Green's function for two points in n-space. **4.** (constant) linear group of points on an algebraic curve. See g. **5.** gravitational constant.

G.C.T.—Greenwich civil time.

GCD—greatest common divisor.

GCS—greatest common subgroup.

GF—Galois field, as in GF(p^n).

GM—geometric mean.

GP—geometric progression.

g—**1.** general function symbol, used with f. **2.** (terrestrial) gravitational attraction. **3.** (variable) linear group of points on an algebraic curve. See G. **4.** g_i, frequency of y_i in bivariate table. **5.** general coefficient in tensor, as in $g_{ij}^k x^i y^i z_k$.

gd—Gudermannian. $e^u = \tan\left(\frac{\pi}{4} + \frac{1}{2}\,\text{gd u}\right)$.

grad—gradient of. Also written ∇.

H—**1.** general symbol for subgroup, as in G/H, particularly for normal (or self-conjugate) subgroup. **2.** Hessian, as $H(f) = \det\frac{\partial^2 f}{\partial x_i \partial x_j}$. **3.** $H_n(x)$, nth Hermite polynomial, $H_n(x)e^{-x^2/2} = (-1)^n D^n e^{-x^2/2}$. **4.** $H(P_1, P_3; P_2, P_4)$ is the proposition that P_1 and P_3 separate harmonically P_2 and P_4. **5.** orthocenter of triangle. **6.** $H(q_1, \cdots, q_n, t, p_1, \cdots, p_n)$ Hamiltonian function (in mathematical physics). **7.** mean curvature of surface, $H = EG - F^2$. **8.** (in mathematical astronomy) hour-angle. Also designated by t.

HCF—highest common factor.

HM—harmonic mean.

HP—(in elementary algebra) harmonic progression.

Hyp.—hypothesis.

h—**1.** (in interpolation theory), distance, between uniformly spaced ordinates. **2.** class interval, in x. **3.** increment of x. Also Δx. **4.** (as superscript) hours, as in $8^{h}15^{m}$. **5.** (terminal) hyperbolic, as in sinh, $\tanh^{-1}$, etc. **6.** altitude ("height").

hav—haversine (of). $\text{hav } x = (\text{vers } x)/2$.

I—**1.** general symbol for interval, and for definite integral. **2.** Roman numeral for "one." Write IV not IIII, IX not VIIII. **3.** $I(\ )$, imaginary part of, also designated by $\mathfrak{I}(\ )$, or $\text{Im}(\ )$. **4.** $I_n(z)$, the Bessel function "of imaginary argument," $I_n(z) = \sum_{m=0}^{\infty} \frac{(\frac{1}{2})z^{n+2m}}{m!\Gamma(n+m+1)}$. **5.** (in geometry of triangle) in center. **6.** sometimes used for the identity as an operation in a group.

$\mathfrak{I}$—(Black letter) imaginary part of. See I.

Im—imaginary part of. See I.

i—**1.** running index, as in a_i, $i = 1, \cdots, n$. **2.** one of the two imaginary square roots of -1. (In electrical engineering, when it is used for the current, j is used for this imaginary unit.)

$\mathbf{i}$—$\mathbf{i}, \mathbf{j}, \mathbf{k}$, unit vectors in a right-handed rectangular system. $\mathbf{i} \times \mathbf{j} = \mathbf{k}$, $\mathbf{j} \times \mathbf{k} = \mathbf{i}$, $\mathbf{k} \times \mathbf{i} = \mathbf{j}$.

inf.—("infimum") greatest lower bound.

J—**1.** Jacobian as in $J\left(\frac{u,v,w}{x,y,z,}\right)$, also designated by $\partial(u,v,w)/\partial(x,y,z)$. **2.** $J_n(z)$, Bessel coefficient of order n. **3.** Jacobian curve. **4.** Jacobian group of points in a linear series of groups of points on an algebraic curve.

j—**1.** running index, with i. **2.** (sometimes in electrical engineering) $\sqrt{(-1)}$. See i.

$\mathbf{j}$—a unit vector. See $\mathbf{i}$.

K—**1.** specific curvature of surface. **2.** kernel of integral equation, as in $u(x) = f(x) + \lambda \int_a^b \bar{K}(x,t)u(t)dt$. K_n, the nth iterated kernel is then defined recursively by $K_1 \equiv K$, $K_n(x,y) = \int_a^b K_{n-1}(x,t)K(t,y)dt$. Also designated by $K^{(n)}$. **3.** K, iK', periods for Jacobian elliptic functions. **4.** Symmedian (Lemoine) center of triangle. **5.** $K_n(z)$, the Bessel function ("second solution") $\lim_{\nu \to n} \frac{(-1)^n}{2}\left[\frac{I_{-\nu}(z) - I_\nu(z)}{\nu - n}\right]$

k—1. proportionality factor for variation. Do not use $y \propto x$. **2.** running index, used with h. **3.** k,k', modulus and complementary modulus respectively of Jacobian elliptic functions. **4.** class interval, in y. **5.** increment in y. Also Δy.

$\mathbf{k}$—a unit vector. See **$\mathbf{i}$**.

kei, ker—Bessel functions defined as real for real z and satisfying, $\ker(z) + i \operatorname{kei}(z) = K_0(z\sqrt{\pm i})$.

L—1. general symbol for linear function. **2.** general symbol for linear system, or linear space. **3.** limit, as in $\underset{n \to \infty}{L}\ e^{-n} = 0$. See "lim." **4.** Roman numeral for "fifty." **5.** length. Also designated by l. **6.** first fundamental differential quantity of second order for surfaces. **7.** Lexis ratio, $\sigma/\sqrt{pq/s}$, for sets of s objects each. **8.** $L_n(x)$, nth Laguerre polynomial, $L_n(x)e^{-x}n! = D^n(e_x{}^{-x}n)$.

LCD—lowest common denominator.

LCM—lowest (or least) common multiple.

l—1. running index. **2.** (in elementary algebra) last term (of arithmetic or geometric progression). **3.** $l = \cos\alpha$, directional cosine, (with x-axis). **4.** length. Also designated by L.

lat.—latitude.

li—logarithmic integral or integral logarithm function, $li(x) = \int_0^x du/\log u$.

lim—limit ( ), $\overline{\lim}$, least upper limit, $\underline{\lim}$, greatest lower limit.

ln—(Sometimes) natural logarithm of.

log—logarithm (of). In theoretical work, the natural base, e, is understood; in numerical computation with tables, the base 10 is understood unless otherwise specified. Some writers use "ln" for natural logarithm of. Where ambiguity is otherwise likely, indicate the base, thus $\log_b x$, $\log_{10} x$, $\log_e x$.

long—longitude.

M—**1.** Roman numeral, thousand. **2.** arithmetic mean. Also designated by superscript bar, as $\bar{X}$, or by AM. **3.** centroid (in geometry of triangle). **4.** second fundamental differential quantity of second order for surfaces.

M.D.—mean deviation.

Md—median.

Mm—mid-mean, arithmetic mean of data in range Q_1 to Q_3.

Mo—mode.

m—1. general symbol for natural number, or integer, usually used with n. **2.** slope of line, dy/dx. **3.** $m = \cos\beta$, directional cosine (with y-axis). **4.** m_a, m_b, m_c, median lines, lengths of medians of triangle. **5.** (as subscript) meridian measurement. **6.** class of an algebraic plane curve (a Plücker number). **7.** (superscript) minutes, as in $10^d 13^h 5^m$. **8.** meters.

max—maximum (of).

meas—measure (of).

mi—miles.

min—**1.** minimum (of). **2.** minutes

mod—**1.** modulus (of), as in $\operatorname{mod}(re^{i\theta}) = r$. **2.** modulo as in $7 \equiv -3 \pmod 5$.

N—1. third fundamental differential quantity of second order for surfaces. **2.** north. **3.** total frequency in a statistical distribution.

n—**1.** general symbol for natural number or integer. **2.** $n = \cos \gamma$, directional cosine (with z-axis). **3.** order or degree of plane algebraic curve (a Plücker number). **4.** (in elementary algebra) number of terms in finite progression. **5.** (sometimes) total frequency. See N. **6.** outward normal to surface, as in $\cos(\theta, n)$.

O—**1.** origin of coordinates. **2.** circumcenter of triangle. **3.** of comparable order with, as $\Sigma_{n=0}^{N} n = O(N^2)$.

o—of inferior order to, as $\log n = o(n)$.

ord—order.

P—**1.** general symbol for polynomial, in particular the interpolational polynomial. **2.** product moment. Also expressed by p. **3.** general symbol for point. The common notation indicating the coordinate system used as $P(x,y,z)$, $P(r,\theta,\varphi)$, etc., is not recommended. **4.** general probability distribution function, in particular any one of Pearson's standard types, or Poisson's forms. **5.** $P_n(x)$, Legendre polynomial, $2^n n! P_n(x) = D^n(x^2 - 1)^n$. **6.** total force due to pressure. **7.** function, as in $Pdx + Qdy$, and in $y' + P(x)y = Q(x)$. **8.** $P_{n,r}$ or ${}_nP_r$, or $P(n,r)$, number of permutations of n distinct things taken r at a time (without repetitions), $= n!/r!$. **9.** general potential due to finite number of particles. In Newtonian case $P = \Sigma_i m_i/r_i$. See U and W. **10.** horizontal parallax. **11.** north celestial pole.

PE—probable error. See $\pm$.

Post.—postulate.

Prob.—**1.** problem. **2.** probability.

Prop.—proposition.

PS—power series.

Pt.—point.

$\wp$—Weierstrassian elliptic function.

p—**1.** general symbol for prime number. **2.** semi-latus rectum. **3.** probability ratio. **4.** genus (or deficiency) or plane algebraic curve (a Plücker number). **5.** perpendicular distance from origin to given line or plane. **6.** p_n, numerator of nth convergent of continued fraction $a_0 + \frac{1}{a_1+} \frac{1}{a_2+} \cdots$ $(p_{-1} = 0,\ p_0 = 1)$, $p_1 = a_0$, $p_{n+1} = a_n p_n + p_{n-1}$. **7.** $p_{12}, p_{13}, p_{14}, p_{23}, p_{24}, p_{34}$, line coordinates (point system). **8.** sometimes "per," as in "*rpm*," revolutions per second. This use is not recommended. **9.** perimeter. **10.** $p(n)$, total number of partitions of n. **11.** p_i, impulse component.

p.—page.

pos.—positive.

Q—**1.** general symbol for quadratic form or quadratic manifold. **2.** Q_1, Q_3 first and third quartile marks. (Q_2 is the median, Md.) **3.** function, as in $Pdx + Qdy$, and in $y' + P(x)y = Q(x)$. **4.** $Q(P_1, P_2, P_3; P_4, P_5, P_6)$, quadrangular set of six points.

QD—quartile deviation.

Q.E.D.—("Quod erat demonstrandum") which was to be proved.

Q.E.F.—("Quod erat faciendum") which was to be constructed.

q—**1.** complementary probability, $q = 1 - p$. **2.** q_n, denominator of nth convergent of continued fraction, $a_0 + \frac{1}{a_1+} \frac{1}{a_2+} \cdots$ $(q_0 = 0)$, $q_1 = 1$,

$q_{n+1} = a_n q_n + q_{n-1}$. **3.** $q_{12}, q_{13}, q_{14}, q_{23}, q_{24}, q_{34}$, line coordinates (plane system). **4.** q_1, q_2, quartile distances from the median. **5.** q_i, force component.

R—**1.** general symbol for remainder. $R_n(x)$, remainder after n turns in power-series in x. **2.** radius, in particular circumradius of triangle. **3.** real part of. Also indicated by $\mathfrak{R}$ (Black letter), and Re. **4.** general symbol for range of variable, as in $\int_{(R)}$.

$\mathfrak{R}$—(Black letter) real value of. See *R*.

R. A.—right ascension. Also designated by α.

Re—real value of. See *R*.

RMS—root-mean-square. $\sqrt{(\Sigma_{i=1}^{n} x^2/n)}$.

r—**1.** general running index, as in *r*th term. **2.** radius (see *R*), in particular in radius of triangle. **3.** coefficient of linear correlation, correlation coefficient. **4.** (in elementary algebra) common ratio between successive terms in a geometric progression. **5.** distance, in polar and in spherical coordinates; projected distances in cylindrical coordinates. **6.** (sometimes) revolutions, as in *r.p.m.* (revolutions per minute). **7.** (sometimes) (superscript) radians, as in $2\pi^{(r)}$. (This usage is not recommended.)

rad—**1.** radius. **2.** radians. Where no units are indicated angles are measured in radians, sin 30 means "sine of 30 radians," not sin 30°. Do not write $\sin a^r$ or $\sin a^{(r)}$ for $\sin a$ (where a is measured in radians), since superscript r is sometimes interpreted as "revolutions."

rot—rotation or curl of vector. Also designated by ∇x.

S—**1.** general symbol for space, as S_n, space of n dimension. See *L*. **2.** general symbol for sum, as in S_n, sum of first n terms of given sequence or series. See *s*. **3.** south. **4.** standard error of estimate. 5. radius of spherical curvature of curve.

Si—1st sine-integral function $\mathrm{Si}(x) = \int_0^x (\sin u/u)du$. See si.

S.T.—siderial time.

s.—**1.** general running index. Used with *r*. **2.** general symbol for sum, as in s_n sum of first n terms of sequence or series. See *S*. **3.** (in elementary algebra), sum of arithmetic or of geometric progression. **4.** $s_k(n)$, sum of *k*th powers of first n natural numbers. **5.** s_k, sum of the *k*th powers of the roots of an algebraic equation. **6.** arc length. **7.** slant height. **8.** (usually as superscript) seconds. **9.** semi-interquartile range. **10.** semi-perimeter of triangle, $s = (a + b + c)/2$. **11.** (sometimes) number of individuals in sample. **12.** root-mean-square deviation about arbitrarily assumed origin, (in "short method").

sec—secant (of).

$\sec^{-1}$—inverse secant (of). Also designated by arc sec.

sech—hyperbolic secant (of). Do not use Sec or $\mathfrak{Sec}$ (in German letters).

sech^{-1}—inverse hyperbolic secant of. Do not use arc sech.

si—2nd sine-integral function, $\beta_i(x) = \int_\infty^x (\sin u/u)du$. See Si.

sgn—(signum) sign (of), more generally for z complex, $\mathrm{sgn}\, z = z/|z|$

sin—sine (of). Do not use Sin.

$\sin^{-1}$—inverse sine (of). Also designated by arc sin.

sinh—hyperbolic sine (of). Do not use Sin, or $\mathfrak{Sin}$ (in German letters),

$\sinh^{-1}$—inverse hyperbolic sine of. Do not use "arc sinh."
sk—skewness of frequency distribution.
sn—(Jacobian elliptic function), sine amplitude.
sq—square.
sup—(supremum) least upper bound. Sometimes designated by **L.U.B.,** or l.u.b.
T—**1.** total time, (as in time of flight of projectile). **2.** clock time. **3.** general symbol for transformation, T^n, nth iterate of T. **4.** tons. **5.** (in logic), true or truth. **6.** absolute temperature.
Th—theorem.
t—**1.** general variable or parameter. **2.** time. See τ. See "dot accent." **3.** ordinary temperature. See T, τ, θ.
tan—tangent (of).
$\tan^{-1}$—inverse tangent (of). Also designated by arc tan.
tanh—hyperbolic tangent (of). Do not use Tan or 𝔗𝔞𝔫 (in German letters).
$\tanh^{-1}$—inverse hyperbolic tangent (of). Do not use arc tanh.
U—general (line surface or volume) potential. In Newtonian case, $U = \int_{(L)} \frac{\mu dL}{r}$ or $\int_{(S)} \frac{\mu dS}{r}$, or $\int_{(V)} \frac{\mu dV}{r}$. See P and W.
u—**1.** general variable, especially dependent variable or real part thereof. See w. **2.** u_n, Lucas' function $u_n = (\alpha^n - \beta^n)/(\alpha - \beta)$, α, β, roots of given quadratic.
V—**1.** Roman numeral, five. **2.** (in Euler's polyhedral formula) number of vertices. **3.** general harmonic function. **4.** volume.
$\boldsymbol{v}$—(linear) velocity.
v—**1.** general variable, especial dependent variable, used with u, or coefficient of pure imaginary part thereof. See w. **2.** v_n, Lucas' function $\alpha^n + \beta^n$, α, β, roots of given quadratic. See u_n. **3.** speed.
W—**1.** west. **2.** general potential of double layer. In Newtonian case, $W = \int_{(S)} \nu \frac{\partial}{\partial n}\left(\frac{1}{r}\right) dS, = -\int_{(S)} \frac{\nu}{r^2} \cos(r,n)\, dS$. See P and U. **3.** Wronskian,

$$W = \begin{vmatrix} y_1 & y_1' & \cdots & y_1^{(n-1)} \\ \cdot & \cdot & \cdots & \cdot \\ y_n & y_n' & \cdots & y_n^{(n-1)} \end{vmatrix}.$$

4. total weight. Also designated by Wt. **5.** work (or energy). Also designated by Wk.
Wt.—weight. See W.
w—**1.** general symbol for variable, particularly dependent variable. Used with u and v as in $J\left(\frac{u,v,w}{x,y,z}\right)$, etc. **2.** dependent complex variable, $w = u + iv$, or $w(z) = u(x,y) + iv(x,y)$ where $z = x + iy$, x,y,u,v, real.
X—**1.** Roman numeral, ten; as in XCIII, etc. **2.** X_i, original numerical data for x-variates, (previous to change of origin or scale). **3.** general symbol for variable point, particularly on x-axis **4.** function, as in $Xdx + Ydy + Zdz$ or $\frac{dx}{X} = \frac{dy}{Y} = \frac{dz}{Z}$.

x—**1.** general symbol for independent variable or unknown. **2.** first rectangular coordinate. In space a right-handed coordinate system such as indicated

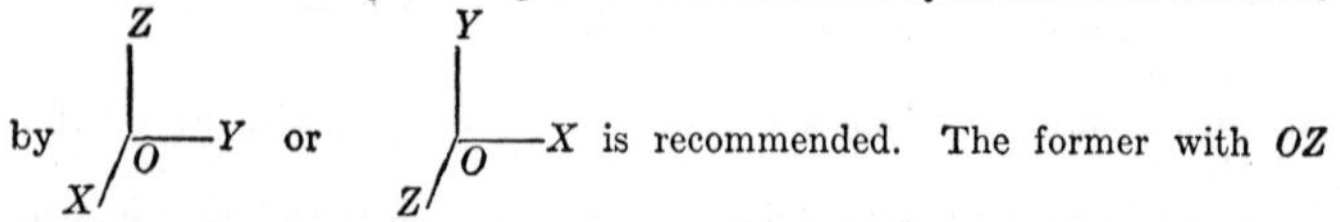

directed to the zenith is more common. **3.** real part of independent complex variable $z = x + iy$.

Y—**1.** Y_i, original numerical data for y-variates (previous to change of origin or scale). **2.** function as in $Xdx + Ydy + Zdz$, or $\frac{dx}{X} = \frac{dy}{Y} = \frac{dz}{Z}$.

y—**1.** general symbol for dependent (real) variable. **2.** general symbol for second independent variable, r unknown. **3.** second rectangular coordinate. See x. **4.** pure imaginary coefficient, in independent complex variable, $z = x + iy$.

Z—zenith.

Z.T.—zone time.

z—**1.** independent complex variable, $z = x + iy$. **2.** general symbol for third independent variable or unknown. **3.** third rectangular coordinate. See x. **4.** axial coordinate in cylindrical coordinates (r, θ, z). **5.** zenith distance, $(90^{\circ} - h)$.

Selected Symbols Used in Financial and Actuarial Theory

α—net premium in first policy year.

β—net premium in each policy year after the first.

δ—force of interest (and of discount) $e^{\delta} = 1 + i$.

ω—terminal recorded age in mortality table, "limiting" age.

A_x—commutation symbol, present value of net single premium for whole life policy on (x), $= M_x/D_x$.

$a_{\overline{n}|i}$—present value of annuity for unit periodic payment, $= (1 - v^n)/i$.

$a_{\overline{n}|i}^{(p)}$—present value of an annuity of 1 per annum at interest rate i, payable p times a year (in installments of $1/p$ each).

a_x—commutation symbol, present value of (ordinary) whole life annuity on (x) of unit annual payment.

$a_x^{(m)}$—present value of whole life annuity on (x), of unit annual payment, payable m times a year.

$n|a_x$—present value of whole life annuity, on (x), deferred n years for unit annual payment.

$a_{x\overline{n}|}$—present value of temporary life annuity, on (x), for n years, for unit annual payment.

$a_{\infty i}$—present value of perpetuity at rate of interest, i.

$\mathbf{a}_{\infty \mathbf{i}}$—present value of perpetuity due at rate of interest, $\mathbf{i}$.

$\mathbf{a}_x$—commutation symbol present value of whole life annuity due, on (x), of unit annual payment.

$\mathbf{a}_{\overline{n}|\mathbf{i}}$—present value of an annuity due, for unit periodic payments at interest rate $\mathbf{i}$.

B—book value.

B_k—book value, after k years.

C—**1.** original cost. **2.** capitalized cost.

C_x—commutation symbol, $= v^{x+1}d_x$.

c_x—natural premium at age x, $= C_x/D_x$.

D—total simple discount.

D_b—total bank discount.

D_c—cash discount, where for example, "terms 4/10, 2/30, n/90" designates 4% discount for payment within 10 days, 2% thereafter but within 30 days, payable net in 90 days.

D_t—trade discount.

D_x—commutation symbol, $= v^x l_x$.

d—rate of simple discount, $= 1 - v = 1 - (1 + i)^{-1} = i/(1 + i)$.

d_x—number dying between ages x and $x + 1$, according to mortality table (for 100,000 alive at age 10).

E—present value of expectation.

${}_nE_x$—present value of an n-year pure endowment to (x), $= v^n l_{x+n}/l_x$.

e_x—curtate expectation of life for (x), $= (l_x + \cdots + l_\omega)/l_x$.

$\overset{\circ}{e}_x$—complete expectation of life, for (x), $= e_x + \frac{1}{2}$.

F—**1.** net-cost-rate factor. **2.** face value of bond.

I—total interest (ordinary simple).

I'—total interest (exact, simple).

i—rate of interest (effective).

$j_{(p)}$—nominal rate of interest convertible p times a year corresponding to effective annual rate i, $= p[(1 + i)^{1/p} - 1]$.

k_x—valuation symbol, $= C_x/D_{x+1}$.

${}_nk_x$—valuation symbol, $= (M_x - M_{x+n})/D_{x+n}$, $[{}_1k_x = k_x]$, accumulated cost of insurance.

L—**1.** list price (for trade discount). **2.** salvage value.

l_x—number living at age x according to mortality table (for 100,000 alive at age 10).

$\mathbb{N}_x$—("open bar N"), commutation symbol, $= D_x + D_{x+1} + \cdots + D_\omega$.

n—number of conversion periods (for compound interest).

P—principal.

P_b—bank proceeds.

P_x—net annual premium for ordinary whole life policy, on (x), for unit annual payment $= A_x/(1 + a_x)$.

${}_rP_x$—net annual premium for r-payment life policy, $= M_x/(\mathbb{N}_x - \mathbb{N}_{x+r})$.

p—**1.** probability of success. **2.** interest period/payment interval.

p_x—probability of living for another year for a person of age x (according to mortality table).

${}_np_x$—probability that a person aged x will live n years, $= l_{x+n}/l_x$.

p_{xy}—the probability that (x) and (y) will survive jointly for one year.

${}_np_{xy}$—the probability that (x) and (y) will survive jointly for n years.

q—probability of failure, $= 1 - p$.

q_x—probability of dying within a year for a person of age x (according to mortality table).

${}_{|n}q_x$—probability that (x) will die within n years.

${}_{n|}q_x$—the probability that (x) will die between ages $x + n$ and $x + n + 1$.

R—**1.** periodic payment or "rent." **2.** replacement cost. **3.** repair charge (annual).

S—amount.

S—**1.** scrap value. **2.** amount of sinking fund. **3.** subscription price. **4.** amount (at simple interest).

s—amount (at compound interest) for unit principal $= (1 + i)^n$.

$s_{\overline{n}|i}$—amount of annuity for unit periodic payment, $= [(1 + i)^n - 1]/i$.

$s_{\infty i}$—amount of perpetuity at interest rate i.

s_{∞}—amount of perpetuity due.

$\mathrm{s}_{\overline{n}|i}$—amount of an annuity due, for unit periodic payments.

$s_{\overline{n}|i}^{(p)}$—amount at end of n years of annuity of 1 per annum at interest rate i, payable p times a year (in installments of $1/p$ each).

u_x—valuation symbol, $= D_x/D_{x+1}$.

${}_nu_x$—valuation symbol, $(\mathrm{N}_x - \mathrm{N}_{x+n})/D_{x+n}$, $[{}_1u_x = u_x]$, accumulated value of individual survivors payments.

V—purchase price (of bond).

${}_tV_x$—terminal reserve of tth policy year on policy on (x) of unit annual payment.

v—present value (at compound interest) for unit principal, $= (1 + i)^{-1}$.

W—wearing value, = original cost minus scrap value.

x—age of insured (to nearest year).

(x)—a person aged x (for use with mortality table).

$x]$—where $[x] + t$ indicates a life, now aged $x + t$, who was accepted for insurance t years ago at age x.

INDEX

A

B

C

D

E

E

I

INDEX

P

Q

R

S

INDEX